PICTORIAL
ATLAS
OF THE WORLD

PICTORIAL
ATLAS
OF THE WORLD

TIGER

Contents

6 **The Earth viewed from space**

8 **A panorama of the Earth**

10 **Space meteorology**
 Cartography

12 **Volcanoes**
 Geysers
 Earthquakes

16 **Caves and grottoes**

17 **The Earth's treasures**

18 **Mountains**
 Formation of mountain ranges
 Orogenesis from the collision of
 two plates

20 **Mountains of the world**

22 **Glaciers**
 The great Quaternary Ice Ages

24 **Rivers**

26 **Lakes**

28 **The oceans**
 Man and the Sea

 Waves
 Tides
 Coastlines

32 **Islands**
 Atolls

34 **Atmospheric phenomena**
 Wind

36 **Climate**
 Climate and Vegetation

38 **Vegetation**

40 **Evolution**

42 **Habit and Habitat**

44 **The Arctic**

45 **The Antarctic**

46 **The tundra**

47 **The taiga**

48 **The temperate forests**

50 **The tropical forests**

52 **The grasslands**

54 **The deserts**

This edition published in 1991 by
Tiger Books International PLC, London

Printed in Italy by Vallardi Industrie Grafiche S.p.A.
Lainate (Mi) - July 1991

PHOTOGRAPHIC AKNOWLEDGEMENTS
Ammann: 192b; Archivio Vallardi: 22tr, 23c, d, 29, 45 cr, 47 bc, 57 bl, 60 c, 62, 63tl, b, 65t,
67tl, 71bl, 76b, 77bl, 189t; B. Coleman: 2s, 24tr, 25t, cr, 28t, 31c, 33tr, 44t, 45t, 46cl, 51ac,
55c, cl, b; Diemberger: 20bd; Dimt: 31br, 48br, 48bd; Explorer: 13bl, tr, 15b, 27bl, 31t, md;
Fantin: 18b, 21bd; Ferrari: 21bs; Fiore: 68bs; Gaggero: 49 c, 57tl, mb; Ghedina: 20tr; Marka:
2/3, 4/5, 9s, 11t, bl, 13tl, 14d, 15tr, 16tl, 17tr, ac, bl, mbr, 20bl, 21cr, 22b, 24cr, 25cl, bsd, 26tr,
27tr, 28c, 30tl, b, 32b, 33tl, 34, t, c, b, 35, 42, 43, 45cl, 46t, b, 47cr, br, 48c, bl, 49t, b, 50tr,
51b, 52c, 53msd, 54, 55t, c, cr, 56, 57cr, mb, 59t, 60cl, br, 63tr, 64c, b, 65 cr, c, 180, 181, 182,
183tr, 184, 185tr, 188b, 189b, 190, 191tr, b, 192t, 197tr, b, 198, 199, 200, 201, 202b, 203tl, b,
206b, 207, 208, 209, 209, 210, 211, 214, 215, 216, 217, 220, 221, 223; Mazza: 53br, 57tr, c, 58t,
59b, 60t, mb; NASA: 6, 7, 8, 9t, br, 10, 11br, 19t, 24tl, 33br, 198as; Pagani: 48tl, d; Pedone:
42, 43; Prato-Previde: 14t, 26tl, 27br, 31bl, 33bl, 37, 43, 47cl, 50c, 63c, 65cl, 69c, 70c, 78cl,
br, 182br, 185tl, 188t, 191tl, 196br, 202t, 203tr; Pubbliaerfoto: 14b (conc. SMA 297 dated
20/7/76), 18t (conc. SMA E1108) 22tl (conc. SMA E707), 23t (conc. SMA E1276), 27c (conc.
SMA 571 dated 29/10/73), 32t (conc. SMA 472 dated 21/10/75) 34tl; Ricatto: 68br, 69t, 183tl;
Ruth: 21cl; SEF/Regaldi: 15tl, 16tr, b, 17c, 24b, 26b, 27tl, 30tr, 42, 44c, 47bl, 50tl, 65cr, 66c,
70bl, 79cl, 183b, 185b, 196b, 197tl, 206t; Stutte: 12d, 21t; Tiofoto: 44b; Zappelli 20tl.
DRAWINGS: GABRIELE POZZI
CARTHOGRAPHY: VALLARDI INDUSTRIE GRAFICHE
Geophysical Globe by Rand McNally and Co. Copyright R.L. 91PG0416A

56 **The mountains**

58 **Fresh water**

60 **The seas and oceans**

62 **The inhabited world**
The population problem

64 **The many races**

65 **Religions**

65 **Languages**

66 **The city**
The problems of urbanisation

68 **Food resources**

70 **Agriculture**
Fishing
Rearing livestock

72 **Food and nourishment**

73 **Economy and society**

74 **Energy resources**

76 **Mineral resources**

77 **Transport**

78 **A changing world**
The works of nature
The works of man

81 **WORLD ATLAS**

177 **COUNTRIES OF THE WORLD**
178 **Europe**
186 **Asia**
194 **Africa**
204 **North America**
212 **South America**
218 **Oceania**
223 **Polar Lands**

225 **INDEX**

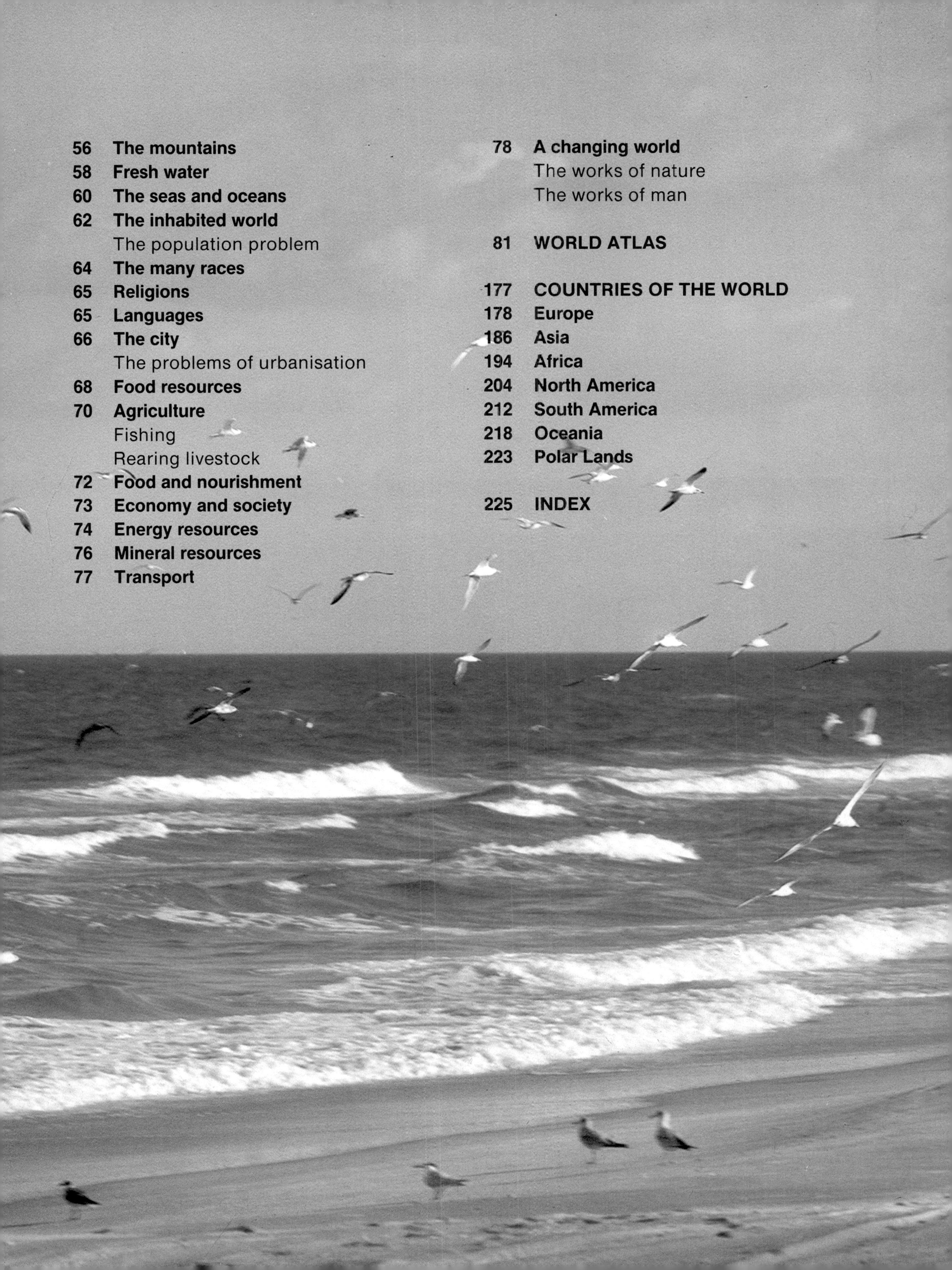

The Earth viewed from space

"It looks like a splendid jewel suspended in space." These words by the American astronaut Neil Armstrong, who became the first man to set foot on the Moon on 21 July 1969, epitomise the fascinating spectacle offered by our planet to an observer in an artificial satellite or on the Moon itself.

Unlike some planets in the solar system, such as Venus and Jupiter, which are constantly obscured by a thick mantle of clouds, the Earth is characterised by a very variable covering of cloud which often permits the actual true surface of the planet to be discerned.

The overall colour of the Earth is a bright blue, but the brilliant white of the cloud formations, the dark blue of the oceans and the deep brown of the continents can be clearly distinguished by an observer in space.

The light with which the Earth shines is due to its "albedo", the process by which all the planets reflect into space a percentage of the Sun's light which falls on them.

The Earth, owing to its mantle of clouds, the polar caps and the vast expanses of water, reflects into space about 40 per cent of the incident light from the Sun.

Naturally, if one were to travel further and further away into space, the Earth would become fainter and less visible. From Mars it would look like a star, but from Jupiter it would be practically invisible without a powerful telescope.

The Earth (above left and below)
This is how the Earth appears from the ATS artificial satellite in orbit at a height of about 35,800 km. The whole hemisphere illuminated by the Sun is visible. As shown in the map below, the South American continent with the Andes mountains and western Africa, which enclose the Atlantic Ocean, may be clearly discerned. The polar caps are obscured by clouds.

North America (left)
This photograph was taken from the Apollo 11 space vehicle at the beginning of the flight which was to carry the astronauts to the Moon in July 1969. The picture covers an area of about 2,600,000 sq km. The long, narrow peninsula of California is clearly visible in the west where a cyclone can also be seen and a sheet of cloud stretching all the way to Los Angeles. The land is almost completely clear of cloud with only tufts of white cumulus cloud indicating fine weather.

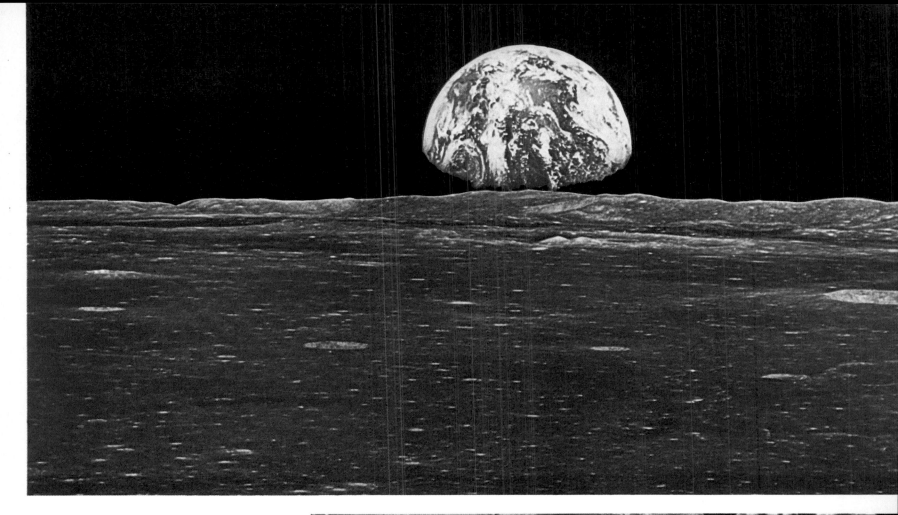

The Earth as seen from the Moon (above)

This is how the Earth looked to the crew of Apollo 10 in May 1969 while in orbit around the Moon at a height of 115 km above its surface.

The picture throws the contrast between the two worlds into sharp relief. On the one hand the Earth, the planet of life, with its atmosphere, its oceans and continents teeming with living creatures, stands out brilliantly against the dark background of space. On the other hand, the Moon with its sombre landscape coloured a monotonous yellowish brown, pockmarked with craters is devoid of any form of life. Our natural satellite, at a distance of 384,400 km from the Earth, appears utterly inhospitable. Lacking an atmosphere which by day filters the Sun's heat rays and at night retains some of the received heat, the Moon is subject to extremes of temperature. In order to survive under these conditions, man must recreate the climatic conditions to which he is accustomed by means of special suits like those of the astronauts or, as in science fiction, by means of huge sealed domes.

Two continents side by side (right)

Only the 25 km wide straits of Bab el Mandeb separate Asia and Africa. This photograph was taken in September 1966 from Gemini 11 from a height of about 850 km looking towards the NNE. Better than any map, the picture shows with extreme clarity one section of the largest fracture in the Earth's crust. This is the famous Rift Valley of East Africa which, starting from Mozambique, extends through the great African lake region, across Ethiopia and then divides into two branches, as the photograph clearly shows. On the left is the Red Sea and on the right the Gulf of Aden. The two opposite edges of the fracture, recent from a geological point of view, are continually evolving. Arabia and Africa are very slowly drifting apart.

In the lower part of the Arabian peninsula (at the top of the photograph) it is possible to distinguish part of the desert of Rub'-al Khali (the large yellowish-brown patch) and the mountains of the Yemen, whose line of peaks is outlined by a row of cumulus clouds. Beyond the Gulf of Aden can be seen the horn of Africa, Somalia, with the sharp Cape Guardafui.

The central Sahara *(left)*
This photograph, taken from Apollo 9, shows the great sand sea of Edeyen Murzuq (edeyen in Berber means sandy desert). We are in Fezzan, the region of central Libya bordering on Niger. On the left, the mountains of Messak Mellet can be seen, the eastern foothills of the Hoggar mountains. The highest areas appear deeply scored and eroded. The action of the wind, together with the rare but violent rainstorms, has a continual scouring and levelling effect which is particularly effective in these areas which are completely devoid of vegetation.

At the upper right hand corner, emphasised by clusters of small cumulus clouds, the edge of the Mediterranean Sea can be seen stretching to the horizon about 1,000 km to the north. In the right hand part of the picture, where there is a vast undulating expanse, the effect of the wind on the landscape is clearly visible in the form of dunes, or mounds of sand heaped up by the wind which are characteristic of deserts and low sandy shorelines.

A panorama of the Earth

The advances in space travel have permitted twentieth century man to observe his own planet from a viewpoint which even the boldest and most imaginative of the explorers of the sixteenth century could probably never have conceived. In less than ten years from his first orbit of the Earth, man has set foot on his own natural satellite, realising what must have seemed an impossible dream, and is now sending probes to other planets such as Venus and Mars. Practical,

scientific and prestigious motives were all important to those assisting with these endeavours to a greater or lesser degree. However, it was really through the unaccustomed aspect from which the Earth was being seen and the photographs taken by the astronauts which were arriving back on the Earth that the variety and beauty of the landscape of this fragment of rock wandering in space, with its burning red deserts and deep blue oceans, was being rediscovered.

Lake Volta (Ghana, West Africa)
This is how Lake Volta looks from space (this photograph was taken from Apollo 6); its dark blue waters contrast with the dark green of the forest and the white tufts of cloud. The artificial basin of Lake Volta, of which only a part is seen in the picture, has an area of 8,500 sq km and is the largest in the world. It was formed by building a large dam at Akosombo about 100 km from the mouth of the river Volta which flows into the Gulf of Guinea.

THE CONQUEST OF SPACE

4 October 1957: first satellite in orbit around the Earth. This was the Russian Sputnik 1.
4 October 1959: the Russian space probe Lunik 3 photographed the hidden side of the Moon.
12 April 1961: first man in orbit; Vostok 1 with Yuri Gagarin on board.
20 February 1962: the American John Glenn completed three Earth orbits.
18 March 1965: first "walk" in space by the Russian Alexei Leonov.
31 January 1966: first hard landing on the Moon (without crew) by the Russian space probe Lunik 9.
16 March 1966: rendezvous in space between the Gemini 8 capsule and an Agena missile.
21 July 1969: Apollo 11 mission. The American astronauts Neil Armstrong and Edwin Aldrin became the first men to set foot on the Moon. Scientific experiments were also carried out. Michael Collins remained in lunar orbit waiting for them.
14 November 1969: two other American astronauts (Apollo 12 mission) walked on the Moon.
30 May 1971: first space vehicle orbits another planet. Mariner 9 transmits thousands of photographs of the planet Mars.
14 May-22 June 1973: first Skylab mission. A space laboratory was placed in orbit to carry out a number of scientific experiments.
17 July 1975: link up in orbit between the American Apollo space capsule and the Russian Soyuz.
22 October 1975: the Russian space probe Venera 9 landed on Venus and transmitted the first photograph of this mysterious planet.
24 July 1976: the Viking probe landed on the surface of Mars and transmitted the first colour photograph.

Socotra (right)
The Isle of Socotra and to
the right the small islands
of The Brothers.
Socotra is about 240 km
east of the easternmost
point of Africa (Cape
Guardafui) to which, from
a geographical point of
view, it belongs. The island
actually consists of a base
of ancient crystalline rocks
covered with more recent
sedimentary rocks
(Mesozoic), similar to
those of the high plain of
Ethiopia.
Politically speaking, the
island is in Asia since it is
an integral part of the
Republic of the Yemen.
This photograph was taken
looking towards the south
and therefore appears
inverted with respect to
normal maps. The colour
effect is caused by
reflection of the Sun in the
surface of the sea and by
the type of filter used.
The difference between the
two coasts of the island is
clearly shown: the
southern coast (uppermost
in the photograph)
descends abruptly and
precipitously to the sea,
while the northern coast is
less barren and steep. The
main town of Socotra,
Hadibu, is situated close to
the northern coast, near to
the smaller bay to the left.

Oman (above)
Oman, the eastern point
of Arabia. Both Cape al
Hadd, which separates
the Arabian Sea from the
Gulf of Oman, and the
hills of Hajar can be seen.
At the lower left there is
an expanse of dunes, the
beginnings of the
Arabian desert of Rub-al
Khali.

The Nile delta (right)
This is how the Nile
delta appears from a
height of over 300 km.
The thin cloud covering
fails to hide the great
fan formed by the river
where it flows into the
Mediterranean. The
whole delta appears to
be highly cultivated and
its blue colours seem
to merge with that of
the Mediterranean, but
it stands out from the
paler colours of the
rocks and the plains of
the desert. The whole of
the Suez canal from
Port Said to the town of
Suez can also be clearly
distinguished.

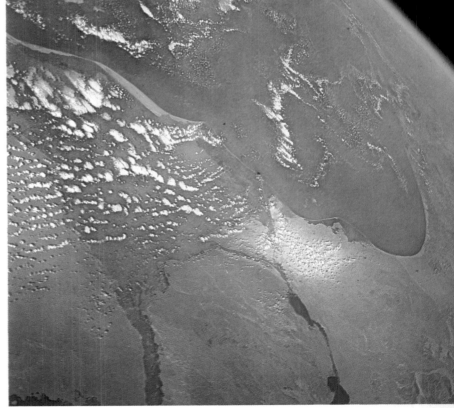

9

Space meteorology

Meteorology, the study of the physical processes and phenomena taking place in the atmosphere on which weather forecasts are based, has benefited enormously from the tremendous advances made in the field of space travel.

Photographs taken from artificial satellites and space probes supply meteorologists with a wealth of data on the Earth's atmosphere and its phenomena, even if sometimes the outlines of the continents and seas are hidden by clouds.

Photographs taken from above the atmosphere have a special practical importance since they show the early stages of development of dangerous tropical cyclones, enabling their subsequent development to be followed and the necessary precautions to be taken in those areas immediately threatened.

In particular, specially designed weather satellites with complex instrumentation have contributed to a greater understanding of the distribution and location of cloud formations. Orbiting at heights of between 200 and 700 km, the satellites transmit television pictures to meteorological stations on the Earth, clearly showing the distribution, shape, type and extent of the various cloud formations.

It is thus possible to differentiate between tropical and non-tropical cyclones, characterised by their spiral shape, and jet streams, recognisable by long streaks of cloud, and high pressure areas with practically no clouds.

A cyclone over the Pacific (above)
This photograph was taken from Apollo 9 at a height of 130 km. The characteristic vortex structure of tropical cyclones is clearly visible. These cyclones, as distinct from the cyclones in temperate zones, are of fairly small diameter (rarely exceeding a few hundred kilometres) and have a high speed of rotation. Inside them are winds blowing anti-clockwise in the northern hemisphere at over 200 km per hour, around a central area called the "eye" where it is relatively calm. This type of cyclone originates in tropical zones in summer and in autumn when the high temperatures of the oceans combine with a very high humidity.

The structure of a cyclone
The diagram below shows the structure of a tropical cyclone (hurricane). The up-currents which form above the surface of the sea in the warmest seasons (**A**) rise rapidly and, being charged with moisture and possessing considerable energy liberated by condensation (**B**), tend to develop a rotational velocity which is anti-clockwise in the northern hemisphere (**C**). Downward currents (**E**) are found around the central nucleus, or eye (**D**).

A cyclone over Colombia (left)
The picture, taken from Apollo 9, shows the circular mass of clouds forming the tropical cyclone or hurricane. The name cyclone should be reserved for hurricanes in the Indian Ocean, while the term "typhoon" applies to those in Japan and "willy-willies" to those in Australia.
In the photograph, a huge area of cumulonimbus cloud can be seen rising up to a height of 6,600 m with cirrus and cumulus clouds at the outer edges.

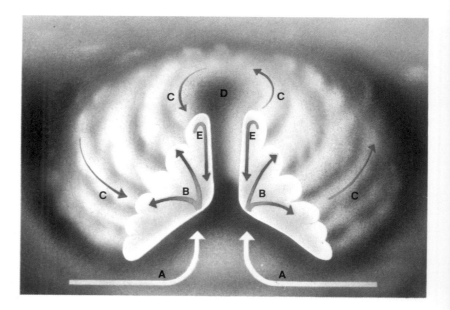

Cartography

Cartography is a very ancient occupation. It was born for obvious practical reasons (delineation of boundaries, for example) and was practised by the Egyptians and the people of Mesopotamia, but it was with the Greek civilisation that it rose to the level of a science.

One of the greatest of the cartographers of the ancient world was Claudius Ptolemy of Alexandria, who lived between AD 120 and 180 and was better known as an astronomer. He devised various types of projections (the cartographic projection is the process which allows the curved surface of the Earth to be represented on a plane surface with the minimum of distortion).

With the ending of the period of the great geographical discoveries and the development of precision optical instruments, he was able to make use of triangulation methods and produced very accurate maps for that time.

A revolution occurred with the use of aerial photographs which, by means of special instruments (such as the stereoscope), were converted into topographical maps permitting accurate representation and faster production. In this way it became possible to make more accurate maps of inaccessible regions like Antarctica.

Photographs taken from the air, however, covered only a fairly small area and therefore to produce maps of relatively large areas required much long and difficult work of co-ordination.

This problem did not arise with photographs taken from space vehicles, since a single picture could depict a very large area. Space photography is of value in other specialised fields. Infra-red pictures can provide valuable information on the state of vegetation and agriculture. Even the sphere of geology can benefit a good deal from space photography, especially regarding structural details, which are clearly revealed in the pictures.

The urban district of Detroit

Detroit, Michigan (USA), is one of the most important industrial centres in the United States. Situated on the right hand side of the river of the same name, Detroit is characterised by a regular grid-like urban structure as can be clearly seen in the right hand part of the photograph.
Taking photographs by infra-red light, which is emitted by everything but not perceived by the human eye, not only gives a detailed view of the urban structure but also clearly shows the green areas, the various types of crops (note the cultivated areas in the bottom left hand corner) and the nature of the wooded areas.
By infra-red light, the vegetation appears in various shades of red which reveals the extent of any pollution.

Italy seen from space (below)

Seen from an artificial satellite, the Italian peninsula clearly reveals its characteristic shape. The surface area covered is over 300,000 sq km and the distance from the Swiss lake of Neuchâtel in the upper left hand corner to Cape Passero in Sicily is about 1,250 km. Using aerial photography, several thousand photographs would have been required. In the picture, the various different types of land structure are revealed: the alluvial plain of the Po and its tributaries divided into the upper Alpine regions and the Paduan trench, the sweep of the crystalline Alps with the swelling of the limestone southern Alps, the characteristic backbone of the Apennines with the upper Tyrrhenian region, the original Mesozoic Apennines and the Adriatic coast.

Space photography (above)

The diagram illustrates the value and effectiveness of a photograph taken from a body orbiting the Earth. An area can be covered by a single photograph which would have required hundreds of the traditional aerial photographs accompanied by the serious problems caused by the inevitable distortion. In order to transform the photographs into maps, it is important to provide a network of points whose co-ordinates are precisely known. For this purpose, "geodetic" satellites are used which permit rapid and exact measurement of distance, a fundamental requirement for precision mapmaking.

Mount Etna (left)

This photograph, taken from the Skylab space laboratory orbiting the Earth, shows one section of the east coast of Sicily. The conical mass of Etna is clearly visible on the right, the highest volcano in Europe, still active, as evidenced by the thin plume of smoke issuing from the crater (**A**). Infra-red photography allows the different lava streams on the sides of the volcano to be distinguished; the most recent streams appear dark blue (**B**) and contrast clearly with the ancient streams and volcanic dust which are coloured red (**C**). Catania, the largest town situated at the foot of Etna, appears as a blue patch on the side on the plain of the same name (**D**). In the left hand part of the photograph, the beginning of the Iblei Mountains can be seen, while numerous lakes stand out because of their dark blue colour, among them Lake Pozzillo.

Volcanoes

Volcanoes, like earthquakes, are the clearest and most spectacular manifestation of the vitality and dynamism of our planet, whose crust has the task of maintaining it in equilibrium.

In fact, underneath the thin rigid crust of the lithosphere, there extends a thick region called the mantle, where the matter, which is subjected to very high temperatures and pressures, becomes plastic. It is thus quite possible for convection currents to exist in the mantle whose very slow movement (a few centimetres per year) is transferred to the overlying crust which consists of several large scales or plates.

Below the Earth's crust there is a completely or partially molten, incandescent substance called magma, made up of silicon compounds and small amounts of gas (water vapour, carbon dioxide, hydrogen sulphide, etc.). Wherever there is a local weakness in the Earth's crust, usually occurring at points where the various plates meet, the magma, because of its fluidity, is able to escape, thereby giving rise to volcanoes. The shape of volcanoes, which are typically conical, depends on the type of lava emitted and the type of volcanic material erupted (ash, small fragments or molten boulders). Also, the manner in which the volcano normally behaves is connected with the type of lava.

The most basic types of lava, that is to say those containing only small amounts of silica (less than 55%) but rich in magnesium and iron, are quite fluid. In this case, the activity of the volcano is seldom violent since the gas within the magma is able to escape easily, while the lava flows in winding rivulets which can travel considerable distances, and forms huge cones of shallow gradient (shield volcanoes of the type found in the Hawaiian islands).

Acid lavas, that is, those rich in silica (over 60%), are rather viscous and obstruct the emission of gases which escape with explosive force, carrying with them liquid and solid matter. These are fragments of rock, molten boulders and ash which form layers on the lava flows giving rise to the group of volcanic structures known as "composite" or "strato-volcanoes", to which nearly all of the existing great volcanoes belong.

Fountains of lava *(left)*
The Kilauea volcano in the Hawaiian islands during the 1959 eruption. A small vent on the side of a large shield volcano whose slopes extend into the Pacific Ocean to a depth of 5,000 m.

Kilimanjaro, an extinct volcano *(below)*
The peak of Kilimanjaro, whose volcanic activity is now almost totally extinct, was formed after the Cenozoic age at the same time as the opening up of the great Rift Valley of East Africa.

A volcanic cone *(above)*
This volcanic structure in Central America has the typical conical form. It is a layered or composite volcano formed by the building up of alternate layers of lava and volcanic material (ash and molten boulders). The former is disposed during periods of relative inactivity of the volcano, the latter associated with explosive activity preceded by shaking and rumbling and, as in the picture, with the ejection from the crater of a high column of gas and magmatic vapour which often spreads upwards, taking on the characteristic shape of a pine tree.

Lava streams
Lava streams winding their way down the sides of Piton de la Fournaise, a volcano on Réunion, an island in the Indian Ocean to the east of Madagascar. The lava, which is at a very high temperature (between 800 and 1,000°C) and of variable viscosity, while still in a fluid state, flows in streams and rivulets, forming cascades and complete lakes.

Section through a volcano *(below)*
The diagram shows a section through the lithosphere in a volcanic region. It illustrates both the fundamental elements of a volcano and the more typical aspects of volcanic terrain. The magma, which collects in the magma reservoir, reaches the surface through cracks or along the lines of least resistance. It then remains within the lithosphere and slowly cools to form a laccolith.

A) Volcanic cone composed of layers of lava and erupted material
B) Volcanic vent
C) Miscellaneous cones
D) Sedimentary rocks (sandstone, limestone, shale)
E) Metamorphic rocks
F) Magma reservoir
G) Laccolith

Santorini, the eruption which destroyed a civilisation
Santorini, which forms part of the Cyclades, a group of islands in the southern Aegean Sea, is one of the remains of the ancient land called Egeide, which linked Greece with Asia Minor. Before 1250 BC Santorini, known by the classical name of Thera, was an island on the circular perimeter where a civilisation of the Cretan-Minoan type was settled. Around 1250 BC a violent eruption destroyed the central inhabited parts of the island, which were reduced to rubble, leaving only a crescent shape and several small islets. Thus a flourishing maritime community was cut off in its prime. Some archaeologists maintain that the Thera disaster explains the sudden downfall of the Cretan-Minoan civilisation. The ashes from Thera would have destroyed all vegetation and rendered the harbours of Crete non-navigable.
In recent years, the Santorin volcano, now dormant, has shown signs of reawakening. In 1956 in less than one minute 2,000 houses on the island were destroyed. In the picture the islet of Néa Kaméni is seen from the island of Santorini.

Types of volcanic eruption

Hawaiian type
Characterised by continuous emission of very fluid lava.

Strombolian type
Small lava flows accompanied by spasmodic explosive activity.

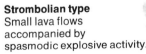

Vulcanian type
Violent emission of ash and larger material accompanied by a characteristic trail of smoke.

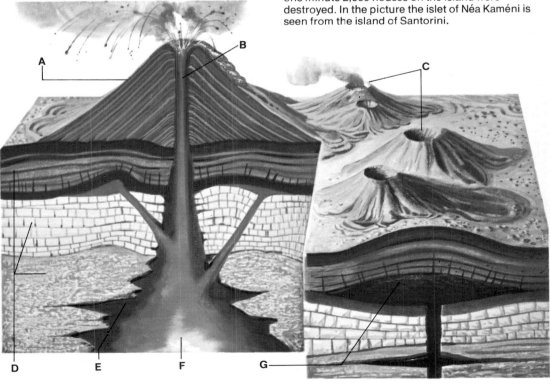

The regular cone of Mount Fuji *(below)*
The highest peak in the Japanese archipelago (island of Honshu, 3,776 m), worshipped as a sacred mountain and the object of pilgrimages, Fuji has been dormant since 1707, when the ashes from its eruption buried the city of Edo, now Tokyo. Japan, which is part of the so-called "fiery ring of the Pacific", is one of the most active and unstable areas in the world where vulcanicity is concerned. Its very large number of active volcanoes mark the line of contact between the Pacific and Eurasian plates. The Pacific plate is slowly creeping under the edge of the second plate giving rise to intense volcanic activity and leading to the formation of deep trenches (the Japan trench, the Kuril trench).

The birth of a volcanic island *(above)*
The island of Surtsey was formed in November 1963 by an underwater eruption. When such an eruption occurs the magma, escaping through a fissure in the floor of the ocean, is suddenly cooled on contact with the cold sea water. There follows a series of violent explosions of water vapour with outpourings of cinder which accumulates around the underwater source to form a volcanic cone which can, as in the case of Surtsey, extend above the surface of the sea. This is usually a short lived structure which is rapidly destroyed by the waves.

GREAT ERUPTIONS

79 AD Vesuvius buries Pompeii, Herculaneum and Stabiae.
1006 Ash from the Merapi volcano on the island of Java (Indonesia) buries the city of Baradur.
1669 Etna destroys part of Catania with flows of lava.
1783 The Asama volcano on the island of Honshu (Japan) causes thousands of deaths.
1883 Explosion of the Krakatoa volcano in Indonesia. More than 40,000 victims.
1902 The Pelé volcano on the island of Martinique destroys the city of Saint Pierre (34,000 dead).
1943 The new volcano Paricutin is born in Mexico.
1963 The Agung volcano on the island of Bali (Indonesia) causes 2,000 deaths.
1968 In Costa Rica the Arenal volcano destroys numerous villages.
1973 On the island of Heimaey (Iceland) the Helgafell volcano destroys part of the city.
1980 Mount St Helens (USA) explodes: 65 dead and 400 sq km of forest destroyed.
1985 The Nevado do Ruiz, in Colombia, kills 20,000 victims.

The crater of Vesuvius
This very famous volcano near Naples is composed of two peaks each of a quite different type. Mount Somma is the remains of an ancient crater shattered by successive explosions; the Great Cone, where the actual crater lies, reaches a maximum height of 1,277 m and is seen reflected in the bay of Naples.
The best recorded eruption was in 79 AD. This was when the nearby cities of Pompeii, Herculaneum and Stabiae were destroyed and buried.

The earthquake and volcanic zones of the Earth
As can be seen from the map, there is a clear correspondence between the regions of the Earth where earthquake activity is common and those where volcanoes are located. These areas are relatively young in geological terms and therefore still unstable, and they comprise the recent great mountain chains (the Alpine-Himalayan chain and the Circumpacific chain) and the mid-ocean ridges.

DISTRIBUTION OF VOLCANIC AND EARTHQUAKE ZONES

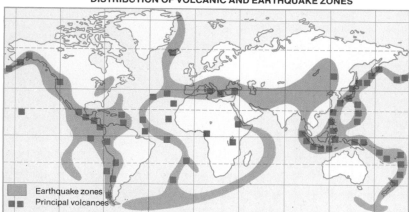

■ Earthquake zones
▪▪ Principal volcanoes

GREAT EARTHQUAKES

1693 In eastern Sicily an earthquake causes 60,000 casualties.
1755 The city of Lisbon is almost completely destroyed by a violent tremor accompanied by a tidal wave.
1906 The city of San Francisco is hit.
1908 An earthquake and tidal wave raze Messina to the ground; 85,000 dead.
1923 Tokyo and Yokohama are destroyed by a tremor. The dead number around 100,000.
1960 The city of Agadir in Morocco is razed to the ground.
1972 In Managua, the capital of Nicaragua, more than three quarters of the buildings are flattened. Casualties number 6,000.
1976 Earthquakes in Friuli (1,000 victims) and in China (one million victims).
1980 In Algeria an earthquake causes 28,000 deaths.
1985 A violent earthquake hits Mexico City: 35,000 dead.
1988 60,000 victims in Armenia.

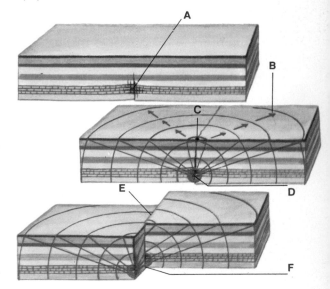

Geysers

Geysers, fumaroles and solfataras (gas vents) belong to the group of phenomena known as "secondary volcanic activity".

Without doubt, the most spectacular of these phenomena is the geyser (the photograph above shows the spout of a geyser near West Thumb in Yellowstone National Park, USA). Geysers are very hot springs which periodically hurl jets of water into the air which can reach a height of 50 m. They are found most frequently in New Zealand, Iceland and in the Yellowstone National Park and are caused by the heating of water from an underground spring by hot volcanic gases. Some of the water reaches boiling point and the resultant pressure violently expels a vertical column of water, causing the familiar spout of the geyser.

Solfatara
The solfatara is a discharge of various gases from small craters or fissures in areas of volcanic activity. The solfatara in the picture emits gases such as hydrogen sulphide which oxidise on contact with the air, depositing the familiarly yellow-coloured sulphur.

Earthquakes

Terrae motus, trembling of the Earth. These Latin words describe exactly that startling natural event, the earthquake.

Earthquakes are felt as sudden rapid movements of the ground caused by a succession of seismic waves, which originate in an area fairly deep down within the Earth's crust. These waves, which are usually due to a shifting of the rocks within the crust, can be divided into three types: longitudinal waves, causing up and down movement of the ground; transverse waves, which travel more slowly than the first type, causing a wave-like movement; and lastly surface waves, which travel even more slowly. The source of these waves is known as the origin or focus and the point on the Earth's surface immediately above the source is known as the epicentre. The geographical distribution of earthquakes is not random but seems to be associated particularly with those zones which are not yet completely stable (recent mountain chains, ocean trenches), and which also exhibit intense volcanic activity.

The most recent research in the field of Earth sciences tends to include earthquakes in an overall view of all the phenomena affecting the Earth's surface (vulcanism, the formation of the mountain chains and the ocean trenches and mid-ocean ridges).

Both seismic and volcanic activity are

The ruins of Gibellina
This picture conveys a very clear idea of the destructive force of an earthquake. Gibellina, a Sicilian settlement in the Belice valley, was hit by a violent tremor in January 1968 and completely razed to the ground, resulting in many casualties.

manifestations of the release of energy occurring along the abutting edges of the many tectonic plates into which the Earth's crust is divided.

Successive phases of an earthquake
A) Rupture point
B) Seismic waves
C) Epicentre
D) Focus
E) Fracture line (fault)
F) Displacement of the edges of the fracture

Caves and grottoes

Natural caves can result from various causes and can be found in many different types of surroundings. We find them on wavebeaten coasts, in the faces of glaciers and in solidified lava streams. The greatest and most spectacular, however, are the result of the dissolving of limestone rocks.

Limestone rocks are mostly composed of calcium carbonate which is insoluble in water. The surface water, however, contains carbon dioxide which causes the insoluble calcium carbonate to be chemically transformed into calcium bicarbonate which is water-soluble and can therefore be carried away by water washing over it.

Closely related to this chemical pheno- menon is the high degree of fissuring in limestone, either vertically (joints) or hori- zontally (strata or bedding planes) which encourages the penetration of water leading to the formation of underground passages, recesses, galleries and later caves and grottoes.

The erosive action of the water and consequent structural collapse has led to the formation of caves which are sometimes of enormous size connected together by a whole system of passages, vertical shafts, and galleries, which are being systematically explored by speleologists. One of the biggest cave systems in the world is the Mammoth Cave National Park system in the United States, whose galleries stretch for 484 km.

Traces of the past *(above)*
Prehistoric man frequently left traces of his existence on cave walls. These were usually figures of animals engraved or painted in vivid colours as in the picture (the Lascaux caves in the Dordogne, France), probably to bring good hunting or for some other ritual purpose.

The karst landscape
The phenomena of natural fissuring and chemical solubility typical of limestone rock give rise to a particular type of land formation known as "karst" (after the Karst plateau in Yugoslavia, where these phenomena are widely displayed), characterised by the almost complete lack of surface water features. The water rapidly penetrates to some depth through numerous sinkholes and fissures and commences active erosion thereby creating the recesses, caves and grottoes shown in the illustration.

A) Stalagmites
B) Stalactites
C) Columns
D) Sinkholes
E) Subterranean river
F) Shaft
G) Cave
H) Subterranean pool
I) Limestone rock

Stalagmites in the Tuckaleechee cave
(Tennessee, USA)
The walls, vaults and floors of the caves are usually covered with calcareous accretions caused by the slow deposition of limestone by the action of water. When the water escapes from fissures in a cave ceiling, dissolved carbon dioxide tends to be released because of the reduced pressure. The bicarbonate of calcium then becomes calcium carbonate which is insoluble and is deposited on the rock. This is how stalactites, which hang down, and the thicker stalagmites, which rise from the ground, are formed.

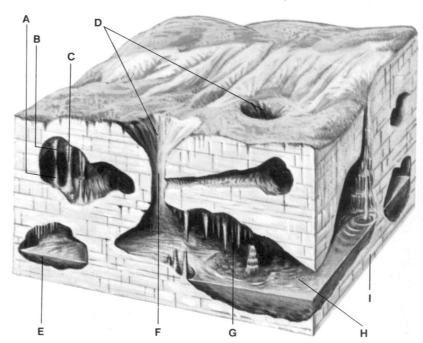

The Earth's treasures

Minerals represent a valuable gift from the Earth, whether from the scientific aspect, for their beauty (as with precious stones), or lastly for their fundamental importance and widespread utilisation in industrial fields, especially metallurgy.

The term "mineral" is applied to a homogeneous body (that is to say a substance in which each particle has the same chemical and physical properties as all the others) formed in the Earth's crust (lithosphere) by natural processes.

Many minerals are formed by the cooling and solidification of magma, others by the deposition of salts dissolved in percolating water, and others still through the phenomenon of metamorphosis, a process by which existing rocks are transformed and recrystallised by the high temperatures and pressures within the lithosphere.

Colombian emerald. A form of beryllium (cyclosilicate of beryllium and aluminium) with a dark green colour which is one of the most precious of gems.

Saxony quartz amethyst. A variety of quartz (silicon oxide) of a violet colour. Quartz is one of the most important minerals found in the various types of rock (igneous, sedimentary and metamorphic).

Gold. A natural element whose preciousness is well known, often found in the form of threads or scales. The most prolific gold-bearing zones in the world are in South Africa and the USSR.

Balangero asbestos. A phyllosilicate formed of whitish flexible fibres which is widely utilised in industry for its insulating properties.

Diamond. A gem which has been prized from antiquity for its qualities of clarity and brilliance which can be greatly enhanced by accurate cutting.

Uranium from the Congo. Oxide of uranium, the best known mineral from which this radioactive element is extracted.

Magnetite with barytes. Magnetite, a translucent black colour, is one of the most useful and commonest oxides of iron found in nature. The white or colourless barytes are the commonest form of the mineral barium.

Graphite. Although, like the diamond, composed of carbon, graphite differs enormously in its physical properties. It is in fact the softest mineral known.

Chilean malachite. A green carbonate of copper often associated with azurite and found in large quantities in Siberia.

Calcite crystals. Calcium carbonate is widely found throughout the Earth's crust and forms the basis of the limestone rocks.

Celestine with sulphur. Celestine, colourless or slightly blue, is a sulphate of strontium often associated with sulphur.

Mountains

It is undeniable that one of the most striking features of the continents is the hills and mountain ranges. These range from the giant Himalayas to the modest peaks of the Alpine foothills. Despite the tremendously wide variety of shapes and formations, those upward projections of the Earth's surface large enough to merit the description "mountain" can be considered to possess two characteristics in common.

The first is the well known fairly steep slope of mountainous territory (greater than 20%). This shows that erosion is at work (principally by water in its many physical states), a process of continual wearing down of these grandiose structures composed of widely differing types of rock, sculpting, chiselling and finally flattening the mountains which were raised up by tectonic activity (above all by the coming together of two tectonic plates).

The second characteristic common to all the mountains in the world is the variation in climate from the base to the peak. The air temperature is known to fall by about one degree Celsius for every 180 m increase in height and precipitation is much heavier in the mountains than on the plains. All this has a significant effect upon vegetation and also on the settlement of man. By climbing only a few kilometres one can pass from a landscape of broadleaved forest to pines, grasslands, arctic tundra and lastly to the region of perennial ice.

The Bernese Alps (Switzerland)
On the left can be seen the highest peak of the range, the Finsteraarhorn, which reaches a height of 4,224 m and from which the Unteraar glacier winds its way down, reaching all the way to Lake Grimsel. The landscape is typical of high Alpine mountains with a rather harsh shape, having crests and steep walls which are continuously subjected to the destructive action of freezing and thawing and to the sculpting action of many glaciers.

The Dru Needle pyramid
The Dru peak, which rises up like a slender obelisk above Chamonix in France, forms a part of the Mont Blanc range (Western Alps) and is composed of the characteristic granite known as protogine. Granite is a type of rock which originates from the cooling and solidification of a magma mass within the Earth's crust, which is then exposed and acted upon by the forces of erosion. The picture shows the vertical west wall of Petit Dru, about 1,000 m in height, characterised by huge slabs and columns of red protogine.

MOUNTAIN RANGES OF THE WORLD

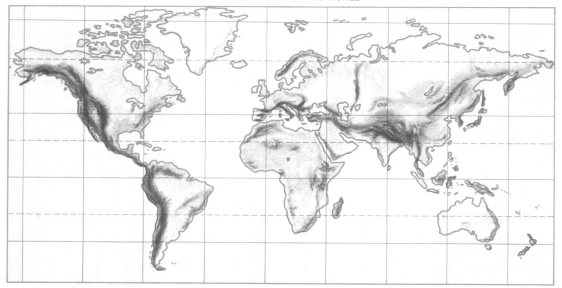

Formation of mountain ranges

The origin of mountains and uplands in general (orogenesis) has always been one of the fundamental problems facing geologists. Modern geologists, believing partly in Alfred Wegener's theory on "continental drift" dating back to 1915, maintain that it is possible to include all the phenomena occurring in the Earth's crust (mountain ranges, vulcanism, earthquakes, ocean ridges and trenches) in a single concept known as the theory of "global tectonics" or "plate tectonics". The Earth's crust (lithosphere) is said to be divided into six major rigid plates (Eurasian, African, Indian, Antarctic, Pacific and American) which float on the upper part of the mantle called the asthenosphere. The plates are subject to slow approaching, receding or tangential movement caused by subcrustal convection currents.

Over the course of the geological ages, the mutual displacement of the plates has carried the continents to many different positions (see below). This phenomenon was and still is always accompanied by the formation of ocean ridges (where two plates are receding) and by partial subduction (when two plates are colliding and their edges tend to overlap, forming mountains).

The birth of the continents
Ridges (green), fractures (black), direction of movement (red)

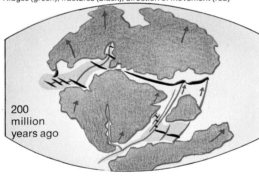

200 million years ago

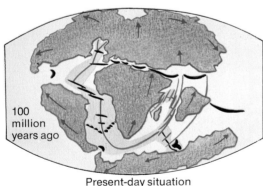

100 million years ago

Present-day situation

Orogenesis from the collision of two plates

The movement of two plates of the lithosphere towards each other can give rise to the formation of mountain ranges. This occurs when the approach velocity is limited (less than 6 cm per years) and the force of impact can therefore be absorbed by means of folding of the two edges of the plates.

In the other case (when the velocity is greater than 6 cm per year) we have the phenomenon of subduction, where one plate dives beneath the other and re-enters the mantle where it again becomes molten.

The drawings on the right show the principal phases in the formation of the Himalayan mountain range. The Asiatic and Indian plates are moving together slowly owing to subcrustal convection currents, causing corrugation of both edges of the plates. The accumulated sedimentary deposits in the basin dividing the two plates become compressed and forced upwards, while part of the crust is reabsorbed and remelted into the mantle. At the point of contact of the two plates there is thus massive deformation of the crust which, compressed and folded, gives rise to new mountain ranges such as that of the Himalayas.

Successive stages of orogenesis *(right)*
A) Two plates of the lithosphere (1) are approaching each other because of convection currents (arrows) in the mantle (2).
B) The edges of the two plates and the sedimentary deposits between them are compressed (3) and become corrugated.
C) The compression continues and leads to the elevation of the mountain range.

The Himalayas seen from space
The central part of Asia's huge mountain range looked like this to the astronauts in the Apollo 9 space capsule. The picture clearly shows the corrugation caused by the collision of the Indian plate (on the right, where the Ganges plain can be faintly seen) and the Asiatic plate on the left (part of the plain of Tibet can be seen). The Himalayas, which boasts the highest land on Earth (there are at least ten peaks there which exceed 8,000 m in height), is a tectonic structure of recent origin. Its formation dates back in fact only to the Tertiary Period and is contemporary with the birth of the Alps.

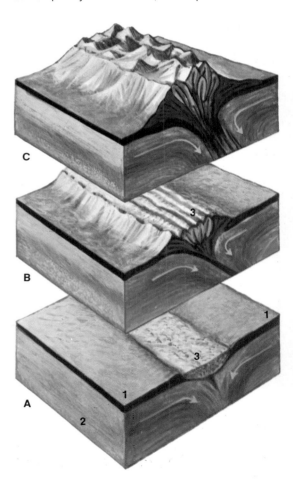

Mountains of the world

Man has always been fascinated by mountains but for century upon century "the cathedrals of the Earth", as John Ruskin called them, were cloaked in a veil of mystery and fear. For many people the mountain was a point of contact with God, or indeed the very seat of God; from Mount Olympus, home of the classical Greek gods, to the prehistoric shrines of Monte Bego in the Maritime Alps and to those of Mount Fuji on the island of Honshu in Japan.

For centuries considered mere landmarks and boundaries among the local people or as inconvenient obstacles by the commercial world, only since the end of the eighteenth century have mountains been appreciated for the scientific curiosity which they arouse and for their fascinating beauty, often wild and bleak, which is well illustrated in the pictures appearing on these two pages.

K2 in the Karakorum *(below)*
The majestic pyramid of rock, K2, rises from the
Godwin-Austen glacier. On the right can be seen the
south-east ridge called the Abruzzi Ridge, along
which the first ascent of the mountain was made (by
Achille Compagnoni and Lino Lacedelli in 1954).
K2, with a height of 8,611 m, is the second highest
mountain in the world. It is in the Karakorum, a
mighty Asian mountain range situated north-west of
the Himalayas at the border between India, Pakistan
and China, and is composed of extremely dense
granitic gneiss. The name K2 comes from the
classification assigned by the Indian geodetic
service and means Peak no. 2 of the Karakorum.

Everest, the roof of the world
(Himalayas) *(left)*
The highest peak in the world (8,848 m) stands out darkly on the left, while in the foreground can be seen the pointed pyramid of Nuptse which reaches the respectable height of 7,879 m. Everest rises from the Himalayas at the borders between Nepal and Tibet which form the most spectacular mountains on the surface of the Earth. The whole structure was formed by Tertiary orogenesis which also caused the formation of the Alps. The name Everest commemorates Sir George Everest who between 1823 and 1842 was head of the British geodetic service in India. The Tibetan name, Chomolungma, is much more poetic, meaning Goddess Mother of the Earth.

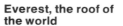

Glaciers at the Equator: Mount Kenya *(right)*
Together with Kilimanjaro and Ruwenzori, Mount Kenya (5,199 m) makes up the great trio of African mountains. Situated just south of the Equator in the African state of the same name, Mount Kenya is the remains of an ancient volcanic structure which has been severely weathered and carved by erosion. The many glaciers have contributed to the sculpturing of this massive structure which, as can be seen in the picture, dominates the high valley of Teleki. Only a small distance from the mountain's perennial glaciers, appear groups of senecios, herbaceous plants which, owing to the particular climate of Kenya, can reach a height of as much as 15 metres.

McKinley, the giant of Alaska *(left)*
At 6,193 m McKinley is the highest peak in the entire North American continent. Situated in the Alaskan Range, it rises imposingly in isolation above the tundra, its sides hidden by glaciers. Visible from a great distance, it was discovered by George Vancouver, the navigator, in 1794, but the summit was not reached until 1913.

Grand Teton, the "Matterhorn of the United States" *(right)*
It is given this name because its slanting strata are vaguely reminiscent of the famous Alpine peak. Grand Teton (4,190 m) is the highest peak in the granite Teton mountains (Teton Range) in the central part of the Rocky Mountains (Wyoming). The area surrounding Teton has been declared a national park.

Cerro Torre, Patagonian Andes *(left)*
The rocky spire of Cerro Torre (3,128 m), with its near vertical granite walls, seems to offer a challenge of nature to the courage of mankind. Continually struck by blizzards from the Pacific Ocean, Torre is covered with a layer of unstable and soft ice ready to turn into a terrifying avalanche.

Aconcagua, the father of the Andes *(right)*
Aconcagua, which reaches a height of 6,960 m, is the highest peak in the whole of both North and South America. It is in the Andean chain in the far west of Argentina. The mountain, which is of volcanic origin, is composed of lava from the Tertiary Period (and therefore a contemporary of the Alpine orogenesis), which was deposited on top of older marine sediment. The picture on the right shows the south-east face with the Lower Horcones glacier.

Glaciers

Confined in small basins called "cirques", squeezed between rocky walls, or flowing in a great frozen mass like a solidified river, glaciers owe their origin to a slow process of transformation of the snow.

Above a certain altitude (known as the limit of permanent snow), which is around 2,700 m in the Alps, the snow which falls in the coldest months does not completely melt in the summer. The snow therefore accumulates from year to year and is slowly transformed by the gradual expulsion of air due to the increasing pressure first into granular snow and then eventually into compacted ice.

The resulting mass of ice does not remain static but, owing to gravity, tends to slide over the ground with a velocity which varies between a few tens and a few hundreds of metres per year.

The glacier will be halted naturally in its downstream movement at the height at which the increasing temperature is high enough to melt it. The survival of a glacier therefore is related to the balance between the accumulation of snow in the coldest months of the year and its melting or dissolution in the warm summer months.

If over a number of years the snowfall is heavy and the summer temperature is low, the glacier will tend to expand and in the opposite case it will tend to contract.

Crevasses
In the foreground can be seen some deep cracks in the ice, or crevasses. These are fractures of the ice mass whose depth varies from a few metres to 50 metres or so. Crevasses are formed when the ice flow, in its descent, encounters a slope that is too steep and which tends to stretch or compress it, thereby exceeding the elastic limit of the ice.

The Colory Glacier in Alaska
The glaciers of Alaska, which together cover an area of over 50,000 sq m, are of the piedmont type. As they flow out of the valleys, their trunks merge into one giant ice flow which sometimes, as in the photograph, reaches all the way to the sea. The dark winding line which appears to divide the glacier is a moraine, which consists of rock debris torn from the mountain face and carried along by the movement of the glacier.

**Longitudinal section
of a valley glacier**

A) Glacial cirques
B) Lateral moraine
C) Glacial stream
D) Base moraine
E) Transverse crevasses
F) Longitudinal crevasse
G) Glacial trunk
H) Central moraine
I) Terminal moraine

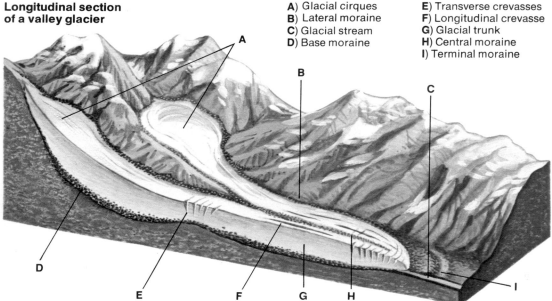

The Aletsch, the greatest glacier in the Alps *(right)*
The Aletsch glacier is in Switzerland, in the Finsteraarhorn mountains. It is a compound valley type glacier; that is, it is formed by the confluence of several single valley glaciers (those glaciers where a single trunk flows down from the collecting basin and occupies the upper part of a valley). The Aletsch glacier is over 20 km in length and covers an area of more than 100 sq km.

The face of an Antarctic glacier
Antarctica is almost totally covered by an ice sheet from which many glaciers flow to the sea. Yet even here, as seen in the photo, right next to fully glaciated terrain there remain a few areas which are not covered with ice.

The Baltoro Glacier (Karakorum)
In the great Karakorum and Himalayan ranges in Asia there are many glaciers which fill entire valley systems. Among the biggest of these is Baltoro which is about 60 km in length and covers over 700 sq km in area.

The great Quaternary Ice Ages

Continental (inland) glaciers and the glaciers of the various mountain ranges on the Earth cover at the present time an area of around 15 million sq km, which represents 10% of the land area. Ice covers nearly all (96%) of the great Antarctic region (12,600,000 sq km) and the island of Greenland (1,800,000 sq km).

By the beginning of the last century several studies had already shown that at one time the glaciers occupied a much larger area. Evidence for this theory were the scattered boulders, the scoured rocks and above all the corries and moraines found well outside the Alpine valleys. Today it is agreed that between one million and 12,000 years ago there were several Ice Ages when the ice coverage increased to around 47 million sq km, about three times more extensive than now. Great ice caps formed, outside Antarctica and Greenland, in North America, Scandinavia and in Central Siberia.

The Alps themselves have been invaded by massive rivers of ice at least four times, reaching right down to the plains.

Much study has been devoted to discovering the cause of the ice ages of the Quaternary Period, which were clearly linked with climatic changes. Nowadays some people believe that the climatic oscillations may have been due to variations in the amount of thermal energy coming from the Sun, resulting from the changes in the eccentricity of the Earth's orbit and the variations in inclination of the Earth's axis.

The expansion of the ice caps during the Quaternary Period
The illustration shows the limits reached by the ice during the great Quaternary Ice Ages when ice covered a large part of North America and Europe.

The Ganges, sacred river of India
The picture on the left shows the plain of the Ganges as it looks from a height of 230 km (the photograph was taken in October 1968 from Apollo 7). On the left, covered by cloud, part of the great Himalayan range can be seen where the Ganges rises in the north at a point about 4,500 m high. After flowing 2,700 km through large cities such as Allahabad and Varanasi (the photograph above shows the Ganges at Varanasi), the Ganges discharges into the Bay of Bengal in a delta having an area of 75,000 sq km.

A bend of the Rio Grande
Called by the Mexicans Río Bravo del Norte, the Rio Grande marks the boundary over a long distance from El Paso to the Gulf of Mexico, between the United States and Mexico.

Rivers

To an observer in an aircraft, the land appears to be frequently covered with winding silver threads of varying width which here and there flow together forming a complex network. These are the water courses, rivers and streams which are fundamental elements in the evolution of the landscape which they alter by erosion and silting but which are also indispensable to man to whom they bring the precious gift of water.

In order for an area to be provided with water courses, certain requirements must be met, such as a sufficient quantity of water, which may come from atmospheric precipitation or from the melting of snow and ice; a suitable gradient to enable the water to flow towards other rivers and thence to lakes or to the sea; and a low surface permeability so that the water is not lost as it flows over the ground.

The water which is not absorbed by the ground first runs down slopes then collects in rivulets, some of which, having greater erosive power, excavate deeper beds and annex nearby streams. Thus a stream is born which grows ever larger until eventually it becomes a river.

The Zaire river *(below left)*
Completely surrounded by dense equatorial forest, the Zaire winds slowly, through sweeping meanders, down to the Atlantic Ocean. These bends are characteristic of slow-running lowland rivers and some valley rivers. To the sides of the river can also be seen some oxbow lakes, remains of more highly developed bends which have been abandoned as small lakes in the typical horseshoe shape. Considered to be among the greatest rivers in the world on account of its length (4,200 km), the Zaire, formerly called the Congo river, is second to the Amazon in the area of its basin (3,822,000 sq km).

The course of a river
A) Upper course
B) Middle course
C) Lower course

1) Valley
2) Alluvial fan
3) Meander

4) Oxbow
5) Delta
6) Sea

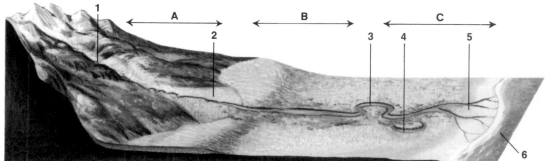

The Amazon

The Spaniards gave the river this name when, in the sixteenth century, they first entered the equatorial forests and were attacked by Indians with long hair whom they mistook for female warriors, like the Amazons of Greek mythology. With a length of 6,280 km, which puts it in second place among the great rivers of the Earth, the Amazon has no rivals where flow rate is concerned. At about 600 km from the ocean, its flow rate is over 200,000 cu m of water per second. Before discharging into the Atlantic, the river divides into a number of branches separated by sandy islands which are continually reshaped by material transported by the river and deposited at the mouth.

Log flotation on the Si Kiang (left)

There are several important rivers in China. Two of the largest are the Yangtse Kiang and the Huang-ho (Yellow River). The Huang-ho is so called because of the large amount of yellowish alluvial material carried by its waters. In fact the river flows across some plains covered with loess, a very soft yellow rock formed by the accumulation of fine desert dust carried by the wind and deposited on the plains.

The Rhine (above)

The Rhine, which flows through several European countries, is essentially a German river which has always figured in the history and economy of Germany.

The falls of the Blue Nile (left)

Rising in Lake Tana in Ethiopia, the Blue Nile then joins the White Nile at Khartoum to form the Nile proper. The Egyptian civilisation grew up along this river which boasts a length of 6,680 km.

The Mississippi, father of all rivers (below)

So called by the American Indians, the Mississippi and its tributary, the Missouri, reaches a length of 6,260 km and is a most significant feature of the United States landscape from the Rocky Mountains to the Gulf of Mexico.

Lake Saimaa (left)
Lake Saimaa, one of the largest in Finland (1,300 sq km), owes its existence to the expansion of the ice caps which occurred during the Quaternary Period which at various times covered the whole of Scandinavia and the Baltic. In Finland, aptly called "land of the 60,000 lakes", the erosive action of the ice has given rise to a very large number of lakes (totalling over 58,000) which cover about one tenth of the land area. The lakes are mostly of irregular outline, dotted with small islands covered with coniferous forest and of a depth which rarely exceeds ten metres.

Crater Lake
Situated in the Cascade Mountains (Oregon, USA), Crater Lake is a typical example of a volcanic or crater lake. This one fills the base of an enormous crater or basin (its diameter exceeds eight kilometres and its depth 800 metres) and it was formed by the subsidence of the upper part of a volcano into the magma reservoir below.

Lakes

Among the most beautiful and picturesque features of the Earth's landscape are lakes; so often associated with an idyllic serenity. A lake is simply a basin filled with water which has no immediate means of flowing to the sea. In keeping with this definition, lakes, which can be filled either by rivers and streams which flow into them or by precipitation, may have a wide variety of different origins.

The most common criterion of classification relates to the origin of the basin, distinguishing between lakes formed by obstruction of water and those formed in original or existing basins.

In the first case, the lake is formed when an obstruction of some kind blocks the normal flow of water which, in order to continue on its way to the valley, obviously has first to fill up the existing hollow upstream of the obstruction.

This obstruction may consist of a landslide (as in the case of Lake Alleghe, for example), a glacial moraine, a glacier, a coastal ridge or a dune.

Among those lakes whose basins are original and not due to some obstruction are crater lakes (for example Crater Lake, Oregon) and tectonic lakes, which fill great fissures in the Earth's crust like those of eastern central Africa (Lake Edward, Lake Tanganyika, Lake Malawi, etc.). There are also karst lakes, formed from caves and sinkholes, glacial lakes formed by the eroding action of flowing ice, and lakes in meteorite craters.

Lake Band-i-Amir
The picture shows two of the Band-i-Amir lakes in Afghanistan. This is a system of seven lakes in the Band-i-Amir Valley in Hazarajat (Koh-i-Baba mountains). The lakes occur along a fissure line, visible evidence of which can be seen in the often vertical rocky walls enclosing them which are one of the edges of this fissure. These lakes are therefore tectonic in origin; that is, they are formed by the filling up of rifts resulting from movements of the Earth's crust.

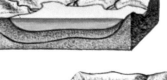

The inflowing rivers of a lake begin to deposit alluvial material on the bottom and to form deltas.

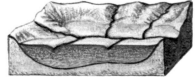

In the intermediate phases, the deposits on the bottom reach a significant thickness and the deltas continue to extend.

By now, the sediment has filled the lacustrine basin and the fate of the lake is sealed.

The stages in the sedimentation of a lake (left)
Lakes are but transitory features of the Earth's landscape, and from a geological point of view have an extremely short life, especially when they are of limited size and depth. The inevitable disappearance of a lake follows the filling up of its basin with alluvial material from the rivers which flow into it, forming deltas which continually advance towards each other until they unite, as illustrated in the drawings on the left.

Lake Baikal (above)
Lake Baikal in eastern Siberia also has its origins in tectonic phenomena of the Earth's crust and fills a deep, asymmetrical fissure between two mountain ranges.
Like the great tectonic lakes of East Africa, the most pronounced characteristic of Lake Baikal is its length rather than its width. With a depth reaching 1,740 metres, Lake Baikal is the deepest lake on Earth.

The Brianza lakes (above)
The three small stretches of water of Alserio, Pusiano and Annone appear blue among the gently rolling hills of Brianza (Lombardy). Of shallow depth (a maximum of ten metres) and limited area (the largest is Annone with 5.7 sq km), these lakes can be described as morainic, as they were formed behind the successive moraines deposited by the ancient ice.

Lake Titicaca (above)
Politically divided between Bolivia and Peru, Lake Titicaca is the largest lake in South America (8,300 sq km) and also one of the highest in the world at a height of 3,800 metres.

Lake Nakuru (above)
Thousands of pink flamingoes inhabit the banks of Lake Nakuru, which with its surrounding land forms one of the national parks of Kenya.
Lake Nakuru is situated in the eastern branch of the Rift Valley, that great fissure that opened up during the Tertiary and Quaternary Periods stretching for thousands of kilometres across eastern Africa and containing numerous lakes of widely varying sizes.

Lake-filled region in New Zealand (below)
Enclosed between steep mountainsides clothed with vegetation, the lakes of the South Island of New Zealand are reminiscent of the great lakes in the foothills of the northern Italian and Swiss Alps. New Zealand has also been subjected to intensive glacial erosion, the most visible evidence of which is in the elongated lake basins carved out during the Ice Ages by the ice masses.

The oceans

The name "Earth" for our planet does not seem very appropriate when we consider that over 70% of its surface is covered by seas and oceans which comprise a single connected system to which various names have been given by geographers. These include the Pacific Ocean (this is the largest, covering an area of 180 million sq km), the Atlantic Ocean and the Indian Ocean together with a number of minor seas. Over the centuries man has learnt to travel over and chart these vast expanses of water, but only recently have some of the secrets hidden below the waves been revealed. The massive submarine mountain ridges, submarine volcanoes, the mid-ocean ridges crossed by fissures and the movement of the sea bed are discoveries of contemporary science.

Despite the fact that modern technology has enabled the enormous depths of the ocean trenches to be explored (the bathyscaphe *Trieste* reached a depth of nearly 11,000 metres in 1960 in the Mariana Trench in the Pacific), our knowledge of the underwater world is still very limited. The future of mankind may well depend upon the expansion of our knowledge in this area. In an overpopulated world which is rashly wasting some of its natural resources, the oceans, with their immense supplies of water, food, minerals and energy could very well play an important part in the determination of our future.

The Cape of Good Hope
Although it is not Africa's most southerly promontory, the Cape of Good Hope is an essential point of reference on the route linking the Atlantic to the Indian Ocean.

The topography of the world beneath the sea
The illustration shows a section through a typical ocean bed in which can be seen the various features which comprise the underwater scene and which are usually hidden by the water.

A) Granite continental mass
B) Continental shelf
C) Basaltic crust
D) Ocean trench
E) Mantle

F) Mid-ocean ridge
G) Guyot (underwater mountain with flat top)
H) Volcano
I) Ocean islands

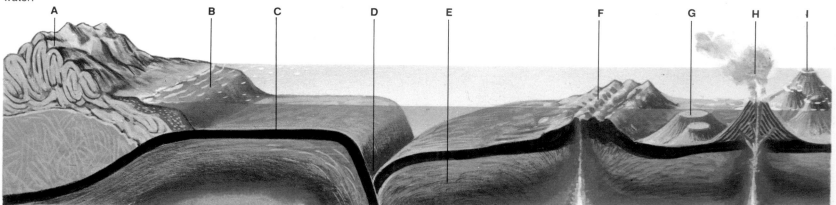

Man and the Sea

Oceanography, the study of the chemical, physical, geological and biological characteristics of the oceans, is a very young science. Today many people are studying this subject. Some have the opportunity to spend long periods in special submarine laboratories (photograph above) and to carry out experiments on the possibility of exploiting the depths.

Submarine exploration
1) Beebe-Barton bathysphere (932 m). **2)** Frogman. **3)** Research submarine Ben Franklin (down to 1,000 m). **4)** Alvin submersible (1,200 m). **5)** FNRS III bathyscaphe (2,300 m). **6)** Deepstar submersible (4,000 m). **7)** Bathyscaphe Trieste (10,911 m).

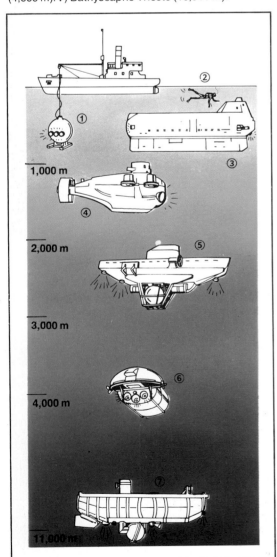

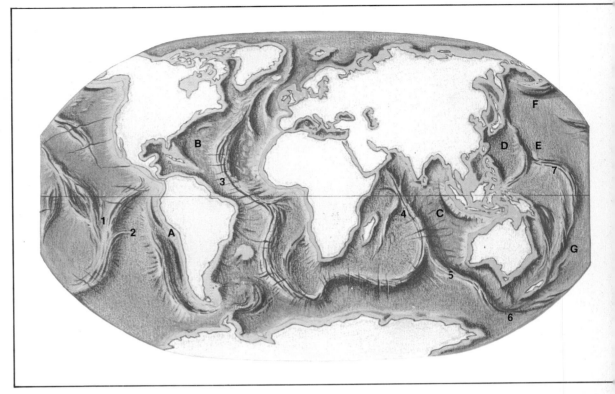

The ocean beds
Contrary to what was thought for centuries, the floor of the oceans is anything but flat and smooth. Modern hydrographic measurements have shown that the beds of the seas and oceans have an extremely varied topography in which, as shown in the map, imposing mountain ranges (ridges) lie alongside deep valleys and trenches.

Ocean ridges
1) Pasque Island
2) Eastern Pacific
3) Mid-Atlantic
4) Indian
5) Antarctic Indian
6) Pacific Antarctic
7) Hawaiian

Ocean trenches
A) Chilean-Peruvian
B) Puerto Rican
C) Andaman
D) Philippine
E) Mariana
F) Aleutian
G) Kermadec

Ocean currents
Caused by the motions of trade winds and the Earth's rotation, to which is added the variation of thermal characteristics of density and salinity different from the waters surrounding them, these currents are like vast rivers moving about in the oceans. Among the best known is the Gulf Stream whose favourable effects are so far-reaching as to be felt even in the coastal areas of north-western Europe.

Ocean currents
(cold currents shown blue and warm currents red)
1) North Pacific
2) North Equatorial
3) East Countercurrent
4) South Equatorial
5) Peruvian
6) Antarctic
7) Cape Horn
8) Brazilian
9) Benguela
10) Canaries
11) Gulf Stream
12) North Atlantic Drift
13) Mozambique
14) Indian Countercurrent
15) Monsoon

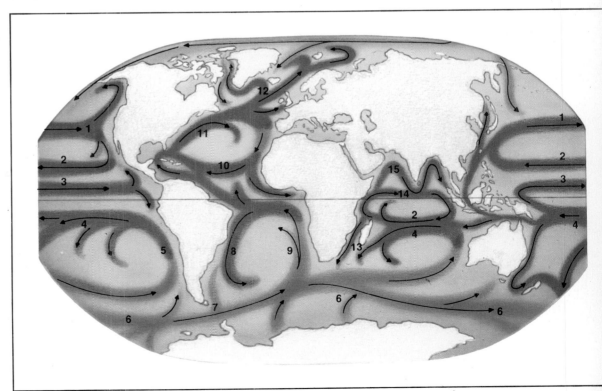

Waves

The surface of the seas and oceans is rarely flat and calm. More often there are undulations or waves to be seen which, in open waters, do not usually exceed a height of ten metres. Waves are usually caused by the action of the wind which, even if not very strong, always exerts a frictional force on the upper layers of water.

In exceptional cases, waves are caused by submarine volcanic action or earthquakes

which are extremely dangerous for inhabited coastal regions for these waves can reach very high velocities of the order of 800 km per hour and a height of over 25 m. These are known as tidal waves or "tsunami".

An observer of the waves on the surface of the sea would notice an apparent forward movement of the waves; this is only an illusion. In deep water, there is no actual forward movement of water, but only movement of energy. The particles of water actually move in closed paths, assuming a circular motion in deep water when the wave only affects a limited depth of water. This motion becomes elliptical, however, when the wave approaches the shore and is slowed down by friction with the bottom.

Breakers *(left)*
When the oscillatory motion of a wave meets the bottom of a gently sloping shore, the water particles are slowed down by friction with the bottom and take on an elliptical movement (see diagram below). Travelling on towards the shore, their orbital path is broken and the crest of the wave falls forward resulting in breakers which exert considerable forces on the shore and harbour installations.

Tides

Tides are periodical fluctuations of the level of the seas and oceans. Every day, or rather every 24 hours and 50 minutes, there are two rises in the level (flowing of the tide) followed by two reductions (ebbing). The principal cause of this phenomenon is the attraction exerted by the Moon on the mass of water on the Earth (see drawing below). In the middle of the oceans and the land-locked seas, the tide is scarcely noticeable (for example, in the Mediterranean it is less than one metre). In bays and estuaries the increase in the water level reaches quite high values and has a significant effect on navigation (the highest tides, 20 metres, have been recorded in the Bay of Fundy in Canada).

The cause of the tides
The principal cause of the tides is lunar gravitational attraction, but the Sun's gravitational pull also has an effect. The highest tides occur when, as shown in the diagram, the Earth, the Moon and the Sun are in line. The Sun and Moon combine then to give the highest high tides and lowest low tides, called spring and neap tides. On the opposite side of the Earth, owing to the reduced gravity, there is a further rising of the tide.

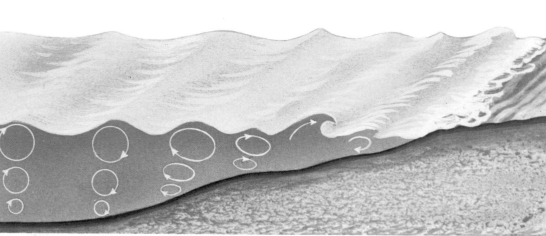

Coastlines

The coast, where the land meets the oceans and the seas, can take on many different aspects which change with time. Its position can change owing to variations in sea level (eustatic phenomena, typical of the Quaternary Period which saw the formation and melting of enormous glaciers) or because of tectonic movements (caused by the shifting of plates) or isostatic movements (rise or fall of the land when, for example, an ice sheet accumulates or melts upon it).

The coast is also continually subjected to reshaping, either through erosion or by the accumulation and deposition of material. Erosion, the effect of which naturally depends on the type and characteristics of the rocks forming the coast, is principally caused by the waves which, because of the pressure of the water and the materials contained in it (sand and shingle) are capable of slowly breaking up the coast which is occasionally protected from being completely eroded away by the accumulation of debris. The waves and the tides can actually deposit suspended materials and thus form beaches or offshore bars.

Different types of coastline
Coasts, whose shapes are due to the effects of erosion and deposition acting alternately, are usually divided into two groups: those with high cliffs and those with low beaches. The photographs on the right, from top to bottom, show three types of high cliffs.

The first shows true cliffs, typical of the French coast of the Channel, steep and sheer, carved in the sedimentary rocks of the Secondary Period.

The second picture shows the Australian coast north of Perth, where the action of the waves has left a series of spurs projecting into the ocean and exposed the various layers of sandstone.

The third photograph shows the coastline of Esterel in Provence (southern France), composed of resistant red porphyry.

The low coast at Oahu (left)
The narrow beach of Oahu, the most important island in the Hawaiian archipelago, is composed of sand and volcanic material, resulting from erosion or the wearing down of ancient volcanic structures.

Islands

Isolated stretches of land of various sizes, but always smaller than a continent, islands are scattered not only in the seas and oceans but also in lakes and rivers. Taking account of their geographical location and neglecting islands and islets in lakes and rivers, islands can be divided into two principal categories: continental and oceanic.

The first type form part of a continent (the British Isles are an example of this) in that they rise from the same base structure as the main continental mass and in past ages were often joined with the main continent.

Oceanic islands, which are mostly volcanic in origin, rise straight from the ocean floor.

The Hawaiian islands are oceanic islands. Islands can also be classified according to their origins. Thus there are, among others, volcanic islands, such as Surtsey in Iceland which is of very recent origin; and coral islands, common in tropical seas, built by living organisms.

The Isle of Levant (above)
Situated a short distance off Trapani and included in the Egadi group, the Isle of Levant is one of the western outcrops of Sicilian territory. It is formed of limestone and dolomite rock and this gives the coastline its often harsh and precipitous appearance.

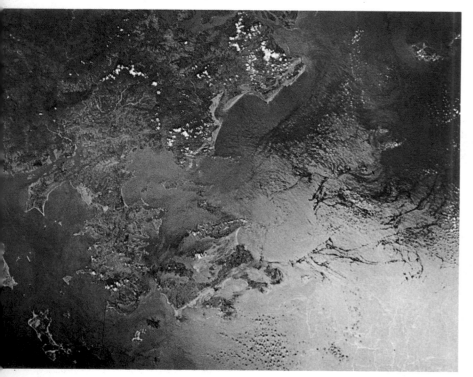

Continental islands off the coast of China
This photograph, taken from a satellite, shows a stretch of the east coast of China in the straits of Taiwan (Formosa) near the city of Fuzhou. As well as the mouths of the Min Chiang, numerous islands and islets can be seen rising from the same foundations as the Asian continent from which they are separated by narrow and often quite shallow stretches of water. Islands of this type were often united with the main continent quite recently in geological time, depending on eustatic, tectonic or isostatic movements (see main text).

THE LARGEST ISLANDS

Greenland	2,175,600 sq km
New Guinea	785,000 sq km
Borneo	736,000 sq km
Madagascar	587,000 sq km
Baffin Island	476,065 sq km
Sumatra	420,000 sq km
Great Britain	229,885 sq km
Honshu	227,414 sq km
Victoria Island (Canada)	212,198 sq km
Celebes	172,000 sq km
South Island (New Zealand)	150,461 sq km
Java	125,900 sq km
Newfoundland	112,300 sq km
Cuba	105,007 sq km
Luzon	104,687 sq km
Iceland	102,820 sq km
Sicily	25,426 sq km

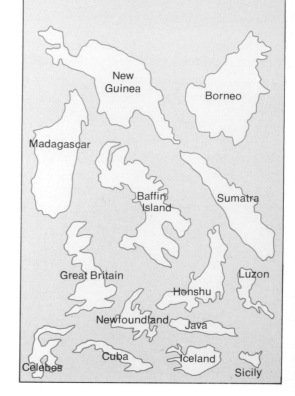

An atoll in the Maldives (Indian Ocean)
The Maldive Islands form a long archipelago between the Arabian Sea and the Indian Ocean to the west of Sri Lanka. There are over 2,000 islands and islets, all formed of natural coral following the slow and gradual sinking of the underwater shelf (subsidence). Most of the islands are surrounded by a coral reef in the shape of a ring covered with foam from the breaking ocean waves.

The birth of an atoll

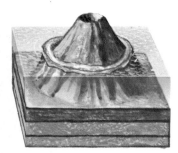

Coral grows around a volcanic island which is slowly sinking.

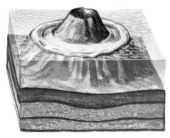

The island continues sinking while the coral structures grow up towards the surface.

The island has completely submerged. Vegetation appears on the coral reef.

An islet in New Caledonia
New Caledonia (French Oceania) comprises the principal island which gives its name to the group and an indefinite number of small islets. These are generally surrounded by a coral reef, which can be clearly seen in the picture.
Within the reef, the waters are calm and lap over a narrow beach of very white sand.

Atolls

The process by which atolls are formed has always posed an interesting scientific problem, made more complex by the special conditions necessary for the life of the organisms of which they are constructed (water temperature over 20°C, depth at the bottom less than 40 metres, continual submersion, and clear water with a high salinity). Yet today Darwin's theory seems to be correct, at least in general terms. He postulated a slow sinking of the rock base on which the first coral colonies had formed and a consequent upward growth of these colonies which could not survive at the increased depth (see drawings on the left).

The island of Bora Bora (above)
The principal features of the landscape of Bora Bora, an island in the Polynesian archipelago of the Society Islands, are the volcanic rocks, sculptured by erosion, the palm trees and the coral reef over which break the waves of the Pacific.

The archipelago of Tuamotu (below)
This photograph was taken from a height of about 250 km. The islands of the archipelago, which forms part of Polynesia, reveal their origin because of their characteristic shape. They are atolls, forming a circular or elliptical coral reef enclosing a lake. From the right, some of the larger atolls can be distinguished: Apotaki, Toau and Fakarawa with the little settlement of Rotoava. The inner lake, which looks the same colour as the surrounding ocean in this picture, is in reality very shallow (one hundred metres maximum).

Cirrus. High clouds (from 6,000 to 12,000 metres, the limit of the troposphere). They are shaped like tufts or thin fibres and are formed from tiny needles of ice which barely obscure the light of the sun. When, as in the picture, cirrus clouds are broken up, this is caused by high winds.

Cumulus. Clouds with very clear outlines which grow vertically up to quite great heights and have dome-shaped tops with white, rounded protuberances. They are convection clouds, caused by upward air currents, and usually indicate fine weather until they tower to great altitudes.

Atmospheric phenomena

Rain, snow and wind together with temperature variations (collectively known as atmospheric phenomena) are the clearest evidence of the way in which the physical characteristics (humidity, pressure and temperature) of the troposphere, that is those layers of the atmosphere between the Earth's surface and an average height of 12 kilometres, change and combine together in different ways.

In particular, rain is associated with the process of condensation of water vapour in the atmosphere which is the result of the phenomenon of evaporation. The amount of water vapour that can be absorbed by a mass of air is not unlimited, but is a function of the temperature. At 0ºC for example, one cubic metre of air cannot absorb more than five grammes of water vapour, while at 30ºC it can absorb more than 30 grammes. Clearly a reduction in the temperature will cause separation of the excess water vapour, which condenses in minute water droplets. The rains, as shown in the map below, are not evenly distributed over the surface of the Earth, but depend on the location of areas of high and low pressures. The most significant rainfall occurs in the equatorial belt where large masses of warm, humid air converge.

Cumulonimbus. Clouds rising to a great height with a very broad upper region. They are accompanied by storms with violent rain and lightning. They are typical of areas where warm and cold air masses meet (fronts) and the cold air drives a wedge under the warm air.

ANNUAL RAINFALL

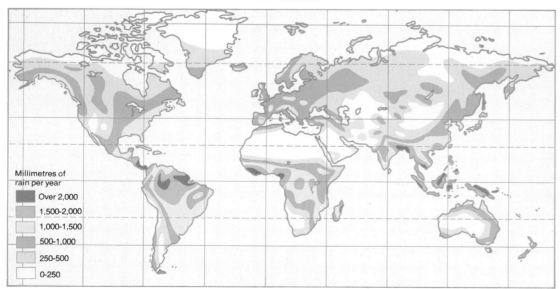

Millimetres of rain per year

- Over 2,000
- 1,500-2,000
- 1,000-1,500
- 500-1,000
- 250-500
- 0-250

Lightning. This is an electrical discharge occurring during thunderstorms between the base of the cloud and the ground or between two clouds. It is due to the potential difference between parts of the atmosphere which have accumulated electrical charges.

34

Snow
Snow is also the result of the condensation of water. This phenomenon occurs when the temperature is below freezing point and the water vapour passes from the gaseous state to the solid state to form tiny ice crystals which, if the temperature of the lower layers of the atmosphere is low enough, can reach the ground without melting.

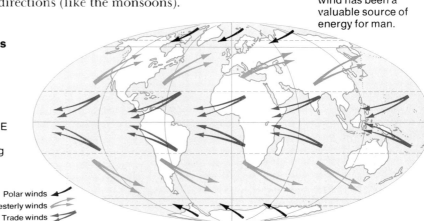

Drops of dew on a leaf
During the night the ground loses heat by radiation and the layer of air in contact with the surface is cooled. The water vapour in the air condenses in minute droplets and is deposited on the vegetation.

A bank of fog forming
Fog, which only affects the lower layers of the atmosphere, is formed of minute water droplets suspended in banks of varying density which can seriously reduce visibility. Near large industrial and urban centres the fog, combining with smoke, can easily become smog.

Wind

The wind, which is usually defined as a mass of air moving parallel to the surface of the Earth, is a phenomenon caused by the variations of pressure occurring in the atmosphere. The pressure, or force exerted by the air, is measured in millibars or millimetres of mercury and varies with height, humidity and temperature.

The air masses tend to move away from areas of high pressure (anticyclones) towards those of low pressure (cyclones, or depressions) like a river which flows from the highest to the lowest level. The winds are known as prevailing if they always blow in the same direction (like the Trade Winds which blow from the north-east in the northern hemisphere) or periodic when they blow alternately from two opposite directions (like the monsoons).

Windmills
Over the centuries, wind has been a valuable source of energy for man.

The prevailing winds
The map shows the directions of the principal prevailing winds. The so-called Trade Winds can be seen blowing towards the Equator from 30° NE and SE as can the westerly winds blowing towards the poles and the polar winds.

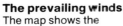

Polar winds
Westerly winds
Trade winds

The water cycle

The water cycle, of which rainfall forms only a part, is the process of the continual transformation of water through various physical states as it passes from the oceans to the Earth and back to the oceans again. This process is of vital importance to every form of life on Earth, water being essential to survival. Energy is provided by the heat of the Sun, together with the force of gravity.

Solar energy acts on the oceans to cause evaporation, i.e. the transformation of water from the liquid state to that of vapour. Part of the water vapour condenses and falls again as rain on to the oceans. But a large part is carried by winds over the Earth on to which it falls in the form of rain or snow. Some of this mass of water evaporates directly from the soil, lakes, rivers and vegetation (transpiration); some runs over the surface to replenish the water courses — snowfall replenishes the glaciers — and part of it penetrates the surface from where it also contributes to the feeding of the rivers (see below). The rivers in their turn flow into the seas and oceans, thus completing the cycle.

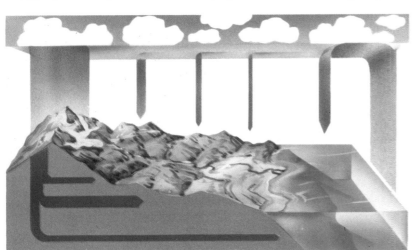

Subterranean water
The water which penetrates the soil filters through porous rocks like sandstone and limestone until it meets impervious rock. The saturation of the porous rocks forms the water table, from which the rivers are also fed.

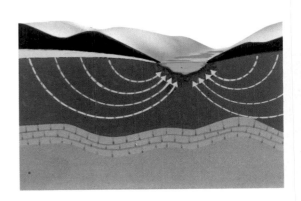

Climate

Climate can be defined as the outcome of the interaction between the diverse factors which characterise the Earth's atmospheric layer. Understanding climatic events requires analysis of the behaviour of the atmosphere over a relatively long time-span. There are three factors to take into consideration: temperature; humidity (and hence rainfall); and pressure (which is responsible for the movement of bodies of air, namely winds). In addition to these factors, latitude is also of importance because of its relationship to heat distribution and seasonal variations. On a lesser scale, in terms of microclimate, it is necessary to take account of many other influences which may give rise to variations in the relationships between the basic climatic factors. Altitude, continental influences, exposure, the presence of forests, the proximity of glaciers and other phenomena are all involved. Climate obviously plays a very important part in the modelling of the Earth's landscapes. In fact, every area of the Earth's surface is continually subjected to the action of factors such as ice, heat, rainfall and winds. These alter surface rocks and bring about a kind of adaptation of the contours of the land and its vegetation to the prevailing type of climate. Man is also subject to the influence of climate, despite the extent to which modern technology permits human beings to tolerate climatic conditions which would otherwise be incompatible with survival. It must also be remembered that the combinations of factors involved have not been stable over time, neither in geological terms nor in historical terms. Geological studies have shown that in past epochs the prevailing climatic conditions were quite different from those found today. For example, in Antarctica geologists have found coal deposits which show that there was once a warm, humid climate in a region now covered in ice. The fact that climate can vary even on a historical scale is demonstrated, among other things, by the retreat of the glaciers as recorded since the first half of the nineteenth century, resulting from a slight increase in world temperatures.

The atmosphere

The atmosphere probably developed at the time when the solid outer crust was forming. Some of the main components of the atmosphere (such as nitrogen, carbon dioxide and water vapour) were liberated during the solidification process; oxygen was produced only later by certain early plants. The atmosphere consists of layers differing both in physical character and in chemical constitution. The troposphere is the layer in contact with the Earth's surface, varying in thickness from 18 kilometres at the equator to 6 kilometres at the poles. Almost all the well-known meteorological phenomena originate in the troposphere, since it is in this layer that vertical movements of air masses and significant quantities of water vapour are to be found. Above the troposphere lies the stratosphere, which has a very low density and is almost completely lacking in water vapour. Above this is the ionosphere, characterized by electrically charged particles; finally there is the exosphere. Beyond that lies the vacuum of interstellar space.

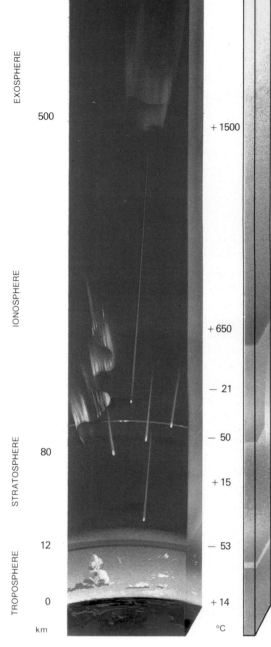

How the Sun heats the Earth

The illustration (*left*) clearly shows how the spherical shape of the Earth influences the distribution of heat at the various latitudes. In fact, because of the Earth's shape, the angle between the Sun's rays and a tangent to the Earth's surface becomes more and more acute as one moves from the Equator towards the poles. As a result, with increasing latitude the area over which the Sun's thermal energy is dispersed also increases, along with the density of the air which filters this energy. Hence regions close to the equator receive more solar radiation. Not only the form of the Earth but also its rotation has an influence on heat distribution, due to the inclination of the Earth's axis and the form of its orbit around the Sun.

Oceanic currents

Oceanic currents which are generated by variations in the density of sea water and by the rotational movement of the Earth, permit a massive transfer of thermal energy from the Equator to the poles. The map (*below*) shows the principal currents in the Atlantic Ocean. It is easy to recognise the northern equatorial current generated by the Trade Winds of the Azores region. After passing the Gulf of Mexico, this current swings northwards and exerts a warming influence on European coasts as the well-known Gulf Stream. In the southern hemisphere, the path followed by the equatorial current is different because of interaction with the cold currents of the subpolar regions.

DISTRIBUTION OF SOLAR ENERGY

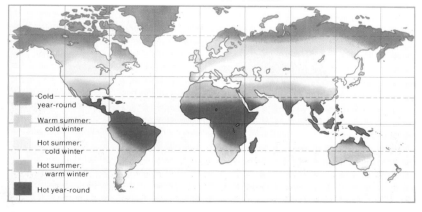

- Cold year-round
- Warm summer; cold winter
- Hot summer; cold winter
- Hot summer; warm winter
- Hot year-round

The large thermal belts delineated by the latitudes are less rigidly defined than they appear as a result of the determining influence of geographical features such as oceans, mountains and ocean currents on the temperature of the atmosphere.

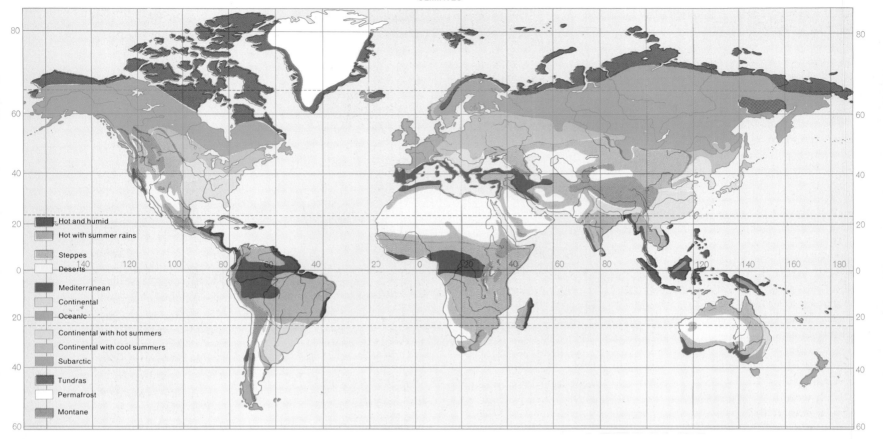

Climate and Vegetation

Vegetation, the fundamental ingredient of the various natural environments of the Earth, depends for its existence on many factors, most importantly the climate. The warming action of the Sun results in the formation of hot and cold air currents, causing winds, which in their turn affect the ocean currents. Winds and ocean currents together largely determine the distribution of humidity which, together with solar radiation, provides the basis of life for all vegetation.

The more humid and hot the climate, the more luxuriant and varied the vegetation. As humidity decreases so does the variety of species (forests of deciduous trees and forests of coniferous trees). Environments become progressively more arid, both in the tropical areas (savannas) and the temperate and cold areas (grasslands and steppes); until we finally arrive at the most barren — the deserts and the polar ice-caps.

The monsoon
Dark skies and trees emerging from fields transformed into lakes are typical of the Indian landscape when battered by monsoons. The torrential rains of the summer months compensate for the dryness of the winter and, despite disastrous flooding, are essential to agriculture and to the survival of vegetation.

Rain and vegetation
The diagram illustrates the relationship between the amount of rainfall and the vegetation. From the equatorial forests with an annual rainfall exceeding 2,000 mm, the vegetation changes gradually to desert as the rainfall decreases.

250
500
1,000
2,000
3,000

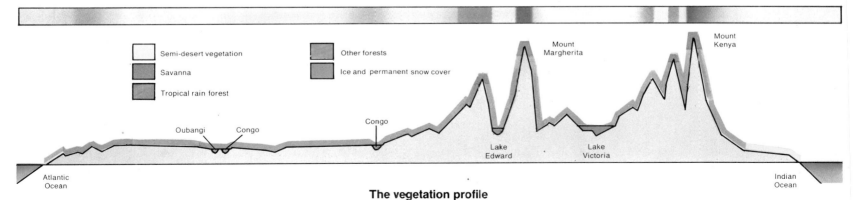

Semi-desert vegetation
Savanna
Tropical rain forest
Other forests
Ice and permanent snow cover

Mount Margherita
Mount Kenya
Congo
Oubangi
Congo
Lake Edward
Lake Victoria
Atlantic Ocean
Indian Ocean

The vegetation profile

There are a number of factors which limit plant growth and hence influence the geographical distribution of plant species: quantity and annual distribution of rainfall; soil type; exposure to sunlight; temperature; and so on. Collectively, these are referred to as climatic and physical factors. The diagram (*above*) shows the different plant associations which occur in sequence from the Atlantic coastline to the Indian Ocean coastline of Africa. It can be seen that the presence of bodies of water, even far inland, gives rise to humid local microclimatic conditions with resulting luxuriant plant growth. The further one moves away from the great oceans or from the lakes, the more arid the conditions become culminating in semi-desert and desert landscapes.

Vegetation

Although we commonly use expressions such as "pine-forest", "chestnut-grove", "beech forest" and "prairie", they are not widely recognised as actual ecological concepts, each defined by a basic set of fundamental constituents. In fact, the analysis of vegetation (that is to say, of the plant groups inhabiting different geographical areas) permits us to identify the structure and composition of the diverse habitats which are present on the Earth's surface by virtue of well-defined climatic and biological processes. The modern science of "phytogeography" combines the descriptive analysis of plant species found in association, that is entire plant communities, and the study of the relationships between plants and their general habitats. A phytogeographical study hence involves identification of the plant species in a given area, investigation of the "community structure" (degree of aggregation and isolation of individuals), and subsequent determination of links with climatic and ecological factors of the region concerned. When such studies are conducted systematically on a global scale it is possible to compile phytogeographical maps and to define vast general areas known as "biomes".

Pollination
Plants exhibit three different types of pollination mechanism which ensure fertilization through transport of male gametes (pollen):
1. Wind-borne pollination, as found (for example) in conifers.
2. Water-borne pollination. This is the most ancient in evolutionary terms and is still found, for instance, in mosses and duckweed.
3. Animal pollination. This is a much more sophisticated mechanism confined to flowering plants, which produce nectar to attract an animal carrier (e.g. insect, bird or bat) which will unwittingly transport pollen from one flower to another.

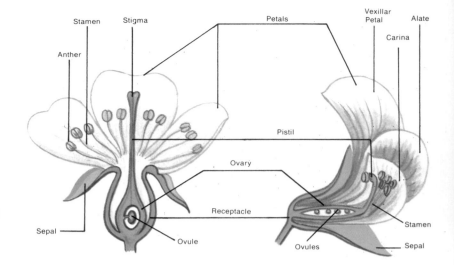

Flowering plants
When a plant is subjected to the appropriate photoperiod (that is to say, a characteristic relationship between the hours of daylight and hours of darkness) the apical meristems (growing tips) stop producing leaves, thus arresting vegetative growth, and begin a series of transformations which lead to flower development. The leaves themselves are responsible for this transition from vegetative to reproductive growth. In fact, when the leaves have reached their definitive size they also become maximally sensitive to the photoperiod. In response to the appropriate ratio between daylight and darkness, the leaves produce certain substances, including the flower-producing hormone, which reach the apical meristems and induce the production of the characteristic floral structures. The diagram (*above*) provides two examples of floral organization.
The exceptional capacity of plants to assess the relative duration of periods of daylight and darkness permits all individuals of a species to flower at the same time and thus increases the chances of cross-fertilization.

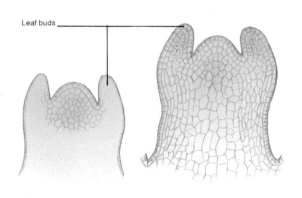

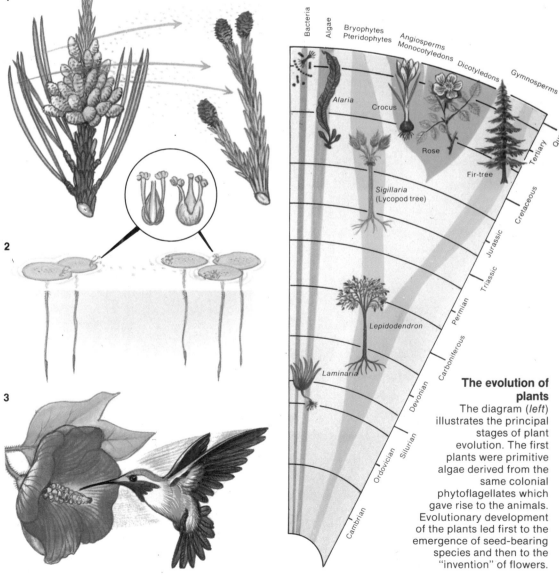

Apical growth
The growing zone of a bud consists of an apical region where cell-division (and hence an increase in cell number) takes place and of a region of cell-growth (where cell number remains constant) in which the embryonic leaves and the internodal segments of the stem develop until they reach their definitive size. The issue of the apical meristem (*see diagram above*) produces new leaves which emerge from the apex in the form of two bulges, each of which subsequently flattens out to form a leaf lamina. Whilst this is happening, the leaf stem grows in length and the vascular elements develop. It should be noted that the entire growth process is governed by plant hormones which respond to external influences such as photoperiod.

The evolution of plants
The diagram (*left*) illustrates the principal stages of plant evolution. The first plants were primitive algae derived from the same colonial phytoflagellates which gave rise to the animals. Evolutionary development of the plants led first to the emergence of seed-bearing species and then to the "invention" of flowers.

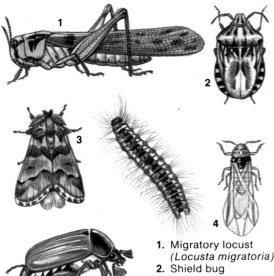

Soils

The term "soil" refers to the relatively thin layer, covering the bed-rock, which is generated by the weathering action of atmospheric factors and biological agents. In climatic regions with regular rainfall distributed throughout the year, deep soil-layers are formed, with all the mineral elements evenly dispersed throughout. By contrast, when rainfall is limited in quantity or rare in occurrence during the year, there is only slow modification of rock, and excess water runs across the surface, carrying away the scarce products of weathering. There is also a temperature influence: for any given combination of bed-rock and pattern of rainfall, low temperatures produce a "podzol" whereas high temperatures lead to laterite formation. Of course, the chemical composition of the soil is also important in determining the character of any vegetation which becomes established. Typical important chemical components are nitrates, carbonates of calcium and magnesium, and various free ions which determine the level of acidity.

1. Migratory locust
   (*Locusta migratoria*)
2. Shield bug
   (*Eurygaster maura*)
3. The oak processionary caterpillar and the adult moth
   (*Thaumetopoea processionea*)
4. Vine-fly
   (*Viteus vitifolii*)
5. Cockchafer
   (*Melolontha melolontha*)
6. Adult and larva of Colorado beetle
   (*Leptinotassa decemlineata*)
7. Spruce bark beetle
   (*Ips typographus*)

Plant parasites

In addition to the numerous examples of positive interaction between plants and animals, there are many examples of parasitism, particularly involving insects. It is indispensable for modern agriculture to be able to recognise such plant pests. A number of common "destroyers" of vegetation are illustrated *above*. Some insects, such as bugs, suck sap from plants; others deposit their eggs in the meristems of leaves and thus cause the formation of galls; yet others (such as locusts) indiscriminately devour the external parts of plants.

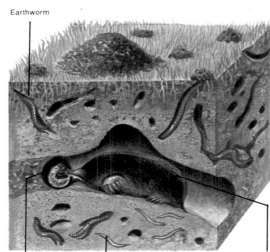

Aeration of the soil

The illustration (*above*) demonstrates the importance of various animal species, such as the mole and the earthworm, for turning the soil and hence aerating it. Any terrain which is poor in soil-living animals is always characterised by compact, poorly ventilated soil (e.g. tundra).

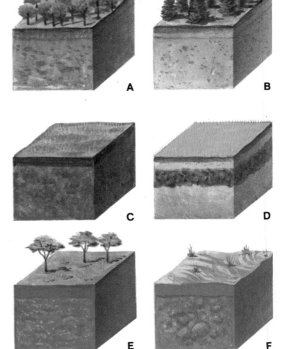

A) Deciduous forest
B) Coniferous forest (taiga)
C) Tundra
D) Prairie
E) Tropical savanna
F) Desert
G) Typical soil
   1. surface layer
   2. humus
   3. bed-rock

SOIL TYPES

- Periglacial soils
- Podzols
- Brown forest soils
- Red soils and laterites
- Neutral prairie soils
- Chernozems
- Rendzine and chestnut soils
- Serozems and desert soils
- Mountain soils

Evolution

Individuals differ from one another at least to some extent, partly because of hereditary differences arising from mutation and genetic recombination and partly because of environmental factors. The structural characteristics of individuals in a population are exposed to the rigours of the environment, and the diversity found within a given species is subject to the filter of natural selection. Those individuals which happen to be best adapted and possess the optimal genetic constitution for a given environment, are favoured. Natural selection operates in a multitude of different ways: predation, competition for food, climatic factors and different resistance to parasites. All these different factors combine to select against those individuals which are least suited to the environment and which therefore succumb to an early death or at least suffer some handicap in reproduction. The outcome of natural selection is that the best adapted members of a species survive to reproduce themselves. With every generation there is some readjustment in adaptation, since evolution is, by definition, no more than a statistical process. Further, there are spatial factors such as ecological and geographical influences which are involved in the evolutionary mechanism.

For terrestrial animals, for example, there are certain characteristic factors which are involved, notably geographical barriers, such as seas or mountain-chains, which isolate populations from one another and prohibit any genetic exchange between them. In the case of the human species, which probably emerged in Africa before spreading to other continental areas, the origin of diverse ethnic groups depended upon geographical isolation brought about by a number of ecological upheavals which prevented genetic exchange between populations which were originally interconnected. In relatively recent times, rapid increases in transport communication and accompanying increases in the rate of intermarriage between ethnic groups have introduced a new element of genetic change which will probably lead to widespread uniformity of the human race.

Animal evolution
The chart (right) summarises the main stages in the evolution of animal life which began with protozoans and led to the array of species living today. According to the most recent interpretations, heterotrophic bacteria (those deriving nourishment from outside) are thought to have given rise to zooflagellates and to have produced a single surviving lineage which terminated in the sponges (Porifera). Another very ancient group of bacteria, with autotrophic (self-nourishing) habits, is thought to have given rise to the phytoflagellates. Colony-living phytoflagellates (of the *Volvox* type) apparently gave rise to two branches, one forming the ancestral stock of the plants and the other leading to the first coelenterates and thus to all other animal species.

The origin of life
By recreating the conditions which are believed to have been present on Earth three thousand million years ago, it has proved possible to confirm a basic hypothesis of the origin of life. According to this hypothesis, the action of ultraviolet radiation brought about the transformation of relatively simple molecules — such as methane, ammonia, hydrogen and water vapour — into complex organic compounds which aggregated together to generate structures of ever-increasing complexity, culminating in *coacervates*. Growth and reproduction are the two essential characteristics of living organisms, but we still do not know how simple coacervates developed to produce the first structure definable as a proper "cell".

Animal and plant cells
The two diagrams below represent schematically typical cells of an animal (*left*), and of a plant (*right*), showing the fundamental differences between them. The characteristic structural components of plants are: 1. chloroplasts, containing chlorophyll and the mechanism required for photosynthesis. 2. other pigments, such as carotenoids and xanthophylls, which are also involved in the absorption of radiant energy. 3. a rigid cell wall composed of cellulose. 4. amyloplasts for the accumulation of starch as a carbohydrate reserve. Animal cells do not possess a rigid cell wall isolating them from the external environment. Instead, they have no more than a cell membrane which in certain cases may be hardened to resist mechanical damage. Carbohydrate reserves in animal cells are stored in the form of glycogen rather than starch.

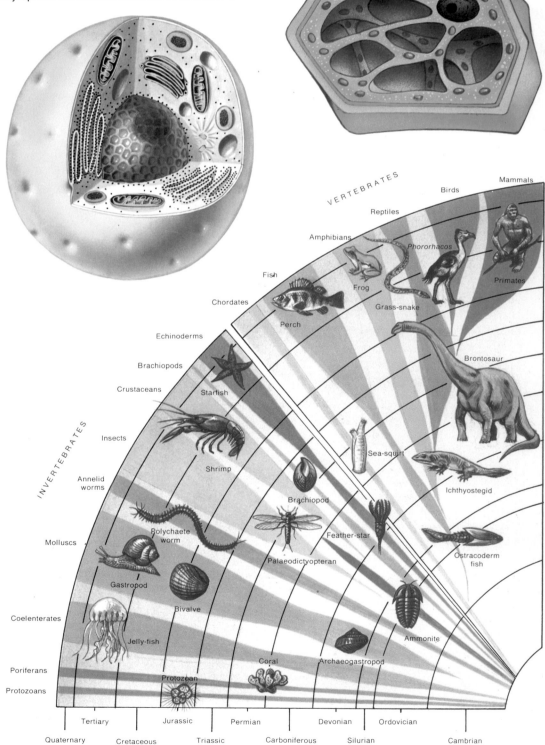

Zoogeographical regions

It is possible to divide land areas into six principal regions: 1. The Palaearctic Region inhabited by cervids (deer), bears and the camel group, in addition to being the zone of origin of the horses, asses, ducks and pigeons. 2. The Nearctic Region, comparable in many respects to the Palaearctic Region as in the presence, for example, of the bison, but very different in terms of amphibians. 3. The Ethiopian Region, characterized by large-bodied apes (gorilla, chimpanzee), elephants, hippopotamus, various antelope and gazelle species, and zebras. 4. The Oriental Region, inhabited by various primate species (lorises, monkeys, gibbons, orang-utans), rhinoceros, tiger, peafowl and various gallinaceous bird species. 5. The Neotropical Region, with armadillos, sloths, certain camelids (llama, guanaco, vicuna), ceboid monkeys and specialized birds such as humming-birds. 6. The Australasian Region, with a special mammalian fauna composed of monotremes (spiny anteater, duck-billed platypus) and marsupials, and completely lacking in native placental mammals.

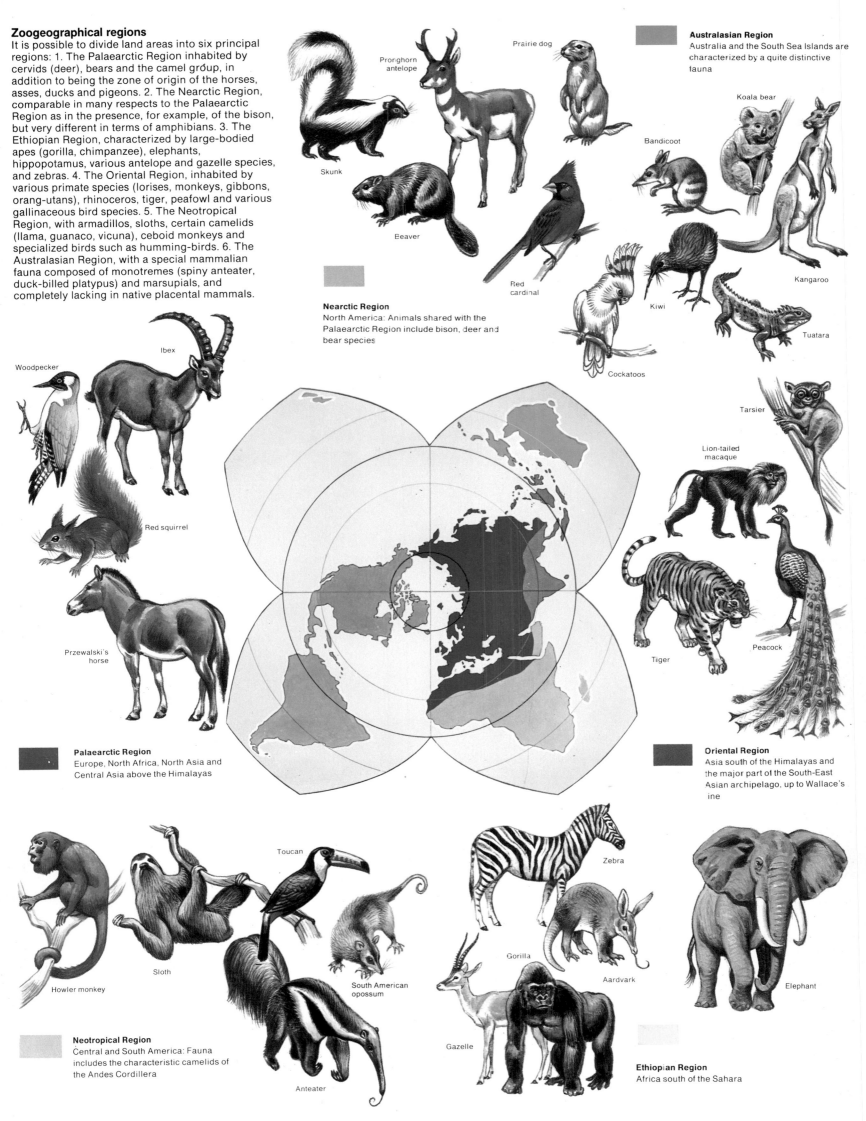

Nearctic Region
North America: Animals shared with the Palaearctic Region include bison, deer and bear species

Prairie dog

Pronghorn antelope

Skunk

Beaver

Red cardinal

Australasian Region
Australia and the South Sea Islands are characterized by a quite distinctive fauna

Koala bear

Bandicoot

Kiwi

Cockatoos

Kangaroo

Tuatara

Tarsier

Lion-tailed macaque

Woodpecker

Ibex

Red squirrel

Przewalski's horse

Palaearctic Region
Europe, North Africa, North Asia and Central Asia above the Himalayas

Tiger

Peacock

Oriental Region
Asia south of the Himalayas and the major part of the South-East Asian archipelago, up to Wallace's line

Howler monkey

Sloth

Toucan

South American opossum

Anteater

Neotropical Region
Central and South America: Fauna includes the characteristic camelids of the Andes Cordillera

Zebra

Gazelle

Gorilla

Aardvark

Elephant

Ethiopian Region
Africa south of the Sahara

41

Habit and Habitat

The study of the relationships between a biocoenosis (an intimate association of animal and plant species) and the inanimate environment is the province of ecology, a branch of biology which begins with the specifics of animals and plants. It provides an overall view of the functioning of each living species in relation to other organisms and to the general habitat in which it lives.

The subject of ecology can be divided into *autoecology* (the individual, its way of life and its relations with members of its own and other species within its natural environment), and *synecology* (the analysis of the interactions between all animal and plant populations constituting a biological community in an area).

Autoecology includes the study of social organization among the members of a particular species, investigation of any territorial behaviour, analysis of communication systems, and indeed analysis of all the ways in which an organism or group of organisms responds to environmental stimuli. Synecology, on the other hand, includes the study of all those biological mechanisms which contribute to the overall development of a species population, and the investigation of environmental constraints which tend to limit such development.

A knowledge of autoecology is an indispensable prerequisite for the study of community ecology, since only the study of individuals living in a given habitat will permit us to understand the operation of a food-chain or to interpret a diagram portraying the way in which a certain number of unstable communities will tend to result in the same climax (the final stage in a biological progression).

The ecological pyramid

Dividing living things into autotrophic and heterotrophic forms, it is possible to construct a simple food-chain which portrays the flow of energy and chemical exchange.
1. Producers, the *plants*, which produce organic carbon compounds by means of photosynthesis.
2. Primary consumers, the *herbivores*, which feed directly on plants.
3. An unlimited number of predators, or *carnivores*, which exist by feeding either on herbivores or on other predators. 4. *Degraders* and *mineralizers*, which restore the inorganic material required by producers for biosynthesis. It is obvious that the

number of individuals occupying different levels in this system must be subject to certain constraints. In fact, any plant community has a threshold of exploitation as a food resource above which ecological imbalance will result in destruction of the ecosystem. The relationships involved can be represented by pyramids portraying biomass, energy or numbers of species.

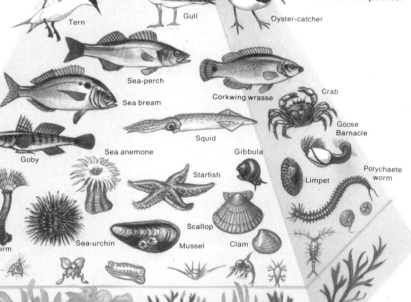

Biomes

Even though the climatic and physical conditions of the Earth's surface do not remain constant over time, certain communities (biomes) tend to be maintained by dynamic replenishment and to develop wherever the appropriate conditions of humidity, temperature, soil chemistry, etc., are available. They include typical plant groups and entire series of animal species whose populations are maintained in balance with the environment. Apart from the obvious marine and freshwater aquatic environments, there is a variety of stable ecological situations which can be found on dry land, ranging from arid desert to luxuriant rain forest and including a large number of intermediate biomes.

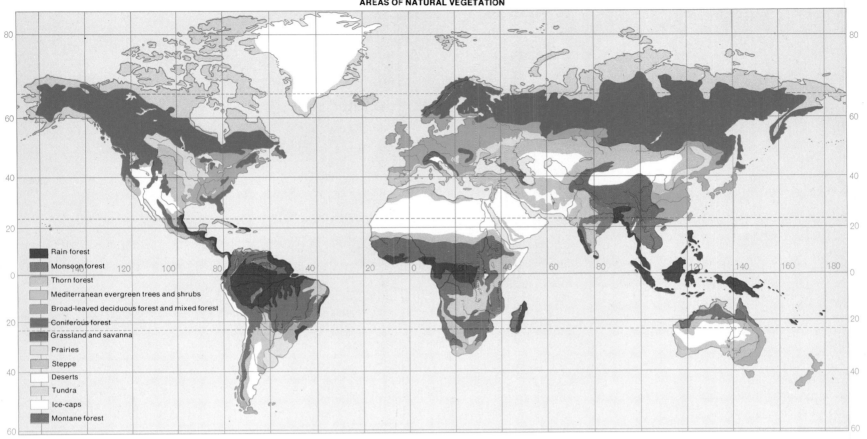

Rain forest
Monsoon forest
Thorn forest
Mediterranean evergreen trees and shrubs
Broad-leaved deciduous forest and mixed forest
Coniferous forest
Grassland and savanna
Prairies
Steppe
Deserts
Tundra
Ice-caps
Montane forest

Parasites
Among the many examples of negative interactions between species, is the case involving man and the tapeworm. This ribbon-like worm lives in a cavity—the intestine—which is actually in communication with the external environment. The intermediate host of the tapeworm is the pig; man becomes infected by eating contaminated pork.

Endoparasites
Endoparasites, which live inside parts of the body which do not communicate directly with the external environment, include the *Plasmodium*, the protozoan responsible for malaria. Human beings are actually intermediate hosts for this endoparasite, since it reproduces asexually within the human body. The *Anopheles* mosquito is the definitive host.

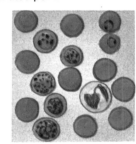

Symbiosis
An example of perfect symbiosis is provided by termites and hyper-mastiginous zooflagellates. In fact, these two species are unable to exist without one another. The termite is only able to obtain its food from wood because the protozoan, which inhabits the intestine of the termite, breaks down the cellulose. Similarly, the zooflagellates are unable to lead a free-living existence if they are not encysted. Whenever moulting occurs, the termite discards its old skin and at the same time loses the lining of its stomach enclosing the zooflagellates. Subsequently, the termite would be unable to digest cellulose if it did not rapidly take steps to re-establish its precious culture of protozoans by ingesting encysted zooflagellates.

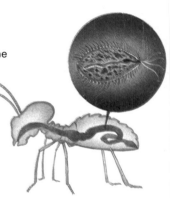

The Arctic

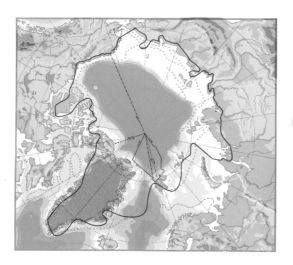

Birds of the Arctic
In the milder season many species of birds, attracted by the tranquillity and plentiful supplies of food, reach the Arctic to nest. These are generally species of flighted birds such as the albatross, petrel and fulmar which spend most of their lives at sea.

Petrel

Steller's albatross

Ice fulmar

Vegetation
In spring, after the thaw, the water-laden soil of the Arctic is covered with mosses and lichens.

Icebergs
In the northern hemisphere the icebergs come mainly from glaciers in Greenland.

The Arctic includes the North Pole and the region beyond the Arctic Circle (latitude 66°32' North). Besides the polar cap, it includes the northern parts of the New and Old World as well as numerous islands.

Polar bear

Carnivores
The largest Arctic carnivore is the polar bear, which wanders restlessly in search of prey. The arctic wolf too is a tireless hunter, whose insatiable appetite makes him very daring.

Arctic wolf

The seals
Seals, sea-lions and walruses visit the shores only during the breeding season. Thanks to a thick layer of subcutaneous fat they are able to survive the low temperatures of the polar regions.

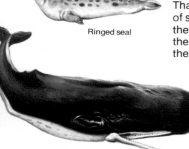

Walrus

Ringed seal

The cetaceans
Whales, dolphins and sperm whales are mammals which have undergone various changes to adapt them to marine life. Their limbs have been transformed into fins, their skin is smooth and waterproof and their bodies have taken on hydrodynamic shapes. A thick layer of subcutaneous fat helps these animals, which spend many months of the year in polar waters, to maintain an even body temperature.

Sperm whale

Narwhal

White dolphin

Killer whale

Herring

Sparidae

Cod

The poles are among the coldest places on Earth, since they receive the least heat from the Sun whose rays there are tangential to the surface of the Earth. In addition the glaciers reflect the solar energy like a mirror, dispersing it in space. The poles differ considerably from each other, for while the North Pole is in the frozen Arctic Ocean, covered with perpetual ice and surrounded by the northern boundaries of the Old and New Worlds, the South Pole lies within a circular-shaped continent which is also covered by perpetual ice. The covering of ice has an uneven surface due to the effect of the strong winds blowing from the Arctic Ocean, and is 2 to 4 kilometres thick.

The fish
The abundance of life in the polar seas depends on the phytoplankton, which are comparable to huge marine prairies. On these feed the zooplankton, a collection of unicellular animals and fish larvae which forms the diet of numerous species of fish, which in turn are preyed upon by larger animals.

Diatom

Fish larva

Sponge

Amphipod crustacean

Euphausiacea

Sand star

Starfish

The Antarctic

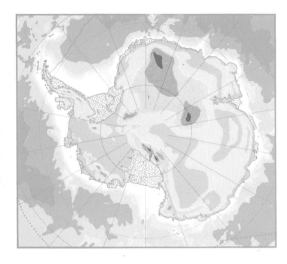

The vegetation
Animal and vegetable life in the Antarctic is restricted by the lack of water and warmth. In the centre of the continent in the brief period of thaw, the only vegetation present is in the form of lichen. By the coasts and on the islands there are also mosses and liverworts. Life is more abundant on the Antarctic Peninsula and on the islands where the only land animals are tiny invertebrates, mites and insects which live on tufts of grass. Many other animals however, like some penguins, visit the islands and Antarctic coasts each year at breeding time.

Grey seal

Leopard seal

The seals
Typical of the South Pole are the enormous elephant seal, over 6 metres in length, the swift and elegant leopard seal which hunts penguins, and the grey seal, which feeds on zooplankton.

Elephant seal

In spite of the basic differences, the two extreme ends of the world have one thing in common. For six months of the year the length of darkness greatly exceeds the length of daylight, and vice versa, and for several weeks of the year there is continuous daylight or continuous darkness. Also at both poles strange luminous phenomena, called auroras, can be seen which paint the polar sky with colour. Much of the Antarctic has never been seen, but it is known to be the most desolate continent in the world. The lowest temperatures in the world are found here (90°C below zero) and the worst climate. Some 90% of the world's ice is found in the Antarctic.

The penguins
In the Antarctic and subantarctic regions, dense colonies of penguins collect at breeding time. These birds are remarkably well adapted to aquatic life in the cold polar regions. Adélie penguins enter the continent to build their nests.

The cetaceans
The cetaceans of the southern seas include a majority of the species of the northern hemisphere but the numbers are different.

The invertebrates
Sponges, starfish and numerous species of molluscs and crustaceans enrich the fauna of the Antarctic.

Sponge

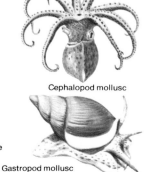

Cephalopod mollusc

Gastropod mollusc

A rich sea
The large amounts of sunlight during the summer months enables a high rate of photosynthesis to be sustained by which the plants containing chlorophyll (phytoplankton) convert inorganic substances into organic substances. That is to say, carbon dioxide and various mineral salts are converted, by means of the solar energy stored in the chlorophyll, into sugars, amides, fats and proteins. Thus the food supply chain begins with plants, on which herbivores live who, in turn, are prey to predators.

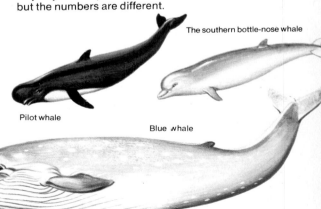

The southern bottle-nose whale

Pilot whale

Blue whale

The tundra

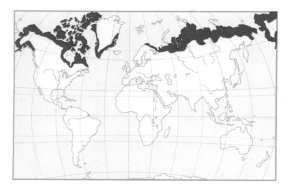

The tundra is a zone without any actual groups of trees, which stretches between the taiga – the band of conifers in the northern hemisphere – and the polar region. There is no equivalent zone in the southern hemisphere where at the same latitude (60°–70°) there is no dry land.

The rodents
In spite of the rigours of the climate, many animals spend the whole year in the tundra. Rodents like the pica (*above left*), the lemming (*left*) and the marmot (*above right*) pass the long winter underground.

Snowy owl

The tundra is characterised by low temperatures (the average in the warmest month is +10°C) and soil which is frozen for most of the year. Even in the brief summer, the soil only thaws on the surface, the lower layer remaining permanently frozen (permafrost).

During the long winter the action of the snow and frost breaks up the rocks, altering the appearance of the terrain and making the growth of vegetation difficult. With the arrival of summer, the snow melts to form marshy areas. Thanks to the moisture and the Sun, which shines for longer each day and for 24 hours a day at the height of summer, the tundra is clothed with mosses and lichens. Animal life is made difficult by the dark and severe winter.

Hibernation and migration
A few mammals merely become lethargic but many hibernate. Others migrate, among them many birds, reindeer and caribou and all animals which obtain their food from rivers and lakes which are frozen for many months of the year. The lynx (*right*) and the arctic fox (*far right*).

The taiga

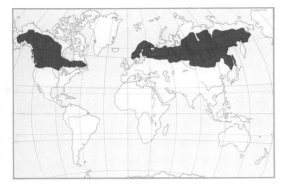

The soil
The damp, cold climate of the taiga encourages the accumulation of dead organic material in the upper layer of the soil (**1**); the formation of humus is slow. Bacteria and earthworms are rare and so decomposition is retarded. Rain washes essential minerals such as iron and aluminium down to lower levels. (**2**) Compact layer resting on the bed-rock (**3**).

The trees
The white spruce has a conical shape with needles and light grey bark. The red spruce has branches which bend downwards, short needles and reddish brown bark. The larch is deciduous with short, soft needles and thick bark. The pine has long slender needles.

White spruce

Red spruce

Larch

Pine

In the coniferous woods
Only specially adapted birds survive in this environment. The turkey (*left*), like other similar birds, feeds on pine needles. The elk (*below*) occurs throughout the polar regions and there are many similar species.

The taiga is found south of the tundra in continental regions which experience long severe winters such as eastern Europe, Siberia and North America. The main varieties of trees are coniferous and include spruce, larch and, near water, mountain maples, poplars, willow and birch. The coniferous forests cover a huge area and the trees are closly spaced. The undergrowth, brambles and bushes, is not very dense. The soil is poor and at times marshy. In spite of the relative poverty of the environment, it still provides food the year round and the fauna are varied. There are wolves, bears, foxes, badgers, beavers, marmots, ermine, martens, lynxes, elk, squirrels, hares, crossbills, eagles, jays and many others.

The birds of prey
The great birds of prey of the taiga hunt in the forest glades, where they dive on their prey and carry it off.

Golden eagle

The great hunters
The numerous rodents, reptiles and birds of the taiga are the usual prey of the weasel family (polecats *(left)*, weasels, ermine, etc.). The great carnivores, bears and wolves (*far left*), hunt elk and deer, but are content with smaller prey if they cannot find sufficient larger prey to meet their needs.

The temperate forests

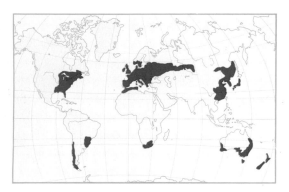

The leaves fall
The biological cycle of the trees is determined more by variation of temperature than by rain. Summer leaves absorb the maximum amount of light from the Sun, but because of their delicate structure cannot survive the rigours of the autumn and fall to the ground. In the winter, the tree lives on its reserves.

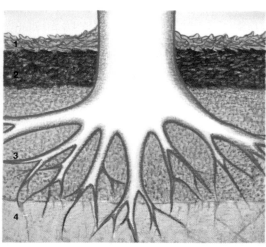

The soil
There are four layers in a cross section through the soil of a broad-leaved forest: **1**) the surface layer, consisting of animal debris (excrement and carrion) and vegetable matter (dead leaves, etc.); **2**) humus; **3**) intermediate layer, with a little decomposed organic material in small particles and a great deal of inorganic matter; **4**) base layer of rock and sand where the true geological substrata begin. The mass of leaves falling on the ground is attacked first of all by the annelids and arthropods, then by bacteria of decomposition which transform it into inorganic material.

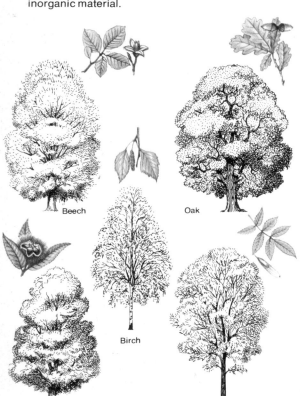

Beech

Oak

Birch

Chestnut

Ash

Deciduous forests occur in the temperate zones where the humidity is constant all the year round and the winters, though short, are severe enough to slow down the biological cycle of the trees. In the cold season, the trees shed their leaves which, falling on the ground, are broken down first of all by worms, woodlice and other creatures, and are then decomposed by bacteria to form mineral salts which enrich the soil, making possible the growth of rich undergrowth. Man's intervention in this region has considerably reduced its original area. At one time the forest covered a large part of North America, central Europe, central Asia, Japan, Chile and the Argentine.

Australian forest
The geographical isolation of Australia has influenced the evolution of animals and vegetation. The temperate forest consists almost exclusively of varieties of the eucalyptus. Numerous marsupials live there (*left:* koala bear), and also many birds (*right:* lyre bird).

The inhabitants of the oak (the caterpillars are hidden)

Dormouse · Jay · Owl · Stag beetle · Green woodpecker · Oak beetle · Squirrel · Goshawk · Oak processionary moth · Bark beetle · Red fox · Wild boar · Satyr butterfly · Great stag · Mole · Cockchafer larva · Earthworm · Badger · Hedgehog

The tree, a world of its own
A large number of animal species find their ecological niche in the giant oak tree. There are three separate habitats: the roots, the trunk and the branches. Among the roots live many animals which are of great benefit to the tree. These include worms which aerate the soil with their tunnels and carry small pieces of leaf into the subsoil where fungi and bacteria transform them into mineral salts which serve to nourish the tree. Predators collect in the root region in search of prey. The trunk is mainly inhabited by insects. Squirrels and birds build their nests in hollow trunks. The branches form the richest habitat and give shelter to wasps, butterflies, caterpillars, spiders and many varieties of birds.

The insects
Many of the insects of this habitat are harmful, like butterfly larvae which eat the leaves or aphids which suck the sap. Others are very useful, like the ladybird (left) which feeds on parasites, or the bees (below) which pollinate the tree.

The herbivores
The forest offers the numerous herbivores a different diet each season; buds and leaves in spring, fruit in summer and dry fruit and berries in autumn. (Above: deer).

The birds
The birds of this habitat have specially adapted beaks to break open the hard fruits of the trees and bushes. The bullfinch (above) has a short, strong beak for crushing seeds and buds and the tit (right) has a long narrow beak to seek out and catch insects. The nightingale (lower right) feeds on both insects and fruit and berries.

The predators
The predators are usually of small size, like the fox, weasel, wild cat and several kinds of snake such as the European smooth snake (below) and numerous birds of prey including kestrels, falcons and owls. Their prey consists mainly of rodents, birds and frogs. With the huge number of insects there are also many animals which feed on them, among them various species of bat (right), hedgehogs, green lizards (below), frogs and toads.

In the bamboo forest
In the bamboo forests of China lives the lesser panda. It feeds exclusively on the stalks and leaves of the bamboo (left).

The raccoon
The raccoon is an inhabitant of the temperate forests of North America. It is skilful at catching crayfish and other aquatic creatures and also eats fruit, berries, eggs and insects.

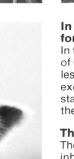

The tropical forests

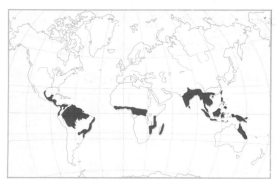

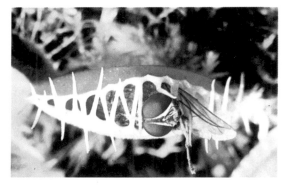

The undergrowth
Many varieties of fern grow in the dark, dense undergrowth shown above. There are also numerous multi-coloured flowers, including several species of orchid. Carnivorous plants (*left*) have strong scents to attract insects. The insects are then trapped and digested.

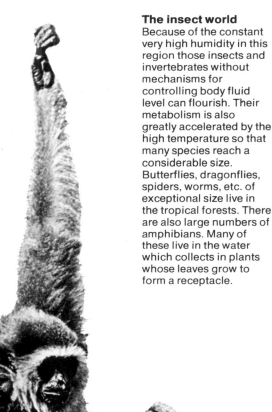

The insect world
Because of the constant very high humidity in this region those insects and invertebrates without mechanisms for controlling body fluid level can flourish. Their metabolism is also greatly accelerated by the high temperature so that many species reach a considerable size. Butterflies, dragonflies, spiders, worms, etc. of exceptional size live in the tropical forests. There are also large numbers of amphibians. Many of these live in the water which collects in plants whose leaves grow to form a receptacle.

A tropical forest region always has a hot and humid climate but other features may vary. Tropical forests can be found in mountainous or low-lying areas, and the rainfall may be constant all the year round or seasonal, as in monsoon areas. Mangroves sometimes grow in coastal swamps.

Vegetation which has no annual dormant period grows very rapidly. Among the many varieties of trees, very tall palms and hardwoods predominate, such as mahogany, teak and ebony, with heights of between 30 and 70 metres. With the abundance and variety of food at every season of the year, this region is rich in animal species.

Life in the trees
Many reptiles and mammals are adapted to tree life and never descend on to the ground. On the left is a gibbon which is an expert at travelling through the trees.

The vegetation
The vegetation in this region is divided into five different height groups, each of which occupies its own habitat. The upper layer includes the branches of the tallest trees which project above the canopy, beneath these are the shorter trees, a layer of bushes and the soil covered with plants.

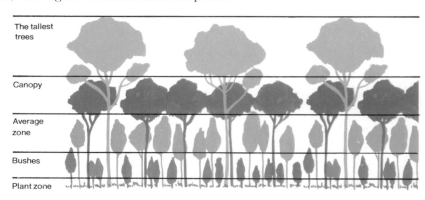

The tallest trees

Canopy

Average zone

Bushes

Plant zone

Above the canopy of the forest, numerous birds of prey seize birds and small mammals which venture on to the highest branches in search of food.

The food offered by the forest – mostly flowers and fruit – is found almost exclusively on the trees. For this reason, the animals have developed certain adaptations to tree life. The most numerous species are those that are confined to the branches of the canopy, where the food is richest. They generally have bright colours which harmonise with their restricted surroundings, and slender shapes necessary for agile movement. The South American monkeys have prehensile tails and the flying squirrels have a membrane attached to their limbs to form a kind of parachute. The beaks of the birds have different shapes according to their food: long and slim in the humming-bird which feeds on nectar, hooked and strong in the parrots which eat hard foods. The creatures drink water which collects in the leaves.

Just as the majority of the animals of the tropical forest live in the trees, so the predators are adapted to tree life. Besides the many snakes which live on birds, small mammals, amphibians and eggs, leopards and wildcats pursue their prey into the trees, restricting themselves mainly to the lower parts where the branches can bear their weight.

The animals which live on the ground, where little light penetrates, generally have subdued colours. Here live stags, antelopes, buffalo and wild boar, tapirs and porcupines. There are many varieties of snake including poisonous ones. Among the predators, the tiger is the largest and most ferocious. Also on the ground live those birds not adapted to much flying, such as the sultana bird and many species of pheasant and peacock. Groups of rodents, insects, molluscs, millipedes and worms live in the damp subsoil.

Common in the forests of South America, the crested eagle is a large bird of prey which feeds exclusively on monkeys.

On the left, from the top: toucan, swallow-tail butterfly, gibbon and humming-bird
Above: Vampire bat
Below: flying squirrel
Right: tarsier

Above: emerald green boa
Right: chimpanzees

Left: leopard, Indian elephant
Above: millipede
Below: cobra
Right: gorilla, tiger

The mountains

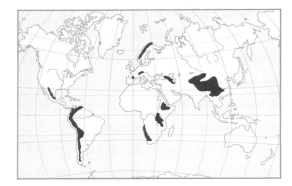

The mountains play an important role with regard to the climate, influencing the direction of the prevailing wind and therefore the rainfall. The wind and rain also erode the slopes, depositing the soil in which the vegetation grows. On the left is a chamois and on the right ibex.

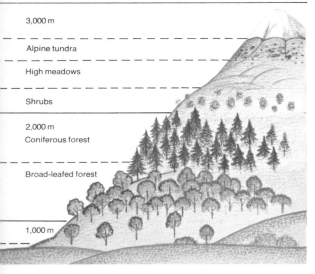

3,000 m

Alpine tundra

High meadows

Shrubs

2,000 m
Coniferous forest

Broad-leafed forest

1,000 m

The vegetation

Ascending the slope of a mountain from the temperate zone, we first come to a strip of deciduous forest, followed by a belt of mixed broad-leaf and coniferous forest. After this we find true coniferous forest which continues up to the limit of tree growth. Before reaching the zone of perennial ice, there is a zone of shrubs, meadows and, finally, a belt of lichen and heather, called the alpine tundra. Latitude has a similar effect to altitude on the distribution of vegetation on the land. In fact, as one travels further from the Equator and moves towards the poles, one passes from the equatorial and tropical rain forests through the temperate forests, the mixed forests and the coniferous forests before finally reaching the Arctic tundra. At the Equator, the upper limit for trees is about 4,500 m while in the Alps, it is about 2,000 m.

The mountain environment varies greatly according to the height and temperature as well as the direction of the prevailing winds. As one climbs the slopes, the temperature falls about 1°C every 150 metres and the soil becomes poorer. The mountains force the winds to rise, so that they are cooled and their water vapour condenses into clouds. As a result, the rain falls on the side of the mountain exposed to the winds. Only dry winds blow down the opposite side and vegetation is therefore scarcer. In Asia, for example, the monsoons which blow from the sea towards the land are cooled by the Himalayas and heavy rains fall on the mountains themselves, while to the north of the range stretch the deserts.

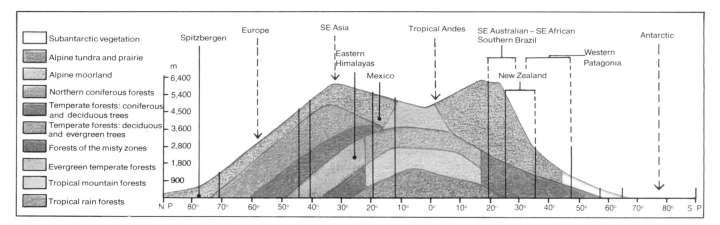

| Subantarctic vegetation |
| Alpine tundra and prairie |
| Alpine moorland |
| Northern coniferous forests |
| Temperate forests: coniferous and deciduous trees |
| Temperate forests: deciduous and evergreen trees |
| Forests of the misty zones |
| Evergreen temperate forests |
| Tropical mountain forests |
| Tropical rain forests |

Spitzbergen · Europe · SE Asia · Tropical Andes · SE Australian – SE African Southern Brazil · Antarctic

Eastern Himalayas · Mexico · Western Patagonia · New Zealand

m
6,400
5,400
4,500
3,600
2,800
1,800
900

N P 80° 70° 60° 50° 40° 30° 20° 10° 0° 10° 20° 30° 40° 50° 60° 70° 80° S P

Life at high altitude

Life for animals above the tree line is made more difficult by their isolation. High mountain ranges actually form natural barriers to migration. The rarefied atmosphere causes certain environmental problems. The air is less rich in oxygen (the gas used by all animals to release energy by the combustion of food); the thin atmosphere allows more ultraviolet rays to penetrate; the soil absorbs more heat with respect to the surrounding air and gives it up more rapidly. Furthermore, the rarefied air is able to absorb less moisture

The animals have developed certain adaptations to their surroundings. Compared with similar species from the plains, the vertebrates have more developed hearts and lungs and their blood contains more red corpuscles whose haemoglobin stores more oxygen. To give additional protection from ultraviolet rays and the cold, many animals have very thick coats. Others have darker colours to absorb the ultraviolet and protect the underlying tissue. Some animals hibernate during the winter, like the marmot (*right*) or the viper (*left*). Others, such as the stags, descend to the valleys, and others, like the Tibetan magpie, hide away in holes supplied with food.

Yak

Alpaca

The herbivores

Herbivores living at high altitudes have very thick coats which protect them from the cold and the harmful ultraviolet rays. They also have hooves which give the best grip on the very uneven ground of their habitat.

Moufflon sheep

Mountain goat

The insects

Above the tree line, the most numerous creatures are the invertebrates (insects, spiders, etc.), which survive the severe winter by sheltering under the ground where the snow protects them from the frost and ultraviolet radiation and also prevents dehydration. The strong winds make flying difficult for the insects so most (over 60%) have no wings. Many butterflies are found at high altitudes and the Apollo (*left*) is found at heights up to 2,000 m.

The birds

Most of the mountain birds are birds of prey (eagles, falcons and vultures), which are strong flyers capable of overcoming the high winds, and members of the sparrow family which fly close to the ground and manage to survive on the available supplies of food. Some small humming-birds live in the South American Andes at heights of between 2,000 and 5,000 metres.

The giant panda

In the bamboo forests of China, at a height of over 2,000 metres, lives the giant panda (*above*). It lives a lonely existence, feeding almost exclusively on bamboo buds and shoots.

The carnivores

The carnivore which reaches the greatest height, 6,000 m, is the snow leopard, found in the Himalayas. There are pumas (*above*), lynxes and various species of bear (*left*, a brown bear), foxes (*right*) and several species of stoats and martens (mink, ermine and polecats, *below*). The carnivores play a vital role in maintaining the balance of life by eliminating old and sick animals and preventing the proliferation of herbivores which would destroy the vegetation

Fresh water

The fresh or inland waters include stretches of water (from the smallest pools to the great lakes), rivers and streams. Stagnant waters are rich in floating plant life offering shelter and food to many animals. The small photographs show two examples of aquatic plants. The large photograph shows a great heron among the lilies of a pond.

Neon Tetra

Angel fish

Life in the rivers
In the upper course of a river, the current is strong, the waters cold and rich in oxygen and there is little plant life. Here carnivorous and well-known varieties of fish like the trout live. The invertebrates have either flat bodies or suckers to attach themselves to the rocks. In the middle course the water becomes gradually warmer, the current slower and plant life more abundant. Here we find grayling, chub, and many invertebrates. In the lower course, the river finally becomes wider and wider and the bed becomes muddy and rich in algae. Here pike, rudd and barbel live.

Source

Upper course

Middle course

Lower course

Mouth

Inland waters offer a great variety of habitats. Rivers flow in all latitudes and in all types of climate. The young, or oligotrophic, lakes are deep and lacking in nutrient salts; consequently there is little plant life and limited animal life. The eutrophic lakes, on the other hand, have gentle slopes and are rich in nutrients and plant and animal life. The older, or dystrophic, lakes are rich in nutrients but lacking in oxygen and have gradually been transformed into marshes. The lake fauna too, like that of the sea, is subdivided into littoral (sponges, crustaceans, molluscs, larvae, insects and fish), pelagic (including well-known fish like trout and grayling) and deep, or benthonic (molluscs and insect larvae).

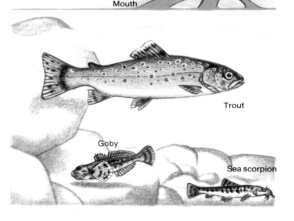

Trout

Goby

Sea scorpion

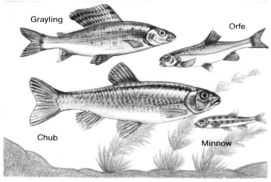

Grayling

Orfe

Chub

Minnow

Pike

Rudd

Perch

Barbel

The aquatic birds found on the shores of lakes and ponds occupy various positions in the ecological spectrum and find their food in many different ways. The waders (1) wait for their prey to approach the shore, while the ducks on the surface (2) feed on what they can reach by shallow diving. The web-footed divers (3) swim under the water to catch their prey. Finally, other birds like the kingfisher (4) dive on the water, seize their prey and fly away.

Fighting fish

A male fighting fish in its mating colours (*above*), so called because during the mating season, it engages in furious struggles with other males of the same species. A pair of sticklebacks (*below*). The male (red) builds a nest of plant material where the female lives prior to laying her eggs.

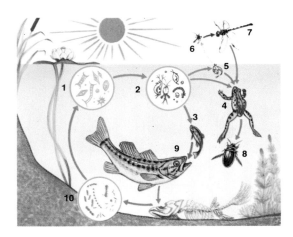

Although they are land insects, dragonflies undergo their larval period in the water. For the amphibians (frogs, toads and newts) water is essential for the growth of their eggs.

Tree frog

Many species of reptile live in fresh water, such as the water snake, which spends its whole life in water. *Above:* a North American terrapin.

Pond life

The water in a pond is usually still and is subject to considerable temperature variations. Furthermore, light does not easily penetrate the water. The abundant plant life offers food and shelter to many amphibians, birds, aquatic mammals and invertebrates. From the surface, rich in plankton, insects and larvae, to the muddy bottom which is host to bivalves, molluscs, crustaceans, worms and larvae there is great activity. The life cycle begins with primary producers (1), that is plants and phytoplankton, which convert inorganic substances into organic materials using the Sun's energy. The zooplankton (2) feed on phytoplankton and both form the diet of small fishes (3) and other vertebrates. These, like the frog (4) eat larvae (5) and insects such as the mosquito (6) and dragonfly (7). The water beetle (8) is a predator, preying on animals much larger than itself. The great predators like the trout (9) complete the feeding cycle. Animal and plant remains are converted into inorganic substances by bacteria of decompositon (10).

Freshwater mammals

There are several species of freshwater mammal, including hippopotamus, shrews, coypu, otters and beavers. They are usually good swimmers who catch their food in the water. The largest aquatic mammal is the hippopotamus, found in Africa (*below*). It is a herbivore and spends most of its life in the water from which only its eyes and nostrils protrude.

Fresh water invertebrates and fish

Invertebrates are the commonest animals found in fresh water. Their presence is a necessary prerequisite for the existence of fish and other aquatic vertebrates. Many land insects, such as the dragonfly, complete their larval development in water. About one third of the known species of fish (over 25,000) live in fresh water. These are usually bony fish. Some, like the eels and salmon, are temporary visitors. Among the cartilaginous fish only rays and some species of shark habitually swim in estuaries.

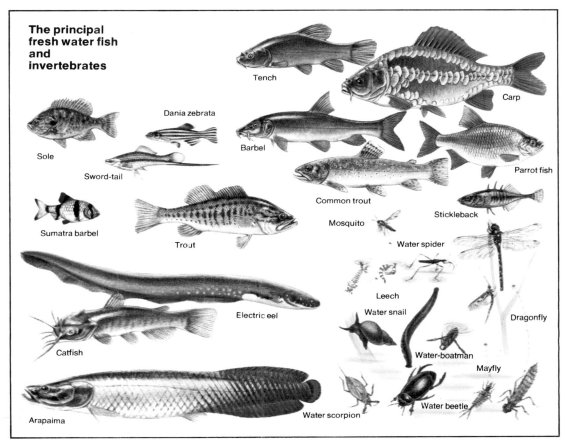

The principal fresh water fish and invertebrates

Tench

Carp

Dania zebrata

Barbel

Sole

Parrot fish

Sword-tail

Common trout

Stickleback

Mosquito

Sumatra barbel

Trout

Water spider

Leech

Dragonfly

Electric eel

Water snail

Catfish

Water-boatman

Mayfly

Arapaima

Water scorpion

Water beetle

The seas and oceans

The body of water comprising the seas and oceans which cover 360 million sq km of the Earth's surface, equal to 71% of the total area, almost constitutes a single entity since most of the seas are in communication with each other. There also exist numerous ecosystems, caused by differences in temperature, salinity and depth, which form barriers to the movement of species.

Phytoplankton and zooplankton

The largest group of marine flora is the phytoplankton, a collection of tiny floating algae, including the diatoms (*above*). The distribution of phytoplankton is not uniform and depends mainly on sunlight and the presence of mineral salts. Small quantities of the latter are carried to the seas by rivers but the larger part comes from rising sea currents which agitate the water and bring nutritive substances to the surface. Phytoplankton is the food of zooplankton, which is composed of unicellular creatures and the larvae of fish and invertebrates. Radiolaria (*above left*), Copepoda (*left*).

The shores

There are three different types of sea shore: rocky, sandy and muddy. Along the rocky coasts live sea anemones, sponges, sea urchins, mussels, limpets, crayfish and fish which have adapted themselves for survival at low tide. Many sea birds nest on the shores. (*Above:* a cormorant.)

The starfish (*above*) is a benthonic creature, that is one which lives on the sea bed. It is a carnivore and feeds on bivalves, among other things, whose valves it can open.

The polychaeta (*below left*) lives on sandy bottoms and feeds on micro-organisms. The sea-horse (*below*) can attach itself to seaweed and coral with its prehensile tail.

The first characteristic of the sea bed is the continental shelf, which extends from the land for about 70 km with a depth of up to 200 metres. In the open sea, the gradient increases rapidly on the continental slope, reaching the bottom of the ocean in a very short distance at a depth of 2,000 metres. The ocean beds are crossed by huge mountain ranges, called ridges, dividing the oceans into several basins. There are also numerous deep trenches. The waters on the shelf comprise the neritic zone and are the home of the littoral fauna, while the waters on the slopes and the ocean bed form the ocean zone, in which the pelagic fauna have their residence.

Protective mimicry among fish

For both predators and their prey, it is essential to attract as little attention as possible. For this purpose, these creatures have developed many adaptations in the course of a long evolution. Deep sea fish are dark-coloured on top, so they are not conspicuous when viewed from above, and light coloured underneath so that, when viewed from below, they blend into the sunlit water. But the real mime artists are the littoral species and, in particular, those of the coral reefs. The octopus can change its colour suddenly to match the bottom over which it is moving. Other species have unusual shapes and many different colours which, against the variegated background of their habitat, make them practically invisible. (*Right:* sea cucumber.)

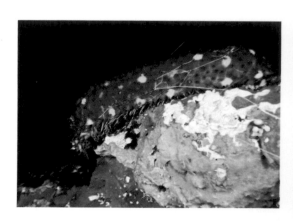

In the pelagic region, that is in the open sea, there is life everywhere, from the surface to the depths. The density of life is, however, much less than in the littoral zone. This is because in the open sea, the surface water, where penetrating sunlight permits the photosynthesis of chlorophyll, contains few mineral salts. These salts are present in large quantities in deeper waters where sunlight, however, cannot reach. Sunlight can only penetrate to a depth of 200 metres.
In consequence, plant life, the first link in the feeding chain, is limited and concentrated in areas where ascending currents carry mineral salts to the surface.
The creatures of the deep sea have developed special adaptations in order to survive in this habitat where there is no cover. For example, tunnyfish, swordfish and squid swim very fast; herrings and anchovies form dense shoals; others, such as the flying fish, squid and manta rays, leap out of the water to escape their predators.

The intermediate, or bathypelagic, zone lies between 2,000 and 3,000 metres. The temperature in this region falls from 10°C to 4°C towards the bottom. As the depth increases, the amount of sunlight decreases and the water pressure increases.
The creatures of the bathypelagic zone are fish, crustaceans and cephalopods, whose body fluids are at the same hydrostatic pressure as the surrounding water.

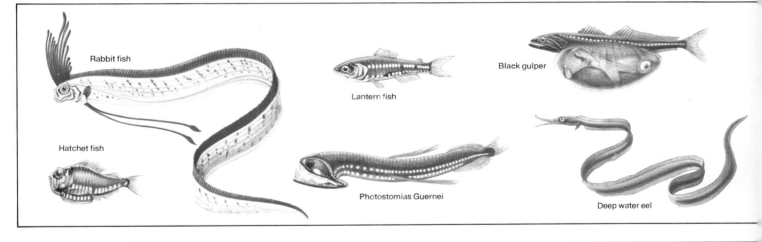

Below 3,000 metres lie the abysses. Here there is total darkness, intense cold and enormous hydrostatic pressure. At 10,000 metres, the pressure exceeds one tonne per sq cm. There is a total absence of vegetation and food is scarce. Because of this, many small fish and some invertebrates rise towards the surface in search of food or develop special modifications to a meagre diet. Others feed on the waste matter which falls to the sea bed. Because of the lack of light, the deep water fish are generally dark in colour. Many species are equipped with light cells, called photophores.

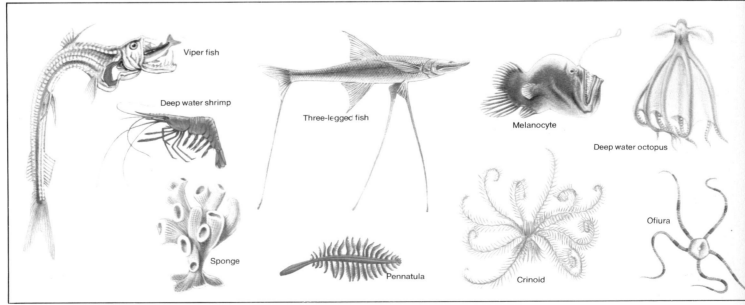

The inhabited world

Compared with the age of the Earth, which according to the most recent determination is around five thousand million years, mankind has existed for only a very brief period.

The first hominids actually appeared only twenty million years ago and about three million years ago, they began to use primitive stone tools. Finally, a little over 70,000 years ago, there appeared Neanderthal man, the direct ancestor of *Homo sapiens*, who spread over nearly all the planet, cultivating the soil and domesticating the animals.

Thus began the wearisome and troubled history of man, whose intelligence caused him to stand apart from all other animals and who, with his science and technology, could bend the very forces of nature to his own wishes and turn his gaze towards the other planets and the stars. The distribution

of man over the Earth was never uniform and still is not. As can be seen from the map of population density (below) there are numerous completely uninhabited zones (the oceans, the poles, the deserts, the forests and the highest mountains), covering an area of about 30 million sq km. The remaining 120 million constitute the inhabited areas.

Among the inhabited areas, there are some zones with a high density of population, mostly located in temperature zones in the northern hemisphere (southern Japan, the plain of the Ganges, central southern China, Western and Central Europe and the United States). This particular population distribution has either been encouraged by natural conditions (climate, relief or type of soil) or by historical, political or economic considerations.

POPULATION DENSITY

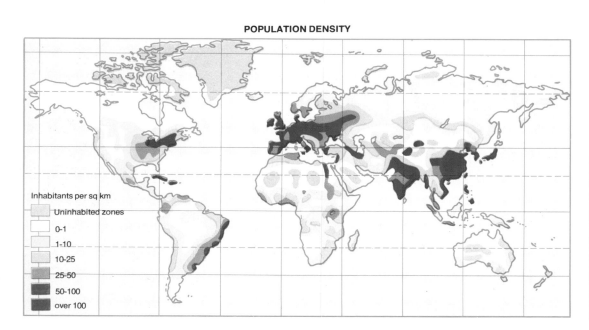

Inhabitants per sq km

- Uninhabited zones
- 0-1
- 1-10
- 10-25
- 25-50
- 50-100
- over 100

THE POPULATION OF THE EARTH

EUROPE
Area	: 10,397,000 sq km
Population	: 705 million
Density	: 68 inhabs/sq km

ASIA
Area	: 44,368,000 sq km
Population	: 3,048 million
Density	: 69 inhabs/sq km

AFRICA
Area	: 30,312,000 sq km
Population	: 613 million
Density	: 20 inhabs/sq km

CENTRAL AND NORTH AMERICA
Area	: 24,216,000 sq km
Population	: 412 million
Density	: 17 inhabs/sq km

SOUTH AMERICA
Area	: 17,842,000 sq km
Population	: 287 million
Density	: 16 inhabs/sq km

AUSTRALIA, NEW ZEALAND AND NEW GUINEA
Area	: 8,935,000 sq km
Population	: 28 million
Density	: 3 inhabs/sq km

Nomadism and urbanisation
Two contrasting life styles in the world today. Nomadism (*left:* nomads in the Algerian desert), which is found among certain peoples who breed animals, is a way of life which is now followed by a very limited portion of the population of the world. Such nomads are continually reducing in number because of the heavy and widespread development of industrialisation and urbanisation (*right*).

Agriculture and commerce in the developing countries
Agriculture based on the plough, which is often made of wood (*above:* an Indian peasant in Orissa), clearly shows the primitive technology and low productivity of many peoples. In such areas, trading in goods (*right:* a market in Rwanda) takes place only in limited areas or not at all, since often agricultural produce barely sustains those who produce it.

Modern industrial installations
Since the second half of the eighteenth century, Western Europe has been undergoing the so-called Industrial Revolution which caused the Earth to be divided into two blocks from an economic point of view (on one side, the economically advanced countries, such as some European countries together with the United States, Japan and Australia, and on the other, the many developing countries).

The population problem

In 1650 the world population reached 500 million, growing to 1,000 million by 1830. In mid-1975 a UN survey estimated that it had reached 3,967 million, an increase of 77,000,000 over the previous twelve months. This shows how the world's population has dramatically increased since the nineteenth century as science and technology have developed. If the present rate of increase is maintained, the population will double by 2014.

The population explosion is largely due to the reduction in the mortality rate (especially among children), owing to progress in medicine and improvement in the standard of living. Clearly this population increase poses enormous problems to the various nations. Many solutions have been put forward, but a real answer has yet to be found. It is clear, however, that the planet will eventually be unable to support its ever-increasing population.

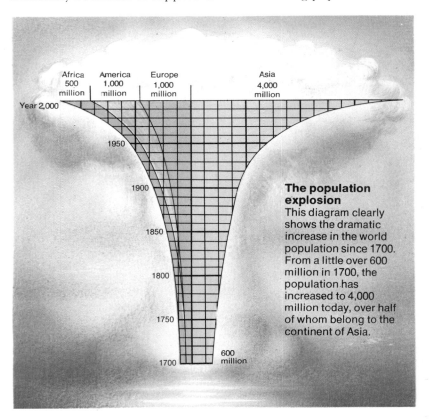

The population explosion
This diagram clearly shows the dramatic increase in the world population since 1700. From a little over 600 million in 1700, the population has increased to 4,000 million today, over half of whom belong to the continent of Asia.

Distribution of the principal racial groups
The map shows the principal zones occupied by the three major racial groups. As can be seen, the mongoloid group occupies the larger part of Asia, and some areas of America and eastern Madagascar. The caucasians occupy the whole of Europe, part of Asia, the northern part of Africa and its southern tip in addition to enormous areas of America. The negroid group is found in Africa, part of Madagascar and a small area of the American continent.
It is a situation which is continually changing; there have been numerous and massive population movements (remember the negro slave trade and the white immigration in America).

Mongoloid
Caucasian
Negroid

The many races

Homo sapiens, who thousands of years ago gained ascendancy over the other species, today has many different outward appearances from one group to another. One can meet very tall people with white skin, blue eyes and fair hair like the inhabitants of northern Europe, and short people with dark skin and hair like the pigmies of Africa. Taking account of these and other physical differences, anthropologists divide humans into three major groups or races: caucasians, mongoloids and negroids, in proximity with whom however there are often people with intermediate characteristics.

Mongoloids
The classic mongoloids have yellowish skin, straight hair and the typical slanting eyes. They are found throughout Asia (with the exception of part of India and western Asia) and in the eastern part of Madagascar.

Negroids
Living in central and southern Africa, the western part of Madagascar, the Philippines and the Indonesian islands, they usually have dark skins and curly hair.

Caucasians
Found throughout Europe, Arabia, India and northern Africa, the caucasians have many different outward appearances. For example, the colour of their skin varies from whitish to brown, while their hair may be either fair, brown or black.

The Eskimos
Spread along the shores of Alaska and Canada, the Eskimos are small in size and have yellowish skins.

The Samburu
The Samburu are a tribe in northern Kenya similar to the Masai, with dark brown skin and tall stature.

The Albanians
The Albanians exhibit characteristics of the Dinaric and Alpine peoples which spread from France to Russia.

The Tibetans
Springing from a mixture of Mongolians and an ancient white people, the Tibetans have slightly narrow, mongoloid faces.

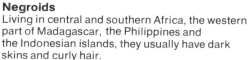

The Bushmen
Small in height, the Bushmen once occupied a large part of southern Africa. Now found in the Kalahari desert, they are becoming extinct.

The Indians
The Indians are one of the largest groups in the world. They have brown skins and slender physiques.

The American Indians
The American Indians are descended from mongoloid groups who reached the New World about 25,000 years ago.

The Papuans
Having come from Asia across the Malay peninsula and Papua, they have very dark skins, curly hair and are found in New Guinea.

The Tuareg
The Tuareg, who belong to the Berber people, live in the Sahara and have dark skins and tall stature.

Religions

If one excludes the religious beliefs in spirits of the primitive peoples, which are still found among people living close to nature, modern religions are found far outside the geographical boundaries within which they originated. Whether monotheistic or polytheistic, throughout history the many religious faiths have been propagated widely among millions of people through evangelism and conversion.

In particular, Christianity and Islam (or Mohammedanism), both monotheistic religions, believe it to be their sacred mission to convert all mankind and they are found in practically every continent.

Judaism is another monotheistic religion, from which both Christianity and Islam have drawn inspiration, and it has grown in strength following the re-establishment of the state of Israel after the Second World War.

The great eastern religions, however, are polytheistic like Hinduism (or Brahmanism), an Indian religion which worships a large number of gods, or Buddhism, based on the teaching of Gautama Buddha.

RELIGIONS

Legend:
- Christian
- Moslem
- Hindu
- Buddhist
- Spirit worship

Christianity
This is the religion with the largest number of followers at the present time (*above*, an Orthodox ceremony). There are over 960 million Christians, subdivided into Catholics, Protestants and Orthodox. Christianity is based on the doctrine of Jesus of Nazareth who lived in Palestine almost two thousand years ago.

Islam
There are today over 500 million followers of Islam. The founder was Mohammed who lived in Arabia between the sixth and seventh centuries AD. *Right:* a place of worship (mosque).

Spirit worship
The worship of spirits is a form of religion found among primitive peoples who believe that every object around them possesses a good or evil spirit, which must be propitiated or driven off by special rituals. There are about 100 million spirit worshippers.

Hinduism
Found almost entirely in the Indian peninsula (*left:* ritual bathing in the sacred Ganges), Hinduism is practised by over 480 million followers.

Buddhism
There are now over 220 million Buddhists found mainly in China, Japan, Sri Lanka and Indochina (*right:* a statue of Buddha).

Languages

Language is another factor which distinguishes the inhabitants of the world. It is difficult to establish how many different languages there are because it is not always possible to differentiate between languages and dialects. It is believed, however, that there are over 2,500 languages, some spoken by small groups like the Basques, others used daily by millions of people like English. The classification criterion is generally historical, that is those languages with a common origin are grouped at various levels. For example, Italian, Spanish, Portuguese and French form the Romance group since they are all derived from Latin (Roman).

LANGUAGES

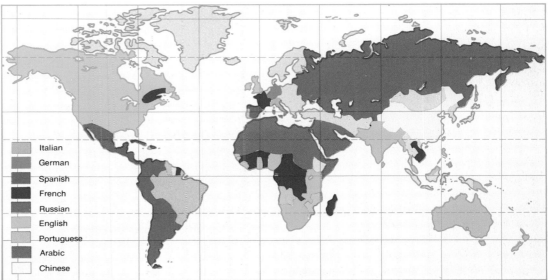

Legend:
- Italian
- German
- Spanish
- French
- Russian
- English
- Portuguese
- Arabic
- Chinese

The city

The birth of the city is not a phenomenon exclusive to the present age, neither is it confined to the economically developed countries.

Long before the Industrial Revolution, which since the eighteenth century has affected many European countries, there were few areas on our planet without cities. One can speak of a complete urban revolution starting in the fourth millennium before Christ in Sumeria, Egypt, and the Indus valley when from a primitive economic culture based on hunting, fishing and agriculture, it progressed to a more complete form which required differentiation of tasks between different members of the group. It is clear that co-ordination and guidance of the various groups could only be achieved if the controlling bodies were concentrated in one well defined area which could form a point of reference for the surrounding region. Thus then was born an urban settlement in an easily accessible position (usually along rivers or on the coasts) which provided services to the remainder of the territory from which, in turn, it received its supplies.

This is how the great settlements developed, like Babylon which 3,000 years before Christ contained 100,000 inhabitants; Athens, dominated by the hill of the Acropolis; or Rome which at the height of its splendour boasted over half a million inhabitants.

One had to wait, however, for the Industrial Revolution of the eighteenth century before this way of life became characteristic of a large proportion of the population and cities with over a million inhabitants developed. In the urban areas of Europe, North America and Japan, this phenomenon was linked to industrial development, while in continental Asia it was due above all to the development of trading centres.

Palmanova
This aerial view reveals the characteristic polygonal layout of Palmanova, the centre of Friuli which was built as a city-fortress by the Venetians at the end of the fifteenth century and whose ramparts and ditches are still intact.

A street walk in Barcelona
The dense crowd strolling along the avenues where there are bars and shops (in Barcelona these avenues are called Ramblas) is perhaps one of the most typical marks of the modern way of life.

THE GREAT URBAN AREAS

Areas with high urbanisation
● Over 1,000,000 inhabitants
○ Over 5,000,000 inhabitants

THE CITIES WITH THE LARGEST POPULATIONS IN EACH CONTINENT

EUROPE:		AFRICA	
Moscow	8,769,000	Cairo	13,300,000
Paris	8,707,000	Alexandria	2,917,000
London	6,735,000	Kinshasa	2,653,000
Madrid	4,925,000	Casablanca	2,904,000
Leningrad	4,456,000	Lagos	1,243,000
Rome	3,784,000	Johannesburg	1,609,000
Berlin	3,339,000	**AMERICA**	
Athens	3,027,000	Mexico City	18,748,000
Kiev	2,587,000	New York	18,054,000
Budapest	2,104,000	São Paulo	10,997,000
Vienna	1,480,000	Buenos Aires	9,766,000
ASIA		Los Angeles	8,296,000
Shanghai	12,320,000	Chicago	8,116,000
Tokyo	11,680,000	Lima	6,053,000
Seoul	9,646,000	Rio de Janeiro	6,011,000
Beijing	9,579,000	San Francisco	5,878,000
Calcutta	9,165,000	Santiago	5,913,000
Bombay	8,227,000	Philadelphia	4,826,000
Tientsin	8,190,000	Detroit	4,601,000
Djakarta	7,829,000	**OCEANIA**	
Tehran	6,022,000	Sidney	3,430,000
Delhi	5,714,000	Melbourne	2,942,000

A village in Kenya
Around the cities where millions of people live, the phenomenon of settlements occurs all over the Earth in the form of villages (the photograph shows a Kikuyu village). The village consists of a group of thatched huts whose inhabitants devote their entire lives to agriculture in order to support themselves.

Pueblo village in New Mexico (USA)
The villages of the Pueblos in the southern part of the Rocky Mountains are usually built under rocky shelters with dwellings reached by flights of steps.

Floating city in Hong Kong (left)
Shortage of space on land and extreme poverty have led to the growth near a number of cities in eastern Asia (for example Hong Kong, Singapore, Bangkok) of actual cities on the water where boats have taken the place of houses.

The problems of urbanisation

Although the birth of the city took place centuries ago, it is only in recent times that the problems of living in large conurbations have appeared. While urban life offers numerous advantages with respect to rural life (the work is usually better paid, there are many opportunities for recreation and meeting people and there are numerous services of which to avail oneself), there are also many disadvantages, frequently associated with the urban areas of industrially and economically developed regions and with those of underdeveloped zones. You only have to think of the noise, the pollution, the traffic congestion, the rising cost of living and the continual influx of people from the country who find it harder and harder to find work and who are forced to live on the outskirts of the city, often in very poor accommodation.

The development of London

| 1750 |
| Population 750,000 |
| 1860 |
| Population 3,000,000 |
| 1960 |
| Population 8,000,000 |

Tokyo, the easternmost city in Asia
The photograph shows the commercial centre and the streets of Ginza (one of the most central parts of the city) teeming with dense and fast-moving traffic.

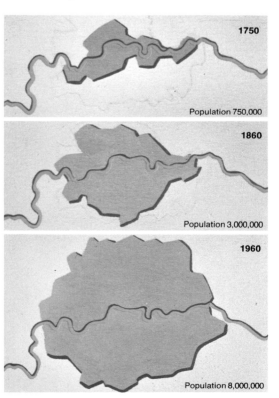

Food resources

The first men lived by hunting, fishing and the gathering of wild fruit. This is the most primitive form of economy and is found today only in the most isolated and inaccessible regions of the world (Amazonia, Indonesia and equatorial Africa). When, about 10,000 years ago, man first discovered that animals could be reared and the soil cultivated a process was begun which has literally changed the face of the Earth. Pastoralism developed for the most part in the marginal areas near the hot and cold deserts of Africa and Asia. Pastoral peoples don't change the land but limit themselves to exploiting it and moving on, in the constant search for new pastures and watering places. Nowadays there are very few completely nomadic populations; most have settled or practice only seasonal nomadism.

Agricultural practice has made continual improvement over the centuries, progressing from primitive cultivation with a hoe, to ploughing with a plough pulled by animals, to modern mechanised agriculture. Farm workers of today are more likely to be specialized technicians than manual labourers.

From the beginning of this process a large part of the planet has been cultivated. First were the tropical areas along the large fluvial basins, favoured with heat all year round and with abundant rainfall. However, the most productive areas now are in the temperate zones, both because of the natural conditions and because, being part of the richest nations, the agriculture is at a high level of technological development.

The greatest problem we face today is whether the food resources of the world are sufficient for its growing population. According to FAO more than a billion people are undernourished and of these 500 million suffer from serious malnutrition. To meet food requirements cultivated areas need to increase by 15% to reach 2 billion hectares by the end of the century. But the modern tendency seems to be the reverse. The increase of urbanisation, erosion, pollution and desertification are causing every year the loss of precious soil.

Fishing
Along the coasts of the countries of the southern hemisphere fishing is still practised by traditional methods and production is for consumption by the family or for domestic trade. *Left*: a Yemeni fisherman. In industrialised countries fishing is a very different affair — huge fleets equipped with sophisticated technology which go further and further from the coasts in order to satisfy the growing demand for fish and its derivatives (meal and fertilisers).

Plantation agriculture
The export of crops does not necessarily bring wealth as is evidenced in the export of so-called secondary priority products such as tea, coffee and cocoa which are cultivated in countries of the southern hemisphere, often in place of more essential products, to be imported by the industrial nations of the north.
Right: a tea plantation in Sri Lanka, the third producer and the largest exporter of tea in the world.

Uncultivated areas | Subsistence-level agriculture | Industrialised agriculture

Cultivated land

Only one tenth of the land above sea-level is cultivated. Most of the rest is occupied by ice-caps, deserts, forests, mountains, grazing land and urban areas with their roads and industries. Arable land is not distributed equally between the continents. In the temperate regions the soil and climate favour the cultivation and rearing of a greater variety of crops and livestock, while in the tropical zones cultivation is limited to a few cereals like rice and maize and specialised products like tea, coffee, cocoa, sugar cane and tropical fruits.

Desertification

Herds of cattle on the move near Bla in Mali. The photograph shows a typical Sahel landscape, an area which is becoming progressively more arid and is subject to dramatic periods of drought. The last, which ended in 1985, caused the death of millions of cattle and the migration of nomadic tribes from the dried-out wells and burnt pastures to the big cities where they could count on the assistance of international aid organisations like FAO. But little has been done or is being done in these and other areas of risk to halt the trend towards desertification.

Land use

The graph shows the current situation, the result of man's transformation of the environment; for example the forests which covered nearly half of the Earth's surface have been destroyed to make room for cultivation. The ratio percentages show in fact a dangerous imbalance: most of the uncultivated and unproductive land is desert, which is increasing to the consequent loss of grazing land (the phenomenon of desertification).

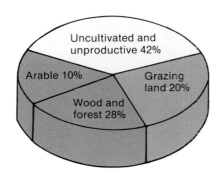

Uncultivated and unproductive 42%
Arable 10%
Grazing land 20%
Wood and forest 28%

Subsistence agriculture

In Afghanistan 58% of the population is involved in agriculture. The methods of cultivation and processing are primitive. Wooden ploughs are still in use. These can neither plough deeply into the soil nor turn the clod, but are however adapted to the relatively powdery soil of the region. In many developing countries, with the advent of the Green Revolution at the end of the sixties, there has been an improvement in agricultural productivity. However, because of a variety of problems, the promised results have not been achieved.

Market agriculture

Left: mechanised harvesting of maize in Italy. Italian agriculture is characterised by a notable variety of products thanks to the climatic variations within the country. *Right*: an agrarian landscape in Pennsylvania, USA. The cultivation is following the level of the land to avoid erosion. In the USA only 3.5% of the active population is involved in agriculture.

Agriculture

Agriculture has been the focus of human activity through the centuries. When man passed from a nomadic life to a sedentary one, he abandoned the simple picking of the fruits provided by nature, realising that the land would provide more abundant and more secure nutrition if he lavished some care on it.

Thus developed the idea of sowing and fertilising, which today is still at the heart of all agriculture. Men began to take a greater and more positive control of nature as they sowed, tended and reaped the crops they needed in the best possible conditions. Following the significant progress of the classical era (the Romans used the rotation of crops and invented many agricultural implements), and the decline of the Middle Ages and subsequent recovery, it was due to the great scientific discoveries of the nineteenth century that agriculture took a decisive step forward with a complete overhaul of the traditional methods of cultivation.

The most important developments were in the field of mechanical and chemical engineering, which overcame man's fatigue in the fields through large-scale mechanisation and led to the maximum growth of the various crops through adequate fertilisation. In spite of the enormous developments in industry which have taken place since the eighteenth century, today still about half of those in business are involved with agriculture. The percentage of activity in this sector varies significantly from country to country.

It ranges from countries where there is intensive mechanisation with high productivity and a low percentage of the people employed in agriculture (in the United States 3.5%, in Belgium 4% and in Canada 5.5%, for example) to countries where mechanisation is almost non-existent, and the entire agricultural output often only supports the population with nothing left over for export. In such countries the percentage of those engaged in agriculture is very high. In Chad, for example, 85% of the population is involved in agriculture, in Tanzania 83% and in Rwanda 82%.

Wheat *(above)*
Now grown all over the world, wheat originated in south-west Asia. (*Right:* barley.)

Rice
The traditional and sometimes the only food of many people in Asia, rice requires high temperatures and plenty of moisture.

CROPS

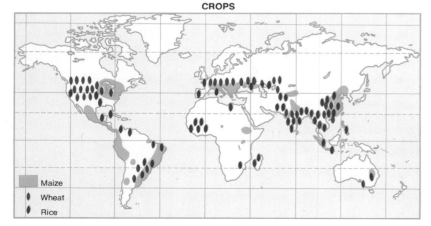

Maize
Wheat
Rice

Maize
Also known as Indian corn, maize is a herbaceous plant from central South America. In many countries, much of the production is destined for livestock feeding.

The olive
Among the most characteristic oil-bearing trees, the olive is typical of the Mediterranean area and is well adapted to rather poor and harsh soil.

Vines
Vines are woody plants, usually climbing, whose fruit is either eaten fresh (usually a little over 10%) or used for wine-making.

Fishing

An activity as old as man himself, fishing has been affected over the centuries by technical limitations and by eating habits which prevented greater expansion. Today, fishing provides only a little over 5% of the food consumed by the entire population of the world and is in a phase of rapid development (the most active country is Japan with over 11 million tonnes of fish landed annually) which could make it one of the decisive factors in the struggle against hunger which affects such a large proportion of mankind.

Rearing livestock

The rearing of livestock is an old and well-established part of the agriculture and economy of many countries of the world. Only since the eighteenth century has significant technical progress been made in Europe leading to the enrichment of the diet of the larger animals and improvement of the breeds.

Today there are two animal breeding methods. The first is the European method, which has benefited from the notable progress in agriculture (rotation of crops, cultivation of fodder crops) and from techniques of conservation and commercialisation. This type of animal breeding is found all over Europe and also in parts of America and Australia where it is managed as a vast business concern.

The second type of breeding is what may be called non-European and is characterised by a lack of rationalisation in the areas of animal feeding and breeding by selection. This is generally carried on on a small scale. A particular case of this type of animal husbandry occurs in India which has the largest population of cattle (about 180 million) but cannot exploit these resources for religious reasons.

Tuna fishing
The tuna, which is much sought after for its tender and tasty flesh, lives at considerable depths. In spring they collect in shoals for breeding and come to the surface where many of them are caught by tuna fishermen. The fishermen use a collection of nets across which the fish must pass to the last net, called the death chamber, where they are finally caught.

Flocks of sheep in Australia
In Australia, the country with the largest number of sheep, this type of livestock farming is used for the production of wool and meat.

Pigs
The pig is very suitable for small breeders, and is found in large numbers in China.

ANIMAL BREEDING AND FISHING

Cattle
Sheep
Pigs
Fishing

Food and nourishment

A useful indication of a population's living standard is found in the type and quantity of food it consumes, and inadequate nourishment is in fact a fundamental characteristic of many of the developing countries of the so-called Third World. It is linked, by cause and effect, to numerous other factors. Developing countries have a higher percentage of their populations involved in agriculture, but yields are low and there is limited industrialisation. The fast increase in population also tends to nullify efforts to reduce the food shortage. Rates of population increase are higher in the Third World. Economic growth is slow as there is little or no money for development, and countries frequently become dependent on foreign aid and investment.

Recent studies have shown that today almost 2,000 million people do not have enough to eat, and that there is always a connection between food consumption and level of income. It has in fact been established that both total protein consumption and total calorie consumption increase with increasing income. The developing countries not only have a lower protein consumption in terms of quantity but also in terms of quality. Their diet is rarely varied, as is the diet of people in more developed countries. It often consists mainly of staple foods, rice perhaps, or cereals. Yields are usually low as fields are poorly irrigated and agricultural machinery and methods are outdated. Reliance on one crop can also be dangerous, as a drought, for example, can ruin the crop and even cause famine.

Daily calorie consumption per inhabitant
The map on the right shows the amount of food available daily to each inhabitant of the countries of the world. It should be noted that, according to the Food and Agriculture Organisation's estimates, an intake of 1,600 calories per day is required in order to sustain a minimum amount of physical activity, whilst about 3,000 are required for a medium-intensity occupation. It is clear from the map that the regions of greatest food shortage coincide with the underdeveloped or developing areas, which are often densely populated. This applies to large areas of Africa and Asia, and many of the Andean countries of South America. The daily calorie consumption is quite adequate in the greater part of the northern hemisphere, and also in Australia and Argentina in the southern hemisphere. Canada, the United States, Australia and Argentina are also great exporters of foodstuffs, cereals in particular. In tropical countries, calorie consumption is markedly lower, and is frequently inadequate to the needs of the population.

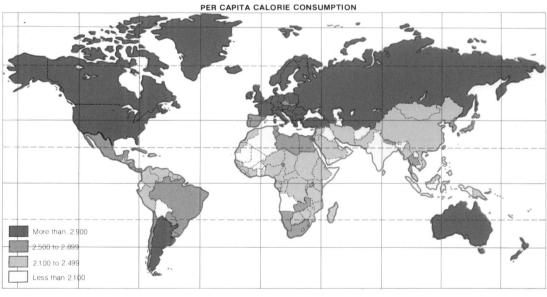

PER CAPITA CALORIE CONSUMPTION

More than 2,900
2,500 to 2,899
2,100 to 2,499
Less than 2,100

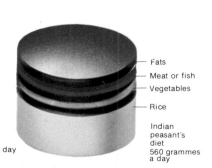

Different foodstuffs available
The diagrams (below and left) serve to illustrate the quantity and quality of the food available daily to an American labourer and to an Indian peasant respectively. In the American diet, the food, apart from being plentiful, is varied, with fruit, milk and vegetables predominating; in the Indian diet, however, the staple ingredient is rice.

Fats
Eggs
Cereals
Sugar
Meat or fish
Milk
Fruit and vegetables

American labourer's diet
2,110 grammes a day

Fats
Meat or fish
Vegetables
Rice

Indian peasant's diet
560 grammes a day

Malnutrition
The effects of malnutrition and starvation, constituted by a prolonged reduction in diet to a point below the minimum required to sustain life, are evident amongst large populations and in vast tracts of our Earth. Many people among the populations of India, numerous African countries, Latin America and the Far East display such symptoms as loss of weight, hypertension, swellings caused by starvation and, particularly in children, retarded growth and conditions such as rickets.

Economy and society

The size and development of population, increased urbanisation and industrialisation, technical and scientific development, the distribution of lines of communication, the efficiency of methods of transport and availability of resources — these are some of the many factors which condition to some degree our economic development, and thus also the standard of living of the peoples of the world.

There is a stark contrast today between those few countries with an abundance of natural resources which are sometimes wasted, and the many countries whose populations struggle for survival. The disparities between countries are enormous, as is illustrated by the map showing the per capita gross national product in 1974-75. The disparities are only partly attributable to the presence of natural resources. It is easy to see that many countries in the process of development have an abundance of resources (minerals and foodstuffs) but that their exploitation has only limited advantages for the producer countries.

GROSS NATIONAL PRODUCT

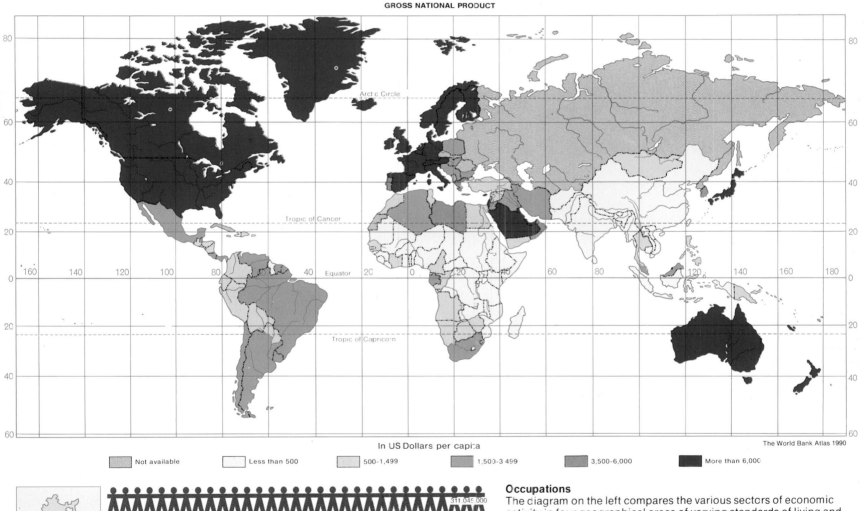

In US Dollars per capita

The World Bank Atlas 1990

Not available	Less than 500	500-1,499	1,500-3,499	3,500-6,000	More than 6,000

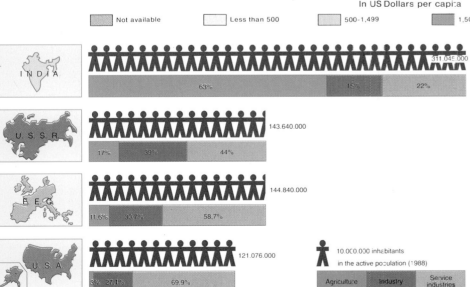

10.000.000 inhabitants in the active population (1988)

Agriculture | Industry | Service industries

Occupations

The diagram on the left compares the various sectors of economic activity in four geographical areas of varying standards of living and with different social, economic and political structures. These areas are India, the USSR, the European Economic Community and the United States. It is clear how the percentage of those engaged in agriculture falls as economic prosperity increases. At the two extremes there is India, where more than half the active population is employed in agriculture, and the United States where the percentage is very small. The countries have diametrically opposed agricultural systems. On the one hand traditional subsistence agriculture in India employs a large number of people, is very much affected by natural conditions (above all by the climate and the soil) and is characterised by a very low level of productivity. On the other hand modern agriculture in the USA is characterised by intense mechanisation, high returns and a limited labour force. In the industrial sector the highest percentages of active employees are found at the intermediate levels (USSR and EEC), whilst the service industries are most developed in countries with the most advanced economies, where the metropolitan facilities and services (sanitation, education, transport) are most plentiful and advanced.

Energy resources

For centuries human and animal muscular power and wind and water power were the most widely used sources of energy and they are still used today in several developing countries.

It was at the beginning of the 18th century that, thanks to technical and scientific developments, coal began to be used on a large scale for the production of energy, both for heating and the powering of machinery.

This was followed by the spread of electricity, produced both in coal-fuelled and hydroelectric power stations, which facilitated industrial development in many countries rich in raw materials. After this came the use of hydrocarbons, particularly oil. Being easy to use and, until very recently,

very cheap, it became the most widely used source of energy.

The continued expansion of industrialization and motorization, and the possibility of a rapid exhaustion of the sources of hydrocarbons, together with political tensions, have encouraged research and development in other areas, for example nuclear power. But inherent in this last are serious problems of various kinds such that attention is now being turned to renewable resources (hydroelectric, geothermal, solar, biomass) and to ways of saving energy.

Careful management of energy resources must also provide for increased efficiency in energy use at all levels, and promising advances are being made in this field.

New York at night
Over 30% of energy used in the USA is for lighting, heating and airconditioning. Construction techniques which provide efficient heating insulation would reduce consumption in this field by one half.

Types of energy consumed
As shown in the graph below more than half of the energy consumed today comes from hydrocarbons (oil and natural gas), a proportion which has been increasing since the beginning of the 20th century. Until then 70% of energy resources were provided by coal; the proportion has now fallen to less than one third. The increasing costs of oil however are making it necessary to re-evaluate the economics of this source. Nuclear energy, due to the high costs of production and the advanced technology required, at present represents only a small proportion.

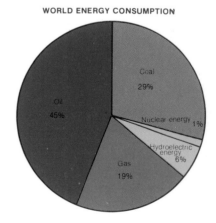

WORLD ENERGY CONSUMPTION

- Coal 29%
- Oil 45%
- Nuclear energy 1%
- Hydroelectric energy 6%
- Gas 19%

CONSUMPTION OF ENERGY

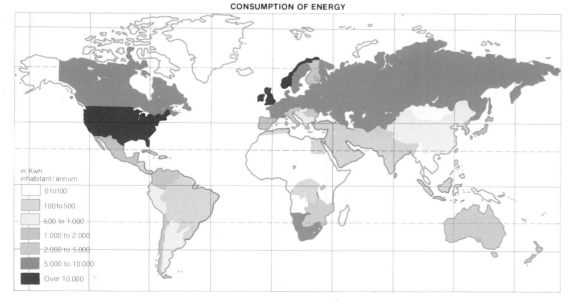

in Kwh inhabitant/annum
- 0 to 100
- 100 to 500
- 500 to 1.000
- 1.000 to 2.000
- 2.000 to 5.000
- 5.000 to 10.000
- Over 10.000

Energy consumption
The annual amount of energy consumed per capita of population has now become a significant indication of the level of development of each country. As can been seen on the map the highest level of consumption is in the most industrialised countries with the highest standards of living (e.g. the USA). These are followed by nearly all the European countries, the USSR and Canada, where consumption is only a little lower. Industry, particularly the metal and chemical industries, and domestic consumption account for these high levels. In most of the remaining areas consumption is distinctly lower but constantly increasing.

COAL DEPOSITS

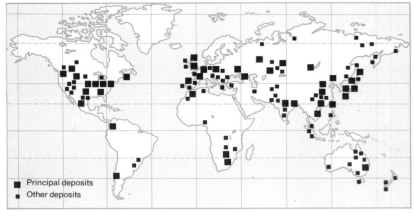

- ■ Principal deposits
- ▪ Other deposits

Coal
Used long ago by the Chinese to produce thermal energy, fossil coal became fundamental to world, and particularly European, economy after the discovery of the steam engine. Heavy concentration of industry occurred in the mining areas (the Ruhr in Germany, the Pittsburgh area in the United States, and the Donetz in the USSR), and the production of coal only slowed down after the introduction of the internal combustion engine, which was fuelled by petroleum products (the photograph on the right shows coal being extracted in an Australian mine). Today coal remains an indispensable raw material in the iron industry, many sectors of the chemical industry and for the generation of electricity.

OIL RESERVOIRS

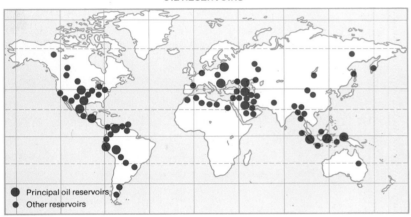

- ● Principal oil reservoirs
- • Other reservoirs

Oil
Oil, which is an extremely important raw material in modern life, is a natural mixture of hydrocarbons. These hydrocarbons are produced by the transformation by bacteria of a mud layer rich in organic substances deposited on the sea bed or in marshes.
Oil is only found in reservoirs consisting of porous and permeable rock, called mother rock, which is impregnated with the precious fluid. World oil production exceeds two thousand million tonnes per year. The oil-producing countries can be divided into four groups: the American group with the United States, Venezuela and Canada; North Africa and the Far East which has only begun to develop its resources; the socialist countries including the USSR and Romania; and Britain which has technically been self-sufficient since 1980.

Drilling for oil
The methods and techniques for the extraction of oil have today been perfected. Drilling is preceded by a complete geological survey in order to minimse the risk of dry wells and the resultant unnecessary expenditure. The drilling installation consists of a metal derrick supporting the drill (*above right:* an oil installation in the Libyan Desert), which is fitted with a rapidly rotating bit which can penetrate to a depth of 6,000-7,000 metres. By means of special platforms (*right:* an exploration drilling platform in the Adriatic) it is possible to drill wells under water. The oil is then piped to the refineries which are on land.

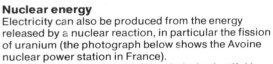

Electrical energy
Electrical energy has to be produced from other forms of energy (mechanical, thermal or nuclear). Electricity offers many advantages over other forms of energy because of its ease of distribution (this applies in practically every case) and its many uses. Electricity can be produced from the energy stored in water in hydroelectric power stations (the photograph below shows the dam of the Aswan station in Egypt) or from the thermal energy of fossil fuels in thermoelectric power stations (the photograph on the left shows the Piacenza thermoelectric power station).

Nuclear energy
Electricity can also be produced from the energy released by a nuclear reaction, in particular the fission of uranium (the photograph below shows the Avoine nuclear power station in France).
Uranium is an element which is relatively plentiful in the Earth's crust, but its extraction is fairly costly and complicated and therefore requires advanced technology as do the power stations themselves. At the present time, the electricity produced by nuclear power stations is more expensive than that produced by either hydroelectric or thermoelectric power stations.

Iron mines in the USA
Along with coal and oil, iron is the other raw material essential to industry and generally to the economy of a country. It is used in many different ways in metallurgy and the iron and steel industry. It is extracted from various minerals including lodestone and haematite. Often, as seen in the illustration, it is produced from open-cast mines. At present about 550 million tonnes of iron are produced every year.

Mineral resources

From prehistoric times man has extracted from the surface of the earth minerals which are useful to him. But today mining activity has reached unprecedented levels in order to supply the industrialized countries with the approximately 80 minerals which are indispensable to modern industry.

Some metals, like iron and aluminium are relatively abundant in the Earth's crust, while others like mercury, tin, silver and platinum are already becoming scarce. The reserves of metals and non-metallic minerals which are economically valuable are distributed irregularly over the Earth, and so there is not one country that does not need to import minerals from another.

The USA and the USSR are the major producers of iron, (which, together with its alloys, is of prior importance), other minerals and fossil fuels. It is in fact the combination of minerals and fuels in that they initially make industrial development possible, which makes these countries rich. Even if a country is rich in precious minerals but not in fuels it may remain poor. This is in fact the fate of many countries in the southern hemisphere, even though they extract and export huge quantities of minerals.

The need to have economically important minerals readily available pushes many countries to accumulate reserves (with the effect of stabilizing price fluctuations) and to substitute with other materials where possible. It also gives the incentive to recycle above all scrap metals.

The copper mines of Chuquicamata (Chile)
Another important raw material is the mineral copper. It is indispensable in various sectors of industry, above all that of electricity, being both a thermal and electrical conductor. It is extracted in large quantities from mines in the USA, the USSR, and Chile.

IRON-STEEL

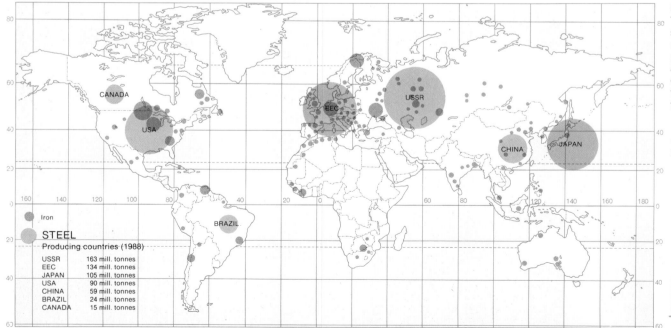

Iron

STEEL
Producing countries (1988)

USSR	163 mill. tonnes
EEC	134 mill. tonnes
JAPAN	105 mill. tonnes
USA	90 mill. tonnes
CHINA	59 mill. tonnes
BRAZIL	24 mill. tonnes
CANADA	15 mill. tonnes

Steel
Though man has been producing steel for centuries, it has been the revolutionary innovations of the past 130 years that have made it an indispensable part of our civilisation. World production today reaches about 770 million tonnes a year.

IRON
Total world production (1987): 553 million tonnes

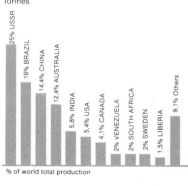

25% USSR
16% BRAZIL
14.4% CHINA
12.4% AUSTRALIA
5.8% INDIA
5.4% USA
4.1% CANADA
2% VENEZUELA
2% SOUTH AFRICA
2% SWEDEN
1.5% LIBERIA
9.1% Others

% of world total production

76

Transport

The economic evolution of a country is fundamentally dependent upon its means of transport and lines of communication. The same is even truer on a worldwide scale today, where the requirements of trade, not only in the economic sector but also in the social and cultural sectors, can be met only if methods of transport and lines of communication develop more rapidly and interconnect more effectively with one another.

For ease of analysis, methods of transport are divided into: continental (road, rail), sea and air. However, obviously there are innumerable combinations of the three types, and for a system of communication to be complete and satisfactory, all transport sectors must develop in parallel with one another.

The range of means of transport, and the layout and density of various lines of communication, are frequently conditioned by natural factors (for instance terrain, rivers, and geological and climatic conditions), though these are sometimes overcome by way of very expensive construction work such as bridges or tunnels. Other factors also have their influence — distance, costs, and the kind of goods to be transported.

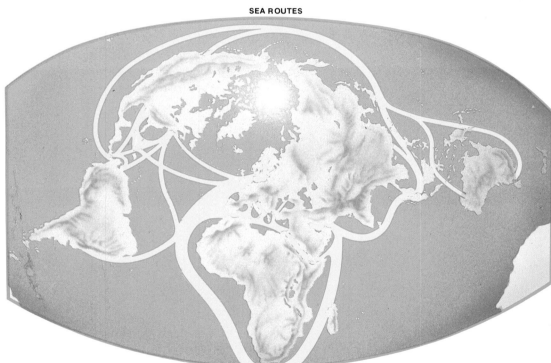

SEA ROUTES

Sea transport
There has been a continuous increase in the amount of goods carried by sea in the course of the 20th century. This is due to the moderate cost of sea transport, making it commerically viable for all goods which do not need to be carried quickly, such as raw materials and fuel. Although little used for passenger transport (ferries excepted), and for the carriage of goods over short distances, ships have increased their useful tonnage appreciably. The main sea routes are shown on the map on the right. Oil accounts for more than half (about 1.5 thousand million tonnes) of the goods carried overall.

Road transport
This ranks foremost in continental transport, above all for passengers and certain types of goods. Motorised transport is often quicker and more comfortable than rail although this is not necessarily true. It is also facilitated by the dense network of roads of various types – trunk roads, main roads and motorways – the development of which has accompanied and promoted the development of motorised transport in general, and the private car in particular. It is estimated that there are almost 19 million vehicles in use on British roads today.

Air transport
In less than 100 years air travel, the last on the scene of all intercontinental means of transport, has revolutionised our concept of distance. It is possible in only a few hours to reach almost any part of the Earth (the Atlantic is crossed in little more than three hours), thanks to the speed of our aircraft. There has been massive development from the 1960s over the principal airline routes. Negative factors are the high costs not only of the planes themselves but also of airports, to which has recently been added the rise in the cost of aviation fuel.

Rail transport
The railways are in close competition with road transport and there has been much development in recent years of advanced passenger and freight trains to improve services. One of the most important areas for rail transport is long-distance passenger travel. For many types of goods, the train has to compete with the lorry, which can carry goods from door to door and therefore does not involve transfer of the goods from factory to station, for example. Rail transport has remained supreme in very large countries with a small and scattered population.

A changing world

The works of nature

To one who has not studied natural phenomena, the surface of the Earth seems changeless and immutable but it is in reality continually undergoing changes. Where man once built busy cities, corals now flourish and where the highest mountain peaks now rise up, were plains inhabited by strange animals of which there are few remains.

These were changes which occurred very slowly, at a rate almost inconceivable by the human mind, being measured in terms of tens of millions of years. Only in exceptional cases (subsidence, earthquakes and the silting up of lakes, for example) can man observe this continual evolution which is forever changing the morphology of the Earth's crust. Many different agents contribute to this transformation, in particular rivers, wind, glaciers and the sea.

The waters
Channelled water constitutes one of the most active agents that change the landscape in temperate climates. Its action may be explained in terms of erosion, transportation and deposition. In mountain stretches, where the slope is steep, rivers have considerable erosive power which is in proportion to their mass, velocity, the amount of abrasive material in suspension and the friability of the rocks on which they act. Thus we have the excavation of a valley with the typical V-shaped cross section (*above:* channels cut by streams in the soft rock of the Goreme in Turkey). It is a slow process of destruction of the mountain started, especially at great heights and in high latitudes, by the disintegration of the rock brought about by the freezing and thawing of water. When the energy of the river has been dissipated, the suspended particles are deposited, which raises the level of the plains and fills up the seas.

The wind
The action of the wind is clearly seen in areas deprived of vegetation whose surface is covered with very fine material (sand and dust) produced by the crumbling of rocks owing to temperature variations. Wind erosion therefore occurs in desert areas and is a form of abrasion called "corrasion" caused by the wind, carrying particles of sand, scouring the rocks which become rounded and smooth (the photograph on the right shows an arch in the Rocky Mountains, USA, formed by wind erosion).
When the wind encounters an obstruction, it deposits the sand it holds to form "dune fields" which are aligned according to the direction of the prevailing wind.

The glaciers
The sculpting action of glaciers is today confined to regions with high mountains or at high latitudes. It is known however that long ago glaciers were much more widely distributed. The last Ice Age, during which much of North America and northern Europe were covered with ice, began about one million years ago. Among examples of the erosive power of glaciers are alpine or prealpine lake basins, cirques (basins of rock with vertical walls found in all the glacial mountain ranges) and the "U"-shaped valleys, so called owing to their typical cross section caused by the action of the channelled glacial mass (the picture on the left is of the St Gottard valley). Deposits left behind by glaciers are called moraines.

The sea
The action of the sea is most clearly seen along its line of contact with the shore. Erosion is mainly caused by the action of the waves, whose considerable mechanical energy gradually wears away the rocky coast which can either appear even or indented according to the degree of disintegration of the rocks of which it is composed and the way in which the rocky strata present themselves to the erosive action of the sea (the photograph below shows a section of the south coast of Australia opposite Tasmania. Erosion has isolated several pinnacles called "The Twelve Apostles").

The works of man

Man has arrogantly included himself among those agents which modify the appearance of the surface of the Earth. He has built towns, he has woven a dense web of communication channels which crosses the rivers and mountains, and he has replaced the forests with the type of agriculture necessary for his own existence. For centuries, man's intervention was on a fairly small scale, but from the beginning of the nineteenth century, with its enormous rate of development of technology and industry, and the growth of population and town planning, the effect of man on his natural environment became more significant and sometimes irreversible. We are now at a point in the history of mankind where, perhaps for the last time, we should reflect whether the description "sapiens" of which our species is so proud is deserved or not.

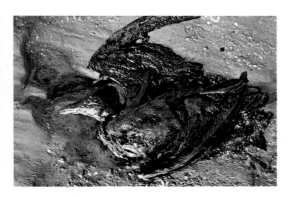

The soil
The soil consists of the very thin surface layer of the Earth's crust formed by the slow disintegration of the rocks, and it also contains organic substances and living organisms. Without the soil, any form of agriculture would be impossible. Solid waste matter constitutes one of the most worrying sources of pollution of the soil, particularly non-degradable substances such as some plastics.

The air
The gaseous envelope called the atmosphere which covers the Earth is formed of a mixture of gases. Oxygen makes combustion possible, including that occurring inside organisms (respiration); nitrogen supports the vigorous oxidising action of oxygen, while carbon dioxide is essential for chlorophyll photosynthesis, the method by which plants make food.
In the last ten years, man has accelerated the process of polluting the atmosphere by introducing into it substances, in ever increasing quantities, which alter its composition such as sulphur dioxide, lead and unburnt particles originating mainly from domestic heating, vehicle exhausts and industrial installations (the photograph above shows the smoke from factories in Cleveland in the United States).

The water
The importance of water is obvious to everybody. Water is synonymous with life; without it those organisms which are composed of high percentages of water (in man, over 65% by weight) could not survive. Although water covers three quarters of the surface of the Earth, it is not an inexhaustible resource, especially when it is subjected to massive industrial pollution (the photograph on the right shows the effluents from a steelworks in Baltimore, USA), and pollution by sewage and agriculture which contributes to the destruction of both the animals and also the birds who live near water. *(Left:* bird killed by oil pollution.)

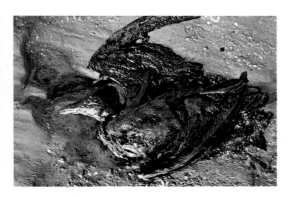

World Atlas

Contents

THE EARTH

Table I   **Physical Features of the Earth**

Table II   **The Oceans**

Table III **Climates and Ocean Currents**

Table IV **Population Density**

Table V   **The Political Divisions of the Earth**

EUROPE

Table 1   **Europe-Physical** 1 : 14 000 000

Table 2   **Europe-Political** 1 : 14 000 000

Table 3   **The British Isles** 1 : 4 500 000

Table 4   **Great Britain and Ireland** 1 : 4 500 000

Table 5   **England and Wales**

Table 6   **Scotland**

Table 7   **Ireland**

Table 8   **The Iberian Peninsula** 1 : 4 500 000

Table 9   **Spain and Portugal** 1 : 4 500 000

Table 10 **France-Physical** 1 : 4 500 000

Table 11 **France-Political** 1 : 4 500 000

Table 12 **Central Europe-Physical** 1 : 4 500 000

Table 13 **Central Europe-Political** 1 : 4 500 000

Table 14 **North-West Europe** 1 : 4 500 000

Table 15 **The Netherlands, Belgium and Luxembourg** 1 : 4 500 000

Table 16 **Scandinavia-Physical** 1 : 4 500 000

Table 17 **Scandinavia-Political** 1 : 4 500 000

Table 18 **Italy-Physical** 1 : 4 500 000

Table 19 **Italy-Political** 1 : 4 500 000

Table 20 **South East Europe-Physical** 1 : 4 500 000

Table 21 **South East Europe-Political** 1 : 4 500 000

Table 22 **The Soviet Union** 1 : 20 000 000

Table 23 **The Baltic lands** 1 : 6 000 000

Table 24 **The Ural Lands** 1 : 6 000 000

Table 25 **The Caucasian Soviet Republics** 1 : 6 000 000

ASIA

Table 26 **Asia-Physical** 1 : 34 000 000

Table 27 **Asia-Political** 1 : 34 000 000

Table 28 **The Near East** 1 : 4 500 000

Table 29 **The Middle East** 1 : 12 000 000

Table 30 **India** 1 : 12 000 000

© Vallardi Industrie Grafiche - Lainate (Mi)
  All rights reserved

Edition 1994/1993/1992/1991
Reprint 1/2/3/4

Table 31 **China and Mongolia** 1 : 12 000 000

Table 32 **Korea and Japan** 1 : 12 000 000

Table 33 **South East Asia** 1 : 12 000 000

Table 34 **Indonesia, Malaysia and the Philippines** 1 : 12 000 000

AFRICA

Table 35 **Africa-Physical** 1 : 34 000 000

Table 36 **Africa-Political** 1 : 34 000 000

Table 37 **Northern Africa** 1 : 12 000 000

Table 38 **East Africa** 1 : 20 000 000

Table 39 **West Africa** 1 : 12 000 000

Table 40 **Central Africa** 1 : 12 000 000

Table 41 **South Africa** 1 : 12 000 000

NORTH AND CENTRAL AMERICA

Table 42 **North America-Physical** 1 : 34 000 000

Table 43 **North America-Political** 1 : 34 000 000

Table 44 **Canada** 1 : 12 000 000

Table 45 **Alaska** 1 : 12 000 000

Table 46 **The United States** 1 : 12 000 000

Table 47 **Mexico** 1 : 12 000 000

Table 48 **The West Indies** 1 : 12 000 000

SOUTH AMERICA

Table 49 **South America-Physical** 1 : 34 000 000

Table 50 **South America-Political** 1 : 34 000 000

Table 51 **Colombia, Venezuela, Guiana** 1 : 12 000 000

Table 52 **Brazil, Ecuador, Peru, Bolivia and Paraguay** 1 : 12 000 000

Table 53 **Chile, Argentina and Uruguay** 1 : 12 000 000

AUSTRALASIA AND OCEANIA

Table 54 **Australasia and Oceania-Physical** 1 : 33 000 000

Table 55 **Australia and New Zealand** 1 : 12 000 000

POLAR REGIONS

Table 56 **The Arctic Regions** 1 : 30 000 000

Table 57 **The Antarctic Regions** 1 : 30 000 000

North Pole

ARCTIC OCEAN

80

Queen Elizabeth Is.
Ellesmere
Greenland

Banks I.
C. Barrow
Beaufort Sea
Victoria I. Boothia
Magnetic Pole
Melville Pen.
Baffin Bay
Davis Strait

70

ASIA
Brooks Range
Mackenzie
Great Bear L.
Baffin I.
Hudson Strait
Ungava Pen.
C. Farewell

Nunivak I.
Bering Strait
Yukon
Mt. McKinley
Mt. Logan
Great Slave L.
Hudson Bay
Ungava Bay

60

Bering Sea
Gulf of Alaska
Coast Range
Belcher Is.
Labrador

Aleutian Is.
7860
Aleutian Trench
Alexander Arch.
L. Winnipeg
Newfoundland

50

Vancouver I.
ROCKY MOUNTAINS
Great Plains
L. Superior
St. Lawrence
G. of St. Lawrence
C. Sable

NORTH AMERICA

Missouri
L. Michigan
L. Huron
L. Ontario
C. Cod
APPALACHIAN MTS.

40

C. Mendocino
Mt. Elbert
Colorado
Arkansas
Mitchell
Mississippi
L. Erie

6741
Mt. Whitney
Sierra Nevada
Rio Grande
Red R.
C. Hatteras

30

Hawaiian Islands
Midway I.
TROPIC OF CANCER
Guadalupe I.
Lower California
G. of California
Eastern Sierra Madre
Western Sierra Madre
Mexican Plateau
Florida
Bermuda
Sargasso Sea
6996

20

Hawaii
Johnston I.
C. San Lucas
Revilla Gigedo Is.
Citlaltepetl
G. of Campeche
Yucatan
Gulf of Mexico
Bahamas
Cuba
Greater Antilles
Jamaica
Hispaniola
Puerto Rico
Guadeloupe
Martinique

10

Palmyra I.
Fanning I.
Christmas I.
Clipperton I.
Tajumulco
G. of Honduras
Caribbean Sea
Lesser Antilles
Barbados
Pta. Gallinas
Trinidad

Baker I.
180
7251
170
160
150
LONGITUDE WEST FROM GREENWICH
L. Nicaragua
Isthmus of Tehuantepec
Isthmus of Panama
Chirripó
G. of Panama
Maracaibo
Lake Maracaibo
Orinoco
Llanos
Guiana Highlands

EQUATOR
Phoenix Is.
Galápagos Is.
Gulf of Guayaquil
Chimborazo
Amazon
Japurá
Amazon
Marajó I.
Fernando de Noronha I.
C. S. Roque

Tokelau Is.
Huascarán
Selvas
Purus
SOUTH AMERICA
Catingas

10

W. Samoa
Marquesas Is.
Ascension

Tonga Is.
(Friendly Is.)
Society Is.
Tahiti
Tuamotu Arch.
Illampú
Bolivian Plat.
Plateau of Mato Grosso
Brazilian Highlands
São Francisco
St. Helena

20

10882
Tonga Trench
Cook Is.
Tubuai Is.
TROPIC OF CAPRICORN
L. Titicaca
Gran Chaco
Paraná
Paraguay
Brazilian Highlands
Pico da Bandeira
C. Frio

30

Kermadec Trench
10047
Kermadec Is.
Rapa Iti
Pitcairn I.
Ducie I.
Sala-y-Gómez
Easter I.
S. Félix
S. Ambrosio
Aconcagua
Pampas
Patagonia
Paraná
Lagoa dos Patos

40

Chatham Is.
Juan Fernández Is.
Chiloé
G. of San Matías
Chonos Arch.
Patagonia
G. of San Jorge
Tristan da Cunha
Gough I.

50

Str. of Magellan
Tierra del Fuego
Horn
Falkland Is.
South Georgia

60

Drake Passage
South Shetland Is.
South Sandwich Is.
South Orkney Is.
8264

70

Antarctic Peninsula
Charcot I.
Alexander I.
Weddell Sea

ANTARCTIC CIRCLE

80

Ross Sea
Byrd Land
Ellsworth I.
Coats Land

South Pole

ATLANTIC

PACIFIC OCEAN

Azores
C. St. Vincent
Madeira
Canary Is.
Toubk
C. Blanco
C. Verde Is.
C. Verde
Mauritania
C. Palmas

HEIGHT

Metres
Over 3000
3000
1500
500
250
0
Sea level
Below sea level

DEPTH
0
150
3000
6000
Below 6000

AVERAGE HEIGHT OF CONTINENTS

Arctic Circle
60
340
960
720
Tropic of Cancer
750
180 150 120 90 60 30 0 30 60 90 120 150 180
Equator
590
Tropic of Capricorn
340
2200
Antarctic Circle
60

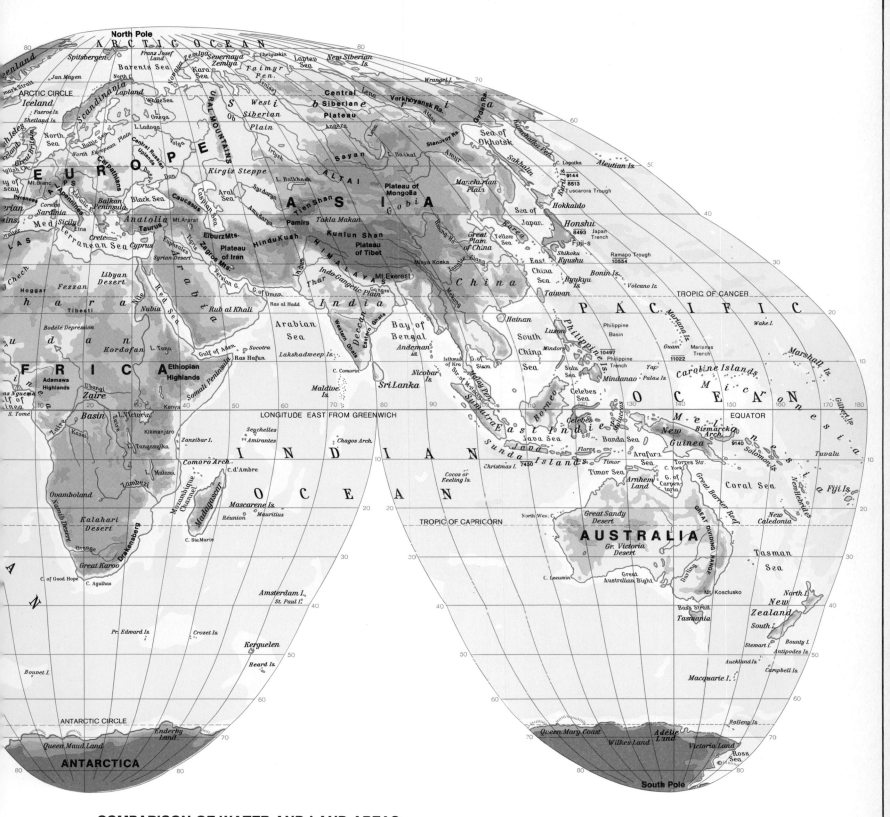

COMPARISON OF WATER AND LAND AREAS AT VARIOUS LATITUDES

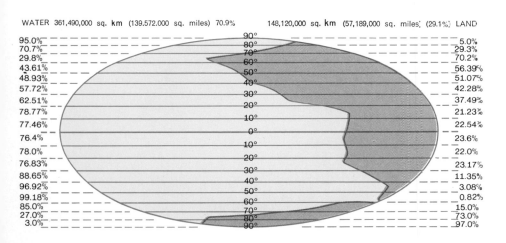

WATER 361,490,000 sq. km (139.572.000 sq. miles) 70.9%   148,120,000 sq. km (57,189,000 sq. miles) (29.1%) LAND

WATER	Latitude	LAND
95.0%	90°	5.0%
70.7%	80°	29.3%
29.8%	70°	70.2%
43.61%	60°	56.39%
48.93%	50°	51.07%
57.72%	40°	42.28%
62.51%	30°	37.49%
78.77%	20°	21.23%
77.46%	10°	22.54%
76.4%	0°	23.6%
78.0%	10°	22.0%
76.83%	20°	23.17%
88.65%	30°	11.35%
96.92%	40°	3.08%
99.18%	50°	0.82%
85.0%	60°	15.0%
27.0%	70°	73.0%
3.0%	80°	97.0%
	90°	

HYPSOMETRIC CURVE
(Average heights of land above and below sea level)

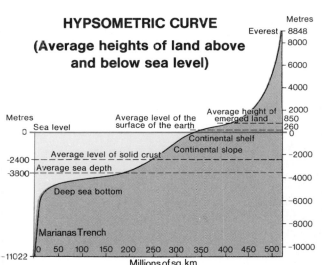

Metres
Everest 8848
8000
6000
4000
2000
850
260

Metres — Sea level — 0 — Average level of the surface of the earth — Average height of emerged land

Continental shelf
Continental slope

Average level of solid crust — −2400 — −2000

Average sea depth — −3800 — −4000

Deep sea bottom — −6000

−8000

Marianas Trench — −11022 — −10000

Millions of sq. km
0 50 100 150 200 250 300 350 400 450 500

ARCTIC

Fletcher Ridge

Canada Basin

Eurasia Basin

Severnaya Zemlya (North Land)

Lomonosov Ridge

Novo Sibirskiye Ostrova (New Siberian Islands)

Chukchi Rise

Parry Is.

Dev

Banks I.

Victoria Island

Ostrow Vrangelya (Wrangel I.)

Ob

Lena

Yenisei

Arctic Circle

Lena

Yukon

Great Bear Lake

Mackenzie

Great Slave Lake

Lake Baikal

St. Lawrence I.

M.t McKinley 6196

Rocky Mountains

Amur

Sakhalin

Nunivak I.

Pribilof Is.

Commander Is.

Aleutian Is.

Kodiak I.

Alexander Archipelago

Lake Superior

Kuril Islands

Paramushir I.

Aleutian Trench

Queen Charlotte Is.

Lake Michigan

-10542

Kuril-Kamchatka Trench

North-East Pacific

Vancouver I.

Hokkaido

North-West

Honshu

Pacific

Basin

Blanca Peak 4386

Japan Trench

Basin

-5697

-6800

Mississippi

-10340

-1276

Hawaiian Islands

Murray Fracture Zone

Guadalupe I.

Ryukyu Is.

Okinawa

Bonin Is.

Marcus-Necker Rise

Midway In.

Tropic of Cancer

-7507

Volcano Is.

Marcus I.

Gardner Pinnacles

Revillagigedo Is.

Taiwan

Batan I.

Wake I.

Kauai

Oahu

Hainan

Babuyan I.

Farallon

Mariana

Johnston

Hawaii

Clarion Fracture Zone

Luzon

Philippine Basin

-8124 Trench

-6662

Mariana

Clipperton I.

Guatemala Basin

Mekong

-10783

Guam

Eniwetok

Marshall Islands

Central Pacific

Clipperton Fracture Zone

Philippine Is.

MICRONESIA

Palmyra I.

Basin

Philippine Trench

Ratak Chain

Palawan

-10497

Palau Is.

Truk I.

Ralik Chain

Fanning I.

Equator

Cocos Is.

Mindanao

Talaud Is.

Kusaie

Makin

Fanning Ridge

Christmas I.

Galapagos Islands

Borneo

Caroline Is.

Caroline Basin

Nukuoro

Gilbert Is.

-7315

Celebes

Molucca Is.

MELANESIA

New Ireland

Nauru

Arorae

Phoenix Is.

Jarvis I.

Isabela

Ceram

Java

New Guinea

Bismarck Arch.

New Britain

Bougainville

Nanumea

Gardner

Malden I.

-5490

Aru

New

Solomon Is.

Malaita

Ellice Is. (Tuvalu Is.)

Manihiki

Marquesas Is.

Peru Basin

Tanimbar I.

Louisiade Arch.

Santa Cruz Is.

Tokelau

Savaii

Suwarrow

Flint

Pukapuka

-7455

Timor

Coral Sea Basin

Wallis Is.

Samoa Is.

Society Is.

Tuamotu Islands

Sumbawa

Sumba

New Hebrides

Fiji Islands

Tonga Is.

Cook Islands

Tahiti

Oeno I.

Christmas

Cocos Is.

Great Barrier Reef

-1570

Loyalty Is.

Tubuai Is.

East Pacific Ridge

Nor-West Australian Basin

-1001

New Caledonia

Fiji Basin

-10882

Gambier Is.

Tropic of Capricorn

Ducie I.

Sala-y-Gomez Reef

Australia

Great Dividing Range

Norfolk I.

Rapa

Pitcairn I.

Easter I.

New Zealand Rise

Eastern Plateau

Murray

Lord Howe

Kermadec Is.

Mt Kosciusko 2228

North Island

Legouve Reef

Maria Theresa Reef

Diamantina Trench

South

-5578

South-East Indian Basin

Australian

East Australian

New Zealand

South Island

Chatham Is.

Bounty Is.

South Pacific

Tasmania

Basin

Tasmania Ridge

Antipodes Is.

Ridge

INDIAN OCEAN

Basin

Auckland Is.

Campbell I.

East Pacific-

Indian-Antarctic Ridge

Macquarie Ridge

Macquarie Is.

South Pacific Basin

-5399

Antarctic Basin

Antarctic Circle

PACIFIC OCEAN

POLYNESIA

Tonga Trench

Kermadec-Tonga Trench

DEPTH Metres
200
2000
4000
6000
over 6000

Scale 1 : 85 000 000

0   500 1000 1500 2000 3000 4000 km

Extreme Limit of Drift Ice
Average Limit of Drift Ice
Limit of Pack Ice

OCEAN

Lomonosov Ridge

Franz-Joseph-Land

Spitsbergen

Murmansk Rise

Novaya Zemlya

Lena

Greenland

Greenland Basin

Bear I.

Kolguev I.

Yenisei

Ural Mountains

Ob

Irtysh

Baffin Sea

Jan Mayen I.

Norwegian Basin

Lake Baikal

Baffin Island

Iceland

Faeroes
Shetland Is.

Volga

Aral Sea

Reykjanes Ridge

British Isles

Labrador Basin

Mt. Bianc 4810

Alps

Danube

Caucasus 5633

Euphrates

Newfoundland

West European Basin

Corsica
Sardinia

Indus

Mt. Everest 8848

Lake Huron
Lake Ontario
Lake Erie

Newfoundland Basin

Iberian Basin

Balearic Is.

Sicily

Crete

Cyprus

Ganges

North American Bermuda I. Basin

Azores

Madeira

High Atlas

4165

Nile

Socotra

Arabian Laccadive Is. Basin

Andaman Is.

-6996

Canary Basin

Canary Is.

-6407

Sri Lanka
Nicobar Is.

Bahamas

Cuba
Hispaniola
-9219
Greater Antilles
-9240
Jamaika
Curacao
Lesser Antilles

Puerto Rico

Cape Verde

Cape Verde Is.

Niger

Carlsberg Ridge

Somali Basin

-5358

Maldive Is.

Guadeloupe
Dominica
Martinique
Barbados
Trinidad

Guiana Basin

Sierra Leone Basin

Guinea

Principe
São Tomé
Annobón

Congo

Lake Victoria

Seychelles

Chagos Archipelago

Mid-Indian Basin

St. Paul Rocks

Fernando de Noronha I.

Romanche Trench

-7730

Guinea Basin

Aldabra I.

Comoro Is.

Farquhar Is.

-5386

-216

Amazon

Brazilian Basin

Ascension I.

South Atlantic

St. Helena

Angola Basin

Drakensberge

Madagascar

Mascarene Is.

Mauritius
Réunion

Indian Basin

Chile Basin

-7973

Andes

Trindade I.

Orange

3650

Madagascar Ridge

Mascarene Basin

San Ambrosio I.
San Felix I.

-5755

-5630

Juan Fernandez Is.

-6960
Aconcagua

Rio Grande Rise

South Atlantic Ridge

Tristan da Cunha

Cape Basin

-2213

South-West Indian Basin

Amsterdam I.
St. Paul I.

Argentine Basin

Gough

Cape Rise

Agulhas Basin

Prince Edward Is.

-5779

Crozet Is.

Indian-Antarctic Ridge

-2899

-6125

South Georgia Rise

Falkland Islands

Scotia Ridge

South Georgia

-8264

South Sandwich Islands

Bouvet I.

Atlantic-Indian Ridge

Kerguelen

Kerguelen-Gaussberg
Heard I.
Ridge

OCEAN

INDIAN

South Shetland Islands

South Orkney Island

Scotia Basin

-5869

Atlantic-Indian-Antarctic Basin

Indian-Antarctic Basin

ANTARCTIC

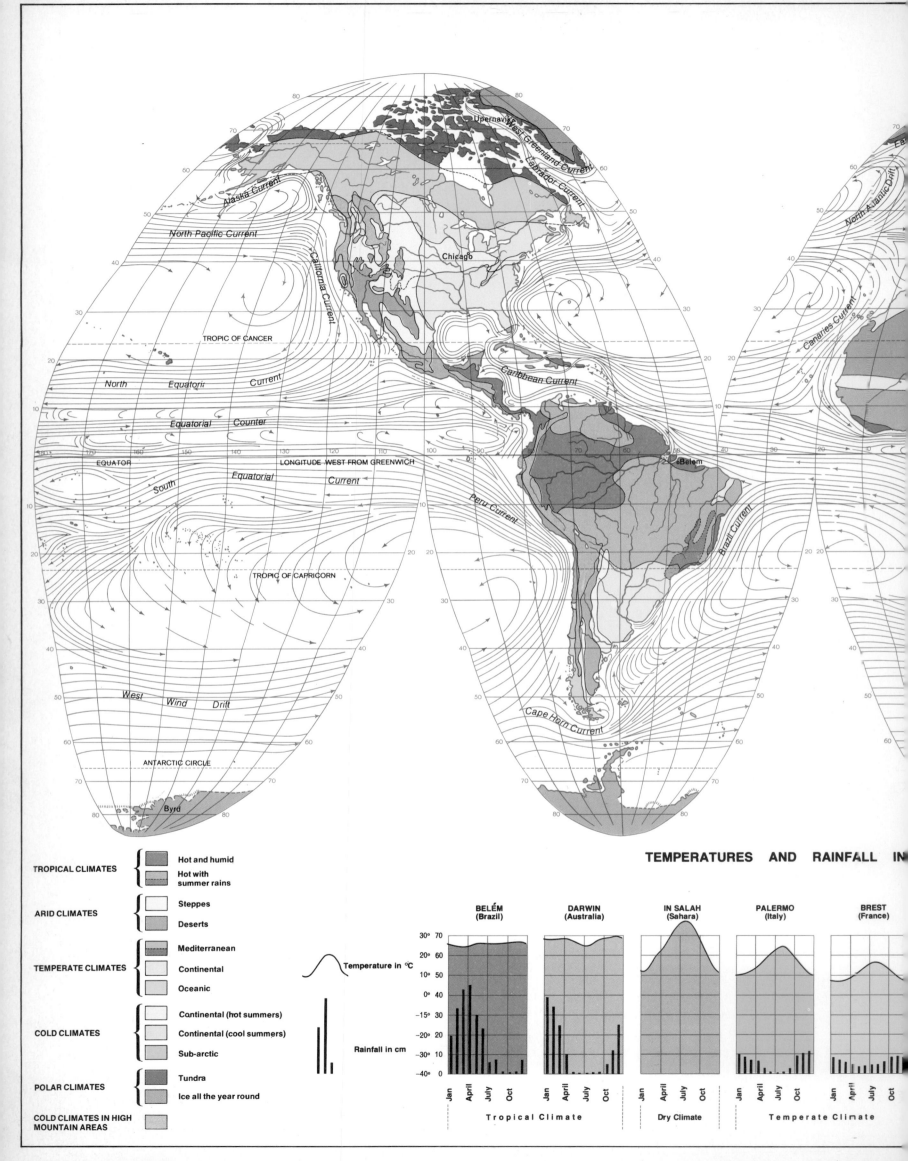

TEMPERATURES AND RAINFALL IN

TROPICAL CLIMATES
- Hot and humid
- Hot with summer rains

ARID CLIMATES
- Steppes
- Deserts

TEMPERATE CLIMATES
- Mediterranean
- Continental
- Oceanic

COLD CLIMATES
- Continental (hot summers)
- Continental (cool summers)
- Sub-arctic

POLAR CLIMATES
- Tundra
- Ice all the year round

COLD CLIMATES IN HIGH MOUNTAIN AREAS

Temperature in °C

Rainfall in cm

BELÉM (Brazil)   DARWIN (Australia)   IN SALAH (Sahara)   PALERMO (Italy)   BREST (France)

Tropical Climate   Dry Climate   Temperate Climate

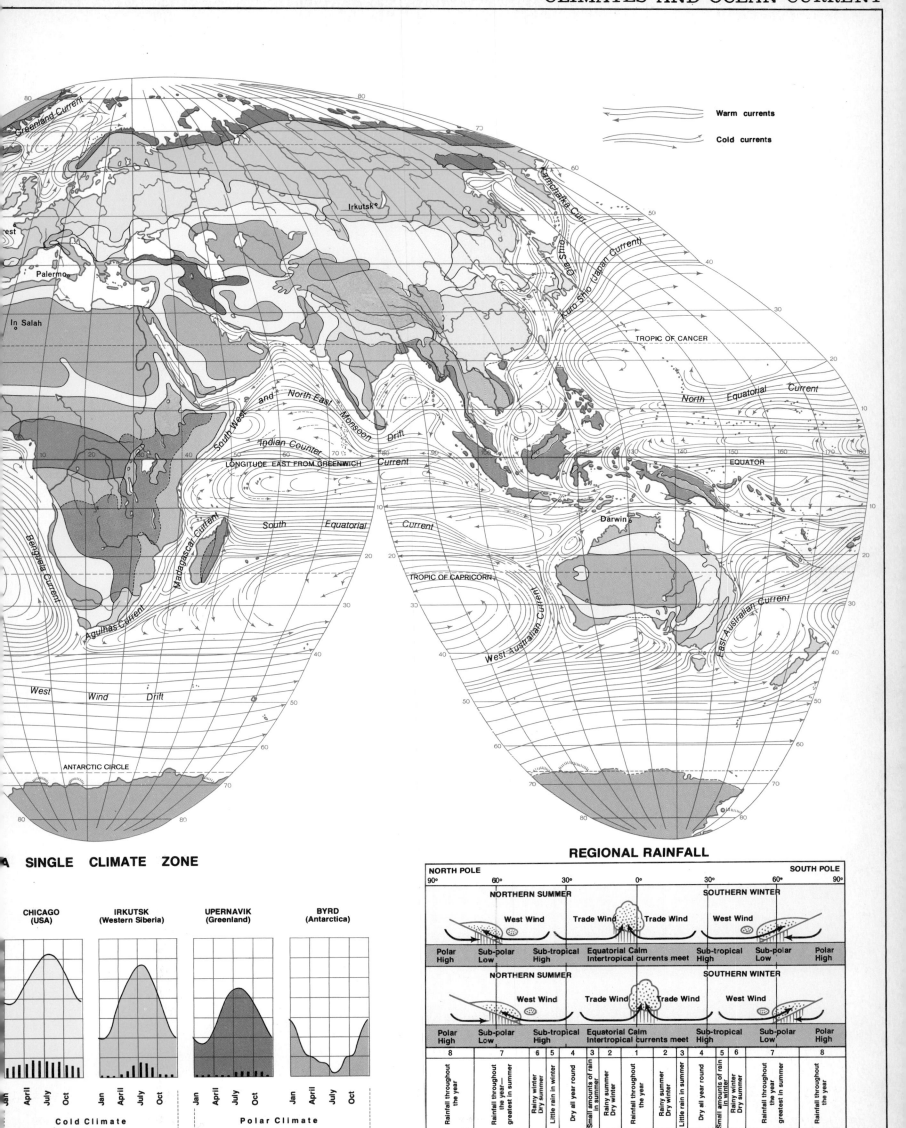

A SINGLE CLIMATE ZONE

CHICAGO (USA) — **IRKUTSK (Western Siberia)** — **UPERNAVIK (Greenland)** — **BYRD (Antarctica)**

Jan · April · July · Oct

Cold Climate — Polar Climate

REGIONAL RAINFALL

| NORTH POLE | | | | | | | | | | | | | | SOUTH POLE |
| 90° | 60° | | 30° | | | 0° | | | 30° | | 60° | | | 90° |

NORTHERN SUMMER — West Wind — Trade Wind — Trade Wind — West Wind — SOUTHERN WINTER

| Polar High | Sub-polar Low | Sub-tropical High | Equatorial Calm Intertropical currents meet | Sub-tropical High | Sub-polar Low | Polar High |

NORTHERN SUMMER — West Wind — Trade Wind — Trade Wind — West Wind — SOUTHERN WINTER

| Polar High | Sub-polar Low | Sub-tropical High | Equatorial Calm Intertropical currents meet | Sub-tropical High | Sub-polar Low | Polar High |

8	7	6	5	4	3	2	1	2	3	4	5	6	7	8
Rainfall throughout the year	Rainfall throughout the year—greatest in summer	Rainy winter Dry summer	Little rain in winter	Dry all year round	Small amounts of rain in summer	Rainy summer Dry winter	Rainfall throughout the year	Rainy summer Dry winter	Little rain in summer	Dry all year round	Small amounts of rain in winter	Rainy winter Dry summer	Rainfall throughout the year greatest in summer	Rainfall throughout the year

Warm currents
Cold currents

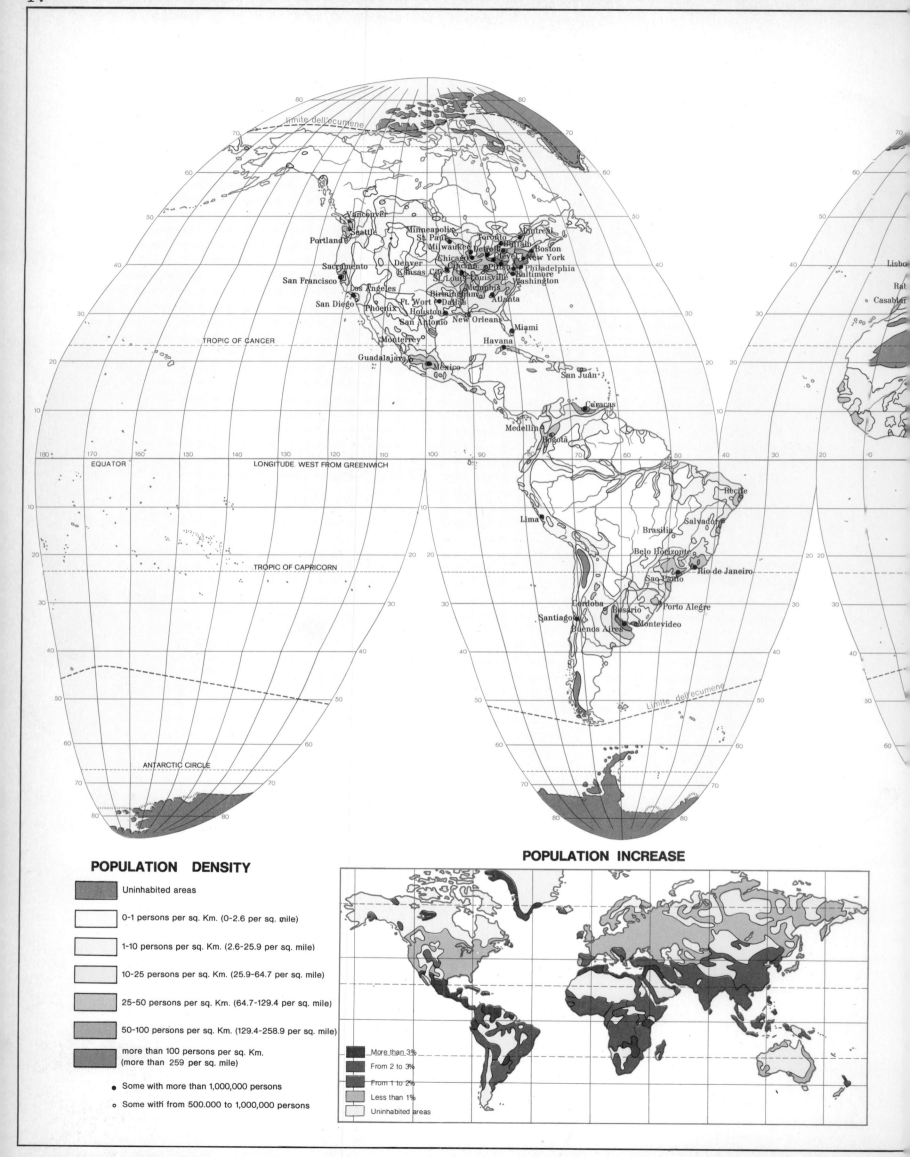

POPULATION DENSITY

Uninhabited areas

0-1 persons per sq. Km. (0-2.6 per sq. mile)

1-10 persons per sq. Km. (2.6-25.9 per sq. mile)

10-25 persons per sq. Km. (25.9-64.7 per sq. mile)

25-50 persons per sq. Km. (64.7-129.4 per sq. mile)

50-100 persons per sq. Km. (129.4-258.9 per sq. mile)

more than 100 persons per sq. Km. (more than 259 per sq. mile)

• Some with more than 1,000,000 persons

○ Some with from 500.000 to 1,000,000 persons

POPULATION INCREASE

More than 3%

From 2 to 3%

From 1 to 2%

Less than 1%

Uninhabited areas

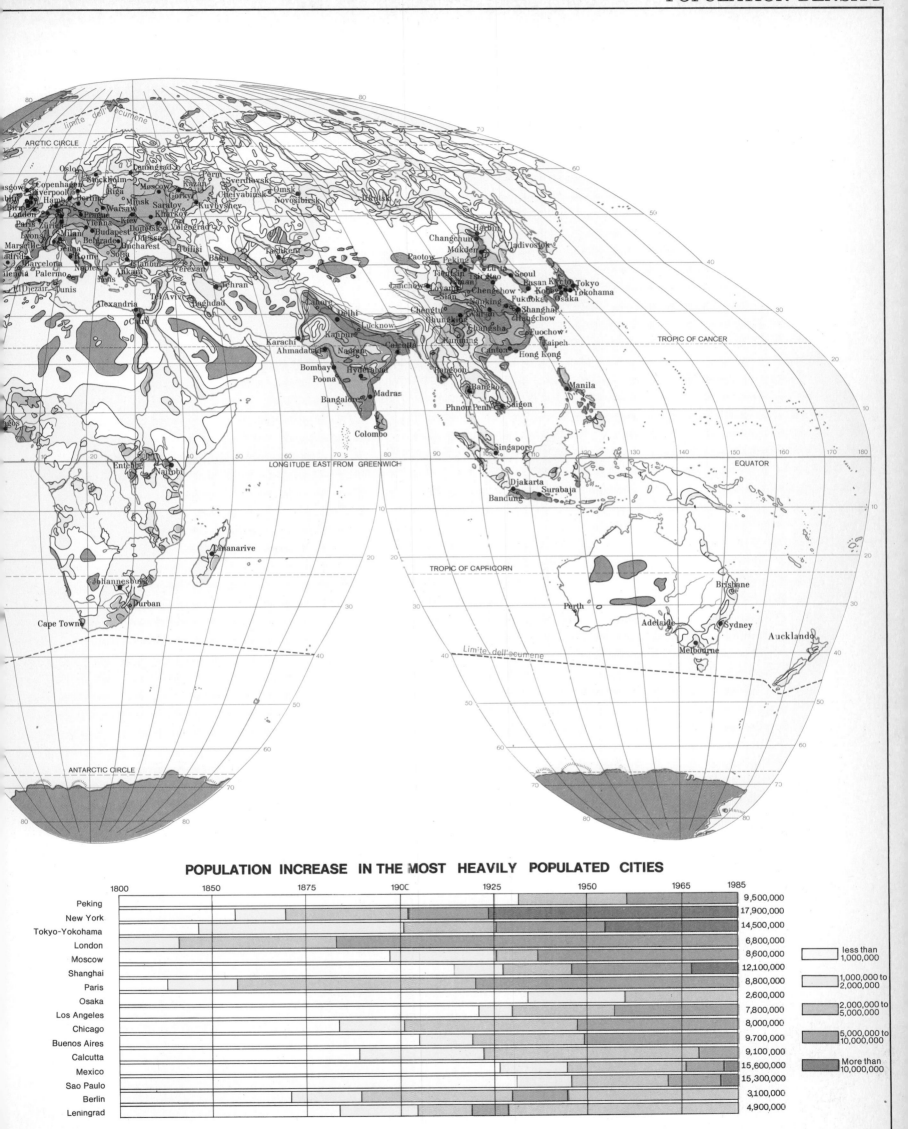

POPULATION INCREASE IN THE MOST HEAVILY POPULATED CITIES

	1800	1850	1875	1900	1925	1950	1965	1985	
Peking									9,500,000
New York									17,900,000
Tokyo-Yokohama									14,500,000
London									6,800,000
Moscow									8,600,000
Shanghai									12,100,000
Paris									8,800,000
Osaka									2,600,000
Los Angeles									7,800,000
Chicago									8,000,000
Buenos Aires									9,700,000
Calcutta									9,100,000
Mexico									15,600,000
Sao Paulo									15,300,000
Berlin									3,100,000
Leningrad									4,900,000

less than 1,000,000

1,000,000 to 2,000,000

2,000,000 to 5,000,000

5,000,000 to 10,000,000

More than 10,000,000

Copyright Vallardi Ind. graf.

ARCTIC
OCEAN
Greenland
(Den.)
Banks I.
Baffin
Bay
Baffin Island
Victoria I.
Davis Strait
U.S.A.
Alaska
Nome
Yukon
Whitehorse
Anchorage
Juneau
Hudson
Bay
Labrador
C A N A D A
Edmonton
Vancouver
Winnipeg
Seattle
Missouri
Newfoundland
Quebec
Portland
Montreal
Ottawa
St. John's
Chicago
Detroit
Halifax
Cleveland
Boston
U N I T E D   S T A T E S
Denver
New York
San Francisco
St. Louis
Washington
Colorado
Bermuda
(Br.)
Los Angeles
Houston
Atlanta
New Orleans
Rio Grande
MEXICO
Gulf of
Mexico
BAHAMAS
Guadalupe I.
(Mex.)
Havana
CUBA
TROPIC OF CANCER
U.S.A.
Hawaiian Islands
Midway Is.
(U.S.A.)
Mexico
Veracruz
BELIZE
HAITI
DOMINICAN REP.
Puerto Rico (U.S.A.)
Revillagigedo Is.
(Mex.)
Hawaii
GUATEMALA HONDURAS
JAMAICA
Guadeloupe (Fr.)
Johnston I.
(U.S.A.)
EL SALVADOR NICARAGUA
Caribbean Sea
Martinique (Fr.)
P A C I F I C
Clipperton
(Fr.)
COSTA RICA
BARBADOS
TRINIDAD
AND TOBAGO
Palmyra I.
(U.S.A.)
Fanning I.
PANAMA
Caracas
VENEZUELA
Georgetown Paramaribo
A T L A N T I C
Christmas I.
Bogotá
GUYANA
Cayenne
Howland I.
(U.S.A.)
COLOMBIA
SURINAM
Fr. Guiana
EQUATOR
Jarois I.
(U.S.A.)
Malden I.
WEST FROM GREENWICH
Galápagos Is.
(Ec.)
ECUADOR
Quito
Belém
Fernando
de Noronha
(Braz.)
Baker I.
(U.S.A.)
Manaus
São Luís
Tokelau Is.
(N.Z.)
Starbuck I.
Marquesas Is.
(Fr.)
PERU
B R A Z I L
Fortaleza
Recife
French Polynesia
Lima
Ascension
(Br.)
SAMOA
Tutuila
(U.S.A.)
Society Is.
(Fr.)
Tuamotu Archipelago
(Fr.)
Callao
Salvador
St. Helena
La Paz
Brasília
TONGA
Cook Is.
(N.Z.)
BOLIVIA
Sucre
TROPIC OF CAPRICORN
Sala-y-Gómez
(Chile)
PARAGUAY
Rio de Janeiro
Trindade
(Braz.)
Pitcairn I.
(Br.)
Ducie I.
(Br.)
Easter I.
(Chile)
Antofagasta
Asunción
S. Paulo
Kermadec Is.
(N.Z.)
ARGENTINA
URUGUAY
O C E A N
Santiago
Rosario
Montevideo
Buenos
Aires
Tristan da Cunha
(Br.)
Chatham Is.
(N.Z.)
Gough I.
(Br.)
Falkland Is.
(Br.)
South Georgia
(Br.)
Punta Arenas
Tierra del Fuego
ANTARCTIC CIRCLE
C. Horn
Drake Passage
South Sandwich Is.
(Br.)
South Shetland
South Orkney Is.
(Br.)
Antarctic
Peninsula
Alexander I.
Weddell
Sea
Ellsworth L.
Byrd Land
Ross Sea
Coats Land

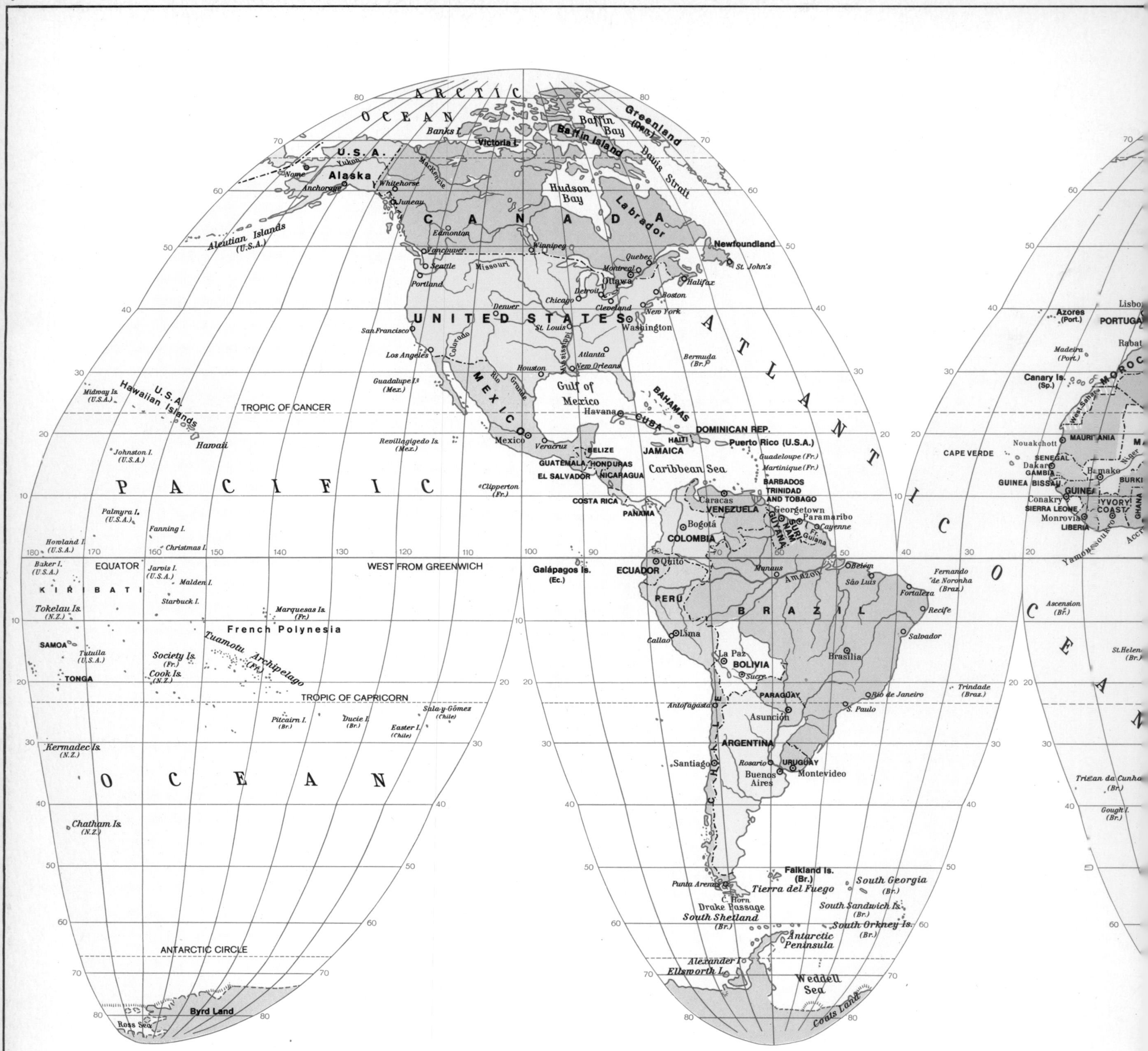

Lisboa
Azores
(Port.)
PORTUGAL
Rabat
Madeira
(Port.)
Canary Is.
(Sp.)
MOROCCO
West Sahara
MAURITANIA
Nouakchott
CAPE VERDE
SENEGAL
Dakar
Niger
Bamako
GAMBIA
GUINEA BISSAU
GUINEA
Conakry
IVORY
COAST
BURKINA
SIERRA LEONE
Monrovia
LIBERIA
Yamoussoukro
Accra
Ascension
(Br.)

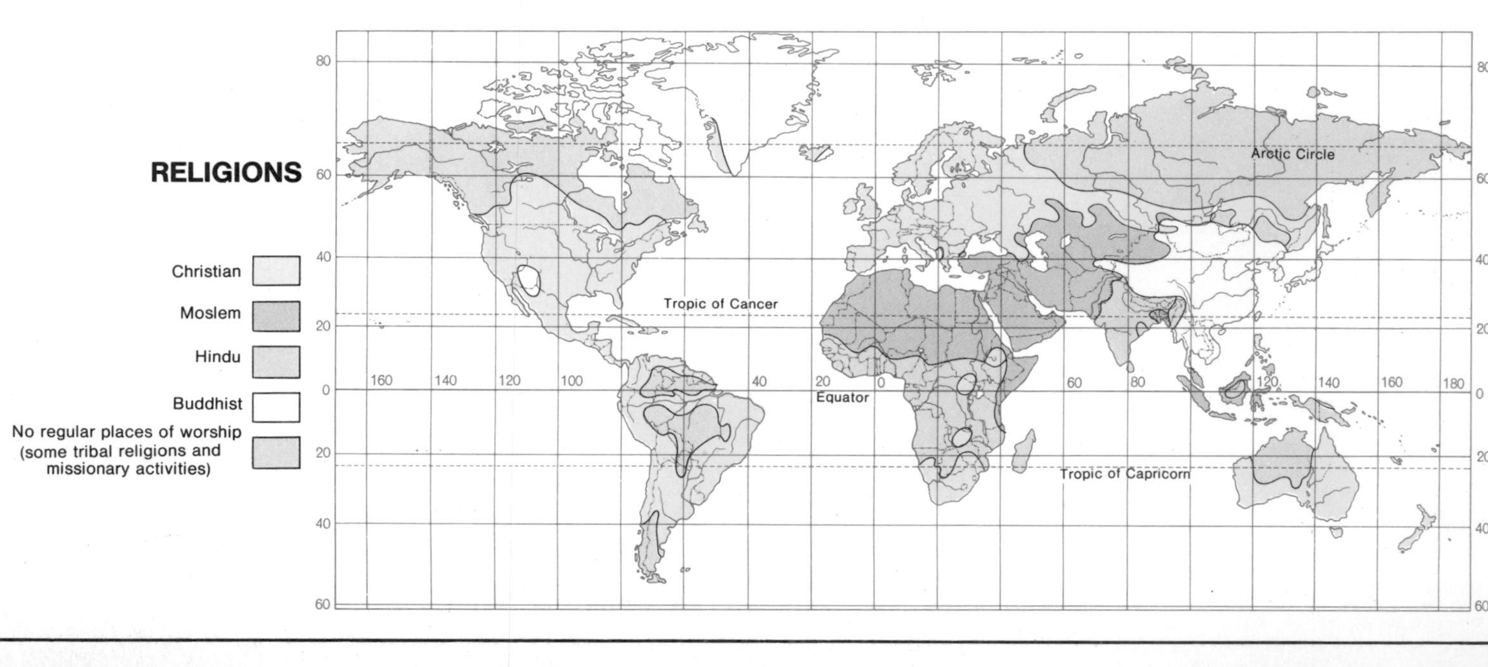

RELIGIONS

Christian

Moslem

Hindu

Buddhist

No regular places of worship
(some tribal religions and
missionary activities)

Arctic Circle

Tropic of Cancer

Equator

Tropic of Capricorn

THE POLITICAL DIVISIONS OF THE EARTH

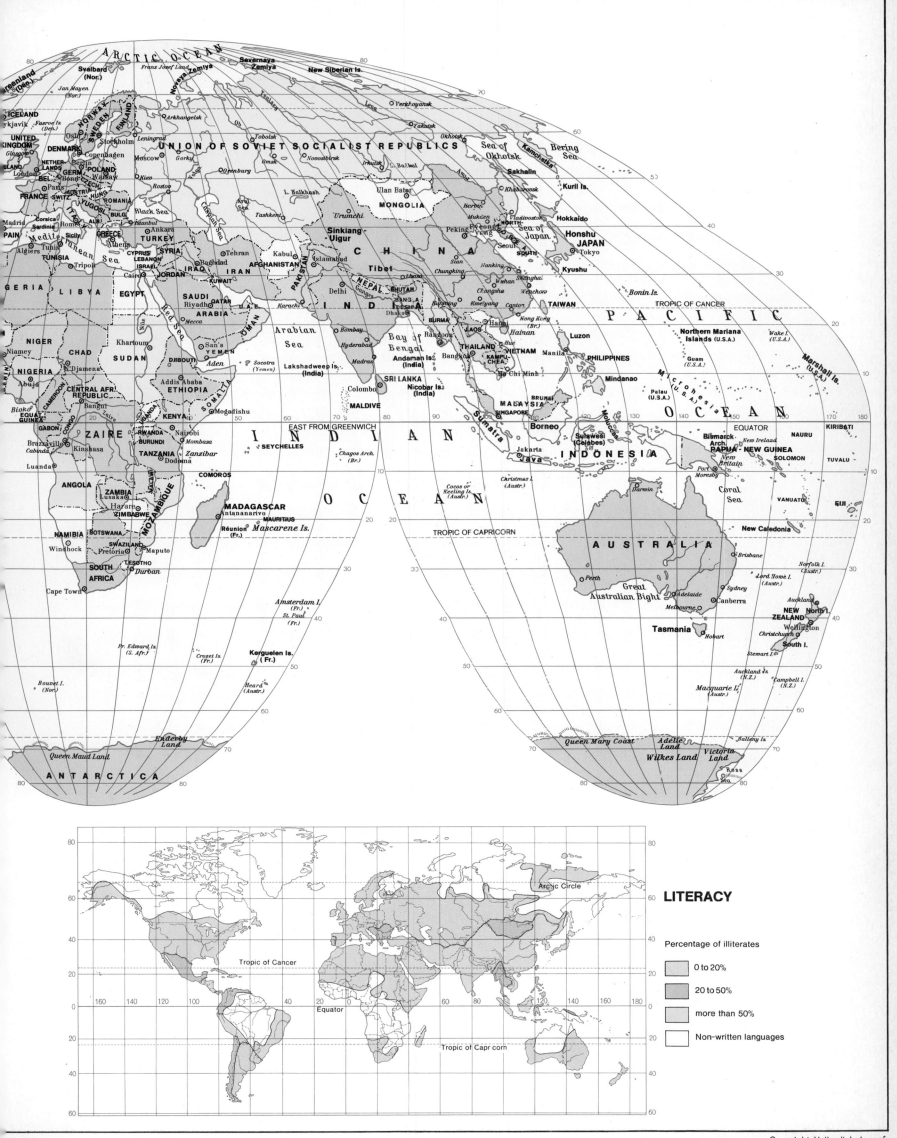

LITERACY

Percentage of illiterates

- 0 to 20%
- 20 to 50%
- more than 50%
- Non-written languages

Copyright: Vallardi Ind. graf.

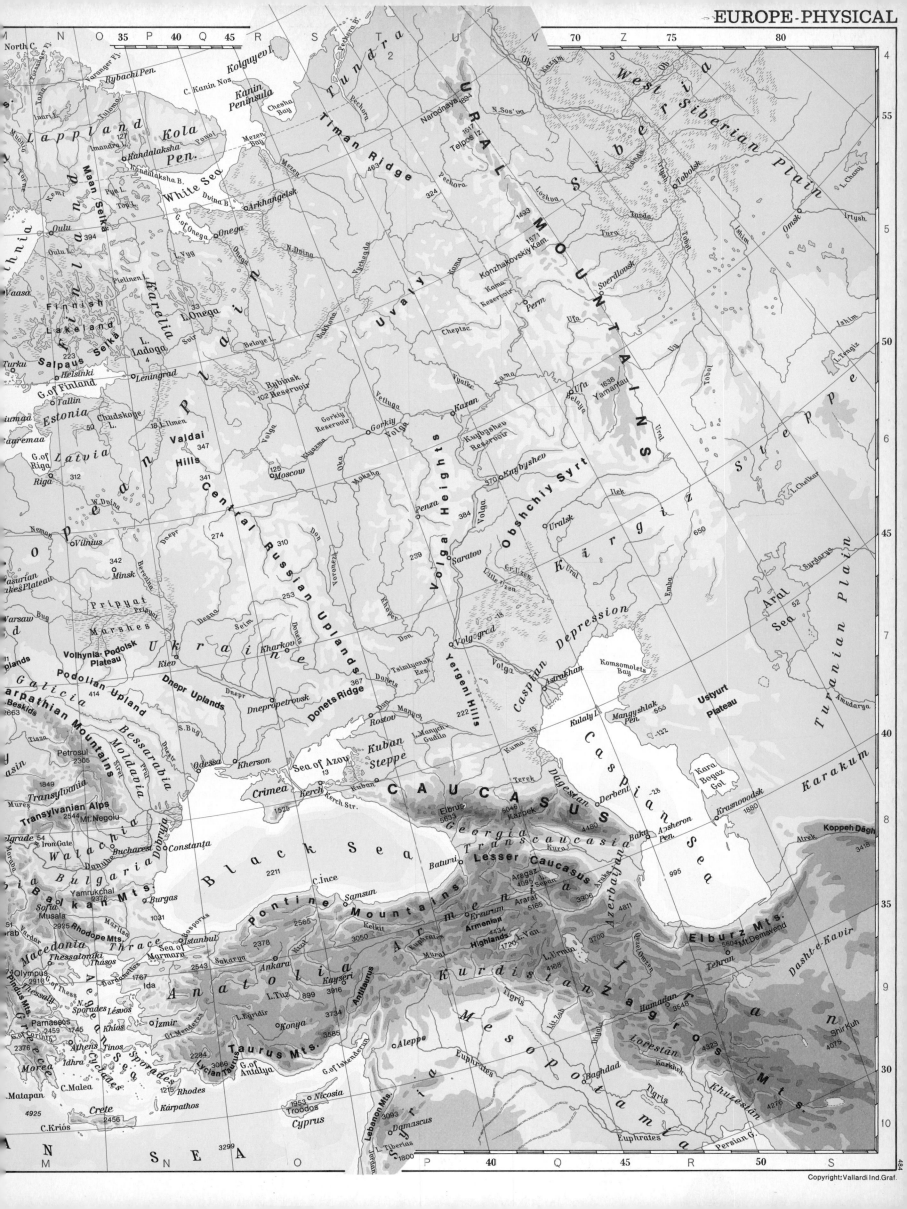

North C.

Lappland

Varanger Fj.
Rybachi Pen.
Kola
Kanin
C. Kanin Nos
Kolguyev I.
Pen.
Kanin
Peninsula

Tundra

West Siberian Plain

Ob

Kazan

URAL MOUNTAINS

Siberia

L. Chang

White Sea
Kandalaksha
Kandalaksha B.
Ponoi
Cheshn
Bay
Mezen
Bay
Mezen

Timan Ridge

Pechora

Narodnaya

N.Sos'va

Ishim

Irtysh

Omsk

Inari
Tuloma
127
Imandra
Maan Selka
Kem
Pya L.
Topl L.
Top L.
Dvina B.
G. of Onega
Arkhangelsk
Mezen
N. Dvina
Dvina
463
324
Pechora
Telpos IZA
1617
1493
Lozhva
Tura
Sverdlovsk
Tobolsk
Tobol
Irtysh

Oulu
394
Kemi
Onega
Onega
N.Dvina
Vashonga
Konzhakovsky Kam.
1571
Kama
Perm
1000

Oulu L.
L.Vyg
Vychegda
Ufa
Ishim

Finland

Vaasa

Karelia
Selka
Sel-
ka
33
L.Onega
Beloye L.
Sukhona
Kama
Reservoir
Uvaly
Chepts e.
Ufa
Yamantau

Finnish
Lakeland
223
Salpaus
Helsinki
L.
Ladoga
4
Sor
Kovzha
Vyatka
Kama
Perm
Sverdlovsk

Turku
G. of Finland
Tallin
Leningrad
Rybinsk
Reservoir
102
Gorky
Reservoir
Vetluga
Gorky
Kazan
Ufa
1638
Yamantau

Estonia
Chudskoye
L.
18 L.Ilmen
Valdai
Hills
347
Klyazma
Vetluga
Volga
Belaya
Obshchiy Syrt

G. of
Riga
312
Latvia
341
Volga
Moksha
Penza
384
Volga
570
Kuybyshev
Reservoir
Kuybyshev
Kama
Ural
1582

Riga
125
Moscow
Oka
Sura
Penza
Volga
Kuybyshev
Ilek
L.Tengiz

W. Dvina
Vilnius
Dnepr
274
310
Don
239
Saratov
Uralsk
Gr.Uzen
Ust-Urt
650
L. Chalkar

Neman
342
Minsk
Berezina
Desna
Seim
Khoper
Saratov
Little Uzen
Gr. Uzen
52
Syrdarya
Aral
Sea

Warsaw
Bug
Pripyat
Marshes
Pripyat
Pripyat
253
Don
Tsimlyansk
Res.
Volga
-18
Caspian
Depression
Emba
Amudarya
Turanian Plain

Volhynia-Podolsk
Plateau
Ukraine
Kharkov
Kiev
367
Donets
Volga
grad
222
Astrakhan
Komsomolets
Bay
Ustyurt
Plateau

Podolian Upland
Dnepr Uplands
Dnepr
Dnepropetrovsk
Donets Ridge
Rostov
Manych
Volga
Kuma
15
Kulaly I.
Mangyshlak
Pen.
555

Galicia
Carpathian Mountains
414
Beskids
Bessarabia
Moldavia
S.Bug
Dnestr
Odessa
Kherson
Sea of Azov
13
Kuban
Steppe
L.Manych
Gudilo
Terek
Caspian
Sea
-28
Kara
Bogaz
Gol
-122

2663
Tisza
Petrosul
2305
Moldavia
Strei
Crimea
Kerch
Kuban
CAUCASUS
Dagestan
Derbent
Krasnovodsk
1880

1849
Transylvania
Mures
Transylvanian Alps
2544
Mt. Negoiu
1525
Kerch Str.
Elbrus
5633
Kazbek
5046
Georgia
Transcaucasia
4480
Apsheron
Pen.
Baku
995
Koppeh Dagh

Belgrade 54
Iron Gate
Walachia
Bucharest
Dobruja
Constanța
Danube
Batumi
Lesser Caucasus
Kura
Azerbaijan
Araks
4811
3418

Bulgaria
Balkan Mts.
2211
Black Sea
C.Ince
Samsun
Pontine
Mountains
Aragaz
4095
Sevan
3306
3700
Gezel Owzen
Elburz Mts.
5604
Mt. Demavend

Macedonia
Yamrukchal
2376
Burgas
1031
Marisa
Pontine
Mountains
2565
Kelkit
Erzurum
Armenian
Highlands
Ararat
5165
Mt.Van
4434
1720
L.Urmia
Tehran

Sofia
Musala
2925
Rhodope Mts.
Thrace
Istanbul
Bosporus
2378
Kizit
3050
Euphrates
Murat
L.Van
4168
Hamadan
3548
Shirkuh
4079

Thessaloniki
Thasos
Sea of
Marmara
Sakarya
2543
Ankara
Kayseri
Anatolia
Armen
Kurdistan
Zagros Mts.
Khuzestan
4276

Olympus
2918
G. of Thess.
Dardanelles
1767
Ida
Izmir
L.Tuz
899
3916
Antitaurus
L.Van
Lit.Zab
Loretan
Baghdad
Karkheh

Pindus Mts.
N.Sporades
Lésvos
2543
Konya
3734
Mesopotamia
Tigris
Bit.Zab

Parnassos
2459
1745
Khios
L.Egridir
3585
Taurus Mts.
Lycian Taurus
G. of
Antalya
Aleppo
Euphrates
Syrian
Desert
Tigris
Persian G.

2376
Athens
Idhra
Cyclades
2294
3066
1215
Rhodes
Nicosia
Troodos
1953
Damascus
Euphrates

Morea
C.Malea
Crete
Karpathos
Cyprus
Lebanon Mts.
3093

4925
C. Kriós
2456
3299
Matapan
1800
L.Tiberias
Jordan

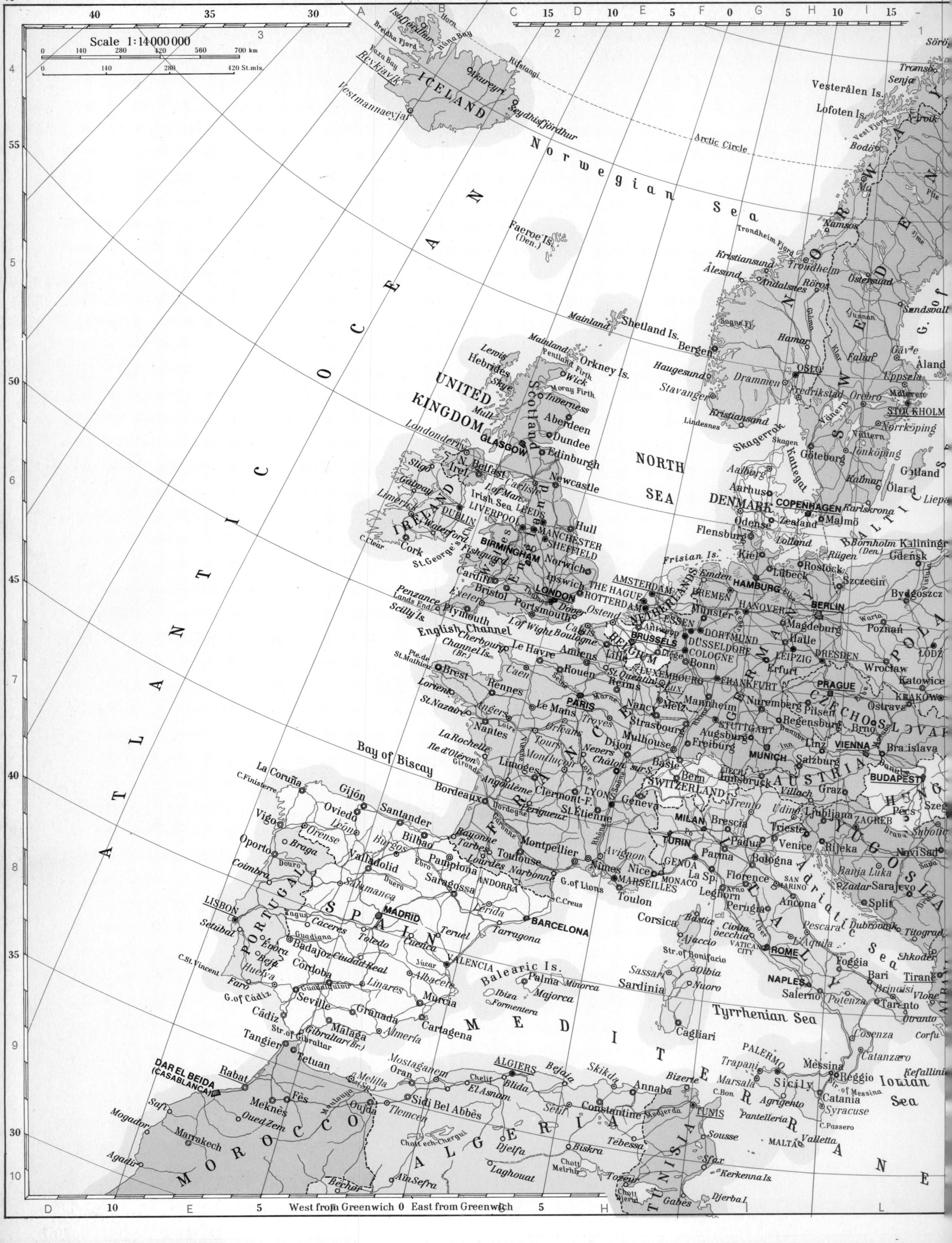

2

Scale 1:14 000 000

0 140 280 420 560 700 km
0 140 280 420 St.mls.

40   35   30   A   B   C   15   D   10   E   5   F   0   G   H   5   10   I   15

A T L A N T I C   O C E A N

ICELAND

Horn Bay
Isafjördhur
Breidha Fjord
Húna Bay
Faxa Bay
Reykjavik
Vestmannaeyjar
Akureyri
Seydhisfjördhur
Rifstangi

N O R W A Y

Norwegian Sea
Arctic Circle
Tromsö
Senja
Vesterålen Is.
Lofoten Is.
Bodö
Vest Fjord
Namsos
Trondheim Fjord
Kristiansund
Ålesund
Andalsnes
Trondheim
Röros
Östersund
Hamar
OSLO
Drammen
Haugesund
Stavanger
Kristiansand
Lindesnes
Fredrikstad

SWEDEN

Falun
Gäv'e
Åland
Uppsala
Örebro
STOCKHOLM
Norrköping
Gotland
Öland
Karlskrona
Malmö
Kalmar
Liepa
Göteborg
Jönköping
Skagerrak
Skagen
Kattegat

Faeroe Is. (Den.)

Mainland
Shetland Is.
Bergen

NORTH SEA

Lewis
Hebrides
Skye
Mull
Mainland
Orkney Is.
Pentland Firth
Wick
Moray Firth
Inverness

UNITED KINGDOM

SCOTLAND
GLASGOW
Aberdeen
Dundee
Edinburgh
Newcastle

Londonderry
N. Belfast
Carlisle
I. of Man

IRELAND
Sligo
Galway
Limerick
DUBLIN
Waterford
Cork
C. Clear
St. George's
Fishguard

Irish Sea
LEEDS
LIVERPOOL
MANCHESTER
Sheffield
Hull
BIRMINGHAM
Norwich
Cardiff
Bristol
Ipswich
THE HAGUE
AMSTERDAM
LONDON
Rotterdam
Penzance
Lands End
Exeter
Plymouth
Scilly Is.
Portsmouth
I. of Wight
Dover
Ostend
Calais
Boulogne

English Channel
Cherbourg
Channel Is. (Br.)
Le Havre
Amiens
Lille
Pte. de St. Mathieu
Brest
Caen
Rouen
St. Quentin
Lorient
Rennes
Angers
Le Mans
PARIS
Troyes
Nancy
Metz
St. Nazaire
Nantes
Orleans
Tours
Dijon
Strasbourg
La Rochelle
Ile d'Oléron
Limoges
Montluçon
Châlon sur S.
Mulhouse
Nevers
Freiburg

DENMARK
COPENHAGEN
Aarhus
Odense
Zealand
Flensburg
Lolland
Kiel
Lübeck
Rostock
Rügen
Frisian Is.
Emden
HAMBURG
BREMEN
HANOVER
BERLIN
Magdeburg
Halle
LEIPZIG
DRESDEN
Erfurt
Wroclaw
Münster
ESSEN
DORTMUND
DÜSSELDORF
COLOGNE
Bonn
FRANKFURT
Nuremberg
Mannheim
STUTTGART
Augsburg
Regensburg
Linz
MUNICH
Salzburg
Innsbruck
VIENNA
Bratislava

GERMANY

BELGIUM
BRUSSELS
Antwerp
Liège
LUXEMBOURG

NETHERLANDS

Bornholm (Den.)
Szczecin
Gdansk
Poznań
Bydgoszcz
Łódź
Katowice
KRAKÓW
Ostrava

POLAND

CZECHOSLOVAKIA
PRAGUE
Pilsen
Brno

Kaliningrad
Warta
Oder

FRANCE
Rochefort
Angoulême
Périgueux
St. Étienne
LYONS
Geneva
Bern
Basle

SWITZERLAND

La Coruña
C. Finisterre
Gijón
Oviedo
Santander
Bilbao
Vigo
Orense
León
Burgos
Bayonne
Oporto
Braga
Valladolid
Pamplona
Saragossa
LISBON
Salamanca
Coimbra

PORTUGAL
SPAIN
MADRID
Caceres
Teruel
BARCELONA
Tarragona
Setubal
Évora
Badajoz
Toledo
Cuenca
Lérida
ANDORRA
VALENCIA
Ciudad Real
Albacete
C. St. Vincent
Faro
Huelva
Córdoba
Linares
Murcia
Seville
Granada
Cartagena
G. of Cádiz
Cádiz
Málaga
Almeria
Str. of Gibraltar
Gibraltar (Br.)
Tangier
Tetuan
Balearic Is.
Palma
Minorca
Ibiza
Majorca
Formentera

Bay of Biscay
Bordeaux
Toulouse
Tarbes
Lourdes
Montpellier
Avignon
Nîmes
MARSEILLES
Toulon
Narbonne
G. of Lions
C. Creus

Corsica
Ajaccio
Bastia
Str. of Bonifacio
Sardinia
Sassari
Olbia
Nuoro
Cagliari

ITALY
TURIN
MILAN
Brescia
Padua
Venice
Trieste
GENOA
La Spezia
Parma
Bologna
Florence
Leghorn
Perugia
SAN MARINO
Ancona
VATICAN CITY
ROME
Civita vecchia
NAPLES
Salerno
Potenza
Foggia
Bari
Brindisi
Taranto
Pescara
L'Aquila
Cosenza
Catanzaro
Reggio
Messina
PALERMO
Trapani
Marsala
Sicily
Agrigento
Catania
Syracuse
C. Passero

Tyrrhenian Sea
Adriatic Sea
Ionian Sea
Pantelleria
MALTA
Valletta

AUSTRIA
Villach
Graz
Trento
Udine
Ljubljana
ZAGREB
YUGOSLAVIA
Rijeka
Zadar
Banja Luka
Sarajevo
Split
Dubrovnik
Titograd
Shkoder
TIRANE
Vlone
ALBANIA
Corfu
Kefallinia

HUNGARY
BUDAPEST
Pécs
Subotica
Novi Sad

MEDITERRANEAN

MOROCCO
DAR EL BEIDA (CASABLANCA)
Rabat
Mogador
Safi
Marrakech
Agadir
Meknès
Fès
Oued Zem
Oujda
Tlemcen

ALGERIA
ALGIERS
Oran
Mostaganem
Sidi Bel Abbès
El Asnam
Blida
Skikda
Béjaia
Annaba
Constantine
Sétif
Biskra
Djelfa
Laghouat
Aïn Sefra
Béchar
Tébessa

TUNISIA
TUNIS
Bizerte
Sousse
Sfax
Kerkenna Is.
Gabes
Djerba I.
C. Bon

West from Greenwich 0 East from Greenwich 5

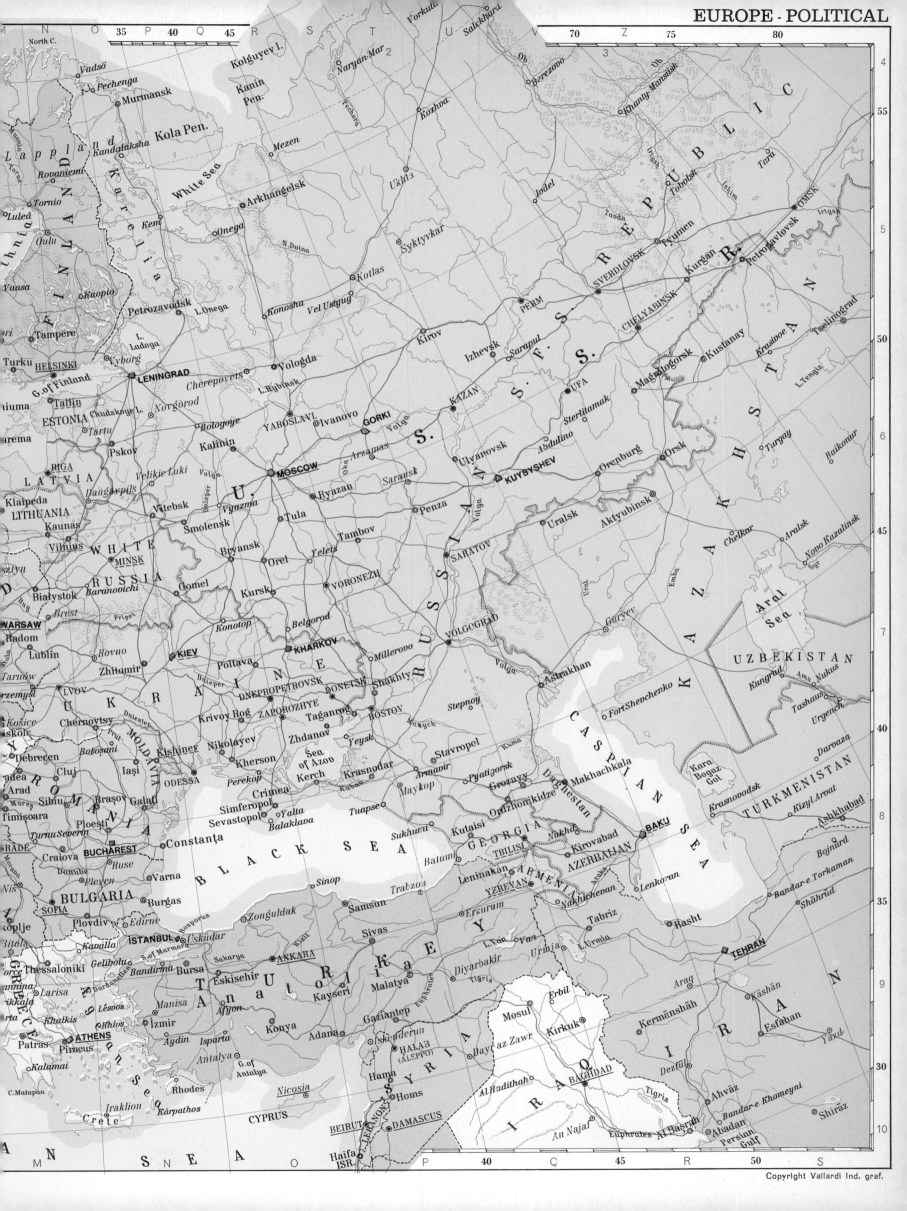

North C.
Vadsö
Pechenga
Murmansk
Kolguyev I.
Kanin
Pen.
Naryan-Mar 2
Vorkuta
Salekhard
Ob
Berezovo
Ob
Khanty-Mansiisk
3
Lappland
Rovaniemi
Kandalaksha
Kola Pen.
Kem
White Sea
Mezen
Pechora
Kozhva
Irtysh
Tobolsk
S. F. S. R.
Tornio
Kuolo
Karelia
Arkhangelsk
N.Dvina
Uklä
Tanda
Tsumen
OMSK
Luleå
Onega
Kotlas
Syktyvkar
Irtysh
Tselinograd
Tampere
Petrozavodsk
L.Onega
Konosha
Vel Ustyug
PERM
SVERDLOVSK
Kurgan
Petropavlovsk
Oulu
Kuopio
L.
Ladoga
Kirov
Izhevsk
Sarapul
CHELYABINSK
Turku
HELSINKI
Vyborg
Vologda
L.Rybinsk
U.
Cherepovets
KAZAN
UFA
Magnitogorsk
Kustanay
Krasnoe
L.Tengiz
Baikonur
Tallin
LENINGRAD
Chudskoye L.
Novgorod
YAROSLAVL
Ivanovo
GORKI
Volga
S.
Sterlitamak
Orsk
Turgay
Estonia
Tartu
Botogoye
Kalinin
Arzamas
Ulyanovsk
Abdulino
Orenburg
Turgay
Pskov
Velikie Luki
S.
F.
Aralsk
LATVIA
RIGA
Volga
MOSCOW
Oka
Ryazan
Saransk
KUYBYSHEV
Chelkar
Novo Kazalinsk
Daugavpils
Vitebsk
Vyazma
S.
Penza
Uralsk
Aktyubinsk
Aral
Sea
LITHUANIA
Smolensk
Tula
Tambov
SARATOV
Emba
Kaunas
WHITE
MINSK
Bryansk
Orel
Yelets
S.
VOLGOGRAD
Guryev
Syr
Vilnius
RUSSIA
Gomel
Kursk
Belgorod
R
U
Volga
Astrakhan
UZBEKISTAN
WARSAW
Baranovichi
Fripet
Konotop
Millerovo
S
Volga
Kungrad
Nukus
Radom
Brest
KHARKOV
S
FortShevchenko
Tashauz
Lublin
Rovno
KIEV
Poltava
DNEPROPETROVSK
Shakhty
I
Urgench
LVOV
Zhitomir
Dnieper
Krivoy Rog
DONETSK
ROSTOV
Volga
A
Darvaza
Kosice
Chernovtsy
Dniester
ZAPOROZHYE
Taganrog
Stepnoy
Kara
Bogaz
Gol
Przemysl
MOLDAVIA
Prut
Kishinev
Nikolayev
Zhdanov
Yeysk
Manych
Stavropol
Kuma
CASPIAN
Krasnovodsk
TURKMENISTAN
Debrecen
Botosani
Iasi
Kherson
Sea
of Azov
Yalta
Krasnodar
Armavir
Pyatigorsk
Grozny
Daghestan
Makhachkala
Kizyl Arvat
Cluj
Perekop
Crimea
Kerch
Maykop
Ordzhonikidze
SEA
Ashkhabad
Arad
ROMANIA
Simferopol
Tuapse
Kutaisi
Sukhumi
GEORGIA
Nukha
BAKU
Brasov
Galati
Sevastopol
Balaklava
Batumi
TBILISI
Kirovabad
Krasnovodsk
Bojnurd
Timisoara
Turnu Severin
Ploesti
Constanta
BLACK
SEA
Leninakan
ARMENIA
AZERBAIJAN
Bandar-e Torkaman
RADE
BUCHAREST
Ruse
Varna
Sinop
Trabzon
YEREVAN
Nakhichevan
Lenkoran
Shahrud
Craiova
Danube
Pleven
Burgas
Samsun
Erzurum
Tabriz
Rasht
BULGARIA
SOFIA
Plovdiv
Edirne
Zonguldak
Sivas
L.Van
Van
L.Urmia
TEHRAN
Skopje
ISTANBUL
Uskudar
S.of Marmara
Bosporus
ANKARA
Kizil
Diyarbakir
Urmia
Bitola
Thessaloniki
Gelibolu
Bandirma
Bursa
T U R K E Y
Sakarya
Eskisehir
Malatya
Tigris
Araq
Kashan
Dardanelles
A n a t o l i a
Kayseri
Gaziantep
Euphrates
Erbil
Kermanshah
Esfahan
Larisa
Manisa
Afyon
Izmir
Konya
Adana
Mosul
Kirkuk
Yazd
Khalkis
Khios
Isparta
Iskenderun
HALAB
(ALEPPO)
Dayr az Zawr
Dezful
ATHENS
Aydin
Antalya
G.of
Antalya
SYRIA
Hama
Al Hadithah
BAGHDAD
Tigris
Ahvaz
Patras
Piraeus
Rhodes
Nicosia
Homs
I R A Q
Euphrates
Bandar-e Khomeyni
Kalamai
Iraklion
Karpathos
CYPRUS
DAMASCUS
An Najaf
Al Basrah
Abadan
Persian
Gulf
Shiraz
C.Matapan
Crete
BEIRUT
Haifa
ISR.

Faeroe Is.
Österö Viderö Fuglö
Strömö Svinö
Bordö
Vågö Thorshavn
Sandö
Syderö

OCEAN

ATLANTIC

GREAT BRITAIN

Shetland Islands
Unst
Yell Fetlar
450
Valsey
Mainland
Foula Lerwick Bressay
Sumburgh H.

Fair

Westray Sanday
Stronsay
Pomona
Hoy **Orkney Islands**
South Ronaldsay
Pentland Firth
Duncansby H.

Butt of Lewis
C. Wrath

Ben Hope Morven
921 705
Ben More B. Klibreck
361 999
L. Shin
Wick

Lewis
Clisham
799
North Uist
South Uist
Hebrides

L. Maree Ben Wyvis
1045
Dornoch Dornoch Firth
Tarbat Ness
Moray Firth

Kinnaird's Head
Peterhead

North-West-Highlands
Raasay S.
Skye Inverness
Carn Eige Loch Ness
1182 Caledonian Canal
Findhorn Spey Don Aberdeen
Ben Macdhui
1309
Dee
N. Esk
466 S. Esk

Canna
Rhum Ben Nevis
Eigg 1343
Coll
Mull B. Lawers
1214
1171 Tay Perth
B. More Dundee
Firth of Tay
Fife Ness
L. Awe
Firth of Forth

Grampian Mts.

Lowlands

Tyree
Colonsay Jura
Firth of Lorne
L. Lomond
Greenock Glasgow Edinburgh
Berwick upon Tweed

Islay Arran
Kintyre Firth of Clyde
Ayr Broad Laws
Ayr 839
Tweed
Cheviot Hills
553 816
Carter Fell
842
Southern Uplands
Nith
Roman Wall
Newcastle
Carlisle Tyne Sunderland
Cross Fell
893
Eden Cumbrian
Mountains
Scafell P.
978
Pennines

Malin H.
L. Foyle
Errigal Trostan
752 554
Londonderry
Teelin H. Donegal
Sperrin Mts.
683
Donegal Bay **Ulster**
L. Erne
L. Neagh Belfast
Rhinns of Galloway
Solway Firth
Man
Douglas

Erris H. Sligo
Achill Cuilcagh
Nephin 667
806 L. Allen
Mulrea **Connacht**
819 L. Mask
Sline Head L. Corrib
Clifden L. Ree
Galway Bay
Mourne Mts.
852
IRELAND
Barrow
Whernside
726
Cumbrian
Mountains
Cleveland Hills
454
Flamborough H.

Dundalk Dundalk B.
Boyne
IRISH SEA

NORTH SEA

Lancashire
Wharfe
Ribble Leeds
Blackpool Manchester
Liverpool Mersey Sheffield
Don
Hull
Spurn H.
Humber

Aran I.s L. Derg
Leinster
Arderin **Wicklow Mts.**
528 926
Lugnaquilla
Dublin
Grand Canal
Royal Canal
Shannon

Anglesey
Holyhead
Snowdon
1085

Lincoln
Witham
The Wash

Limerick
704
Kilkenny
Leinster
795
Nore Barrow Suir
Munster
Galty
919
Blackwater
Waterford
Wexford
Carnsore P.
Saint George's Channel
Cardigan Bay
Tremadoc B.
Aran Mawddwy
752
Cambrian Mountains
Plynlimon
Radnor F.
660
Wye
Stoke
Derby
Nottingham
Trent
Leicester
Birmingham
Nene
Norfolk
Norwich
Great Yarmouth
Waveney
Suffolk
Ipswich
Cambridge
Ouse
Stour

Dingle
Tralee
Loop Head
Dingle B.
Carrantuohill
1042
Knockboy
707
Kenmare Lee Cork
Bantry B. Bantry
Mizen H.

Cardigan
536
Wales
Towy Usk
Carmarthen B.
Swansea Glamorgan
Cardiff
Bristol Channel
326
Lundy
Hartland Point
Exmoor
520
Mendip Hills
Bristol
Avon Severn Worcester
Gloucester
Cotswold Hills
326
Thames Oxford
Reading
Chiltern Hills
Lea London
Thames
Dover
Kent
Strait of Dover

CELTIC SEA

Devon
Dartmoor Forest
621 Dart
Tamar
Plymouth
Cornwall
Start Point
Exeter
Lyme B.
Weymouth
Portland Bill
Parrett
Avon Test
Southampton Stour
Portsmouth
Wight
Brighton
Beachy H.
Sussex
Downs

Land's End
Scilly I.s
Lizard Point

English Channel

C. de la Hague
Alderney
Cherbourg
B. de la Seine
Guernsey
Channel Islands

Dieppe
Caux Amiens
Somme
Le Havre Seine
Normandy

Flanders

West from Greenwich 0 East from Greenwich

Scale 1:4.500.000
0 25 50 100 150 200 km

Copyright. Vallardi Ind.Graf.

The British Isles

For many centuries, the British Isles took little part in commercial and cultural exchanges with other nations. In particular when the Mediterranean was the centre of west European civilisation, it was forced into a position of isolation.

During the 15th century, Britain became less insular and began to develop as a powerful sea-going nation. The south-coast and Atlantic-facing ports developed, and Englishmen explored and traded throughout the known world and Britain became a great commercial sea power.

With the Industrial Revolution of the 18th century, helped by the country's natural resources, particularly coal and iron, Great Britain became the world's major power in both political and economic terms. This changed following the two World Wars, and the growing influence and industrialisation of the United States and the USSR, which became the two superpowers. The British Empire was broken up and the United. Kingdom began to strengthen its links with the European continent. In 1973 it became part of the EEC.

Tower Bridge
Tower Bridge was opened in 1894 and is London's most famous bridge. It stands more than 50 metres above water level, and opens to allow vessels with large tonnages to pass along the River Thames.

The great invasions
Britain was invaded many times between the 1st and the 11th centuries, and this influenced its language, customs and the civilisation of its peoples. The Romans were the first to conquer the island in 55 and 54 BC under the leadership of Julius Caesar. The Romans later penetrated as far as Hadrian's Wall. The Romans were followed in succession by Saxons, Jutes, Vikings, Danes and Normans.

THE MANY INVASIONS OF BRITAIN

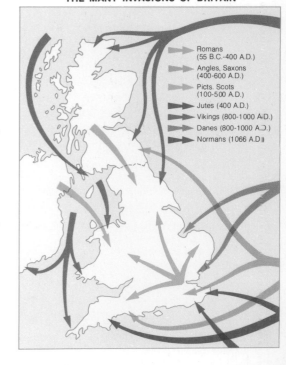

Romans (55 B.C.-400 A.D.)
Angles, Saxons (400-600 A.D.)
Picts. Scots (100-500 A.D.)
Jutes (400 A.D.)
Vikings (800-1000 A.D.)
Danes (800-1000 A.D.)
Normans (1066 A.D.)

Stonehenge
When the sea level rose with the melting of the great Pleistocene ice cap, it transformed Britain into an island. Britain's few inhabitants were hunters, using weapons of stone and bone. Stonehenge was erected in about 2000 BC. during the early Bronze Age. It is one of the major examples of primitive architecture in Great Britain, and consists of concentric circles of colossal stones, often forming a three-stoned arch. Stonehenge may have been a temple for sun-worshippers.

THE GREAT VOYAGES OF DISCOVERY

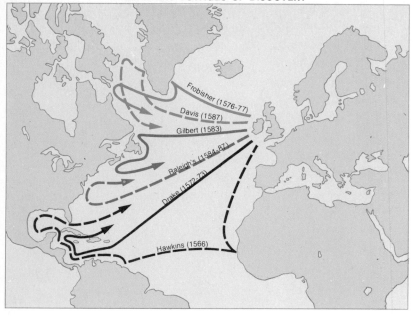

Frobisher (1576-77)
Davis (1587)
Gilbert (1583)
Raleigh's (1584-87)
Drake (1577-79)
Hawkins (1566)

Conquests and discoveries
For Great Britain, the 16th century meant the splendour of the Elizabethan era. Elizabeth I understood that the destiny of her country was indissolubly linked with the sea. She therefore did all she could to promote the development of her fleet and to encourage explorations and maritime trading, triumphantly keeping pace in this with the other great sea power of the period, Spain. Elizabeth made use in her service of the most able navigators of the time, Sir Walter Raleigh, Sir Francis Drake, Sir Martin Frobisher, and others who were pirates. Frobisher made many voyages in the northern Atlantic, looking for the North-West Passage, which it was hoped would be an alternative trade route to the East; however he got no farther than Baffin Island. John Davis also looked for the North-West Passage; he was stopped by the ice floes off the coast of Greenland, close to the strait which bears his name and which is the entry to the passage he was looking for. Richard Chancellor sought the North-East Passage, which was supposed to link Europe with East Asia.

Sir Francis Drake
Sir Francis Drake was a bold and daring navigator who sank many Spanish vessels. Between 1577 and 1580 he led an expedition around the world. He was knighted by Elizabeth I and took part as vice-admiral in the battle which routed the supposedly invincible Spanish Armada.

Castle and fortifications
The civil and religious architecture of Great Britain reflects the styles and tastes not only of the native Saxons, but also of the numerous peoples who came to settle in succession in the island, right up to the end of the Middle Ages, such as Normans, Vikings and Danes. One area which has particularly diverse architecture is south-east England, the region most frequented by the invaders because it led them to the heart of the country and to London. Romans, Vikings and Normans all passed through it. Each of these peoples left behind them a number of fortifications to add to the castles erected for defence purposes in successive eras. There are also many castles in Wales and Scotland. The photograph above right shows Caernarvon Castle in Wales, which was begun by Edward I. The present Prince of Wales was invested there in 1969.

The British Empire
The British Empire reached its greatest extent following the First World War. Its bases had already been established during the reign of Queen Victoria, however, and it was at the height of its power in the second half of the 19th century, during which period the Empire had been extended into various other continents. In Africa, Britain colonised Egypt, Nigeria, Kenya, Uganda and the Sudan, in an effort to establish a continuous route linking the Mediterranean to South Africa. Links with the colonies frequently took on the character of dominions, allowing a greater degree of autonomy to the native peoples. Examples of this are Canada, Australia, New Zealand and South Africa.

Abbeys and monasteries
Many cathedrals were built in Great Britain following the Norman conquest. Some of the most famous are those of Canterbury, St Albans, Winchester and Lincoln, built in the Romanesque/Norman style and in the Gothic style which followed it. Lincoln cathedral (the west facade of which is shown in the photograph on the right) was originally built between 1075 and 1090. It was restored 1922-32 and is one of the finest cathedrals in Britain and, with its light stone, dominates the centre of the city.

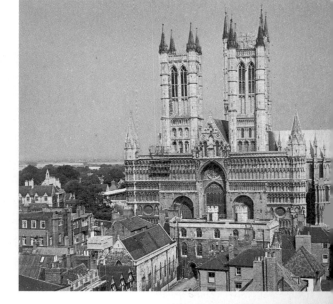

The British Constitution
The British Constitution has seen many changes down the centuries. The sovereign, for example, enjoyed absolute powers for some time, whereas today the United Kingdom, is in fact ruled by its government in the Queen's name, the monarch acting on the government's advice. It is a constitutional monarchy. Legislative power rests in the hands of the Sovereign and Parliament. The Parliament is divided into two houses: the House of Lords (below right) and the House of Commons. The former is made up of hereditary and life peers and peeresses; the second consists of 635 members of parliament, elected by popular vote at least once every five years. Executive power is exercised by the government, through its prime minister.

The Victorian era
The Victorian era had a profound effect on the history of Great Britain. Queen Victoria (right) reigned from 1837 to 1901. She was a great monarch, although her powers were restricted by her prime ministers, Palmerston, Disraeli and Gladstone. One of the things that made her popular was the effect she had on the spread of education.

THE BRITISH EMPIRE 1919

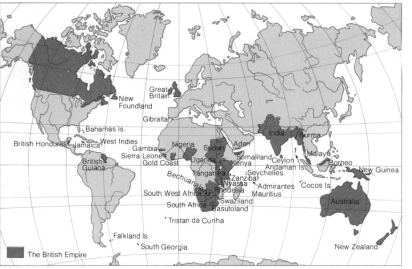

Great Britain
New Foundland
Gibraltar
Bahamas Is.
British Honduras
Jamaica
West Indies
Gambia
Sierra Leone
Gold Coast
British Guiana
Nigeria
Sudan
Uganda
Kenya
Bechuanaland
Nyassa
Rhodesia
Tanganika
South West Africa
South Africa
Swaziland
Basutoland
Somaliland
Zanzibar
Seychelles
Admirantes
Mauritius
Aden
India
Ceylon
Burma
Andaman Is.
Malaya
Borneo
New Guinea
Cocos Is.
Australia
Falkland Is.
South Georgia
Tristan da Cunha
New Zealand

■ The British Empire

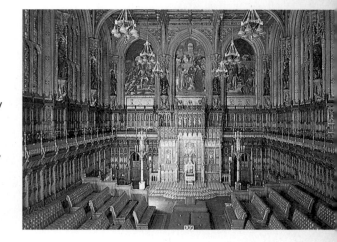

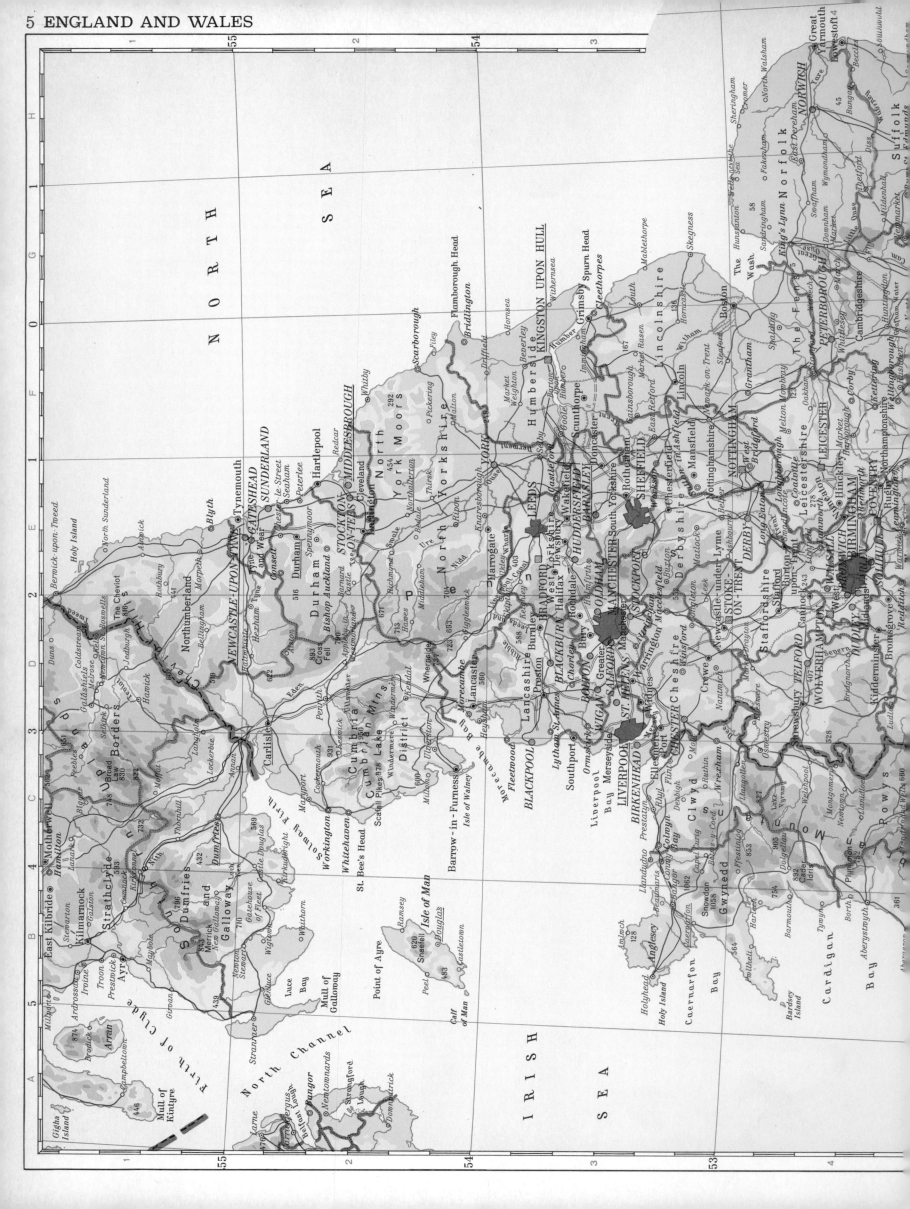

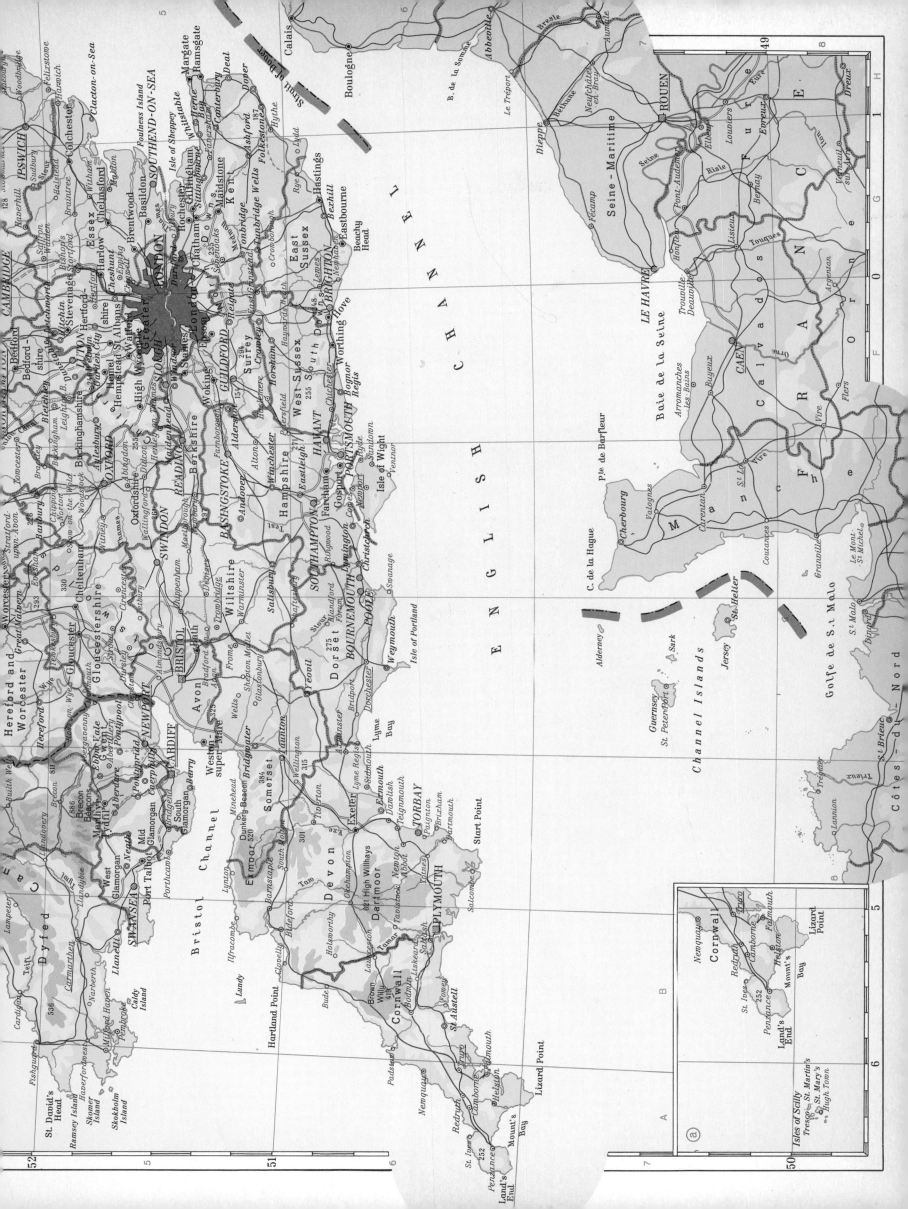

6 SCOTLAND

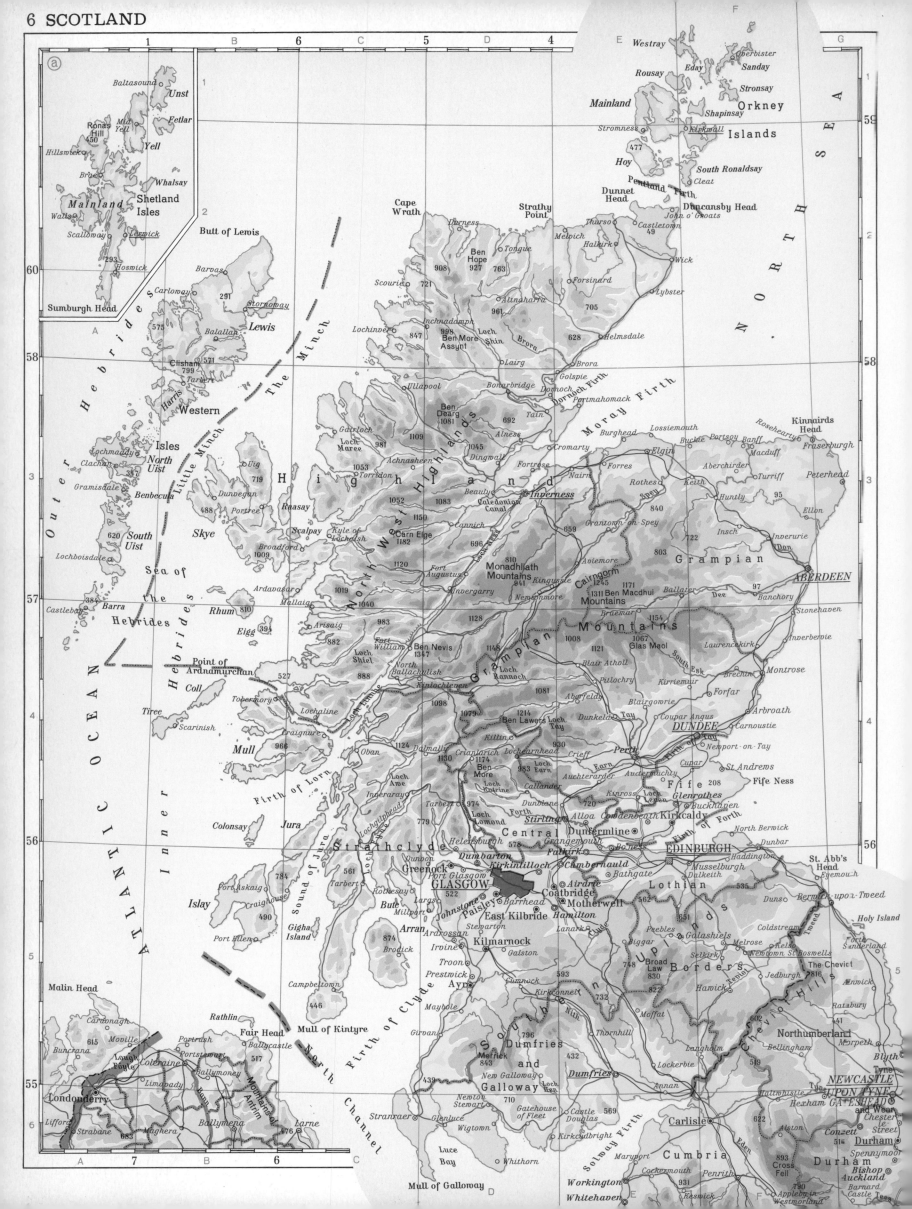

(a) Shetland Isles inset

Baltasound, Unst, Fetlar, Ronas Hill 450, Mid Yell, Yell, Hillswick, Brae, Whalsay, Mainland, Shetland Isles, Watts, Scalloway, Lerwick, 293, Hosmick, Sumburgh Head

Butt of Lewis

ORKNEY ISLANDS
Westray, Rousay, Eday, Sanday, Oberbister, Stronsay, Mainland, Shapinsay, Orkney, Stromness, Kirkwall, Islands, 477, Hoy, Cleat, South Ronaldsay, Dunnet Head, Pentland Firth, Duncansby Head, John o' Groats, Castletown, 49, Thurso, Melvich, Halkirk, Wick, Forsinard, Lybster

Cape Wrath, Strathy Point, Durness, Tongue, Ben Hope 927, 763, Scourie, 721, Altnaharra, 961, 705, Helmsdale, Inchnadamph, 998 Ben More Assynt, 847, Loch Shin, Brora, 628, Lochinver, Lairg, Brora, Golspie, Bonarbridge, Dornoch Firth, Portmahomack, Ullapool, Domoch, Tain, Ben Dearg 1081, 692, Alness, Moray Firth, Lossiemouth, Burghead, Buckie, Portsoy, Banff, Kinnairds Head, Rosehearty, Gairloch, 1109, Achnasheen, Dingwall, Cromarty, Elgin, Aberchirder, Turriff, Macduff, Fraserburgh, Peterhead, Loch Maree, 981, 1053, Torridon, Beauly, Caledonian Canal, INVERNESS, Forres, Nairn, Rothes, Keith, Huntly, Insch, Inverurie, 95, Ellon, Don, 1052, 1083, Cannich, 659, Grantown-on-Spey, 840, 722, GRAMPIAN, Carn Eige 1182, 696, 810, Aviemore, 803, Kyle of Lochalsh, 1150, Monadhliath Mountains 841, Kingussie, Cairngorm, 1245, ABERDEEN, 1120, Fort Augustus, Invergarry, Newtonmore, 1171, 1311 Ben Macdhui, Ballater, Dee, 97, Banchory, 1019, Mountains, 1128, Braemar, 1154, Stonehaven, 1040, 983, 1008, 1067 Glas Maol, Laurencekirk, Inverbervie, 882, Grampian, 1148, 1121, Mountains, Fort William, North Ballachulish, Ben Nevis 1347, Loch Rannoch, Blair Atholl, Pitlochry, Kirriemuir, Brechin, Montrose, 888, Kinlochleven, 1081, Aberfeldy, Blairgowrie, Forfar, Arbroath, 1098, 1079, 1214, Dunkeld, Coupar Angus, DUNDEE, Ben Lawers, Loch Tay, Tay, Carnoustie, Killin, 930, Crieff, Perth, Newport-on-Tay, 1124, Dalmally, Crianlarich, Lochearnhead, 1130, 1174, Ben More, Loch Earn, 983, Auchterarder, Auchtermuchty, Cupar, St Andrews, Oban, Callander, Kinross, Fife 208, Fife Ness, Dunblane, Loch Leven, Glenrothes, 720, Buckhaven, Loch Katrine, Alloa, Cowdenbeath, Kirkcaldy, 974, Forth, STIRLING, Firth of Forth, 779, Loch Lomond, Central, Dunfermline, North Berwick, Helensburgh, 578, Grangemouth, Dunbar, EDINBURGH, Haddington, Dunoon, Dumbarton, Falkirk, Bo'ness, St. Abb's Head, Greenock, Kirkintilloch, Cumbernauld, Musselburgh, Eyemouth, Port Glasgow, Airdrie, Bathgate, Dalkeith, Lothian, 535, GLASGOW, 522, Johnstone, Coatbridge, Dunse, Berwick-upon-Tweed, Paisley, Barrhead, Motherwell, 562, Holy Island, East Kilbride, Hamilton, 651, Rothesay, Largs, Lanark, Clyde, Peebles, Galashiels, Coldstream, Tweed, Bute, Millport, Stewarton, Biggar, Selkirk, Melrose, Kelso, Arran, Ardrossan, Irvine, Kilmarnock, Galston, 748, Broad Law 830, Borders, Newtown St Boswells, The Cheviot, Brodick, Troon, Prestwick, 593, Hawick, Jedburgh, 816, Alnwick, Ayr, Cumnock, Kirkconnel, 732, Langholm, 602, Rothbury, Malin Head, Maybole, Nith, Moffat, Northumberland, Morpeth, Girvan, South, 796, Thornhill, Lockerbie, 519, Bellingham, Merrick 843, Dumfries, 432, 893 Cross Fell, 439, and, Annan, NEWCASTLE UPON TYNE, GATESHEAD, Galloway, Dumfries, Carlisle, Hexham, Chester-le-Street, New Galloway, Loch Ken, Castle Douglas, Kirkcudbright, Solway Firth, Eden, 622, Alston, Durham, Stranraer, Glenluce, Wigtown, Gatehouse of Fleet, Maryport, Cumbria, Bishop Auckland, Whithorn, Cockermouth, 931, Penrith, 790, Appleby in Westmorland, Barnard Castle, Tees, Workington, Keswick, Whitehaven, Mull of Galloway

Western Isles / Hebrides
Outer Hebrides, North Uist, Lochmaddy, Clachan, 337, Gramisdale, Benbecula, Balallan, Lewis, Clisham 799, Tarbert, Harris, The Minch, Little Minch, Stornoway, 575, Carloway, 291, Barvas, Callanish, Scalpay, Raasay, Skye, Portree, Dunvegan, 719, Uig, 488, Broadford, 1009, Kyle of Lochalsh, South Uist, 620, Lochboisdale, Sea of the Hebrides, Castlebay, 384, Barra, Rhum 810, Eigg 394, Point of Ardnamurchan, Coll, Tiree, Scarinish, Mull, 966, Tobermory, Lochaline, Craignure, Inner Hebrides, Colonsay, Jura, Islay, Port Askaig, 784, Craighouse, 490, Port Ellen, Gigha Island, 446, Campbeltown, Mull of Kintyre, Firth of Clyde, Firth of Lorn, Sound of Jura, ATLANTIC OCEAN, NORTH SEA, North Channel

Northern Ireland inset
Malin Head, Cardonagh, 615, Moville, Buncrana, Lifford, Strabane, 683, Londonderry, Lough Foyle, Limavady, Coleraine, Portrush, Portstewart, Ballycastle, Ballymoney, 517, Rathlin, Fair Head, Ballymena, Larne, 476, Maghera, Mountains of Antrim, Bann

Gairloch, Ardvasar, Mallaig, Arisaig, Loch Shiel, Fort William, Loch Linnhe, Loch Awe, Inveraray, Lochgilphead, Tarbert, Strathclyde

1. Carrickfergus
2. Newtownabbey
3. Belfast
4. Castlereagh
5. North Down

ATLANTIC OCEAN

IRISH SEA

North Channel

Firth of Clyde

St. George's Channel

Malin Head
Bloody Foreland
Gweedore
Errigal 752
Aran Island
Rossan Point
Killybegs
Donegal Bay
Ballyshannon
Erris Head
Belmullet
Killala
Achill Head
Achill Island 672
Nephin 806
Clare Island
Clew Bay
Inishbofin
Slyne Head
Mweelrea 819
Aran Islands
Loop Head
Ballybunion
Kerry
Slea Head
Dingle Bay
Valencia Island
Dursey Head
Mizen Head
Clear Island

GLASGOW
Colonsay
Jura
Islay
Port Askaig
Port Ellen
Gigha Island
Mull of Kintyre
Rathlin
Fair Head
Strathclyde
Arran
Campbeltown
Dumfries and Galloway
Luce Bay
Mull of Galloway
Stranraer

Londonderry
Donegal
Derryveagh Mountains
Letterkenny
Buncrana
Cardonagh
Moville
Lough Swilly
Lough Foyle
Coleraine
Portrush
Portstewart
Ballymoney
Mountains of Antrim
Ballycastle
Larne
Antrim
Newtownabbey
BELFAST
Lisburn
Bangor
Newtownards
Ballymena
Carrickfergus
Belfast Lough
Strabane
Omagh
Sperrin Mountains
Sawel Mountain
Magherafelt
Cookstown
Lough Neagh
Dungannon
Craigavon
Lurgan
Portadown
Armagh
Banbridge
Down
Downpatrick
Strangford Lough
Fermanagh
Lower Lough Erne
Upper Lough Erne
Enniskillen
Monaghan and Mourne
Newry
Newcastle
Mourne Mountains
Slieve Donard
Sligo
Leitrim
Cavan
Carrick-on-Shannon
Roscommon
Longford
Westmeath
Mullingar
Meath
Drogheda
Clogher Head
Louth
Dundalk
Dundalk Bay
Balbriggan
Swords
Dublin
DUBLIN
Dun Laoghaire
Bray
Greystones
Kildare
Naas
Wicklow
Wicklow Mountains
Lugnaquillia Mountain 926
Wicklow Head
Arklow
Carlow
Galway
Galway Bay
Clare
Ennis
Limerick
Tipperary
Kilkenny
Wexford
Rosslare
Cahore Point
Carnsore Point
Offaly
Laois
Portlaoise
Mountmellick
Tullamore
Birr
Nenagh
Keeper Hill 694
Thurles
Cashel
Clonmel
Carrick-on-Suir
New Ross
Enniscorthy
Gorey
Waterford
Tramore
Dungarvan
Hook Head
Galty Mountains
Galtymore 920
Mallow
Fermoy
Blackwater
Lismore
Youghal
CORK
Cork
Midleton
Cobh
Macroom
Killarney
Tralee
Brandon Mountain 953
Carrauntoohill 1041
Mountains of Kerry
Cahersiveen
Kenmare
Bantry Bay
Bantry
Skibbereen
Clonakilty
Kinsale
Old Head of Kinsale
Baltimore

Greenock
Dumbarton
Paisley
Johnstone
Kilmarnock
Ayr
Maybole
Girvan

Fishguard
St. David's Head
Ramsey Island
Skomer Island
Skokholm Island
Milford Haven

IBERIAN PENINSULA

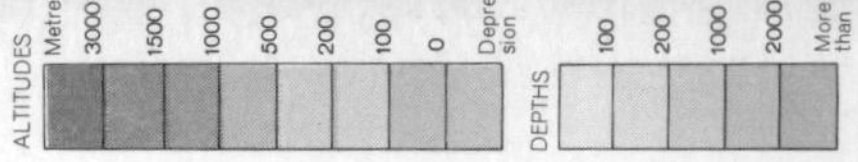

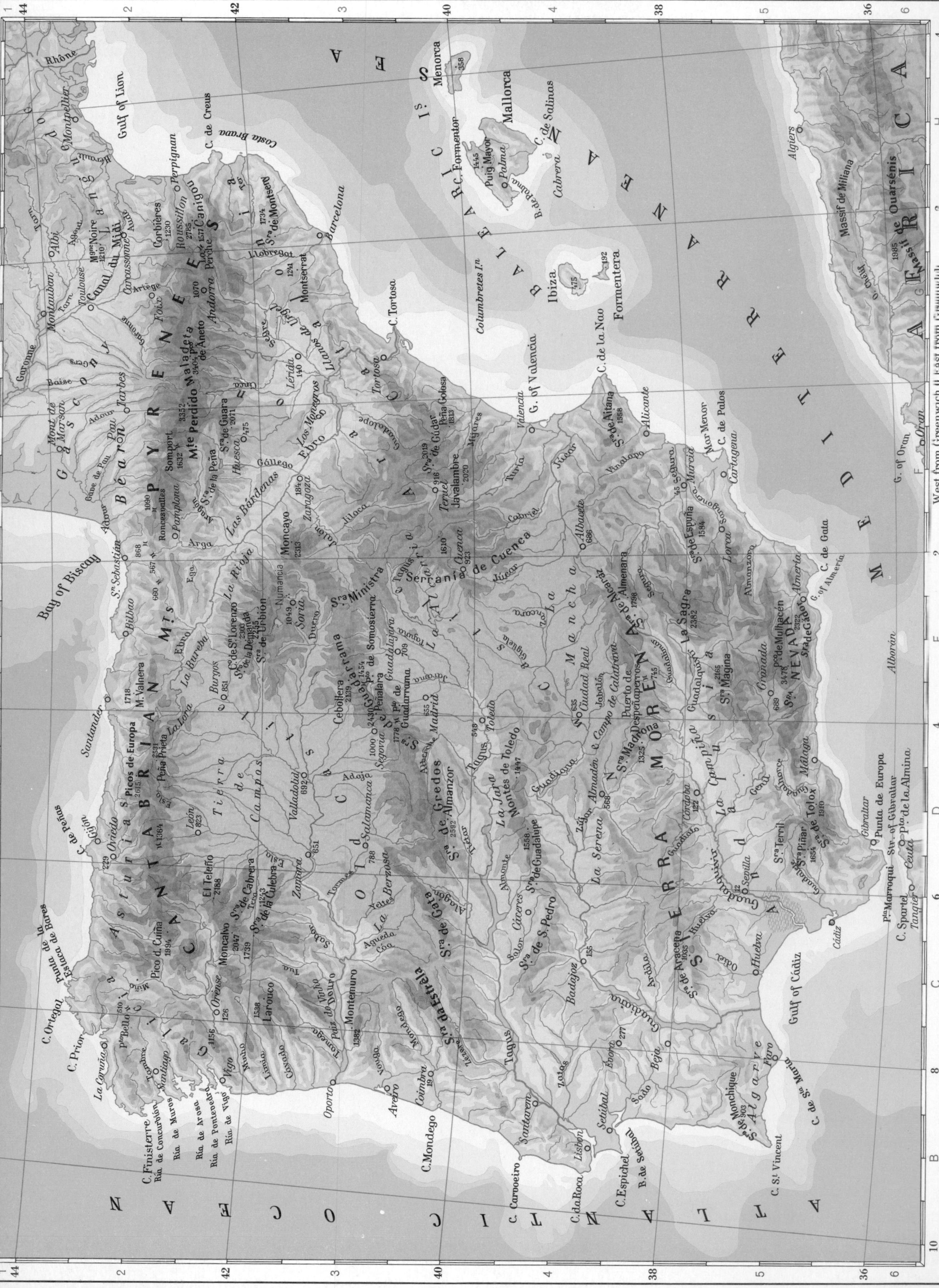

ALTITUDES Mètres 3000 1500 1000 500 200 100 0 Depression DEPTHS 100 200 1000 2000 More than

West from Greenwich 0 East from Greenwich

Scale 1:4.500.000

0 25 50 100 150 200 km

Bodies of water and regions:

Gulf of Lion
Costa Brava
C. de Creus
BALEARIC Is.
Menorca
Mallorca
Palma
Puig Mayor
C. de Salinas
Ibiza
Formentera
Columbretes I.
MEDITERRANEAN
AFRICA
Massif de Ouarsénis
Massif de Miliana
Algiers
Oran
G. of Oran
G. of Valencia
C. de la Nao
Mar Menor
C. de Palos
Cartagena
Alicante
Alborán
G. of Almería
C. de Gata
Bay of Biscay
ATLANTIC OCEAN
Gulf of Cádiz

Pyrenees / North:

Rhône
Montpellier
Canal du Midi
Mgne Noire
Carcassonne
Toulouse
Montauban
Mont de Marson
Gascony
Béarn
Gave de Pau
Bayonne
Adour
Gulf of Biscay
Corbières
Roussillon
Perpignan
Canigou 1557
1230
Sra de Montseny 1734
Barcelona
Andorra
Mte Perdido 3352
Maladeta 3404
Pic d'Aneto 3404
Somport 1632
PYRENEES
Pamplona
Roncesvalles 1090
Aragón
Sra de Guara 2071
Huesca 475
Sra de la Peña
Montserrat 1241
Llobregat
Lérida 140
Ebro
C. Tortosa
Tortosa
Peña Golosa 1813
Gudar 2019
Teruel
Javalambre 2020

Central:

S. Sebastián 868
Bilbao 680 567
Santander
Picos de Europa
Peña Prieta 2535
CANTABRIAN Mts
M. Valnera 1718
Burgos 851
La Rioja
Sra de S. Lorenzo 2303
Sra de la Demanda 2303
Sra de Urbión 2249
Soria 1049
Numancia
Moncayo 2313
Zaragoza 187
Las Bárdenas
Gállego
Jalón
Jiloca
Moncayo
Valladolid 692
Adaja
Segovia
Madrid 655
Pº de Guadarrama 1778
Sra de Guadarrama
Guadalajara 709
Serranía de Cuenca
Cuenca 923
Júcar
Toledo 548
Tagus
Sra Ministra
Cebollera 2430
Guadalope
Ebro

Northwest / Portugal:

C. Ortegal
Punta de la Estaca de Bares
C. Prior
C. de Peñas
Gijón
Oviedo 229
ASTURIAS
GALICIA
La Coruña
C. Finisterre
Ría de Corcubión
Santiago
Ría de Muros
Ría de Arosa
Ría de Pontevedra
Ría de Vigo
Vigo
Miño
Orense 126
El Teleno 2188
León 823
Tierra de Campos
Moncalvo 2047
Sra de Cabrera
Sra de la Culebra
La Cabrera
Zamora 651
Tormes
Salamanca 788
Sra de Gata
Sra de Gredos
Almanzor 2592
Pº de Somosierra 1454
Sra de Peñalara
Serra da Estrêla 1991
Montemuro 1382
Larouco
Montesinho
Douro
Oporto
Aveiro
C. Mondego
Coimbra 19
Santarém
Lisbon 903
C. da Roca
C. Espichel
B. de Setúbal
Setúbal
Algarve
Monchique 903
C. de S. María
C. S. Vincent

South:

La Mancha
Ciudad Real 635
Campo de Calatrava
SIERRA MORENA
Sra Madrona
Despeñaperros
La Jara
Montes de Toledo 1447
Guadiana
La Serena
Badajoz
Cáceres
Sra de S. Pedro
Sra de Guadalupe 1558
Mérida
Córdoba 123
Sevilla 155
Guadalquivir
Huelva
Odiel
Tinto
Sra de Aracena 1035
Ronda 1122
La Campiña
Sra Nevada
Mulhacén 3478
Veleta 3478
Granada 689
Guadix
SRA NEVADA
Sra Mágina 2165
Jaén
Sra Segura 2018
Sra de Cazorla
Sra de Espuña 1584
Lorca
Murcia
Almería
Málaga
C. de Gata
Marbella
Gibraltar
Punta de Europa
Str. of Gibraltar
Ceuta
Tánger
C. Spartel
Pta de la Almina
Pta Marroquí
Cádiz

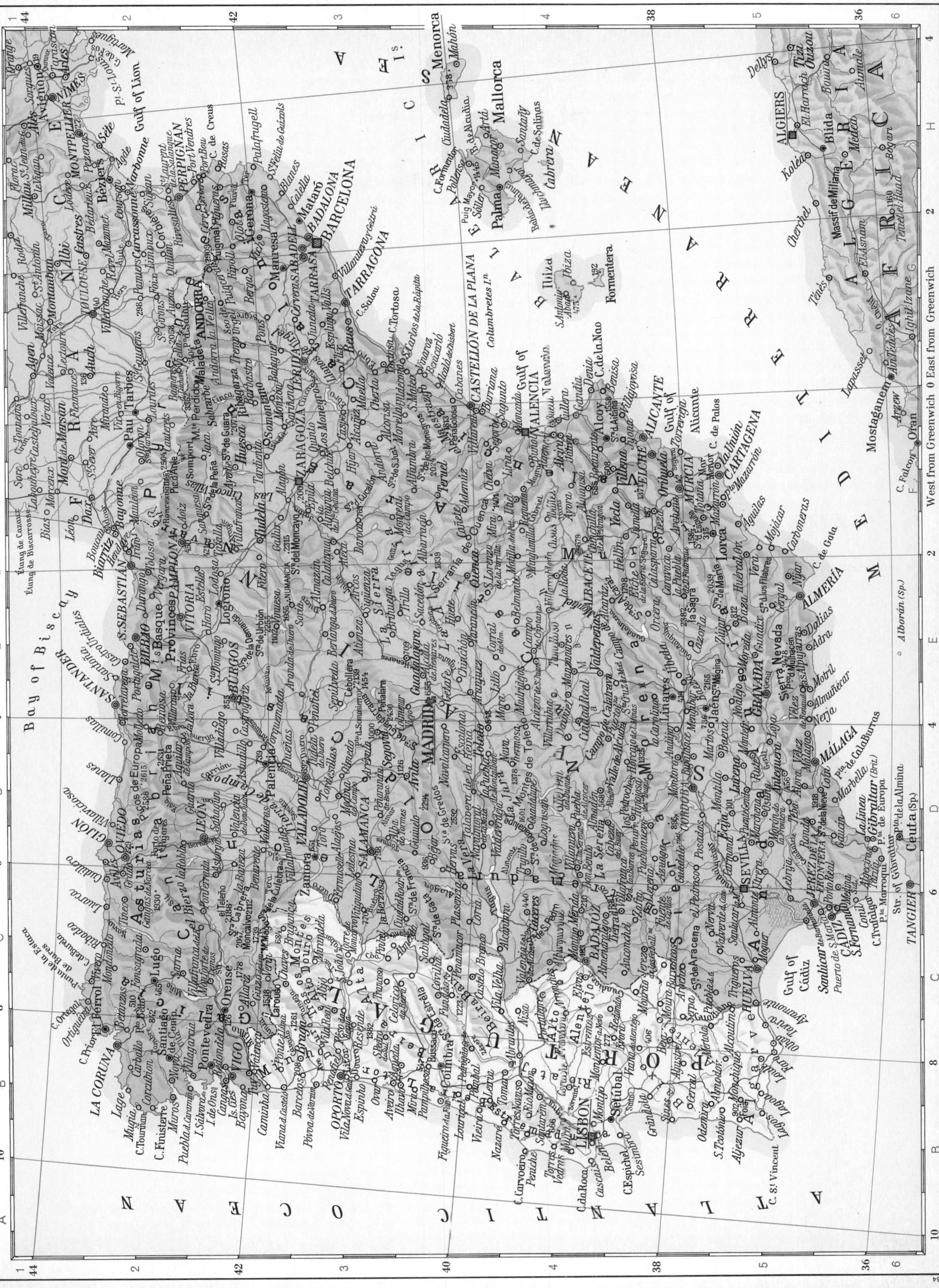

Copyright: Vallardi Ind. Graf.

Scale 1:4.500.000

West from Greenwich 0 East from Greenwich

Bay of Biscay

ATLANTIC OCEAN

MEDITERRANEA

ALGERIA

AFRICA

MADRID
LISBON
BARCELONA
VALENCIA
SEVILLA
MÁLAGA
ZARAGOZA
BILBAO
GRANADA
MURCIA
CARTAGENA
ALICANTE
ALMERÍA
VALLADOLID
SALAMANCA
BURGOS
OVIEDO
GIJÓN
LA CORUÑA
VIGO
OPORTO
BADAJOZ
CÁDIZ
HUELVA
TARRAGONA
CASTELLÓN DE LA PLANA
ALBACETE
PAMPLONA
VITORIA
S. SEBASTIÁN
SANTANDER
LÉRIDA
GERONA
BADALONA
SABADELL
TARRASA
Palma
Mallorca
Menorca
Ibiza
Formentera
ALGIERS
Gibraltar (Brit.)
Ceuta (Sp.)
TANGIER
ANDORRA
Gulf of Lion
Gulf of Cádiz
Gulf of Valencia
PERPIGNAN
MONTPELLIER
BÉZIERS
NÎMES
TOULOUSE
BAYONNE
Biarritz

ALTITUDES Metres: 3000 | 1500 | 1000 | 500 | 200 | 100 | 0 | Depression

DEPTHS: 100 | 200 | 1000 | 2000 | More than

ATLANTIC OCEAN
MEDITERRANEAN SEA
LIGURIAN SEA
English Channel
Gulf of Lion
G. of Biscay
Strait of Dover
Channel Islands
Bretagne
Normandie
Vendée
Poitou
Saintonge
Médoc
Landes
Gascogne
Béarn
Pyrenees
Massif Central
Cévennes
Mts du Vivarais
La Margeride
Périgord
Guyenne
Limousin
Marche
Sologne
Beauce
Nivernais
Burgundy
Plateau de Langres
Côte d'Or
Champagne
Argonne
Lorraine
Ardennes
Vosges
Black Forest
Dauphiné
Provence
Jura
Alps
Cantabrian Mts
Asturias
Picos de Europa
Tierra de Campos
Scale 1:4.500.000
West from Greenwich 0 East from Greenwich
Copyright Vallardi Ind. Graf.

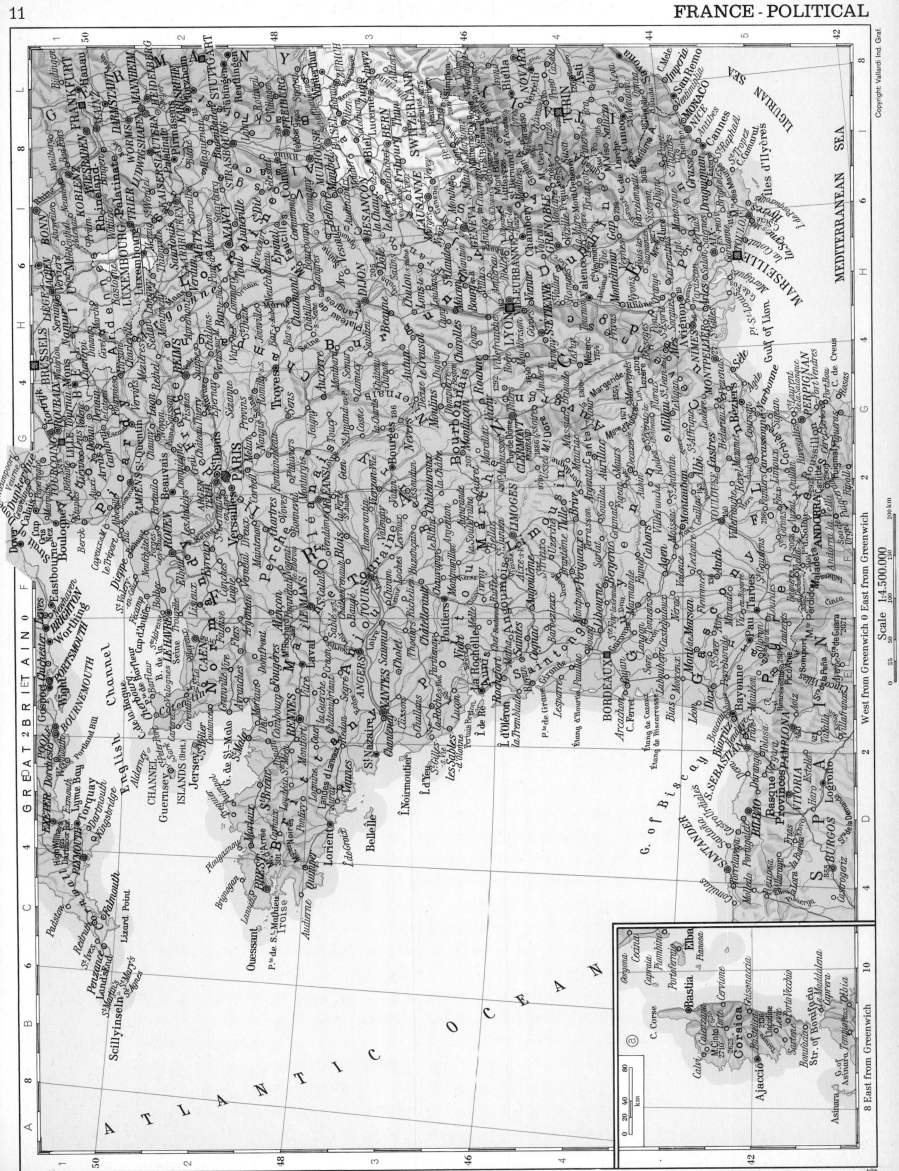

Scale 1:4.500.000

West from Greenwich 0 East from Greenwich

0 25 50 100 150 200 km

CENTRAL EUROPE - PHYSICAL

Scale 1:4.500.000

10 East from Greenwich

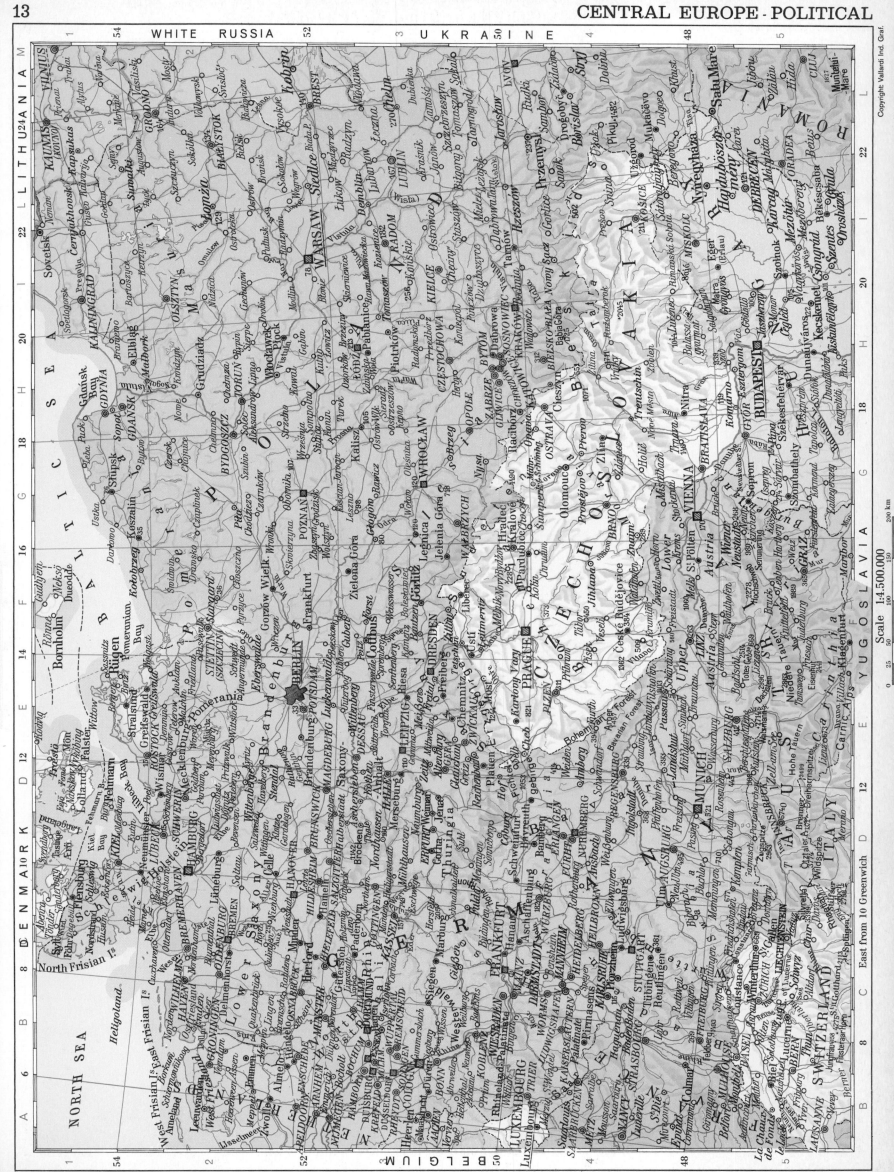

Scale 1:4.500.000

0 25 50 100 150 200 km

ALTITUDES   Métres   3000 1500 1000 500 200 100 0   Degres sion   DEPTHS   100 200 1000 2000 More than

Copyright: Vallardi Ind. Graf.

NORTH SEA

Zealand   Fyn   Langeland   Falster   Rostok   Lübeck Bay

Schleswig-Holstein   North Frisian I.s   Heligoland

Mecklenburg   Hamburg   Lüneburg   Elbe

Harz   Brocken 1142   Thuringian Forest   Halle   Fichtel-Geb.

West Friesland   Holland   Gelderland   Amsterdam   Haarlem   The Hague   Rotterdam   Utrecht

Weser   Bremen   Hanover   Wesergeb.   Teutoburger Wald   Bielefeld   Osnabrück

Westphalia   Münster   Dortmund   Essen   Cologne   Bonn

Bavaria   Nuremberg   Würzburg   Franconia   Swabia   Augsburg

Black Forest   Swabian Jura   Zugspitze 2963   Stuttgart   Ulm   L. Constance   Vaduz   Chur

Frankfurt   Mainz   Odenwald   Spessart   Darmstadt

Hunsrück   Haardt   Palatinate   Erbeskopf   Strasbourg   Freiburg   Basel   Bern

Ardennes   Luxembourg   Liège   Maastricht   Düsseldorf   Duisburg

Lorraine   Metz   Nancy   Moselle   Meuse   Trier   Koblenz

Brabant   Brussels   Antwerpen   Namur   Kempenland

Flanders   Lille   Ostend   Scheldt   Ghent

Artois   Picardy   Arras   Amiens   Somme

Argonne   Champagne   Reims   St. Quentin   Châlons

Plateau de Langres   Côte d'Or   Dijon   Besançon   Chasseral

Paris   Île de France   Seine   Marne   Aube   Troyes

Beauce   Orléans   Loire   Sologne   Bourges   Nevers

Chartres   Eure   Rouen   Dieppe   Le Havre

Normandy   Caen   Cherbourg   Cotentin   C. de la Hague

Maine   Anjou   Le Mans   Angers   Tours   Touraine

Brittany   Rennes   St. Malo   St. Brieuc   Brest   Quimper   Nantes

Channel Islands   Guernsey   Jersey   Alderney   Belle Île   Noirmoutier

English Channel

C. Gris Nez   Calais   Strait of Dover   Dover   Boulogne

Kent   Sussex   Beachy H.   Brighton   Portsmouth   Wight   Southampton   Weymouth   Portland Bill

England   London   Thames   Reading   Oxford   Chiltern Hills   Cotswold Hills   Gloucester

Norfolk   Great Yarmouth   Norwich   Suffolk   Ipswich   Cambridge   The Wash

Lincoln   Nottingham   Leicester   Derby   Sheffield   Birmingham   Worcester

Pennines   Manchester   Leeds   Hull   Humber   Flamborough H.   Spurn H.

Cleveland Hills   Newcastle   Sunderland   Cross Fell 893   Carlisle

Cumbrian Mountains   Scafell P. 978   Barrow   Blackpool   Liverpool   Lancashire

Southern Uplands   Cheviot Hills   Merrick 842

IRISH SEA   Isle of Man   Douglas

North Channel   Belfast   Sperrin Mts.   Mourne Mts. 852   Ulster   L. Neagh   Dublin

Leinster   Wicklow Mts.   Lugnaquilla   Waterford   Wexford   Carnsore P.

Anglesey   Holyhead   Snowdon 1085   Cambrian Mountains   Cardigan Bay

Wales   Plynlimon   Radnor F.   Glamorgan   Swansea   Cardiff

Bristol Channel   Bristol   Mendip Hills   Lundy   Hartland Point

Devon   Exmoor   Dartmoor Forest   Exeter   Plymouth   Start Point

Cornwall   Land's End   Lizard Point   Scilly I.s

St. George's Channel

Scale 1:4.500.000

200 km   150   100   50   25   0

West from Greenwich   0   East from Greenwich

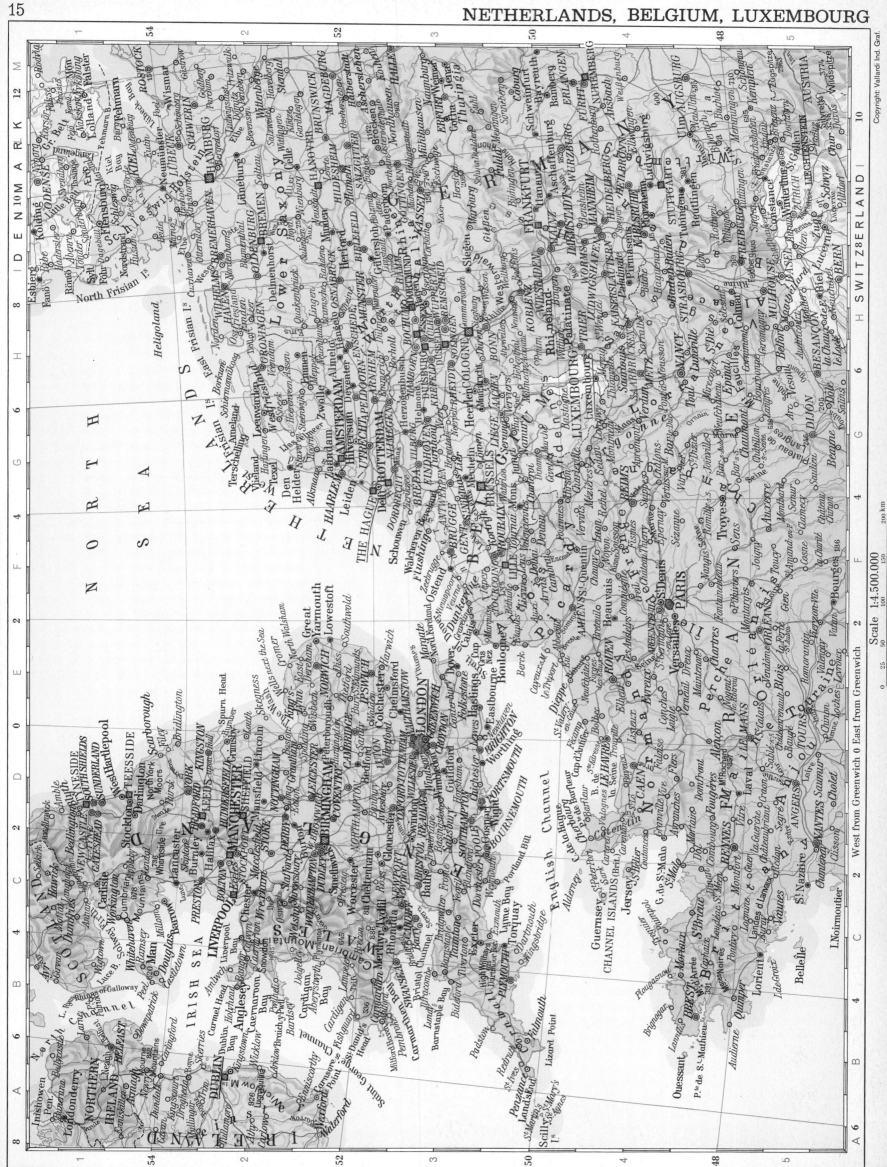

Scale 1:4.500.000

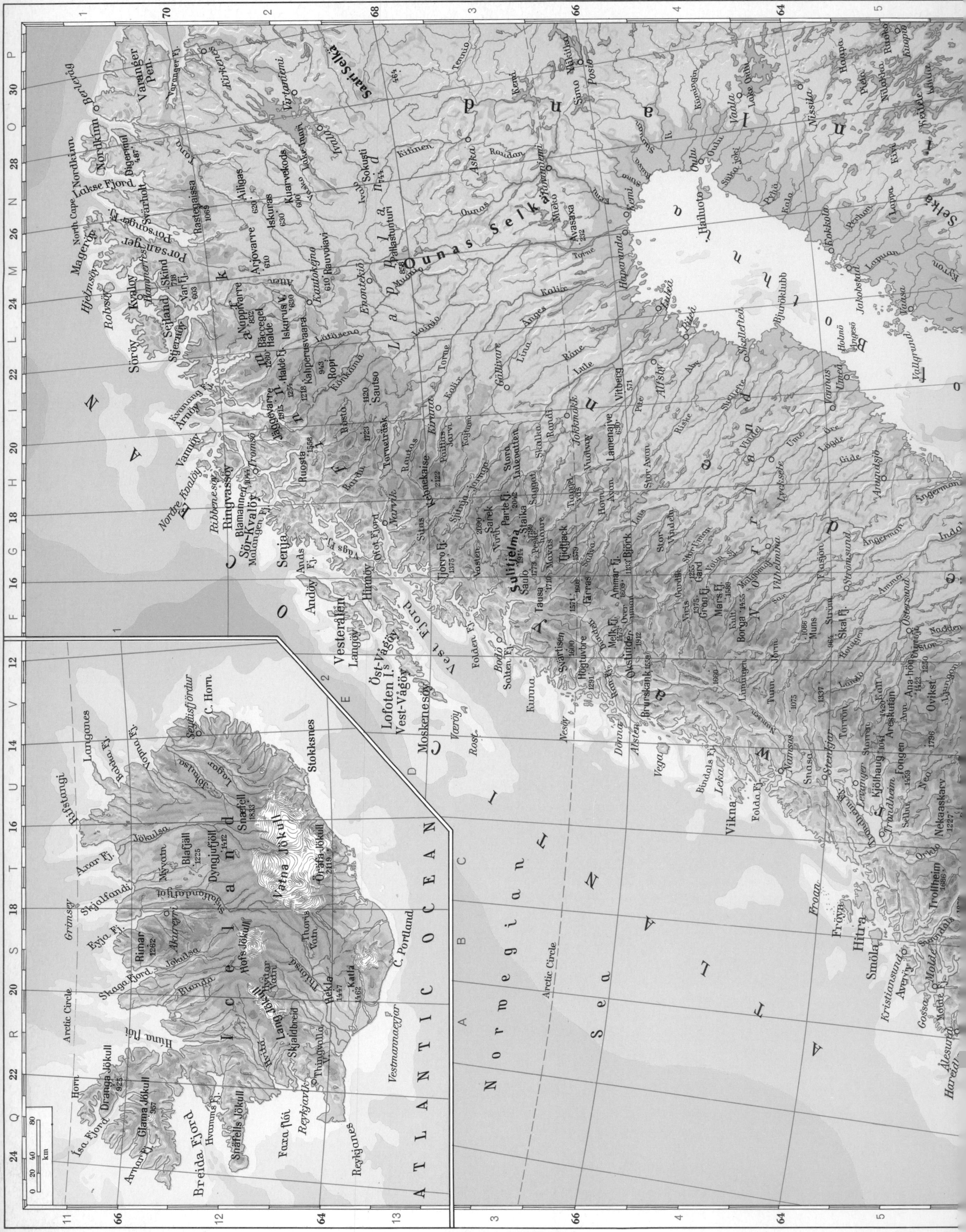

16

Map (Scandinavia / Iceland inset)

Place names as read from the map:

Varanger Pen., North Cape, Nordkinn, Berlevåg, Laxe Fjord, Magerøy, Hjelmsøy, Kvaløy, Seiland, Søröy, Robvsøy, Stjernöy, Porsanger Fj., Arnöy, Vannöy, Kvænangen Fj., Ringvassöy, Tromsö, Senja, Andöy, Langöy, Vesterålen, Lofoten Is., Vest-Vågöy, Öst-Vågöy, Moskenesöy, Vest Fjord, Bodö, Sulitelma 1914, Sarek 2090, Kvikkjokk, Gällivare, Kiruna, Pallastunturi, Kautokeino, Enontekiö

Ounas Selkä, Lappland, Sver ige, Norway, Norwegian Sea, Atlantic Ocean, Arctic Circle

Iceland inset
C. Horn, Langanes, Seydisfjördur, Snæfell 1833, Vatna Jökull, Öræfa-Jökull 2119, Hofs-Jökull, Dyngjufjöll 1442, Blafjall 1225, Myvatn, Hekla 1447, Katla 1362, Reykjanes, Faxa flói, Breida Fjord, Snæfells Jökull, Drangs Jökull, Glama Jökull, C. Portland, Vestmannaeyjar

Scale 1:4.500.000
0 25 50 100 150 200 km

East from 24 Greenwich

Scale 1:4.500.000

0 25 50 100 150 200km

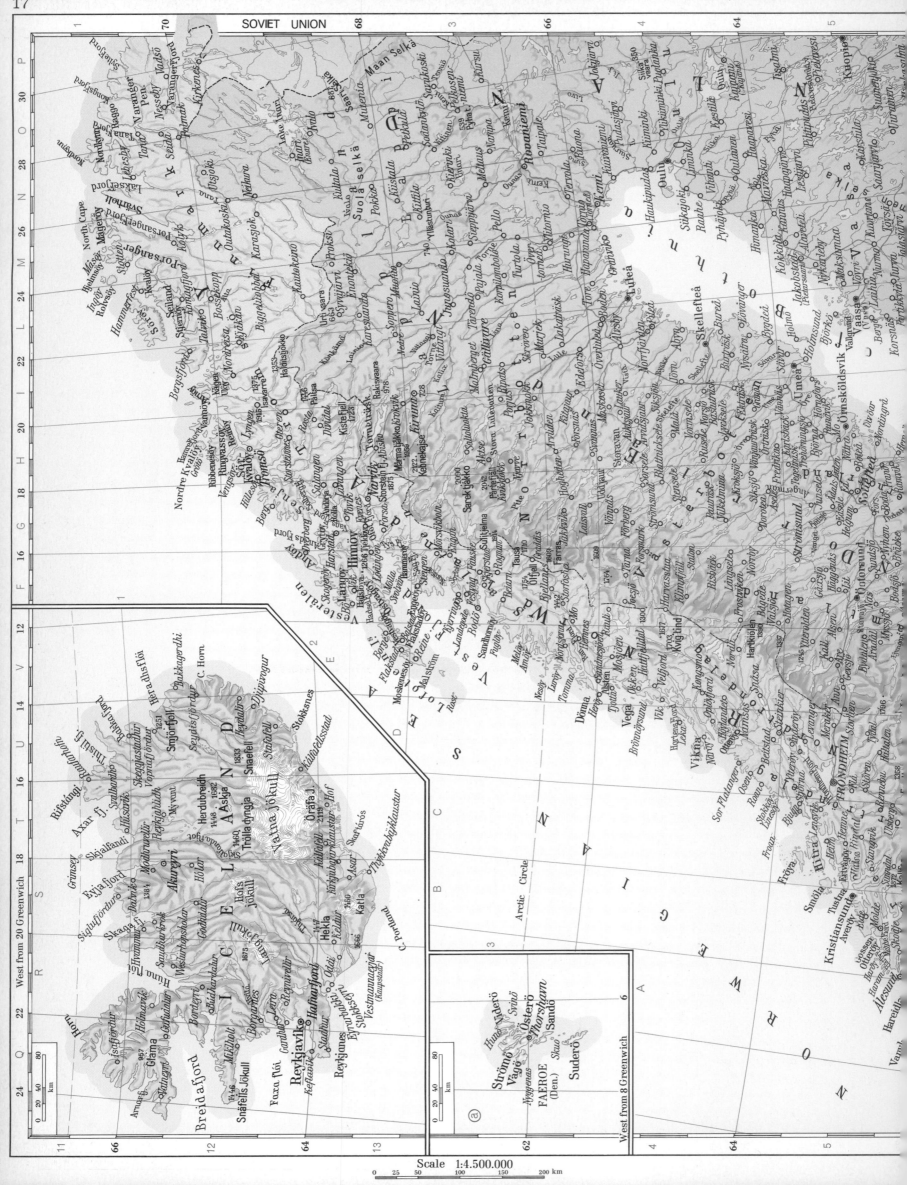

ITALY - PHYSICAL

Major seas and regions:

- LIGURIAN SEA
- TYRRHENIAN SEA
- ADRIATIC SEA
- IONIAN SEA
- MEDITERRANEAN SEA
- G. of Venice
- G. of Genoa
- G. of Taranto
- Gulf of Manfredonia
- G. of Squillace

Islands and regions:

- Corsica
- Sardinia
- Sicily
- Elba
- Lipari Is.
- Egadi Is.
- Tuscan Archipelago

Mountains and peaks:

- Mont Blanc 4810
- Matterhorn 4505
- M. Rosa 4638
- Gr. Paradiso 4061
- M. Viso 3841
- Marmolada
- M. Amiata 1734
- Vesuvius 1277
- Etna 3263
- Gran Sasso d'Italia

Cities:

- Turin
- Milan
- Genoa
- Venice
- Bologna
- Florence
- Rome
- Naples
- Bari
- Brindisi
- Taranto
- Cagliari
- Palermo
- Catania
- Syracuse
- Reggio C.
- Messina

Neighbouring regions:

- Tunisia
- AFRICA
- Slovenia
- Karst
- Dinaric Alps
- Bosnia
- Herzegovina

East from 10° Greenwich

Scale 1:4.500.000

0   25   50   100   150   200 km

ITALY - POLITICAL

SWITZERLAND AUSTRIA HUNGARY

FRANCE

YUGOSLAVIA

AFRICA

Major cities and features:

ZÜRICH · INNSBRUCK · BERN · GRAZ · Székesfehérvár · Klagenfurt · Maribor · PÉCS · ZAGREB · TRIESTE · RIJEKA · LJUBLJANA · UDINE · VENICE · PADUA · VERONA · VICENZA · TREVISO · BRESCIA · MILAN · MONZA · BERGAMO · COMO · NOVARA · TURIN · ALESSANDRIA · PIACENZA · PARMA · CREMONA · Mantua · FERRARA · MODENA · BOLOGNA · REGGIO NELL'EMILIA · RAVENNA · FORLI · FAENZA · RIMINI · GENOA · Savona · LA SPEZIA · Carrara · Massa · Lucca · PISTOIA · PRATO · FLORENCE · LEGHORN · PISA · Arezzo · SIENA · PERUGIA · ANCONA · Pesaro · Fano · Senigallia · Macerata · Ascoli Piceno · Teramo · PESCARA · Chieti · L'Aquila · TERNI · Viterbo · Grosseto · Civitavecchia · ROME · VATICAN CITY · Latina · NAPLES · Pozzuoli · Ischia · Caserta · Benevento · Avellino · SALERNO · Potenza · CAMPOBASSO · FOGGIA · Barletta · Trani · Molfetta · BARI · Brindisi · Lecce · Matera · TARANTO · COSENZA · Crotone · Catanzaro · REGGIO DI CALABRIA · MESSINA · PALERMO · Trapani · Marsala · Agrigento · CATANIA · SYRACUSE · Ragusa · Gela

Islands / Regions:
Corsica · Sardinia · CAGLIARI · SASSARI · Elba · Sicily · MALTA · Valletta · Lipari Is. · Pantelleria

Seas:
LIGURIAN SEA · TYRRHENIAN SEA · ADRIATIC SEA · IONIAN SEA · Sicilian Channel · Gulf of Taranto · Str. of Bonifacio

Tunis · Bizerte · Annaba · Sousse · Kairouan

Scale 1:4.500.000

0 25 50 100 150 200 km

East from Greenwich

SOUTH EAST EUROPE - PHYSICAL

Scale 1:4.500.000

0 25 50 100 150 200 km

Copyright: Vallardi Ind. Graf.

BERLIN

WARSAW · **KIEV** · **ŽITOMIR** · **VINNITSA** · **ODESSA**

PRAGUE · **VIENNA** · **BRATISLAVA** · **BUDAPEST** · **BELGRADE** · **BUCHAREST** · **ZAGREB**

POZNAŃ · **WROCŁAW** · **KRAKOW** · **LVOV** · **LUBLIN** · **BREST** · **ČERNIGOV** · **RÓVNO**

DRESDEN · **LEIPZIG** · **KATOWICE** · **GRAZ** · **TIMIŞOARA** · **ARAD** · **CRAIOVA** · **PLOEŞTI**

DEBRECEN · **SZEGED** · **ORADEA** · **CLUJ** · **SIBIU** · **BRAŞOV** · **GALAŢI** · **BRĂILA**

SARAJEVO · **NOVI SAD** · **PÉCS** · **SPLIT** · **RIJEKA** · **TRIESTE** · **CONSTANŢA** · **VARNA** · **RUSSE**

KISHINEV · **TIRASPOL** · **ČERNOVTSY** · **IAŞI** · **BOTOŞANI** · **TARNOPOL** · **BERDIČEV**

WHITE RUSSIA · SOVIET UKRAINE · POLAND · CZECHOSLOVAKIA · HUNGARY · ROMANIA · TRANSYLVANIA · AUSTRIA · YUGOSLAVIA · Hercegovina · Krajina

Scale 1:4.500.000

0   25   50   100   150   200 km

ITALY

BULGARIA

SOFIA

TURKEY

ISTANBUL

Bosporus

ÜSKÜDAR

İZMİT

BURSA

Sea of Marmara

İZMİR

EPHESOS

CARIA

RHODES

Rhodes

Karpathos

Kasos

SEA OF CRETE

CRETE

Iraklion

Chania

MEDITERRANEAN SEA

AEGEAN SEA

Cyclades

Naxos

Andros

Tinos

Mikonos

Paros

Milos

Santorini

Samos

Ikaria

Chios

Lesbos

Mitilini

Lemnos

Thasos

Samothraki

Alexandroupolis

Komotini

THESSALONIKI

Chalkidike

G. of Thessaloniki

Mt Olympus

Larisa

Volos

Thessaly

Trikala

Ioannina

Epirus

EUBOEA

ATHENS

Piraeus

Corinth

G. of Corinth

Patras

Peloponnesus

Tripolis

Sparta

Kalamata

C. Matapan

Kithira

Northern Sporades

Skopelos

Skiros

Zakinthos

Kefallinia

Lefkas

Ithaka

Korfu (Kerkira)

IONIAN SEA

Strait of Otranto

Brindisi

Lecce

BARI

FOGGIA

NAPLES

SALERNO

PESCARA

Chieti

Teramo

Taranto

Gulf of Taranto

COSENZA

CATANZARO

REGGIO DI CALABRIA

MESSINA

CATANIA

SYRACUSE

Lipari Is.

TYRRHENIAN SEA

CALABRIA

BASILICATA

Etna

ADRIATIC SEA

ALBANIA

Durrës

Tiranë

Shkodër

Titograd

YUGOSLAVIA

SKOPJE

Bitola

Florina

Pristina

Prizren

Kosovo

Veles

Ohrid

Nish

MACEDONIA

PLOVDIV

Stara Zagora

BURGAS

Edirne

Central Balkan

Eastern Balkan

Pirin Pl.

Scale 1:4.500.000

0   25   50   100   150   200 km

East from 20 Greenwich

Copyright: Vallardi Ind. Graf.

22

Scale 1:20.000.000

0 100 200   400   600   800   1000 km

East from 100 Greenwich

ARCTIC OCEAN
Laptev Sea
East Siberian Sea
New Siberia
New Siberian Is.
Kotelny I.
Lyakhov Is.
Bolshevik I.
Chelyuskin
Wrangel I.
De Long Str.

UNITED STATES
Alaska
Bristol Bay
Alaska Pen.
Platinum
C. Lisburne
Kotzebue
Nome
Teller
C. Prince of Wales
Bering Str.
C. Dezhnëv
Norton Sound
Nunivak
Unimak
Dutch
Unalaska
Umnak
Seguam
Amlia
Atka
Adak
Kanaga
Tanaga
Amchitka
Kiska
Near Is.
Attu
Angattu
Andreanof Is.
Rat Is.
Aleutian Islands

S. Lawrence I.
S. Matthew I.
Pribilof Is.
Bering Sea
C. Navarin
Gulf of Anadyr
Anadyr
Providenija
Nunligran
Chukchi Pen.
C. Chukotskiy
Arctic Circle

PACIFIC OCEAN

Kamchatka
Petropavlovsk-Kamchatskiy
Ust'-Kamchatsk
Sredne Kamchatsk
Komandorskiye Is.
C. Lopatka

Sea of Okhotsk
Okhotsk
Magadan
Ajan
Nikolaevsk
Sakhalin
Aleksandrovsk Sakh.
Yuzhno-Sakhalinsk
Tartary Str.

Kuril Is.
Paramušir
Onekotan
Matua
Rassua
Ketoj
Simušir
Urup
Iturup
Kunašir
Šikotan

Yakutsk
Verkhoyansk
Cherskiy Ra.
Y A K U T S. S. R.
Verkhoyansk Ra.
Stanovoy Ra.
Dzhugdzhur Ra.
Oymyakon
Aldan
Tommot
Lena

Chita
Ulan Ude
Ulan Bator (Urga)
MONGOLIA
Inner Mongolia
Gobi
Manchuria
Great Khingan

HARBIN
CHIANG CHUN
MUKDEN
AN SHAN
FU SHUN
CHI CHI HA ERH
PEKING
TIENTSIN
TAIYÜAN
Paotou
Yinchuan
Kalgan
Huh-Hoto

Khabarovsk
Komsomolsk
Birobidžan
Blagoveščensk
Belogorsk
Svobodnyj
Vladivostok
Ussuriysk
Nachodka

Sea of Japan
NORTH KOREA
PYEONGYANG
Hungnam
Wonsan
SOUTH KOREA
SEOUL
INCHEON
Daejeon
DAEGU
BUSAN
Kunsan
Masan
Yellow Sea
LÜ-DA
Chefoo

Hokkaido (Ezo)
SAPPORO
Otaru
Muroran
Hakodate
Kushiro
Obihiro
JAPAN
Aomori
Akita
Morioka
SENDAI
Niigata
Nagano
TOKYO
YOKOHAMA
NAGOYA
KOBE
OSAKA
KYOTO
Hiroshima
Shikoku
Tokushima

Scale 1:20.000.000
0 100 200 400 600 800 1000 km

Copyright: Vallardi Ind. Graf.

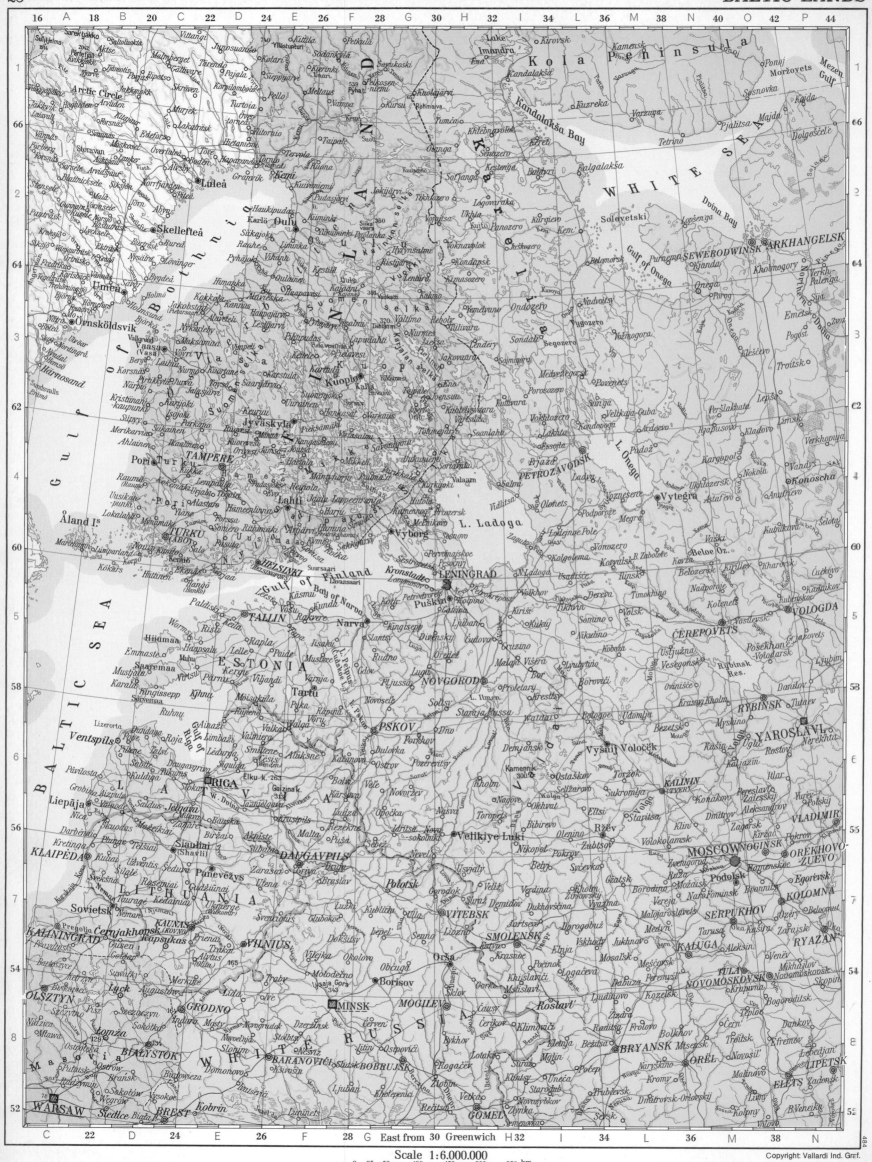

Scale 1:6.000.000

0 25 50   100   150   200   250 km

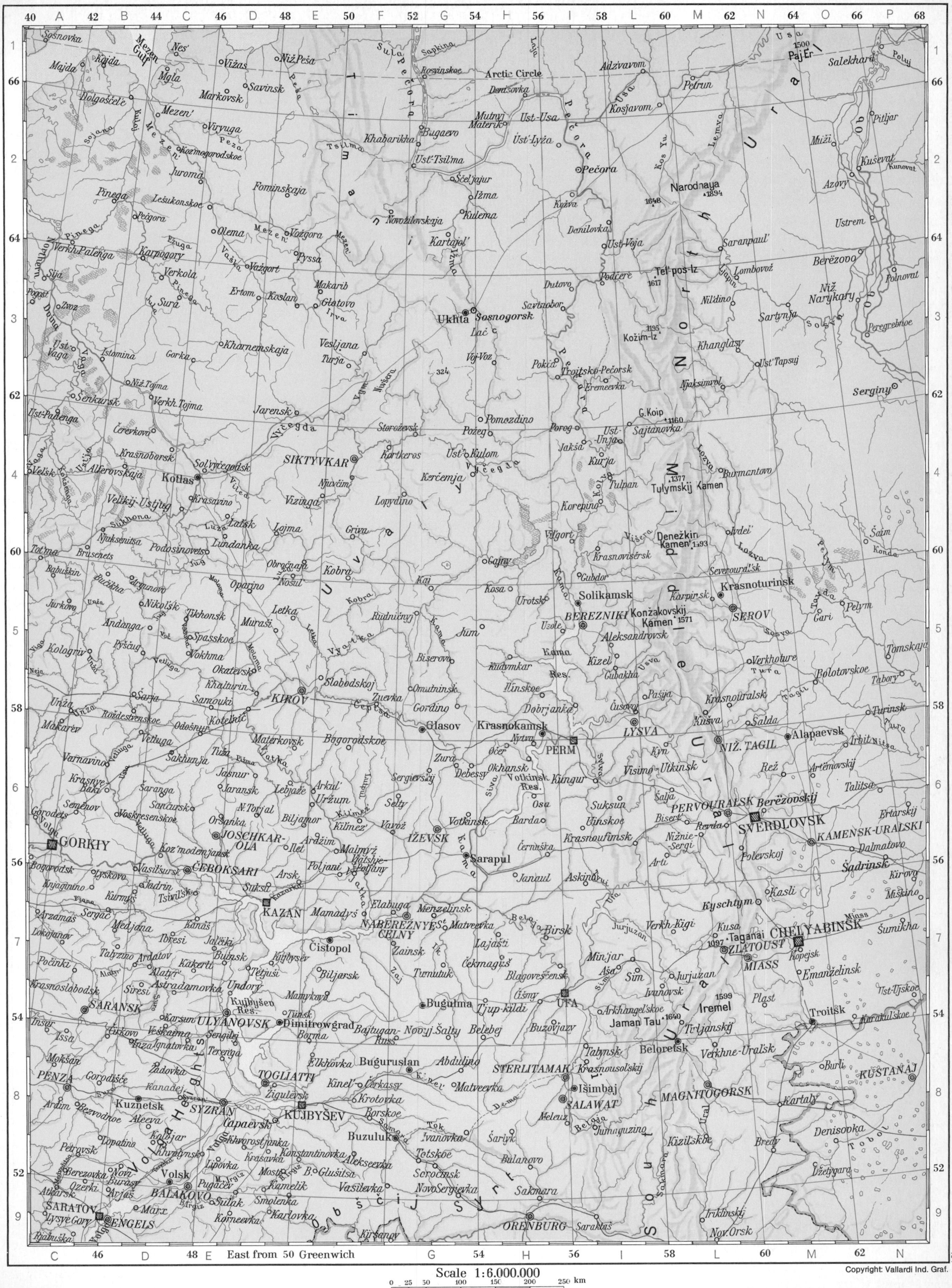

Arctic Circle

Mezen Guf

Pečora

Narodnaya

SIKTYVKAR

Ukhta Sosnogorsk

BEREZNIKI

Solikamsk

Krasnoturinsk

SEROV

Kotlas

Velikij-Ustjug

KIROV

Glasov Krasnokamsk

LYSVA

PERM

NIŽ. TAGIL Alapaevsk

PERVOURALSK Berëzovskij

SVERDLOVSK

KAMENSK-URALSKI

Šadrinsk

GORKIY

JOSCHKAR-OLA

ČEBOKSARI

KAZAN

IŽEVSK

Sarapul

Votkinsk

Kyshtym

Kasli

CHELYABINSK

Taganai ZLATOUST

MIASS Kopejsk

NABEREŽNYES' ČELNY

Bugulma

UFA

Iremel

Jaman Tau

SARANSK

ULYANOVSK Dimitrowgrad

Belebej

Beloretsk

KUSTANAJ

PENZA

TOGLIATTI

STERLITAMAK

MAGNITOGORSK

KUZNETSK

SYZRAN

KUJBYŠEV

Išimbaj

SALAWAT

SARATOV

ENGELS

BALAKOVO

Volsk

ORENBURG

East from 50 Greenwich

23

Scale 1:6.000.000

0 25 50 100 150 200 250 km

Copyright: Vallardi Ind. Graf.

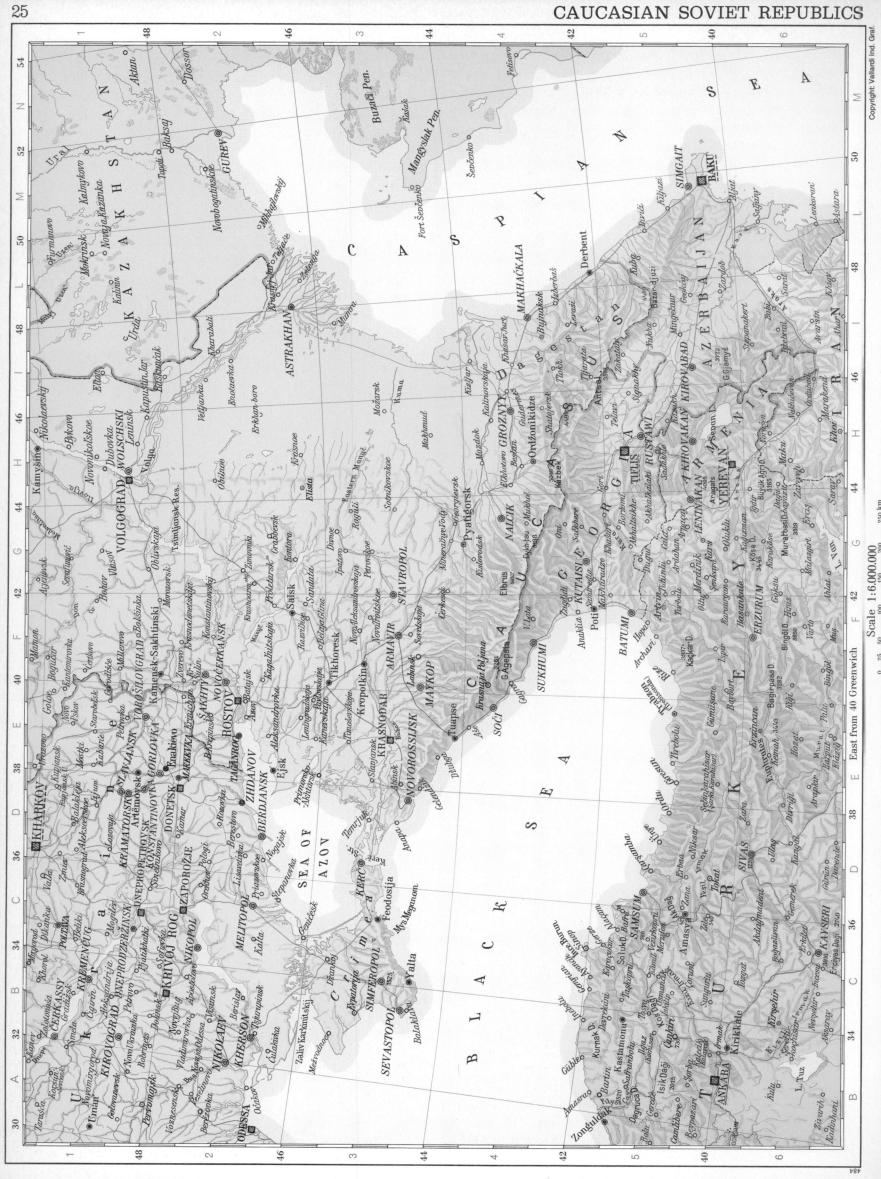

Scale 1:6.000.000

0 25 50   100   150   200   250 km

East from 40 Greenwich

U.S.S.R.: AGRICULTURAL AND INDUSTRIAL REGIONS

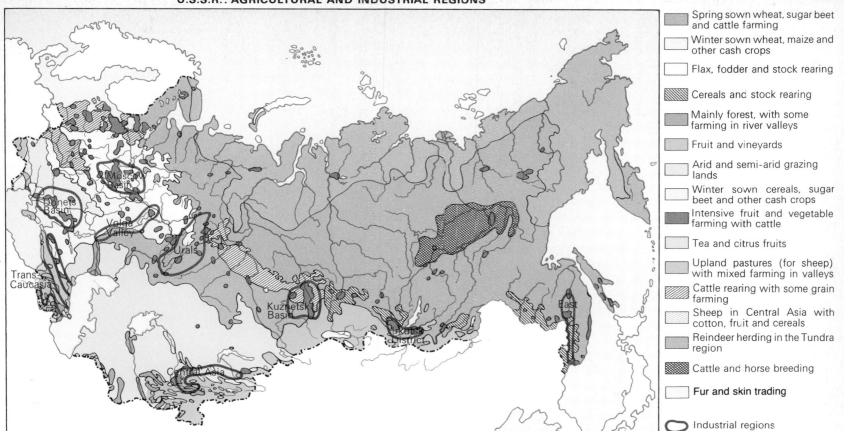

Spring sown wheat, sugar beet and cattle farming
Winter sown wheat, maize and other cash crops
Flax, fodder and stock rearing
Cereals and stock rearing
Mainly forest, with some farming in river valleys
Fruit and vineyards
Arid and semi-arid grazing lands
Winter sown cereals, sugar beet and other cash crops
Intensive fruit and vegetable farming with cattle
Tea and citrus fruits
Upland pastures (for sheep) with mixed farming in valleys
Cattle rearing with some grain farming
Sheep in Central Asia with cotton, fruit and cereals
Reindeer herding in the Tundra region
Cattle and horse breeding
Fur and skin trading
Industrial regions

STAGES OF RUSSIAN EXPANSION

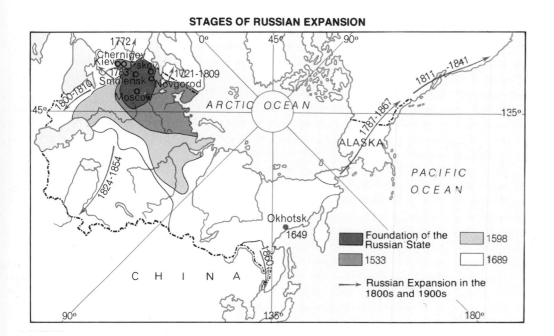

Foundation of the Russian State
1533
1598
1689
Russian Expansion in the 1800s and 1900s

THE USSR

With an area of 22,402,200 sq km the Union of Soviet Socialist Republics is the largest country in the world, occupying more than one-seventh of the world's land surface. At its greatest width it stretches nearly half way round the Earth from about longitude 20°E to 17°W, and from latitude 77°N as far south as 35°N on the border with Afghanistan. This means that there is a time difference of 11 hours between one side of the country and the other. Three-quarters of the USSR is in Asia and most of this comprises the grasslands of the Steppes. Forests also cover large areas. The climate shows wide variation over this vast country, but on the whole it is continental with hot summers and cold winters, becoming most severe at Verkhoyansk in North-east Siberia. Rainfall is usually moderate (an average of 500–800 mm per year) although it is much less in the south-west. The USSR has immense resources in fuel and timber. The population is most dense in the regions around Moscow and least in Northern Siberia and the deserts of Central Asia.

SOVIET UNION: AIR AND SEA ROUTES

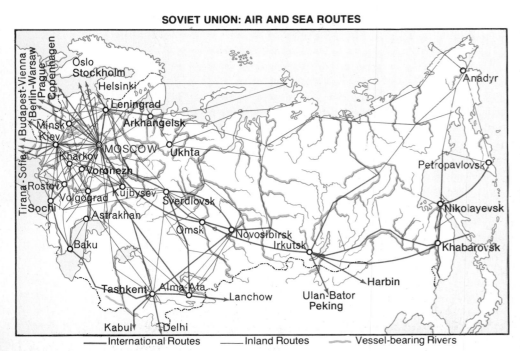

International Routes — Inland Routes — Vessel-bearing Rivers

COMPARISONS OF AREA BETWEEN THE USSR, USA AND CHINA

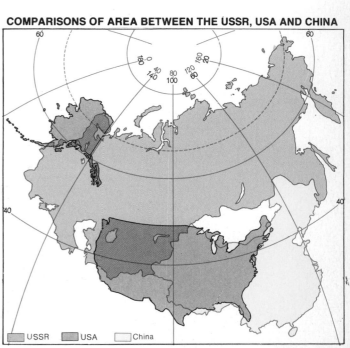

USSR USA China

26

ATLANTIC OCEAN ARCTIC OCEAN

Greenland Iceland Reykjavik North Pole 4290

Jan Mayen 2545 3830 West Spitsbergen North East Land Komsomolets I. Oct. Revolution I. Bolshevik I. C. Chelyuskin

British Isles Faeroe Is. 3970 Norwegian Sea Svalbard Franz Josef Land Severnaya Zemlya Kotelny I. New Siberian Is. De Long Is.

Ireland Dublin Shetland Is. Bear I. Barents Sea Novaya Zemlya Taymyr Pen. Byrranga Mts. Laptev Sea

Great Britain North Sea North Cape Pen. Kolguyev I. Kara Sea Bely I. Putorana Mts. 2037 Central

London English Channel Oslo Scandinavia Lappland Kola Pen. Kanin Pen. Yamal Pen. Gydan Pen. Siberian Plateau

Bay of Biscay Loire Amsterdam Berlin Jutland Copenhagen G. of Bothnia Finland White Sea Pechora Ob West Siberian

Paris Elbe Oder Stockholm L. Ladoga Leningrad Timani Ridge Narodnaya 1894 Lower Tunguska Stony Tunguska

Iberian Peninsula Lisbon Ebro Madrid Pyrenees Rhine Vistula Warsaw Riga Lake Onega Vychegda Uvaly Volga Yenisey Tobolsk Tomsk

Barcelona Alps Mt Blanc 4810 Sudeten Mts. 342 Dvina Central-Russian Uplands Moscow Kama Ural Mountains Ob 454

Balearic Is. Corsica Apennines Vienna Carpathians 347 Valdai Hills Volga Yamantau 1638 Omsk Irtysh Eastern Sayan

Algiers Sardinia Rhone Budapest 2305 Ukraine Dnieper Volga Heights 359 Uralsk Ural L. Chany 140 Barnaul Western Sayan 3491 Irkutsk

Atlas Mediterranean Sea Tyrrhenian Belgrade Danube Dniester Don Caspian Depression Astrakhan Kirgiz Steppe L. Tengiz Belukha 4506 Altai

Tunisia Sicily Ionian Sea Balkans Rhodope Crimea S. of Azov Elbrus 5633 Caspian Sea -28 Kazakh Uplands L. Zaysan Hangay Mts 4030 Ulan Bator

Tripoli Morea Athens Aegean Sea Black Sea Bosporus 2271 Caucasus Tbilisi Muyunkum L. Balkhash 340 Plateau of Mongolia

Algeria Libyan Sea Crete Anatolia Pontine Mts. Ankara Ararat 5165 Araks Turanian Plain Ili L. Issyk-Kul 1609 Dzungaria Tien Shan 7439 Turfan Depression -28

Cyprus Taurus Mts. 3347 1953 L. Van L. Urmia Caspian Sea 995 Kyzylkum Syrdarja 5485

Fezzan Libyan Desert Egypt Jerusalem Lebanon Mts. Mesopotamia Kurdistan Plateau of Iran Karakum Amudarja Hari Alai Ra. Kashgar Tarim Tarim Basin Lop Nor Nan Shan

Kufra Oasis Tropic of Cancer 1934 J. Uwaynat Cairo Sinai 2637 Damascus Baghdad Euphrates Tigris Tehran Demavend 5604 Elburz Mts. Dasht-i-Kavir Communism Peak 7495 Pamirs 7700 Takla Makan Desert Altyn Tagh Tsaidam Koko Nor Lancho

Arabian Des. 2187 Syrian Desert Nafud Desert 1500 Zagros Mts. Dasht-i-Lut Hindu Kush Ra. 8611 Kabul 1122 Karakoram Ra. 8611 Kunlun Shan 7723 Bayan Kara Shan Hwang-ho Minya Konka 7590

Nubian Desert Red Sea Dahna Des. Persian Gulf 4420 Khyber P. Indus Plateau of Tibet Trans-Himalaya Nam Tso

Mecca Riyadh Arabian Peninsula Qatar G. of Oman Makran Baluchistan Kirthar Ra. Indus Plain Great Indian (Thar) Desert Delhi Mt. Everest 8847 Brahmaputra Assam Salween Mekong

Port Sudan 2217 Rub' al Khali Str. of Hormuz Mascat 3107 Ras al-Hadd Karachi 1721 Aravalli Ra. Ganges Himalaya Ganges Plain Yunnan

Sudan Khartoum Asmara Sana 2380 Hadhramaut 3217 Aden Al Masirah I. Kuria Muria Is. India Vindhya Mts. Narmada Satpura Ra. Mahanadi Bengal Calcutta Chittagong Arakan Yoma Burma

Kordofan Bahr el Ghazal Ras Dashan 4620 Ethiopian Highlands Djibouti G. of Aden Bab el Mandeb Socotra Nagpur Godavari G. of Cambay G. of Bombay Hyderabad Krishna Deccan Ganges Delta Rangoon

Addis Ababa L. Abaya 4340 Harjeisa Ras Hafun Arabian Sea Western Ghats Eastern Ghats Bay of Bengal Andaman Sea Bangkok

L. Turkana Somali Plateau Somali Peninsula Lakshadweep Is. Malabar Coast Coromandel Coast Andaman Is. Isthmus of Kra

L. Kyoga Mt Kenya 5199 Lugh Ganane 5826 Malsan Coast 2695 Polk Str. Sri Lanka Pidurutalagala 2524 Ten Degree Channel 4360 Nicobar Is. Phuket

L. Victoria 1134 Nairobi 5895 Kilimanjaro Shebelle Mogadishu 4790 Maldive Islands C. Comorin G. of Manaar Dondra Head Nicobar Is.

Ruwenzori 2980 Pemba Zanzibar Dar es Salaam Equator Suvadiva Atoll Simeulue Nias 5400 Mentawai

L. Malawi INDIAN OCEAN

Scale 1:34 000 000
0 250 500 750 1000 1250 1500 km
0 250 500 750 1000 St.mls.

East from 80 Greenwich

Main map (left)

Alaska   Nome
Bering   Pr.of Wales
C. Dezhnev (East C.)   St.Lawrence I.

70   60   4   50   5   40

Wrangel I.
Chukchi Pen.
Chukot Ra.   2320
Koryak Ra.   Gulf of Anadyr   St.Matthew I.
Gydan Ra. (Kolyma)   2115   C.Navarin
Bear Is.
Kolyma Plain   Omolon   2222
Kamchatka Pen.
Indigirka   3147
Verkhoyansk
Cherskiy Ra.   2959
oyansk Range
Anga   Stanovoy Ra.   2800
Dzhugdzhur Ra.   Okhotsk
Uchur   2520
Sakhalin
Shantar Is.
Tartary Str.
Sea of Okhotsk
Amur   2078
Bureya   Aldan   Olekma
Manchurian Plain
Great Khingan Mts.   Little Khingan Mts.
Kerulen   Sungari   Res.
Sikhote Alin Ra.
Khanka   Vladivostok   2741
Korea Bay   Yellow Sea   Seoul
Peking   2996
Wutai Shan   3681
Hwang-Ho (Yellow)
Great Plain of China
Tapa Shan   3052
Wuhan
Yangtse-Kiang   Poyang L.
Nan Shan
Tung-Ting L.
Wu Yi Shan
Canton   Si-Kiang   Hong Kong
Hainan   1879
G. of Tonking   Tonking (Red)
Mui Varella   2598
Atacuat
Mekong
Ho Chi Minh (Saigon)
Ca Mau Pt.

Bering Sea
Atka I.   567
Andreanof Is.
Rat Is.   Aleutian Is.
Karaginl.   4775   Near Is.   7679
Komandorskiye Is.
Kamchatka Pen.
4450   Klyuchevsk Mt.
Paramushir I.   2339
Simushir I.   3658   1609
Kuril Is.   9144   8513
Urup I.
La Perouse Str.
Hokkaidō   2290
Hakodate
Honshu   Sado
Fuji Yama   2542   Tokyo
3775   Osaka
Kyoto   1708
Korea Str.   3230
Shikoku
Kyūshū   Tanega I.
Nagasaki   5996
Cheju Do
Amami Is.
Okinawa   7505
Ryū kyū Is.
Ishigaki I.
Taiwan (Formosa)   3950
Batan Is.
Babuyan Is.
Luzon   2928   Pulog
Manila   5176   2698   2428
Mindoro   Samar
Panay   Leyte   10497
Negros
Palawan   5576
Mindanao   2953
Sulu Sea   6218
Balabac Str.
Kinabalu   4100
Sulu Arch.   Celebes Sea
Bunguran Is.   Talaud Is.   Sanghe Is.
Borneo   Molucca Sea   Halmahera
Kapuas   G. of Tomini   Molucca Sea
Schwaner Ra.   3440   Celebes
Kutai   Ujung Pandang   Banda Sea
Singapore   Mahakam   5800   2429   Buru   Ceram
Riau Arch.   Butung   2871   Kais Is.
Lingga Arch.   Sula Is.   Weter   Aru Is.
Bangka   Greater   Ujung   Str.of   Alor
Belitung   Sunda Is.   Flores   Flores   Timor
Barisan Mts.   2190   Java Sea   Roti
Sumatra   Java   Semeru   3676   Bali
Jakarta   3019   Sumbawa   Sumba   Lesser Sunda Is.

Bonin Is.
Volcano Is.
10554
Daitō Is.
Yap Is.   8527
Palau Is.   9133
Caroline Islands

Sea of Japan
Korea
East China Sea
PACIFIC OCEAN
Philippines
South China Sea
Khmer   Vietnam
New Guinea   2399   Biak   Waigeo
Arafura Sea

6   30   7   20   8   10   9   0   10   130   R

Altitude legend
ALTITUDES
Feet / Metres
16404 / 5000
13123 / 4000
9843 / 3000
65E2 / 2000
32E1 / 1000
1640 / 500
656 / 200
Sea level / 0
Depression / 0
DEPTHS
656 / 200
6562 / 2000
13123 / 4000
Over 4000

Inset a–h: NORTH PACIFIC OCEAN

140 a 150 b 160 c 170 d 180 e 170 f 160 g 150 h 140

NORTH PACIFIC OCEAN
0   300   600 km

Arctic Ocean
Bear Is.   Wrangel I.   Pt.Barrow
Kolima Plain   Aion I.   De Long Str.   Barrow   2816
Sredne Kolymsk   Nizhne Kolymsk   C.Dezhnev   Brooks Ra.
Cherskiy Ra.   Kolyma   Yuzhne Kolymsk   Chukot Ra.   Kotzebue   Yukon   Fairbanks
Siberia   2320   Chukchi Pen.   Seward Pen.   Mt.Mc Kinley   Alaska Ra.
Arctic Circle   Nome   6196   3063
Anadyr   St.Pr.of Wales   Anchorage
Gydan Ra. (Kolyma)   Gulf of Anadyr   Alaska
Magadan   Shelekhov Bay   Penzhina G.   St.Lawrence I.
Koryak Range
Sea of Okhotsk   C.Navarin
Kamchatka Pen.   3335   C.Olyotorski
Karaginsk I.   St.Matthew I.   Bering Sea   Nunivak I.   Bristol B.   Alaska Pen.   Kodiak I.
4850   Ust.Kamchatsk   Pribilof Is.
4750   Klyuchevsk Mt.   Komandorskiye Is.
Petropavlousk Kamchatsky   Unimak I.
C.Lopatka   Near Is.   Rat Is.   Aleutian Islands   Unalaska I.   Umnak I.
Andreanof Is.   Atka I.

60   11   60   12   50

Inset l–m / n–o: JAVA

l   m

Sepuik   Karamian
Sumatra   Java Sea   Selembu Is.
Teluk Betang   Karimunjava Is.   Bawean
C.Krawang   Sunda Strait   Surabaya Str.
Jakarta   C.indramayu   C.Bugel   Madura I.
Krakatau I.   Bogor   Cirebon   1602   Muryo   Madura Str.
Panaitan I.   2211   3078   Careme   Semarang   Solo   Surabaya
Jungkulot Pen.   3019   Bandung   Slamet   Merbabu   Surakarta   Arjuno   Raung
C.Genteng   Pangrango   2821   Sumbing   3428   3142   3348   3088   3332
Cikurai   3371   Lawu   Semero   Buli
Yogyakarta   3265   Barung   3676
Java   3900   Barung   Blambangan Pen.
INDIAN OCEAN   1200
Christmas I.
JAVA
0   100   200 km
110 East from Greenwich

5   5   13   10   10

Inset n–o / p–q: NEW GUINEA

n   o

Waigeo   Jamursba   Equator
Tandrawasih   Tamrau   Manokwari   Biak   Ninigo Is.   St.Matthias Group
Misool   2999   Japen   d'Urville C.   Admiralty Is.
Berau G.   Sarera B.   Jayapura   Manus   Lavongat   New Ireland
Seram   Kamrau Bay   Puncak Jaya   Mamberamo   Torricelli Mts.   Schouten Is.   Bismarck Arch.
Banda Sea   Kai Is.   5030   Maoke Mts   4700   Sepik   Central Range   Astrolabe B.   Umboi   Rabaul   9140
6505   Wokam   Finisterre Range   Vitiaz Str.   New Britain
Trangam   Aru Is.   New Guinea   Papua   4100   C.Cretin   G.of Huon
Jamdena   Digul   Gulf of Papua   Mt.Victoria   Trobriand Is.
Tanimbar Is.   Kolepom   4074   Owen Stanley Range   D'Entrecasteaux Is.
Selaru   Torres Str.   Pt.Moresby
Babar Is.   Arafura Sea   York C.
Melville   Cobourg Pen.   Wessel Is.   Coral Sea
Bathurst   C.Arnhem   C.York Pen.   150
Darwin   Arnhem Land   Gulf of Carpentaria   Melville C.
NEW GUINEA
0   200   400 km
130   East from 140 Greenwich

0   14   20   10   15

Inset p–q: CENTRAL HIMALAYA

p   q

CENTRAL HIMALAYA
0   5   10 km

8189   7897   Gyachung Kang   Khartaphu   7205
Cho Oyu   West Rongbuk Gl.   Khartachangri   Karma Changri   6267
Nup La   Changtse   Karpo La   6076
Lingtren   Pumori   7547   Rapiu La   Pethang Ringmo
7145   6660   Lho La   6510   Kangshung Glacier
8006   8847   Everest (Chomolungma)
Changri   6145   7879   Lhotse   Pethangtse
Lobuche   Nuptse   7589   Chomo Lonzo   7797
Dzonglu   6840   Pk.38   Dho Pola   Makalu II
Cholatse   Tsubmu   Dingboche   7660
Nang   6542   Sheng   Chukung   8481   Makalu
Khumbu   Pheriche   Tharu
Khumbila   Koner   Ama Dablam   Baruntse   Peak 4
Thangmoche   5881   Yaral   6856   7751   Peak 3
Tesinga   Thammu   Thyangboche   8477
Namche Bazar   6623   Thamserku   7317
Bhate Kosi   Kangtega   Chamlang
Thamserku   7317

28   16   28   17

130   R   Q   48A
Copyright:Vallardi Ind.Graf.

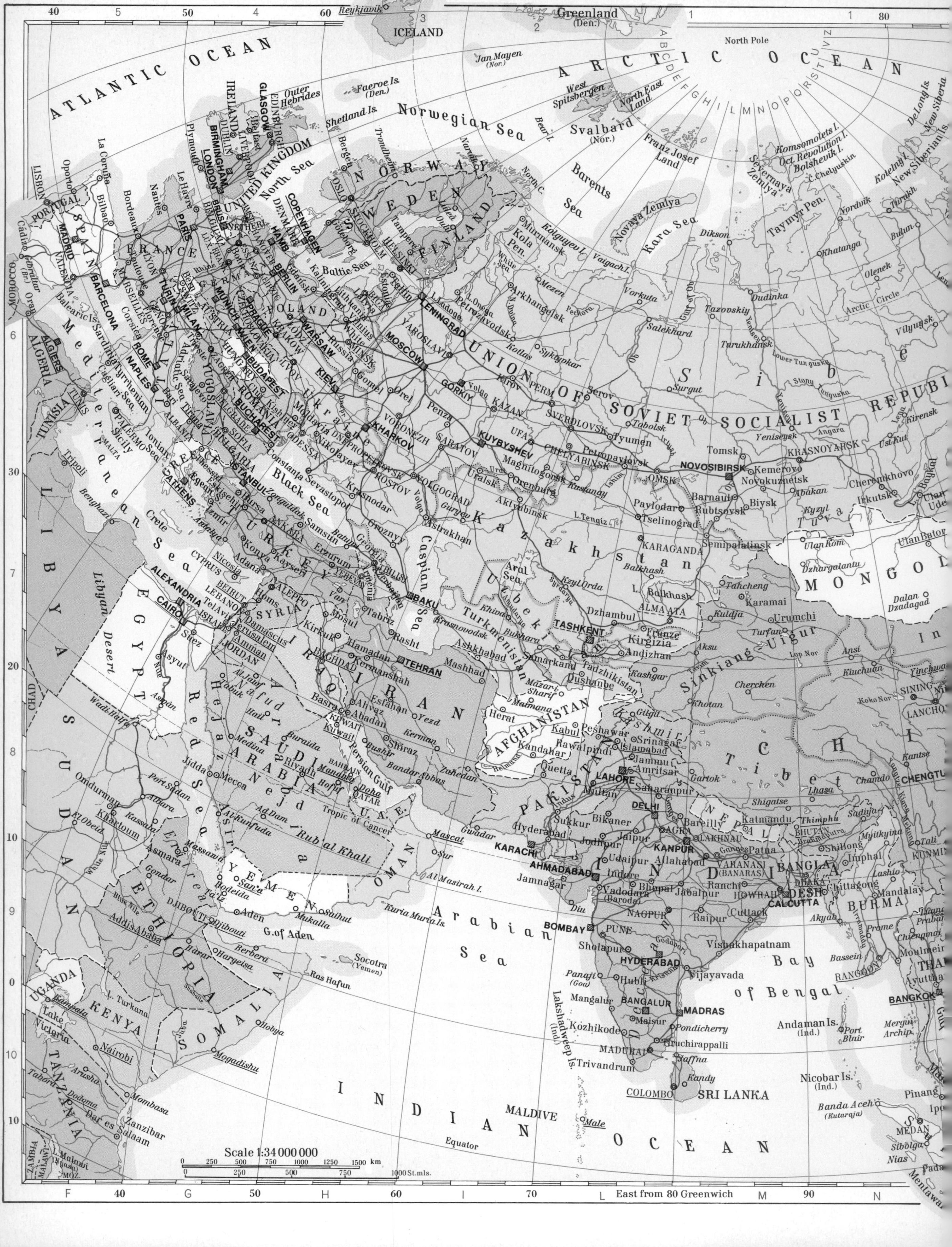

27

ATLANTIC OCEAN

ARCTIC OCEAN

Greenland (Den.)

North Pole

ICELAND
Reykjavik

Jan Mayen (Nor.)

Svalbard (Nor.)

Franz Josef Land

Komsomolets I.
Oct. Revolution I.
Bolshevik I.

Novaya Zemlya

Kara Sea

Barents Sea

Norwegian Sea

NORWAY
SWEDEN
FINLAND

UNITED KINGDOM
IRELAND
GLASGOW
EDINBURGH
BELFAST
DUBLIN
LIVERPOOL
BIRMINGHAM
LONDON
Plymouth

OSLO
STOCKHOLM
HELSINKI
COPENHAGEN
DENMARK

North Sea
Baltic Sea

PORTUGAL
LISBON
Oporto
SPAIN
MADRID
BARCELONA

FRANCE
PARIS
BRUSSELS
NETHERLANDS
HAMBURG
BERLIN
GERMANY
MUNICH
PRAGUE
WARSAW
POLAND

Murmansk
Arkhangelsk
LENINGRAD
MOSCOW
GORKIY
KAZAN
PERM
SVERDLOVSK
CHELYABINSK
UFA
KUYBYSHEV

UNION OF SOVIET SOCIALIST REPUBLICS

S i b e r i a

Tomsk
NOVOSIBIRSK
KRASNOYARSK
Irkutsk
OMSK

KHARKOV
KIEV
ROSTOV
VOLGOGRAD
Astrakhan

MONGOLIA
ULAN BATOR

Mediterranean Sea

ALGERIA
ALGIERS
TUNISIA
TUNIS

LIBYA
Tripoli

ROME
NAPLES
ITALY
YUGOSLAVIA
ROMANIA
BUCHAREST
BULGARIA
SOFIA
ALBANIA
GREECE
ATHENS
ISTANBUL
ANKARA
TURKEY

Black Sea

Caspian Sea
BAKU
TBILISI
YEREVAN

K a z a k h s t a n
Aral Sea
KARAGANDA
ALMA ATA
TASHKENT
Uzbekistan
Turkmenistan
ASHKHABAD
Kirgizia
Tadzhikistan
DUSHANBE

Sinkiang Uigur

Tibet

EGYPT
CAIRO
ALEXANDRIA
Libyan Desert

SYRIA
DAMASCUS
LEBANON
BEIRUT
ISRAEL
JORDAN
AMMAN
Jerusalem
IRAQ
BAGHDAD
Basra

IRAN
TEHRAN
Esfahan
Shiraz

AFGHANISTAN
Kabul
Herat
Kandahar

Kashmir
Srinagar
PAKISTAN
Islamabad
LAHORE
Amritsar
Quetta

NEPAL
Katmandu
BHUTAN
Thimphu

CHENGTU
Lhasa

SUDAN
Khartoum

SAUDI ARABIA
RIYADH
Mecca
Medina
Nejd
Rub' al Khali

Red Sea

U.A.E.
QATAR
Doha
BAHRAIN
KUWAIT
Persian Gulf
Tropic of Cancer

OMAN
Mascat

DELHI
AGRA
KANPUR
LAKHNAU
VARANASI (BANARAS)
Allahabad
KARACHI
AHMADABAD
I N D I A
BOMBAY
PUNE
NAGPUR
HYDERABAD
BANGALUR
MADRAS

BANGLA DESH
DHAKA
CALCUTTA
HOWRAH
Chittagong

BURMA
Mandalay
RANGOON

ETHIOPIA
Addis Ababa

DJIBOUTI
SOMALIA
Mogadishu

UGANDA
KENYA
Nairobi
Mombasa

TANZANIA
Dar es Salaam

Socotra (Yemen)

YEMEN
San'a
Aden
G. of Aden

Arabian Sea

Bay of Bengal

THAILAND
BANGKOK

Andaman Is. (Ind.)
Port Blair

Nicobar Is. (Ind.)

SRI LANKA
COLOMBO

INDIAN OCEAN

MALDIVE
Male
Equator

Scale 1:34 000 000

0 250 500 750 1000 1250 1500 km
0 250 500 750 1000 St. mls.

East from 80 Greenwich

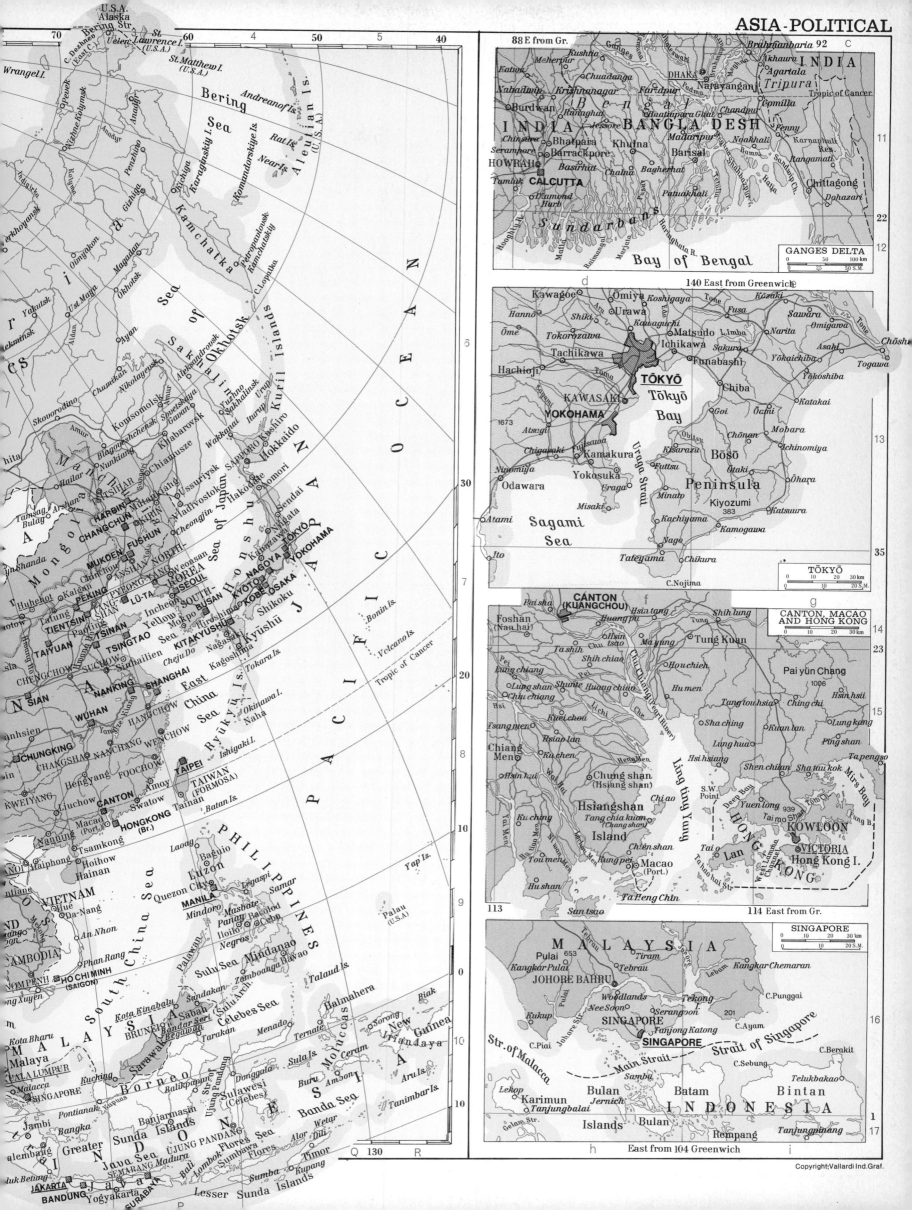

28

A 32 B 34 C 36 D 38 E 40 F 42

Konya
L. Beyşehir
Beyşehir
Karapinar
Niğde
Säimbeyli
Tavsu
Çermik
Diyarbakir
Batman
Kabilcevaz
Sürt

T U R
Seytan D. 2403
Kilbasan
Ereğli
3488 Aydos D.
Durak
Kozan
K. Maraş
Besni
Adiyaman
Siverek
Viranşehir
Mardin

Geyik D. 2890
Karaman
Tarsus
ADANA
Ceyhan
Osmaniye
Gaziantep
Birecik
Urfa
Harran
Nusaybin
Cizre
El Qāmishh

Antalya
Manavgat
Ermenak
Mağara
Mersin
Ayas
Karataş
İskenderun
Kilis
Nizip
İslâhiye

Gulf of Antalya
Alanya
Yenidamlar
Silifke
Dracik
İskenderun G.
Arsuz
Mustiniye
Membij
El-Bab
Tell Abyad
Çerlanpinar
Ain
Mo

Gazipaşa
Anamur
C. Anamur
C. Andreas
Yayladagi
Antakya
ALEPPO
Er-Raqqah
Balad Sinjar

C. Kormakiti
Alaja
Idlib
Meskeneh
Euphrates
Tibni
Tell-Sheikh Ahmed

C. Arnaoutis
Morfu
Nicosia
Famagusta
Latakia
Ma'arret en Näman
Isriyah
Deir-ez-Zor

Troodos 1953
Larnaka
C. Greko
Baniyas
Deir-Shemeyil
Hama
Selemiyeh
Sukhne
Meyadin

Pafos
Qimassol
C. Gata
Tartus
Masyaf
Tadmor

CYPRUS
Tripoli
Haba
El-Qusair
Homs
Abu Kemal

MEDITERRANEAN
LEBANON
El-Hermel
Al-Qaim
Haditha
Alu

BEIRUT
Baalbek
El-Nebq
Yabrud

SEA
Zahleh
Duma
Sab'Biyar

Saida
DAMASCUS
Syrian Desert

Sur
'Akko
Haifa
L. Tiberias
Jebel-ed
Es-Suweida
Druz
Rutba

CÆSAREA
Nazareth
Irbid

Ramat Gan
Jordan
J. Aneiza 940

TEL AVIV -JAFFA
Nablus
Es-Salt
Ez-Zarqa'
AMMAN

Pétah Tiqwa
Holon
Damietta
Port Said
Ashqelon
Ghaza
Jerusalem
Turayf

El-Matariya
Rafah
Dead Sea
Kaf

El Qantara
El-Arish
El-Khalil
Be'er Sheva
Dimona
El-Kerak
Al-Badana

El-Ismailia
Suez Canal
Et-Tafilah
Wadi Sirhan

Et-Tih
Esh-Shobak
SAUDI

Suez
Ma'an
Shaghar
Al-Jauf
Al Qarah

Nakhl
Râs en-Naqb
Sakakah

EGYPT
Eilat
El-Aqaba

Gulf of Suez
Sinai
1204
Abu Zenima
Bir es-Suweir
Al-Haql

Feiran
Al-Himeida
Hallat 'Ammar

G. Katherina 2637
Bir al-Mashi
Dhat al Haggi
Al-Musaywid

Et-Tor
Magna
Al-Khamis

G. Gharib 1751
Nabq
Tiran Is
Savrah
Al-Khuraybah
Tabuk
Ubait
Jubba

Gemsa
Ras Muhammad
Qal'at Khamis Akhadar
Jabal Sha

Hurghada (El Ghurdaqa)
Shadwan I.
Ras Mahrash
Al-Muwailih
Qal'at al-Muladhar
Qnaa

Arabian Desert
RED SEA
Duba
Dar al Hamra
Hail

Bir el-'Anz
Jaz. an-Naman
Taima
Al Qufar
Faid

Ras Abu Soma
Bor Safaga
Ras 'Ubid
Madain Salih
Al-'Ula
Taba
Qasr

East from Greenwich

Scale 1:4.500.000
0 25 50 100 150 200 km

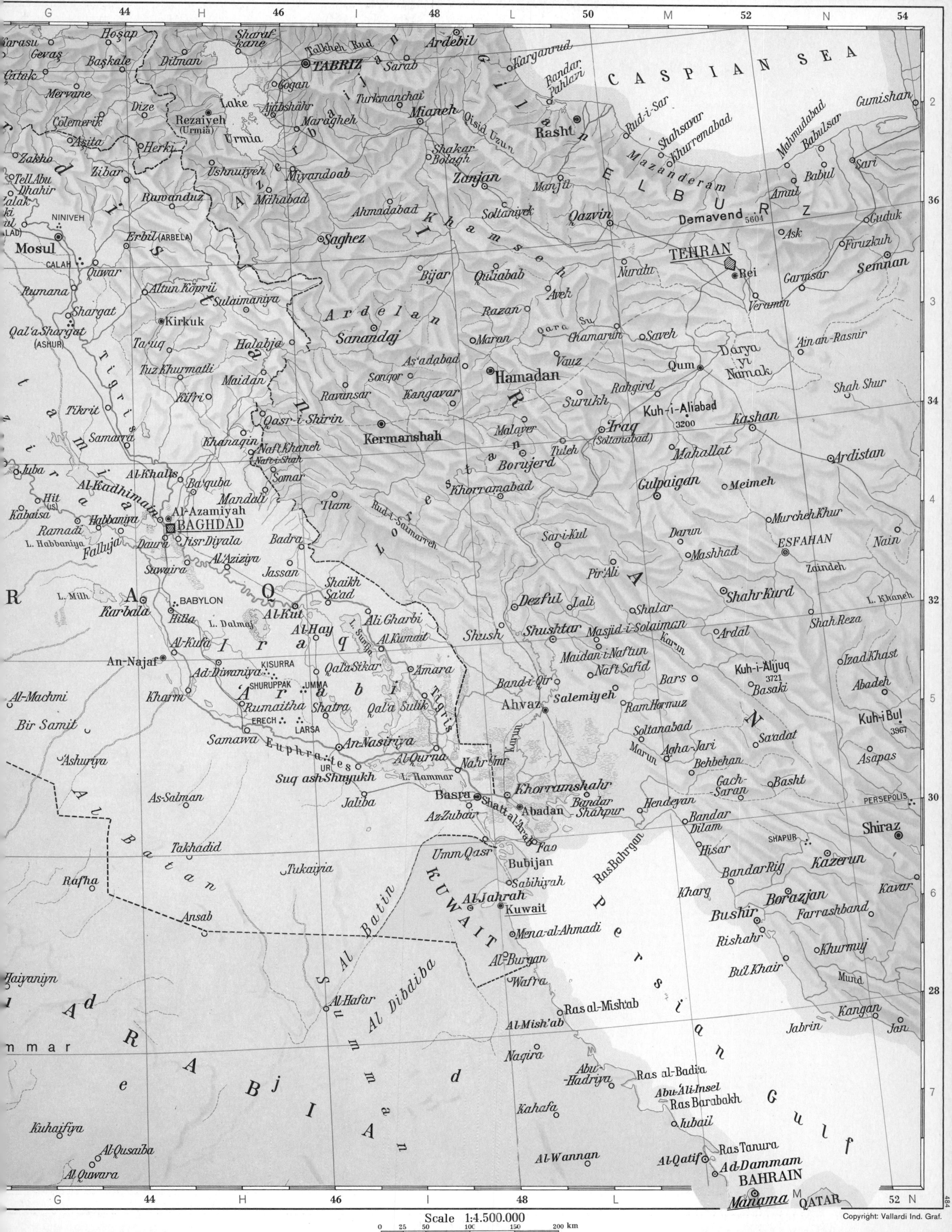

CASPIAN SEA

Grid references (top): G 44 H 46 I 48 L 50 M 52 N 54

Right edge: 2, 36, 3, 34, 4, 32, 5, 30, 6, 28, 7

Hoşap · Sharaf-kane · Talkheh Rud · Ardebil · Karganrud
Gevaş · Başkale · Dilman · **TABRIZ** · Sarab · Randar Pahlavi
Çatak · Mervane · Dize · Gogan · Turkmanchai · Mianeh · Qisid Uzun · Rud-i-Sar · Shahsavar · Gumishan
Çölemerik · Rezaiyeh (Urmia) · Ajabshahr · Maragheh · Rasht · Khurramabad · Mahmudabad · Babulsar
Asita · Herki · Lake · Urmia · Shakar Bolagh · Mazanderam · Sari
Zakho · Zibar · Ushnuiyeh · Miyandoab · Zanjan · Manjil · Babul
Tell Abu Dhahir · Ruwanduz · Mahabad · Ahmadabad · Soltaniyeh · Qazvin · Demavend 5604 · Amul · Guduk
Zalak · NINIVEH · Erbil (ARBELA) · Saghez · ELBURZ · Ask · Firuzkuh
ki ul LAD · **Mosul** · CALAH · Quwar · **TEHRAN** · Rei · Garmsar · Semnan
Rumana · Altun Köprü · Bijar · Quliabab · Nuralu · Veramin
Shargat · Sulaimaniya · Sanandaj · Razan · Aveh · Chamarun · Saveh · Darya-y Namak · Ain an-Rasnir
Qal'a Shargat (ASHUR) · Kirkuk · Ardelan · Maran · Qara Su · Vauz · Shah Shur
Ta'uq · Halabja · As'adabad · Songor · Kangavar · Surukh · Rahgird · Kuh-i-Aliabad 3200 · Kashan
Tikrit · Tuz Khurmatli · Maidan · Ravinsar · **Hamadan** · Iraq (Soltanabad) · Ardistan
Samarra · Kifri · Malayer · Tuleh · Mahallat
Juba · Qasr-i-Shirin · **Kermanshah** · Borujerd · Gulpaigan · Meimeh
Al-Khalis · Khanaqin · Naft Khaneh · Khorramabad · Murcheh Khur
Hit · Naft-i-Shah · Sari-i-Kul · Darun · ESFAHAN · Nain
Kabaisa · Al-Kadhimain · Somar · Mandali · Mashhad · Zaindeh
Ramadi · Ba'quba · Badra · **BAGHDAD** · Al-Azamiyah · 'Ilam · Pir'Ali · Shahr Kurd · L. Khaneh
L. Habbaniya · Habbaniya · Jisr Diyala · Dezful · Lali · Shalar · Shah Reza
Falluja · Daura · Al-'Aziziya · Jassan · Rud-i-Saimarreh · Shush · Shushtar · Masjid-i-Solaiman · Ardal · Izad Khast
Suwaira · BABYLON · Shaikh Sa'ad · Maidan-i-Naftun · Karun · Kuh-i-Alijuq 3721 · Abadeh
Karbala · Hilla · L. Dalmaj · Al-Kut · Ali Gharbi · Naft Safid · Bars · Basaki
An-Najaf · Al-Kufa · Al-Hay · L. Sunia · Al Kumait · Shush · Bandi-Qir · Ram Hormuz · Saadat · Kuh-i-Bul 3967
Al-Machmi · Ad-Diwaniya · KISURRA · Qal'a Sikar · Amara · Ahvaz · Salemiyeh · Soltanabad · Kharm · SHURUPPAK · UMMA · Marun · Agha-Jari · Behbehan · Asapas
Bir Samit · Kharm · Rumaitha · Shatra · Qal'a Sulik · ERECH · LARSA · Tigris · Gach-Saran · Basht
Ashuriya · Samawa · Euphrates · An-Nasiriya · Nahr Umr · Khorramshahr · Hendeyan · PERSEPOLIS
As-Salman · Suq ash-Shuyukh · UR · Al-Qurna · L. Hammar · Basra · Abadan · Bandar Shahpur · Bandar Dilam · SHAPUR · **Shiraz**
Jaliba · Shatt al-'Arab · Az-Zubair · Fao · Hisar · Bandar Rig · Kazerun
Takhadid · Umm Qasr · Bubijan · Ras Bahrgan · Kharg · Bushir · Borazjan
Rafha · Tukaiiya · Sabihiyah · KUWAIT · Al-Jahrah · Kharg · Rishahr · Farrashband
Ansab · Al Batın · Kuwait · Mena-al-Ahmadi · Khurmuj · Bul Khair
Haiyaniyn · Al Dibdiba · Al-Burgan · Wafra · Mund
Kuhaifiya · Al-Hafar · Ras al-Mish'ab · Kangan
Al-Qusaiba · Al-Mish'ab · Jabrin · Jan
Al-Quwara · Naqira · Abu-Hadriya · Ras al-Badi'a · Abu-Ali-Insel · Ras Barabakh
Kahafa · Jubail
Al-Wannan · Ras Tanura · Al-Qatif · Ad-Dammam · BAHRAIN
Manama · QATAR

A R A B I A N · Nejd · As-Summan

PERSIAN GULF

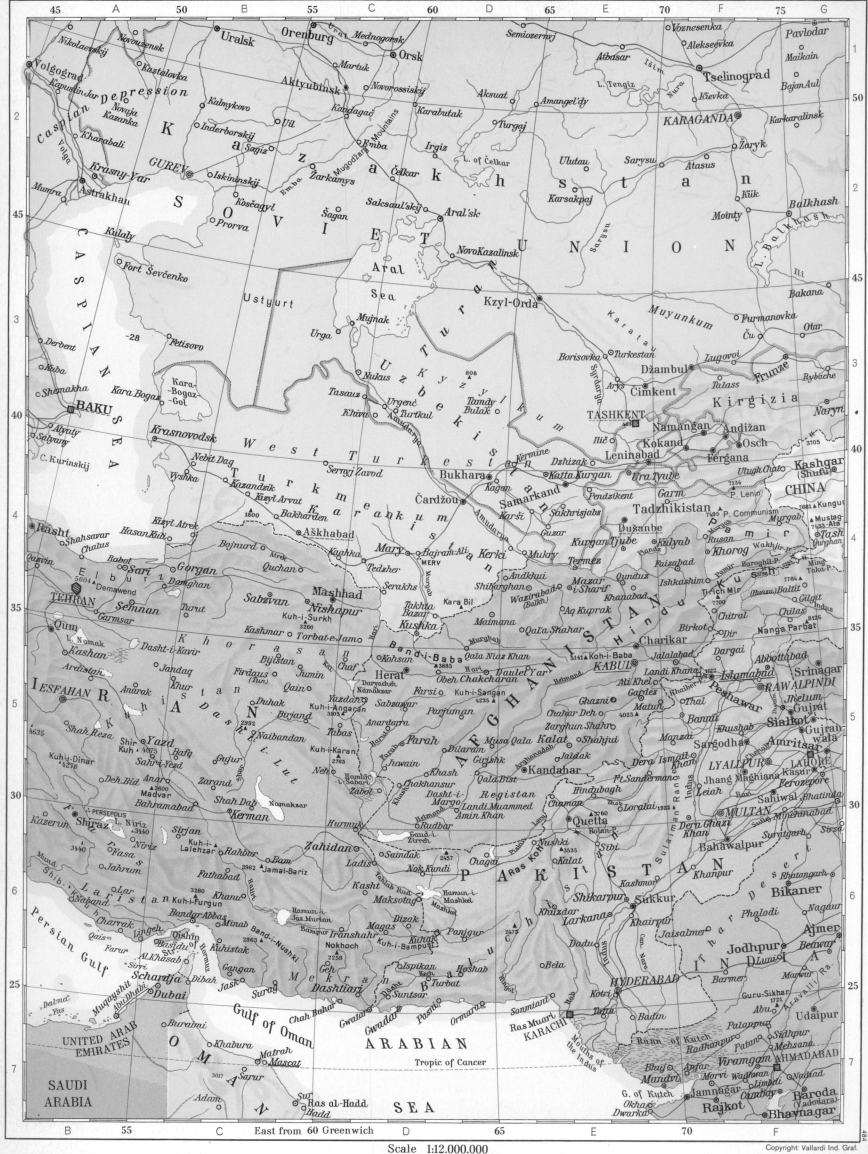

Scale 1:12.000.000

East from 60 Greenwich

0 50 100   200   300   400   500 km

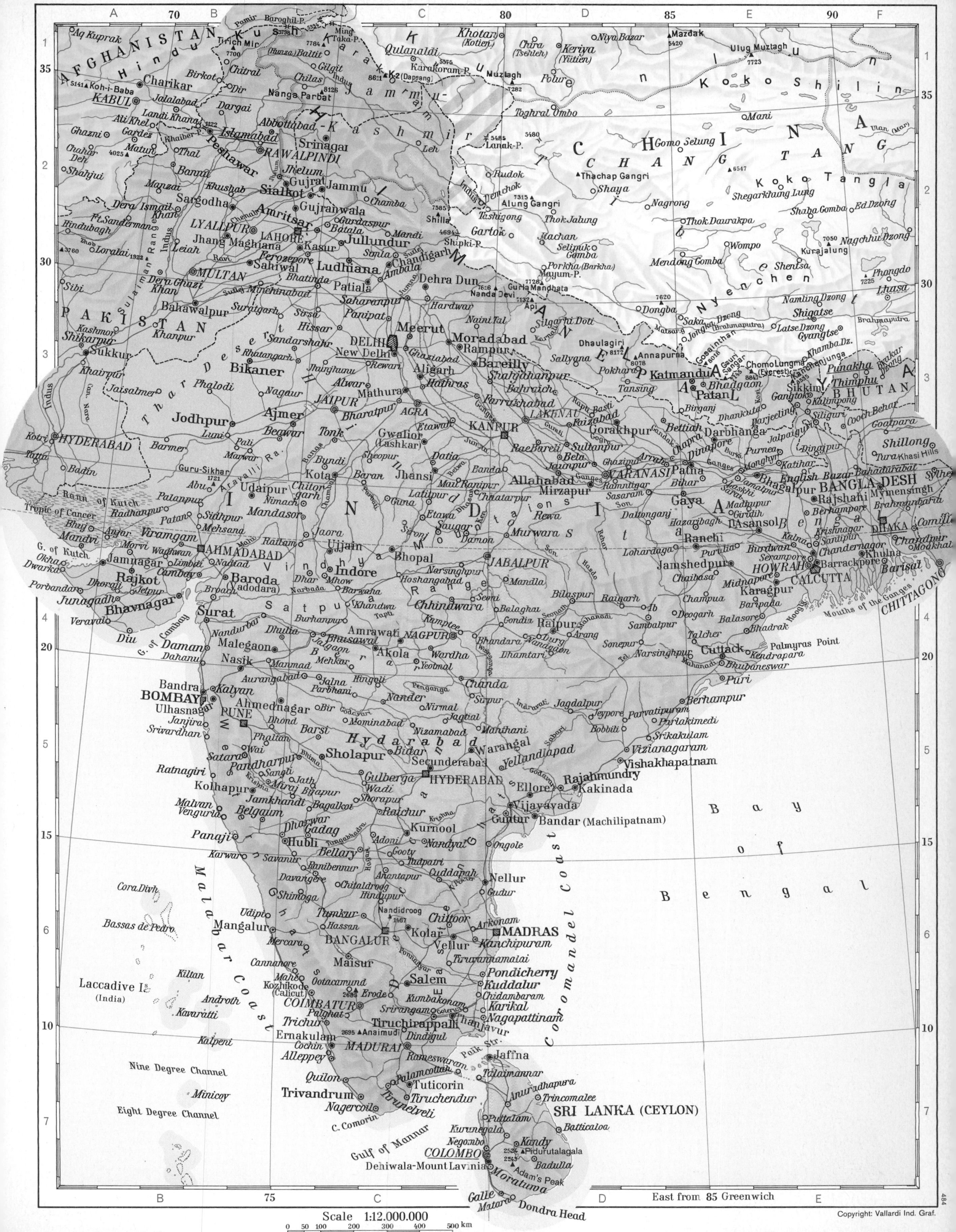

AFGHANISTAN

PAKISTAN

CHINA

CHANG TANG

Koko Shili

Koko Tangla

Nyenchen

I N D I A

NEPAL

BHUTAN

BANGLA DESH

SRI LANKA (CEYLON)

Tibet

Kashmir

Thar Desert

Rann of Kutch

Tropic of Cancer

G. of Cutch

G. of Cambay

Arabian Sea

Bay of Bengal

Laccadive Is. (India)

Nine Degree Channel

Eight Degree Channel

Malabar Coast

Coromandel Coast

Palk Str.

Gulf of Mannar

Mouths of the Ganges

CHITTAGONG

Major cities: KABUL, Islamabad, RAWALPINDI, Peshawar, LAHORE, MULTAN, DELHI, New Delhi, JAIPUR, AHMADABAD, BOMBAY, PUNE, HYDERABAD, BANGALUR, MADRAS, CALCUTTA, HOWRAH, DHAKA, Katmandu, Thimphu, COLOMBO

East from 85 Greenwich

Scale 1:12.000.000

0 50 100   200   300   400   500 km

Copyright: Vallardi Ind. Graf.

484

MONGOLIA

Ulan Bator (Urga)

The Great Wall

Gobi (Shamo)

Inner Mongolia

Ordos

Manchuria

HARBIN (HA ERH PIN)

CHI CHI HA ERH (TSI TSI KAR)

CHANG CHUN

KIRIN (CHI LIN)

MUKDEN (SHEN YANG)

Liaoning

FU SHUN

AN SHAN

LÜ-DA

NORTH KOREA

PYONGYANG

SEA OF JAPAN

SOUTH KOREA

SEOUL

INCHEON

BUSAN

DAEGU

GWANGJU

Jeju (Quelpart)

HONSHU

HIROSHIMA

KITAKYUSHU

FUKUOKA

Kyushu

Nagasaki

PEKING

TIENTSIN

Po Hai

Shansi

TAIYUAN

SHIHCHIACHUANG

Shantung

CHINAN

CHING TAO

YELLOW SEA (HUANG HAI)

Honan

CHENG CHOU

Kaifeng

Loyang

SIAN

Shensi

Szechuan

CHUNG CHING

Hupei

WUHAN

Anhwei

NANKING

SHANGHAI

WUHSI

HANGCHOU

Chekiang

Kiangsu

Kiangsi

NANCHANG

Hunan

CHANG SHA

Kweichow

KWEIYANG

Kwangsi

Kuang Hsi

Chuang

Nanning

Kwangtung

CANTON

KOWLOON

VICTORIA

Hong kong (Br.)

Macao (Port.)

Fuchien

FOU CHOU

Amoy

TAIPEI

TAIWAN (FORMOSA)

Taichung

Tainan

Kaohsiung

RYU KYU (Japan) (Nansei Shoto)

EAST CHINA SEA

Tropic of Cancer

NAM (Vietnam)

HANOI

Haiphong

Scale 1:12.000.000

0 50 100 200 300 400 500 km

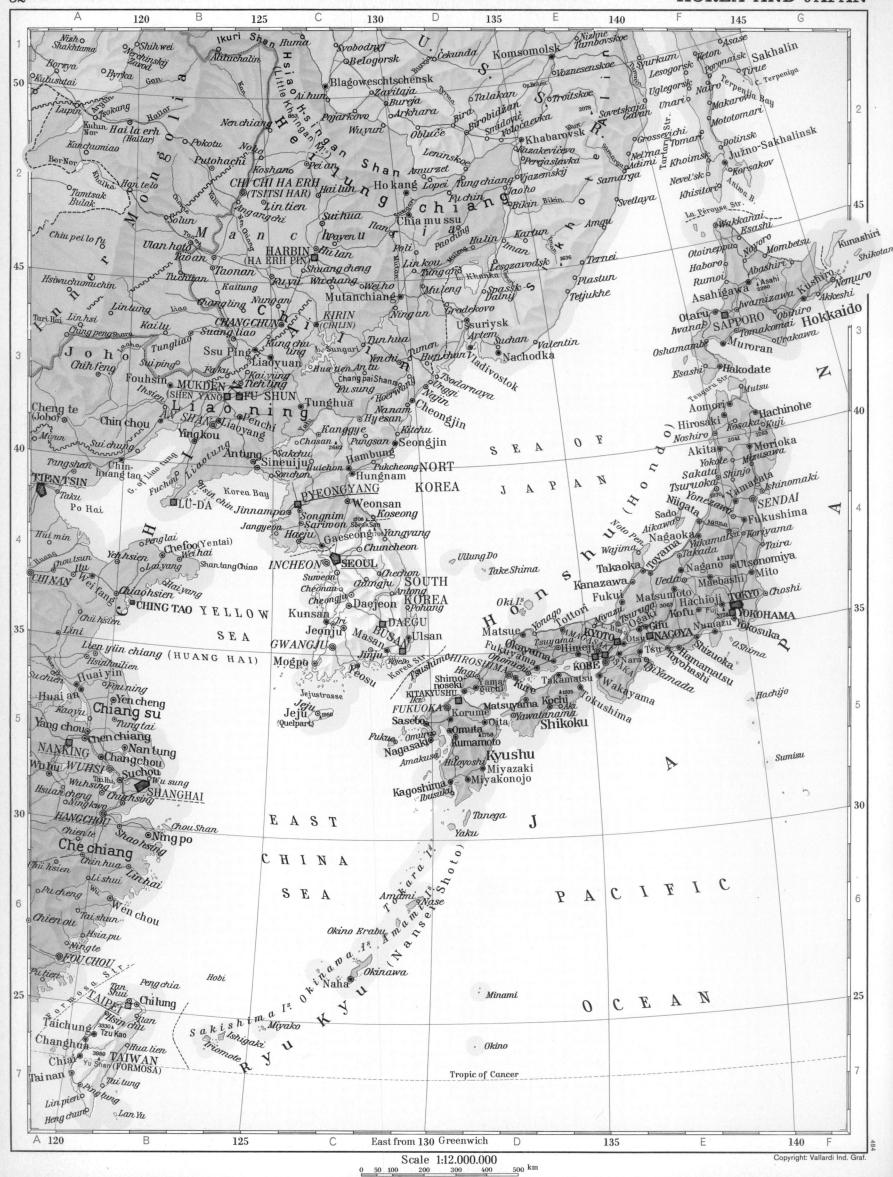

Scale 1:12.000.000

0 50 100   200   300   400   500 km

Copyright: Vallardi Ind. Graf.

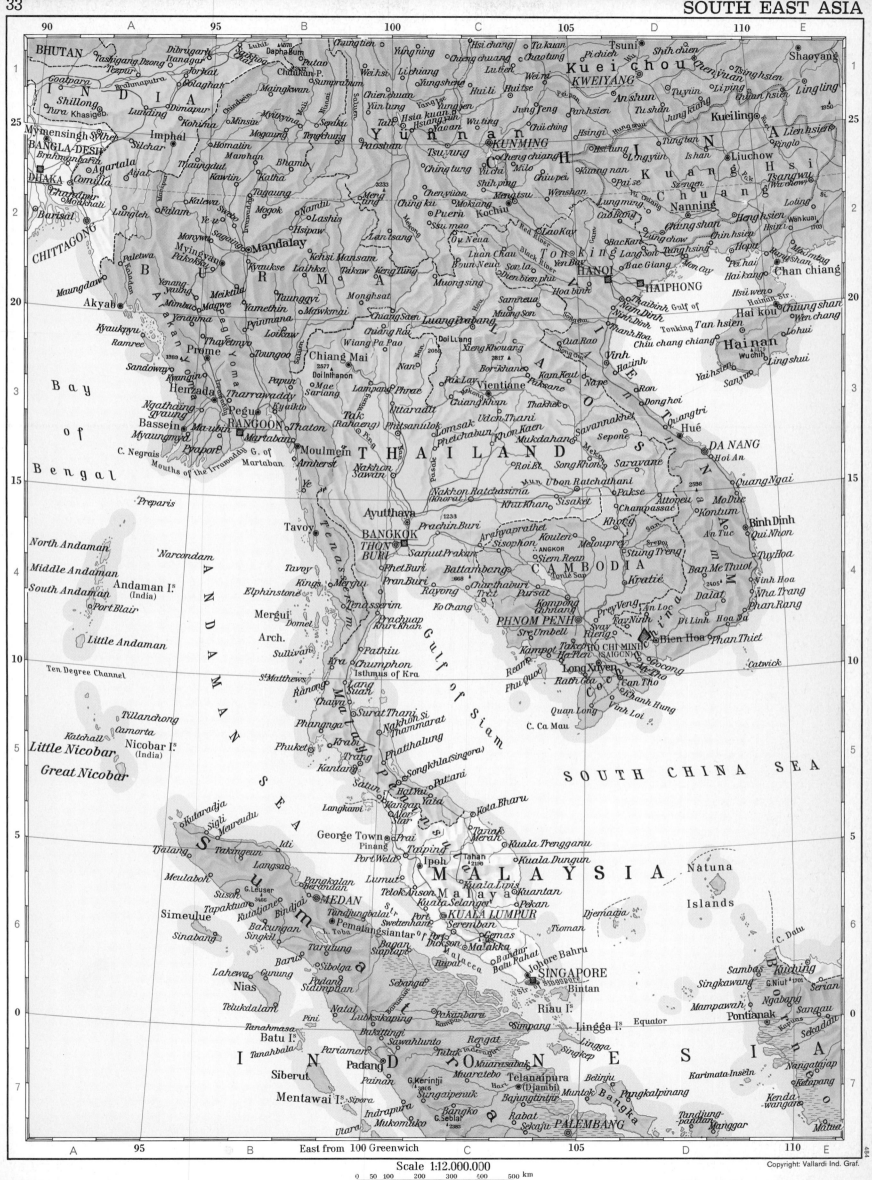

East from 100 Greenwich

Scale 1:12.000.000

Copyright: Vallardi Ind. Graf.

0 50 100   200   300   400   500 km

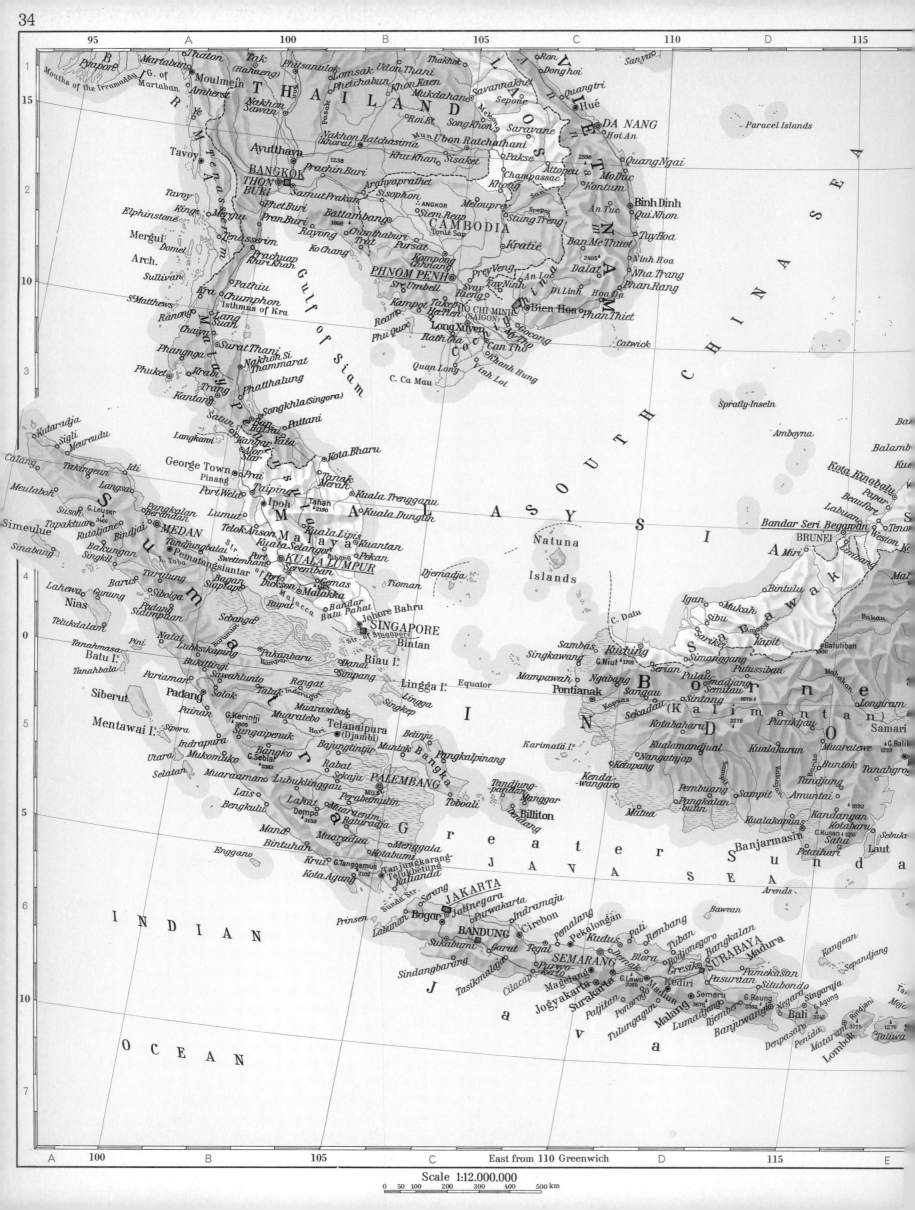

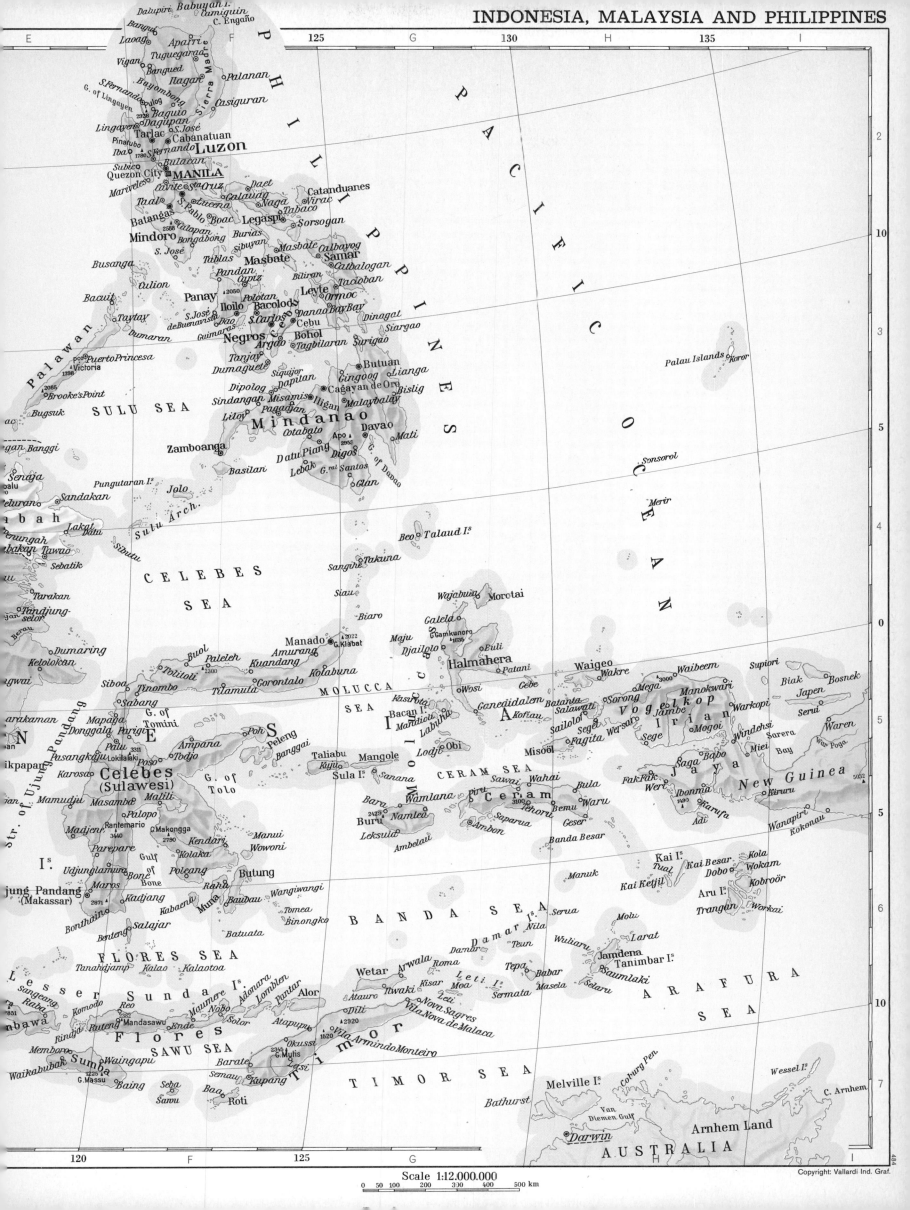

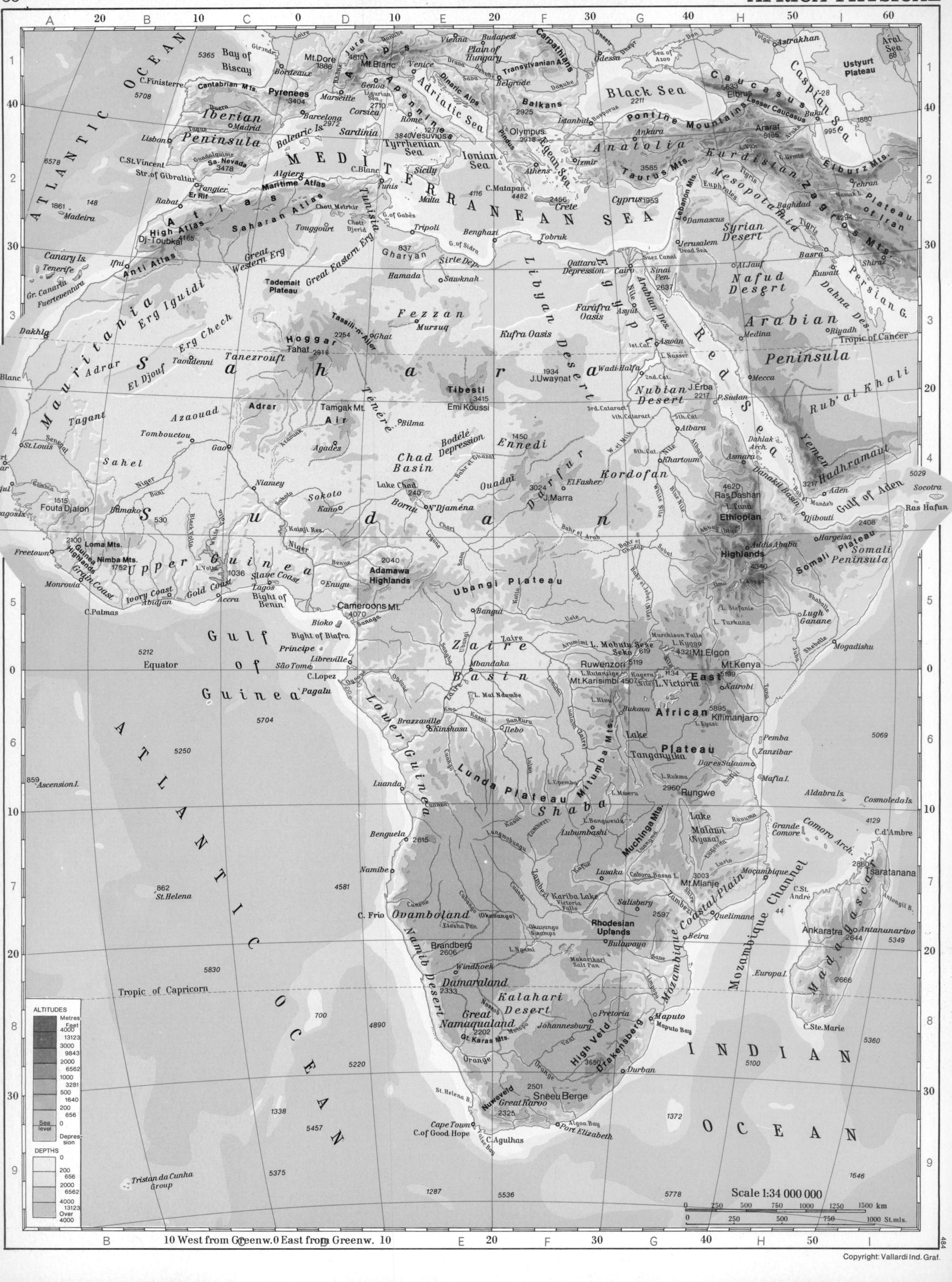

ATLANTIC OCEAN

MEDITERRANEAN SEA

Bay of Biscay
C. Finisterre
Cantabrian Mts.
Pyrenees 3404
Iberian Peninsula
Lisbon
Madrid
C. St. Vincent
Sa. Nevada 3478
Tangier
Rabat
Madeira
Canary Is.
Tenerife
Gr. Canaria
Fuerteventura
Ifni
Dj-Toubkal 4165
High Atlas
Anti Atlas
Atlas
Saharan Atlas
Maritime Atlas
Algiers
Tunis
Tunisia
Chott Melrhir
Touggourt
Chott Djerid
Tripoli
G. of Gabès
Gharyan
Sirte Dep.
G. of Sidra
Benghazi
Tobruk

Mt. Blanc
Genoa
Marseille
Barcelona
Corsica
Rome
Sardinia
Vesuvius
Tyrrhenian Sea
Sicily
Malta
C. Blanc
Crete
Ionian Sea
Aegean Sea
Olympus 2918
Athens
Izmir
Pindus
Anatolia
Taurus Mts. 3585
Cyprus 1953
Lebanon Mts.
Damascus
Syrian Desert
Jerusalem
Dead Sea
Sinai Pen. 2637

Vienna
Budapest
Plain of Hungary
Carpathians
Transylvanian Alps
Belgrade
Danube
Balkans 2925
Black Sea
Istanbul
Ankara
Pontine Mountains
Caucasus 5633
Elbrus
Lesser Caucasus
Ararat 5165
Baku
Caspian Sea
Tehran
Astrakhan
Aral Sea 68
Ustyurt Plateau
Elburz Mts.
Zagros Mts.
Plateau of Iran
Baghdad
Basra
Persian G.
Kuwait
Riyadh
Shiraz
Mesopotamia
Euphrates
Tigris
Kurdistan

SAHARA

Sudan

Mauritania
Erg Iguidi
Erg Chech
Adrar
Tanezrouft
Tademait Plateau
Great Western Erg
Great Eastern Erg
Hamada
Fezzan
Murzuq
Ghat
Hoggar
Tahat 2918
Tassili-n-Ajjer
Ténéré
Tibesti 3415
Emi Koussi
Libyan Desert
Qattara Depression
Cairo
Suez Canal
Farafra Oasis
Asyut
Nile
Arabian Des.
Kufra Oasis
J. Uwaynat 1934
Wadi Halfa
Nubian Desert
J. Erba 2217
P. Sudan
Nafud Desert
Medina
Mecca
Arabian Peninsula
Rub' al Khali
Tropic of Cancer
Aswan
L. Nasser
1st Cat.
2nd Cat.
3rd Cataract
4th Cataract
5th Cat.
6th Cat.
Khartoum
Atbara
Yemen
Hadhramaut 3217
Aden
Gulf of Aden
Socotra
Ras Hafun
5029

C. Blanc
Adrar
Azaouad
Tagant
Sahel
Tombouctou
Gao
Air
Tamgak Mt.
Agadès
Bilma
Bodélé Depression
Ennedi 1450
Chad Basin
Lake Chad 240
Ouadaï
Darfur 3024
J. Marra
El Fasher
Kordofan
Bahr el Ghazal
Bahr el Arab
Wel Nile
Ras Dashan 4620
L. Tana
Ethiopian Highlands 5340
Addis Ababa
Asmara
Dahlak Arch.
Massawa
Danakil Basin
Djibouti
Hargeisa
Somali Plateau
Somali Peninsula

C. Vert
Dakar
St. Louis
Senegal
Banjul
Gambia
Bissagos Is.
Bissao
Fouta Djalon 1515
Freetown
Loma Mts. 2100
Guinea Highlands
Nimba Mts. 1752
Grain Coast
Monrovia
C. Palmas
Ivory Coast
Abidjan
Gold Coast
Accra
Upper Guinea
Niger
Bamako 530
Black Volta
L. Volta 1036
Niamey
Sokoto
Kano
Kainji Res.
Bornu
N'Djaména
Chari
Benue
Lagos
Bight of Benin
Enugu
Slave Coast
Adamawa Highlands 2040
Ubangi Plateau
Bangui
Bahr el Jebel
Sobat
Omo
L. Stefanie
L. Turkana
Lugh Ganane

Gulf of Guinea
Equator
Principe
São Tomé
Pagalu
Bioko
Libreville
Cameroons Mt. 4070
Bight of Biafra
C. Lopez
Sanaga
Zaire Basin
Mbandaka
L. Mai Ndombe
Ubangi
Uele
Ruwenzori
L. Mobutu Sese Seko 619
Murchison Falls
L. Kyoga
Mt. Elgon 4321
Mt. Kenya 5199
Nairobi
East African Plateau
Kilimanjaro 5895
L. Victoria
Mt. Karisimbi 4507
L. Rutanzige
L. Kivu
Bukavu
Mafia I.
Mogadishu

ATLANTIC OCEAN

Ascension I. 859
Lower Guinea
Brazzaville
Kinshasa
Kasai
Kwango
Sankuru
Lomami
Ilebo
Luanda
Lunda Plateau
Mitumba Mts.
Lake Tanganyika
Dar es Salaam
Zanzibar
Pemba
Rungwe
L. Rukwa
2960
Aldabra Is.
Cosmoledo Is.
5069

St. Helena 862
Benguela 2615
Namibe
Shaba
Lubumbashi
L. Bangweulu
Muchinga Mts.
Lusaka
Lake Malawi (Nyasa)
Cabora Bassa L.
Mt. Mlanje 3003
Comoro Arch.
Grande Comore
Moçambique
Quelimane
C. d'Ambre 4129

C. Frio
Ovamboland
Etosha Pan
Okavango
Okavango Swamps
Kariba Lake
Victoria Falls
Zambezi
Salisbury 2597
Beira
Rhodesian Uplands
Coastal Plain
Tsaratanana 2880
C. St. André
Madagascar
Antananarivo 5349
Ankaratra 2644

Namib Desert
Brandberg 2606
Windhoek
Damaraland 2333
Kalahari Desert
Great Namaqualand
Gt. Karas Mts. 2202
Makarikari Salt Pan
L. Ngami
Bulawayo
Pretoria
Johannesburg
Maputo
Maputo Bay
C. Ste. Marie
Europa I.
2666
Mozambique Channel
Tropic of Capricorn

INDIAN OCEAN

Orange
High Veld
Vaal
Drakensberg 3650
Durban
Nuweveld 2501
Sneeu Berge
Great Karoo 2325
Cape Town
C. of Good Hope
False Bay
C. Agulhas
Port Elizabeth
Algoa Bay
St. Helena B.
Tristan da Cunha Group

ALTITUDES
Metres / Feet
4000 / 13123
3000 / 9843
2000 / 6562
1000 / 3281
500 / 1640
200 / 656
Sea level 0
Depression

DEPTHS
0
200 / 656
2000 / 6562
4000 / 13123
Over 4000

Scale 1:34 000 000
0 250 500 750 1000 1250 1500 km
0 250 500 750 1000 St. mls.

A   20   B   10   C   0   D   10   E   20   F   30   G   40   H   50   I   60

ATLANTIC OCEAN

Nantes   Bordeaux   La Coruña   Bilbao   FRANCE   LYONS   Toulouse   SWITZ.   Bern   GERM.   MUNICH   AUSTRIA   VIENNA   BUDAPEST   HUNGARY   Clu   Kishinev   U.   ROSTOV   Astrakhan   Aral Sea

Oporto   Valladolid   MADRID   BARCELONA   ANDORRA   TURIN   GENOA   MILAN   Venice   Florence   ZAGREB   YUGOSLAVIA   ROMANIA   BUCHAREST   ODESSA   Sevastopol   Black Sea   Georgia   TBILISI   BAKU   Krasnovodsk   Turkmenistan

LISBON   PORTUGAL   SPAIN   Tagus   VALENCIA   Palma   Balearic Is.   Corsica   ITALY   ROME   NAPLES   Bari   Tirane   ALB.   GREECE   BULGARIA   SOFIA   ISTANBUL   Esküdar   ANKARA   Samsun   Erzurum   YEREVAN   Azerbaijan   Tabriz   Caspian Sea

Seville   Cartagena   MEDITERRANEAN SEA   Sardinia   Cagliari   PALERMO   Sicily   Messina   ATHENS   Crete   Rhodes   Izmir   TURKEY   Konya   Adana   Kaiseri   L. Van   L. Urmia   Rasht   TEHRAN   Ashkhabad

Str. of Gibr.   Gibraltar (Br.)   ALGIERS   Oran   Annaba   Bizerte   TUNIS   Tripoli   Nicosia   CYPRUS   HALAB   BEIRUT   SYRIA   Mosul   IRAN

Madeira (Port.)   Tangier   Fés   Melilla   Tlemcén   Constantine   Sfax   LEBANON   DAMASCUS   BABYLON   BAGHDAD   Kermanshah   Esfahan

Canary Is. (Sp)   Tenerife   Gr. Canaria   Las Palmas   Fuerteventura   Rabat   DAR EL BEIDA (CASABLANCA)   MOROCCO   Marrakech   Sidi Ifni   Ain Sefra   Djelfa   Biskra   Touggourt   Ghadames   Tripolitania   Benghazi   Tobruk   ALEXANDRIA   CAIRO   Tel Aviv   Jerusalem   ISRAEL   AMMAN   JORDAN   Al Başrah   Abadan   KUWAIT   El Kuwait   Shiräz

El Aiun   Western Sahara   Tropic of Cancer   Tindouf   Abadla   Adrar   ALGERIA   Ft. Flatters   Ghat   Fezzan   Sabhah   LIBYA   Cyrenaica   Sirte   Siwa   EGYPT   El Faiyum   Asyüt   Suez   Al Jawf   SAUDI   BAHRAIN   QATAR   Persian Gulf

Dakhla   C. Blanc   Fderik   Taoudenni   Djanet   Tummo   Djado   Bardai   Kufra Oasis   Al Jawf   Qena   Aswan   L. Nasser   Wadi Halfa   Medina   Riyadh   Buraida

Nouakchott   MAURITANIA   Atar   Araouane   Tamanrasset   Faya Largeau   Fada   Dongola   Port Sudan   Jidda   Mecca   ARABIA   Hejaz   Red Sea

St. Louis   C. Vert   Dakar   SENEGAL   Riffa   Kayes   Bamako   MALI   Timbuktu   Gao   Bourem   Agadès   NIGER   Tahoua   Zinder   N'Guigmi   CHAD   Abéché   El Fasher   Omdurman   KHARTOUM   Kassala   Asmara   Massawa   San'a   YEMEN   Mukalla   Socotra

GAMBIA   Banjul   GUINEA-BISSAU   Bissau   Bissagos Is.   Conakry   GUINEA   Siguiri   Kankan   BURKINA   Ouagadougou   Bobo Dioulasso   Sokoto   Kano   Maiduguri   NIGERIA   Kaduna   N'Djamena   Maroua   Am Timan   Nyala   El Obeid   Kordofan   SUDAN   Wad Medani   Gondar   Adwa   DJIBOUTI   Djibouti   Aden   G. of Aden   Berbera   C. Guardafui

SIERRA LEONE   Freetown   Beyla   IVORY COAST   Bouake   GHANA   Kumasi   ACCRA   Tamale   TOGO   BENIN   Lome   Porto Novo   LAGOS   IBADAN   Abuja   Enugu   Makurdi   Yola   Garoua   CAMEROON   CENTRAL AFRICAN REPUBLIC   Bangui   Bangassou   Wau   Tambura   Jimma   ADDIS ABABA   ETHIOPIA   Dire Dawa   Hargeisa   SOMALI REP.   Eil

LIBERIA   Monrovia   Greenville   Abidjan   Sekondi-Takoradi   Benin   Pt. Harcourt   Yaoundé   Douala   MALABO   Bioko   Bata   EQ. GUINEA   S. TOMÉ AND PRÍNCIPE   São Tomé   Libreville   GABON   Port Gentil   Lambarene   ZAIRE   Kisangani   UGANDA   Kampala   KENYA   Nairobi   Marsabil   L. Turkana   Moyale   Negelli   Mogadishu

Gulf of Guinea   Equator   Annobón   Mouila   CONGO   Makokou   Ouesso   Mbandaka   Lisala   Aketi   Mungbere   L. Albert   L. Edward   RWANDA   Kigali   BURUNDI   Bujumbura   L. Kivu   L. Victoria   Kisumu   Mwanza   Arusha   Mombasa   Pemba   Malindi   Kismayu   SEYCHELLES

ATLANTIC OCEAN   Ascension (Br.)   Pointe Noire   Brazzaville   KINSHASA   Cabinda (to Angola)   Mbandaka   Kindu   Bukavu   Kalemie   TANZANIA   DODOMA   Tabora   Tanga   ZANZIBAR   Dar-es-Salaam   Mafia I.

St. Helena (Br.)   Matadi   Nzeto   Kananga   Lusambo   Kabalo   Manono   Kasanga   Mahenge   Mtwara   Aldabra Is.   Cosmoledo Is.

Luanda   Malange   Dundo   Dilolo   Likasi   Lubumbashi   L. Bangweulu   L. Mweru   Karonga   Manda   COMOROS

Gunza   Lobito   Benguela   Huambo   Luena   ANGOLA   Ndola   Luanshya   Chipata   Lichinga   MALAWI   Nampula   Moçambique   Mahajanga   Marovantsétra

Namibe   Lubango   Menongue   ZAMBIA   Lusaka   LILONGWE   Blantyre   Zomba   Nampula   Mocuba   MOZAMBIQUE   Quelimane   Maintirano   MADAGASCAR   Toamasina   Antananarivo

C. Fria   Tsumeb   Caprivi Strip   L. Kariba   Tete   Harare   Maramba   Beira   Morondava   Fianarantsoa   Manakara

Walvis Bay (South Africa)   Outjo   NAMIBIA   Groot-fontein   L. Ngami   Makarikari Salt Pan   Bulawayo   ZIMBABWE   Masvingo   Inhambane   Mozambique Channel   Bassas da India (Fr.)

Tropic of Capricorn   Windhoek   BOTSWANA   Kalahari Desert   Gaborone   Messina   VENDA   Pietersburg   Pretoria   Maputo   Toliary   C. d'Ambre   Antsiranana

Lüderitz   Gobabis   Gibeon   Transvaal   JOHANNESBURG   Mafikeng   SWAZILAND   C. Ste. Marie

Seeheim   Keetmanshoop   SOUTH   Kimberley   Kroonstad   Orange   Natal   Pietermaritzburg

Port Nolloth   Orange   Upington   Bloemfontein   Maseru   LESOTHO   DURBAN   AFRICA   Cape Province   TRANSKEI   East London

Bitterfontein   Worcester   CISKEI   Port Elizabeth   INDIAN OCEAN

CAPE TOWN   C. of Good Hope   C. Agulhas

Tristan da Cunha (Br.)   Gough I. (Br.)

Scale 1:34000000

0   250   500   750   1000   1250   1500 km

0   250   500   750   1000 St.mls.

10 West from Greenw. 0 East from Greenw. 10

Mascarene Islands

Port Louis   MAURITIUS   St Denis   St Pierre   Réunion (Fr.)

Map: Northwest Africa and Iberian Peninsula

ATLANTIC OCEAN

Azores (Port.) — Corvo, Flores, Graciosa, São Jorge, Terceira, Faial, Pico, Vila das Lagens, São Miguel, Pta. Delgada, Sta. Maria, Vila do Porto, Angra do Heroismo

PORTUGAL — LISBON, Leiria, Évora, Beja, Sines, Faro, Huelva, C. S.t Vincent

SPAIN — MADRID, Toledo, Ciudad Real, Salamanca, Ledesma, Segovia, Calatayud, SARAGOSSA, Sabadell, BARCELONA, Tarragona, Teruel, Castellón de la Plana, VALENCIA, Albacete, Villena, Alicante, Elche, Murcia, Lorca, Cartagena, Almería, Granada, Jaén, Linares, Cordoba, SEVILLA, Cadiz, Jerez de la Frontera, Málaga, Gibraltar, Mallorca, Menorca, Ibiza, Palma, **Balearic Is.**

MOROCCO — Tangier, Tetuan, Ceuta, Melilla, Chechaouen, El-Araich, Ksar-el-Kebir, Kénitra, Salé, Rabat, DAR-EL-BEIDA (CASABLANCA), El-Jadida, Meknes, Fez, Azrou, Oujda, Marrakech, Agadir, Safi, Essaouira, Taroudant, Ouezzane, Taza

Madeira (Port.) — Porto Santo, Vila Baleira, Funchal, S. Vicente

Canary Is. — Tenerife, S.ta Cruz, Pico de Teide, Las Palmas, Gran Canaria, Gomera, Ferro (Hierro), Valverde, La Palma, S. Cruz de la Palma, Lanzarote, Graciosa, Fuerteventura, Puerto del Rosario

ALGERIA — ALGIERS, Oran, Tlemcen, Sidi-Bel-Abbès, Mostaganem, Biskra, Laghouat, Ghardaia, Ouargla, Great Western Erg, Great Eastern Erg, El Goléa, Bechar, In Salah, Tamanrasset, Reggan, Adrar, Tanezrouft

Sahara — Tindouf, Taoudenni, Terhazza, Araouane

MAURITANIA — Nouakchott, Nouadhibou, C. Blanc, Atar, Chinguetti, Tidjikja, Tichit, Néma, Aleg, Boutilimit, Zouérate, Dakhla, Bir-Enzaran

SENEGAL — DAKAR, S.t Louis, Diourbel, Kaolack, Louga, Thiès

MALI — Bamako, Ségou, Tombouctou (Timbuktu), Gao, Mopti, Kayes, Kita, Nioro

GUINEA — Conakry, Kindia, Mamou, Labé, Kouroussa, Kankan

GUINEA-BISSAU — Bissau, Bafatá

GAMBIA — Banjul

BURKINA — Ouagadougou, Bobo Dioulasso

NIGER — Niamey, Tillabéry

NIGERIA — Kaduna, Katsina, Sokoto

Scale 1:12,000,000 — 0 50 100 200 300 400 500 km

West from 0 East from Greenwich

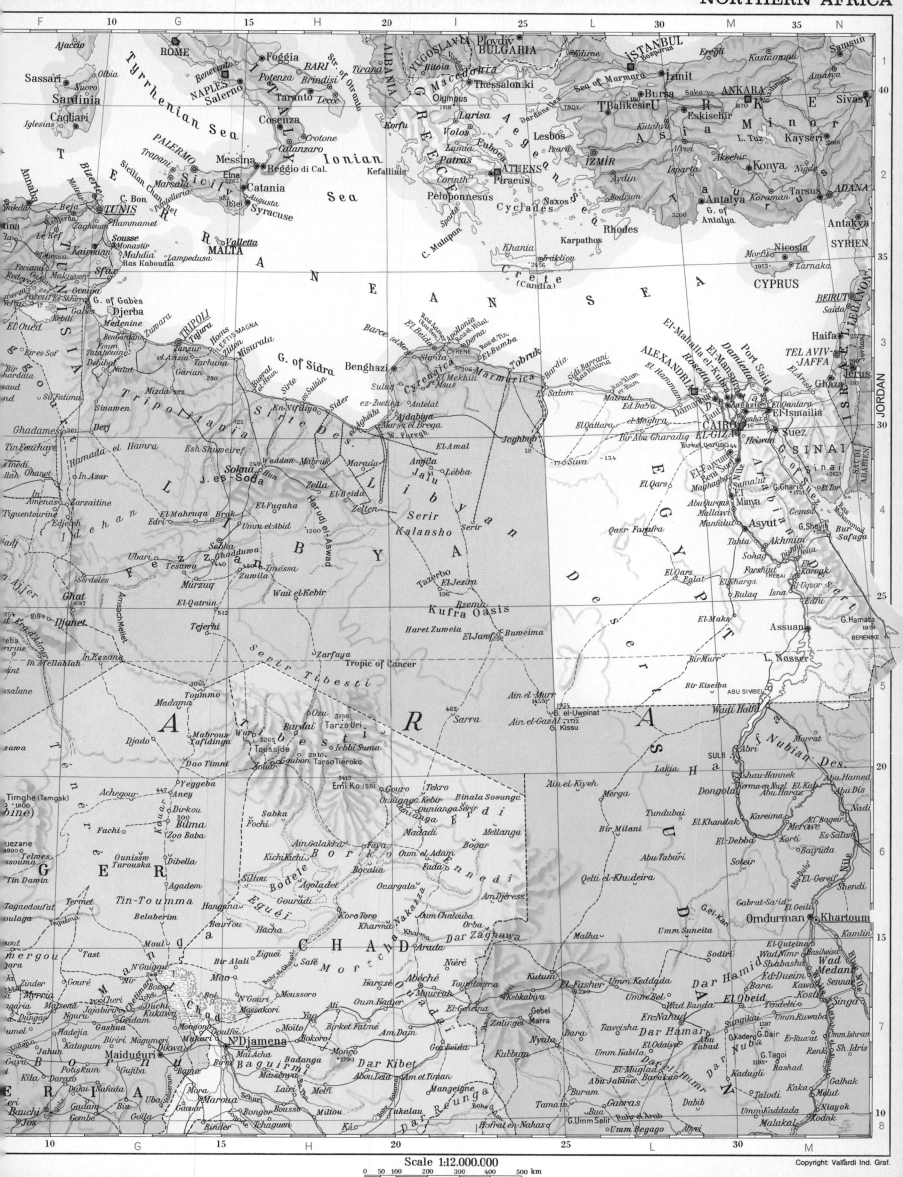

NORTHERN AFRICA

Scale 1:12.000.000

0 50 100   200   300   400   500 km

Copyright: Valfardi Ind. Graf.

EGYPT · **SUDAN** · **SAUDI-ARABIA** · **IRAQ** · **IRAN** · **JORDAN** · **ETHIOPIA** · **KENYA** · **UGANDA** · **SOMALIA** · **YEMEN** · **KUWAIT** · **BAHRAIN** · **QATAR** · **UNITED ARAB EMIRATES**

Seas and water bodies: *Red Sea* · *Persian Gulf* · *Gulf of Aden* · *Indian Ocean* · *Dead Sea* · *L. Nasser* · *L. Tana* · *L. Stefanie* · *L. Abaya* · *L. Shama*

Deserts / regions: *Rub al-Khali (Great Arabian Des.)* · *Nubian Desert* · *Nafud* · *Sinai* · *Ogaden* · *Borana* · *Bale* · *Hadramaut*

Selected cities:
CAIRO · EL-GIZA · Suez · Port Said · TEL AVIV-JAFFA · Jerusalem · Gaza · AMMAN · An Najaf · Basra · Abadan · Ahwaz · KUWAIT · Shiraz · Kerman · BAHRAIN · Manama · QATAR · Doha · Abu Dhabi · Dubai · Sharja · Riad (Riyadh) · Medina · Mecca · Jidda · Ta'if · Hodeida · San'a · Ta'izz · Mokha · Aden · DJIBOUTI · Zeila · Berbera · Hargeisa · Mogadishu · Merca · ADDIS ABABA · Asmara · Makale · Gondar · Dessye · Harar · Dire Daua · Jimma · Khartoum · Omdurman · Port Sudan · Suakin · Wad Medani · El-Obeid · Malakal · Juba · Aswan · Asyut · El-Minya · Wadi Halfa

Tropic of Cancer

Scale 1:20.000.000
0 50 100   200   300   400   500 km

Copyright: Vallardi Ind. Graf.

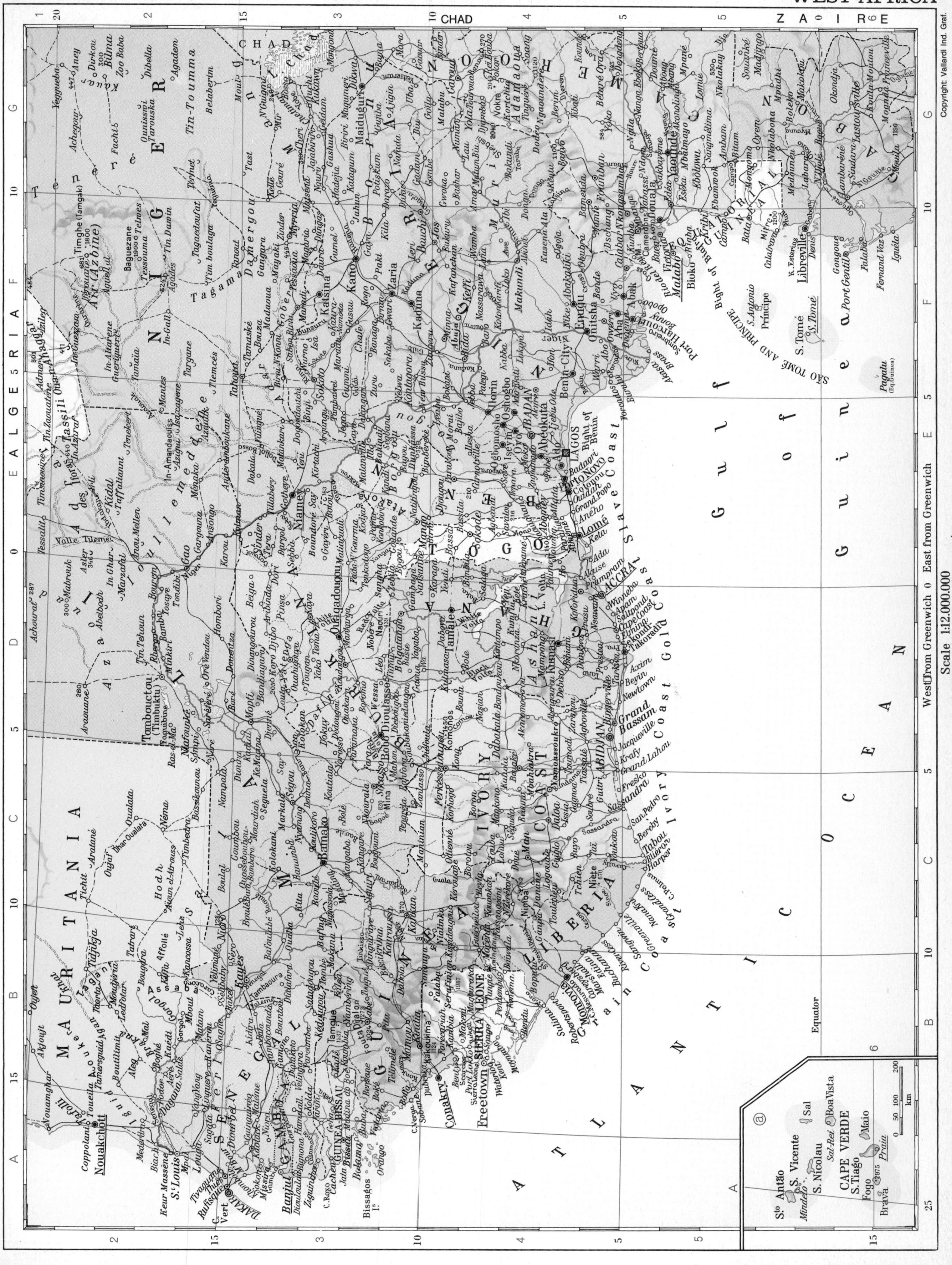

CHAD

ZAIRE

ALGERIA

NIGER

MAURITANIA

MALI

SENEGAL

GAMBIA

GUINEA-BISSAU

GUINEA

SIERRA LEONE

LIBERIA

IVORY COAST

GHANA

TOGO

BENIN

NIGERIA

CAMEROON

EQUATORIAL GUINEA

GABON

Aïr (Azbine)

Adamaoua

Ashanti

Borgou

Gold Coast

Slave Coast

Ivory Coast

Grain Coast

Bight of Benin

Bight of Bonny

Gulf of Guinea

ATLANTIC OCEAN

SÃO TOMÉ AND PRÍNCIPE

CAPE VERDE

Nouakchott · St. Louis · DAKAR · Banjul · Bissau · CONAKRY · Freetown · MONROVIA · ABIDJAN · Grand Bassam · Takoradi · Sekondi · Cape Coast · Elmina · ACCRA · Lomé · Porto-Novo · LAGOS · IBADAN · Abeokuta · Benin-City · Onitsha · Enugu · Port Harcourt · Calabar · Victoria · Douala · Yaoundé · Libreville · Port Gentil

Kano · Zaria · Kaduna · Katsina · Sokoto · Maiduguri · Jos · Bauchi

Timbuktu (Tombouctou) · Gao · Mopti · Bamako · Ségou · Kayes

Niamey · Zinder · Agadès · Tahoua

Ouagadougou · Bobo-Dioulasso

Agadem · Bilma · Djado

Malabo · Bioko · Fernando Po · S. Tomé · Príncipe · Pagalu (Eq. Guinea)

Scale 1:12.000.000
West from Greenwich 0 East from Greenwich

0 50 100 200 300 400 500 km

Copyright: Vallardi Ind. Graf.

Equator

Scale 1:12.000.000

0 50 100 200 300 400 500 km

East from 20 Greenwich

NORTH AMERICA - PHYSICAL

ASIA

ARCTIC OCEAN

Greenland Sea

North Pole

Greenland

Iceland

Beaufort Sea

Queen Elizabeth Islands

Baffin Bay

Baffin Island

Davis Strait

Brooks Ra.

Alaska

Alaska Range
Mt. McKinley 6198

Yukon

Gulf of Alaska

Mt. Logan 6050

Mt. St. Elias 5489

Mackenzie Mts.

Franklin Mts.

Barren Grounds

Great Bear Lake

Arctic Circle

Great Slave Lake

Hudson Bay

Hudson Strait

Ungava Pen.

Labrador

Newfoundland

Queen Charlotte Is.

Vancouver I.

ROCKY MOUNTAINS

Coast Range

Mackenzie Lowlands

Canadian Prairies

L. Athabasca

Reindeer Lake

Lake Winnipeg

L. Manitoba

Winnipeg

L. Superior

L. Huron

L. Michigan

L. Ontario

L. Erie

Niagara Falls

Laurentian Plateau

Quebec

Ottawa

New England

Gaspé Pen.

Nova Scotia

St. John's

Grand Banks

Columbia Plateau

Cascade Range

Blue Mts.

Yellowstone National Park

Black Hills 2176

Great Plains

Interior Lowlands

Chicago

Allegheny Mts.

Appalachian Mts.

Mt. Mitchell 2038

New York

Boston

C. Cod

Long I.

C. Hatteras

Chesapeake Bay

Piedmont Plat.

PACIFIC OCEAN

C. Mendocino

Mt. Shasta 4317

Sierra Nevada

Great Basin

Wasatch Ra.

Front Ranges

Mt. Elbert 4401

Colorado Plateau

Grand Canyon

Blanca Pk. 4386

Mt. Whitney 4418

Death Valley -85

Salton S. -75

Great Salt Lake

Denver

Kansas

St. Louis

Ozark Plateau

Mississippi

Ohio

Tennessee

Arkansas

Red

San Francisco

Los Angeles

San Diego

Pt. Concepción

Llano Estacado

El Paso

Rio Grande

Pecos

Brazos

Colorado

Gulf Coastal Plain

New Orleans

Mississippi Delta

Savannah

Florida

C. Canaveral

C. Sable

Miami

Bahama Islands

Bermuda Is.

ATLANTIC OCEAN

Tropic of Cancer

Lower California

Gulf of California

Guadalupe I.

Cedros I.

Western Sierra Madre

Eastern Sierra Madre

Mexican Plateau

Corpus Christi Bay

Gulf of Mexico

Havana

Cuba

Florida Strait

Andros

Greater Antilles

Hispaniola

Puerto Rico

Jamaica

Caribbean Sea

Revillagigedo Is.

C. San Lucas

Tres Marías Is.

C. Corrientes

Colima

Mexico

Popocatepetl 5452

Citlaltépetl 5700

Southern Sa. Madre

Isthmus of Tehuantepec

Yucatán

Gulf of Campeche

Gulf of Honduras

Cayman Is.

Tajumulco 4220

San Salvador

Honduras

L. Nicaragua

G. of Fonseca

C. Gracias a Dios

Sierra Nevada de Santa Marta

Maracaibo

Caracas

Curaçao

Clipperton I.

Cocos I.

Malpelo I.

Isthmus of Panama

G. of Panama

ANDES

Western Cord.

Central Cord.

Eastern Cord.

Bogotá

Quito

Chimborazo 6272

Galápagos Is.

Equator

Amazon

Orinoco

Llanos

Scale 1 : 34 000 000

| km | 0 | 250 | 500 | 750 | 1000 | 1250 | 1500 km |
| St. mls | 0 | 250 | 500 | 750 | 1000 St. mls. |

ALTITUDES

Metres	Feet
5000	16404
4000	13123
3000	9843
2000	6562
1000	3281
500	1640
200	656
0	0
Sea level	
Depression	

DEPTHS

Metres	Feet
0	0
200	656
2000	6562
4000	13123
Over 4000	

West from 100 Greenwich

North Pole

U.S.S.R.

ARCTIC OCEAN

Wrangel I.

Chukchi Pen.

C. Dezhnev (East C.)

G. of Anadyr
St. Lawrence I.

Bering Strait
C. Prof. Wales
Seward Pen.
Nome

Bering Sea

Nunivak I.

Pribilof I.

Aleutian Is.

Alaska Peninsula

Kodiak I.

Gulf of Alaska

Alexander Arch.

Queen Charlotte Is.

Vancouver I.

Beaufort Sea

Jan Mayen (Nor.)

Shetland Is.
Orkney Is.
Faeroe Is. (Den.)

ICELAND
Reykjavik

Greenland

Peary Land
King Frederik VIII Land
King Christian X Land
King Christian IX Land
King Frederik VI Coast

Denmark Strait

Knud Rasmussen Land
Thule
Etah
Melville Bay
Upernavik (Den.)
Disko
Godhavn
Godthåb
Julianehåb
C. Farewell

Davis Strait

Baffin Bay

ATLANTIC OCEAN

Queen Elizabeth Islands
Sverdrup Is.
Parry Is.
Melville I.
Bathurst I.
Devon I.
Ellesmere I.
Lancaster Sound
Somerset
Prince of Wales I.
Boothia Pen.
Prof. I.

Viscount Melville Sound
Banks I.
Victoria Island

Baffin Island

Foxe Basin
Foxe Pen.
Melville Pen.
Southampton
Hudson Strait
Resolution I.

Ungava Bay
Ungava Pen.
Hebron

Newfoundland

ALASKA

Mt. McKinley
Anchorage
Fairbanks
Yukon

Aklavik
Mackenzie
Dawson
Whitehorse
Skagway
Juneau

Yukon Territory

Mt. Logan 6000

Coppermine
Great Bear Lake
Port Radium
Norman Wells
Fort Simpson
Great Slave Lake
Fort Resolution

Arctic Circle

Northwest Territories

Reindeer
L. Dubawnt

Churchill

Hudson Bay

Port Nelson
Belcher Is.
Fort George

Port Harrison
Fort Chimo

CANADA

British Columbia
Prince Rupert
Prince George

Peace
Dawson Creek
L. Athabasca
Ft. McMurray
Athabasca

Alberta
Edmonton
Calgary
Lethbridge
Medicine Hat

Saskatchewan
Saskatoon
Prince Albert
Regina

Manitoba
L. Winnipeg
Winnipeg

Ontario
L. Nipigon
Thunder Bay
L. Superior
Sudbury
North Bay
Cochrane
Moosonee

Quebec
Chicoutimi
Quebec
Ottawa
Montreal
Toronto

Sept Iles
St. Lawrence
Anticosti I.
Gaspé
Cap aux Basques
New Brunswick
Newfoundland
St. John's
Miquelon I. (Fr.)
Prince Edward I.
Sydney
Cape Breton I.
Charlottetown
Fredericton
Saint John
Maine
Halifax
Nova Scotia
Battle Harbour
Schefferville

Vancouver
Victoria
Seattle
Tacoma
Spokane
Wash.
Portland
Salem
Oregon
Medford
C. Mendocino

UNITED STATES

Montana
Butte
Idaho
Boise
Helena
North Dakota
Bismarck
South Dakota
Wyoming
Cheyenne
Nebraska
Omaha
Des Moines
Iowa
Minneapolis
St. Paul
Minnesota
Wisconsin
Milwaukee
Michigan
Grand Rapids
Duluth
L. Huron
Detroit
Toledo
L. Erie
Cleveland
Buffalo
Pittsburgh
Ohio
Columbus
Cincinnati
Indiana
Indianapolis
Illinois
Chicago
St. Louis
Kansas City
Kansas
Wichita
Colorado
Denver
Pueblo
Trinidad
Utah
Salt Lake City
Ogden
Great Salt Lake
Nevada
Las Vegas
California
Sacramento
Oakland
San Francisco
Fresno
Mt. Whitney 4418
Los Angeles
Long Beach
San Diego
Arizona
Phoenix
Tucson
New Mexico
Albuquerque
Santa Fe
Amarillo
Oklahoma
Oklahoma City
Tulsa
Texas
Fort Worth
Dallas
Austin
El Paso
San Antonio
Houston
Galveston
Corpus Christi
Laredo

Missouri
Nashville
Tennessee
Memphis
Little Rock
Arkansas
Kentucky
West Virginia
Virginia
Richmond
Washington
Baltimore
Philadelphia
New York
New Haven
Albany
Boston
C. Cod
N.H.
Vt.
Portland
New Jersey
Bermuda I. (Br.)

North Carolina
Charlotte
C. Hatteras
South Carolina
Charleston
Atlanta
Georgia
Savannah
Alabama
Montgomery
Mississippi
Jackson
Louisiana
Baton Rouge
New Orleans
Florida
Jacksonville
Tampa
Miami
Key West
Florida Str.

BAHAMA
Gr. Bahama
Gr. Abaco I.
Nassau
Eleuthera I.
S. Salvador
Long I.
Gr. Inagua I.

Gulf of Mexico

CUBA
Havana
Pinar del Rio
Sta. Clara
Camagüey
Santiago de Cuba
Guantánamo
I. de Pinos
Yucatán Str.
Cayman Is. (Br.)

JAMAICA
Kingston

HAITI
Port-au-Prince

DOMINICAN REP.
Santo Domingo
Puerto Rico (U.S.A.)
San Juan
Virgin Is. (U.S.A.)

Caribbean Sea

MEXICO
Mexicali
Hermosillo
Ciudad Juárez
Chihuahua
Guaymas
Torreón
Saltillo
Monterrey
Nuevo Laredo
Durango
Mazatlán
Culiacán
La Paz
Cedros I.
Guadalupe I. (Mex.)
Lower California
Gulf of California
San Luis Potosí
Tampico
León
Guadalajara
Mexico
Puebla
Veracruz
Manzanillo
Acapulco
Oaxaca
Coatzacoalcos
G. of Campeche
Mérida
Campeche
Tehuantepec
G. of Tehuantepec

Repúblicas de California
Revillagigedo Is. (Mex.)

Clipperton (Fr.)

Tropic of Cancer

BELIZE
Belmopan
GUATEMALA
Guatemala
San Salvador
EL SALVADOR
HONDURAS
Tegucigalpa
NICARAGUA
Managua
Bluefields
L. Nicaragua
COSTA RICA
San José
PANAMA
Panama
Colón
Las Tablas
Panama Canal Zone

Cocos I. (Cost.)
Malpelo I. (Col.)

VENEZUELA
Caracas
Maracaibo
Barranquilla
Cartagena
Barquisimeto
Bucaramanga
S. Fernando de Ap.

COLOMBIA
Medellín
Manizales
Tunja
Bogotá
Cali
Ibagué
Neiva
Pasto

ECUADOR
Quito
Guayaquil
Ibarra
Galápagos Is. (Ec.)
Isabela

PERU
Iquitos
Putumayo

BRAZIL

PACIFIC OCEAN

Equator

Scale 1:34 000 000

0 250 500 750 1000 1250 1500 km
0 250 500 750 1000 St. mls.

West from 100 Greenwich

Copyright: Vallardi Ind. Graf.

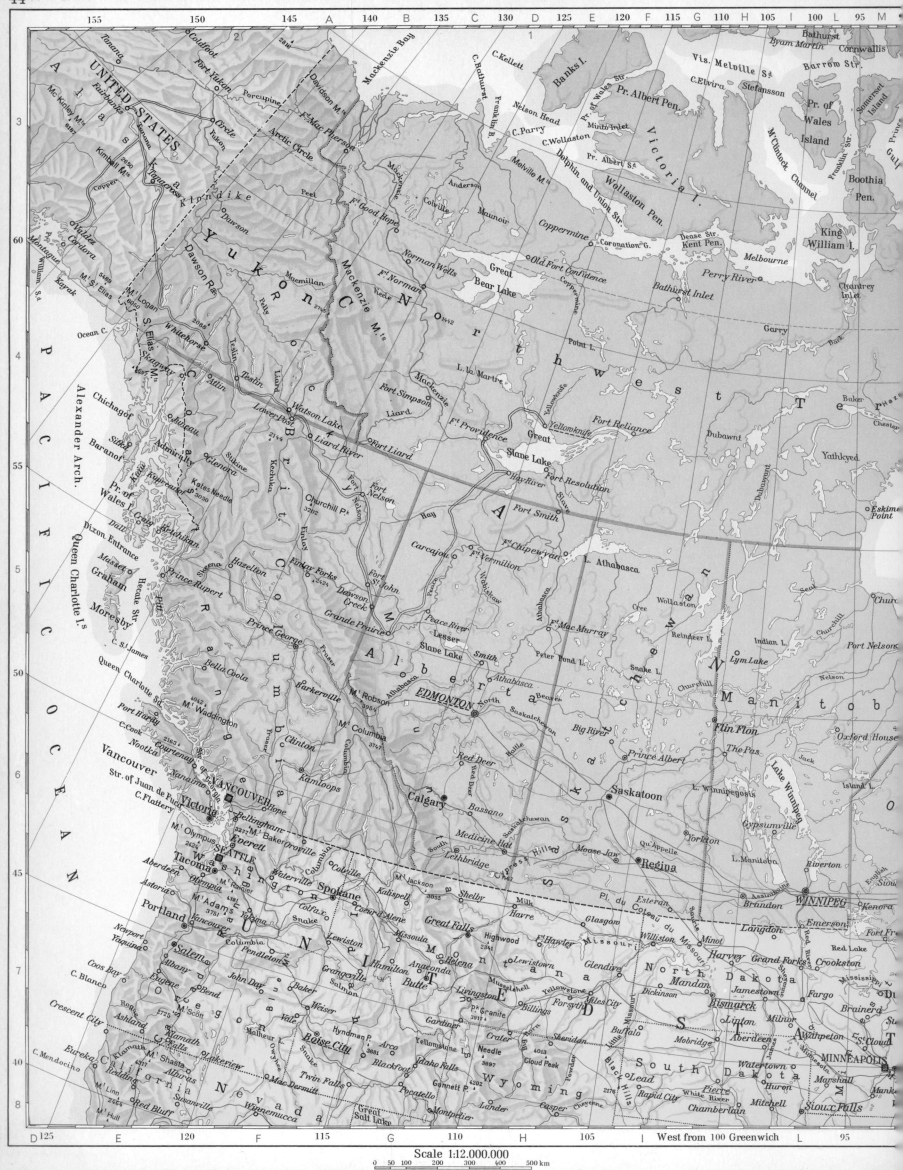

44

Scale 1:12.000.000

0 50 100   200   300   400   500 km

N 85 O 80 P 75 Q 70 R 65 S 60 T 55 U 50 V 45 W 40 Z 35 30

Devon

Lancaster Sound
Dundas Harb.
Bylot
Borden Pen.
Brodeur Pen.
Admiralty Inl.

Baffin Bay

Scott Inlet
C. Christian
Home Bay

Davis Strait

Disko
Vaigat
Umanak Fj. Umanak
Godhavn Bugt
Disko Bugt
Svartenhuk

Mt Forel
Ekatep
Angmagssalik
Dannebrogs
Pikiudleg
C. Mösting

Greenland (Den)

Arctic Circle

Kong Frederik VI Kyst

Ikermiut
Anoritôq

Boothia

Committee Bay

Iglootik
Spicer
Pr. Charles I.
C. Wilson

Melville Pen.

Baffin

Island

Cumberland
Pangnirtung
Pen.

Nettiling L.
C. Mercy
Cumberland Sd.
Angijak
Kangârniut
Sukkertoppen
Lichtenfels

Napassoq
Godhåb

Skjoldungen

Aputasiusok

60

Vansittart

Foxe
Basin

Foxe Pen.

Amadjuak
Hall Pen.

Brevoort
Loks
Frobisher Bay
Lake Harbour
Resolution

C. Dyer

Holsteinsborg

Frederikshåb
Sydpröven
Juliaehåb
C. Farewell

55

Southampton I.
Coral Harbour
Bell Pen.
Evans Str.
C. Low
Roes Welcome Sound
Fisher Str.
Mill
Salisbury
Nottingham
Charles Isl.
Coats
Mansel
Saglouc
Chubb Crater 680
Ungava Pen.

Hudson Strait

Akpatok

Atlantic

Hudson Bay

C. Smith
Kingwa
Povungnituk
Kogaluk
Inoucdjouac
Sleepers
Belcher Is.
Nastapoka Is.

Bellin
Ungava Bay

Leaf
Larch
Koksoak
Fort Chimo
Kaniapiskau
Whale

Hebron
Cod
Nain
Newark

Hopedale
Naskaupi
Rigolet
Cartwright
Hamilton Inlet

Byron B.

50

C. Tatnam
York Factory
Fort Severn
C. Henrietta Maria

Great Whale
Kanaaupscow
Kaniapiskau L.

Dyke L.
Michikamau L.
Hamilton
Melville

Eagle
Belle Isle
C. Bauld
Battle Harbour

Fort George
Fort George
Opinaka
Eastmain
Otish Mts 1128

Natashquan

Str. of Belle Isle

Grand Falls
Newfoundland
C. Freels
Bonavista B.
Bonavista

45

A
Fawn
Winisk
Ekwan
Trout L.
Attawapiskat
Kapiskau

James Bay
Akimiski
Charlton
Albany
Moose Factory
Rupert House
L. Evans
Lake Mistassini
Nottaway
Moose

Labrador

Mingan
Sept Iles
Anticosti
Manikuagan
Ouardes
Peribonka

G. of St. Lawrence

St. Pierre (Fr)
Miquelon (Fr)
Grand Bank

St. John's
Avalon Pen.
Trepassey
C. Race

60

Osnaburgh House
Lookout
L. Nipigon
Savanne
Longlac
Schreiber
Thunder Bay
Ft William
Port Arthur

L. Superior

Kenogami
Cochrane
Timmins
Kirkland Lake
Chapleau
Taschereau

Chicoutimi
Saguenay
Robeva
La Tuque
Trois Rivières

Rimouski
Notre Dame Mts
Gaspé Pen.
Edmundston
Fort Kent
Houlton

New Brunswick
Moncton
Fredericton
St. John

Pr. Edward I.
Charlottetown

Magdalen I.
Cabot Strait
C. North Strait
C. Breton I.
Sydney

45

St. Paul
Ontonagon
Marquette
Ashland
Sault Ste Marie
Sudbury
North Bay
Pembroke
Hull
QUEBEC
MONTREAL
OTTAWA
Blue Mts 911
St. Albans
Sherbrooke
Thetford Mines
Dover
Foxcroft
Bangor

Bay of Fundy
Digby
Nova Scotia
Truro
Dartmouth
Halifax
Liverpool
C. Sable

L. Huron
Manitoulin
Escanaba
Alpena
Orillia
Lindsay
Peterborough
Kingston
Ogdensburg
Watertown
Montpelier
Concord
Mt Washington
Augusta
Portland
Portsmouth
C. Cod

40

Eau Claire
Green Bay
Manistee
Cadillac
Saginaw
Muskegon
Flint
Owen Sound
Goderich
London
Brantford
Niagara Falls
L. Ontario
TORONTO
HAMILTON
BUFFALO
Rochester
Syracuse
Utica
Troy
Albany
Lowell
BOSTON
Worcester
New Bedford
Nantucket

Wausau
Oshkosh
La Crosse
Rapids
Lansing
DETROIT
Windsor
Chatham
L. Erie
St. Thomas
Huron
Sheboygan

Kingston
Springfield
Providence

M 90 N P 75 Q 70 R 65 S 60

Scale 1:12.000.000

0 50 100 200 300 400 500 km

Copyright: Vallardi Ind. Graf.

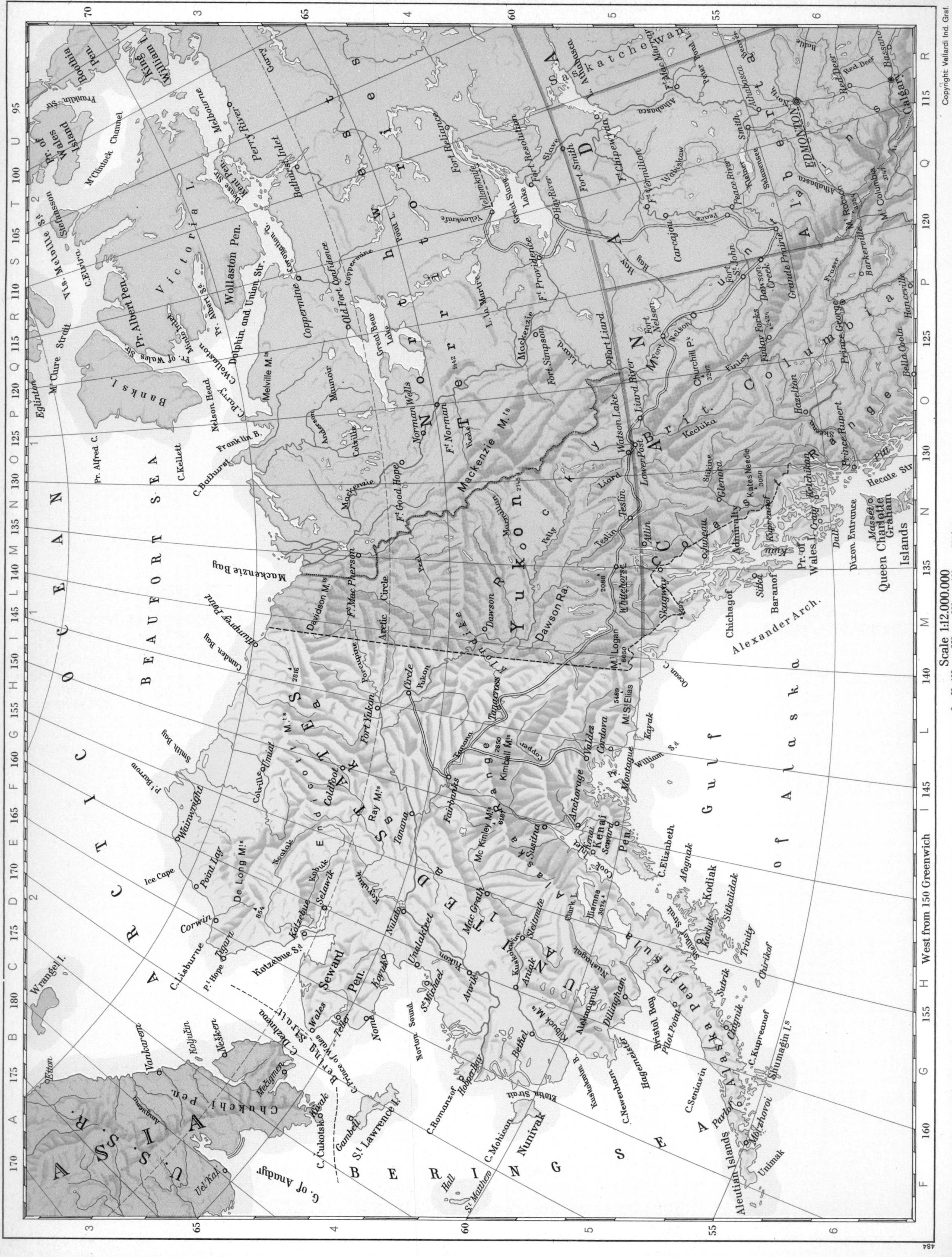

ALASKA

ARCTIC OCEAN

BEAUFORT SEA

BERING SEA

Gulf of Alaska

U.S.S.R.

CANADA

ALASKA

Yukon

Mackenzie

Scale 1:12,000,000

West from 150 Greenwich

EDMONTON

Queen Charlotte Graham Islands

Alexander Arch.

Aleutian Islands

Seward Pen.

Bristol Bay

Kenai Pen.

Alaska Peninsula

Copyright: Vallardi Ind. Graf.

0 50 100 200 300 400 500 km

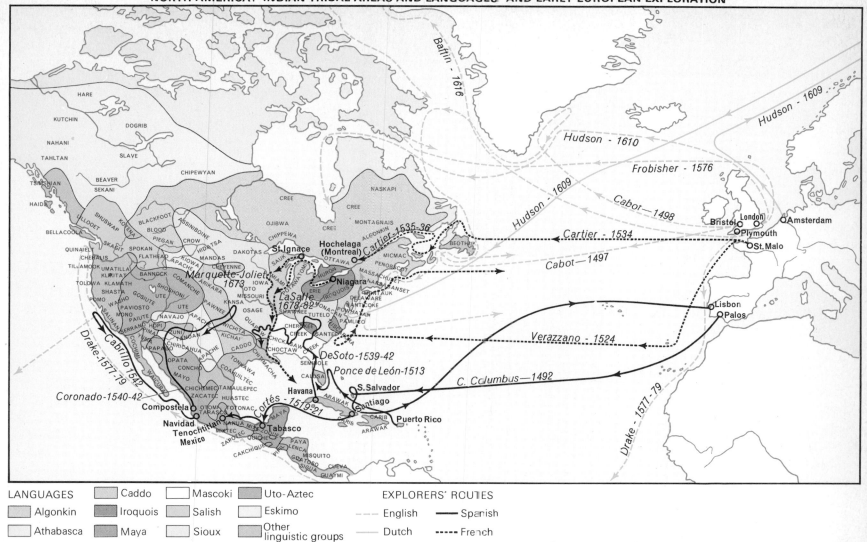

LANGUAGES
- Caddo
- Mascoki
- Uto-Aztec
- Algonkin
- Iroquois
- Salish
- Eskimo
- Athabasca
- Maya
- Sioux
- Other linguistic groups

(Names of North American Indian tribes are printed in red)

EXPLORERS' ROUTES
- English
- Spanish
- Dutch
- French

THE UNITED STATES AND CANADA

The North American continent is composed of two huge countries which possess enormous mineral and agricultural wealth. There are 52 States in the USA and 12 Provinces in Canada. Both countries are approximately the same size (9.9 million sq km) but have been developed very differently. Over 220 million people live in the United States while in Canada there are scarcely 24 million. About 87% of the people living in the USA are white, descended mainly from English and French settlers, 11% are black, descended from the slaves who were brought over from Africa in days gone by. Indians, Japanese and Chinese make up a further 1.4% of the population. Two-thirds of the 800,000 American Indians live on reservations. A further 220,000 Indians live in Canada, also mainly on reservations. In the far north, and on the islands of the Arctic archipelago, live 13,600 Eskimos.

THE UNITED STATES AND CANADA: AGRICULTURAL REGIONS

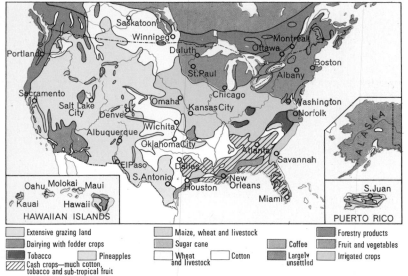

- Extensive grazing land
- Dairying with fodder crops
- Tobacco
- Pineapples
- Cash crops—much cotton, tobacco and sub-tropical fruit
- Maize, wheat and livestock
- Sugar cane
- Wheat and livestock
- Cotton
- Coffee
- Largely unsettled
- Forestry products
- Fruit and vegetables
- Irrigated crops

UNITED STATES – CANADA: MINERALS AND INDUSTRIAL AREAS

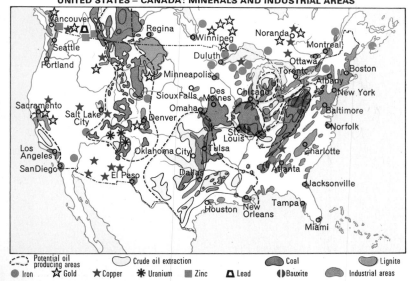

- Potential oil producing areas
- Crude oil extraction
- Coal
- Lignite
- Iron
- Gold
- Copper
- Uranium
- Zinc
- Lead
- Bauxite
- Industrial areas

NORTH AND CENTRAL AMERICA: EXPLORATION AND COLONISATION

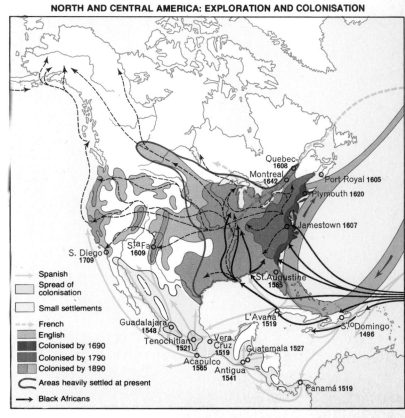

- Spanish
- Spread of colonisation
- Small settlements
- French
- English
- Colonised by 1690
- Colonised by 1790
- Colonised by 1890
- Areas heavily settled at present
- Black Africans

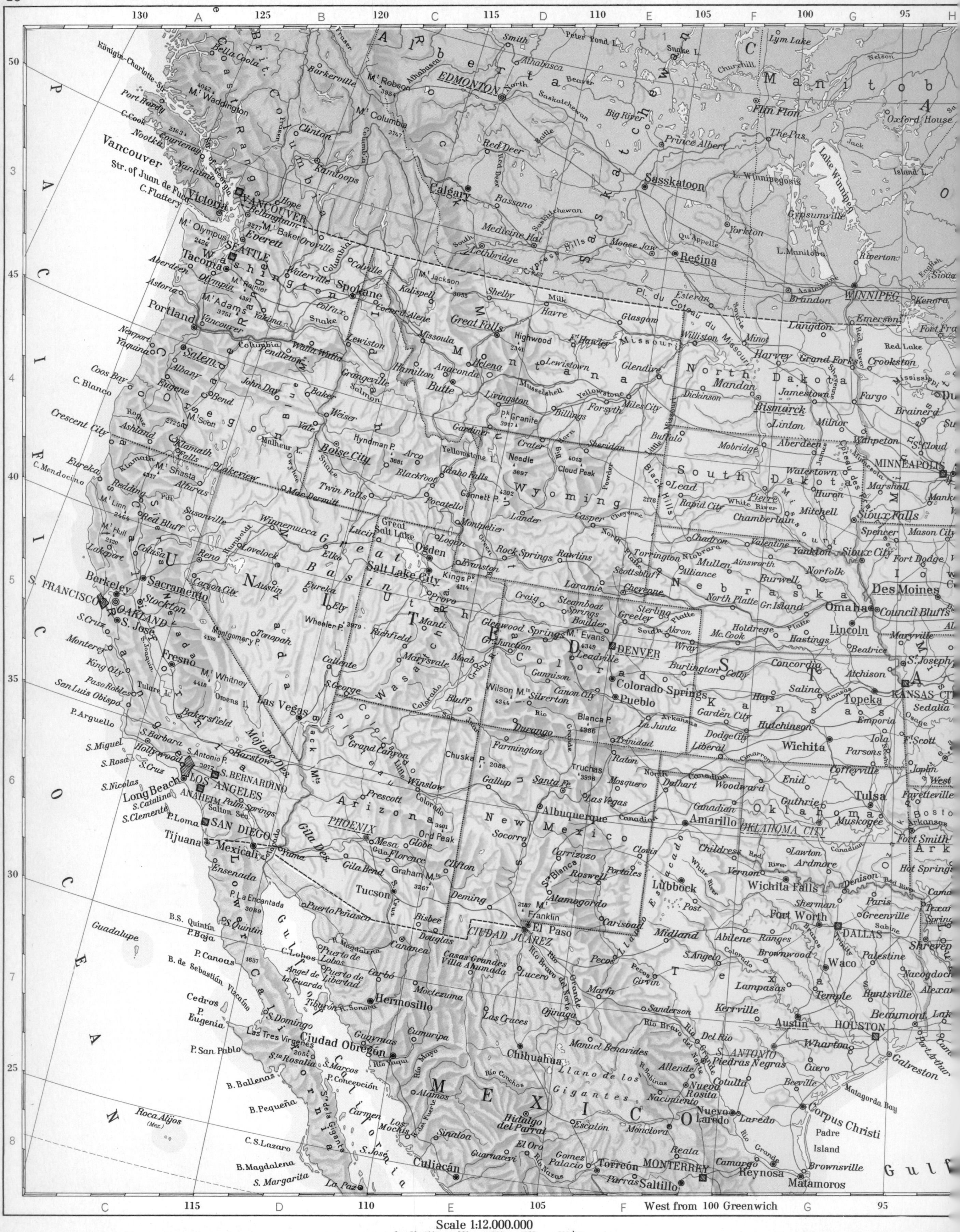

46

130 A 125 B 120 C 115 D 110 E 105 F 100 G 95 H

50

PACIFIC OCEAN

Königin-Charlotte-Str. Bella Coola Barkerville M.¹ Robson
Port Hardy M.¹ Waddington 4042 EDMONTON
C. Cook Courtenay or Comox M.¹ Columbia Athabasca
Nootka Nanaimo 2163 M.¹ Robson 3954 Peter Pond L. Snake L. Lynn Lake
Vancouver Clinton Calgary Big River Churchill Nelson
Str. of Juan de Fuca Victoria Hope VANCOUVER Kamloops Red Deer Bassano Prince Albert The Pas Oxford House
C. Flattery Bellingham Medicine Hat Sasskatoon Jack Island L.

Everett M.¹ Baker 3277 Oroville Lethbridge Moose Jaw L. Winnipegosis Lake Winnipeg
SEATTLE Waterville Spokane Shelby Cypress Hills Regina Gypsumville Riverton
Tacoma M.¹ Rainier 4391 Kalispell M.¹ Jackson 3035 Milk Pt. du Coteau Brandon WINNIPEG Kenora
Aberdeen Olympia Coeur d'Alene Havre Glasgow Langdon Emerson
Astoria M.¹ Adams 3751 Yakima Missoula Great Falls Glasgow Williston Minot Red Lake Fort Francis
Portland Vancouver Colfax Helena Glendive Harvey Grand Forks Crookston
Newport Pendleton Snake Anaconda Butte Lewistown Mandan Jamestown Fargo Mississippi Duluth
Yaquina Salem Albany Walla Walla John Day Grangeville Livingston Billings Dickinson Bismarck Linton Milnor Brainerd
Coos Bay Eugene Baker Salmon Musselshell Forsyth Miles City Sheridan Buffalo Mobridge Aberdeen Wahpeton St. Cloud MINNEAPOLIS
C. Blanco Bend Weiser Yellowstone Pk. Granite 3917 Cloud Peak Lead Pierre Mitchell Watertown Marshall Mankato
Crescent City Roslyn M.¹ Scott 2725 Boise City Arco 3681 Idaho Falls Needle Rapid City White River Huron Sioux Falls
Ashland Malheur L. Twin Falls Pocatello Gannett 4202 Crater 3697 Black Hills Chamberlain Mitchell Sioux City Fort Dodge
Eureka Klamath Falls Lakeview McDermitt Montpelier Lander Casper Cheyenne Torrington Niobrara Valentine Yankton Sioux City Iowa
C. Mendocino M.¹ Shasta 4317 Alturas Winnemucca Great Salt Lake Ogden Rock Springs Rawlins Laramie Scottsbluff Alliance Ainsworth Burwell Norfolk Des Moines
Redding M.¹ Linn 2464 Susanville Lovelock Elko Logan Evanston Wyoming Craig Steamboat Springs Greeley Sterling North Platte Gr. Island Omaha Council Bluffs
Red Bluff Lakeport Reno Carson City Austin Eureka Ely Provo Salt Lake City Kings Pk. 4114 Glenwood Springs M.¹ Evans Boulder Akron Holdrege McCook Hastings Lincoln Maryville St. Joseph
S. FRANCISCO Berkeley Sacramento Stockton Montgomery P. Tonopah Wheeler P. 3979 Richfield Manti Moab Gunnison DENVER Leadville 4349 Burlington Colby Salina Concordia Atchison KANSAS CITY
Oakland S. Jose Fresno M.¹ Whitney 4418 Caliente Marysvale Colorado Colorado Springs Garden City Hays Sedalia
S. Cruz Monterey King City Paso Robles Tulare L. Omens L. Las Vegas S. George Bluff 4344 Silverton Wilson Mtn. Canon City Pueblo La Junta Dodge City Hutchinson Emporia KANSAS CITY
San Luis Obispo Bakersfield Mojave Des. Barstow Grand Canyon Durango Blanca P. 4386 Trinidad Liberal Wichita Iola F. Scott
P. Arguello S. Barbara Hollywood S. Antonio 3072 S. Bernardino Winslow Gallup Santa Fe Raton Dalhart Woodward Enid Guthrie Parsons Coffeyville Joplin West
S. Miguel S. Rosa S. Cruz Long Beach ANAHEIM Palm Springs Salton Sea Prescott Ord Peak 3401 Albuquerque Las Vegas Mosquero Canadian Amarillo OKLAHOMA CITY Tulsa Fayetteville Boston
S. Nicolas LOS ANGELES Salton Sea PHOENIX Mesa Globe Socorro New Mexico Childress Muskogee Fort Smith Ark.
S. Clemente P. Loma SAN DIEGO Gila Des. Florence Clifton Carrizozo Clovis Lubbock Lawton Ardmore Vernon Wichita Falls Denison Hot Springs
Tijuana Mexicali Gila Bend Graham Mts. 3267 Deming Roswell Portales Post Sherman Paris Camargo
Ensenada Tucson Bisbee Alamogordo M.¹ Franklin 2187 Carlsbad Midland Abilene Ranges Fort Worth Greenville Palestine Shreveport
B.S. Quintín P. Baja La Encantada 3089 Puerto Peñasco Douglas CIUDAD JUAREZ EL PASO Pecos S. Angelo Brownwood Waco Sabine Nacogdoches Alexander
P. Canoas Cananea Casas Grandes El Paso Lucero Marfa Girvin Lampasas Temple Huntsville
B. de Sebastián Vizcaíno 1657 Puerto de Lobos Carbó Villa Ahumada Rio Bravo del Norte Sanderson Kerrville Austin HOUSTON Beaumont
Cedros Angel de la Guarda Puerto de Libertad Moctezuma Ojinaga Rio Bravo del Norte Del Río S. ANTONIO Wharton Galveston
P. San Pablo Hermosillo Cumuripa Chihuahua Manuel Benavides Piedras Negras Cicero Beeville
Ciudad Obregón 2052 S.ta Rosalia Guaymas S. Marcos Rio Yaqui Rio Conchos Llano de los Gigantes Allende Nuevo Laredo Corpus Christi Matagorda Bay
Roca Alijos (Mex.) La Paz B. Ballenas P. Concepción Álamos Hidalgo del Parral Escalón MEXICO Monclova Rosita Nacimiento Reata Laredo Padre Island
C.S. Lazaro B. Pequeña Carmen Los Mochis S.ta Fuerte El Oro Gomez Palacio Torreón Nuevo Laredo Reynosa Brownsville
B. Magdalena S. Margarita S. José Culiacán Sinaloa Guamuchi Parras Saltillo MONTERREY Matamoros Gulf

45

40

35

30

25

Scale 1:12.000.000

0 50 100 200 300 400 500 km

West from 100 Greenwich

Title / scale:

Scale 1:12.000.000

0 50 100 200 300 400 500 km

Oceans / seas:

ATLANTIC OCEAN

G. of Mexico

Florida Str.

Bay of Fundy

Delaware Bay

Chesapeake Bay

Raleigh Bay

James Bay

L. Superior · L. Michigan · L. Huron · L. Erie · L. Ontario

Major cities / places (selection, as labelled):

MONTREAL · QUEBEC · OTTAWA · TORONTO · HAMILTON · BUFFALO · DETROIT · CHICAGO · MILWAUKEE · CLEVELAND · PITTSBURGH · COLUMBUS · CINCINNATI · INDIANAPOLIS · ST LOUIS · LOUISVILLE · NASHVILLE · MEMPHIS · BIRMINGHAM · ATLANTA · MONTGOMERY · NEW ORLEANS · BATON ROUGE · TAMPA · St Petersburg · MIAMI · Ft Lauderdale · JACKSONVILLE · Tallahassee · WASHINGTON · BALTIMORE · PHILADELPHIA · NEW YORK · NEWARK · Trenton · Camden · Atlantic City · BOSTON · Providence · New Bedford · Hartford · New Haven · Bridgeport · Albany · Syracuse · Rochester · Utica · Worcester · Springfield · Portland · Concord · Montpelier · Augusta · Halifax · Dartmouth · Nova Scotia · New Brunswick · Fredericton · Moncton · St John · Bangor · Liverpool · Yarmouth · Sydney · Charlottetown · St John's · Newfoundland · Grand Falls · St Pierre (Fr) · Miquelon (Fr)

RICHMOND · NORFOLK · Newport News · Petersburg · Lynchburg · Roanoke · Raleigh · Charlotte · Greensboro · Winston Salem · Durham · Wilmington · Columbia · Charleston · Savannah · Augusta · Macon · Chattanooga · Knoxville · Asheville · Spartanburg · Greenville · Huntsville · Jackson · Vicksburg · Meridian · Mobile · Pensacola · Gainesville · Orlando · Lakeland · Fort Myers · Key West

DETROIT · Windsor · Toledo · Akron · Youngstown · Canton · Dayton · Flint · Lansing · Grand Rapids · Kalamazoo · South Bend · Gary · Ft Wayne · Fort Wayne · Muncie · Peoria · Springfield · Decatur · Danville · Rockford · Aurora · Rock Island · Davenport · Dubuque · Madison · Racine · Green Bay · Oshkosh · Sheboygan · Manistee · Saginaw · Muskegon · Marquette · Escanaba · Rhinelander · Wausau · Eau Claire · La Crosse

Regions / states labelled:

NEW FOUNDLAND · Anticosti · Gaspé · Nova Scotia · QUEBEC · ONTARIO · Pennsylvania · West Virginia · Virginia · Kentucky · Tennessee · North Carolina · South Carolina · Georgia · Alabama · Mississippi · Massachusetts · Connecticut · Long Island · Nantucket · BAHAMAS · Gr. Bahama · Gr. Abaco · Eleuthera · Nassau · S. Salvador (Watling) · Bermuda Is · Cabot Strait · Str. of Belle Isle · Avalon Pen. · Magdalen I. · C. Breton I. · Pr Edward I.

Capes / points:

C. Cod · C. Hatteras · C. Lookout · C. Fear · C. Sable · C. Canaveral (C. Kennedy) · C. Romano · C. Race · C. North · C. Freels · C. Whittle · C. Henrietta Maria · Belcher Is · Florida Keys · Oregon Inlet · Tropic of Cancer

Grid / coordinate numbers (top): 90 I 85 L 80 M 75 N 70 O 65 P 60 Q 55 R

Grid (bottom): 90 I 85 L 80 M 75 N 70 O

Grid (right margin): 1 · A · 3 · 45 · 40 · 5 · 35 · 6 · 30 · 7 · 25 · 8

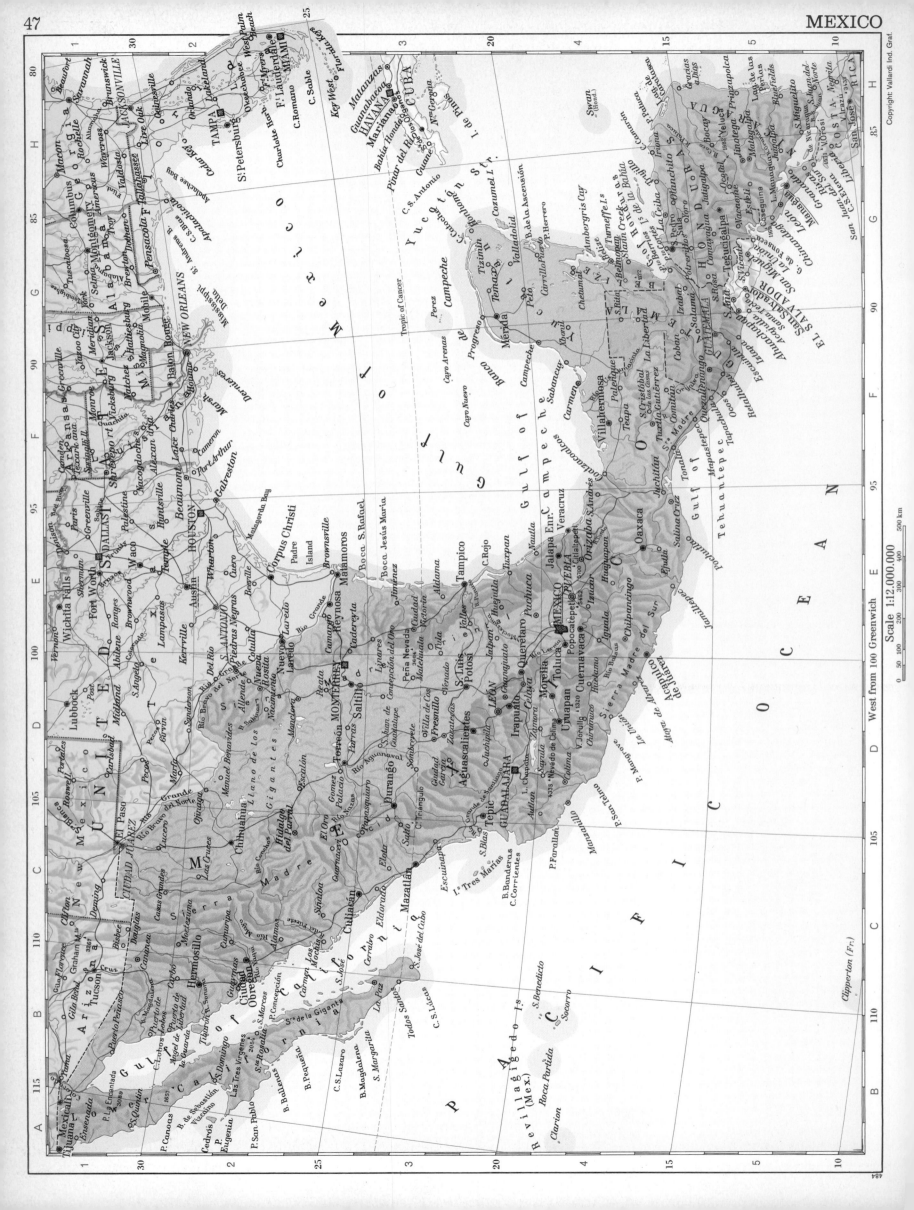

Scale 1:12.000.000

West from 100 Greenwich

0   50   100   200   300   500 km

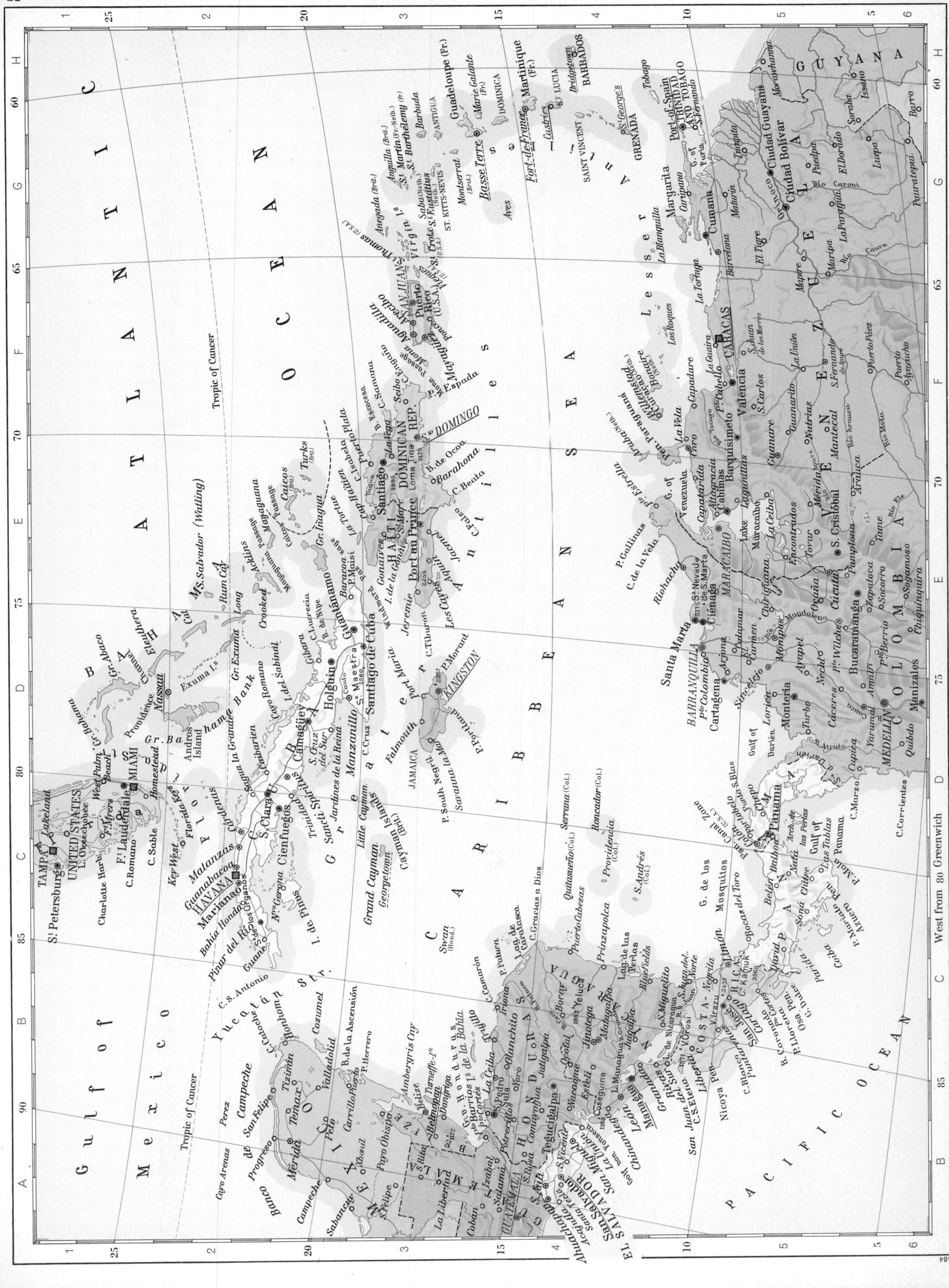

A T L A N T I C   O C E A N

Tropic of Cancer

Gulf of Mexico

UNITED STATES

TAMPA
S. Petersburg
Lakeland
Tampa Bay
West Palm Beach
Ft. Lauderdale
MIAMI
Homestead
Key West
Charlotte Harb.
Ft. Myers
C. Sable
C. Romano

Gr. Bahama
Gr. Abaco
Eleuthera
Nassau
Andros Island
Exuma Is.
Gr. Exuma
Cat I.
S. Salvador (Watling)
Rum Cay
Long I.
Crooked
Acklins
Mayaguana
Caicos (Brit.)
Turks (Brit.)
Gr. Inagua

Bahama Bank
Gr. Bahama Bank

C U B A
HAVANA
Marianao
Guanabacoa
Matanzas
Cárdenas
Pinar del Río
Guane
Bahía Honda
I. de Pinos
S. Clara
Cienfuegos
Trinidad
Sancti Spíritus
Camagüey
Jardines de la Reina
Manzanillo
S. Maestra
Santiago de Cuba
Holguín
Gibara
B. de Nipe
Baracoa
Guantánamo

Florida Str.
Florida Keys
C. S. Antonio

Yucatan Str.
Grand Cayman
Georgetown
Little Cayman
Cayman Islands (Brit.)

JAMAICA
KINGSTON
Falmouth
Port Maria
Port Antonio
Montego
P. Morant
P. South Negril
Savanna la Mar

HAITI
Cap Haïtien
Port au Prince
Jacmel
Gonaïves
Jérémie
C. Tiburon
Les Cayes
P. Maisi
P. Mouant
I. de la Gonâve
La Tortue

DOMINICAN REP.
S.to DOMINGO
Santiago
Loma Tina 3995
La Vega
Puerto Plata
Samaná
B. de Samaná
Barahona
B. de Ocoa
C. Beata
C. Engaño
Seibo
Mona Passage
Mona (P.R.)
P.ta Espada

Puerto Rico (U.S.A.)
SAN JUAN
Ponce
Mayagüez
Arecibo
Aguadilla
Humacao

Virgin Is.
St. Thomas (U.S.A.)
St. Croix (U.S.A.)
Anegada (Brit.)
Sombrero

Anguilla (Fr.-Neth.)
St. Martin (Fr.)
St. Barthélemy (Fr.)
Saba (Neth.)
St. Eustatius (Neth.)
ST. KITTS-NEVIS
ANTIGUA
Barbuda
Montserrat (Brit.)
Guadeloupe (Fr.)
Basse-Terre
Marie Galante
DOMINICA
Martinique (Fr.)
Fort-de-France
SAINT VINCENT
St. Lucia
Castries
Aves
BARBADOS
Bridgetown
GRENADA
St. George's
Tobago
TRINIDAD AND TOBAGO
Port-of-Spain

L e s s e r   A n t i l l e s

C A R I B B E A N   S E A

G r e a t e r   A n t i l l e s

MEXICO
Yucatán
Mérida
Progreso
Campeche
Valladolid
Tizimín
Cozumel
B. de la Ascensión
Chetumal
Banco de Campeche
Cayo Arenas
Perez
Payo Obispo

BRITISH HONDURAS
Belize
Belmopan
Ambergris Cay
Turneffe Is.
Corozal

GUATEMALA
Cobán
Puerto Barrios
Izabal
L. de Izabal

HONDURAS
Tegucigalpa
S. Pedro Sula
La Ceiba
Trujillo
Olanchito
Juticalpa
Puerto Cortés
I. de la Bahía
Roatán
Gracias

EL SALVADOR
San Salvador
La Libertad
San Miguel
Santa Ana
Sonsonate
Gulf of Fonseca

NICARAGUA
Managua
L. de Nicaragua
L. de Managua
Matagalpa
Jinotega
Estelí
León
Granada
Bluefields
Puerto Cabezas
Prinzapolca
C. Gracias a Dios
Log. de Perlas

COSTA RICA
San José
Limón
Puntarenas
Nicoya Pen.

PANAMA
PANAMA
Colón
Balboa
Panama Canal
Canal Zone (U.S.A.)
Gulf of Panama
Las Perlas
G. de los Mosquitos
Bocas del Toro

COLOMBIA
BARRANQUILLA
Cartagena
Santa Marta
MEDELLÍN
Manizales
Bucaramanga
Cúcuta
S. Cristóbal
Montería
Turbo
Quibdó
Sincelejo
Lorica
Magangué
Cáceres
Mompós
Socorro
Sogamoso
Chiquinquirá
Gulf of Darién
C. Corrientes
G. de Urabá
Serrana (Col.)
Roncador (Col.)
Providencia (Col.)
S. Andrés (Col.)
Quitasueño (Col.)

VENEZUELA
CARACAS
La Guaira
Maracaibo
Lake Maracaibo
Valencia
Barquisimeto
Mérida
Cumaná
Barcelona
Cabimas
Coro
La Vela
Riohacha
C. de la Vela
P. Gallinas
Margarita
La Blanquilla
La Tortuga
Los Roques
Los Testigos
Gulf of Venezuela
Gulf of Paria
Pen. Paraguaná
Aruba (Neth.)
Curaçao (Neth.)
Bonaire (Neth.)
S. Fernando
S. Carlos
Guanare
Carúpano
Maturín

GUYANA
Ciudad Bolívar
Ciudad Guayana
Orinoco
Río Caroní
El Dorado
El Tigre

P A C I F I C   O C E A N

Scale 1:12.000.000

0 50 100 200 300 400 500 km

West from 80 Greenwich

Scale 1:34 000 000

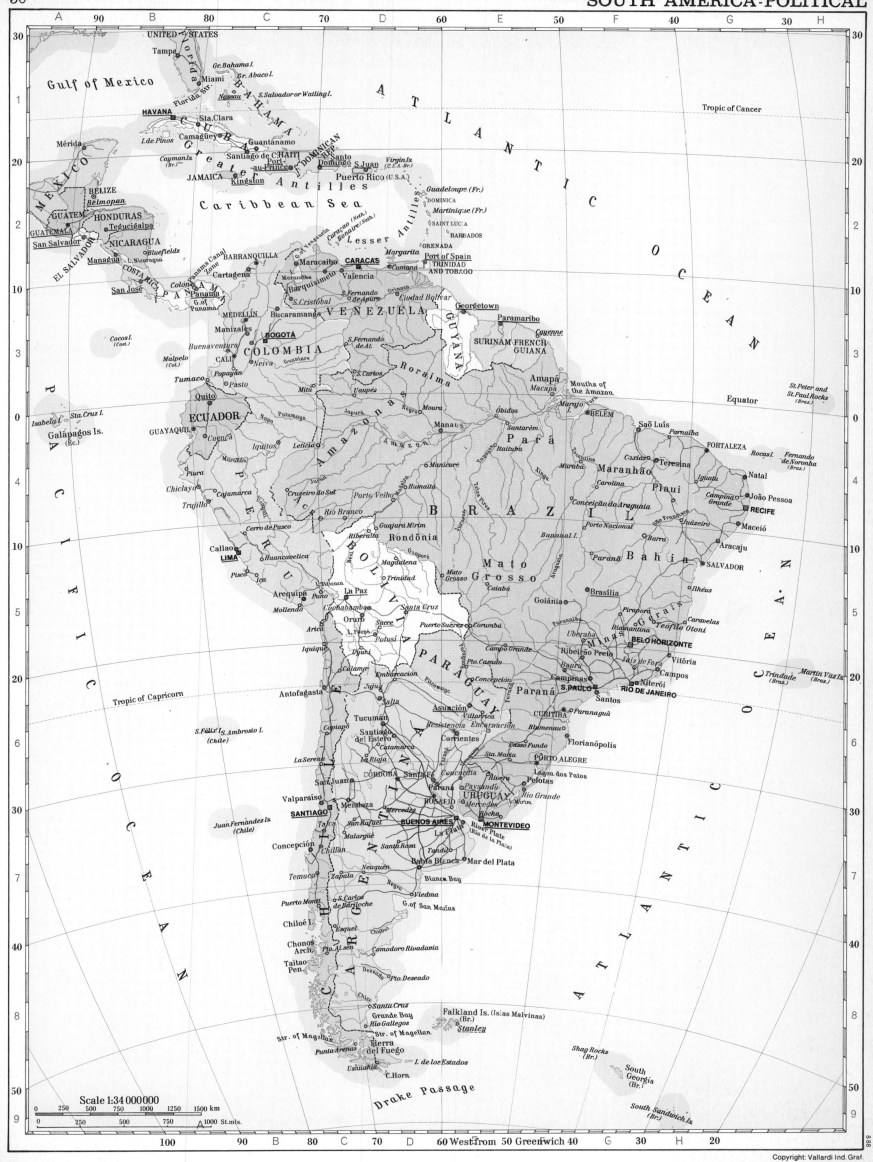

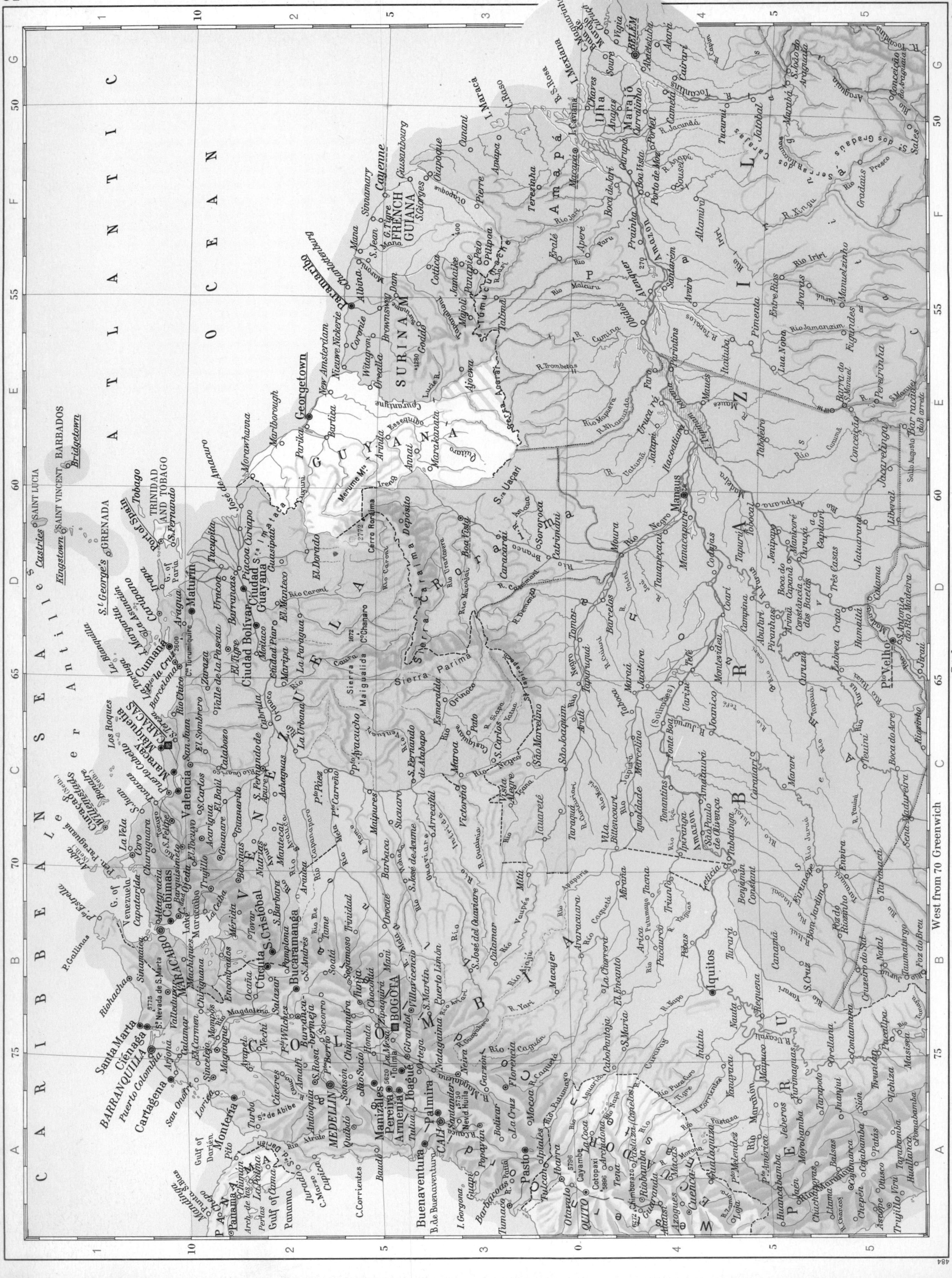

ATLANTIC OCEAN

CARIBBEAN SEA

Lesser Antilles

SAINT LUCIA — Castries
SAINT VINCENT — Kingstown
BARBADOS — Bridgetown
St. George's — GRENADA
TRINIDAD AND TOBAGO — Port of Spain — S. Fernando
Tobago

COLOMBIA
VENEZUELA
GUYANA
SURINAM
FRENCH GUIANA
BRAZIL
PERU
ECUADOR

Santa Marta, Barranquilla, Cartagena, Cartagena, Cienaga, Riohacha, Medellín, Manizales, Pereira, Armenia, Palmira, CALI, Buenaventura, Pasto, Popayán, BOGOTÁ, Bucaramanga, Cúcuta, S. Cristóbal, Maracaibo, Cabimas, Valencia, CARACAS, Maracay, Puerto Cabello, Barquisimeto, Coro, Cumaná, Barcelona, Maturín, Ciudad Bolívar, Ciudad Guayana, El Tigre, San Fernando de Apure, Puerto Ayacucho, Georgetown, New Amsterdam, Paramaribo, Nieuw Nickerie, Albina, Cayenne, St. Laurent, BELÉM, Manaus, Pto. Velho, Iquitos, QUITO, Cuenca

Golfo de Venezuela, Gulf of Maracaibo, Lago de Maracaibo, Gulf of Darién, Gulf of Panama, Golfo de Paria, Golfo de Cariaco, Isla de Margarita, La Blanquilla, Los Roques, Las Aves

Rio Orinoco, Rio Magdalena, Rio Caquetá, Rio Putumayo, Rio Negro, Rio Branco, R. Amazon, R. Madeira, R. Xingu, R. Tapajós, R. Tocantins, Rio Marañón, Rio Napo, Essequibo, Corantyne, Maroni, Oyapock

Sierra Parima, Sierra Pacaraima, Serra do Tumucumaque, Menume Mts., Sierra Nevada de S. Marta

Marajó, Ilha de Marajó, Amapá, Macapá

Scale 1:12,000,000

0 50 100 200 300 400 500 km

West from 70 Greenwich

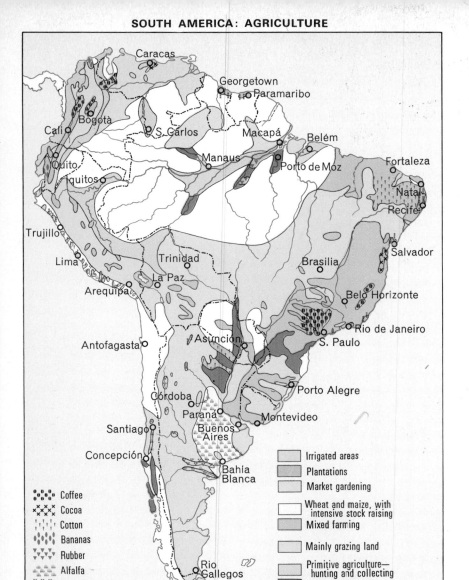

Legend (Agriculture map):
- Coffee
- Cocoa
- Cotton
- Bananas
- Rubber
- Alfalfa
- Vines and fruits
- Sugar cane

- Irrigated areas
- Plantations
- Market gardening
- Wheat and maize, with intensive stock raising
- Mixed farming
- Mainly grazing land
- Primitive agriculture—hunting and collecting
- Forestry products
- Unproductive areas—forests, mountains and deserts

Cities labelled: Caracas, Georgetown, Paramaribo, Bogotá, Cali, S. Carlos, Macapá, Belém, Quito, Manaus, Porto de Moz, Fortaleza, Iquitos, Natal, Recife, Trujillo, Trinidad, Brasilia, Salvador, Lima, La Paz, Belo Horizonte, Arequipa, Rio de Janeiro, S. Paulo, Asunción, Antofagasta, Córdoba, Porto Alegre, Paraná, Montevideo, Santiago, Buenos Aires, Concepción, Bahía Blanca, Rio Gallegos

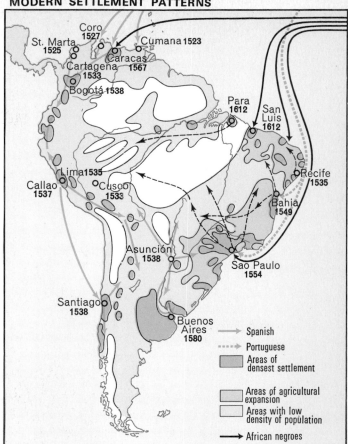

Settlement dates: Coro 1527, St. Marta 1525, Cumana 1523, Cartagena 1533, Caracas 1567, Bogotá 1538, Para 1612, San Luis 1612, Lima 1535, Callao 1537, Cusco 1533, Recife 1535, Bahia 1549, Asunción 1538, Sao Paulo 1554, Santiago 1538, Buenos Aires 1580

Legend (Migrations map):
- → Spanish
- ┈┈ Portuguese
- Areas of densest settlement
- Areas of agricultural expansion
- Areas with low density of population
- → African negroes

SOUTH AMERICA

The total area of South America is 17.8 million sq km, which makes it the fourth largest continent on Earth. It is attached to North America by the narrow isthmus of Central America and stretches south nearly as far as the Antarctic. From the tropical climate of the equatorial rainforest of the Amazon, to the sub-arctic Tundra in the far south, a wide variety of climates prevail. South America is dominated by the huge mountain range of the Andes which stretches for over 6,440 km along the west coast, from the mountainous regions of Guiana and Brazil in the north to the highlands of Patagonia in the south. In the middle lie the great plains, cut through by the waters of three mighty river basins: the Orinoco, Amazon and the Parana-Paraguay which opens out into the estuary of the River Plate. The 12 countries of South America are Brazil, Argentina, Peru, Colombia, Venezuela, Chile, Paraguay, Uruguay, Ecuador and Guyana; French Guiana is a French Colony; until independence in 1975, Surinam was a dependency of the Netherlands.

VENEZUELA: PETROLEUM AND IRON

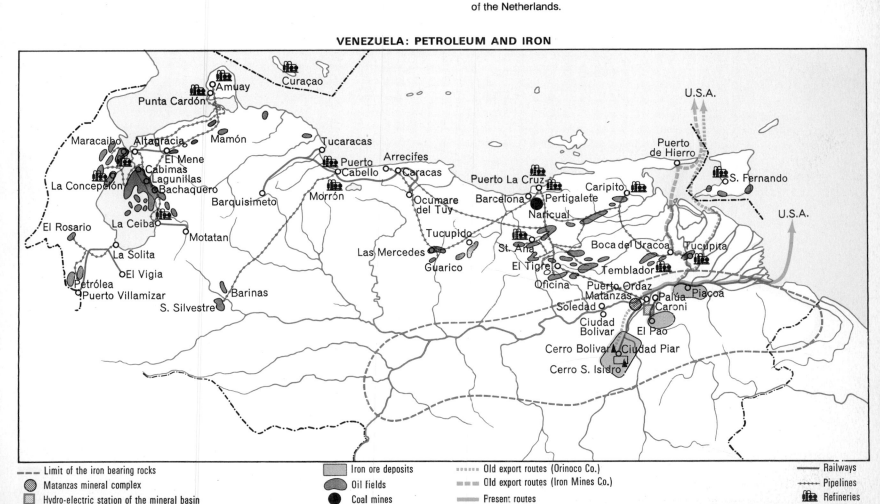

Places labelled: Amuay, Curaçao, Punta Cardón, U.S.A., Puerto de Hierro, Maracaibo, Altagracia, Mamón, Tucaracas, Arrecifes, S. Fernando, El Mene, Puerto Cabello, Caracas, Puerto La Cruz, Caripito, Cabimas, Lagunillas, Bachaquero, Morrón, Ocumare del Tuy, Barcelona, Pertigalete, La Concepción, Barquisimeto, Naricual, Boca del Uracoa, Tucupita, La Ceiba, Motatan, Tucupido, St. Ana, El Rosario, Las Mercedes, El Tigre, Tembladôr, Piacoa, La Solita, Guarico, Oficina, Puerto Ordaz, Palúa, El Vigia, Matanzas, Caroni, Petrólea, Barinas, Soledad, Ciudad Bolivar, El Pao, Puerto Villamizar, S. Silvestre, Cerro Bolivar, Ciudad Piar, Cerro S. Isidro, U.S.A.

Legend (Venezuela map):
- ┈┈ Limit of the iron bearing rocks
- Matanzas mineral complex
- Hydro-electric station of the mineral basin
- Iron ore deposits
- Oil fields
- Coal mines
- Old export routes (Orinoco Co.)
- Old export routes (Iron Mines Co.)
- Present routes
- Railways
- Pipelines
- Refineries

A 80 B 75 C 70 D 65 E 60

PACIFIC OCEAN

COLOMBIA

Tumaco Patía La Cruz Florencia
Esmeraldas Pasto Mocoa Caquetá
P. Galera Ipiales Río Ajojú Mitú Vista Alegre S. Carlos
Pedernales Tulcán Ibarra Macujer S. Marcelino Roraima
Otavalo 5796 Río Putumayo Araracuara S. Joaquim Negro Tomar Tapera
QUITO Cayambe La Coca Río Napo Caquetá Taraquá Tapuruquá Manaus
Latacunga Cotopaxi Archidona Cabo Pantoja La Chorrera Vila Bittencourt Maraá Barcelos Moura
Portoviejo Ambato Tena S. Maria El Encanto Miraña Igualdade Marcelino Jacitara Manacapuru
C.S. Lorenzo Chimborazo Riobamba Pastaza (Canelos) Arica Tonantins Fonte Boa Tefé Coari Itacoatiara
Jipijapa Guaranda Putumayo Tacna Ipiranga São Paulo de Olivença Uarini
GUAYAQUIL Macas Pucaurco Triunfo Amazon Benjamín Constant Tabatinga Carauari Montevideu
Azogues Gualaquiza Pebas Nauta Turará Leticia Coari
G. of Guayaquil Cuenca Iquitos Requena
Machala Canamá

PERÚ

Tumbes Zaruma Loja Pto. Melendez Yanayacu Maipuco
Mancora Celica Jeberos
Talara Sullana Huancabamba Moyobamba Yurimaguas
Paita Piura Inén Tarapoto Juanjui Orellana Contamana
P. de Aguja Catacaos Olmos Chachapoyas Balsas Masisea
Sechura Chiclayo Cajamarca Sión Tiruntan Pucallpa
Cherrepe Chepén Cajabamba Patás Atalaya
Pacasmayo Otusco Trujillo Huánuco
Ascope Trujillo Salaverry Virú Tarabamba Huallanca Cerro de Pasco
Chimbote Casma Huascarán Ambo La Merced
Huarmey Recuay Huánuco Junín
Paramonga Chiquián Supé Tarma La Oroya
Huacho Canta Jauja
Chancay Yauli Huancayo
LIMA Callao Yauyos Anco Huanta
Lurín Chilca Huancavelica Ayacucho Cuzco
S. Vic. de Cañete Chincha Alta Pisco Paico Abancay Acomayo
Ica Laramate Antabamba Ayaviri Poto
Nazca S. Juan S. Tomás Cailloma Juliaca Huancané
P. S. María Coracora Chuquibamba Chivay Puno Titicaca
Lomas Ampato Juli LA PAZ

BOLIVIA

Pto. Velho
Río Branco Guajará-Mirim Riberalta
Cobija Conquista Principe da Beira
Carmen Reyes Trinidad
Arequipa Cochabamba Sta. Cruz de la Sierra
Moquegua Oruro Sucre Potosí
Tacna Arica Sajama Uyuni Tarija
Iquique Tarapacá
Tocopilla Calama Ollagüe La Quiaca
Antofagasta Salta
Mejillones Jujuy
Tropic of Capricorn

ARGENTINA

CHILE

Paposo Taltal
Chañaral Tucumán Resistencia
Caldera Copiapó Catamarca Santiago del Estero
Huasco Vallenar La Rioja
La Serena Coquimbo Chamical

Galápagos Is. (Ecuador)
Darwin Wolf
Marchena Genovesa
Fernandina P. Albemarle Pinta
Isabela S. Salvador S. Cruz S. Cristóbal
P. Cristóbal S. Fé
S. María Española
0 50 100 200 km

Scale 1:12.000.000
0 50 100 200 300 400 500 km

90 80 A 75 B C 70 D 65 E 60

ATLANTIC OCEAN

ATLANTIC OCEAN

Scale 1:12,000,000

0 50 100 200 300 400 500 km

West from 50 Greenwich

Tropic of Capricorn

Major cities and places:

Antofagasta, Mejillones, P. Angamos, Baquedano, Los Dones, La Quiaca, Abra Pampa, Tartagal, Fortín Ballivián, Pín. Falcón, Concepción, Horqueta, Amambaí, Antônio João, Londrina

Palestina, Los Vientos, Llullaillaco 6210, C. Pular 6723, Salar de Macana, Humahuaca, Orán, Embarcación, Río Pilcomayo, F. Ávalos Sánchez, Lima, Igatimí, Pto. Guairá, R. Iguatemi

Taltal, Paposo, C. Aguas Blancas, Aguada, Sal. de Arizaro, Jujuy, S. Antonio de los Cobres, S. Martín (Ledesma), Nm. Población, El Pintado, Villa Hayes, ASUNCIÓN, Cnl. Oviedo, Villarrica

Chañaral, Pueblo Hundido, Antofagasta de la Sierra, Alemania, Cafayate, El Quebrachal, Castelli, Clorinda, Formosa, Pilar, Caazapá, União da Vitoria

Caldera, Copiapó, Ojos del Salado 6870, Puquios, Tucuman, Monteros, Pozo Hondo, Burruyacú, Campo Gallo, Ariá Terai, Pirané, S. Juan Bautista, Encarnación, Posadas, S. Pedro, S. Catarina, Joaçaba

Carrizal Bajo, B. Salada, Mercditas, Villa Castelli, La Madrid, Andalgalá, Catamarca, Quimili, S. Sylvina, La Sábana, Reconquista, Corrientes, Mburucuyá, Bella Vista, S. Tomé, São Borja, S. Ángelo, Erechim, Passo Fundo

Huasco, Vallenar 6380, Cerro del Toro, Chilecito, Mazán, Frías, Gral. Mitre, Bandera, Tostado, Goya, Curuzú Cuatiá, Monte Caseros, Uruguaiana, Alegrete, Santiago, Cruz Alta, S. Maria, Estrela, Caxias do Sul, PORTO ALEGRE

Punta Colorada, La Rioja, Oja de Agua, Ceres, Calchaquí, Concordia, Salto, Rivera, Livramento, Bagé, S. Lourenço do Sul, Lavras do Sul, Río Grande do Sul

La Serena, Coquimbo, Rivadavia, Jáchal, Chamical, Dean Funes, S. Cristóbal, Mar Chiquita, Rafaela, S. Justo, La Paz, Artigas, Tacuarembó, Pelotas, Jaguarão, Lag. dos Patos

P. Lengua de Vaca, Tongoy, Ovalle, Zanjón, Serrezuela, Cruz del Eje, S. Jorge, S. Francisco, CÓRDOBA, Alta Gracia, Santa Fé, Galvez, Nogoyá, Victoria, Paraná, Villaguay, Paysandú, Salto, Negro Reservoir, Blanquillo, Melo

Maitencillo, Illapel, Marquesado, Villa d. Salvador, Chepes, Quines, Villa Dolores, Villa Maria, Bell Ville, Rosario, S. Nicolás, Gualeguaychú, Mercedes, Durazno, Trinta y Tres, Vico Pérez, S. Vitória do Palmar

La Ligua, Quillota, San Juan, Retamito, Renca, Río Cuarto, La Carlota, Rufino, Zárate, Campana, Colonia, Florida, Minas, Lag. da Mangueira

Los Vilos, Aconcagua 6960, Mendoza, Junín, San Luis, Sampacho, V. Mackenna, Rojas, BUENOS AIRES, Avellaneda, Maldonado, Rocha

Viña del Mar, Valparaíso, Los Andes, Lujan, S. Carlos, Mercedes, La Seña, Oral. Villegas, Lincoln, Lomas de Zamora, La Plata, MONTEVIDEO

SANTIAGO, S. Bernardo, Tunuyán, Villa Huidobro, Chivilcoy, 9 de Julio, Lobos, Chascomús, Las Pipinas

Rancagua, S. Fernando, S. Rafael, Gral. Alvear, Ing. Luiggi, Oral. Pico, Pehuajó, 25 de Mayo, Las Flores, Gral. Belgrano, C. S. Antonio

Pichilemu, Curicó, La Jaula, Malargüe, Lag. Llancanelo, Bordas Blancas, Arizona, Winifreda, S. Rosa, Trenque Lauquen, Gen. Alvear, Bolivar, Olavarría, Azul, Maipú, Dolores

Talca, Linares, Telén, Cereales, Doblas, Gen. Acha, A. Alsina, Cnel. Suárez, Juárez, Tandil, Ayacucho, Balcarce, Gén. Madariaga

Constitución, Cauquenes, Chillán, Algarrobo del Aguila, Río Colorado, Cnel. Pringles, Mar del Plata, C. Corrientes

Talcahuano, Concepción, Lota, Los Angeles, Chos Malal, El Huecú, Añelo, Neuquén, Gral. Roca, Bernasconi, Tornquist, Tres Arroyos, Defferrari, Copetonas, Necochea

P. Carnero, Lebu, Angol, Victoria, Zapala, Puelches, Bahía Blanca, Pedro Luro, I. Trinidad, Bahía Blanca

Carahue, Cunco, Temuco, Junín de los Andes, El Cuy, Choele-Choel, Cnel. F. Sosa, Gen. Conesa, I. Gama

Valdivia, Corral, P. Galera, Los Lagos, Neuquén, Río Negro, Valcheta, S. Antonio Oeste, Viedma, Carmen de Patagones, P. Bermeja

Osorno, L. Llanquihue, Tronador 3554, S. Carlos de Bariloche, Maquinchao, Pto. Lobos, G. of San Matías

Puerto Montt, Ancud, Pilcaniyeu, Norquinco, Valdés Pen., Pto. Madryn, P. Delgada

Chiloé, Castro, Esquel, Gastre, Gangán, Pto. Madryn, Rawson

C. Quilán, G. del Corcovado, V. Corcovado 2300, Techá, Vas Plumas, Cabo Raso

Archip. de los Chonos, I. Magdalena, Nueva Lubeca, Paso de Indios, Camarones, C. Dos Bahías

Sarmiento, Comodoro Rivadavia, G. of San Jorge

Puerto Aisén, Balmaceda, Holdich, Col. Las Heras

C. Taitao, Taitao Pen., C.° S. Valentín 4058, L. Buenos Aires, Deseado, Jaramillo, Deseado, C. Tres Puntas

C. Tres Montes, G. de Penas, C.° S. Lorenzo, Tres Cerros, P. Medanosa

I. Stuven, I. Campana, M. Puntudo 1047, Bahía Laura

I. S. Martín, L. Cardiel, S. Julián, C. Desengaño

I. Wellington, C.° Murallón 3600, L. Viedma

I. Madre de Díos, I. Duque de York, L. Argentino, Pto. Coig, Santa Cruz, R. Santa Cruz, Falkland I.s (Islas Malvinas) (Brit.)

I. Hanover, Bahía Grande, Río Gallegos, West Falkland (Gran Malvina), Stanley, East Falkland (I. Soledad), Falkland Sound

Pto. Natales, Esperanza, C. Vírgenes, Strait of Magellan

Strait of Magellan, Punta Arenas, Pen. Brunswick, B. S. Sebastián, Río Grande, San Diego, Le Maire Str., I. de los Estados

I. Desolación, I. S. Inés, Dawson, Tierra del Fuego, Ushuaia, C. San Juan, I. Navarino

I. Clarence, I. Londonderry, B. Cook, I. Hoste, Cap Horn

Ocean labels: PACIFIC OCEAN, ATLANTIC OCEAN

Region labels: CORDILLERA DE LOS ANDES, PATAGONIA, PARAGUAY, BRASIL, URUGUAY, CHILE

West from 50 Greenwich

Scale 1:12.000.000

0   50   100   200   300   400   500 km

BOLIVIA: AGRICULTURE AND MINING

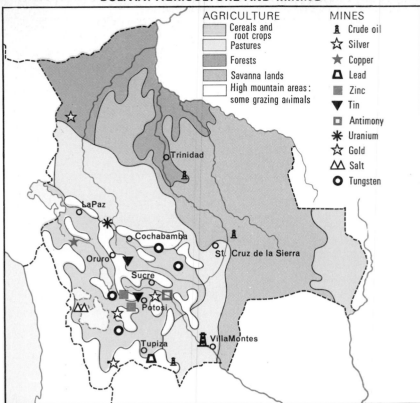

AGRICULTURE
- Cereals and root crops
- Pastures
- Forests
- Savanna lands
- High mountain areas: some grazing animals

MINES
- Crude oil
- Silver
- Copper
- Lead
- Zinc
- Tin
- Antimony
- Uranium
- Gold
- Salt
- Tungsten

BRAZIL: ACTUAL AND POTENTIAL MINERAL RESOURCES

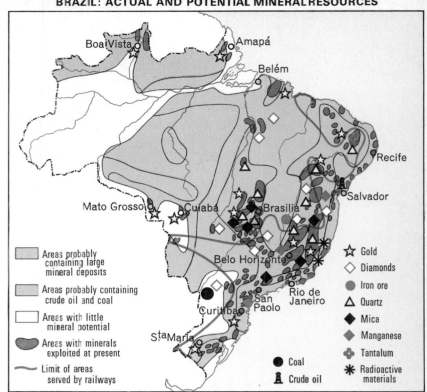

- Areas probably containing large mineral deposits
- Areas probably containing crude oil and coal
- Areas with little mineral potential
- Areas with minerals exploited at present
- Limit of areas served by railways

- Gold
- Diamonds
- Iron ore
- Quartz
- Mica
- Manganese
- Tantalum
- Radioactive materials
- Coal
- Crude oil

SOUTH AMERICA

The first inhabitants of South America were Indians. During the colonisation by European settlers the numbers of Indians became greatly reduced and in one area they were even totally exterminated. Today the population of South America is one-third white, about one-third Indian and the remaining third is made up of blacks, mestizos (mixed European and Indian), mulattoes and zambos (mixed Indian and black). The population is growing rapidly. In 1900 4% of the population of the Earth lived in South America. In 1981 this figure was nearly 5.6% (230 million). At this rate it will be 10% by the year 2000. The initial development of the continent followed more or less along the coastline, so that large areas of the interior were very sparsely settled. The white settlers were mainly interested in the exporting of South America's mineral wealth, so the first small townships were built near the coast. It was only in the last century that the interior was properly explored. With the exception of poor coal deposits, South America is well provided with mineral wealth. Before the conquest by the Spanish there existed the ancient and highly advanced civilisations of the Incas in modern-day Peru, and of the Mayas and Aztecs in Mexico. Many architectural and sculptural remains were discovered during the last century and today these form a tremendous source of tourist interest from all over the world.

THE EXPANSIONS OF THE INCA CIVILISATION

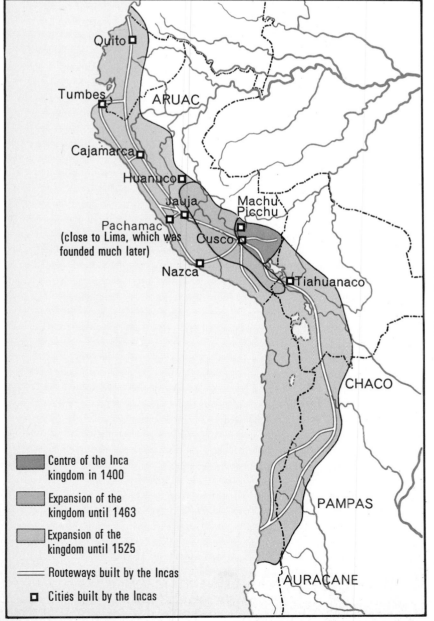

- Centre of the Inca kingdom in 1400
- Expansion of the kingdom until 1463
- Expansion of the kingdom until 1525
- Routeways built by the Incas
- Cities built by the Incas

ARGENTINA: AGRICULTURE

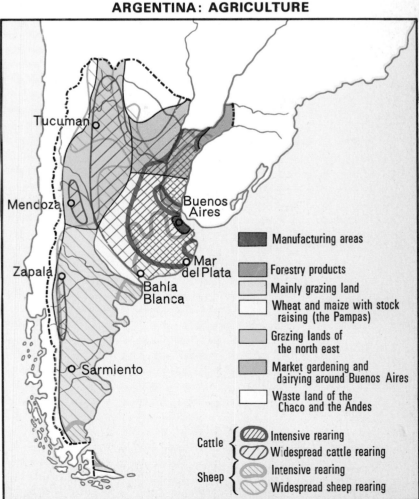

- Manufacturing areas
- Forestry products
- Mainly grazing land
- Wheat and maize with stock raising (the Pampas)
- Grazing lands of the north east
- Market gardening and dairying around Buenos Aires
- Waste land of the Chaco and the Andes

Cattle
- Intensive rearing
- Widespread cattle rearing

Sheep
- Intensive rearing
- Widespread sheep rearing

100 A 110 B 120 C 130 D 140 E 150 F 160 G 170 H

1

C H I N A

Yangtze-Kiang

Shikoku
Kyūshū
Tanega
Tokara Is.
Amami I.
Nampo Shotō

Ramapo Trench
(Izu Tr.)

A
S
I
A

Si-Kiang

East China Sea

2

Ryukyu Is.
Miyako
Okinawa 7507
Ishigaki
Taiwan
(Formosa)
3950

Formosa Str.

Bonin Is.

8848

Volcano Is.

10554

877

Minami Tori Shima
(Marcus)

Hong Kong

20

Ryukyu Trench

Philippine

Batan Is.
1879 Hainan

Babuyan Is.
4224

Parece Vela

Farallon de Pajaros

1379

Wake I.

P
A
C
I

Paracel
Islands

Luzon
267

Basin

Asuncion
Agrihan
Pagan

Mariana Is.
Anatahan
Saipan
Tinian
Rota
Guam

Taongi Atoll

Marshall Islands

S
o
u
t
h

C
h
i
n
a

S
e
a

Mindoro

Samar
Panay
Philippines
Negros
Leyte
10497

10793

1859

11022

Mariana Trench

Bikini
Rongelap

Eniwetok

M I C R O N E S I A

Ralik Chain
Ratak Chain

Kiribati

Palawan

Philippine Trench

Yap Is.
8527

Ulithi
Gaferut

Caroline

Hall Is.
Pulap
Truk Is.

Islands

Kwajalein
Atoll

Maleolap
Ailinglapalap
Jaluit

Arno
Mili

Balabac Str.
2867

Mindanao
Apo 2953
9580
6218

Palau Is.
(Belau)

Woleai
Eauripik

Ponape
Senyavin Is.

Makin

Bandar
Seri Begawan
Bunguran Is.
Kinabalu
4100

Sulu Sea

Sulu Arch.

Talaud Is.

Pulo-Anna

Mortlock Is.
Kusaie

Tarawa Atoll

Gilbert Is.

Iran Ra.

Tobi

M E L A N E S I A

Celebes Sea

Morotai

6920

Nukuoro

Kapingamarangi
Atoll

Nauru
Ocean I.

Nonouti

Kingsmill Is.
Arorae

Schwaner Ra.

B
o
r
n
e
o

M
o
l
u
c
c
a
s

Halmahera
Mapia Is.
Waigeo
Dampier Str.

G.of Tomini

Str. of Ujung
Pandang

Celebes
3440
Rantemario

Buru
Ceram

Sula Is.
Obi Is.

Waigeo
Kwoka
2999

Biak
Japen
Sarera
B.

Ninigo Group

C.d'Urville
Jayapura
New
Guinea

5050

St. Matthias
Group

Admiralty
Is.
New Hanover I.
New Ireland

Bougainville

Nakumanu Is.

Nanumea

Kapuas
Mahakam

0

Billiton

Banjarmasin

Barito

Java Sea Ujung Pandang
2871

Banda Sea

Aru Is.

Central Range
Finisterre Ra.
4694

4100

New
Britain

Bismarck
Archipelago

New Georgia
Choiseul
Sta. Isabel

Tuvalu
Ellice Is.

Nui
Vaitupu

Semarang
Madura

Flores Sea

5800

5400

Tanimbar Is.

Fly

Dia
4074
Owen Stanley Ra.

Trobriand Is.

Malaita

Funafuti
Atoll

Java

Lesser Sunda Is.
Wetar

Kai Is.

Kolepom I.

G. of
Papua

Port
Moresby

D'Entrecasteaux Is.

Duff Is.

Solomon Is.

Semeru 3676
Bali
Lombok
Sumbawa

Flores
Timor

Babar Is.

Arafura Sea

Torres Str.
C. York

Guadalcanal
S. Cristobal
Rennell

6061

Santa Cruz Is.

Mitre I.

Rotuma

Sumba

Roti

Timor
Sea

Melville I.
Cobourg Pen.

Cape
York
Pen.

Louisiade Arch.

Coral

4842

Banks Is.
Aurora

Fiji

Java Trench

7450

Arnhem
Land

Darwin
Jos.
Bonaparte
Gulf

G. of
Groote
Eylandt
Carpentaria

C. Melville

Cooktown

Sea

Mellish Reef

Espiritu Santo Is.
Malekula

Efate

Vanuatu
New
Hebrides

Viti Levu
132

10

6840

King Sd.

Kimberley
Fitzroy

Roper
Wellesley
Is.

Mitchell
Mt. Bartle Frere
1612

Great Barrier Reef

Chesterfield Is.

Bellona Reefs

New Hebrides Tr.
1631
Mt.Panie

Loyalty Is.
Uvea
Maré

Eromanga
Kandavu

Fiji

Barrow I.
De Grey

Hamersley Ra.
1227

L.Mackay
L. Disappointment

Great Sandy
Desert

Macdonnell Ranges
1510 Alice Springs

Barkly Tableland

Selwyn Ra.
Flinders
1213
1277

Rockhampton Cato

New
Caledonia

I. des Pins

Matthew

20

Exmouth G.
N.W.Cape
2910

Ashburton

1106
Mt.Augustus

Gibson Desert
L.Amadeus

A U S T R A L I A

1515

Diamantina

Barcoo

Brisbane
1356
C.Byron

Middleton Reef

South Fiji
5303

Basin

Tasman

Norfolk I.
3566

5548

Shark B.

Murchison
425
L.Austin

Mt.Augustus

Musgrave Ranges

Great Victoria
Desert

L.Eyre

Cooper's Cr.
Bourke

Warrego
Bulloo

New England
Ra.
1555

Lord Howe I.
870

4656

Dirk Hartog I.

L.Barlee

Nullarbor Plain

L.Torrens

Flinders

Macquarie Ra.

Liverpool Ra.

Darling

5944
Sydney

Sea

North C.
New

Perth

L.Moore
L.Cowan

Gawler Ra.
1189

Pt. Augusta

Lachlan
Murrumbidgee
Canberra

30

Geographe B.
1109
C.Leeuwin

Eyre
Pen.

Spencer
G.

Kangaroo I.

Encounter B.

Adelaide

Murray
2228
Australian
Alps
1167

Melbourne

Wilson's Prom.

Tasman

5364

Zealand
Ruapeh
2797

Southern Alps

Wellington

1105

I N D I A N

2498

Great Australian
Bight

South
Australian
Basin

5560

Port Phillip B.
King I.
1573
Ben Lomond
Hobart

Bass Strait

Furneaux Group

Basin

Mt.Cook
3764

Christchurch

Canterbury Bight

South Island

Scale 1:33 000 000

0 250 500 750 1000 1250 1500 km

0 250 500 750 1000 St.mls.

O C E A N

Tasmania

South East
Cape

West C.

Stewart I.

9

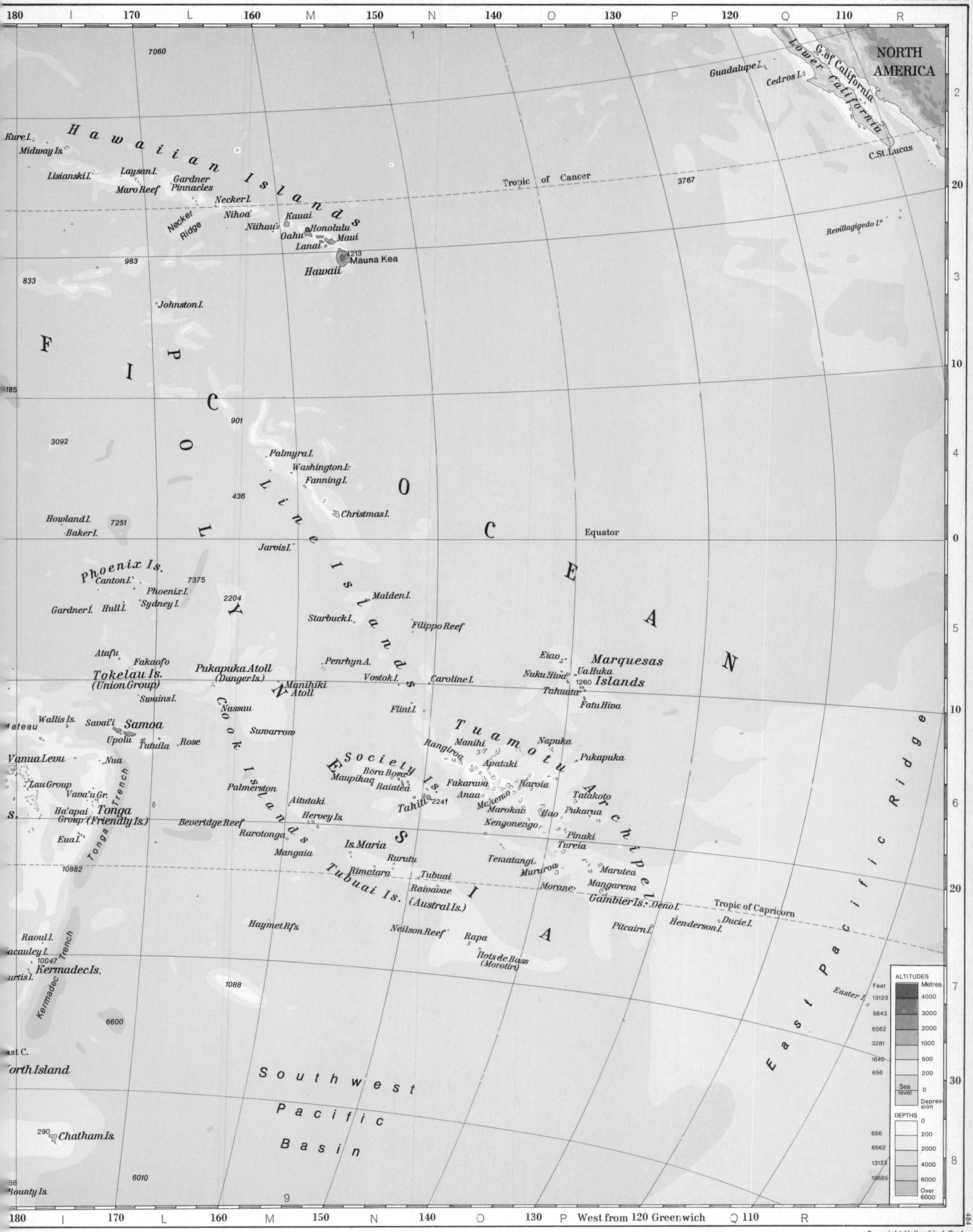

180   I   170   L   160   M   150   N   140   O   130   P   120   Q   110   R

7060

NORTH AMERICA

G. of California
Lower California

Guadalupe I.
Cedros I.

C. St. Lucas

Kure I.
Midway Is.
Lisianski I.
Laysan I.
Maro Reef
Gardner Pinnacles
Necker I.

Hawaiian Islands

Tropic of Cancer   3767

Revillagigedo I.ˢ

Necker Ridge
Nihoa
Niihau
Kauai
Oahu
Honolulu
Lanai
Maui
Hawaii
4213 Mauna Kea

983
833

Johnston I.

F

PACIFIC

Palmyra I.
Washington I.
Fanning I.

901

5185

3092

436

Christmas I.

Howland I.
Baker I.
7251

Line Islands

Jarvis I.

Equator

O C E A N

Phoenix Is.
Canton I.
7375
Phoenix I.
Sydney I.
Gardner I.
Hull I.
2204

Malden I.

Starbuck I.
Filippo Reef

Eiao
Ua Huka
Marquesas Islands
Nuku Hiva
1260
Tahuata
Fatu Hiva

Atafu
Fakaofo
Tokelau Is.
(Union Group)
Swains I.
Pukapuka Atoll
(Danger Is.)
Manihiki Atoll
Nassau
Penrhyn A.
Vostok I.
Caroline I.

Flint I.

Suvarrow

Wallis Is.
Savai'i
Samoa
Upolu
Tutuila
Rose

Nua

Vanua Levu
Lau Group
Vava'u Gr.
Ha'apai
Tonga Group (Friendly Is.)
Eua I.

Cook Islands
Palmerston
Aitutaki
Hervey Is.
Beveridge Reef
Rarotonga
Mangaia
Is. Maria
Rurutu

Society Is.
Bora Bora
Maupihaa
Raiatea
Tahiti 2241

Tuamotu Archipelago
Rangiroa
Manihi
Apataki
Fakarava
Anaa
Makemo
Marokau
Nengonengo
Pinaki
Tureia

Napuka
Pukapuka
Haraia
Tatakoto
Pukarua
Hao

Marutea
Mururoa
Mangareva
Morane
Gambier Is.
Oeno I.
Tropic of Capricorn

Rimatara
Tubuai
Raivavae
Tubuai Is. (Austral Is.)
Tematangi

Duale I.
Henderson I.

Haymet Rfs.
Neilson Reef
Rapa
Ilots de Bass (Morotiri)
Pitcairn I.

Vateau

Tonga Trench
Kermadec Trench

Raoul I.
Macauley I.
10047
Curtis I.
Kermadec Is.

6600

1088

Easter I.

ast C.
North Island

Southwest Pacific Basin

290 Chatham Is.

6010

Bounty Is.

East Pacific Ridge

ALTITUDES

Feet	Metres
13123	4000
9843	3000
6562	2000
3281	1000
1640	500
656	200
Sea level	0
	Depression

DEPTHS

656	200
6562	2000
13123	4000
19685	6000
	Over 6000

484

A 115 B 120 C 125 D 130 E 135

SURABAYA
Pasuruan
Java
Malang 3332 Singaraja 3142 Lombok
Semeru 3676 Banyuwangi Bali 3775
Mataram
2851 Raba
Ruteng Maumere Lomblen Alor
2382 Ocussi Dili
Ramelau 2920
2345 Timor
Sumbawa Flores Sawu Sea
Waingapu
Sumba 1225
Sawu Roti Kupang

INDONESIA
Arafura Sea
INDIAN OCEAN
Timor Sea

Sandy I. L
Scott Reef
Melville I.
Dundas Str. Croker I. Wessel Is.
Bathurst I. Cobourg Pen.
Pt. Hurd Van Diemen Gulf
Clarence Str. Arnhem
Darwin Aboriginal Reserve Land

Anson B.
Adelaide River
C. Talbot Joseph Bonaparte Gulf Pine Creek
Admiralty G. Aboriginal Reserve Daly Katherine
Bonaparte Archip. Mataranka Limmen Bight
Brunswick B. Birdum
Wyndham Ord Victoria Daly Waters Borroloola
Durack Newcastle Waters
King Sound Kimberley Inverway Wave Hill L. Woods Anthony Lagoon
Collier B. King Leopold Ranges Powell Creek
Dampier Land 1936 Derby Victoria River Downs Alexandria
Rowley Shoals Broome Fitzroy Hall's Creek NORTHERN
Fitzroy Crossing Gordon Downs Tennant Creek
La Grange Kura Soak Tanami TERRITORY
Eighty Mile Beach Gregory Salt Sea The Granites Elkedra
Joanna Spring Barrow Creek Sandover
Dampier Archipelago Great Sandy Desert L. Mackay Aileron Marshall
Port Hedland De Grey Percival Lakes
Barrow I. Roebourne L. Dora Macdonnell Ranges 1510
Fortescue Marble Bar L. Blanche L. Macdonald Alice Springs
North West C. Hamersley Ra. Roy Hill Patience Well Aboriginal Reserve
Exmouth G. Onslow 1227 L. Disappointment Gibson Desert L. Hopkins Lake Amadeus Finke Simpson
Yanrey Ashburton Mundiwindi 1219 Bundooma Desert
Lyndon WESTERN Mt. Deering Charlotte Waters
Geographe Ch. Salt Lake Lyons Mt. Augustus 1106 Weld Springs Musgrave Ranges 1515 Alberga Ilbunga
Gascoyne Peak Hill Carnegie Aboriginal Reserve Oodnadatta
Carnarvon Gascoyne L. Carnegie SOUTH Warrina Lake Eyre (North)
Naturaliste Ch. Shark B. Wooramel Wiluna L. Wells Wandunya L. Wright Coober Pedy Strangways Springs
Dirk Hartog I. Hamelin Pool Meekatharra AUSTRALIA L. Meramangye AUSTRALIA
Steep Pt. Big Bell Yeo L. Serpentine Lakes L. Dey-Dey Warrina
Ajana Murchison Cue L. Austin Mount Magnet Lavlers Laverton Rason L. L. Maurice
Northampton Greenough Mullewa Yalgoo L. Barlee Morgans Jubilee L. Ooldea Tarcoola Kingoonya Woomera
Geraldton L. Ballard Great Victoria Desert L. Gairdner
Geelvink Ch. L. Moore Menzies L. Carey Deakin L. Everard
Miling Broad Arrow Rawlinna Haig Nullarbor Plain Colona Penong L. Gairdner
Kalannie Kalgoorlie Forrest Nullarbor Eucla Fowlers Bay Ceduna
Moora Bullfinch Boulder Zanthus Eyre Iron Kno. 473
Darling Ra. Southern Cross L. Lefroy Streaky B. Minnipa
Northam Merredin L. Cowan Eyre Kimba
Perth The Johnston Lakes Norseman Balladonia Great Australian Bight Elliston Pen.
Fremantle Narrogin Newdegate L. Dundas
Geographe B. Wagin Ravensthorpe Esperance Port Lincoln
Collie 1122 Katanning Ongerup Hopetoun Archip. of the Recherche C. Catastrophe C. Spencer
C. Naturaliste Augusta 1109 Kingsco
C. Leeuwin Northcliffe Albany Kangaroo I.
Pt. D'Entrecasteaux Nornalup Bald Hd.

INDIAN OCEAN

Scale 1:12 000 000
0 50 100 200 300 400 500 km

110 A 115 B 120 C 125 D East from 130 Greenwich E 135

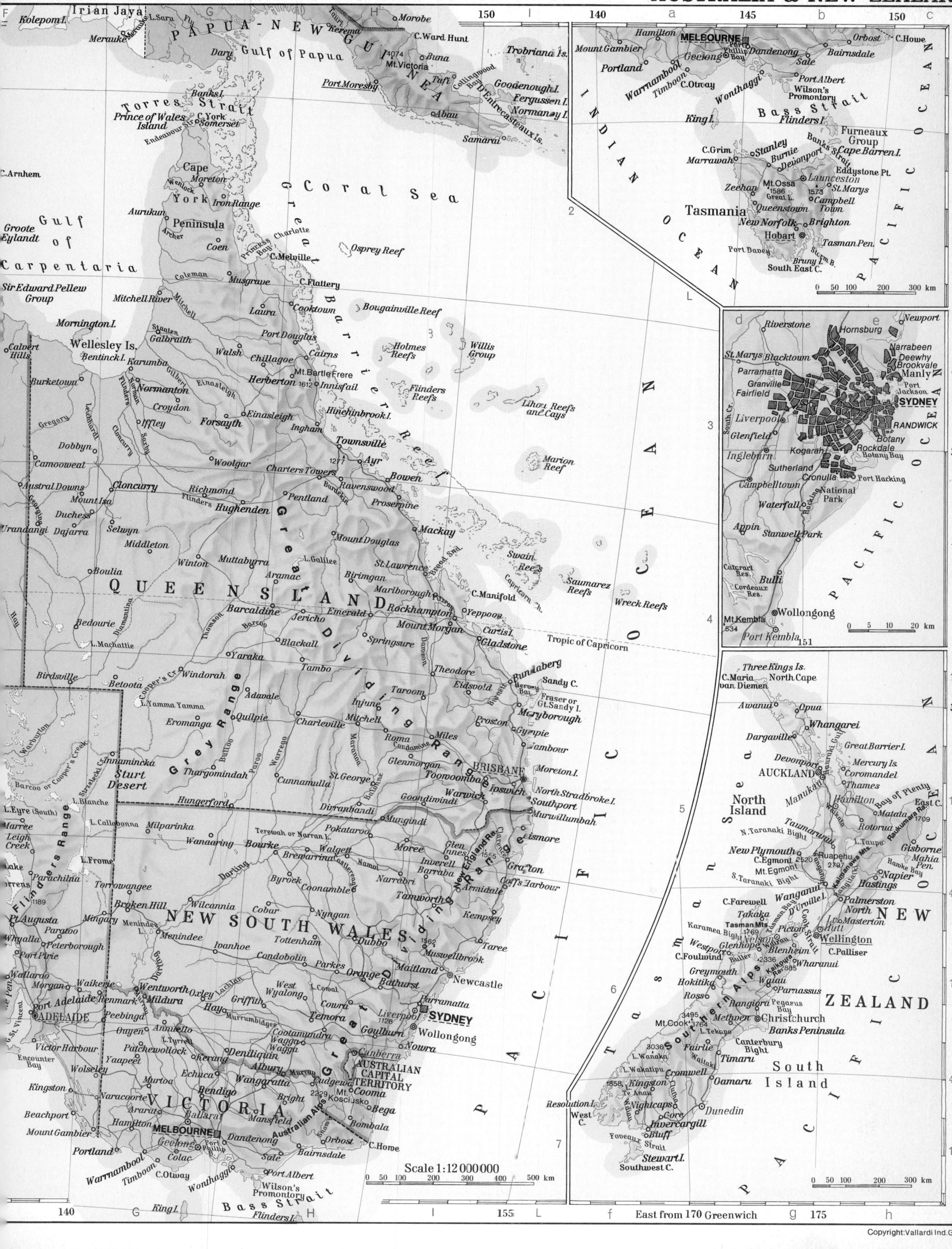

AUSTRALIA & NEW ZEALAND

Irian Jaya PAPUA-NEW GUINEA Gulf of Papua Morobe C. Ward Hunt Port Moresby Samarai

Torres Strait Prince of Wales Island Cape York Peninsula Coral Sea

Gulf of Carpentaria Sir Edward Pellew Group Groote Eylandt C. Arnhem

Wellesley Is. Mornington I. Burketown Normanton Croydon Forsayth

QUEENSLAND Cairns Townsville Charters Towers Mackay Rockhampton Gladstone Bundaberg Maryborough Gympie BRISBANE Ipswich Toowoomba Warwick

Tropic of Capricorn

Great Barrier Reef Willis Group Marion Reef Swain Reefs

NEW SOUTH WALES Broken Hill Bourke Dubbo Newcastle SYDNEY Wollongong Canberra AUSTRALIAN CAPITAL TERRITORY

Great Dividing Range Grey Range Flinders Range Sturt Desert

ADELAIDE Port Adelaide Mildura Murray

VICTORIA Ballarat Bendigo MELBOURNE Geelong Bass Strait

INDIAN OCEAN PACIFIC OCEAN

MELBOURNE Geelong Mount Gambier Portland Warrnambool King I. Bass Strait Flinders I. Furneaux Group

Tasmania Burnie Devonport Launceston Mt. Ossa 1586 Zeehan Queenstown New Norfolk Hobart Bruny I. South East C.

SYDNEY Parramatta Liverpool Botany Bay Manly Port Jackson Randwick Campbelltown National Park Wollongong Port Kembla

NEW ZEALAND North Cape Three Kings Is. Whangarei AUCKLAND Hamilton Bay of Plenty Rotorua L. Taupo New Plymouth Mt. Egmont Napier Hastings Wellington Cook Strait

South Island Southern Alps Mt. Cook 3764 Christchurch Greymouth Hokitika Timaru Oamaru Dunedin Invercargill Bluff Stewart I. Foveaux Strait

Tasman Sea PACIFIC OCEAN

Scale 1:12 000 000 0 50 100 200 300 400 500 km

East from 170 Greenwich

Copyright: Vallardi Ind. Graf.

m 150 M 160 West from 170 Greenwich L 180 East from 170 Greenwich 160 h 150 H

140 140

ALTITUDES
Metres Feet
3000 9843
1500 4921
500 1640
200 656
0

DEPTHS
0
200 656
1000 3281
2000 6562
3000 9843
Over 3000

PACIFIC OCEAN

Aleutian Islands
Andreanof Is.
Rat Is.
Near Is.
C. Lopatka
Kuril Islands
Uruppu I.
Iturup I.
La Pérouse Str.
Hokkaido

N g

Komandorskiye Is.
Petropavlovsk Kamchatski
Paramushir I.
Sea of Japan

Unimak I.
Bristol Bay
Pribilof Is.
Bering Sea
St. Matthew I.
C. Navarin
Mt. 4850 Klyuchevsk

Kamchatka Pen.
Sea of Okhotsk
Sakhalin

Kodiak I.
Nunivak I.
60
Gulf of Anadyr
Anadyr
Shelekhov Gulf
Magadan
Shantar Is.
Nikolayevsk

G. of Alaska
Seward
Alaska Pen.
Alaska Ra.
Norton Sound
Nome
Bering Strait
Chukchi Pen.
Koryak Ra.
Anadyr
Okhotsk
Dzhugdzhur Ra.
Amur

130 130

Queen Charlotte Islands
Alexander Archipelago
Kotzebue
De Dezhneva (east C.)
Chukot Ra.
Gydan Ra. (Kolyma)
Cherskiy Ra.
Verkhoyansk Ra.
Stanovoy Ra.

n f

Juneau
Mt. McKinley 6196
Yukon
U.S.A.
Alaska
Fairbanks
Brooks Ra.
Nizhne Kolymsk
UNION OF

Coast Range
Rocky Mountains
C A N A D A
Mackenzie Mts.
Dawson
Barrow
2816
C. Barrow
Kolyma
Wrangel I.
De Long Str.
Bear Is.
Indigirka
Verkhoyansk
Yakutsk
Aldan

120 120

Fort Liard
Ft. Mc Pherson
Peace
Mackenzie
Beaufort Sea
New Siberia
De Long Is.
New Siberian Islands
Lyakhov Is.
SOVIET

O f

Great Slave Lake
Great Bear Lake
Amundsen Gulf
80
Kotelny I.
Olenek
Lena
Vilyuysk
Lena

110 110

L. Athabasca
Banks I.
M'Clure Str.
Laptev Sea
Nordvik
L. Taymyr
SOCIALIST

o P

Dubawnt L.
Victoria I.
Melville I.
Pr. Patrick I.
C. Chelyuskin
Bolshevik I.
Taymyr Pen.
Tunguska
Lower

100 100

Garry
Melville Pen.
Borden I.
Severnaya Zemlya
October Revolution I.
Dudinka
Stony
Yenisey

P E

Churchill
King William Wales I.
Prince of Wales I.
Queen Elizabeth Islands
Sverdrup Is.
North Pole
Komsomolets I.
90
3

Hudson
I. Boothia
Somerset I.
A. Heiberg I.
1
ARCTIC
1
Yenisey
Gydan Pen.
Salekhard
Surgut

90 90

Southampton I.
Boothia Pen.
Brodeur Pen.
G. of Boothia
Ellesmere I.
OCEAN
Franz Josef Land
Graham Bell I.
Wilczek Ld.
Bely I.
Gulf of Ob
Irtysh

p D

Melville Pen.
Bylot I.
Smith Sd.
George Land
Novaya Zemlya
Gydan Pen.
Taz
Ob
Tobolsk

80 80

Foxe Pen.
Foxe Basin
Baffin Island
Baffin Bay
Peary Ld.
80
North East Land
Kara Sea
Kolguyev I.
1894 Narodnaya
Tobolsk

Nettilling L.
Cumberland Peninsula
Disko I.
Spitsbergen
Svalbard
Barents Sea
Kanin Pen.
Pechora
Yamantau 1638

70 70

C. Chidley
Davis Strait
Kg. Christian X Id.
Shannon
Greenland Sea
Bear I.
North C.
Murmansk
Kola Pen.
White Sea
Arkhangelsk
N. Dvina

q C

Labrador
Ungava Bay
2941
Greenland (Den.)
Jan Mayen
70
L. Inari
Lappland
Onega
L. Onega

60 60

Frederikshåb
King Christian IX Ld.
Mt. Forel 3385
Scoresby Sd.
NORWAY
Narvik
Lofoten Is.
Gorkiy
Kazan
Volga
Kuybyshev

r B

ATLANTIC
King Frederik VI Ld.
Angmagssalik
Denmark Strait
C. Farewell
Norwegian Sea
Trondheim
SWEDEN
FINLAND
Ladoga
Helsinki

Öraefajökull 2119
ICELAND
Reykjavik
Arctic Circle
Umeå
Luleå
Oulu
Umeå
Indalo
G. of Bothnia
Estonia
2481

50 50

OCEAN
Faeroe Is.
Shetland Is.
60
Bergen
Oslo
Vänern
Stockholm
Åland
Gotland
Riga
Latvia
Lithuania

Rockall
Orkney Is.
British Isles
Scotland
Glasgow
North Sea
Vättern
Skagerrak
Copenhagen
Kattegat
Gdańsk
Warsaw

Scale 1:30000000
0 250 500 750 1000 1250 1500 km
0 250 500 750 1000 St. mls.

Itineraries of the main Arctic expeditions
Peary-1908-1909
Amundsen-Nobile (Norwegian) -1926
Byrd-1926
Nobile-1928
Limit of the inhabited areas

South Limit of Drift Ice

DENMARK
GREAT
Dublin IRELAND
BRITAIN
England
London
St. George's Ch.
Bristol Ch.
English Channel
FRANCE
Le Havre
NETH. Amst.
BELGIUM
LUX.
Hamburg
Bonn Berlin
W. GERM. E. GERM.
Frisian Is.
Oder
POLAND
Prague CZECHOSLOVAKIA
Vienna AUSTRIA HUNGARY
Munich
Danube

SPITSBERGEN inset:
10 20 30
Sjuøyane
North C. C. Platen
C. Smith
White I.
Danskøya
Moffen
Wijdel
Haakon VII Land
Hinlopen Strait
North-East Land
Storøya
Ny Ålesund
Friesland
Newton
C. Mohn
King Karls Land
Prins Karls Forland
Spitsbergen
Barents
Svenskøya
Is. Fjorden
Bell Sun.
Edge
Stor Fjorden
Abeløya
Forell Land
Freeman Str.
Negerpynten
C. South

SPITSBERGEN
Scale 1:10000000
0 50 100 150 200 km

Copyright: Vallardi Ind. Graf.

m   30   M   20   l   West from 10 Greenwich   L   0   i   East from 10 Greenwich   I   20   h   30   H

Stations for scientific researches

- ● Argentina
- ▲ Australia
- ■ Chile
- ⬟ France
- ✳ United Kingdom
- ◆ New Zealand
- ✦ South Africa
- ★ United States
- ✶ U.S.S.R.

Northern limit of drift ice
Average limit of drift ice
Limit of pack ice

ATLANTIC OCEAN

Bouvet I. (Nor.)

Prince Edward I. (S. Afr.)   Marion Is.

Traversay Is.

Grytviken

South Georgia

Shag Rocks

South Sandwich Islands

Scotia Sea

Falkland Is.Dependency

Antarctic Circle

60

70

Sanae

Novolazarevskaya

Princess Martha Coast   Princess Astrid Coast   Princess Ragnhild Coast

Lazarev

Princess Astrid

Wohlthat Mts.

Ritscher Upland
4200

2717

Queen Maud Land

Prince Harald Coast

3426

Prince Olaf Coast

Lützow-Holm Bay

C.Ann

1216

Mt.Chr stensen

Enderby Land

Amundsen Bay

Proclamation I.

2260

Edward VIII Bay

Kemp Coast

Mawson

Colbeck Arch.

Douglas Is.

South Orkney Islands

Laurie I.

Coronation I.

Signi Is.

Orcadas

Falkland Is. (Islas Malvinas)

SOUTH AMERICA

Drake Passage

Elephant I.

South Shetland Islands

King George I.

Cap. A. Pratt

Deception

Pres. Pedro Aguirre Cerda

Livingston I.

Pres.G.Gonzales Videla

Palmer Arch.

Anvers I.

Biscoe Is.

Joinville I.

Hope Bay

Esperanza

Gen.Bernardo O'Higgins

Ross I.

Ten. Matienzo

Bransfield Str.

Graham Land

Larsen Ice Shelf

Antarctic Peninsula

Halley

Weddell Sea

Coats Land

Luitpold Coast

Caird Coast

Gen. Belgrano

Ellsworth

Theron Mts.

80

Adelaide I.

Adelaide

Marguerite B.

Fossil Bluff

Alexander I.

Charcot I.

Ashley Snow I.

George VI Sound

Wilkins Coast

Dyer Plateau

Palmer Land

Joerg Plateau
2896

Filchner Ice Shelf

Berkner I.

Edith Ronne Land

Pensacola Mountains
3658

Robert English Coast

Mac Robertson Land
2646

3353

Pr. Charles Mts.

Amery Ice Shelf

C.Darnley

Mackenzie Bay

Ingrid Christensen Land

Prydz Bay

Davis

American Highland

4267

Leopold and Astrid Coast

Gaussberg
371

Bellingshausen Sea

Peter I°I.

Rights Coast

Ellsworth Land

ANTARCTICA

Ellsworth Mts.
5139

Vinson Massif

Thiel Mts.
2812

South Pole
2800

Amundsen-Scott

Polar

Sub-Glacial

Basin

1

2

Wilhelm II Coast

Queen Mary Coast

Davis Sea
1609

Mirny

Drygalski I.

Masson I.

Shackleton Ice Shelf

Thurston I.

C.Flying Fish

Pine I.Bay

Hudson Mts.

Byrd

Hollick Kenyon Plateau
3022

Horlick Mts.

3932

Queen Maud Ra.

Mt.Nansen

Mt.Amundsen

Mill I.

Bowman I.

Amundsen Sea

Martin Pen.

Walgreen Coast

Byrd Land

Byrd

Sub-Glacial

Basin

Mt.Sidley
4221

Rockefeller Plateau

Queen Alexandra Ra.

Mt.Markham

Shackleton Inlet

Ross Ice Shelf

Wilkes Sub-Glacial Basin

Wilkes

Vincennes Bay

Wilkes

Budd Coast

C.Poinsett

C.Dart

Mt.Siple
4575

Wrigley G.

Hobbs Coast

Cruzen I.

Edsel Ford Ra.
3496

Rockefeller Mts.

Edward VII Pen.

Roosevelt I.

Little America

Ice Barrier

Mt.M'Clintock
3609

Mt.Erebus
3794

Ross I.

McMurdo

Scott

Victoria Land

Prince Albert Mts.

Sabrina Coast

Banzare Coast

Paulding B.

C.Goodenough

Porpoise Bay

Ross Sea

Terra Nova B.
2774

Kay Is.

Coulman I.

Mt.Levick

Mt.Sabine
3350

Hallett

C.Adare

C.North

Oates Coast

George V Coast

Adélie Land

Dumont D'Urville

Rennick B.

C.Hudson

Robertson B.

70

Scott I.

Balleny Islands

South Magnetic Pole

Antarctic Circle

60

Macquarie Is.

Campbell I.

Auckland Is.

Antipodes Islands

Bounty Is.

Stewart I.

Tasmania

Tasman Sea

PACIFIC OCEAN

INDIAN OCEAN

ALTITUDES

Metres	Feet
3000	9843
2000	6562
1000	3281
Sea level	0
Depression	

DEPTHS

0	0
1000	3281
2000	6562
3000	9843
4000	13123
5000	16404
Over 4000	

Itineraries of the main Antarctic expeditions

- —— Cook-1773-1775
- – – – Gauss-1901-1902
- ·—·—· Scott-1903-1911-1913
- ········ Amundsen-1911
- +++++++ Ellsworth's flight-1935
- —··—··— Hillary-Fuchs-1957-1958

Scale 1:30 000 000

0   250   500   750   1000   1250   1500 km

0   250   500   750 St.mls.

NEW ZEALAND   East from 160 Greenwich   AUSTRALIA

West from 170 Greenwich   180

150   S   160   T   A   B   b

COUNTRIES AND COLONIAL DEPENDENCIES IN 1914

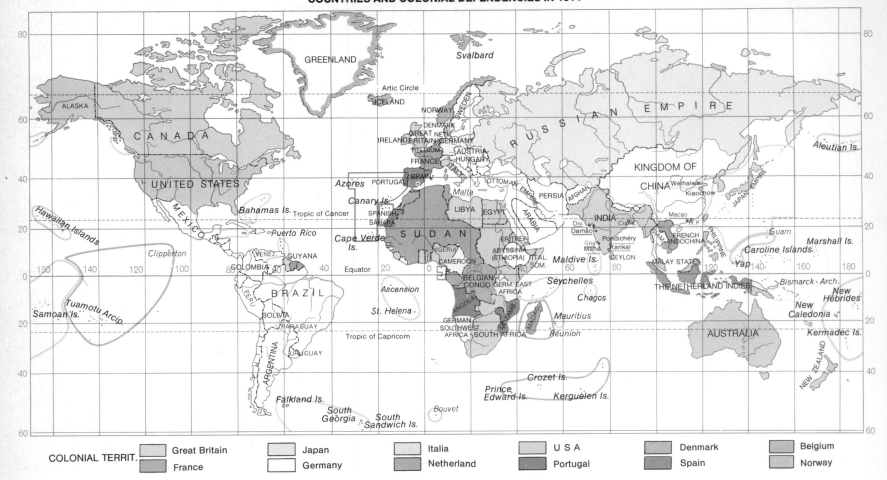

GREENLAND
Svalbard
ALASKA
Artic Circle
ICELAND
NORWAY SWEDEN
CANADA
DENMARK
GREAT NETH.
IRELAND BRITAIN GERMANY
BELGIUM AUSTRIA
FRANCE HUNGARY
SPAIN
ITALY
PORTUGAL
Azores
Canary Is.
Bahamas Is. Tropic of Cancer
SPANISH
SAHARA
Puerto Rico
Cape Verde
Is.
Clipperton
COLOMBIA
VENEZ. GUYANA
SUDAN
Equator
NIGERIA
CAMEROON
BRAZIL
Ascension
PERU
BOLIVIA
PARAGUAY
St. Helena
GERMAN
SOUTHWEST
AFRICA
Tropic of Capricorn
ARGENTINA
URUGUAY
Samoan Is.
Tuamotu Arcip.
Falkland Is.
South
Georgia
South
Sandwich Is.
Bouvet
Prince
Edward Is.
Crozet Is.
Kerguelen Is.
RUSSIAN EMPIRE
KINGDOM OF CHINA Weihaiwei
Kiaochow
OTTOMAN EMPIRE PERSIA
AFGHAN.
Malta
LIBYA EGYPT
ARABIA
Diu
Damão
INDIA
Goa
Mahé
Pondichéry
Karikal
ABYSSINIA
(ETHIOPIA)
ERITREA
ITAL.
SOM.
Maldive Is.
CEYLON
BELGIAN
CONGO GERM. EAST
AFRICA
ANGOLA
Seychelles
Chagos
Mauritius
Réunion
MADAGASCAR
SOUTH AFRICA
Macao
FRENCH
INDOCHINA
MALAY STATES
THE NETHERLAND INDIES
JAPAN EMPIRE
Aleutian Is.
PHILIPPINE
Guam
Caroline Islands
Yap
Marshall Is.
Bismarck - Arch.
New
Hebrides
New
Caledonia
AUSTRALIA
NEW ZEALAND
Kermadec Is.
Hawaiian Islands
UNITED STATES
MEXICO

COLONIAL TERRIT.
Great Britain
France
Japan
Germany
Italia
Netherland
Portugal
USA
Spain
Denmark
Norway
Belgium

WORLDWIDE POLITICAL AND ECONOMIC ORGANISATION

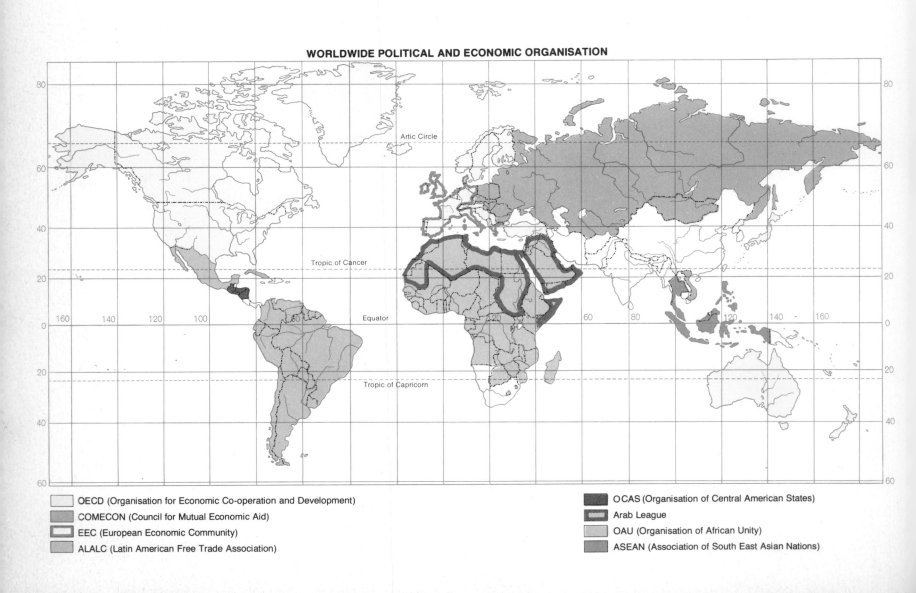

Artic Circle
Tropic of Cancer
Equator
Tropic of Capricorn

OECD (Organisation for Economic Co-operation and Development)
COMECON (Council for Mutual Economic Aid)
EEC (European Economic Community)
ALALC (Latin American Free Trade Association)
OCAS (Organisation of Central American States)
Arab League
OAU (Organisation of African Unity)
ASEAN (Association of South East Asian Nations)

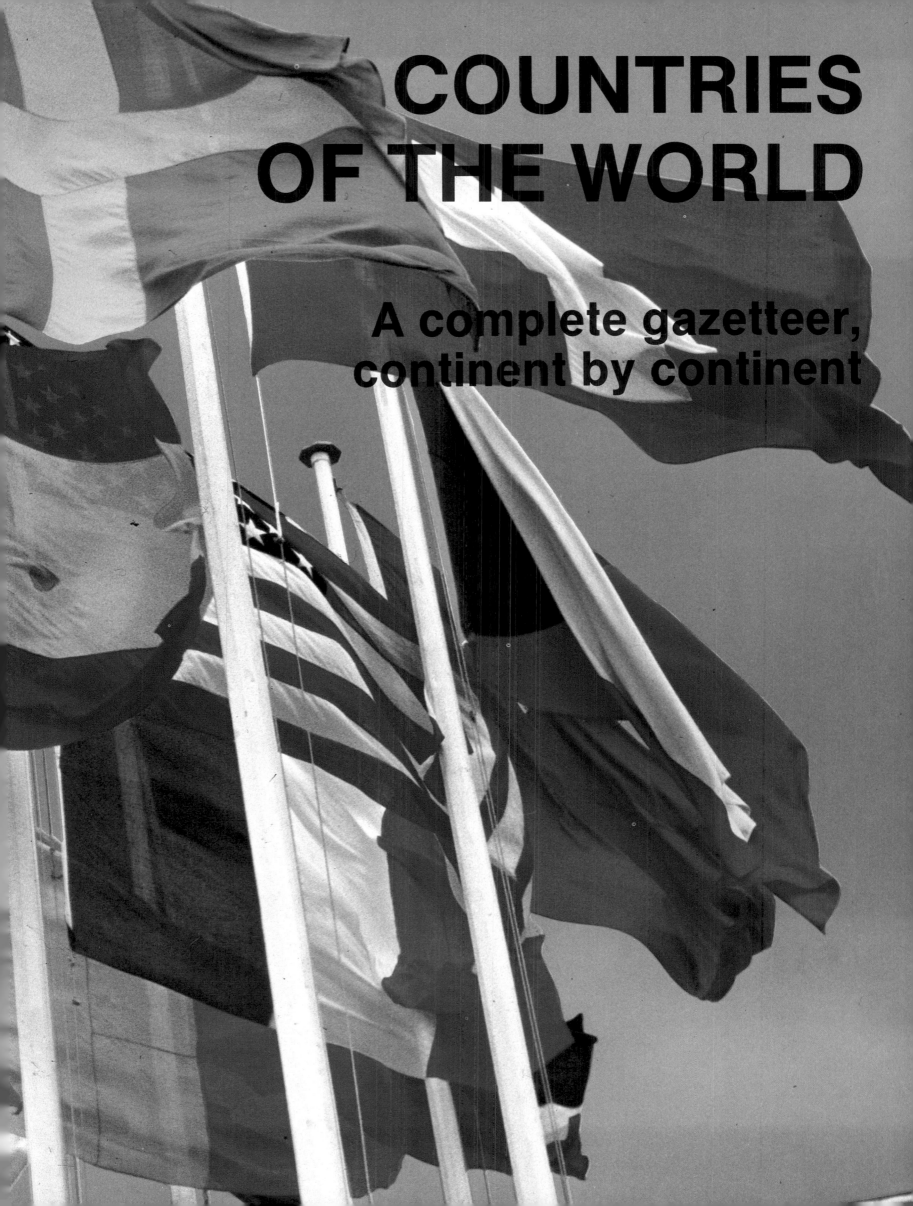

COUNTRIES OF THE WORLD

A complete gazetteer, continent by continent

Europe

The limited surface of the continent of Europe and its geographical position make it in effect an extension of the continent of Asia. Historically and economically, however, it is an area of unique importance. Natural conditions and historical motivations have created strong concentrations of population in the low-lying areas, which are often also the most industrialized and subject to the most intense agricultural exploitation. The temperate climate, the nearness of the sea to practically all areas, the abundance of inland sources of water and the richness in raw materials have encouraged human settlement and made it a focal point for exchange and contact. In contrast the enormously varied physical, ethnic, cultural and economic character of the area is reflected in the large number of states into which the continent is divided.

In the north the Scandinavian countries have overcome the difficult conditions created by the climate by the shrewd exploitation of their natural resources and the harmonious development of their political institutions. Great Britain, which for a long time occupied a marginal position in terms of European history and economics, became with her industrial revolution the leading economic and political power in the world. Only after the two world wars, the accompanying emergence of the USA and the USSR and the break-up of her empire did she re-establish ties with continental Europe by entering the European Community.

The variety, both of natural and human landscapes, of ethnic groups and languages, and of political and economic structures, make it difficult to find an equivalent common denominator between the peoples of central Europe. In the south we have Alpine states like Austria and Switzerland whose history and economics have been influenced by their position within the confines of mountain ranges of over 4,000 metres in height. At the centre there is Germany at the hub of the Slav, Anglo-Saxon and Latin worlds. It is already one of the most important industrial powers in the world. After the Second World War it was divided into West Germany which, thanks to an exceptional economic recovery, enjoyed a high standard of living, and East Germany which was the most advanced of the Socialist countries. In October 1990 the two countries re-united. The other states of central-eastern Europe were linked, though in varying degrees to the political and economic systems of the USSR.

In the west France, with its variety of natural and human landscapes, is like a compendium of European geography. Political unity, achieved and consolidated many centuries ago, was accompanied by attempts to become the dominant European power. Meanwhile in common with the neighbouring Benelux countries France enjoys a comfortable standard of living, fruit of a well balanced combination of agricultural and industrial economies.

Among the states of southern Europe Spain and Portugal have recently initiated modern economic policies which are bringing them in line with the rest of Europe. Italy, which occupies a central position both in the Mediterranean and with respect to the continent, has a large population on limited and mountainous territory. It is characterised by a socio-economic structure which has moved in a short time from being fundamentally agricultural to essentially industrial, and by the unequal distribution between north and south of development and earnings, in favour of the north. Of the remaining Mediterranean states Yugoslavia and Albania are more open to establishing relationships with the Danube areas. The federal character of the political structure of the former is the result of ethnic differences and the fragmented nature of the territory, which are also having repercussions on the transition from an agricultural to an industrial economy. The second is still lagging economically, partly because of its political isolation. Greece with its harsh mountainous landscape encouraging maritime communications is by tradition Mediterranean. However, with its predominantly agricultural economy, it suffers today from a marginal position in respect to European traffic. Romania and Bulgaria, united physically and geographically by the Danube but separated by ethnic and linguistic differences, are both behind in respect to other Eastern European countries. This is due in part to their centuries-old isolation from the rest of Europe. Lastly, situated on the vast East European Plain, is the Republic of Russia, the largest of the states of the USSR with borders on Eastern Europe. After the 1917 Revolution and its victory in the Second World War the Soviet Union changed its economic structure and, from being a predominantly agricultural country, it became one of the most important industrial powers in the world.

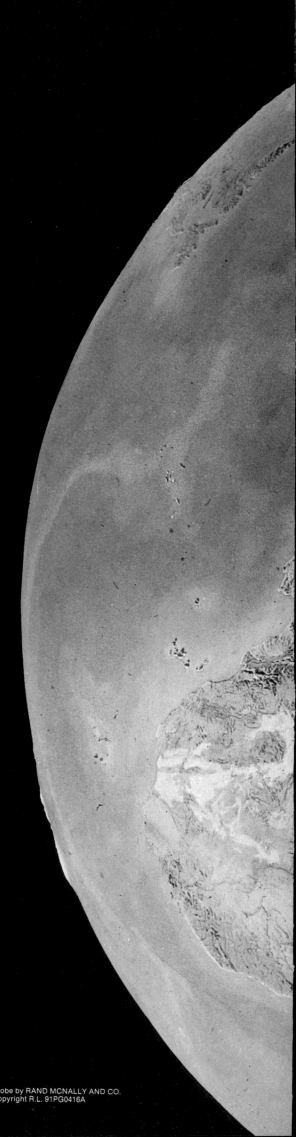

Austria: The Schönbrunn Palace in Vienna

ALBANIA

Shqipëria/Republika Popullóre Socialiste e Shqipërisë

Albania is a Socialist People's Republic. The head of state is the President of the Presidium, whose members are elected from the uni-cameral People's Assembly. This is in turn elected for 4 years by direct universal suffrage from the list of candidates provided by the Democratic Front (the name taken by the Communist Party in 1949). It has legislative power which is, however, endowed by the government and subject to government veto. Thus executive power in fact resides with the Presidium and the government.
Albania is a member of UNO and lays claim to the areas of Kosovo in Yugoslavia and Epirus in northern Greece.
It is a mountainous country, bordering on the Adriatic Sea. The soil is predominantly chalky, with limestone features in the north.
Area: 28,750 sq km.
Population: 3,100,000; 107 per sq km. Albanian 98%; Macedonian and Montenegran minorities.
Annual growth rate: 2.5%; birth rate 26‰; death rate 5‰; average life expectancy: 68 years.
Capital: Tirana (pop 225,000).
Other important towns: Cërrik (61,000); Durrës (79,000); Elbasan (78,000); Shkodër (76,000); Vlorë (67,000).
Land use: cultivated 23%; grazing 20%; wooded 43%; uncultivated 14%. Main agricultural products: wheat, maize, sugar beet, potatoes. Mineral resources: oil, bitumen.
Official language: Albanian.
Religion: Muslim; Orthodox and Catholic minorities.
Gross National Product: US $ 2,600 million; per capita US $ 860.
Currency: Lek = 100 quindarka.

ANDORRA

Principat d'Andorra/
Principauté d'Andorre

A principality, founded in 1278, Andorra is a republic under the joint suzerainty of the French head of state and the Bishop of Urgel in Spain. These two co-protectors are represented respectively by the Viguier Français and the Veguer Episcopal to whom are submitted motions and proposals on the part of the legislative and executive bodies. The General Council of the Valleys (Concell General) is formed of 28 members elected for 4 years by direct universal suffrage. It has

legislative power and nominates the government which has the executive power.
A small mountainous state in the Pyrenees, it is covered with forest and pastureland.
Area: 455 sq km.
Population: 47,000; 103 per sq km.
Annual growth rate: 5%.
Capital: Andorra la Vella (pop 15,000).
Land use: cultivated: 2%; grazing 56%; wooded 22%; uncultivated 20%. Main agricultural products: cheese, potatoes, tobacco.
Official language: Catalan.
Religion: Catholic.
Currency: French franc and Spanish peseta.

AUSTRIA

Österreich/Republik Österreich

Austria is a federal republic, composed of the following 9 federal units (Bundesländer): Vienna, Lower Austria, Upper Austria, Burgenland, Carinthia, Salzburg, Styria, Tyrol and Vorarlberg, each of which enjoys a large degree of autonomy. Within the federation legislative and executive power is exercised by the parliament, which is made up of the National Council (Nationalrat), elected for 4 years by direct universal suffrage, and the Federal Council (Bundesrat), whose members are appointed by the Diets of each Bundesland, the numbers being proportional to the population of each Bundesland. Executive power is entrusted to the Chancellor, who is nominated by the President of the Republic, and to the government. Both are answerable to the National Council. The President of the Republic is elected for 6 years by direct universal suffrage.
Austria is a member of UNO, the Council of Europe, EFTA, and OECD. It has no outlet to the sea, is mountainous in the south with a vast Alpine area, and descends gradually in the north and the north-east towards the Danube plain.
Area: 83,855 sq km. Political-administrative division into 9 federal units (Bundesländer): Lower Austria, Upper Austria, Burgenland, Carinthia, Salzburg, Styria, Tyrol, Vienna, Vorarlberg.
Population: 7,503,000; 90 per sq km. Annual growth rate: 0.1%; birth rate: 11‰; death rate: 12‰; average life expectancy: 72 years.
Capital: Vienna (pop 1,562,000).
Other important towns: Graz (250,000); Innsbruck (120,000); Klagenfurt (85,000); Salzburg (140,000); Villach (55,000); Wels (53,000).
Land use: Cultivated: 18%; grazing 24%; wooded 39%; uncultivated 19%. Main agricultural products: wheat, barley, maize, rye, oats, sugar beet, potatoes. Mineral resources: lignite, iron.
Official language: German. Minority languages: Slovene in Carinthia and Styria; Hungarian in Burgenland; Croatian in Burgenland and Styria.
Religions: Catholic (89%); Protestant (6%).
Gross National Product: US $ 94,000 million; per capita US $ 12,400.
Currency: Schilling = 100 groschen.

BELGIUM

Belgique/België
Royaume de Belgique/Koninkrijk België

Belgium is a hereditary constitutional monarchy. The sovereign exercises executive power through the royally appointed Council of Ministers and legislative power together with the bicameral parliament. The two chambers are the Senate, composed of the Crown Prince and members who are mostly elected for 4 years by direct universal suffrage; and the Chamber of Deputies who are

also elected by direct universal suffrage for 4 years.
Belgium is a member of UNO, Benelux, the Council of Europe, the EEC, OECD and WEU.
It borders on the North Sea, is nearly completely flat, with fertile soil and a damp marine climate.
Area: 30,515 sq km.
Population: 9,900,000; 325 per sq km. Annual growth rate: 0.3%; birth rate: 12‰; death rate: 11‰; average life expectancy: 71 years.
Capital: Brussels (pop 1,010,000).
Other important towns: Antwerp (480,000); Brugge/Bruges (120,000); Charleroi (225,000); Ghent (245,000); Liège/Luik (440,000); Louvain/Leuven (88,000); Namur (105,000).
Land use: cultivated 27%; grazing 24%; wooded 21%; uncultivated 28%. Main agricultural products: sugar beet, potatoes, barley, wheat, oats. Mineral resources: coal.
Official languages: Flemish (57%) and French (32%).
Religion: Catholic.
Gross National Product: US $ 111, 770 million; per capita: US $ 11,250.
Currency: Belgian franc = 100 centimes.

BERLIN

The city was governed from 1st July 1948 by a four-party government: American, British, French and Soviet. On 30th November 1948 in the sector occupied by the Soviet troops a separate Municipal Administration was created, subsequently to be transferred to the German Democratic Republic. Thus began a more and more marked distinction between West Berlin under American, British and French administration, and East Berlin. This division reached its culmination with the building of the Berlin Wall. With it, though not officially part of East Germany, East Berlin became the "de facto" capital of the German Democratic Republic. With German reunification Berlin has once again become the state capital.
Area: 885 sq km.
Population: 3,050,000.

BULGARIA

Bulgariya/Narodna Republika Bulgariya

Bulgaria is a People's Republic. The governing body was the Council of State, whose chairman was also head of state. The members of the Council of State were chosen by the National Assembly, which exercised legislative power. The National Assembly was composed of members elected for 4 years by direct universal suffrage from the Communist Party (Patriotic Front), but was subject to nomination and revocation by the government, who had executive power. Profound institutional changes are now taking place.
Bulgaria is a member of UNO, Comecon and the Warsaw Pact.
There are alternating mountainous and low-lying areas with the Rhodope and Balkan mountains and the plain in between and, to the north, the Danube valley. The eastern coast borders on the Black Sea.
Area: 110,910 sq km.
Population: 8,900,000; 80 per sq km.
Bulgarians (89%), Turks (8%), gypsies (1.5%). Annual growth rate: 0,1%; birth rate 13.5‰; death rate 12‰; average life expectancy: 71 years.
Capital: Sofia (pop 1,130,000).
Other important towns: Burgas (168,000); Pleven (125,000); Plovdiv (345,000); Ruse

France: Mont St Michel Abbey

(170,000); Stara Zagora (135,000); Varna (288,000).
Land use: cultivated 38%, grazing 18%, wooded 35%, uncultivated 9%. Main agricultural products: wheat, sunflowers, tobacco. Mineral resources: lignite, copper, iron ore, oil.
Official language: Bulgarian.
Religion: Orthodox, with Catholic and Muslim minorities.
Gross National Product: US $ 47,000 million; per capita: US $ 5,200.
Currency: Lev = 100 stótinki.

CZECHOSLOVAKIA

Československo/Československá Republika

Czechoslovakia was a socialist federal republic, composed of the two federal units Bohemia/Moravia and Slovakia. The head of state is the President of the Republic, who used to be elected for 6 years by parliament. Legislative power lay with the bicameral parliament, which consisted of the Chamber of the People and the Chamber of the Nations. Members of the first were elected from the list of Communist Party members and of the second equally from the two federal units. Executive power was in the hands of the federal government. According to the constitution the Communist Party had the function of guide to society and state. Since 1989 profound institutional changes have been taking place.
Czechoslovakia is a member of UNO, Comecon, and the Warsaw Pact.
Completely landlocked, it is predominantly hilly. There are three geographical regions: Bohemia and Moravia which are surrounded by mountains, but are low-lying and cultivated; and Slovakia which is mountainous and predominantly grazing land and woods.
Area: 127,880 sq km. Political-administrative division into 2 federal units: Bohemia/Moravia and Slovakia.
Population: 15,600,000; 122 per sq km.
Annual growth rate: 0,2%; birth rate 14‰; death rate 12‰; average life expectancy: 71 years.
Capital: Prague (pop 1,195,000).
Other important towns: Bratislava (375,000); Brno/Brünn (373,000); Košice (205,000); Liberec (85,000); Ostrava (325,000); Pilsen (170,000).
Land use: cultivated 38%, grazing 13%, wooded 36%, uncultivated 13%. Main agricultural products: sugar beet, wheat, barley, rye, potatoes. Mineral resources: coal, lignite.

Belgium: The Grand-Place in Brussels

France: Chenonceaux Castle in the Loire valley

Official languages: Czech and Slovak.
Religion: Catholic with Protestant minorities.
Gross National Product: US $ 100,000 million. per capita US $ 6,500.
Currency: Czechoslovakian koruna = 100 haleru.

DENMARK

Danmark/Kongeriget Danmark

Denmark is a hereditary constitutional monarchy. The sovereign exercises legislative power through the unicameral parliament, whose members are elected for 4 years by direct universal suffrage. The sovereign also exercises executive power through the Ministers who are created by royal appointment but nominated by the parliament.
Denmark is a member of UNO, the EEC, the Council of Europe, the Nordic Council, NATO and OECD.
The country is flat and includes the northern part of the Jutland peninsula and 383 islands. It dominates the passage between the Baltic and the North Sea.
Area: 43,070 sq km, excluding the Faroe Islands and Greenland.
Population: 5,125,000; 119 per sq km.
Annual growth rate: 0.1%; birth rate: 12‰; death rate: 10‰; average life expectancy: 74 years.
Capital: Copenhagen (pop 1,343,000).
Other important towns: Ålborg (155,000); Århus (245,000); Gentofte (70,000); Odense (170,000); Randers (65,000).
Land use: cultivated 62%; grazing 7%; wooded 12%; uncultivated 19%. Main agricultural products: sugar beet, potatoes, barley, wheat, oats. Other activities: fishing.
Official language: Danish.
Religion: Protestant.
Gross National Product: US $ 80,400 million; per capita US $ 15,750.
Currency: Danish krone = 100 øre.
Dependencies: Faroe Islands and Greenland.

FAEROE ISLANDS

Føroyar

The Faeroes are Danish dependencies, but have had a large degree of autonomy since 1948. Foreign policy and defence are decided by Denmark. The islands are represented by 2 delegates in the Danish parliament (Folketing) and have their own legislative assembly (Lagting).
They are a group of islands in the Atlantic, between Iceland and Scotland. The largest and most important is Strømø. The landscape is bleak, but covered with good grazing land.
Area: 1,400 sq km.
Population: 4,000; 34 per sq km.
Annual growth rate: 1.1%.
Capital: Tórshavn (pop 14,000).
Land use: cultivated: 2.1%.
Official languages: Danish and Faeroese.
Religion: Protestant.
Gross National Product: US $ 440 million; per capita US $ 10,620.
Currency: Danish krone = 100 øre.

FINLAND

Suomi/Finland - Suomen Tasavalta/Republiken Finland

Finland is a parliamentary republic. The president is elected by an assembly of 300 electors for 6 years and nominates the government, which exercises executive power. Legislative power is in the hands of the unicameral parliament (Eduskunta), whose members are elected for 4 years by direct universal suffrage.
Finland is a member of UNO, the Nordic Council, EFTA and OECD.
The country, which is situated between the Scandinavian peninsula and USSR, is lowlying and in the centre and south broken up into about 50,000 large and small lakes. About 2/3 of the country is covered with forest.
Area: 337,010 sq km, of which 31,625 sq km are inland water.
Population: 4,940,000; 14 per sq km.
Annual growth rate: 0.4%; birth rate: 13‰; death rate: 10‰; average life expectancy: 72 years.
Capital: Helsinki/Helsingfors (pop 970,000).
Other important towns: Espoo/Esbo (164,000); Oulu (95,000); Pori/Björneborg (80,000); Tampere/Tammerfors (165,000); Turku/Åbo (165,000).
Land use: cultivated: 8.5%; grazing: 0.5%; wooded: 77%; uncultivated: 14%. Main agri-

Germany: Cologne Cathedral

cultural products: barley, oats, potatoes, sugar beet, wheat; timber.
Official languages: Finnish (93,6%) and Swedish (6%).
Religion: Protestant.
Gross National Product: US $ 70,500 million; per capita US $ 12,700.
Currency: Finnish mark = 100 penniä.

FRANCE

France/République Française

France is a parliamentary republic in which, however, the President of the Republic holds a position of particular importance. It is made up of 96 departments (départements) in mainland France, which are grouped into 22 administrative regions (régions), 6 overseas departments (Guadeloupe, Martinique, French Guiana, Réunion, Mayotte, Saint Pierre et Miquelon) and 4 overseas territories (New Caledonia, Wallis and Futuna Island, French Polynesia and French Southern and Antarctic Territories.) All the departments and territories are represented in the French parliament. The President of the Republic is elected for 7 years by direct universal suffrage, and exercises executive power in conjunction with the Prime Minister and the ministers, who are nominated by him. Over and above the right to dissolve the National Assembly the constitution of the 5th Republic gives the president other extraordinary powers in the case of emergency and legal powers over subjects which are normally the prerogative of parliament. The parliament is composed of two chambers the National Assembly and the Senate. Deputies to the National Assembly are elected for 5 years by direct universal suffrage and may not become ministers. The Senate is composed of some ministers nominated for life by the President of the Republic and others elected for 9 years by an electoral body formed of deputies from the National Assembly and delegates from the department and municipal councils. A third of this last group are renewable every three years.
France is a member of UNO, the EEC, the Council of Europe, the WEO, the OECD and NATO.
The country is mostly low-lying, with the highland area of the Central Massif towards the south. It is crossed by many rivers. It is bordered by the Atlantic in the west, the Alps and the Jura mountains in the east and the Mediterranean and the Pyrenees in the south. It includes the island of Corsica in the Mediterranean.

Area: 547,025 sq km including Corsica. Divided into 22 administrative regions, which are subdivided into 96 departments.
Population: 55,750,000; 102 per sq km.
Annual growth rate: 0.4%; birth rate: 14‰; death rate: 10‰; average life expectancy: 73 years.
Capital: Paris (pop 10,210,000).
Other important towns: Bordeaux (843,000); Brest (291,000); Cannes (295,000); Dijon (205,000); Le Havre (265,000); Lilles (1,100,000); Lyons (1,170,000); Marseilles (1,110,000); Montpellier (220,000); Nantes (440,000); Nice (445,000); Orléans (210,000); Rheims (200,000); Rouen (395,000); Strasbourg (375,000); Toulon (410,000); Toulouse (541,000).
Land use: cultivated 35%; grazing 24%; wooded 27%; uncultivated 14%. Main agricultural products: wheat, barley, oats, wine, sugar beet, potatoes, rye, vegetables, fruit. Other activities cattle rearing. Mineral resources: iron ore, coal, oil.
Official language: French.
Religion: Catholic.
Gross National Product: US $ 705,500 million; per capita US $ 12,730.
Currency: French franc = 100 centimes.
Dependencies: Guadeloupe, Martinique, French Guiana, Réunion, Mayotte, Saint Pierre et Miquelon New Caledonia, French Polynesia, Wallis and Futuna, French Southern and Antarctic Territories.

GERMANY

Deutschland/Bundesrepublik Deutschland

Germany is a federal republic, composed of the following 16 federal units (Länder): Baden-Württemburg, Bavaria, Berlin, Brandenburg, Bremen, Hamburg, Hesse, Lower Saxony, Mecklenburg, North Rhine-Westphalia, Rhineland Palatinate, Saarland, Saxony, Saxony-Anhalt, Schleswig-Holstein, Thuringen. Each Land enjoys a large degree of legislative and executive autonomy.
After its defeat in the Second World War Germany was deprived of its eastern regions (Prussia, Pomerania, East Brandenburg and Silesia) and was occupied by the winning powers. On 23rd May 1949 the area occupied by the American, British and French armed forces became known as the Federal Republic of Germany (Bundesrepublik Deutschland) or West Germany. On the 7th October in the same year the area occupied by the Soviet armed forces became known as the German Democratic Republic (Deutsche Demokratische Republik) also known as East Germany. The capitals of the two countries were respectively Bonn and the Pankow area of Berlin.
The city of Berlin and the surrounding area remained under the military administration of the winning powers and had a special legal status. However, after the erection of the Berlin Wall, Berlin became divided into two areas. West Berlin was politically linked to the Federal Republic of Germany, while East Berlin, linked to the German Democratic Republic, later became accepted as its capital.
On 3rd October 1990 East Germany was officially dissolved and incorporated into West Germany, while the whole area became called simply Germany, though preserving its original official title of the Federal Republic of Germany.
The German Democratic Republic was a people's republic. Legislative power was in the hands of the unicameral parliament (People's Chamber-Volkskammer), whose members were elected for 5 years from the Socialist Unity Party and from the political

Germany: Navigation on the Rhine

Great Britain: London - The House of Lords

and union organisations of the extreme left. The People's Chamber elected the Council of State (Staatsrat) for 4 years, whose president was also head of state. Executive power lay with the Council of Ministers which was answerable to the People's Chamber. The German Democratic Republic was a member of UNO, Comecon and the Warsaw Pact.
The Federal Republic of Germany has, after the unification of the two states, preserved its previous political and administrative structures. Legislative power is exercised by parliament, which consists of the Chamber of Deputies (Bundestag) and the Federal Council (Bundesrat). Members of the first are elected by direct universal suffrage for 4 years, while the Federal Council is made up of representatives from each of the Federal units, nominated by their respective governments. An Assembly, composed of members of the Chamber of Deputies and an equal number of members nominated by the parliaments of the various Länder is responsible for the election of the President of the Republic, who is the head of state. The Federal Government which is formed of the Chancellor and the various ministers, has executive power.
Germany is a member of UNO, the EEC, the Council of Europe, OECD, WEO and NATO.
The country extends from the Alps to the North and Baltic seas, which are divided by the Jutland peninsula, the southern part of which belongs to Germany. In the north there is an extensive lowland area which forms part of the Great European Plain. In the centre is a highland region including the mountain groups of the Harz, the Eifel, the Westerwald, the Hunsruck, the Taunus, the Spessart and the Franconian and Swabian Jura. Also in this region are the Thuringen Forest, the High Palatinate Forest and the Black Forest. In the south this highland region rises slowly to form the foothills to the Alps. The country is crossed by numerous navigable rivers, including the Rhine, the Weser, the Elbe and part of the Danube.
Area: 356,970 sq km. Divided into 16 federal units (Länder): Baden-Wurttemburg, Bavaria, Berlin, Brandenburg, Bremen, Hamburg, Hesse, Lower Saxony, Mecklenburg, North Rhine-Westphalia, Rhineland Palatinate, Saarland, Saxony, Saxony-Anhalt, Schleswig-Holstein, Thuringen.
Population: 80,030,000; 252 per sq km.
Annual growth rate: 0%; birth rate: 10.1‰; death rate: 11.6‰; Average life expectancy: 72 years.
Capital: Berlin (pop 3,308,000).
Other important towns: Aachen (245,000); Bonn (former seat of the government - 290,000); Bremen (555,000); Chemnitz (315,000); Cologne (975,000); Dortmund (610,000); Dresden (515,000); Duisburg (560,000); Dusseldorf (590,000); Erfurt (215,000); Essen (650,000); Frankfurt-on-Main (630,000); Halle (235,000); Hamburg (1,640,000); Hanover/Hannover (535,000); Kiel (255,000); Leipzig (565,000); Lübeck (225,000); Magdeburg (290,000); Mannheim (310,000); Munich/München (1,300,000); Nuremberg/Nürnberg (490,000); Rostock (235,000); Stuttgart (590,000); Wuppertal (395,000); Zwickau (125,000).
Land use: cultivated 32%, grazing 18%, wooded 29%, uncultivated 21%. Main agricultural products: potatoes, sugar beet, barley, wheat, oats, rye, vegetables, fodder, beer, wine. Other activities: cattle rearing. Mineral resources: coal, lignite, potash, iron ore.
Official language: German.
Religions: Protestant 47%; Catholic 42%.
Gross National Product: US $ 890,000 million;

Greece: The Temple of Aphaia on the island of Aegina

per capita: US $ 14,590 in ex-West Germany. In ex-East Germany the Gross National Product was US $ 130,000 million and per capita US $ 7,800.
Currency: German mark = 100 pfennig.

GIBRALTAR
Dominion of Gibraltar

Gibraltar is a British colony with autonomy over internal affairs and administered by a Governor who exercises legislative power in conjunction with an Executive Council and a Legislative Council composed of elected and nominated members. The territory, which was conquered by Great Britain in 1704 during the Spanish War of Succession is being officially claimed by Spain.
A rocky promotory at the southernmost point of the Iberian peninsula, it dominates the straits which link the Atlantic Ocean and the Mediterranean Sea.
Area: 6 sq km.
Population: 30,000; 5,000 per sq km.
Annual growth rate: 1.0%.
Official languages: English and Spanish.
Religion: Catholic.
Gross National Product: US $ 150 million; per capita: US $ 5,040.
Currency: UK £ sterling = 100 pence.

GREAT BRITAIN
United Kingdom of Great Britain and Northern Ireland

Great Britain is a constitutional monarchy, hereditary in both male and female lines. By law the sovereign is head of the executive and an integral part of the legislative, but in practice his/her role is purely formal, reigning but not ruling. Executive power is exercised through the government, whose prime minister, nominated by the sovereign, is also leader of the majority party. Legislative power is exercised through the bicameral parliament which is composed of the sovereign, again in a purely formal role, the House of Commons or Lower House and the House of Lords or Upper House. Members of the House of Commons are elected by direct universal suffrage for 5 years on the single-member-constituency system. The House of Lords is composed of members of the Royal Family, hereditary members and life-peers. By law particular importance is given to the opposition, whose leaders are called Leaders of the Opposition. Northern Ireland, though it sends members to the British House of Commons, has its own legislative and executive bodies.
The Isle of Man and the Channel Islands do not form part of the United Kingdom, but are directly dependent on the British Crown and are governed by Governors nominated by the sovereign and their own executive and legislative bodies.
Great Britain is a member of UNO, the EEC, the Council of Europe, OECD, WEO and NATO.
The British mainland is the largest island in Europe. The landscape is mostly undulating, becoming increasingly mountainous towards the north and in Scotland and Wales. Low-lying areas are found in the south and the east. The north-west coastline is rugged and indented.
Area: 244,045 sq km, excluding the Isle of Man and the Channel Islands, but including Northern Ireland.
Population: 56,930,000; 233 per sq km.
Annual growth rate: —0.2%; birth rate: 13‰; death rate: 12‰. Average life expectancy: 75 years.
Capital: London (pop 6,875,000).
Other important towns: Belfast (355,000); Birmingham (2,695,000); Bristol (387,000); Cardiff (285,000); Edinburgh (455,000); Glasgow (1,730,000); Leeds (2,065,000); Liverpool (1,535,000); Manchester (2,650,000); Newcastle-upon-Tyne (300,000); Plymouth (260,000); Sheffield (1,305,000).
Land use: cultivated 29%; grazing 47%; wooded 9%; uncultivated 15%. Main agricultural products: barley, wheat, sugar beet, potatoes, vegetables. Other activities: cattle rearing. Mineral resources: coal, oil, natural gas.
Official language: English. Celtic dialects are spoken in Scotland, Wales and Northern Ireland.
Religions: Anglican and Protestant in England with Catholic, Jewish and Muslim minorities; Presbyterian in Scotland; Protestant and Catholic in Northern Ireland.
Gross National Product: US $ 544,700 million; per capita: US $ 9,600.
Currency: UK £ sterling = 100 pence.
Dependencies: in Europe: Gibraltar; in Asia: Hong Kong; in Central America: British Virgin Islands, Cayman, Anguilla, Turks and Caicos, Montserrat; in Oceania: Pitcairn Island; in the Indian Ocean: British Indian Ocean Territory; in the Atlantic Ocean: Bermuda, Saint Helena, Falkland Islands; in the Antarctic: British Antarctic Territory. All these areas, whether colonies or protectorates, form part of the British Commonwealth, together with Great Britain and the following independent sovereign states, which are ex-dependencies of Great Britain: Canada, Australia, New Zealand, India, Sri Lanka, Ghana, Nigeria, Cyprus, Sierra Leone, Jamaica, Trinidad and Tobago, Uganda, Kenya, Zambia, Gambia, Singapore, Guyana, Botswana, Lesotho, Barbados, Mauritius, Swaziland, Tonga, Fiji, Bangladesh, Bahamas, Samoa, Grenada, Papua New Guinea, Seychelles, Solomon Islands, Saint Kitts and Nevis, Dominica, Saint Lucia, Kiribati, Vanuatu, Belize, Antigua and Barbuda, Zimbabwe, Brunei and, as special members: the Maldives, Nauru, Tuvalu, Saint Vincent and the Grenadines.

Italy: Orvieto Cathedral

The Channel Islands
Iles Normandes

The Channel Islands do not form part of the United Kingdom of Great Britain and Northern Ireland, but are directly dependent on the British Crown, to which they were transferred by the Duke of Normandy at the time of the conquest of Britain by William the Conqueror. They are administered by governors, who represent the British Crown, one for Jersey and one for Guernsey. Both also have their own executive and legislative bodies, some of whose members are nominated by the Crown whereas others are elected by direct universal suffrage.
Situated off the north-west coast of France, in the centre of the Channel, they include the islands of Jersey and Guernsey.
Area: 195 sq km, divided administratively into two governorates.
Population: 136,000; 697 per sq km.
Annual growth rate: 0.7%.
Other important towns: Saint Helier/Saint Hélier (30,000) and Saint Peter Port/Saint Pierre (17,000).
Main agricultural products: vegetables, fruit, flowers.
Official languages: English and French.
Religions: Protestant and Catholic.
Gross National Product: US $ 900 million; per capita: US $ 6,780.
Currency: UK £ sterling = 100 pence.

The Isle of Man

The Isle of Man does not form part of the United Kingdom of Great Britain and Northern Ireland, but depends directly on the British Crown. The island is administered by a governor who is nominated by the British sovereign and who rules the territory in conjunction with a Representative Assembly and a Legislative Council. It is situated in the Irish Sea, between north-west England and Northern Ireland.
Area: 590 sq km.
Population: 65,000; 109 per sq km.
Annual growth rate: 1.0%.
Main town: Douglas (20,000).
Main agricultural products: vegetables and fodder.
Official language: English. Manx, a Celtic dialect, is also spoken.
Religion: Christian.
Gross National Product: US $ 300 million; per capita: US $ 4,500.
Currency: UK £ sterling = 100 pence.

GREECE
Ellás/Eliniki Dimokratia

Greece is a parliamentary republic. Democratic freedom was reinstated on 23rd July 1974 with the fall of the military junta which had maintained power by authoritarian methods since the coup of 21st April 1967. With the referendum of 8th December 1974 the republican regime chosen by the people in the referendum of 29th July 1973, during the period of the military dictatorship, was confirmed. According to the constitution of 7th June 1975 legislative power is in the hands of parliament, whose 300 members are elected from the various parties. Parliament in turn elects the President of the Republic, who is also head of state. He has wide-ranging powers, including the control of the operations of the government which has executive power.
Greece is a member of UNO, the EEC, the Council of Europe, OECD and NATO.
The country is formed of peninsulas and nearly 400 islands. Many are rocky and situated to the south of the peninsula. The landscape is almost entirely mountainous, of limestone character with many karst features. The largest island is Crete in the eastern Mediterranean.
Area: 131,945 sq km, excluding the monastic republic of Mount Athos.
Population: 9,700,000; 74 per sq km.
Annual growth rate: 0.4%; birth rate: 10.6‰; death rate: 9.5‰; average life expectancy: 72 years.
Capital: Athens (pop 3,030,000).
Other important towns: Heraklion/Iraklion (102,000); Larissa (102,000); Patras (142,000); Saloniki/Thessaloniki (406,000); Vólos (71,000).
Land use: cultivated 32%; grazing 40%; wooded 20%; uncultivated 8%. Main agricultural products: wine, citrus fruit, olive oil, tobacco, cereals.
Official language: Greek.
Religion: Greek Orthodox.
Gross National Product: US $ 39,100 million; per capita: US $ 3,900.
Currency: Drachma = 100 lepta.

Mount Athos
Áion Óros

Mount Athos is a small autonomous monastic republic, under the sovereignity of Greece. No women are allowed. It is administered by a Permanent Committee, elected by the Holy Synod, which is formed of 20 members, each representing one of the 20 monasteries.
It is the most eastern of the three peninsulas of the Chalcidice, with the highest point being the Holy Mount (Agion Oros) itself, which rises to 2,000 m.
Area: 335 sq km.
Population: 1,470, all of whom are Greek Orthodox monks.
Most important town: Karves (pop 230).
Official language: Greek.
Religion: Greek Orthodox.
Currency: Drachma = 100 lepta.

HUNGARY
Magyarország/Magyar Köztársaság

Hungary was a People's Republic. The head of state was the President of the Presidential Council, whose members were elected by the National Assembly. Members of this last were elected for 4 years from the party lists of the Marxist Patriotic Front, and had legislative power, though subject to nomination and revocation by the Council of Ministers. Since 1989 profound institutional changes have been in progress.
Hungary is a member of UNO, Comecon and the Warsaw Pact.
Most of the country consists of the vast Hungarian Plain, crossed by the Danube and the Tisza rivers. The plain is fertile in the west and arid steppeland (the puszta) in the east. Only in the north, towards the borders with Czechoslovakia, and in the west are there highland areas.
Area: 93,030 sq km.
Population: 10,715,000; 115 per sq km.
Annual growth rate: —0.2%; birth rate: 11.8‰; death rate: 14‰; average life expectancy: 70 years.
Capital: Budapest (pop 2,065,000).
Other important towns: Debrecen (195,000); Gÿor (125,000); Miskolc (210,000); Nyiregyháza (115,000); Pécs (170,000); Szeged (175,000); Székesfehérvár (110,000).
Land use: cultivated 57%, grazing 14%, wooded 17%, uncultivated 12%. Main agricultural products: wheat, maize, wine, paprika, fruit. Mineral resources: bauxite, coal.
Official language: Hungarian (96%). Slovene, German, Romanian and Serbo-Croat minorities.
Religions: Catholic (65%), Protestant (25%), Orthodox (3%).
Gross National Product: US $ 22,700 million; per capita: US $ 2,140.
Currency: Hungarian florin (forint) = 100 filler.

ICELAND
Ísland/Lýdhveldidh Ísland

Iceland is a parliamentary republic. The President of the Republic is elected for 4 years by direct universal suffrage and exercises executive power through the ministers, who are answerable to parliament. The bicameral parliament, composed of the Upper

Italy: View of the Dolomites

182

and Lower Houses, has legislative power. Members to both are elected for 4 years by direct universal suffrage.

Iceland is a member of UNO; the Council of Europe, the Nordic Council, OECD, EFTA and NATO.

The Island is composed of solidified lava and there are volcanoes, some still active, geysers and glaciers. There is very little arable land.

Area: 103,000 sq km.
Population: 247,000; 2 per sq km.
Annual growth rate: 0.9%; birth rate 17‰; death rate: 7‰; Average life expectancy: 76 years.
Capital: Reykjavik (pop 120,000).
Other important towns: Akureyri (13,000); Hafnarfjördhur (12,000); Kopavogur (14,000).
Land use: cultivated 0.1%; grazing 23%; wooded 1.2%; uncultivated 76%. Main agricultural products: fodder. Other activities: fishing.
Official language: Icelandic.
Religion: Protestant.
Gross National Product: US $ 3,500 million; per capita: US $ 14,330.
Currency: Icelandic krona = 100 aurar.

IRELAND/EIRE

Irish Republic/Poblacht Na h'Éireann

Ireland is a parliamentary republic, whose President, the head of state, is elected for 7 years by direct universal suffrage. He holds executive power which he exercises through the government, which is answerable to the Chamber of Deputies. Legislative power is exercised by the bicameral parliament, made up of the Chamber of Deputies and the Senate. Members of the Chamber of Deputies are elected for 7 years by direct universal suffrage, while the Senate is for the most part composed of representatives from the various professions.

Ireland is a member of UNO, the EEC, the Council of Europe and the OECD.

The country is for the most part low-lying, with mountains in the north and south. There are many lakes. Because of the abundance and lushness of its pastureland it is known as the "Emerald Isle".

Area: 70,285 sq km.
Population: 3,540,000; 51 per sq km.
Annual growth rate: 0.5%; birth rate 15‰; death rate: 9‰; average life expectancy: 71 years.
Capital: Dublin/Baile Atha Cliath (pop 921,000).
Other important towns: Cork/Corcaigh (140,000); Galway/An Ghaillimh (35,000); Limerick/ Luimneach (62,000); Waterford/Port Láirge (35,000).
Land use: cultivated 14%; grazing 69%; wooded 5%; uncultivated 12%. Main agricultural products: barley, sugar beet, potatoes, wheat.
Official languages: Irish and English.
Religion: Catholic.
Gross National Product: US $ 25,100 million; per capita: US $ 7,100.
Currency: Irish pound/punt = 100 pence.

ITALY

Italia/Repubblica Italiana

Italy is a parliamentary republic. The head of state is the President of the Republic, who is elected for 7 years, with a majority of two-thirds. At the third ballot count however an absolute majority is required. He is elected by an Assembly composed of members of the two houses of parliament, together with delegates elected from the regional councils. Executive power is exercised by the President together with the ministers who are nominated by him, but who must subsequently obtain the votes of confidence of parliament. Parliament is composed of a Chamber of Deputies and the Senate of the Republic. Members of the first are elected for 5 years by direct universal suffrage under the system of proportional representation. Some of the members of the second are also elected for 5 years by direct universal suffrage, but on a regional basis; while others, including the ex-President of the Republic, are nominated senators for life as a result of outstanding scientific or artistic merit.

The country is divided administratively into 20 regions, 5 of which — the Val d'Aosta, Trentino Alto Adige, Friuli-Venezia Giulia, Sicily and Sardinia — are, because of their isolated or peripheral positions and the presence of different cultural and linguistic groups, autonomous regions by special statute (instituted between 1946 and 1963). The provinces of Bolzano and Trento form ano-

Norway: View of a fjord

ther region of special statute, with an autonomy comparable to those above and with special legislative powers. The other 15 regions are partly autonomous by ordinary statute instituted between May and July 1971.

Italy is a member of UNO, the EEC, the Council of Europe, OECD, WEO and NATO.

The country is a long peninsula extending into the Mediterranean Sea, bordered in the north by the Alps and divided down its length by the Apennines. In the central north is the Po valley which extends down to the Po estuary on the Adriatic Sea. It includes various islands, including the two biggest n the Mediterranean, Sicily and Sardinia.

Area: 301,265 sq km, divided into 20 administrative regions.
Population: 57,580; 191 per sq km.
Annual growth rate: 0.7; birth rate: 13‰; death rate: 10‰; average life expectancy: 72 years.
Capital: Rome (pop 2,830,000).
Other important towns: Bari (370,000); Bologna (417,000); Florence (413,000); Genoa (706,000); Milan (1,449,000); Naples (1,200,000); Palermo (700,000); Turin (1,005,000); Trieste (233,000); Venice (335,000).
Land use: cultivated 41%; grazing 18%; wooded 21%; uncultivated 20%. Main agricultural products: wheat, maize, sugar beet, citrus fruit, tomatoes, olive oil, potatoes; wine.
Official language: Italian (also German in Alto Adige and French in Val d'Aosta. The Ladino language is also spoken in Friuli-Venezia and Sardinian language in Sardinia. Albanian and Greek are spoken in some areas.
Religion: Catholic.
Gross National Product: US $ 504,000 million; per capita: US $ 8,800.
Currency: Italian lira.

LIECHTENSTEIN

Fürstentum Liechtenstein

Liechtenstein is a constitutional hereditary principality. The Prince exercises legislative power in conjunction with parliament and executive power through the head of government and the ministers. Members of parliament are elected for 4 years by direct universal suffrage, while the ministers are nominated by the Prince and hold office for 6 years. Diplomatic and consular representation is entrusted to neighbouring Switzerland, which has since 1921 managed its postal and telegraphic services, though Liechtenstein issues its own stamps. From 1924 there has existed duty-free exchange between Switzerland and Liechtenstein, and the latter has adopted Swiss currency.

Liechtenstein is a member of the Council of Europe.

The country is in Alpine territory in the upper Rhine valley. It is completely mountainous except for a narrow strip of low-lying land on the border with Switzerland.

Area: 155 sq km.
Population: 28,000; 176 per sq km.
Annual growth rate: 1.1%.
Capital: Vaduz (pop 5,000).
Land use: cultivated 25%; grazing 31%; wooded 19%; uncultivated 25%. Main agricultural products: cereals, vegetables, fruit, fodder, potatoes.
Official language: German.
Religions: Catholic (over 80%); Protestant (6%).
Currency: Swiss franc = 100 rappen.

LUXEMBOURG

Lezeburg/Grand-Duché de Luxembourg/ Grousherzogdem Lezebuurg

Luxembourg is a constitutional grand-duchy, hereditary in both male and female lines. The Grand Duke exercises executive power through the Prime Minister and the ministers, whom he nominates. He also has legislative power, exercised together with the Chamber of Deputies who are elected for 5 years by direct universal suffrage.

Luxembourg is a member of UNO, Benelux, the EEC, the Council of Europe, the OECD, WEO and NATO.

The country is predominantly hilly, with a fairly high wooded plateau in the north.

Area: 2,585 sq km.
Population: 365,000, including 95,000 foreigners; 142 per sq km.
Annual growth rate: 0.4%; birth rate: 11‰; death rate: 10‰; average life expectancy: 71 years.
Capital: Luxembourg (pop 86,000).
Other important towns: Differdange/Differdingen (8,600); Dudelange/Dudelingen (14,000); Esch (26,000).
Land use: cultivated: 22.5%; grazing 27%; wooded 42%; uncultivated 8.5%. Main agricultural products: cereals, sugar beet, potatoes, vegetables. Mineral resources iron ore.
Official language: French. German dialects are also commonly spoken.
Religion: Catholic.
Gross National Product: US $ 5,100 million; per capita: US $ 13,800.
Currency: Luxembourg franc = 100 centimes.

MALTA

Republic of Malta/Repubblika ta' Malta

Malta has been an independent state since 21st September 1964. It became a republic on 18th December 1974, though remaining part of the Commonwealth. The head of state is the President of the Republic. Executive power is entrusted to the Prime Minister and the Council of Ministers who are accountable to the unicameral parliament. The last is elected for 5 years by direct universal suffrage, by the system of proportional representation and has legislative power.

Malta is a member of UNO and the Council of Europe.

It is composed of a small group of two islands south of Sicily. It is mountainous, with limestone rock.

Area: 315 sq km.
Population: 345,000; 1,095 per sq km.
Annual growth rate: 0.8%; birth rate: 15‰; death rate: 9‰; average life expectancy: 71 years.
Capital: Valletta (pop 9,200).
Land use: cultivated: 44%. Main agricultural products: cereals, wine, fruit, vegetables.
Official languages: English, Maltese.
Religion: Catholic. Protestant minority.
Gross National Product: US $ 1,370 million; per capita: US $ 3,800.
Currency: Maltese pound = 100 cents.

MONACO

Principauté de Monaco

Monaco is a hereditary constitutional princip-

Netherlands: View of Amsterdam

ality divided into the three urban areas of Monaco, Monte Carlo and La Condamine. The Prince exercises executive power through the Minister of State and the Council of State, and legislative power together with the National Council, whose members are elected for 5 years by direct universal suffrage.

The principality is situated on the French Mediterranean coast not far from the Italian-French border.

Area: 1.95 sq km.
Population: 27,000, 80% of which are foreigners; 13,800 per sq km.
Annual growth rate: 0.3%; birth rate: 19.6‰; death rate: 16.6‰.
Capital: Monaco (pop 1,700).
Official language: French.
Religion: Catholic.
Currency: French franc = 100 centimes.

NETHERLANDS

Nederland/Koninkrijk der Nederlanden

The Netherlands, popularly referred to as Holland, is a constitutional monarchy, hereditary in both male and female lines. According to the constitution the kingdom consists of the Netherlands and the Netherlands Antilles, both of which have complete autonomy but are linked by close ties of friendship and mutual defence. The sovereign exercises executive power through the Prime Minister and the ministers, who must however obtain the vote of confidence of the parliament (States-General); and legislative power through parliament. Parliament is composed of two chambers, the Upper, whose members are elected for 6 years by the Provincial Councils and who are renewable every 3 years; and the Lower, whose members are elected for 4 years by direct universal suffrage on the proportional representation system.

The Netherlands is a member of UNO, Benelux, the Council of Europe, OECD, WEO and NATO.

The country is completely flat, with part of it below sea-level and protected by dykes. The battle against the sea is unending; new dykes are continually being built and new land reclaimed.

Netherlands: The port of Rotterdam, one of the largest in the world

Spain: View of Granada

Area: 40,845 sq km, of which 7,350 sq km are inland waters.
Population: 14,000,000; 346 per sq km.
Annual growth rate: 0.5%; birth rate: 12‰; death rate: 8‰; average life expectancy: 75 years.
Capital: Amsterdam (pop 1,015,000). The Hague is the seat of government and the royal residence.
Other important towns: Arnhem (290,000); Breda (155,000); Eindhoven (400,000); Enschede (250,000); Groningen (205,000); Haarlem (225,000) Leiden/Leyden (175,000); Nijmegen (230,000); Rotterdam (1,025,000); Utrecht (490,000).
Land use: cultivated: 26%; grazing 35%; wooded 9%; uncultivated 30%. Main agricultural products: plant bulbs, potatoes, barley, wheat, sugar beet, tomatoes, cucumbers. Mineral resources: oil, natural gas.
Official language: Dutch. Friesan minorities in Friesland.
Religions: Catholic (39.5%); Protestant (37.5%).
Gross National Product: US $ 171,100 million; per capita: US $ 11,000.
Currency: Guilder = 100 cents.

NORWAY

Norge/Kongeriket Norge

Norway is a hereditary constitutional monarchy. The sovereign exercises executive power through the Prime Minister and the various ministers, who are accountable to parliament; and legislative power through the parliament (Storting). Members of parliament are elected for 4 years by direct universal suffrage. The Storting is then divided into an upper house (Lagting) with one quarter of the members, and a lower house (Odelsting) with three quarters of the members.
Norway is a member of UNO, the Council of Europe, the Nordic Council, OECD, EFTA, and NATO.
The country is situated on the west of the Scandinavian peninsula and is entirely mountainous, its coastline deeply indented with fjords. It is warmed by the Gulf Stream, which moderates the climate, leaving the ports free of ice all year round. There are also numerous lakes.
Area: 324,220 sq km.
Population: 4,220,000; 14 per sq km.
Annual growth rate: 0.4%; birth rate: 12‰; death rate: 10‰; average life expectancy: 75 years.
Capital: Oslo (pop 460,000).
Other important towns: Bergen (210,000); Drammen (50,000); Kristiansand (60,000); Narvik (20,000); Stavanger (90,000); Tromsø (45,000); Trondheim (135,000).
Land use: cultivated 2.6%; grazing 0.3%; wooded 27%; uncultivated 70%. Main agricultural products: barley, potatoes, oats, vegetables; paper pulp. Other activities: fishing. Mineral resources: oil, iron ore.
Official language: Norwegian (Riksmål - formal Dano-Norwegian and Landsmål - based on the local dialects of Norway). Finnish and Lapp minorities.
Religion: Protestant.
Gross National Product: US $ 68,700 million; per capita: US $ 16,500.
Currency: Norwegian krone = 100 øre.
Dependencies: Spitsbergen/Svalbard and Jan Mayen in the Arctic; Bouvet in the south Atlantic; Peter Island in the Bellinghausen Sea; and the section of Antarctica between the longitudes 20°W and 45°E.

Sweden: Kalmar Castle

POLAND

Polska/Polska Rzeczpospolita

Poland was a People's Republic. The head of state was the President of the Council of State, whose members were voted by parliament (Sejm). Parliament, which had legislative power, was composed of members of the Communist Party (United Party of Polish Workers) elected for 4 years by direct universal suffrage. Since 1989 profound institutional changes have been taking place.
Poland is a member of UNO, Comecon and the Warsaw Pact.
The country borders on the Baltic Sea and most of it forms part of the Great European Plain that extends from Germany to the USSR. Only in the south is there some higher land. There are numerous rivers, the most important being the Vistula.
Area: 312,675 sq km.
Population: 37,735,000; 120 per sq km.
Annual growth rate: 0.7%; birth rate 16.5‰; death rate: 9.9‰; average life expectancy: 71 years.
Capital: Warsaw (pop 1,580,000).
Other important towns: Bydgoszcz/Bromberg (345,000); Czestochowa (235,000); Gdansk (450,000); Katowice (350,000); Kraków/Craców (710,000); Lódz (830,000); Lublin (300,000); Poznan (550,000); Szczecin (390,000); Wroclaw (610,000).
Land use: cultivated: 48%; grazing 13%; wooded 28%; uncultivated 11%. Main agricultural products: wheat, barley, rye, potatoes, sugar beet, vegetables. Other activities: cattle rearing. Mineral resources: coal, lignite, copper, lead.
Official language: Polish (96%). German, Ukrainian, Russian and Lithuanian minorities.
Religion: Catholic.
Gross National Product: US $ 72,520 million; per capita: US $ 2,075.
Currency: Zloty = 100 groszy.

PORTUGAL

Republica Portuguesa

Portugal is a parliamentary republic. Following the bloodless military coup of 25th April 1974, which put an end to the dictatorship introduced in 1966, power was provisionally assumed by a military junta and a Revolutionary Council. With the institution of the new constitution, approved on 2nd April 1976 by the Constituent Assembly which was elected on 25th April 1975, democratic freedom was re-instated. The head of state is the President of the Republic, who is elected for 7 years by direct universal suffrage, and who has wide-ranging powers. Executive power is in the hands of the Prime Minister and the government, who are accountable to the unicameral parliament. This last, elected by direct universal suffrage for 5 years, has legislative powers. The Revolutionary Council is an advisory body, composed of military personnel, whose task it is to guarantee the defence of the constitution.
Portugal is a member of UNO, the EEC, the Council of Europe, OECD, EFTA and NATO.
The country borders on the Atlantic and to the east is situated on the edge of the Spanish highlands, with parallel ranges of mountains alternating with the fluvial valleys of the main rivers, e.g. the Tagus and the Douro.
Area: 92,080 sq km, including the Azores and Madeira which, though considered politically part of the mainland, enjoy a large degree of autonomy.
Population: 10,203,000; 111 per sq km.
Annual growth rate: 0.8%; birth rate: 12‰; death rate: 10‰; average life expectancy: 69 years.
Capital: Lisbon (pop 2,010,000).
Other important towns: Braga (60,000); Coimbra (71,000); Funchal (48,000); Oporto (1,565,000); Setubal (50,000); Villa Nova de Gaia (52,000).
Land use: cultivated 39%, grazing 6%; wooded 40%; uncultivated 15%. Main agricultural products: potatoes, wine, olive oil, wheat, maize, citrus fruit, tomatoes; cork. Other activities: fishing. Mineral resources: coal, copper, iron ore.
Official language: Portuguese.
Religion: Catholic.
Gross National product: US $ 28,900 million; per capita: US $ 2,850.
Currency: Escudo = 100 centavos.
Dependency: Overseas province of Macao in South-East Asia.

ROMANIA

România/Republica România

Romania was a socialist republic. The head of state was the President of the Council of State, whose members were voted by the Grand National Assembly. This last, which exercised legislative power, was composed of members elected from the Communist Party list for 5 years, by direct universal suffrage, but subject to nomination and revocation by the Council of Ministers. Since 1989 profound institutional changes have been taking place.
Romania is a member of UNO, Comecon and the Warsaw Pact.
The country is crossed by the mountain ridges of the Transylvanian Alps and the Carpathians. Towards the south the Walachian and Moldavian plains are crossed by tributaries of the Danube river.
Area: 237,500 sq km.
Population: 22,940,000; 96 per sq km.
Annual growth rate: 0.4%; birth rate: 16‰; death rate: 11‰; average life expectancy: 72 years.
Capital: Bucharest/Bucuresti (pop 2,190,000).
Other important towns: Arad (180,000); Brăila (215,000); Brasov (305,000); Cluj (285,000); Constanța (285,000); Craiova (225,000); Galati (260,000); Oradea (175,000); Ploiesti (210,000); Sibiu (160,000); Timisoara (290,000).
Land use: cultivated 41%; grazing 19%; wooded 27%; uncultivated 13%. Main agricultural products: wheat, maize, sunflowers, tobacco. Mineral resources: oil, natural gas, coal, lignite, iron ore.
Official language: Romanian. Hungarian, German and Ukrainian minorities.

Switzerland: The Clock Tower in Berne

Religion: Orthodox (88%); Catholic and Protestant minorities.
Gross National Product: US $ 86,000 million; per capita: US $ 3,700.
Currency: Leu = 100 bani.

SAN MARINO

Repubblica di San Marino

San Marino has been a republic since its origin, in the 10th century. Legislative power is exercised by the the Grand General Council, whose members are elected for 5 years by direct universal suffrage. Every 6 months 2 of these are appointed as regents (Capitani Reggenti). These, together with the Congress of State, have legislative power. San Marino has been linked to Italy by a friendship treaty since 1897. It also has customs union with Italy and common telephonic, telegraphic and postal services. Italian currency has free circulation.
Completely enclosed within Italian territory the country consists almost entirely of a single mountain, Mount Titano.
Area: 61 sq km.
Population: 21,000; 344 per sq km.
Capital: San Marino (pop 2,800).
Main agricultural products: wheat, wine, vegetables, fruit.
Official language: Italian.
Religion: Catholic.
Currency: Italian lira.

SPAIN

España/Reino de España

Spain is a constitutional monarchy. After the death on 20th November 1975 of General Franco who had governed the country as a dictatorship since the Civil War, the country has gradually returned to democratic systems of government. Constitutional reform, formulated by the government, was approved by the Cortes on 18th November 1976 and confirmed by referendum on 15th December 1977. Executive power is exercised by the king, Juan Carlos, and the government. Legislative power is in the hands of the bicameral parliament (Cortes), which consists of the Chamber of Deputies, elected for 4 years by direct universal suffrage, and the Senate, some of whose members are elected for 4 years, also by direct universal suffrage, but on the system of proportional representation, and others, but not more than one fifth of the whole, by royal appointment.
Spain is a member of UNO, the EEC, the Council of Europe, OECD and NATO.
The country is composed almost entirely of mountains and plateaux. There are only two real plains — Andalusia in the Guadalquivir valley and Aragon in the Ebro valley. In the centre are two vast, barren plateaux, the "meseta". In Spanish possession also are the Canary Islands in the Atlantic and the Balearic Islands in the Mediterranean.
Area: 504,780 sq km, including the Balearic and Canary islands and the African territories of Ceuta and Melilla. The territory is divided into 14 administrative regions, 4 of which are autonomous (Catalonia, the Basque provinces, Galicia and Asturias).
Population: 38,870,000; 77 per sq km.
Annual growth rate: 0.4%; birth rate: 11‰; death rate: 8‰; average life expectancy: 72 years.
Capital: Madrid (3,100,000).
Other important towns: Barcelona (1,920,000); Bilbao (450,000); Granada (230,000); Las Palmas (345,000); Malaga (455,000); Murcia (285,000); Saragossa (560,000); Seville (625,000); Valencia (750,000); Valladolid (310,000).
Land use: cultivated 41%; grazing 22%; wooded 31%; uncultivated 6%. Main agricultural products: wheat, rice, maize, potatoes, sugar beet, wine, olive oil, citrus fruit. Mineral resources: coal, iron ore, copper, lead, zinc.
Official language: Spanish. Regional languages are recognised in their respective regions: Catalan in Catalonia, Basque in the Basque provinces, and Galician in Galicia.
Religion: Catholic.
Gross National Product: US $ 226,700 million; per capita: US $ 5,950.
Currency: Peseta = 100 céntimos.
Dependencies: the African territories of Ceuta and Melilla.

SWEDEN

Sverige/Konungariket Sverige

Sweden is a hereditary, constitutional monarchy. The sovereign exercises executive

Switzerland: The Matterhorn seen from Zermatt

power through the Council of State, which is accountable to parliament, and legislative power through the unicameral parliament (Riksdag). Members of this last are elected for 3 years by direct universal suffrage.
Sweden is a member of UNO, the Council of Europe, the Nordic Council, OECD and EFTA. The country is situated in the eastern part of the Scandinavian peninsula and extends nothwards beyond the Arctic Circle. In the south are extensive lowland areas suitable for cultivation. In the centre and north are the foothills of the Scandinavian Alps, through which run numerous rivers.
Area: 449,965 sq km, of which 38,485 sq km are inland waters.
Population: 8,450,000; 20 per sq km.
Annual growth rate: 0.2%; birth rate: 12‰; death rate: 11‰; average life expectancy: 75 years.
Capital: Stockholm (pop 1,470,000).
Other important towns: Göteborg/Gothenburg (440,000); Helsingborg (100,000); Linköping (110,000); Luleå (70,000); Malmö (240,000); Norrköping (120,000); Örebro (120,000); Uppsala (145,000); Västerås (120,000).
Land use: cultivated 7.3%, grazing 1.8%, wooded 64.2%, uncultivated 26.7%. Main agricultural products: barley, wheat, oats, sugar beet, potatoes; timber and wood pulp. Mineral resources: iron ore.
Official language: Swedish (93%). Finnish and Lapp are also spoken.
Religion: Protestant.
Gross National Product: US $ 131,500 million; per capita: US $ 15,700.
Currency: Swedish krona = 100 öre.

SWITZERLAND

Schweiz/Suisse/Confederatio Helvetica

Switzerland is a federal republic composed of 26 federal states, each of which has its own government (Council of State) and legislative assembly (Grand Council). The 26 states correspond to the 22 cantons into which Switzerland is traditionally divided (plus the newly formed canton of Jura), 3 of the cantons being divided into 2 states each. The 26 federal states are as follows: Aargau/Argovie, Ausser Rhoden and Inner Rhoden (divisions of the canton of Appenzell), Basle-Stadt and Basle-Land (divisions of the canton of Basle/Basel, Bern/Berne, Fribourg/Freiburg, Geneva, Glarus/Glaris, Grisons/Graubunder, Jura, Lucerne/Luzern, Neuchâtel, Obwalden and Nidwalden (divisions of the canton of Unterwalden), Sankt Gallen/St Gall, Schaffausen/Schaffouse, Schwyz, Solothurne/Soleure, Thurgan, Ticino, Uri, Valais, Vaud, Zug/Zoug, Zurich. At federal level legislative power is in the hands of the Federal Assembly (Bundesversammlung), which is divided into the National Council, whose members are elected for 4 years by direct universal suffrage, and the Council of States, whose members are representatives of the individual states. There are 2 representatives for each state except the 6 states which are subdivisions of 3 cantons, which have only one member each. The Federal Assembly elects the 7 members of the executive Federal Council, from whom one is elected every years as President, and also as President of the Confederatio Helvetica.
Switzerland, which is not a member of UNO, is a member of OECD, EFTA and the Council of Europe.
The country is completely landlocked, with the Alps and part of the Ticino valley in the south and a high-level plain in the north. There are numerous lakes and rivers.
Area: 41,295 sq km. Political-administrative division into 26 federal states.
Population: 6,630,000; 157 per sq km.
Annual growth rate: 0.4%; birth rate: 12‰; death rate: 9‰; average life expectancy: 73 years.
Capital: Berne (pop 285,000).
Other important towns: Basel (365,000); Geneva (325,000); Lausanne (225,000); Lucerne (160,000); Saint Gall (85,000); Winterthur (110,000); Zurich (710,000).
Land use: cultivated 9.5%, grazing 39.5%, wooded 26%, uncultivated 25%. Main agricultural products: potatoes, wheat, maize, wine, sugar beet; dairy products.
Official languages: German (73%), French (20%), Italian (5%). Romansch is a regional language spoken in the canton of Grisons.
Religions: Catholic (47%) and Protestant (44%).
Gross National Product: US $ 134,000 million; per capita: US $ 20,400.
Currency: Swiss franc = 100 rappen or centimes.

UNION OF SOVIET SOCIALIST REPUBLICS/USSR

Soyuz Sovietskih Socialisticheskih Respublik/SSSR

The Soviet Union is a socialist federal republic, formed of the following 15 socialist states: The Russian Soviet Federated Socialist Republic (RSFSR), Armenia, Azerbaijan, Estonia, Georgia, Kazakh SSR, Kirghiz SSR, Latvia, Lithuania, Moldavia, Tadzhik SSR, Turkmen SSR, Ukraine, Uzbek SSR, White Russia, each with its own legislative and executive bodies. Each of the federal republics, apart from the smaller ones, are in turn subdivided into provinces and territories, some of which include autonomous republics and national districts. All of these have been instituted in order to safeguard the cultural and linguistic identies of the various ethnic and linguistic groups which, together with the Russian nation, contribute to the formation of the Soviet Union.
Legislative power is exercised by the Supreme Council, or Supreme Soviet (Verchovnyi Soviet), whose members are in power for 4 years. This is divided into the Council/Soviet of the Union (Soviet Soyuza) whose members are elected by direct universal suffrage from the party lists of the Communist Party, on the basis of one member for every 30,000 of the population; and the Council/Soviet of Nationalities (Soviet Natsionalnostei), which consists of deputies from each of the Federal Republics on the basis of 32 deputies for each Federal Republic, 11 for each autonomous republic, 5 for each autonomous province and 1 for each national district. The Supreme Soviet elects the Presidium of the Soviet Supreme of the USSR and nominates the Council of Ministers, who have executive power. The Presidium, which is elected by both houses of the Supreme Soviet, is composed of a President who is also head of state, 15 vice-presidents who represent the 15 federal states, another 14 members and a secretary. According to the constitution, the Communist Party held a position of prime importance in all sectors of national life, performing the function of guide of society and state. However, since 1989, profound institutional changes have been taking place.
The Soviet Union is a member of UNO Comecon and the Warsaw Pact. The Ukraine and White Russia are also members of UNO.
The Soviet Union is the largest country in the world. The European part is almost completely low-lying with only a few highland areas. In the north it borders on the Arctic Ocean; in the south are the impressive Caucasus Mountains. There are many important rivers, including the Volga, the longest river in Europe. The Asian part of the country includes western Siberia, for the most part low-lying, and eastern Siberia, which is mountainous and fed by the Ob, Yenisey and Lena rivers. Central Soviet Asia is low-lying and often semi-desert.
Area: 22,274,900 sq km, of which 5,571,000 sq km are in Europe.
Political-administrative division into 15 federal republics, which are subdivided into provinces, autonomous provinces, territories, national districts, and autonomous republics.
Population: 286,700,000, of which most are Russian (over 50%); the remainder are Ukrainians, White Russians, Uzbekis, Tartars, Kazakhs, Azerbaijanis, Georgians, Tadzhikis, Jews, Chuvash, Turkmen, Kirghiz, Latvians, Estonians etc.

Hungary: View of Budapest

Density: 12 per sq km.
Annual growth rate: 0.9%; birth rate: 19‰; death rate: 10‰; average life expectancy: 70 years.
Capital: Moscow (pop 8,700,000).
Other important towns: Alma-Ata (1 130,000); Baku (1,760,000); Chelyabinsk (1 145,000); Donetsk (1,035,000); Gorky (1,360,000); Kharkov (1,470,000); Kiev (2,580,000); Kuybyshev (1,230,000); Leningrad (5,020,000); Minsk (1,600,000); Novosibirsk (1,430,000); Odessa (1,115,000); Omsk (1,130,000) Rostov (950,000); Tashkent (2,070,000); Tbilisi (1,250,000); Vladivostok (550,000); Volgograd/Stalingrad (940,000).
Land use: cultivated: 10%; grazing 17%; wooded 42%; uncultivated 31%. Main agricultural products: wheat, barley, rye, oats, sunflowers, sugar beet, potatoes, vegetables, fruit, cotton, tobacco, hemp, linen. Other activities: fishing, cattle rearing. Mineral resources: oil, natural gas, manganese, nickel, mercury, potash, iron ore, platinum, gold, silver, diamonds.
Official language: Russian (68%). Among the other 200 languages spoken in the country the most widespread are Uzbeki, Azerbaijani, Kazakh, Tartar, Georgian, Armenian, Ukrainian, Lithuanian, Moldavian.
Religion: Orthodox. Protestant, Catholic, Muslim, and Jewish minorities.
Gross National Product: US $ 1,595,800 million, per capita: US $ 5,700.
Currency: Rouble = 100 kopecks.

VATICAN CITY

Città del Vaticano

The Vatican is an elected absolute monarchy, the Pope being its supreme head. Sovereign Pontiff of the Roman Catholic Apostolic Church, the Pope is elected by secret vote by the College of Cardinals. He has absolute legislative, executive and judicial powers, but delegates the government of the city state to the Pontifical Commission. The College of Cardinals, who are nominated exclusively by the Pope, rules the Church in times of a "vacant see" i.e. between the death of one pope and the election of his successor.
It is the smallest state in the world and includes St Peter's Basilica and the Vatican Palace.
Area: 0.44 sq km.
Population: 1,000; 2.5 per sq km (approx).
Official languages: Latin and Italian.
Religion: Catholic.
Currency: Italian lira.

YUGOSLAVIA

Jugoslavija/Socijalistička Federativna Republika Jugoslavija

Yugoslavia is a socialist federal republic, composed of the following 6 federal republics: Bosnia-Herzegovina, Croatia, Macedonia, Montenegro, Serbia, Slovenia. In Serbia there are the two administratively autonomous regions of Kosovo and Vojvodina. In accordance with the constitution which came into effect on 21st February 1974 legislative power is in the hands of the Federal Parliament. Parliament is composed of a Federal Chamber of 220 deputies, and the Chamber of the Republic whose members are chosen as representatives of the individual federal republics and the autonomous regions. The Presidential College of the Federation, consisting of 9 members representing the federal republics and the autonomous regions, every year elects its own president who is also the head of state. Profound institutional changes are in progress.
Yugoslavia is a member of UNO and by special statute also of OECD and Comecon.
Rugged and mountainous along the coast and in the south, the country has low-lying areas only inland along the valleys of the Danube and its tributaries.
Area: 255,805 sq km with political-administrative division into 6 federal republics: Bosnia-Herzegovina, Croatia, Macedonia, Montenegro, Serbia, Slovenia.
Population: 23,560,000; 92 per sq km.
Annual growth rate: 0.7%; birth rate: 15‰; death rate: 9‰; average life expectancy: 70 years.
Capital: Belgrade (pop 1,475,000).
Other important towns: Fiume (Rijeka-Susak) (160,000); Ljubljana (303,000); Novi Sad (170,000); Pula (60,000); Sarajevo (447,000); Skopje (410,000); Split (169,000); Zagreb (763,000).
Land use: cultivated 31%; grazing 25%; wooded 36%; uncultivated 8%. Main agricultural products: maize, wheat, wine, tobacco, fruit; timber. Mineral resources: coal, bauxite, oil, natural gas, iron ore.
Official languages: Serbo-Croat, Slovene and Macedonian. Albanian and English minorities.
Religions: Orthodox (41%), Catholic (32%), Muslim (12%).
Gross National Product: US $ 41,500 million; per capita: US $ 1,780.
Currency: Dinar = 100 para.

USSR: Red Square in Moscow, with St Basil's Cathedral in the background

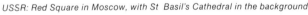

Asia

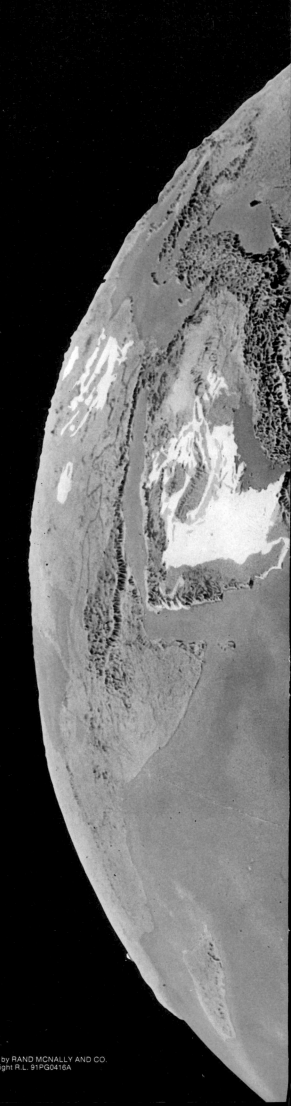

Asia covers more than 44 million square kilometres, stretching from the frozen Arctic icecap to the steaming monsoon regions and is thus the largest continent on Earth. If we add that more than 50% of the world's population lives there, it will be realized how very important this continent is and how very varied its climates, landscapes, human and economic characteristics must be. Climate and morphology roughly form four wide horizontal bands. To the north there are the Arctic landscapes of Siberia where the tundra and taiga (conifer forests) prevail. Further south we find the deserts, hot in the western sector (Arabian Peninsula, Iran, India), cold and continental to the east with the great Gobi desert. Still further south we find the enormous mountain ranges that form a continuous chain from the Anatolian Peninsula (Turkey) to the Pamirs, the Himalayas, Tibet. Here the range breaks up into two branches, one going north-east (Manchuria), the other south-east (Indochina). In the southernmost part of the continent we find the rain forests and river deltas where rain-bearing monsoon winds blow from the south-west.

Asia can be divided into five main regions. The USSR, which covers more than one-third of the continent, has a particular place. Its enormous territory is not heavily populated.

With less than 300 million inhabitants it has a population density of only 12/sq km, which only recently has shown a tendency to rise because of the industrialization of Siberia, encouraged by the enormous wealth of raw materials, and the introduction of irrigation into parts of Kazakhstan. Pioneer cities built in these regions have populated the semi-desert areas.

Western Asia, usually known as the Middle East is a vast area stretching from Arabia to India. The landscape is mostly composed of deserts and barren plateaux. The climate is arid with very low rainfalls (less than 100 mm per year). The important characteristics of this region are the common culture and religion — Islam with all its many internal divisions (and the outstanding exception of Israel) — and the wealth of oil beneath the desert floor. The output of oil products is approximately one-third of the entire world production and is the reason why this is one of the world's hotspots.

Separated from the rest of Asia by the gigantic mountain ranges of the Karakorum and Himalaya, the sub-continent of India forms a world of its own, with over 3 million square kilometres and 700 million inhabitants. The Himalayas are linked to the Deccan Peninsula by the Indus-Ganges Plain, formed down the ages by sediment from the rivers Ganges, Brahmaputra and Indus and their network of tributaries. This is the most densely populated region of India, being the most suitable for farming, which is practised by 70% of the active population.

China and Japan are probably the most emblematic political entities of eastern Asia. However they are very different from one another, to the point of being opposites. On the one hand there is China with over 9 million square kilometres, third only in size after the Soviet Union and Canada. It is an immense territory with an equally enormous population of more than 1,000 million people. Its social order and economy are agriculturally based. On the other hand there is Japan, which is only a little larger than Italy but has more than twice its population. It is a highly industrialized country with average per capita incomes among the highest in the world, but it also suffers from profound social and economic problems.

South-East Asia is an area halfway between Asia and Australia. The Strait of Malacca has always been the most widely used passage between the Pacific Ocean and the Indian Ocean. Still today it is the most important routeway for Japanese industry and the Middle East petrol which is its lifeblood.

Nature and history have both contributed to making this area extremely diverse. Physically the unifying aspects are the monsoons with their heavy rains that go to feed the Indochinese rivers, and the constant seismic and volcanic activity. Economically South-East Asia continues to suffer from enormous differences, made more serious by the wars of recent decades. The agricultural methods used are those typical of underdeveloped countries. Industrialisation is not widespread enough and every effort to improve the situation is rendered vain by the constant rise in population levels.

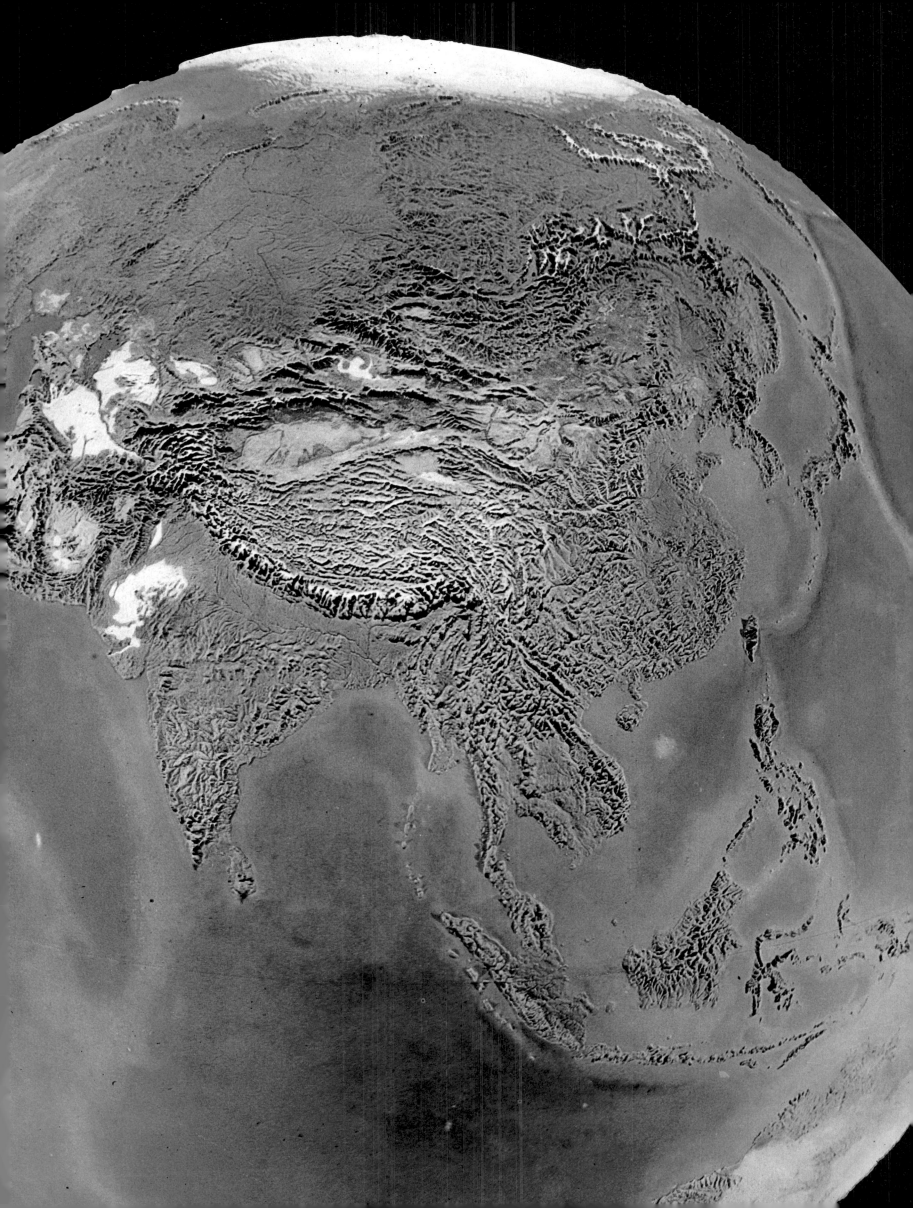

AFGHANISTAN

Da Afghanistan dimukratik jomhuriyat

Afghanistan is a People's Republic founded on 27th April 1978, when a military coup d'état abolished the authoritarian regime established by the previous military coup of 17th July 1973. Power is now in the hands of the Revolutionary Council, which is controlled by the leaders of the Communist Party. From 1979 to 1989 a strong contingent of Soviet troups gave military aid to the government forces against the anti-Communist freedom movements. Guerilla warfare is still going on, however, all over the country.
Afghanistan is a member of UNO.
Its territory is composed of a central mountainous area with long fertile valleys, surrounded by deserts. The rivers disperse into the desert areas except for the Kabul which flows into the Indus.
Area: 652,900 sq km.
Population: 15,900,000, mostly Afghans and Pathans (comprising together over 55%), Uzbekis 09%), Hazaris, Kirghiz, Baluchis, Turkomen; density: 24 per sq km.
Annual growth rate: 1.1%; birth rate: 48‰; death rate: 22‰; average life expectancy: 41 years.
Capital: Kabul (pop 1,297,000).
Other important towns: Baghlan (41,000); Charikar (25,000); Herat (160,000); Jalalabad (55,000); Kandahar (210,000); Konduz (57,000).
Land use: cultivated 12%, grazing 9%, wooded 3%; uncultivated 76%. Main agricultural products: wheat, maize, barley, rice, cotton, sugar beet, sesame, fruit and potatoes. Mineral resources: natural gas.
Official languages: Pashto and Tadzhiki.
Religion: Sunni Muslim.
Gross National Product: US $ 5,000 million; per capita: US $ 290.
Currency: Afghani = 1,000 puls.

BAHRAIN

Al-Bahrayn

A nominally constitutional, hereditary monarchy, Bahrain was formerly a British protectorate which obtained its independence on 14th August 1971. Although the constitution granted in 1973 allows for a Legislative Assembly of 30 members elected by suffrage limited to male citizens, in practice all legislative and executive powers are in the hands of the royal family.
Bahrain is a member of UNO and the Arab League.
The country is formed by a group of five main islands plus other smaller islands in the Gulf. The most important island is Bahrain.
Area: 670 sq km.
Population: 421,000, the vast majority of whom are Arabs; 620 per sq km.
Annual growth rate: 2.3%; birth rate 44‰; death rate 9‰; average life expectancy: 63 years.
Capital: Manama (pop 115,000).
Other important towns: Muharraq (75,000); Rifa (45,000).
Land use: cultivated 3%; grazing 6%; uncultivated 91%. Main agricultural products: dates, rice, vegetables. Mineral resources: oil, natural gas.
Official language: Arabic.
Religion: Muslim (86%).
Gross National Product: US $ 3,850 million; per capita: US $ 9,000.
Currency: Dinar = 1,000 fils.

BANGLADESH

Gana Projatantri Bangladesh

Bangladesh is a presidential republic, proclaimed on 26th March 1971 following the separation from Pakistan of what was its former Eastern Province. It has been effective since 22nd December of the same year. According to the 1972 Constitution, which was modified in January 1975, the executive and legislative powers are held by the Prime Minister who is also the President of the Republic, aided in the exercise of his functions by the ministers in office who are responsible directly to him. The single-chamber Parliament, elected by universal suffrage for 5-year terms from the lists of the only party, the People's Peasants' and Workers' League, is almost exclusively a consultative organ. Following repeated military coups d'état since 1975, however, a military junta now holds full power and has suspended all constitutional rights.
Bangladesh is a member of UNO and the Commonwealth of Nations.

Afghanistan: Caravan of camels

The country consists of plains and the vast Ganges delta. There are many river valleys, swamps and jungle areas. It has a monsoon climate.
Area: 144,000 sq km.
Population: 102,800,000, the vast majority of whom are Bengalis (98%); 714 per sq km.
Annual growth rate: 3%; birth rate 47‰; death rate 18‰; average life expectancy: 49 years.
Capital: Dacca (pop 4,500,000).
Other important towns: Barisal (160,000); Chittagong (1,400,000); Khulna (620,000); Narayangang (275,000); Saidpur (130,000).
Land use: cultivated 68%; grazing 4.5%; wooded 16.5%; uncultivated 11%. Main agricultural products: rice, wheat, jute, bananas, sugar cane, pineapples, tobacco, tea.
Official language: Bengali.
Religion: Muslim (86%). More than 12% are Hindus.
Gross National Product: US $ 15,550 million; per capita: US $ 150.
Currency: Taka = 100 poisha.

BHUTAN

Druk-Yul

Bhutan has a hereditary monarchy, since October 1969 no longer with absolute powers. It is under the protection of India which, in conformity with a treaty signed in 1949, is responsible for defence and external affairs, leaving full autonomy to the Maharajah in home affairs. The Maharajah has religious, legislative and executive powers, which he exercises together with the single-chamber Parliament (Tsongdu). Parliament has the power to pass a vote of no confidence and compel the sovereign to abdicate.
Bhutan is a member of UNO.
It is a small country in the Himalayan area, mountainous and covered in forests. It includes the fertile valleys of the Bhutan river basin.
Area: 46,000 sq km.
Population: 1,300,000, mostly Tibetans, Nepalese and Bhutanese; 28 per sq km.
Annual growth rate: 2.1%; birth rate 43‰; death rate 21‰; average life expectancy: 44 years.
Capital: Thimphu (pop 15,000) in summer, Punakha in winter.
Land use: cultivated 2%; grazing 4%; wooded 70%; uncultivated 24%. Main agricultural products: rice, wheat, maize, barley, potatoes.
Official language: Dzongka.
Religion: Lamaism.
Gross National Product: US $ 205 million; per capita: US $ 162.
Currency: Ngultrum = 100 chetrum.

Saudi Arabia: The Ka'aba in Mecca

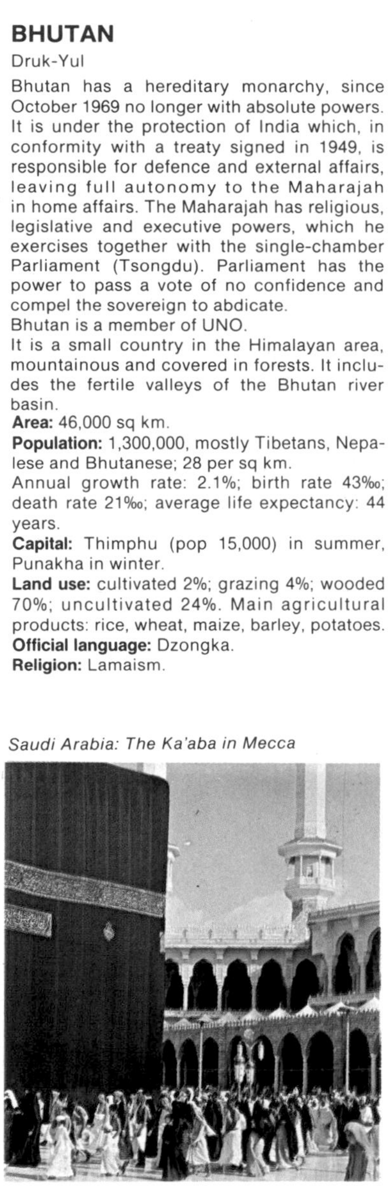

BRITISH INDIAN OCEAN TERRITORY

A British colony, established in November 1965, important for its military installations, the BIOT is made up of the Chagos Islands in the Indian Ocean, south of the Maldives. The main island is Diego Garcia, with a military base shared by both Britain and the United States.
Area: 45 sq km.
Population: 1,000.
Official language: English.
Religion: Christian.
Currency: UK £ sterling = 100 pence.

BRUNEI

Negara Brunei Darussalam

Brunei is a hereditary monarchy, independent since 31st December 1983. Since 1888 it had been under the protection of Great Britain, which was responsible for defence and external affairs. The Sultan has executive power, aided by the Privy Council, and legislative power through the Legislative Council.
Brunei is a member of UNO and the Commonwealth of Nations.
The country lies along the northern coast of the island of Borneo. It is almost entirely covered by equatorial forests.
Area: 5,765 sq km.
Population: 230,000; mostly Malays (65%), and Chinese (20%); 39 per sq km.
Annual growth rate: 3.4%; birth rate 28‰; death rate 3.5‰; average life expectancy: 66 years.
Capital: Bandar Seri Begawan (pop 55,000).
Land use: cultivated 2.5%; grazing 1.5%; wooded 45%; uncultivated 51%. Main agricultural products: copra, rubber, rice, bananas, citrus fruit. Mineral resources: oil.
Official languages: Malay and English. Chinese also widely used.
Religion: Muslim.
Gross National Product: US $ 2,820 million; per capita: US $ 12,500.
Currency: Brunei dollar = 100 cents.

BURMA

Myanmar

Burma is a federal, socialist republic that has been independent since January 1948, formed by Burma itself together with the seven nation states of Kachin (capital Myitkyina), Kayah (capital Loi-Kaw), Shan (capital Taunggyi), Karen (formerly Kawthule, capital Pa-an), Chin (capital Falam), Arakan (capital Sittwe) and Mon (capital Moulmein). These last three states were formed in 1974. In accordance with the new constitution which came into force on 4th January 1974, legislative power is in the hands of the People's National Council, whose members are elected in the lists of the only existing party, the Party of the Burmese Socialist Programme. The People's National Council elects the Supreme Council which is the executive organ presided over by the President of the Republic.
Following the popular uprising of summer 1988, the power is held by a military junta.
Burma is a member of UNO.
The country stretches in a north-south direction and is generally mountainous around the central basins of the Chindwin and Irrawaddy Rivers, with the Irrawaddy delta in the south.
Area: 676,550 sq km; politically and administratively divided into 7 federal states.
Population: 35,300,000 mostly Burmese (72%); Shan (9%); Karen (6%); Kachin, Chin and Chinese; density: 52 per sq km.
Annual growth rate: 2.2%; birth rate 39‰; death rate 14‰; average life expectancy: 54 years.
Capital: Rangoon (pop 2,660,000).
Other important towns: Akyab (145,000); Bassein (360,000); Henzada (285,000); Mandalay (420,000); Moulmein (205,000); Pegu (260,000); Prome (150,000); Tavoy (105,000).
Land use: cultivated 15.5%; grazing 0.5%; wooded 48.5%; uncultivated 35.5%. Main agricultural products: rice, sugar cane, jute, groundnuts, sesame, rubber; fishing. Mineral resources: oil, natural gas, lead.
Official language: Burmese.
Religion: Buddhist (94%); Muslim (3%); Hindu (2%); Roman Catholic (1%).
Gross National Product: US $ 8,340 million; per capita: US $ 220.
Currency: Kyat = 100 pyas.

CHINA

Zhong-guà Renmin Gongheguó

China is a People's Republic founded in 1949 following the taking of power by Communist forces over the whole of mainland China. The nationalists only managed to conserve power over the island of Formosa (now Taiwan) and small groups of islands such as Matsu and Quemoy. The supreme organ of the state is the National People's Congress composed of more than 3,000 deputies elected for 5-year terms in multiple elections. The National People's Congress exerts the legislative power and controls the Council of State with the aid of the Permanent Committee and the Committee for the Nationalities. The Council of State is the Central Government of the People to which the executive power is devolved. The Political Consultative Assembly of the Chinese People has only a consultative role, being convened once a year on political matters.
China lays claim to vast territories in the eastern part of the Soviet Union, northern India and the whole territory of the Republic of China (Taiwan). The archipelagoes of Xsisha (Paracel Islands), Dongsha (Pratas Islands) and Nanshan (including the Spratly Islands) in the South China Sea are disputed with Taiwan. The Paracel Islands, which were militarily occupied on 20th January 1974 are also claimed by Vietnam. The Nanshan Islands are also claimed by Vietnam and the Philippines.
China is a member of UNO.
The country, which covers a fifth of all Asia, has very varied physical characteristics. It is mountainous in the south-west, with the high Tibetan plateau surrounded by the Himalayan mountain range. It is very arid in the north-west with semi-desert uplands and the cold Gobi desert. The most fertile area is in eastern China, where vast plains are crossed by large rivers that flow down to the Pacific, the Huang-ho, the Yangtze Kiang and the Si Kiang. There are also many lakes.
Area: 9,560,980 sq km; politically and administratively divided into three municipalities, 21 Provinces and 5 Autonomous Regions.
Population: 1,057,210,000; 94% of whom are Chinese (Han), with numerous minorities especially in the Autonomous Regions; density: 111 per sq km.
Annual growth rate: 1.3%; birth rate 20‰; death rate 6‰; average life expectancy: 64 years.
Capital: Beijing (pop 9,579,000).
Other important towns: Gouangzhou/Canton (3,360,000); Changchun (1,910,000); Chengdu (2,640,000); Chongqing (2,770,000); Fuzhou (1,210,000); Harbin (2,600,000); Lhasa (105,000); Nanjing (2,290,000); Shangai (12,320,000); Shenyang (4,290,000); Taiyuan (1,955,000); Tientsin (8,190,000); Urumchi (1,040,000); Wuhan (3,490,000); Xi'an (2,370,000).
Land use: cultivated 10.3%; grazing 33%; wooded 12.2%; uncultivated 44.5%. Main agricultural products: rice, wheat, maize, millet, soya bean, barley, sorghum, sugar cane and sugar beet, groundnuts, potatoes, tobacco, cotton, pineapples, bananas, citrus fruit. Other activities: fishing, livestock rearing. Mineral resources: antimony, asbestos, coal, iron ore, mercury, tin, tungsten.
Official languages: Chinese; in the Autonomous Regions Mongol, Tibetan, Uigur and tens of other languages are also spoken.

China: The Forbidden City in Beijing

Religions: Confucianism, Buddhism and Taoism.
Gross National Product: US $ 258,690 million; per capita: US $ 246.
Currency: Yuan = 100 fen.

CYPRUS

Kipriaki Dimokratia / Kibris Cumhuriyeti

Cyprus is a presidential republic independent since 16th August 1960, and a member of the Commonwealth of Nations. According to the 1960 constitution the executive power is exerted by the President of the Republic, a Greek Cypriot, aided by a vice-president, a Turkish Cypriot, seven Greek Cypriot ministers and three Turkish Cypriot ministers. The legislative power is with the single-chamber Parliament whose members are elected for 5-year terms by direct universal suffrage in the proportions of 70% and 30% of the two ethnic groups. The delicate balance between the two communities has been upset more than once in recent years. Particularly dramatic was the military coup d'état on 15th July 1974 which deposed the President of the Republic Archbishop Makarios and put the power in the hands of a pro-Greek military junta. The Turkish government would not accept this state of affairs and sent a military contingent to Cyprus on 20th July. To defend the interests of the Turkish Cypriot community it occupied the whole northern part of the island. On 13th February 1975, in the sector occupied by the Turkish troops, a Turkish Cypriot Federal State was proclaimed (with its own Parliament and President). This was an autonomous political entity, not independent, therefore an integral part of the Federal Independent Republic of Cyprus, as the Cypriot State is called by the Turks. The Greek Cypriot community does not accept this situation partly because the Turkish Cypriot minority, which is less than 20% of the population, at present occupies 40% of the territory. On 15th November 1983 the Federal Turkish Cypriot State unilaterally declared its independence from Cyprus, and established the Turkish Republic of Northern Cyprus, which was immediately recognised by Turkey and later also by Bangladesh.
Cyprus is a member of UNO and the Council of Europe.
It is an island in the eastern part of the Mediterranean Sea with two mountain ranges separated by the fertile plain of Mesaoria.
Area: 9,250,000 sq km.
Population: 680,000, 80% of whom are Greek Cypriots and 18% Turkish Cypriots; density: 68 per sq km.
Annual growth rate: 1.3%; birth rate 18‰; death rate 10‰; average life expectancy: 70 years.
Capital: Nicosia (pop 125,000).
Other important towns: Famagusta (40,000); Larnaca (20,000); Limassol (80,000).
Land use: cultivated 17%; grazing 0.5%; wooded 13%; uncultivated 69.5%. Main agricultural products: barley, sultanas, wine, potatoes, wheat, oats, vegetables. Mineral resources: copper.
Official languages: Greek and Turkish.
Religions: Greek Orthodox (Autonomous Church of Cyprus) and Muslim.
Gross National Product: US $ 2,510 million; per capita: US $ 3,700.
Currency: Cypriot pound = 1,000 mils.

HONG KONG

Xianggang

Hong Kong is a British Crown Colony formed by the island of the same name leased by China to Great Britain in 1841, the Kowloon Peninsula, leased in 1860, and the so-called New Territories on the Chinese mainland, leased in 1898 for 99 years. The Colony is administered by a Governor aided by an Executive Council and a Legislative Council. In accordance with an agreement which came into force in December 1984, Hong Kong will be returned to China on 1st July 1997.
The territory is formed by the island of Hong Kong with other smaller islands and the Kowloon Peninsula which is crossed by the Chinese border.
Area: 1,045 sq km.
Population: 5,400,000, 98% of whom are Chinese; density: 5,160 per sq km.
Annual growth rate: 1.2%; birth rate 12.5‰; death rate 5‰; average life expectancy: 76 years.
Colonial capital: Victoria (pop 680,000).
Land use: cultivated 9%; grazing 1%; wooded 13%; uncultivated 77%. Main agricultural products: rice, vegetables, fruit, timber.
Official languages: English and Cantonese.
Religion: Buddhism; strong Taoist and Confucian minorities.
Gross National Product: US $ 37,410 million; per capita: US $ 6,800.
Currency: Hong Kong dollar = 100 cents.

INDIA

Bharat Juktarashtra

India is a federal republic, and a member of the Commonwealth of Nations. It has been an independent state since August 1947 and became a republic in 1950. It is formed by 25 federal states: Andhra Pradesh, Arunachal Pradesh, Assam, Bihar, Goa, Gujarat, Haryana, Himachal Pradesh, Jammu and Kashmir, Karnataka (former name Mysore), Kerala, Madhya Pradesh, Maharashtra, Manipur, Meghalaya, Mizoram, Nagaland, Orissa, Punjab, Rajasthan, Sikkim (annexed by the Indian Republic in 1975), Tamil Nadu, Tripura, Uttar Pradesh, West Bengal and also by seven territories under the direct dependency of the federal government. Each federal state has its own government and Parliament. These can be one-chamber or two-chamber bodies and are elected for 5-year terms. The President of the Republic and the vice- president are elected for 5-year terms (and can be re-elected) by an electoral body formed by the members of the federal Parliament and those of each separate federal state. The government is designated by the President of the Republic to exert the executive power and is responsible to the Parliament for its action. The Parliament exerts the legislative power and is composed of two chambers. One is the Council of States or Raiya Sabha which has 244 members, 12 of whom are nominated by the President of the Republic, the others being elected by the federal states in proportion to their number of inhabitants. One-third of these seats is renewed every two years. The other chamber is the House of the People or Lok Sabha composed of 543 members elected for 5-year terms by direct universal suffrage.
Bhutan is tied to the Republic of India by a treaty of protection. India lays claim to north-west Kashmir, administered by Pakistan which in its turn lays claim to south-east Kashmir, administered by the Republic of India. The People's Republic of China lays claim to eastern Kashmir, part of Bhutan and Arunachal Pradesh.
India is a member of UNO.
The country covers most of the Indian subcontinent, the enormous peninsula that extends southwards into the Indian Ocean. It can be divided into three geographic areas: the mountainous northern part with the Himalayan peaks rising to 7,817 m.; the great central plains where the Indus, Ganges and Brahmaputra rivers flow, and the vast Deccan plain in the south, rimmed by mountain ranges to the east and west, covered with thick forests. The climate is characterised by monsoon winds.
Area: 3,287,780 sq km; administratively and politically divided into 25 federal states and 7 territories.
Population: 685,184,000; 72% Indo-Aryan (Hindis, Bengalis, Marathis, Biharis, Punjabis, Gujarati, Oriya, Rajasthanis, Assamese, Urdus, Kashmiris, etc.), 25% Dravidians (Tamils, Telugu, Kannada, etc.) and 3% Mongols.
Annual growth rate: 2.1%; birth rate 34‰; death rate 15‰; average life expectancy: 52 years.
Capital: Delhi (pop 5,730,000).
Other important towns: Agra (640,000); Allahabad (616,000); Bangalore (2,650,000); Varanasi (formerly Benares) (710,000); Bombay (8,227,000); Calcutta (9,165,000); Hyderabad (2,528,000); Jaipur (977,000); Kanpur (1,480,000), Lucknow (895,000); Madras (4,276,000); Madurai (920,000); Nagpur (1,297,000); Poona (1,685,000), Srinagar (588,000).
Land use: cultivated 57%; grazing 4%; wooded 22%; uncultivated 17%. Main agricultural products: rice, wheat, millet, maize, barley, sorghum, potatoes, sugar cane, groundnut, hemp, sweet potatoes, bananas, jute, tea, cotton, coffee, tobacco, citrus fruit. Other activities: fishing, cattle rearing. Mineral resources: bauxite, coal, iron ore.
Official languages: Hindi and English. In some of the federal states use of the local language is recognized; Assamesse in Assam; Bengali in West Bengal, Punjabi in the Punjab etc.
Religions: Hindu (80%); Muslim (11.5%); Christian (2.5%); Sikhism (2%); Buddhism (0.7%); Jainism (0.4%).
Gross National Product: US $ 214,960 million; per capita: US $ 276.
Currency: Rupee = 100 paisas.
Protectorate: Bhutan has a Treaty of Protection with India, which is responsible for its external affairs, defence and communications.

INDONESIA

Republik Indonesia

A presidential republic, Indonesia was a colony of the Netherlands under the name of the Dutch East Indies until 1945. The head of state is the President of the Republic, elected for five years by the People's Congress. He directly exerts the executive power with the aid of the Council of Ministers, and the legislative power with the Chamber of Representatives, over three-quarters of whom are elected by direct universal suffrage, while the rest are nominated by the government.
Indonesia is a member of UNO and ASEAN.
The country consists of approximately 3,000 islands in the Indian Ocean and Pacific Ocean. They form a great curve from north-west to south-east with a central mountain range running through them all. There are numerous volcanic peaks several of which are active. The soil is fertile, the climate humid and there are vast tracts of virgin forest. The main islands are Java, Sumatra, Borneo, New Guinea and Sulawesi (Celebes). They a l have a monsoon climate.
Area: 1,904,345 sq km, including the eastern part of the island of Timor, a former Portuguese overseas province, which was occupied by Indonesia and annexed in 1975.
Population: 172,244,000, the majority of whom are Indonesians; 65% of whom are Javanese; density: 89 per sq km.
Annual growth rate: 2.3%; birth rate 29‰; death rate 8‰; average life expectancy: 53 years.
Capital: Jakarta (pop 7,800,000).
Other important towns: Bandung (1,460,000); Banjarmasin (385,000); Jayapura (149,000); Medan (1,380,000); Palembang (785,000); Pontianak (304,000); Semarang (1,020,000); Surabaya (2,020,000); Ujung Pandang (709,000); Yogyakarta (390,000).
Land use: cultivated 10.5%; grazing 7%; wooded 67%; uncultivated 15.5%. Main agricultural products: rice, sugar cane, maize, rubber, tea, coffee, tobacco, soya bean, copra, bananas, pineapples; timber. Other activities: fishing. Mineral resources: oil.
Official language: Indonesian.
Religions: Muslim (88%); Christian (9%); Hindu (1.5%); Buddhism (0.5%).
Gross National Product: US $ 71,910 million; per capita: US $ 435.
Currency: Indonesian rupiah = 100 sen.

IRAN

Jumhuri-e Islami Iran

Iran became an Islamic republic following a referendum held on 30th March 1979 after the expulsion of the former ruler, the Shah Reza Pahlavi. The legislative power is held by the single-chamber Parliament, whose members are elected by universal suffrage.
The Faghih, a charismatic religious dignitary, holds the right to control the laws and the organs of the state and nominate the majority of the members of the Council of Prevention and Vigilance, a political body that controls the Parliament.
Iran is a member of UNO.
The country, which covers the area that was once ancient Persia, reaches south to the Gulf and the Arabian Sea, and north to the Caspian Sea. It consists mainly of a high desert plateau surrounded by high mountains, with a few rivers that disperse into the desert sands. Cultivation is possible only in the oases.
Area: 1,648,000 sq km.
Population: 49,764,000; 65% of whom are Iranians; 20% Azerbaijani, 10% Kurds and 2% Arabs; density: 30 per sq km.
Annual growth rate: 3.2%; birth rate 35‰; death rate 4‰; average life expectancy: 54 years.
Capital: Tehran (pop 6,000,000).
Other important towns: Abadan (300,000); Ahwaz (330,000); Esfahan (670,000); Imanshahr (290,000); Mashhad (680,000); Oramiyeh (165,000); Qom (250,000); Rasht (190,000); Shiraz (420,000); Tabriz (600,000).
Land use: cultivated 10%; grazing 27%; wooded 11%; uncultivated 52%. Main agricultural products: wheat, barley, maize, cotton, soya bean, tobacco, tea, potatoes, citrus fruit. Mineral resources: oil.
Official language: Farsi.
Religion: Shia Muslim (90%).
Gross National Product: US $ 140,000 million; per capita: US $ 3,100.
Currency: Rial = 100 dinars.

IRAQ

Al-Jumhuriyah al-Iraqiyah ad-Dimuqratiyah ash-Shaabiyah

Iraq has been a presidential republic since 1958. Following a military coup d'état in 1968

The Philippines: Rice cultivation

a provisional constitution was promulgated in 1970, according to which the National Revolutionary Council and the President of the Republic, whom it elects, are considered the highest authorities of the state.
In order to procure better access to the sea, Iraq fought a war against Iran for the control of the Shatt al-Arab, with much bloodshed. In August 1990 it invaded Kuwait, which it declared to be its nineteenth province. This annexation was not recognized by the international community which freed Kuwait by force in February 1991.
Iraq is a member of UNO and the Arab League.
The country stretches from Turkey to the top of the Gulf where it has a brief tract of coast. There are three geographical zones: the mountainous northern one; the southern plain which is low-lying and damp and crossed by the Tigris and Euphrates rivers (ancient Mesopotamia); the desert plateau to the west.
Area: 434,900 sq km.
Population: 16,335,000; most of whom are Iraqi Arabs (80%); then Kurds (15%) and Turks (2%); density: 37 per sq km.
Annual growth rate: 3.1%; birth rate 45‰; death rate 12‰; average life expectancy: 56 years.
Capital: Baghdad (pop 3,810,000).
Other important towns: Arbil (334,000); Basra (1,540,000); Mosul (1,220,000).
Land use: cultivated 12%; grazing 9%; wooded 4%; uncultivated 75%. Main agricultural products: dates, cotton, wheat, rice, sesame, sugar cane, vegetables, fruit. Mineral resources: oil.
Official language: Arabic.
Religion: Sunni and Shia Muslim.
Gross National Product: US $ 39,500 million; per capita: US $ 2,500.
Currency: Dinar = 1,000 fils.

ISRAEL

Medinat Yisra'el

Israel as a parliamentary republic was created on 14th May 1948. It has no constitution. Its political and legal organization are determined as needed by special laws. The President of the Republic, elected by Parliament for five years, nominates the Prime Minister who exerts the executive power together with the various ministers. Legislative power is in the hands of the Parliament (Knesset) whose members are elected for 4-year terms by universal suffrage.
Following the campaigns of June 1967 and October 1973, Israel currently holds under military administration, while awaiting the signature of a peace treaty, the Gaza strip (which area was previously administered by Egypt, but was of uncertain sovereignty); the West Bank of the River Jordan (which is also of uncertain sovereignty since Jordan, which had unilaterally annexed the zone in 1950, renounced sovereignty in 1988); the western sector of Jerusalem (annexed unilaterally by Israel) and the Golan Heights on the frontier with Syria.
Israel is a member of UNO.
The country lies along the eastern coast of the Mediterranean Sea between Egypt to the south and the Lebanon to the north. The northern part of the country is a barren plateau that falls steeply down to the fertile valley of the Jordan, the only river of any importance. South of the Dead Sea depression that separates Israel from Jordan stretches the Negev desert, covering almost half Israel's territory.
Area: 20,770 sq km.
Population: 4,331,000 mostly Jews, the rest (6.5%) Arabs; density: 214 per sq km.
Annual growth rate: 1.9%; birth rate 23‰; death rate 7‰; average life expectancy: 72 years.
Capital: Jerusalem (pop 469,000, of whom 65,000 reside in the eastern sector).
Other important towns: Bat Yam (132,000); Beersheba (105,000); Bethlehem (25,000); Elat (20,000); Haifa (230,000); Hebron (45,000); Jericho (13,000); Jerusalem (65,000); Petah Tiqwa (130,000); Ramat Gan (120,000); Tel Aviv-Jaffa (340,000).
Land use: cultivated 25%; grazing 39%; wooded 6%; uncultivated 30%. Main agricultural products: wheat, barley, wine, citrus fruits, olive oil, tobacco, vegetables.
Official language: Hebrew.
Religion: Jewish (85%); Muslim (12%); Christian (3%).
Gross National Product: US $ 28,300 million; per capita: US $ 6,580.
Currency: Israeli pound = 100 agorots.

Japan: The Temples of Kyoto

JAPAN

Nippon/Nihon

Japan is a constitutional, hereditary monarchy, following the male line. The head of state is the Emperor who only has representative functions. The legislative power is exerted by the two-chamber Parliament, formed by the Chamber of Counsellors and the Chamber of Deputies, both elected by universal suffrage, the first for six years, half being renewed every three years, the second for four years. The executive power is in the hands of the Prime Minister and the government who are responsible for their action to the Parliament. Japan disputes with the Soviet Union the territory of the Southern Kuril Islands, while Taiwan lays claim to the Senkaku group of islands situated to the north-east of Taiwan at the south-western end of the Ryukyu chain of islands.
Japan is a member of UNO.
The country consists of four main islands surrounded by numerous other smaller islands. It is mostly mountainous, subject to earthquakes almost daily. There are numerous volcanoes, the highest and most famous being Fujiyama. There are very few plains and the coastline is very jagged.
Area: 372,839 sq km counting the Kuril Islands, which have been administered by the Soviet Union since the Second World War but are disputed by Japan.
Population: 122,779,000; 99% of whom are Japanese; 329 per sq km.
Annual growth rate: 0.6%; birth rate 11‰; death rate 6.5‰; average life expectancy: 76 years.
Capital: Tokyo (pop 12 million).
Other important towns: Fukuoka (1,190,000); Hiroshima (1,044,000); Kawasaki (1,045,000); Kitakyushu (1,070,000); Kobe (1,370,000); Kyoto (1,475,000); Nagasaki (445,000); Nagoya (2,135,000); Okayama (540,000); Osaka (6,180,000); Sapporo (1,410,000); Yokohama (2,775,000).
Land use: cultivated 13.5%; grazing 1.5%; wooded 67%; uncultivated 18%. Main agricultural products: rice, sugar beet, potatoes, sweet potatoes, tea, tobacco, citrus fruit, fruit, vegetables. Other activities: fishing.
Official language: Japanese.
Religions: Shinto, Buddhism.
Gross National Product: US $ 1,958,000 millions; per capita: US $ 16,100.
Currency: Yen = 100 sen.

JORDAN

Al-Mamlakah al-Urdunniyah al-Hashimiyah

Jordan is a hereditary, constitutional monarchy which gained its independence in March 1946 with the end of the British mandate established in 1922 by the League of Nations. The head of state is the Sovereign. The legislative power is with the two-chamber Parliament, formed by the Senate which is nominated by the Sovereign, and the Chamber of Deputies, directly elected for 4-year terms by male suffrage. Executive power is in the hands of the Sovereign, who exerts it through the Prime Minister and government, who are responsible to him and the Chamber of Deputies. In 1988 Jordan renounced sovereignty over the West Bank territories which it had annexed unilaterally in 1950. This area is still militarily occupied by Israel.
Jordan is a member of UNO and the Arab League.
The country, except for the left bank of the River Jordan, which follows the frontier with Israel, is desert, an arid plateau extending eastwards. In the south there is the Dead Sea, a salt lake at 397 m. below sea level.
Area: 97,700 sq km, including the West Bank, occupied by Israel.
Population: 3,600,000, chiefly Jordanian Arabs and Palestinians, but also Armenians, Circassians, Kurds and Turkmenians; density: 38 per sq km.
Annual growth rate: 3.9%; birth rate: 34‰; death rate 6‰; average life expectancy: 61 years.
Capital: Amman (pop 972,000).
Other important towns: Aqaba (40,000); Zarqa (270,000).
Land use: cultivated 5%; grazing 9%; wooded 1%; uncultivated 85%. Main agricultural products: barley, wheat, grapes, olive oil, citrus fruit, tobacco, vegetables. Mineral resources: phosphates.
Official language: Arabic.
Religion: Sunni Muslim.
Gross National Product: US $ 4,330 million; per capita: US $ 1,195.
Currency: Dinar = 1,000 fils.

KAMPUCHEA

Cambodia/République Populaire du Kampuchéa

Kampuchea is a People's Republic. Since 1978 political power has been in the hands of the United National Front for the Salvation of Cambodia, supported with military aid between 1978 and 1989 by the Vietnamese army. Legislative power is in the hands of the National Assembly whose members are all elected in the lists of the only existing party, the Front, which is strongly based on Communist ideals.
Kampuchea is a member of UNO, but it is represented by the exiled government that was in power until 1979.
The country covers two distinct areas. One is mountainous to the north and west. The other is the vast plain of the Mekong River, mostly covered by jungle, that reaches down to the South China Sea.
Area: 181,035 sq km.
Population: 6,689,000, mostly Khmers, or Cambodians (93%), then Vietnamese (4%) and Chinese (3%); density: 37 per sq km.
Annual growth rate: 2.9%; birth rate 43‰; death rate 17‰; average life expectancy: 45 years.
Capital: Phnom Penh (pop 750,000).
Other important towns: Batambang (40,000); Kompong Cham (30,000); Kompong Chhnang (15,000); Pursat (13,000).
Land use: cultivated 17.5%; grazing 3.5%; wooded 75.5%; uncultivated 3.5%. Main agricultural products: rice, maize, bananas, rubber, tobacco, jute, cotton.
Official language: Khmer.
Religion: Buddhism.
Gross National Product: US $ 1,100 million; per capita: US $ 150.
Currency: Riel = 100 sens.

KOREA, DEMOCRATIC PEOPLE'S REPUBLIC OF

(North Korea)
Choson Minju-juui Inmin Konghwa-guk

North Korea is a People's Republic. The head of state is the President of the Presidium whose members are elected by the National Assembly which has the legislative power and is elected for 4-year terms by direct universal suffrage from the lists of the only party, the Workers' Party, based on Marxism. Parliament is also responsible for the nomination and revocation of the government, which holds the executive power. The constitution states that the function of the Workers' Party is to be a guide for the state.
The country covers the northern part of the Korean Peninsula up as far as the border with China. It is prevalently mountainous. Only along the Yellow Sea coastline are there some plains with rivers.
Area: 120,540 sq km.
Population: 18,450,000, almost all Koreans; 161 per sq km.
Annual growth rate: 2.5%; birth rate 33‰; death rate 8‰; average life expectancy: 63 years.
Capital: Pyongyang (pop 2,639,000).
Other important towns: Ch'ongjin (720,000); Kaesong (330,000); Kanggye (135,000); Wonsan (220,000).
Land use: cultivated 20%; grazing 0.5%; wooded 74.5%; uncultivated 5%. Main agricultural products: rice, maize, millet, soya bean, sweet potatoes, tobacco, vegetables, fruit. Other activities: fishing. Mineral resources: coal, copper, iron ore.
Official language: Korean.
Religion: Buddhism and Confucianism.
Gross National Product: US $ 20,000 million; per capita: US $ 1000.
Currency: Won = 100 chon.

Japan: Fujiyama

KOREA, REPUBLIC OF

(South Korea)
Daehan-Minkuk

South Korea is a presidential republic. Legislative power is held by the National Assembly whose members are elected by direct universal suffrage. An electoral body of over 5,000 members, also elected by direct universal suffrage, elects the President of the Republic who has very wide powers.
The country covers the central and southern part of the Korean Peninsula that stretches towards Japan. Hilly ranges alternate with fertile plains.
Area: 99,143 sq km.
Population: 40,467,000, almost all Koreans; 408 per sq km.
Annual growth rate: 1.3%; birth rate 24‰; death rate 7‰; average life expectancy: 63 years.
Capital: Seoul (pop 9,600,000).
Other important towns: Inchon (1,390,000); Kwangju (910,000); Mokpo (200,000); Pusan (3,500,000); Taegu (2,030,000); Ulsan (555,000).
Land use: cultivated 22.5%; grazing 0.5%; wooded 67%; uncultivated 10%. Main agricultural products: rice, sweet potatoes, soya bean, tobacco, vegetables, fruit, barley, potatoes, cotton, tobacco. Other activities: fishing. Mineral resources: coal, iron ore, tungsten.
Official language: Korean.
Religion: Buddhism (40%); Christian (28%); Confucianism (17%).
Gross National Product: US $ 95,110 million; per capita: US $ 2,287.
Currency: Won = 100 chon.

KUWAIT

Dawlat al-Kuwait

Kuwait has been an independent hereditary constitutional monarchy since 19th June 1961. It is the Sheikh who exerts the executive power through the Prime Minister and Council of Ministers, who are directly responsible to him for all they do. He exerts the legislative power together with the single-chamber Parliament, whose members are elected for 4-year terms by male, literate voters. In August 1990 Kuwait was occupied by Iraq, which announced that Kuwait was its nineteenth province. This unilateral action was not recognized by the international community which liberated Kuwait by force on 27th February 1991.
Kuwait is a member of UNO and the Arab League.
It is a small desert area lying at the top of the Gulf between Iraq and Saudi Arabia.
Area: 17,800 sq km.
Population: 2,048,000, more than half of whom are foreigners, mostly Arabs (85%); density: 115 per sq km.
Annual growth rate: 4.6%; birth rate 30‰; death rate 2.4‰; average life expectancy: 70 years.
Capital: Kuwait City (pop 168,000).
Other important towns: Hawalli (110,000); Jaleeb al-Shuyukh (114,000).
Land use: cultivated 0.6%; grazing 8%; uncultivated 92%. Main agricultural products: veg-

Jordan: Petra

etables, fruit. Mineral resources: oil, natural gas.
Official language: Arabic.
Religion: Muslim.
Gross National Product: US $ 20,500 million; per capita: US $ 11,000.
Currency: Dinar = 1,000 fils.

LAOS

Sathalamalath Pasathi Patai/République Démocratique Populaire Lao

Part of French Indochina until 1949, Laos became an independent monarchy in 1955. Since December 1975 it has been a People's Republic. The head of state is President of the Supreme Council of the People, the legislative body, whose members are chosen from the Revolutionary Party of the Laotian People.
Laos is a member of UNO.
The country is the only part of the Indochinese peninsula without access to the sea. It is almost all mountainous except for the plains along the left bank of the Mekong River, which separates Laos from Thailand.
Area: 236,800 sq km.
Population: 3,720,000 inhabitants, the majority of whom are Laotians (51%); Vietnamese, Meo, Chinese; density: 16 per sq km.
Annual growth rate: 2%; birth rate: 44‰; death rate 20‰; average life expectancy: 42 years.
Capital: Vientiane (pop 380,000).
Other important towns: Luang Prabang (45,000); Paksé (45,000); Savannakhet (52,000).
Land use: cultivated 3.5%; grazing 3.5%; wooded 57%; uncultivated 36%. Main agricultural products: rice, maize, cotton, tobacco, opium, coffee; timber.
Official language: Lao.
Religion: Buddhism.
Gross National Product: US $ 650 million; per capita: US $ 170.
Currency: New kip.

LEBANON

Al-Jumhuriyah al-Lubnaniyah

Lebanon has been an independent republic since 16th January 1941, with effect from 1st January 1944. The constitution designates functions and responsibilities among the various ethnic, cultural and religious groups living in the country in order to safeguard their respective liberties in a situation of effective instability. The presence of hundreds of thousands of Palestinian refugees that has altered the equilibrium between the Christian and the Muslim communities, has provoked military intervention by the neighbouring countries, Syria and Israel, which both currently occupy parts of the country.
The Lebanon is a member of UNO and the Arab League.
What was in ancient times the land of the Phoenicians, lies on the eastern Mediterranean coast. The coastal plains are followed in parallel by two mountain ranges, the Lebanon Mountains and the Anti-Lebanons, which are separated by the fertile valley of the River Beka'a.
Area: 10,400 sq km.
Population: 2,200,000 prevalently Arabs; Armenian and Circassian minorities; density: 204 per sq km.
Annual growth rate: 1.5%; birth rate 30‰; death rate 8‰; average life expectancy: 66 years.
Capital: Beirut (pop 900,000).
Other important towns: Saida (Sidon) (25,000);

Tripoli (157,000); Zahlé (33,000).
Land use: cultivated 34%; grazing 1%; wooded 7%; uncultivated 58%. Main agricultural products: wheat, barley, wine, olive oil, citrus fruit, groundnuts.
Official language: Arabic.
Religions: Christian and Muslim.
Gross National Product: US $ 3,000 million; per capita: US $ 1000.
Currency: Lebanese lira = 100 piastres.

MACAO

Macau/Provincia de Macau

Macao is a Portuguese overseas province with administrative and financial autonomy. It is administered by a Governor and sends representatives to the Portuguese Parliament. An agreement signed with China in January 1988 lays down that Macao will be returned to China on 20th December 1999.
The country consists of the Macao Peninsula which is linked to the mainland by an isthmus which marks the Chinese frontier.
Area: 16.9 sq km.
Population: 275,000 inhabitants the great majority of whom are Chinese; 17 per sq km.
Annual growth rate: 2.7%; birth rate 31‰; death rate 6‰.
Capital: Macao (pop 230,000).
Main agricultural products: vegetables, fruit, tobacco. Other activities: fishing.
Official language: Portuguese; Chinese and English widely spoken.
Religion: Buddhism.
Gross National Product: US $ 1,240 million; per capita: US $ 3,150.
Currency: Pataca = 100 avos.

MALAYSIA

Persekutuan Tanah Malaysia

Malaysia is an independent federation founded on 16th September 1963 by the political union of the 11 states forming the former Federation of Malaya, (which had already been an independent country and a member of the Commonwealth since 1957), the former British territories of Sabah (formerly North Borneo) Sarawak and Singapore. The latter seceded in 1965. The present federated states are therefore the following: Johore, Kedah, Kelantan, Malacca, Negeri Sembilan, Pahang, Perak, Perlis, Penang, Selangor, Terengganu — which form West Malaysia — and Sabah and Sarawak which form East Malaysia. Each state has its own executive and legislative bodies. The head of the whole federation is elected for five years by the Conference of the Heads of the Federated States, each of which is governed by a hereditary monarch or a Governor. On the federal level, the legislative power is held by the federal Parliament formed by the Chamber of Deputies and the Senate. The executive power is in the hands of the Prime Minister and ministers who are responsible to the federal Parliament.
Malaysia is a member of UNO, the Commonwealth of Nations and ASEAN.
The country covers the southern part of the Malay Peninsula which is mountainous with fertile coastal plains, and the northern part of the island of Borneo, two-thirds of which are covered by tropical forests.
Area: 329,750 sq km, politically and administratively divided into 13 federated states.
Population: 16,280,000, the majority of whom are Malaysians (53%), and Chinese (35%), then Indians and Pakistanis (11%).
Annual growth rate: 2.6%; birth rate 31‰;

India: The Temple of Shiva in Madras

death rate 6‰; average life expectancy: 69 years.
Capital: Kuala Lumpur (pop 1,100,000).
Other important towns: Johore Baharu (250,000); Kuching (75,000); Melaka (90,000); George Town (Penang, 250,000); Seremban (140,000).
Land use: cultivated 13%; grazing 0.1%; wooded 60%; uncultivated 27%. Main agricultural products: rice, copra, rubber, palm (for oil), pineapples, bananas, cocoa. Mineral resources: tin.
Official language: Malay.
Religion: Muslim (over 50%); also numerous Buddhists, Confucians, Hindus and Christians.
Gross National Product: US $ 25,770 million; per capita: US $ 1,620.
Currency: Ringgit = 100 sen.

MALDIVES

Divehi Rajje

The Maldive Islands have been a presidential republic since November 1968, and independent since 1965. The head of state is the President of the Republic, elected for 5-year terms by direct universal suffrage. He is also head of the government and therefore exerts the executive power directly. The legislative power is devolved to the single-chamber Parliament (Majlis), the majority of whose members are elected for 5-year terms by direct universal suffrage.
The Republic of the Maldives is a member of UNO and the Commonwealth of Nations.
It is an archipelago of 20 atolls with 1,087 coral islands in the Indian Ocean south of India.
Area: 300 sq km.
Population: 181,000, mostly Sinhalese and Arabs; density: 497 per sq km.
Annual growth rate: 4%; birth rate 50‰; death rate 23‰.
Capital: Malé (pop 55,000).
Main agricultural products: coconuts, copra; fishing.
Official language: Divehi.
Religion: Sunni Muslim.
Currency: Rupee = 100 laari.

MONGOLIA

Bügd Nayramdah Mongol Ard Uls

Mongolia is a People's Republic independent since 1924. The head of state is the President of the Presidium, elected by the People's Assembly which exerts the legislative power and is composed of members elected for 3-year terms by direct universal suffrage in the lists of the Communist Party, the only party admitted. Between one legislative session and another the legislative power is devolved to the Presidium. The executive power is in the hands of the Council of Ministers, nominated by the People's Assembly and responsible for its action to the Presidium.
Mongolia is a member of UNO and Comecon. The country is landlocked. It borders on the USSR and China. It is formed of a high undulating barren steppe plateau. The Gobi desert extends over the southern and eastern parts.
Area: 1,565,000 sq km.
Population: 1,900,000; mostly Mongols (87%); 1 per sq km.
Annual growth rate: 2.9%; birth rate 36‰; death rate 9‰; average life expectancy: 63 years.
Capital: Ulan Bator (pop 500,000).
Other important towns: Cecerleg (14,000),

India: Varanasi

Choybalsan (28,000); Suhe-Bator (13,000).
Land use: cultivated 0.7%; grazing 79%; wooded 10%; uncultivated 10.3%. Main agricultural products: wheat, barley, oats. Other activities: livestock rearing.
Official language: Khalkha.
Religion: Lamaism.
Gross National Product: US $ 1,580 million; per capita: US $ 820.
Currency: Tugrik = 100 mongo.

NEPAL

Nepal Adhirajya

Nepal is a hereditary constitutional monarchy. The King exerts the executive power aided by the Council of Ministers whom he nominates and who is reponsible to him and the Parliament. The King also exerts the executive power together with the Parliament, one-third of which is renewed every two years. It consists in part of members nominated by the King and in majority by members elected by the professional organizations and district assemblies.
Nepal is a member of UNO.
The country lies in the Himalayan area between India and China. It has the highest peaks in the world including Everest. Only the southern part of its territory is flat.
Area: 147,180 sq km.
Population: 15,022,000 mostly Gurkhas, Tibetans and Indians; density: 102 per sq km.
Annual growth rate: 2.6%; birth rate 44‰; death rate 21‰; average life expectancy: 44 years.
Capital: Katmandu (pop 393,000).
Other important towns: Bhadgaon (48,000); Patan (50,000).
Land use: cultivated 17%; grazing 14%; wooded 16%; uncultivated 53%. Main agricultural products: rice, maize, millet, wheat, jute. Other activities: cattle rearing.
Official language: Nepali.
Religions: Hinduism and Buddhism.
Gross National Product: US $ 2,570 million; per capita: US $ 152.
Currency: Rupee = 100 paisa.

OMAN

Sultanat Oman

Known until 1970 as Muscat and Oman (in Arabic Masqat wa Oman), Oman is a hereditary absolute monarchy. The Sultan exerts both the executive and the legislative power directly with the aid of a Consultative Council which he himself nominates.
The oasis of Buraimi is disputed with Saudi Arabia and the Emirate of Abu Dhabi (United Arab Emirates). The islands of Kuria Muria are disputed by the People's Democratic Republic of the Yemen. The region of Dhofar is currently controlled by the fighters of the Front for the Liberation of Oman and the Arabian Gulf, who have made of it a practically autonomous state with its own administration and economic structure.
Oman is a member of UNO and the Arab League.
The country is situated at the south-eastern tip of the Arabian Peninsula. The interior is mountainous with vast tracts of desert. The coastline gives on to the Arabian Sea and the Gulf of Oman.
Area: 212,500 sq km.
Population: 1,370,000, mostly Arabs (88%); Beluchis (4%); Indians, Pakistanis, Iranians and black Africans; density: 6 per sq km.
Annual growth rate: 3.7%; birth rate 49‰; death rate 19‰; average life expectancy: 45 years.

Iran: Esfahan Mosque

Capital: Muscat (pop 50,000).
Other important towns: Matrah (15,000); Sohar (30,000).
Land use: cultivated 0.2%; grazing 4.8%; uncultivated 95%. Main agricultural products: dates, citrus fruit. Mineral resources: oil.
Official language: Arabic (88%).
Religion: Sunni Muslim.
Gross National Product: US $ 8,500 million; per capita: US $ 6,620.
Currency: Rial = 1,000 baizas.

PAKISTAN

Islami Jamhuriya-e-Pakistan

Pakistan is a federal republic founded in August 1947 following the division of the former Indian Empire which gained independence as India and Pakistan. The state included West Bengal until 1971 when there was a war of secession and West Bengal became the Republic of Bangladesh. The new constitution dated April 1973 gives the executive power to the Prime Minister and the Council of Ministers. Legislative power is in the hands of the two-chamber Parliament. This consists of the Chamber of Deputies (207 members), elected by direct universal suffrage and the Senate, whose 87 members are designated by the regional parliaments. For political and administrative purposes Pakistan is divided into four federal provinces: Baluchistan, Punjab, Sind, North-West Frontier plus the Federal District of the capital Islamabad. Pakistan disputes the part of Kashmir administered by India. The populations of the Pathans and the Baluchistanis who live in Baluchistan and the North-West Frontier region want independence or at least a good measure of autonomy within the Republic.
Pakistan is a member of UNO.
The country is in the north-western part of the Indian sub-continent. It is flat in the southern part and mountainous to the north and north-west of the River Indus. It is mainly arid except for the central area where the Indus flows. The coast lies on the Arabian Sea.
Area: 803,945 sq km divided into four political and administrative provinces.
Population: 89,740,000, mostly Punjabis, Sindhis, Hindus, Baluchis; density: 113 per sq km.
Annual growth rate: 3.1%; birth rate 40‰; death rate 14‰; average life expectancy: 52 years.
Capital: Islamabad (pop 200,000).
Other important towns: Hyderabad (750,000); Karachi (5,180,000); Lahore (2,965,000); Multan (730,000); Peshawar (566,000); Quetta (285,000); Rawalpindi (790,000).
Land use: cultivated 26%; grazing 6%; wooded 4%; uncultivated 64%. Main agricultural products: wheat, rice, millet, sorghum, sugar cane, citrus fruit, cotton, dates, tobacco. Mineral resources: natural gas.
Official language: Urdu and English; widely spoken also Punjabi (67%); Sindhi (14%); Pashto and Baluchi.
Religion: Muslim.
Gross National Product: US $ 34,900 million; per capita: US $ 350.
Currency: Pakistan rupee = 100 paisa.

PHILIPPINES

Republika ng Pilipinas

An independent republic since 12th June 1946, the Philippines had previously, from 1898, been a dependency of the USA, which still maintains some airforce and naval bases in the archipelago.
The constitution approved on February 1987 gives legislative power to the two-chamber Parliament. The Chamber of Deputies has 250 members, of whom 200 are elected by universal suffrage, the others nominated by the President; the Senate has 24 members, all elected by universal suffrage.
The Nanshan Islands (including the Spratly Islands) in the South China Sea are disputed between China, the Philippines, Taiwan and Vietnam. The Philippines claim Sabah.
The Philippines belong to UNO and ASEAN.
The islands lie between the Pacific Ocean and the South China Sea. They form an archipelago of 7,100 islands all very mountainous, with numerous volcanoes and thick equatorial forests. A little under seven-tenths of the territory is formed by the islands of Mindanao and Luzon, which are the most densely inhabited, with their coastal plains and fertile river valleys. The northern islands lie in the track of cyclones and suffer frequent earthquakes.
Area: 300,000 sq km.
Population: 48,070,000, the great majority of whom are Philippines; 2% Chinese; density: 160 per sq km.
Annual growth rate: 2.6%; birth rate 34‰; death rate 8‰; average life expectancy: 62 years.
Capital: Manila (pop 1,750,000).
Other important towns: Bacolod (260,000); Batangas (140,000); Butuan (175,000); Cagayan de Oro (227,000); Cebu (490,000); Davao (610,000); Iloilo (240,000); Tarlac (175,000); Zamboanga (343,000).
Land use: cultivated 27%; grazing 4%; wooded 36%; uncultivated 33%. Main agricultural products: rice, maize, copra, sugar cane, coffee, pineapples, rubber. Mineral resources: gold, coal.
Official language: Tagalog; English and Spanish also widely spoken.
Religions: Mostly Roman Catholic; numerous animists, Protestants and Muslims.
Gross National Product: US $ 30,110 million; per capita: US $ 538.
Currency: Peso = 100 centavos.

QATAR

Dawlat al-Qatar

An absolute hereditary monarchy independent since 1st September 1971, Qatar was a British protectorate from 1916 to 1971, with Great Britain ensuring defence and diplomatic representation. The Emir exerts both executive and legislative power with the aid of a Consultative Council which he himself nominates. It is mostly formed by members of his family.
Qatar is a member of UNO and the Arab League.
The country is formed by a peninsula extending into the Gulf to the west of Saudi Arabia. It is an arid low-lying plain.
Area: 11,000 sq km.
Population: 370,000, mostly Arabs (56%); then Persians (23%) and Pakistanis (7%); density: 33 per sq km.
Annual growth rate: 8%.
Capital: Doha (pop 217,000).
Land use: cultivated 0.2%; grazing 4.5%; uncultivated 95.3%. Main agricultural products: dates, fruit, vegetables. Mineral resources: oil.
Official language: Arabic.
Religion: Sunni Muslim.
Gross National Product: US $ 3,100 million; per capita: US $ 11,400.
Currency: Riyal = 100 dirhams.

SAUDI ARABIA

Al-Mamlaka al-'Arabiya as-Sa'udiya

Saudi Arabia is a hereditary absolute monarchy formed in September 1932 by the personal union of the Kingdoms of Hejaz and Nejd and the principates of Asir and Al-Hasa. Although the 1961 constitution introduced a parliamentary political system, the executive and legislative powers are entirely in the hands of the sovereign, who is aided by collegial bodies and ministers who are reponsible to him alone. The oasis of Buraimi is disputed with Oman and the emirate of Abu Dhabi (United Arab Emirates).
Saudi Arabia is a member of UNO and the Arab League.
The country is formed by an immense desert of sand and stones with occasional oases. It is a plateau that slopes gradually from the Red Sea down to the Gulf.
Area: 2,149,700 sq km.
Population: 7,200,000, the vast majority of whom are Arabs; 3 per sq km.
Annual growth rate: 4%; birth rate 44‰; death rate 14‰; average life expectancy: 54 years.
Capital: Riyadh (pop 1,300,000).
Other important towns: Dammam (130,000); Jeddah (1,500,000); Mecca (370,000); Medina (198,000); Taif (300,000).
Land use: cultivated 0.5%; grazing 39.5%; wooded 0.5%; uncultivated 59.5%. Main agricultural products: barley, wheat, rice, dates, citrus fruit, bananas. Mineral resources: oil.
Official language: Arabic.
Religion: Sunni Muslim.
Gross National Product: US $ 82,700 million; per capita: US $ 7,800.
Currency: Riyal = 20 qirshes.

SINGAPORE

Republik Singapura

Singapore as a parliamentary republic has been independent since 1965 when it separated from the Federation of Malaysia of which it had been a founder member from 16th September 1963. Legislative power is exerted by Parliament whose members are elected for 5-year terms. Executive power is in the hands of the Prime Minister and ministers who are responsible to Parliament for their action.
Singapore is a member of UNO and ASEAN.
It is a small island separated from the tip of the Malacca Peninsula by the Strait of Malacca. It also includes other smaller islands. The main island is low-lying and covered by equatorial vegetation.
Area: 625 sq km.
Population: 2,635,000, mostly Chinese (76%), and Malays (14%); density: 4,216 per sq km.
Annual growth rate: 1.1%; birth rate 20‰; death rate 5‰; average life expectancy: 71 years.
Land use: cultivated 4.8%; wooded 5.3%; uncultivated 90%. Main agricultural products: fruit, vegetables.
Official languages: English, Chinese, Malay and Tamil.
Religions: Buddhist, Muslim and Hindu.
Gross National Product: US $ 18,000 million; per capita: US $ 6,960.
Currency: Singapore dollar = 100 cents.

SRI LANKA

Sri Lanka Janarajaya

Sri Lanka has been a presidential republic since 4th February 1978. It was a British colony until 1948 when it gained independence and became a member of the Commonwealth of Nations. It became a republic in 1972 when it changed its name from Ceylon. The head of state is the President of the republic, who exerts the executive power directly, aided by the ministers. Legislative power is in the hands of the Parliament, almost all of whose members are elected for 6-year terms by direct universal suffrage.
Sri Lanka is a member of UNO and the Commonwealth of Nations.
The country is an island in the Indian Ocean off the south-east coast of India. It is mostly a high-plateau whose highest point is a peak of 2,500 m. It then slopes gradually down towards the sea in a series of terraces. The climate is affected by the monsoons and the vegetation is luxurious.
Area: 65,610 sq km.
Population: 16,300,000 mostly Sinhalese (71%) and Tamil (28%); density: 249 per sq km.

Mongolia: A typical yurt

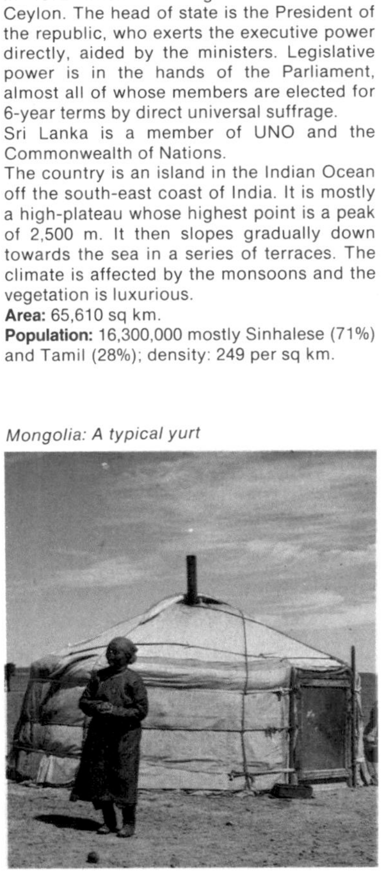

Annual growth rate: 1.7%; birth rate 21‰; death rate 6‰; average life expectancy: 66 years.
Capital: Colombo (pop 664,000), but the official capital is Sri Jayewardenepura.
Other important towns: Galle (80,000); Jaffna (120,000); Kandy (105,000); Moratuwa (110,000); Negombo (65,000); Trincomalee (50,000).
Land use: cultivated 32%; grazing 6.5%; wooded 26.6%; uncultivated 35%. Main agricultural products: rice, rubber, tea, copra, coffee, maize, cocoa. Mineral resources: gemstones, graphite.
Official language: Sinhalese (71%); Tamil also widely spoken (28%).
Religions: Buddhist (69%) and Hindu (15%).
Gross National Product: US $ 6,400 million; per capita: US $ 397.
Currency: Rupee = 100 cents.

SYRIA

Al-Jumhuriya al-'Arabiya as-Suriya

Syria is a presidential republic, independent since 1946. The President of the Republic is also head of the government and as such exerts the executive power directly. Legislative power is devolved to the one-chamber Parliament which is elected by direct universal suffrage. Currently, after the campaigns of June 1967 and October 1973 a strip of territory in the south-western part of the country (the Golan Heights) is occupied by Israeli troups awaiting the signature of a peace treaty between the two neighbouring states.
Syria is a member of UNO and the Arab League.
The country lies on the eastern coast of the Mediterranean Sea. It is a high plateau, mostly desert except for the coastal strip, an area along the course of the River Euphrates and some oases.
Area: 185,200 sq km.
Population: 11,338,000, mostly Arabs, then Kurds, Armenians and Circassians; density: 61 per sq km.
Annual growth rate: 3.4%; birth rate 45‰; death rate 8‰; average life expectancy: 65 years.
Capital: Damascus (pop 1,330,000).
Other important towns: Aleppo (985,000); Hamah (170,000); Homs (350,000); Latakia (190,000).
Land use: cultivated 31%; grazing 45%; wooded 3%; uncultivated 21%. Main agricultural products: wheat, barley, vegetables, potatoes, wine, olive oil, celery, groundnuts, cotton. Mineral resources: oil.
Official language: Arabic (88%); also spoken, Kurdish and Armenian.
Religion: Muslim; Christian (10%).
Gross National Product: US $ 17,300 million; per capita: US $ 1,590.
Currency: Syrian pound = 100 piastres.

TAIWAN

Ta Chunghua Min-kuo

Taiwan is a presidential republic founded in 1949 by the Kuomintang government that withdrew to the island of Formosa, as it was then called, with most of the Nationalist forces after power had been taken in China by the revolutionary Communist forces at the end of the long and bloody civil war. The state includes some groups of islands such as the Pescadores, Quemoy and Matsu. The President of the republic is the head of state and has vast powers. He is elected for six years by the National Assembly. He is aided by five collegial bodies, of which one is legislative, one executive and the others have control functions. The archipelagoes of Dongsha (or Pratas Islands), Xsisha (Paracel Islands), and Nanshan are disputed between Taiwan and China which took the Paracel islands by force on 20th January 1974. The Philippines claim the Nanshans; Vietnam claims both the Nanshans and the Xsishas. Taiwan also lays claim to the Senkaku islands at the southwestern tip of the Ryukyu group on the grounds that they are on its continental shelf, to the north-east of the island.
The country covers the island of Taiwan and other smaller islands. It is prevalently mountainous, with a mild climate and considerable rainfall.
Area: 35,980 sq km, excluding the Pescadores, the Quemoy and the Matsu.
Population: 19,672,000, the vast majority of whom are mainland Chinese; 546 per sq km.
Annual growth rate: 1.4%; birth rate 16‰; death rate 5‰; average life expectancy: 71 years.

Capital: Tai-pei (pop 2,637,000).
Other important towns: Hsin-chu (310,000); Kao-hsiung (1,340,000); Keelung (345,000); Panchiao (506,000); Tai-chung (715,000); Tai-nan (650,000).
Land use: cultivated 24%; wooded 52%; uncultivated: 24%. Main agricultural products: rice, sugar cane, maize, pineapples, sweet potatoes, soya bean, bananas, citrus fruit, tobacco. Mineral resources: coal, gold, silver.
Official language: Mandarin Chinese.
Religion: Confucianism and Buddhism widespread.
Gross National Product: US $ 73,240 million; per capita: US $ 3,740.
Currency: Dollar = 100 cents.

THAILAND

Prathet Thai / Muang Thai

Thailand's official name was Siam until 1939 and between 1945 and 1949. On the basis of the present constitution (18th December 1978), which is the twelfth since 1932, it is a constitutional monarchy. The executive power is held by the Government, which is reponsible to the Parliament. The two chambers of the Parliament are the Senate whose members are all nominated by the Sovereign, and the Chamber of Deputies whose members are elected by universal suffrage.
Thailand is a member of UNO and ASEAN.
The country lies on the Gulf of Siam between Laos and Burma. The southern part covers part of the Malay peninsula. It is mountainous in the north and flat in the centre and south. It is semi-arid except for the fertile valley of the River Chao Phraya (Menam).
Area: 514,000 sq km.
Population: 54,960,000, the majority of whom are Thai (98%), then Chinese and Malay; density: 107 per sq km.
Annual growth rate: 2.1%; birth rate 16.5‰; death rate 4.3‰; average life expectancy: 62 years.
Capital: Bangkok (pop 5,716,000).
Other important towns: Ayutthaya (60,000); Chieng Mai (165,000); Nakhon Pathom (35,000); Phitsanulok (75,000).
Land use: cultivated 39%; grazing 1.5%; wooded 28%; uncultivated 31.5%. Main agricultural products: rice, maize, sorghum, sugar cane, rubber, bananas, cotton, jute, tobacco, copra, timber. Other activities: fishing, cattle rearing. Mineral resources: tin.
Official language: Thai (90.5%).
Religion: Buddhism.
Gross National Product: US $ 40,160 million; per capita: US $ 763.
Currency: Baht = 100 Stangs.

TURKEY

Turkiye Cumhuriyeti

Turkey is a parliamentary republic proclaimed in 1923. The head of state is the President of the republic who is elected for seven years by the Parliament. Executive power is exerted by the Prime Minister and the Council of Ministers, legislative power by the two-chamber parliament which is formed by the Senate, the majority of whose members are elected for six years by direct universal suffrage, one-third being elected every two years, and the Chamber of Deputies, who are elected by universal suffrage for 4-year terms. Following a military coup d'état on 12th September 1980, however, constitutional rights were suspended and political power is held by a military junta whose president is the head of state. A new constitution was approved in 1982.
Turkey is a member of UNO, the Council of Europe, OECD and NATO; it is an associate member of EEC.
Approximately one-third of the country, Eastern Thrace, is in Europe. The part beyond the Bosporus and the Dardanelles is in Asia, where the land is a stony, arid and impervious plateau, rising in height to the north. The north coast lies on the Black Sea and the west and south coasts are on the Mediterranean Sea.
Area: 755,690 sq km.
Population: 46,318,000, the majority of whom are Turks (90%); and then Kurds, Armenians, Georgians, Arabs and Greeks; density: 61 per sq km.
Annual growth rate: 2.5%; birth rate 40‰; death rate 12‰; average life expectancy: 61 years.
Capital: Ankara (pop 2,800,000).
Other important towns: Adalia (258,000); Adana (776,000); Antioch (110,000); Bursa (614,000); Edirne (86,000); Gaziantep (466,000); Istanbul (5,494,000); Konya (438,000); Izmir, (formerly Smyrna, 964,000) Trabzon (150,000).
Land use: cultivated 36%; grazing 11% wooded 26%; uncultivated 27%. Main agricultural products: cotton, sugar cane, tobacco, fruit, vegetables, wine, sultanas, walnuts, wheat, barley. Mineral resources: coal, lignite, iron ore, chromium.
Official language: Turkish.
Religion: Sunni Muslim.
Gross National Product: USA $ 59,000 million; per capita: US $ 1,160.
Currency: Lira = 100 piastres (kurus).

Nepal: Annapurna

UNITED ARAB EMIRATES

Al-Imarat al-'Arabiya al-Muttahida

The United Arab Emirates is a federal independent state formed by the union of the following seven hereditary absolute principates: Abu Dhabi, Dubai, Sharjah, Ajmar, Umm al Qaiwain, Ras el Khaimah and Fujairah.
Known in the past as the Trucial States for the treaty that concluded a truce between Great Britain and the pirates that infested the coastal area, it became a British protectorate in 1892. It obtained its independence on 2nd December 1971. On the federal level the highest state body is the Supreme Council of the Union, formed by the sovereigns of the seven emirates. This body exerts the executive and legislative power through the Prime Minister and ministers. The President of this Council is also the head of state.
The oasis of Buraimi is disputed with Oman, Saudi Arabia and the emirate of Abu Dhabi. The Tunb Islands near the Strait of Hormuz in the Gulf and the island of Abu Musa, which were taken by force by Iran in November 1971, are claimed respectively by the emirates of Ras el Khaimah and Sharjah
The United Arab Emirates belongs to UNO and the Arab League.
The country covers a desert area on the eastern coast of Arabia that almost closes the Gulf.
Area: 83,600 sq km.
Population: 1,622,000 including the foreign workers present in the country; 19 per sq km.
Annual growth rate: 6.4%; birth rate 44‰; death rate 14‰; average life expectancy: 48 years.
Capital: Abu Dhabi (pop 243,000).
Other important towns: Dubai (265,000); Sharjah (126,000).
Land use: cultivated 0.1%; grazing 2.4%; uncultivated 97.5%. Main agricultural products: dates, vegetables. Other activities: fishing. Mineral resources: oil, natural gas.
Official language: Arabic.
Religion: Muslim.
Gross National Product: US $ 21,500 million; per capita: US $ 15,000.
Currency: Dirham = 100 fils.

VIETNAM

Viet Nam Cong Hoa Xa Hoi Chu'Nghia

Vietnam is a People's Republic, independent within the French Union from 8th March 1949, but with complete sovereignty since 29th December 1954. After the Japanese invasion of 1940-1945, France had attempted to regain her possessions in Indochina and at the same time the Communist-led Viet Minh forces had established a People's Republic in the Tonkin and Annam regions. An armistice was signed in Geneva on 20th July 1954 under which the country was divided along the 17th parallel. This was intended to be a temporary division but the two parts of the country developed into two completely different political, social and economic organizations. Thus two States of Vietnam were created: North Vietnam or the Democratic Republic of Vietnam and South Vietnam or Republic of Vietnam. The northern state was supported by the Communist countries and the southern one by the USA. A long and harsh civil war broke out between the government forces of Saigon (then capital of the southern state, now Ho Chi Minh City), with the military support of the USA, and the National Liberation Front backed by North Vietnam. It was a long and cruel war which ended on 30th April 1975 when the forces of the Democratic Republic of Vietnam and the National Liberation Front entered Saigon and then took over all the territory of South Vietnam. On 2nd July 1976 the re-unification of the two parts of the country was officially proclaimed as the Socialist Republic of Vietnam. According to the new constitution promulgated on 19th December 1980 the head of state is the President of the republic. He is elected for four years by the National Assembly which holds the legislative power and whose members are elected for 4-year terms by direct universal suffrage from the lists of the only existing party, the Communist Party. The National Assembly also nominates and revokes the nomination of the Council of Ministers which holds the executive power and elects the Permanent Committee, which holds the legislative power between legislative sessions of the National Assembly.
Vietnam claims the Xsisha (or Paracel Islands) which were occupied by China on 20th January 1974. It also disputes with China, Taiwan and the Philippines the Nanshan Islands (including the Spratly Islands) in the South China Sea. Kampuchean control of the so-called "Duck's Bill" and other land on the left bank of the Mekong River is strongly disputed by Vietnam, whose troops occupied Kampuchea until 1989.
Vietnam is a member of UNO and Comecon.
The country lies on the continental side of the South China Sea. Two vast fertile plains crossed by many rivers form the northern and southern halves of the country. The central part is a narrow coastal strip crossed by a range of mountains.
Area: 329,555 sq km.
Population: 58,770,000 mostly Vietnamese (84%); 177 per sq km.
Annual growth rate: 2.1%; birth rate 41‰; death rate 18‰; average life expectancy: 63 years.
Capital: Hanoi (pop 2,870,000).
Other important towns: Da Nang (495,000); Haiphong (1,400,000); Ho Chi Minh City (3,420,000); Hué (210,000).
Land use: cultivated 19%; grazing 1%; wooded 39%; uncultivated 41%. Main agricultural products: rice, sugar cane, sweet potatoes, rubber, copra, bananas, tea. Mineral resources: coal, phosphates.
Official language: Vietnamese.
Religions: Buddhist and Taoist.
Gross National Product: US $ 12,000 million; per capita: US $ 190.
Currency: Dong = 10 hao.

Thailand: Bangkok

YEMEN, REPUBLIC OF

Al-Jumhuriya al-Yamaniyah

The Republic of the Yemen is a recently-formed state founded on 22nd May 1990 by the union of Northern and Southern Yemen, respectively the former Arab Republic of the Yemen and the People's Democratic Republic of the Yemen. The political structures of the new state are not yet known. It is a member of UNO and the Arab League.
The Yemen covers the whole southern tip of Arabia, between the Red Sea and the Gulf of Aden. It is prevalently mountainous around its borders, flat desert in the interior. Between the high plateaux of the former Northern Yemen and the coast of the Red Sea there is a narrow inhospitable coastal strip. The climate is characterised by a wide temperature range, with very high day-time summer temperatures, a fair amount of rain on the highlands, very little along the coasts and in the interior. The Yemen includes the islands of Perim and Socotra. It also lays claim to the Kuria Muria Islands which belong to the sultanate of Oman.
Area: 482,000 sq km.
Population: 11,380,000 the majority of whom are Arabs; 23 per sq km.
Annual growth rate: 2.5%; birth rate 7‰; death rate 22‰; average life expectancy: 43 years.
Capital: Sana (pop 427,000).
Other important towns: Aden (300,000), Dhamar (30,000); Hodeida (150,000); Mukallah (50,000); Taiz (178,000).
Land use: cultivated 7%; grazing 36%; wooded 8%; uncultivated 49%. Main agricultural products: cotton, tobacco, sugar cane, qat, millet, wheat, maize, sesame, coffee, dates, bananas. Mineral resources: oil.
Official language: Arabic (99%).
Religion: Muslim.
Gross National Product: US $ 3,400 million; per capita: US $ 445.
Currency: Riyal = 100 fils.

Yemen Arab Republic

Al-Jumhuriyah al-'Arabiyah al-Yamaniyah

Formerly a republic, in northern Yemen (from 26th November 1962). Following a military coup d'état on 13th June 1974 all political power was deferred to the ten-member Council of the Armed Forces whose president was the head of state. The Council exerted the legislative power directly and entrusted the executive power to the Prime Minister and Government who were responsible to the Council.

Yemen, people's democratic republic of Southern Yemen

Al-Jumhuriyah al-Yaman ash-Shaabiyah ad-Dimuqratiyah

Formerly an independent republic in southern Yemen (from 30th November 1967). The highest organ of the state was the Presidential Council composed of five members whose President was head of state. The executive power was exerted by the Government which was nominated by the Presidential Council. Legislative power was held by the Higher People's Council.

Africa

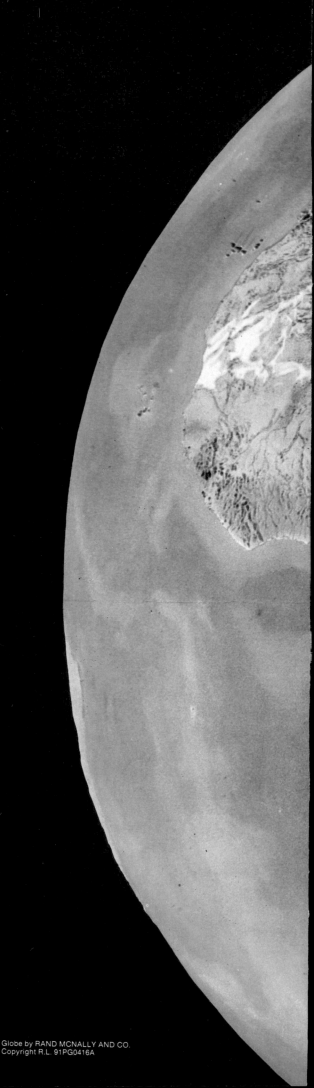

Africa was, with all probability, the cradle of mankind. In the Olduvai Gorge, in what is now Tanzania, have been found the remains of prehistoric man, dating back over one million years. It was from this region that the first migrations are thought to have begun, and here, also, that the diversification of the species got under way. The descendants of these prehistoric men from the Olduvai include both the white Berber of the north and the black African.

White Africa. Black Africa. These two differing worlds are in many respects divided by the vast Sahara. To the north lies white, Mediterranean Africa which gave life to the Egyptian civilisation and then saw the passage of those peoples — Greeks, Romans, and, lastly, Arabs — who gave the region its definitive and unifying traits. To the south lies black Africa, whose negroid population had, for many centuries, little contact with the outside world. The physical features of Africa contributed to this isolation.

The continent's size and inhospitable coastline mean that huge inland areas are still extremely hard to penetrate: over 50% of Africa is more than 500 kilometres from the sea; rivers, like the Congo (Zaire) and the Niger, are often unnavigable, their courses obstructed by waterfalls and rapids. To these obstacles can be added climatic conditions. With the Equator crossing the central regions, there is a symmetry of inhospitable climes (deserts, rain forests).

To the north, a distinction can be made between western and eastern regions.

North-western Africa is physically and anthropologically varied. The ethnic characteristics and religion (Islam) of the Mediterranean-facing countries are close to those of the Middle East than to those of the rest of Africa. Only recently has the exploitation of mineral resources, in particular, oil, helped ease the burdens of poor, agricultural economies. In the central regions, the Sahara forms an almost insuperable barrier, its expanses of dunes and shattered rocks crossed only by caravan trails. To the south, the steppe and savanna gradually give way to the equatorial forests and, beyond, black Africa.

North-eastern Africa is a land of deserts and mountains; from the eastern areas of the Sahara, like the oil-rich Libyan desert, to the slopes of the Tibesti range, and the Ethiopian plateau, which rises to over 4,000 metres. The only large river is the Nile, flowing northwards to the Egyptian desert, where intense evaporation greatly reduces the flow before it reaches the Mediterranean. Further south, and as in north-western Africa, there is the steppe and the savanna. Here, the dry tropical climate becomes more equatorial, with summer rains. Here, too, Islam predominates, with the exception of Ethiopia where Coptic Christians are the largest religious group. Most populations work the land, concentrated in the few fertile zones, like the banks and delta of the Nile.

From the Red Sea to Lake Malawi in Mozambique stretches the world's greatest tectonic rift. In Kenya, this longitudinal fault is known as the Rift Valley. Here Africa's highest peaks, volcanic giants, tower to over 5,000 metres, their summits, despite the nearness of the Equator, permanently covered in snow and ice.

South of the Equator, the succession of changes in climate and vegetation mirrors that of the north. Along the Equator are virgin forests, hot and humid, with annual rainfall exceeding 2,000 millimetres. In an environment so hostile to human settlement, population density is very low. Much of this region lies in the huge Congo Basin. It is rich in minerals: Katanga, in Zaire, is situated in the Copper Belt. The oldest metamorphic rocks of southern Africa hold seams of precious stones. As a result of European colonisation, and also of tribal conflicts and foreign influences, the nations of this part of Africa have still not reached a balance between the exploitation of their resources and the well-being of their populations. Beyond the steppe, the savanna, and the Namib desert, is the Republic of South Africa. Political and economic power in South Africa is still in the hands of the descendants of Dutch and British colonisers, with the black population distinctly subordinate.

Separated from the mainland by the Mozambique Channel, Madagascar is the world's fourth largest island. Its flora and fauna resemble those of South-East Asia, and its population is partly black African and partly of Asian origin.

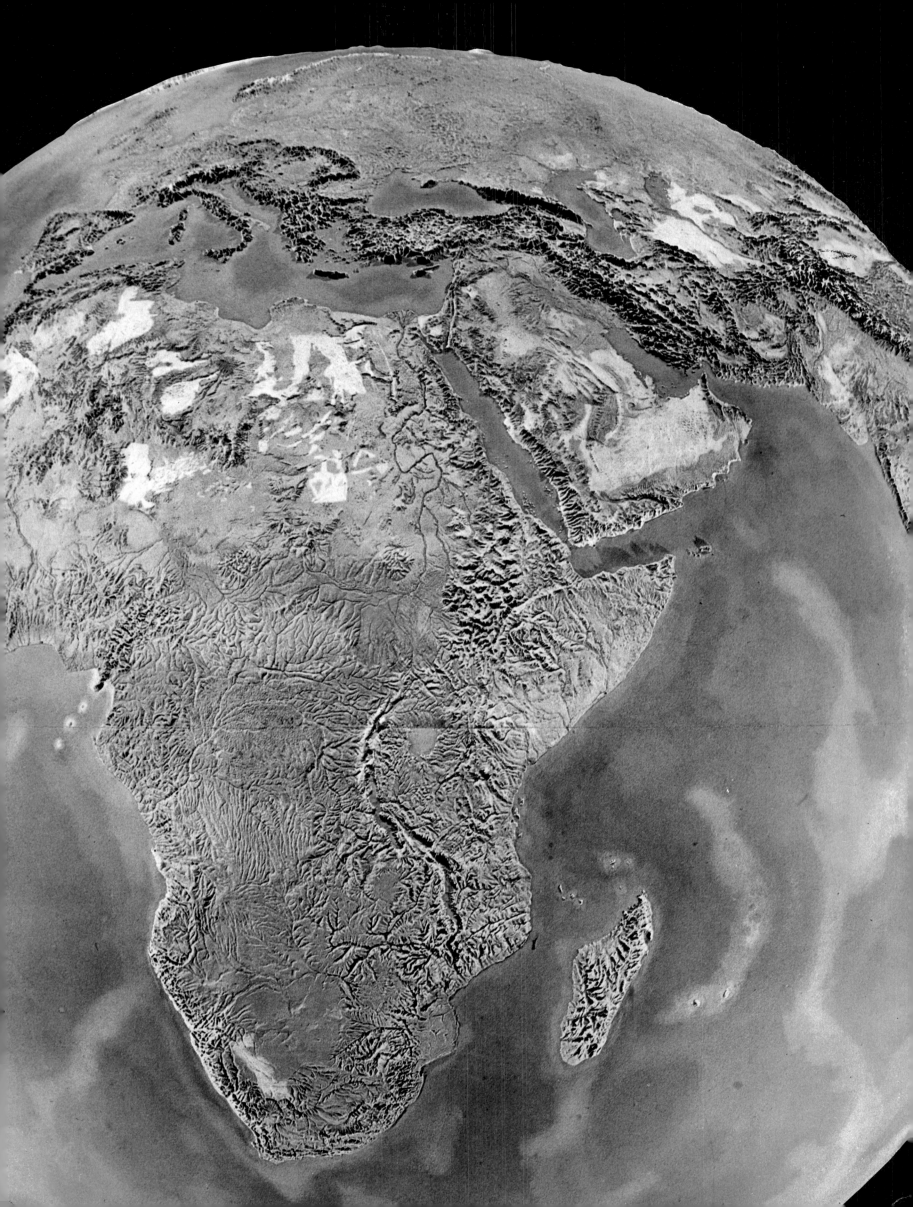

Algeria: The Sahara at Taghit

ALGERIA

Al-Jumhuriya al-Jaza'iriya ad-Dimuqratiya ash-Sha'biya

As a presidential democratic People's Republic Algeria has been independent since 3rd July 1962. Head of state is the President of the Republic, elected every 6 years by universal suffrage. The President has both executive powers, assisted by a Prime Minister and Government, and legislative ones, through the National Assembly, formed by general elections every 5 years.
Algeria is a member of UNO, the OAU, and the Arab League.
Algeria faces the Mediterranean. Some 90% of the country is covered by the Sahara. In the north there is a narrow coastal strip with a Mediterranean climate, backed by the Atlas Mountains.
Area: 2,380,000 sq km
Population: 22,971,000; 9 per sq km. Annual growth rate: 3.3%; birth rate 40‰; death rate: 8‰; average life expectancy: 56 years.
Capital: Algiers (pop 1,690,000).
Other important towns: Annaba (227,000); Constantine (450,000); Oran (600,000); Sidi Bel Abbès (155,000); Skikda (110,000).
Land use: cultivated 3%; grazing 15%; wooded 2%; uncultivated 80%. Main agricultural products: wheat, wine, olive oil, tobacco, vegetables, cotton, dates. Other activities: livestock rearing.
Official language: Arabic. French and Berber are also spoken.
Religion: Muslim.
Gross National Product: US $ 58,880 million; per capita: US $ 2,608.
Currency: Algerian dinar = 100 centimes.

ANGOLA

República Popular de Angola

Angola is now a People's Republic, but was formerly a colony and, later, an overseas province of Portugal. Angola declared independence on 11th November 1975 after a long and bloody civil war which ended in victory for the strongly Marxist People's Movement for the Liberation of Angola (MPLA). The highest authority is the Revolutionary Council, formed of members of the MPLA's political office, army chiefs-of-staff, and military and political representatives of the country's various districts. Head of state is the President of the Republic, who is also President of the MPLA.
Angola is a member of UNO and the OAU.
The country covers a vast area of southern Africa facing the Atlantic. Inland there is a series of plateaux, and, to the west, a large coastal plain.
Area: 1,247,000 sq km, including the enclave of Cabinda.
Population: 9,385,000; mainly Bakongo, Mbundu, Lunda, Ambo, Nganguela, Herero, and whites of Portuguese descent; density: 7 per sq km.
Annual growth rate: 3%; birth rate 48‰; death rate 22‰; average life expectancy: 42 years.
Capital: Luanda (pop 1,134,000).
Other important towns: Benguela (42,000); Huambo (65,000); Lobito (63,000); Lubango (35,000); Malanje (35,000).

Land use: cultivated 3%; grazing 23%; wooded 43%; uncultivated 31%. Main agricultural products: sisal, citrus fruits, sugar cane, coffee, cotton, fruit, maize, cocoa. Mineral resources: diamonds, oil.
Official language: Portuguese. Bantu dialects spoken.
Religion: Animist (50%), Catholic (40%), Protestant (10%).
Gross National Product: US $ 9,000 million; per capita: US $ 1,000.
Currency: Kwanza = 100 lwei.

BENIN

République Populaire du Bénin

Formerly a French colony, independent since 1st August 1960 under the name Dahomey, this People's Republic was renamed Benin on 30th November 1975.
The constitution of August 1979 gives legislative power to the People's Revolutionary Assembly, composed of members of the Benin People's Revolutionary Party, which governs the country.
Benin is a member of UNO and the OAU.
The country is prevalently flat, extending from the Gulf of Guinea to the River Niger.
Area: 112,600 sq km.
Population: 4,300,000; Fon (27%), Adja (12%), Yoruba (13%).
Annual growth rate: 2.9%; birth rate 49‰; death rate 21‰; average life expectancy: 47 years.
Capital: Porto Novo (pop 160,000).
Other important towns: Abomey (40,000); Cotonou (478,000); Natitingou (55,000); Parakou (23,000).
Land use: cultivated 16%; grazing 4%; wooded 32%; uncultivated 48%. Main agricultural products: cotton, cocoa, groundnuts, palm oil. Mineral resources: oil.
Official language: French. Sudanese dialects also spoken.
Religion: Animist (70%), Catholic (15%), Muslim (13%).
Gross National Product: US $ 1,380 million; per capita: US $ 300.
Currency: CFA franc = 100 centimes.

Algeria: The market in Ghardaia

BOTSWANA

Lefatse la Botswana

Formerly a British protectorate, Bechuanaland, the country is now a presidential republic, having become independent (though remaining a member of the British Commonwealth) on 30th September 1966. Executive power is exercised by the President of the Republic, assisted in his duties by the ministers which he, himself, appoints. Legislative power lies with the single-chamber parliament, most of whose members are directly elected by the people every 5 years.
Botswana is a member of UNO and the OAU.
The country is a vast inland plateau, semidesert, in southern Africa. It contains the Kalahari desert and, to the north, the great swamps of the Okovango delta and Ngami Depression.
Area: 600,400 sq km.
Population: 1,127,000; mainly Sotho-Tswana; 1 per sq km.
Annual growth rate: 3.7%; birth rate 51‰; death rate 19‰; average life expectancy: 56 years.
Capital: Gaborone (pop 111,000).
Other important towns: Molepolole (20,000); Kanye (20,000); Serowe (23,000).
Land use: cultivated 2.5%; grazing 76%; wooded 1.5%; uncultivated 20%. Main agricultural products: vegetables, cereals, fruit. Mineral resources: diamonds, copper, nickel.
Official language: English. Setswana is the national language.
Religion: Animist. Small Christian minority.
Gross National Product: US $ 980 million; per capita: US $ 900.
Currency: Pula = 100 thebe.

BURKINA

Burkina Faso

An independent republic since 5th August 1960, Burkina Faso was formerly a French colony. The constitution of November 1977 was abolished following military coups in 1980 and 1983. Power is totally in the hands of a military junta, and the Supreme Commander of the Armed Forces is now also the President of the Republic. Much of the border region between Burkina Faso and neighbouring Mali is claimed by both countries.
Burkina Faso, known as Upper Volta until 1984, is a member of UNO and the OAU.
This western African state lies on an inland plateau covered partly by savanna and partly by desert, and is crossed by three rivers which are sources of the Volta.
Area: 274,000 sq km.
Population: 7,900,000; Mossi (50%), Fulani, Bobo, also Dioula, Hausa and Tuareg; density: 29 per sq km.
Annual growth rate: 3.1%; birth rate 48‰; death rate 23‰; average life expectancy: 43 years.
Capital: Ouagadougou (pop 442,000).
Other important towns: Bobo Dioulasso (231,000); Koudougou (51,000).
Land use: cultivated 11%; grazing 36%; wooded 25%; uncultivated 28%. Main agricultural products: groundnuts, sesame, tobacco, cotton.
Official language: French. Bantu and Sudanese dialects.
Religion: Animist (75%), Muslim (20%), Christian (5%).
Gross National Product: US $ 1,470 million; per capita: US $ 182.
Currency: CFA franc = 100 centimes.

BURUNDI

République du Burundi/Republika y'Uburundi

Burundi, formerly part of Belgian-controlled Ruanda-Urundi, became an independent kingdom on 1st July 1962, and a presidential republic on 29th November 1966. Following a military coup in November 1987, power passed to the National Committee and the constitution was suspended.
Burundi is a member of UNO and the OAU.
This small nation is situated on an inland plateau which is covered by savanna and crossed by the Kagera River, east of Lake Tanganyika.
Area: 27,800 sq km.
Population: 4,780,000; mainly Hutu (85%) and Tutsi (14%); density: 184 per sq km.
Annual growth rate: 3%; birth rate 45‰; death rate 22‰; average life expectancy: 42 years.
Capital: Bujumbura (pop 270,000).
Other important towns: Gitega (95,000); Muhinga (20,000); Muramvya (14,000).

Land use: cultivated 48%; grazing 33%; wooded 3%; uncultivated 16%. Main agricultural products: coffee, cotton, fruit, cereals, tobacco.
Official languages: French and Kirundi. Swahili is also spoken.
Religion: mainly Catholic (more than 60%).
Gross National Product: US $ 830 million; per capita: US $ 200.
Currency: Burundi franc = 100 centimes.

CAMEROON

République du Cameroun

Formerly under French trusteeship, Cameroon became independent on 1st October 1961, following the unification of British-administered southern Cameroon. The country constituted a federal state until May 1972, when it became a presidential unitary republic. The President of the Republic, who also heads the Government, is elected every 5 years by direct universal suffrage, and exercises executive power together with the ministers appointed by him. Legislative power lies with the single-chamber Parliament, also elected every 5 years by direct universal suffrage.
Cameroon is a member of UNO and the OAU.
The country lies on a huge plateau facing the Gulf of Guinea, dominated by volcanic mountains. The climate is warm and humid.
Area: 475,000 sq km.
Population: 11,210,000; over 130 ethnic groups, mainly Bantu-speaking; density: 23 per sq km.
Annual growth rate: 3.2%; birth rate 42‰; death rate 21‰; average life expectancy: 47 years.
Capital: Yaoundé (pop 653,000).
Other important towns: Bafoussam (75,000); Bamenda (60,000); Buea (30,000); Douala (850,000); Kumba (50,000); Maroua (81,000).
Land use: cultivated 14%; grazing 18%; wooded 54%; uncultivated 14%. Main agricultural products: coffee, cocoa, tea, bananas, rubber, palm oil, timber. Mineral resources: bauxite, oil.
Official languages: English, French. Bantu and Sudanese dialects.
Religion: Muslim (30%), Catholic (22%), Protestant (16%).
Gross National Product: US $ 9,000 million; per capita: US $ 860.
Currency: CFA franc = 100 centimes.

CAPE VERDE ISLANDS

República do Cabo Verde

Formerly an administratively autonomous Portuguese Overseas Province, the islands have, since 5th July 1975, been an independent People's Republic. Legislative power lies with the Assembly, whose members all belong to the Marxist-oriented African Party for the Independence of Cape Verde (PAICV). Executive power is in the hands of the Prime Minister and his Government, who answer to the Assembly.
Cape Verde is a member of UNO and the OAU.
The islands are situated in the Atlantic, north-west of Cape Verde. There are 10 main islands, the largest of which is São Tiago.
Area: 4,035 sq km.
Population: 325,000; mainly Mulatto (70%), also Black African (28%), and White (1%); density: 78 per sq km.

Algeria: Tassili cave paintings

Algeria: A Saharan Tuareg

Annual growth rate: 2.4%; birth rate: 28‰; death rate 9‰; average life expectancy: 58 years.
Capital: Praia (pop 50,000).
Other important towns: Mindelo (30,000); São Filipe (4,500).
Land use: cultivated 10%; grazing 6%; uncultivated 84%. Main agricultural products: bananas, other fruit, vegetables, cereals, sweet potatoes.
Official language: Portuguese.
Religion: Catholic.
Gross National Product: US $ 156 million; per capita: US $ 170.
Currency: Cape Verde escudo = 100 centavos.

CENTRAL AFRICAN REPUBLIC

République Centrafricaine

The Central African Republic, previously the French colony of Ubangui-Shari, became an independent parliamentary republic on 13th August 1960. From 1st January 1966, the country was governed in an authoritarian manner by a President who, in March 1972, declared himself President for life, and, on 4th December 1976, transformed the republic into an empire and assumed the title of Emperor. A coup restored the republic on 20th September 1979, but as a result of a second coup (1st September 1981), constitutional guarantees were suspended and power passed into the hands of a military junta.
The Central African Republic is a member of UNO and the OAU.
The country lies inland, just north of the Equator, on a plateau, covered by savanna and forests, which forms the watershed between the Shari and the Zaire rivers.
Area: 623 000 sq km.
Population: 2,900,000; mainly Bantu and Sudanese dialects; density: 4 per sq km. Annual growth rate: 2.5%; birth rate 41‰; death rate 21‰; average life expectancy: 44 years.
Capital: Bangui (pop 596,000).
Other important towns: Bambari (52,000); Berbérati (45,000); Bouar (49,000).
Land use: cultivated 5%; grazing 5%; wooded 58%; uncultivated 32%. Main agricultural products: coffee, cotton, groundnuts, millet, maize, vegetables, fruit; timber, rubber. Mineral resources: diamonds, uranium, gold, iron ore.
Official languages: French and Sango.
Religion: mainly Animist (60%), also Catholic (15%), and Muslim (5%).
Gross National Product: US $ 980 million; per capita: US $ 371.
Currency: CFA franc = 100 centimes.

CHAD

République du Tchad/Jumhuriyat Tashad

Chad, a French colony until 11th August 1960, is now a presidential republic. On the basis of the constitution approved in December 1989, the National Assembly and the President are elected by direct universal suffrage.
Libya claims sovereignty over a large stretch of uranium-rich desert in northern Chad and occupied the area militarily until 1987. Also active in the north is the National Liberation Front (FROLINAT), supported economically and militarily by Libya.
Chad is a member of UNO and the OAU.
The country is situated inland in northern central Africa. It is in a low-lying plain of steppe and desert which rises to the north to form the Tibesti mountains. It is separated from Nigeria and Cameroon to the south-west by the swamps of Lake Chad.
Area: 1,284,000 sq km.
Population: 4,950,000; mainly Arabian tribal groups (53%), and Sara (25%), also Fulani; density: 4 per sq km.
Annual growth rate: 2%; birth rate 44‰; death rate: 23‰; average life expectancy: 41 years.
Capital: N'Djamena (pop 512,000).
Other important towns: Abéché (71,000); Moundou (90,000); Sarh (100,000).
Land use: cultivated 2.5%; grazing 35%; wooded 10%; uncultivated 52.5%. Main agricultural products: cotton, groundnuts, millet, maize, vegetables. Mineral resources: tin.
Official languages: French, Arabic. Sudanese dialects.
Religion: Muslim (50%), Animist (44%), Christian (10%).
Gross National Product: US $ 811 million; per capita: US $ 158.
Currency: CFA franc = 100 centimes.

COMOROS

République Fédérale Islamique des Comores

Formerly a French Overseas Territory, the islands have been an independent presidential republic since 6th July 1975. The President of the Republic has extensive powers and, as head of government, directly exercises executive power. Legislative power is entrusted to the Parliament, elected by universal suffrage.
The Comoros claim sovereignty over the island of Mayotte which rejected independence in favour of status as a French Overseas Department, thus maintaining its links with France.
The Comoros are a member of UNO and the OAU.
The Comoros are three islands, the largest of which is Grande Comore, off the north-west coast of Madagascar.
Area: 1,862 sq km.
Population: 355,000; mainly Arab and half-caste; 152 per sq km.
Annual growth rate: 3.4%; birth rate 44‰; death rate 19‰; average life expectancy: 45 years.
Capital: Moroni (pop 20,000).
Land use: cultivated 42%; grazing 7%; wooded 16%; uncultivated 35%. Main agricultural products: sisal, copra, cocoa, vanilla, rice, maize, cassava.
Official languages: French, Arabic. Swahili is widely spoken.
Religion: Muslim.
Gross National Product: US $ 162 million; per capita: US $ 352.
Currency: CFA franc = 100 centimes.

CONGO

République Populaire du Congo

This former French colony became independent on 16th August 1960 and is now a People's Republic. Power is held by a military junta which pursues the policies expressed by the Marxist-inspired Congolese Labour Party, the only lawful political party in Congo. The members of the People's National Assembly all represent this party.
Congo is a member of UNO and the OAU.
The country straddles the Equator on a plateau sloping towards the Atlantic. The River Congo flows along much of the south-western border. Forest covers most of the country.
Area: 342,000 sq km.
Population: 1,912,000; Kongo (45%), also Sangha, Téké; density: 5 per sq km.
Annual growth rate: 3.9%; birth rate 45‰; death rate 18‰; average life expectancy: 47 years.
Capital: Brazzaville (pop 595,000).
Other important towns: Loubomo (49,000); Pointe Noire (297,000).
Land use: cultivated 2%; grazing 30%; wooded 62%; uncultivated 6%. Main agricultural products: groundnuts, sugar cane, coffee, cocoa, cassava; palm oil, timber, rubber. Mineral resources: copper.
Official language: French. Lingala, Sangha, Téké and Kikongo (Bantu group of languages) are also spoken.
Religion: Animist (50%), Catholic (40%), Protestant (10%).
Gross National Product: US $ 1,980 million; per capita: US $ 1,023.
Currency: CFA franc = 100 centimes.

DJIBOUTI

République de Djibouti

Djibouti has been an independent parliamentary republic since 27th June 1977. Until 1967 it was the French colony of French Somaliland, or the French Coast of the Somalis. Until independence it was then the French Overseas Territory of the Afars and Issas. Legislative power is held by the single-chamber Parliament, whose members, all representing the African People's Independence League, are elected by direct universal suffrage. Executive power is held by the Government, which is answerable to Parliament.
Djibouti is a member of UNO, the OAU, and the Arab League.
This small nation is situated in the Gulf of Aden, at the mouth of the Red Sea.
Area: 23,200 sq km.
Population: 405,000; mainly Danaki (Afar) (37%), Somali (Issa) (47%), also Arab and European density: 17 per sq km.
Annual growth rate: 4.8%; birth rate 42‰; death rate 8‰.
Capital: Djibouti (pop 200,000).
Land use: cultivated 0.5%; grazing 11%; uncultivated 88.5%.
Official languages: French, Arabic. Cushitic dialects also spoken locally.
Religion: Muslim (88%), Catholic (12%).
Gross National Product: US $ 500 million; per capita: US $ 1300.
Currency: Djibouti franc = 100 centimes.

EGYPT

Al-Jumhuriya Misr al-'Arabiya

Egypt is a presidential republic whose head of state, the President, is elected for a 6-year term by direct universal suffrage. As head of government, the President also has direct executive power and appoints government ministers. The single-chamber Parliament, most of whose members are elected for 5 years by direct universal suffrage, is the nation's legislative body.
Egypt is a member of UNO, the OAU, and the Arab League.
Some 96% of Egypt is desert. Only 3%, along the banks of the Nile, is inhabitable and farmable. The Aswan Dam has created a lake 250 kilometres long.
Area: 1,000 000 sq km, of which 59,000 are in Asia (Sinai).
Population: 48,205,000; mostly Hamitic Arabs, Bedouin and Berbers; density: 875 per sq km in the Nile Valley which, apart from the oases, is the only inhabited part of Egypt.
Annual growth rate: 2%; birth rate 41‰; death rate 11‰; average life expectancy: 57 years.
Capital: Cairo (pop 13,300,000).
Other important towns: Alexandria (2,920,000); Asyut (213,000); Aswan (180,000); Dumyat/Damietta (90,000); El-Mansura (311,000); Isma'iliya (145,000); Luxor (93,000); Port Said (400,000); Suez (327,000); Tanta (283,000).
Land use: cultivated 2.8%; uncultivated 97.2%. Main agricultural products: rice, cotton, sugar cane, wheat, maize, citrus fruits, dates, bananas. Mineral resources: oil, phosphates, iron ore.
Official language: Arabic.
Religion: Muslim.
Gross National Product: US $ 38,440 million; per capita: US $ 773.
Currency: Egyptian pound = 100 piastre.

Benin: The stilt-elevated village of Ganvié

Botswana: The Kalahari Desert

EQUATORIAL GUINEA

República de Guinea Ecuatorial

Equatorial Guinea has been an independent presidential republic since 12th October 1968. Prior to this it was a Spanish colony, with autonomous status from 1964. Following the military coup of 3rd August 1979, all political power was placed in the hands of a military junta. Further to the constitution approved in 1982, the President, elected by universal suffrage, is aided by a Chamber of Representatives of 41 members and by the Council (6 members).
Equatorial Guinea is a member of UNO and the OAU.
The country consists of a mountainous, wooded area surrounding the final 200 kilometres of the River Mbini as it flows to the Gulf of Guinea, and a number of islands.
Area: 28,000 sq km, of which 26,000 are continental.
Population: 300,000; mostly Black African and Mulatto; 10 per sq km.
Annual growth rate: 2.2%; birth rate 42‰; death rate 21‰; average life expectancy: 42 years.
Capital: Malabo (pop 40,000).
Other important towns: Bata (30,000); Ebebiyin (25,000); Luba (15,000).
Land use: cultivated 8%; grazing 4%; wooded 46%; uncultivated 42%. Main agricultural products: coffee, cocoa, cassava, copra, bananas.
Official language: Spanish. Bantu dialects widely spoken.
Religion: Catholic (80%).
Gross National Product: US $ 100 million; per capita: US $ 250.
Currency: CFA franc = 100 centimes.

ETHIOPIA

Yetyopiya Hizbawi Dimokrasiyawi Ripublik

The republic was born on 21st March 1975 following the military coup which deposed the Emperor (Negus), and thus ended a constitutional hereditary monarchy.
In 1987 it became a People's Republic. Political power is in the hands of the Parliament (Shengo) whose 485 members are elected from the only lawful party, the WEB. The President of the Council of State (24 members) is also head of state.
Since 1956, when Eritrea, already federally united to Ethiopia since 1950, was annexed, a violent war of liberation has been going on. Eritrea seeks independence or a form of real autonomy. More recent but no less bloody is the war of liberation which the Somali population of the Ogaden region have been waging against the government of Addis Ababa since 1977, with the support of Somalia.
The political and military situation in the so-called Horn of Africa remains unstable.
Ethiopia is a member of UNO and the OAU.
The country is formed of vast plateaux divided by a deep fault. Altitude makes the climate more moderate than in other regions, and rainfall is higher. Ethiopia borders on the Red Sea.
Area: 1,251,900 sq km.
Population: 47,300,000; mainly Galla (30%); Amhara and Tigrina (48%); Somali, Danakil and Nilotic; density: 38 per sq km.
Annual growth rate: 2.8%; birth rate 50‰; death rate 24‰; average life expectancy: 40 years.
Capital: Addis Ababa (pop 1,423,000).
Other important towns: Aduwa (13,000); Asmara (275,000); Dessye (68,000); Dire Dawa

The Horn of Africa

(80,000); Gonder (68,000); Harer (60,000); Massawa (15,000).
Land use: cultivated 11%; grazing 37%; wooded 22%; uncultivated 30%. Main agricultural products: maize, sorghum, barley, wheat, coffee, tobacco, potatoes, citrus fruits, bananas, groundnuts, sugar cane, sesame and castor oil; timber. Other activities: livestock rearing.
Official language: Amharic.
Religion: Coptic Christian (60%) and Muslim (30%).
Gross National Product: US $ 5,680 million; per capita: US $ 130.
Currency: Birr = 100 cents.

GABON
République Gabonaise

Formerly a French colony, Gabon is now a presidential republic (independent since 17th August 1960). The President of the Republic, who is also Prime Minister, is elected, as is the vice president, by direct universal suffrage for a term of 7 years, and holds direct executive power. Legislative power is exercised by the single-chamber Parliament whose members, all representing the Gabonese Democratic Party, are elected for 7 years by direct universal suffrage.
Gabon is a member of UNO and the OAU.
The country borders on the equatorial Atlantic, with a coastal plain backed by a forested plateau.
Area: 267,000 sq km.
Population: 1,300,000; mainly Fang (32%); Njebi, Eshira-Epunu, Omyene, Batéké; density: 5 per sq km.
Annual growth rate: 1.9%; birth rate 31‰; death rate 23‰; average life expectancy: 41 years.
Capital: Libreville (pop 255,000).
Other important towns: Port-Gentil (85,000); Lambaréné (25,000).
Land use: cultivated 1.7%; grazing 18%; wooded 75%; uncultivated 5%. Main agricultural products: cassava, potatoes, maize, cocoa, groundnuts, coffee, bananas; timber. Mineral resources: oil, natural gas, manganese, uranium.
Official language: French. Bantu dialects also spoken.
Religion: Catholic (50%); Animist (35%); Protestant (15%).
Gross National Product: US $ 2,920 million; per capita: US $ 2,860.
Currency: CFA franc = 100 centimes.

GAMBIA
Republic of the Gambia

This former British colony became independent on 18th February 1965, and, since 24th April 1970, has been a republic. It is a member of the Commonwealth of Nations. The single-chamber Parliament, most of whose members are elected by direct universal suffrage, holds legislative power. Executive power is held by the Prime Minister and his Council of Ministers, both proposed by Parliament and appointed by the President of the Republic.
Since February 1st, 1982, Gambia has been united with Senegal in the Confederation of Senegambia, a confederation in which both states do, however, retain their international juridical status.
Gambia is a member of UNO and the OAU.
The country lies along the banks of the Gambia River, forming an enclave in Senegal.

Area: 11,295 sq km.
Population: 687,000; mainly Mandinka (40%); Wolof (20%); Fulani (20%); density: 64 per sq km.
Annual growth rate: 3.1%; birth rate 47‰; death rate 23‰; average life expectancy: 41 years.
Capital: Banjul (pop 45,000).
Other important towns: Brikama (20,000). Serekunda (69,000).
Land use: cultivated 15%; grazing 8%; wooded 16%; uncultivated 61%. Main agricultural products: groundnuts, palm oil, rice, millet and maize.
Official language: English. Sudanese dialects also spoken.
Religion: Muslim (65%); Animist (8%).
Gross National Product: US $ 190 million; per capita: US $ 280.
Currency: Dalasi = 100 bututs.

GHANA

Formerly the British colony of the Gold Coast, now a member of the Commonwealth of Nations, Ghana has been independent since 6th March 1957, and a republic since 1st July 1960. As a result of recent military coups, the constitution has been suspended, political parties dissolved, and power is in the hands of a provisional National Defence Council, formed of both army officers and civilians.
Ghana is a member of UNO and the OAU.
The country borders on the Gulf of Guinea. It is flat and crossed by the River Volta, on which a dam has created a lake 400 kilometres long.
Area: 238,535 sq km.
Population: 13,578,000; mainly Akan (53%) and Mole Daghani (16%); also Gonya, Ewe, Yoruba, Mossi, Dagomba, Fulani, Hausa; density: 57 per sq km.
Annual growth rate: 3%; birth rate 48‰; death rate 13‰; average life expectancy: 49 years.
Capital: Accra (pop 1,580,000).
Other important towns: Kumasi (489,000); Sekondi-Takoradi (170,000); Tamale (185,000).
Land use: cultivated 12%; grazing 14%; wooded 35%; uncultivated 39%. Main agricultural products: cotton, cocoa, maize, millet, coffee, tobacco, sisal, pineapples, sugar cane; latex. Mineral resources: bauxite, gold, manganese, diamonds.
Official language: English. Sudanese dialects also spoken.
Religion: Christian (52%); Muslim (14%); and Animist (35%).
Gross National Product: US $ 5,630 million; per capita: US $ 420.
Currency: Cedi = 100 pesewas.

GUINEA
République de Guinée

Formerly a French colony, Guinea is now a presidential republic, independent since 2nd October 1958. Head of state is the President of the Republic. After the death of President Sékou Touré, a coup brought to power a military junta which has supended the constitution and dissolved the Parliament.
Guinea is a member of UNO and the OAU.
Guinea borders on the Atlantic, with a coastal plain, and an inland plateau dominated by the Fouta Djallon to the north and the Nimba Mountains to the south.
Area: 245,855 sq km.

Egypt: The Nile near Aswan

Population: 5,780,000; Susu, Kissi, Tenda, Mandinka and Fulani; density: 23 per sq km.
Annual growth rate: 2.9%; birth rate 46‰; death rate 20‰; average life expectancy: 44 years.
Capital: Conakry (pop 705,000).
Other important towns: Kankan (100,000); Kindia (50,000).
Land use: cultivated 6%; grazing 12%; wooded 40%; uncultivated 42%. Main agricultural products: rice, groundnuts, sisal, palm oil, citrus fruits, coffee and tobacco. Mineral resources: bauxite.
Official language: French. Sudanese dialects and Fulani also spoken.
Religion: Muslim (60%); Animist and Christian.
Gross National Product: US $ 1,590 million; per capita: US $ 243.
Currency: Syli = 100 cauris.

GUINEA-BISSAU
República da Guiné-Bissau

Formerly a Portuguese Overseas Province, Guinea-Bissau has been an independent republic since 10th September 1974. After the military coup of 14th November 1980, power was restricted to the Revolutionary Council, made up predominantly of army officers. This has now been substituted by the National People's Assembly whose 150 members are elected by local councils. The new constitution was approved in May 1984.
Guinea-Bissau is a member of UNO and the OAU.
The country comprises a swathe of West African territory with a jagged Atlantic coastline, and the archipelago of the Bijagos and Bolama Islands.
Area: 36,125 sq km.
Population: 768,000; predominantly, Balante (33%); and Fulani (20%); density: 21 per sq km.
Annual growth rate: 2.1%; birth rate 40‰; death rate 25‰; average life expectancy: 39 years.
Capital: Bissau (pop 110,000).
Other important towns: Bafatá (14,000); Catió (6,000).
Land use: cultivated 9%; grazing 30%; wooded 30%; uncultivated 31%. Main agricultural products: groundnuts, copra, maize, barley, rice.
Official language: Portuguese. Sudanese dialects and Fulani.
Religion: Animist (60%); Muslim (30%); and Catholic (8%).
Gross National Product: US $ 162 million; per capita: US $ 160.
Currency: Guinea peso = 100 centavos.

IVORY COAST
République de Côte d'Ivoire

The Ivory Coast is now a presidential republic, and was formerly a French colony. Head of state is the President, elected for 5 years by direct universal suffrage. As head of government, the President also holds executive power. Legislative power lies with the single-chamber Parliament, whose members, all representing the Ivory Coast Democratic Party, are elected every 5 years.
Ivory Coast is a member of UNO and the OAU.
The country is situated on a vast plateau above the Gulf of Guinea. It is covered by thick forests and numerous rivers, and it has a hot, humid climate.

Egypt: The Sphinx

Area: 322,465 sq km.
Population: 6,898,000; mainly Akan (38%); Kru (16%); Mande; density: 21 per sq km.
Annual growth rate: 4.3%; birth rate 47‰; death rate 18‰; average life expectancy: 47 years.
Capital: Yamoussoukro (pop 100,000). The de facto capital is, however, still Abidjan (2,534,000).
Other important towns: Bouaké (175,000); Daloa (60,000); Gagnoa (45,000); Korhogo (48,000).
Land use: cultivated 11%; grazing 10%; wooded 20%; uncultivated 59%. Main agricultural products: coffee, cocoa, pineapples, bananas, cotton, palm oil, tobacco; latex; timber.
Official language: French. Sudanese dialects and Kru also spoken.
Religion: Animist (37%); Muslim (34%); Christian (22%).
Gross National Product: US $ 8,850 million; per capita: US $ 850.
Currency: CFA franc = 100 centimes.

KENYA
Jamhuri ya Kenya

Formerly a British colony, Kenya became an independent member of the Commonwealth of Nations on 12th December 1963, and a republic on 12th December 1964. Head of state is the President of the Republic, elected for 7 years by direct universal suffrage. The President is also head of government and, as such, directly exercises executive power in collaboration with the ministers he appoints. Legislative power belongs to the single-chamber Parliament, whose members all represent the Kenya African National Union (KANU) and are elected by direct universal suffrage.
Kenya is a member of UNO and the OAU.
Kenya is a very varied land made up of plateaux between Lake Victoria, Lake Rudolph and the Indian Ocean, crossed by rift valleys and dominated by Mount Kenya (5,199 metres).
Area: 582,600 sq km.
Population: 19,540,000; mainly Kikuyu (20%); Luo (13%); Luhya (13%); Kamba (11%); Meru, Masai and Turkana; density: 33 per sq km.
Annual growth rate: 4.1%; birth rate 55‰; death rate 14‰; average life expectancy: 55 years.
Capital: Nairobi (pop 1,160,000).
Other important towns: Kisumu (150,000); Malindi (23,000); Mombasa (425,000); Nakuru (92,000); Nyeri (35,000); Thika (41,000).
Land use: cultivated 4%; grazing 7%; wooded 6%; uncultivated 83%. Main agricultural products: coffee, tea, sisal, pineapples, cotton, maize, vegetables, fruit. Other activities: livestock rearing.
Official language: Swahili. English and Bantu, Nilotic and Cushitic dialects are widely spoken.
Religion: Animist (40%); Protestant (30%); Catholic (22%); Muslim (5%).
Gross National Product: US $ 6,630 million; per capita: US $ 314.
Currency: Kenya shilling = 100 cents.

LESOTHO
Kingdom of Lesotho/Muso oa Lesotho

Formerly the British protectorate of Basutoland, Lesotho, a constitutional monarchy, has been an independent member of the Commonwealth of Nations since 4th October

Egypt: The golden mask of Tutankhamon

1966. Until 1986 the Monarch exercised executive power through his Prime Minister and ministers. Since January 1986, the power has been held by a military junta.
Lesotho is a member of UNO and the OAU.
Lesotho is a small, mountainous, inland nation in southern Africa. In it lies the upper valley of the Orange River, characterized by steppe and grassland.
Area: 30,400 sq km.
Population: 1,577,000; mostly Basotho; 52 per sq km.
Annual growth rate: 2.6%; birth rate 40‰; death rate 16‰; average life expectancy: 51 years.
Capital: Maseru (pop 109,000).
Other important towns: Mafeteng (6,000); Leribe (6,500).
Land use: cultivated 12%; grazing 66%; uncultivated 22%. Main agricultural products: maize, barley, wheat, vegetables. Other activities: livestock rearing. Mineral resources: diamonds.
Official languages: Sesotho and English.
Religion: Christian (80%).
Gross National Product: US $ 620 million; per capita: US $ 390.
Currency: Loti = 100 lisente.

LIBERIA

Liberia has been an independent republic since 1822, with a constitution modelled on that of the United States of America. The President and the two-chamber Parliament, are elected by universal direct suffrage.
Liberia is a member of UNO and the OAU.
The nation borders on the Atlantic and is formed of a plain, characterized by rivers and forests, rising gradually towards the Nimba Mountains.
Area: 111,400 sq km.
Population: 2,211,000; mainly Bassa, Kpelle, Mandinka, and Kru; density: 22 per sq km.
Annual growth rate: 3.3%; birth rate 50‰: death rate 21‰: average life expectancy: 54 years.
Capital: Monrovia (pop 465,000).
Other important towns: Buchanan (25,000); Greenville (8,500); Harper (12,000).
Land use: cultivated 3.5%; grazing 2%; wooded 19%; uncultivated 75.5%. Main agricultural products: coffee, cocoa, bananas, rice, cassava, citrus fruits, sugar cane, groundnuts, palm oil; latex, timber. Mineral resources: iron ore.
Official language: English. Sudanese dialects and Kru also spoken.
Religion: Animist (75%); Muslim (20%); Christian (5%).
Gross National Product: US $ 1,000 million; per capita: US $ 444.
Currency: Liberian dollar = 100 cents.

LIBYA

Al-Jamahiriya al-'Arabiya al-Libiya
Libya was an Italian dependency until 24th December 1951, when it became a federal (unitary from April 1963), hereditary monarchy. It has been a Socialist People's Republic since the military coup of 1st September 1969, which brought the Revolutionary Council to power. Following the constitutional reforms of 2nd March 1977, the General Congress of the People became the supreme organ of state. From it emanate the General Committee of the People, and the five-member General Secretariat (which replaced the Revolutionary Council). Head of state is the President of this Secretariat who, in practice, is authoritarian ruler of the nation.
Libya is a member of UNO, the OAU, and the Arab League.
Libya occupies a large part of the Sahara from the Tibesti mountains to the Mediterranean coast. With the exception of the oases, the coastal strip is the only farmable and inhabitable area.
Area: 1,760,000 sq km.
Population: 3,638,000; mainly Arab, Berber and Tuareg; density: 2 per sq km.
Annual growth rate: 4.5%; birth rate 49‰; death rate 15‰; average life expectancy: 56 years.
Capital: Tripoli (pop 989,000).
Other important towns: Al Bayda (31,000); Benghazi (650,000); Misratah (285,000); Sebha (28,000); Tobruk (26,000).
Land use: cultivated 1.5%; grazing 8%; wooded 0.3%; uncultivated 90%. Main agricultural products: dates, olives, citrus fruits, potatoes, tobacco. Other activities: livestock rearing. Mineral resources: oil.
Language: Arabic.

Ethiopia: Coptic priests in Addis Ababa

Religion: Muslim.
Gross National Product: US $ 20,000 million; per capita: US $ 5,500.
Currency: Libyan dinar = 1,000 dirhams.

MADAGASCAR

République Malgache/Repoblika Malagasy
Formerly a French colony, independent since 26th June 1960, Madagascar became a presidential People's Republic on 15th June 1975. According to the constitution of December 1975, head of state is the President of the Republic, elected for 7 years by direct universal suffrage. The President is also head of the Supreme Revolutionary Council, which has executive power. Legislative power lies with the People's National Assembly, whose members, elected for 5 years by direct universal suffrage, all represent the Marxist-oriented National Front for the Defence of the Revolution.
Madagascar is a member of UNO and the OAU.
Madagascar, the world's fourth largest island, lies in the Indian Ocean, 400 kilometres off the east coast of southern Africa. A mountain range runs along the eastern side of the island while, to the west, a series of fertile plateaux slope down towards the Mozambique Channel, which separates Madagascar from the rest of Africa.
Area: 587,000 sq km.
Population: 10,012,000; mainly Madagascan (99%), some Indian, French and Chinese; density: 17 per sq km.
Annual growth rate: 2.9%; birth rate 46‰; death rate 25‰; average life expectancy: 47 years.
Capital: Antananarivo (pop 1,050,000).
Other important towns: Antseranana (100,000); Fianarantsoa (130,000); Mahajanga (85,000); Toamasina (100,000); Toliara (50,000).
Land use: cultivated 5%; grazing 58%; wooded 25%; uncultivated 12%. Main agricultural products: coffee, vanilla, cotton, sugar cane, pepper, cocoa, cloves, tobacco, coconut, copra, fruit; timber. Mineral resources: gold, chromite, graphite.
Official language: Madagascan. French is also widely spoken.
Religion: Animist (55%); Catholic (20%); Protestant (18%); Muslim (5%).
Gross National Product: US $ 2,490 million; per capita: US $ 237.
Currency: Madagascan franc = 100 centimes.

MALAWI

Formerly the British protectorate of Nyasaland, Malawi is now a presidential republic (independent since 6th July 1964, a republic since 6th July 1966) and member of the Commonwealth of Nations. The current President (elected for life in 1971) is also head of government and, as such, exercises executive power with the assistance of the ministers he appoints. A single-chamber Parliament has legislative power and its members all represent the Malawi Congress Party.
Malawi is a member of UNO and the OAU.
This inland nation occupies a thin strip of the southern African plateau, along the western edge of Lake Malawi (Nyasa).
The Great Rift Valley runs along its length.
Area: 118,500 sq km.
Population: 7,982,000; 85 per sq km.
Annual growth rate: 3.7%; birth rate 51‰; death rate 27‰; average life expectancy: 47 years.

Capital: Lilongwe (pop 220,000).
Other important towns: Blantyre (400,000); Mzuzu (115,000).
Land use: cultivated 20%; grazing 15%; wooded 36%; uncultivated 29%. Main agricultural products: tobacco, cotton, tea, millet, groundnuts, rice, maize, cassava; timber. Mineral resources: coal.
Official language: English. Bantu dialects are widely spoken.
Religion: Animist (50%); Christian (40%); Muslim (10%).
Gross National Product: US $ 1,116 million; per capita: US $ 159.
Currency: Kwacha = 100 tambala.

MALI

République du Mali
Mali, formerly a French colony, has been an independent presidential republic since 22nd September 1960. The President of the Republic, who is also head of government, holds direct executive power, while legislative power lies with the National Assembly whose members all represent the Mali People's Democratic Union.
Mali is a member of UNO and the OAU.
It covers a vast inland area between the northern part of the Fouta Djallon and the Sahara, part of which lies inside Mali. Crossed by the Niger and the Senegal rivers, the country is also characterized by huge swamps.
Area: 1,240,000 sq km.
Population: 7,620,000; predominantly Bambara (32%), Fulani (17%), Songhai (7%), and Tuareg; density: 6 per sq km.
Annual growth rate: 1.7%; birth rate 49‰; death rate 23‰; average life expectancy: 41 years.
Capital: Bamako (pop 640,000).
Other important towns: Kayes (67,000); Mopti (78,000); Ségou (100,000); Sikasso (70,000); Timbuktu (20,000).
Land use: cultivated 2%; grazing 24%; wooded 7%; uncultivated 67%. Main agricultural products: cotton, groundnuts, millet, rice, maize, cassava; timber. Other activities: livestock rearing.
Official language: French. Berber, Arabic, Sudanese dialects and Fulani are widely spoken.
Religion: Muslim (90%) and Animist (10%).
Gross National Product: US $ 1,580 million; per capita: US $ 210.
Currency: Mali franc = 100 centimes.

MAURITANIA

Al-Jumhuriya al-Islamiya al-Muritaniya/ République Islamique de Mauritanie
Formerly a French colony, now a presidential republic, Mauritania has been independent since 28th November 1960. Following the military coup of 9th July 1978, the country's only political party, the Mauritanian People's Party, was dissolved, constitutional guarantees suspended, and power assumed by a military junta, the Military Committee for National Salvation.
Mauritania is a member of UNO, the OAU, and the Arab League.
Most of the country is Saharan desert plateau. Fertile land is to be found along the Atlantic coast to the west, and, to the south, along the banks of the Senegal River, which forms the border between Mauritania and Senegal.
Area: 1,030,000 sq km.
Population: 1,890,000; mainly Mauri (80%); also Bambara, Soninké, Wolof, Sarakalles, and Fulani; density: 2 per sq km.
Annual growth rate: 2.6%; birth rate 50‰; death rate 23‰; average life expectancy: 43 years.
Capital: Nouakchott (pop 600,000).
Other important towns: Kaédi (22,000); Nouadhibou (23,000); Zouérate (18,000).
Land use: cultivated 0.2%; grazing 38%; wooded 15%; uncultivated 46.8%. Main agricultural products: millet, maize, dates, potatoes, rice. Other activities: livestock rearing. Mineral resources: iron ore.
Official languages: Arabic and French.
Religion: Muslim.
Gross National Product: US $ 750 million; per capita: US $ 432.
Currency: Ouguiya = 5 khoum.

MAURITIUS

Now a constitutional monarchy and member of the Commonwealth of Nations, this former British colony has been independent since 12th March 1968. Head of state is the British monarch, represented in Mauritius by a Governor General who acts in accordance with the decisions of the Council of Ministers. A single-chamber Parliament with members elected for 5 years by direct universal suffrage forms the legislature. Executive power is exercised by the Council of Ministers, which is responsible to Parliament.
Mauritius is a member of UNO and the OAU.
The country is a mountainous, volcanic island in the Mascarene Islands, north of Madagascar in the Indian Ocean. Its climate is hot and humid.
Area: 1,865 sq km.
Population: 1,008,000; mainly Asiatic Indian (65%) and half-caste (20%); density: 541 per sq km.
Annual growth rate: 0.9%; birth rate 19‰; death rate 7‰; average life expectancy: 63 years.
Capital: Port Louis (pop 145,000).
Other important towns: Quarte Bornes (65,000); Curepipe (63,000).
Land use: cultivated 58%; grazing 4%; wooded 31%; uncultivated 7%. Main agricultural products: sugar cane, vanilla, tobacco, tea, coffee.
Official language: English. A French Creole dialect is widely spoken.
Religion: Hinduism (50%); Catholic (26%); Muslim (14%).
Gross National Product: US $ 1,340 million; per capita: US $ 1,302.
Currency: Mauritius rupee = 100 cents.
Dependencies: The Rodrigues, Agalega and St Brandon Islands.

Egypt: The Temple of Abu Simbel

Kenya: A village market

MAYOTTE

Mayotte is a French territory, created following a referendum on 8th February 1976, administered by a Governor with the help of an elected Council.
The Mayotte group of islands dissociated itself from the decisions taken concerning independence by the rest of the Comoros archipelago. The Republic of the Comoros, in fact, claims sovereignty over Mayotte, which also, once, was a part of the French Overseas Territory of the Comoros.
Mayotte is at the easternmost end of the Comoros archipelago.
Area: 375 sq km.
Population: 67,000; 179 per sq km.
Administrative capital: Dzaoudzi (pop 6,000).
Main agricultural products: sugar cane, vanilla, sorghum, maize, coffee, copra.
Official language: French.
Religion: Muslim and Christian.
Currency: French franc = 100 centimes.

MOROCCO

Al-Mamlaka al-Maghrebiya

Independent since 28th March 1956, Morocco is a constitutional hereditary monarchy. The King exercises executive power through the Prime Minister and his ministers (who are answerable to both monarch and Parliament), and legislative power together with the single-chamber Parliament, whose members are elected by universal suffrage.
Morocco claims sovereignty over the towns of Ceuta and Melilla, Peñón de Vélez de la Gomera, Peñón de Alhucemas, and the Chafarinas Islands, small territories along or just off the North African coast which the Spanish government considers 'plazas de soberania', integral parts of Spanish territory. Morocco has also occupied militarily what was Western Sahara, a territory with a government in exile, and officially recognized by many nations.
Morocco is a member of UNO, the OAU, and the Arab League.
The country faces the Atlantic to the west, and the Mediterranean to the north. It can be divided into three geographical areas: the Sahara Desert to the south, the steppe-like Atlas Mountains, and the long, fertile coastal strip.
Area: 458,730 sq km, not including former Western Sahara, whose annexation by Morocco is contested by many countries.
Population: 23,200,000; mainly Arab and Berber; density: 50 per sq km.
Annual growth rate: 2.8%; birth rate 47‰; death rate 16‰; average life expectancy: 46 years.
Capital: Rabat (pop 600,000).
Other important towns: Agadir (110,000); Casablanca (2,139,000); Fès (430,000); Kénitra (188,000); Marrakech (440,000); Meknès (320,000); Oujda (260,000); Tangier (200,000); Tétouan (200,000).
Land use: cultivated 19%; grazing 47%; wooded 12%; uncultivated 22%. Main agricultural products: wheat, barley, vegetables, citrus fruits, wine, olive oil, dates, cotton, groundnuts. Other activities: livestock rearing. Mineral resources: phosphates, iron ore, lead.
Official language: Arabic (63%). Berber (24%) and French are also widely spoken.
Religion: Muslim.
Gross National Product: US $ 14,000 million; per capita: US $ 626.
Currency: Dirham = 100 centimes.

MOZAMBIQUE

República Popular de Moçambique

Formerly a Portuguese Overseas Province, Mozambique has been a People's Republic since 25th June 1975. Under the constitution of the same date, the political and social administration of the country was assigned to the Marxist 'Frente de Libertaçao de Moçambique' (Frelimo), formed in 1962 with the merger of three political parties, and power behind the armed revolt against the Portuguese. The President of Frelimo is also President of the Republic, Mozambique's head of state. He directly exercises executive power together with his Council of Ministers. Legislative power belongs to the People's Assembly, formed entirely of Frelimo members.
Mozambique is a member of UNO and the OAU.
The country borders on the Indian Ocean, facing the Island of Madagascar. It is formed of a series of plateaux crossed by the Zambesi and lesser rivers.
Area: 799,380 sq km.
Population: 14,362,000; 90% Bantu-speaking tribes (Makua, Shona, Tonga, etc.); density: 18 per sq km.
Annual growth rate: 2.6%; birth rate 46‰; death rate 21‰; average life expectancy: 43 years.
Capital: Maputo (pop 1,007,000).
Other important towns: Beira (350,000); Lichinga (40,000); Nampula (130,000); Pemba (20,000); Quelimane (180,000); Tete (55,000); Xai-Xai (65,000).
Land use: cultivated 4%; grazing 56%; wooded 19%; uncultivated 21%. Main agricultural products: cotton, sugar cane, sorghum, rice, groundnuts, sisal, cassava, sweet potatoes, tobacco, citrus fruits, coconut; timber. Other activities: livestock rearing. Mineral resources: coal, gold, bauxite, copper, iron ore.
Official language: Portuguese. Bantu dialects are widely spoken.
Religion: Animist (48%); Catholic (14%); Muslim (16%).
Gross National Product: US $ 4,290 million; per capita: US $ 300.
Currency: Metical = 100 centavos.

NAMIBIA

This parliamentary republic came into being on 21st March 1990. Previously known as South-West Africa, the territory belonged to Germany until the First World War. In December 1920, the League of Nations assigned it to the then Union of South Africa. At the end of the Second World War, the United Nations confirmed this mandate but then revoked it on 26th October 1966, and took Namibia under direct UN control. The following year, the United Nations set up a special commission whose task was to administer the territory until the right conditions for independence existed. On independence, South-West Africa would take the name Namibia, a denomination officially recognized by UNO with the resolution of the General Assembly of 12th June 1968. The Republic of South Africa, which considered South-West Africa as de facto South African territory, refused to accept the UN move. Following the independence of Angola and Mozambique, however, the government in Pretoria agreed to take part in a conference, which opened in Windhoek on 1st September 1975, on the future of Namibia. The Windhoek conference favoured tribal divisions, with eleven different black delegations representing the various ethno-cultural groups, but no representative of SWAPO (South-West African People's Organization), considered the only legitimate representative both by UNO and by neighbouring African states. South Africa thus hoped to perpetuate its position of authority over Namibia under a new formula, with a federal state and a multi-racial government in which whites played a dominant role. After lengthy negotiations, independence was finally declared on 21st March 1990.
Head of state is the President of the Republic, elected for 5 years, after which he may stand for a second term. With his government, the President exercises executive power. The Government is answerable to the single-chamber National Assembly. This, the legislature, has 72 deputies, directly elected for 5 years, and a maximum of 6 members appointed by the President in recognition of their services to the Republic.
The country is situated in south-western Africa and is almost totally desert, both towards the coast and on the inland plateau.
Area: 824,300 sq km.
Population: 1,000,000; mainly Bantu-speaking tribes (Herero, Ovambo, Damara, Okavango etc.), also Hottentot, Bushmen and Mulatto; density: 1 per sq km.
Annual growth rate: 2.4%; birth rate 44‰; death rate 17‰.
Capital: Windhoek (pop 115,000).
Other important towns: Keetmanshoop (14,000); Tsumeb (12,000).
Land use: cultivated 0.8%; grazing 64%; wooded 22%; uncultivated 13.2%. Main agricultural products: maize, millet, sorghum. Mineral resources: diamonds, zinc, lead, copper, tin.
Official languages: English, Afrikaans and German. Various Bantu and Hottentot dialects are also spoken.
Religion: Animist (68%); Christian (32%).
Gross National Product: US $ 1,420 million; per capita: US $ 1.410.
Currency: South African rand = 100 cents.

Libya: The Roman theatre of Leptis Magna, east of Tripoli

Kenya: A view of Mount Kenya

NIGER

République du Niger

Formerly a French colony, now a presidential republic, Niger has been independent since 3rd August 1960. According to the constitution approved on 24th September 1989, the President of the Republic, elected by direct universal suffrage for a 7-year term, holds direct executive power. The legislative power is devolved to a single-chamber Parliament whose 93 members are elected every 5 years by direct universal suffrage from the only lawful political party, the Progressive Party of Niger.
Niger is a member of UNO and the OAU.
Niger lies inland, and is mainly desert in the Saharan regions between the Hoggar and Tibesti mountains and Lake Chad. The only real vegetation is to be found in the south-west, an area crossed by the River Niger.
Area: 1,186,000 sq km.
Population: 7,250,000; mainly Hausa (53%); Djerma-Songhay (24%); Fulani (11%); Manga (9%), and Tuareg (3%); density: 6 per sq km.
Annual growth rate: 3%; birth rate 51‰; death rate 23‰; average life expectancy: 41 years.
Capital: Niamey (pop 400,000).
Other important towns: Agadez (21,000); Maradi (40,000); Tahoua (30,000); Zinder (60,000).
Land use: cultivated 2.8%; grazing 7.2%; wooded 2%; uncultivated 88%. Main agricultural products: groundnuts, sugar cane, dates, cotton, vegetables. Other activities: livestock rearing.
Official language: French. Kanuri, Tuareg, Fulani, Hausa, and Songhay-Djerma are all considered national languages.
Religion: Muslim (90%); Animist (10%).
Gross National Product: US $ 2,000 million; per capita: US $ 300.
Currency: CFA franc = 100 centimes.

NIGERIA

Federal Republic of Nigeria

Formerly a British colony and protectorate, Nigeria is now a federal republic and member of the Commonwealth of Nations.
Independent since 1st October 1960, and a republic since 1st October 1963, the federation is formed of 21 states. The President of the Republic, elected by direct suffrage every 4 years, was also head of government and, as such, exercised executive power. Parliament, the legislative organ, had two chambers, a Senate and a House of Representatives, both elected by universal suffrage. Following the military coup of 13th December 1983, the President was deposed, the Parliament dissolved and the constitution suspended. Since then the power has been in the hands of a military junta.
Nigeria is a member of UNO and the OAU.
The country, facing the Gulf of Guinea, is mostly flat with some higher land between the valleys of the Niger and its tributary, the Benue.
Area: 923,800 sq km divided into 21 states and a federal territory in which the capital is situated.
Population: 112,260,000; mainly Hausa (20%); Yoruba (20%); Ibo (17%); Tuareg and Fulani; density: 121 per sq km.
Annual growth rate: 3.4%; birth rate 50‰; death rate 20‰; average life expectancy: 49 years.
Capital: Lagos (pop 1,250,000). The new capital, Abuja, is under construction.
Other important towns: Abeokuta (350,000); Benin City (187,000); Enugu (260,000); Ibadan (1,170,000); Ilorin (390,000); Iwo (296,000); Kaduna (280,000); Kano (552,000); Maiduguri (262,000); Ogbomosho (598,000); Oshogbo (390,000); Port Harcourt (336,000); Zaria (311,000).
Land use: cultivated 34%; grazing 23%; wooded 17%; uncultivated 26%. Main agricultural products: cocoa, sugar cane, tobacco, cotton, groundnuts, soya bean; timber. Other activities: fishing, livestock rearing. Mineral resources: oil.
Official language: English. Hausa, Yoruba, Ibo, and other dialects are widely spoken.
Religion: Muslim (46%); Christian (38%); Animist.
Gross National Product: US $ 40,000 million; per capita: US $ 350.
Currency: Naira = 100 kobo.

RÉUNION

La Réunion

Réunion is a French Overseas Department, governed by a Prefect and an elected General Council, and represented in the French Parliament by 2 senators and 3 deputies.
It lies in the Indian Ocean, east of Mada-

Morocco: A nomad camp

gascar, in the Mascarene Islands.
Area: 2,510 sq km.
Population: 525,000; 199 per sq km.
Annual growth rate: 1.7%; birth rate 22.3‰; death rate 6‰.
Administrative capital: Saint-Denis (pop 109,000).
Other important towns: Saint-Louis (30,000); Saint-Paul (58,000); Saint-Pierre (50,000).
Land use: cultivated 22%; grazing 4%; wooded 35%; uncultivated 39%. Main agricultural products: sugar cane, coffee, bananas, tobacco, tea.
Official language: French. French Creole is widely spoken.
Religion: Catholic. Hindu minority.
Currency: French franc = 100 centimes.

RWANDA

République Rwandaise/Republika y'u Rwanda
Formerly part of the territory of Rwanda-Urundi, placed, by the United Nations, under Belgian trusteeship, Rwanda has been an independent presidential republic since 1st July 1962. Under the constitution of December 1978, the President of the Republic, who is also Prime Minister, is elected by direct universal suffrage and exercises executive power with the help of the ministers he appoints. Legislative power is held by a single-chamber Parliament whose members all represent the National Revolutionary Movement for Development.
Rwanda is a member of UNO and the OAU.
It is a small inland nation in central Africa, lying on a plateau between Lake Kivu and the Kagera river.
Area: 26,300 sq km.
Population: 5,660,000; mainly Hutu (90%); also Tutsi (9%) and Pigmy; density: 215 per sq km.
Annual growth rate: 3.4%; birth rate 50‰; death rate 19‰; average life expectancy: 44 years.
Capital: Kigali (pop 180,000).
Other important towns: Butare (26,000); Gisenye (15,000); Ruhengeri (17,000).
Land use: cultivated 43%; grazing 15%; wooded 19%; uncultivated 23%. Main agricultural products: cereals, sweet potatoes, potatoes, tea, tobacco, cassava, vegetables, coffee, groundnuts. Mineral resources: tin ore.
Official languages: French and Kinyarwanda. Swahili is also spoken.
Religion: Animist (40%); Catholic (36%); Protestant (12%); Muslim (9%).
Gross National Product: US $ 1,640 million; per capita: US $ 260.
Currency: Rwanda franc = 100 centimes.

SAINT HELENA

St Helena is a British colony, under the administration of a Governor assisted by an Executive Council and a Legislative Council, both of which are formed largely of elected members.
Saint Helena is a small volcanic island in the middle of the South Atlantic.
Area: 420 sq km, including the islands of Ascension and Tristan da Cunha.
Population: 7,000; mainly Black African and Mulatto; 16 per sq km.
Administrative capital: Jamestown (pop 1,400).
Official language: English.
Religion: Protestant.
Currency: UK £ sterling = 100 pence.
Dependencies: Ascension, Tristan da Cunha.

SÃO TOMÉ AND PRÍNCIPE

República Democratica de São Tomé e Príncipe
São Tomé and Príncipe was a Portuguese colony from 1522 until June 1951, when it acquired autonomy as a Portuguese Overseas Province. On 12th July 1975 it became an independent People's Republic. Under the 1975 constitution, the supreme organ of state is the People's Assembly, whose members are elected for 4 years by direct universal suffrage and all represent the Marxist-oriented São Tomé and Príncipe Liberation Movement. The Assembly has legislative power, while executive power is held by a Prime Minister and his ministers. Head of state is the President of the Republic, who is elected for 4 years by the People's Assembly. The São Tomé and Príncipe Liberation Movement guides the nation's politics.
São Tomé and Príncipe is a member of UNO and the OAU.
The country is formed of two islands in the Gulf of Guinea. The southern tip of the largest of these, São Tomé, touches the Equator.
Area: 965 sq km.
Population: 117,000; mainly Black African and Mulatto; 121 per sq km.
Annual growth rate: 2.9%; birth rate: 42‰; death rate 10‰.
Capital: São Tomé (pop 35,000).
Land use: cultivated 38%. Main agricultural products: cocoa, coffee, copra, coconut oil, cassava.
Official language: Portuguese. Portuguese Creole also spoken.
Religion: Catholic. Animist minority.
Currency: Dobra = 100 centimos.

SENEGAL

République du Sénégal
Formerly a French colony, Senegal has been an independent presidential republic since 11th September 1960. The legislature is a single-chamber Parliament with members elected every 5 years by direct universal suffrage. The President of the Republic, also elected every 5 years by direct universal suffrage, holds executive power. Since 1st February 1982, Senegal and Gambia have been united in the Confederation of Senegambia, both retaining, however, their own international juridical status.
Senegal is a member of UNO and the OAU.
The country is predominantly flat and covered by steppe, savanna and forest. It faces the Atlantic, and the Senegal River runs along its northern border.
Area: 197,000 sq km.
Population: 7,188,000; mainly Wolof (41%); Serer (15%); Fulani (12%); Toucouleur (11%); Malinka etc.; density: 36 per sq km.
Annual growth rate: 2.9%; birth rate 47‰; death rate 23‰; average life expectancy: 43 years.
Capital: Dakar (pop 1,382,000).
Other important towns: Kaolack (127,000); Rufisque (125,000); Thiès (150,000).
Land use: cultivated 27%; grazing 30%; wooded 30% uncultivated 13%. Main agricultural products: groundnuts, cotton, millet, cassava, rice, maize, sweet potatoes, citrus fruits. Other activities: fishing. Mineral resources: phosphates.
Official language: French. Wolof is the national language.
Religion: Muslim (85%); Catholic (5%); Animist.
Gross National Product: US $ 3,140 million; per capita: US $ 470.
Currency: CFA franc = 100 centimes.

Morocco: The Great Atlas Mountains

Morocco: Marrakech

SEYCHELLES

République des Seychelles/Repiblik Sesel
Colonised by France until 1814, and then by Britain, the Seychelles have been an independent presidential republic and member of the Commonwealth of Nations since 28th June 1976. In accordance with the constitution of June 1979, executive power is exercised by the President of the Republic and his ministers. Legislative power lies with the single-chamber Parliament, whose members are elected by direct universal suffrage, and all represent the Marxist-oriented Seychelles People's Progressive Front.
The Seychelles is a member of UNO and the OAU.
The country is formed of a group of islands, the biggest of which is Mahé, north-east of Madagascar.
Area: 453 sq km, including the Amirante Islands, the Cosmoledo Islands, and other small groups of islands.
Population: 67,000; mainly Black African, Mulatto; 148 per sq km.
Annual growth rate: 0.8%; birth rate 25.4‰; death rate 7‰: average life expectancy: 65 years.
Capital: Victoria (pop 25,000) on the island of Mahé.
Land use: Main agricultural products: copra, coconuts vanilla, tea, cinnamon. Mineral resources: phosphates.
Official language: French Creole.
Religion: Catholic.
Gross National Product: US $ 196 million; per capita: US $ 2,920.
Currency: Seychelles rupee = 100 cents.

SIERRA LEONE

This independent presidential republic (independent since 27th April 1961, a republic since 19th April 1971) was formerly a British colony and protectorate, and remains a member of the Commonwealth of Nations. Legislative power lies with the single-chamber Parliament, whose members, all representing the People's Congress Party, are, for the most part, elected every 5 years by direct universal suffrage. Executive power is held by the President of the Republic, who is elected every 5 years by the Parliament.
Sierra Leone is a member of UNO and the OAU.
The country faces the Atlantic, and has a jagged coastline backed by an inland plateau.
Area: 71,700 sq km.
Population: 3,820,000; 49 per sq km.
Annual growth rate: 1.9%; birth rate 46‰;

death rate 21‰; average life expectancy: 44 years.
Capital: Freetown (pop 470,000).
Land use: cultivated 25%; grazing 31%; wooded 29%; uncultivated 15%. Main agricultural products: rice, coffee, cocoa, copra, maize, cassava, barley, potatoes. Mineral resources: iron ore, diamonds, bauxite.
Official language: English. Sudanese dialects including Mende (33%); Temne (25%); and Limba (8%).
Religion: Animist (51%); Muslim (39%); Catholic and Protestant.
Gross National Product: US $ 1,140 million; per capita: US $ 300.
Currency: Leone = 100 cents.

SOMALIA

Jamhuuriyadda Soomaaliya
Somalia has been a presidential People's Republic since 1st July 1960, when Italian-administered Somalia was united with the former British protectorate of Somaliland. The parliamentary regime established by the constitution of July 1960 was overthrown in the military coup of 21st October 1969, which brought to power the Marxist-oriented Supreme Council of the Somali Revolution. On 1st July 1976, full powers were transferred to the Central Committee of the Somali Revolutionary Socialist Party (the country's only lawful party), whose President was both head of state and head of government. Under the constitution approved in 1979, there was a single-chamber Parliament, formed entirely of members of the Revolutionary Socialist Party, which constituted the legislature. In early 1991 a civil war overthrew the military dictatorship.
Somalia is a member of UNO and the OAU.
The country occupies the easternmost tip of the African continent. The rough uplands of the north slope down to a series of arid plains in the south.
Area: 637,700 sq km.
Population: 5,075,000; mainly Somali (95%); 8 per sq km.
Annual growth rate: 2.8%; birth rate 47‰; death rate 22‰; average life expectancy: 44 years.
Capital: Mogadishu (pop 500,000).
Other important towns: Afgoi (18,000); Berbera (65,000); Hargeysa (70,000); Kismaayo (18,000); Johar (18,000); Merca (60,000).
Land use: cultivated 1.5%; grazing 45%; wooded 14%; uncultivated 39.5%. Main agricultural products: sorghum, maize, sesame, dates, bananas, groundnuts, cassava, cotton, citrus fruits, timber. Other activities: livestock rearing.
Official language: Somali.
Religion: Muslim.
Gross National Product: US $ 850 million; per capita: US $ 270.
Currency: Somali shilling = 100 cents.

SOUTH AFRICA

Republic of South Africa/Republiek van Suid-Afrika
South Africa left the British Commonwealth in 1910, and was known as the Union of South Africa until 1961. Since 31st May 1961, it has been a federal republic formed of the four provinces: Cape Province, Natal, Transvaal and the Orange Free State. Head of state is the President of the Republic, elected for a 7-year term by the Parliament. He exercises executive power through the Prime Minister and other ministers and is aided by the President's Council. The ministers are ap-

pointed by the President but must have the approval of Parliament.
Under the Constitution approved on 2nd November 1983, the Parliament has three chambers, elected by Whites (178 members), Coloureds (85) and Asians (45). Each chamber is autonomous for decisions concerning its own community; general issues must be approved by the three chambers.
As part of the Government's former policy of racial segregation, autonomous Bantu Homelands, or Bantustans, have been created.
These are reserved for tribal groups of the Black population, and are under the direct control of the Department of Bantu Administration and Development. Four of them, Transkei, Bophuthatswana, Venda and Ciskei, have already obtained from the South African government a special form of independence. There are plans to extend this status to the other homelands — KwaZulu, Lebowa, Gazankulu, KaNgwane, QwaQwa (formerly Basotho-Qwaqwa), and Ndebele — over the next few years.
South Africa is a member of UNO.
Most of the country lies on a vast plateau corresponding largely to the basin of the Orange River, which rises in the Drakensberg mountains. South Africa occupies the southern tip of the continent, between the two oceans. The south-east coast has many natural harbours. The climate is temperate, with low rainfall.
Area: 1,150,000 sq km, including the four federal Provinces and the Bantu Homelands.
Population: 29,690,000; Blacks (68%); Whites (19%); Coloureds and Asians from India and Pakistan; density: 26 per sq km.
Annual growth rate: 2.6%; birth rate 38‰; death rate 12‰; average life expectancy: 65 years for Whites, 48 years for Blacks.
Capital: legislative - Cape Town (pop 1,910,000), administrative - Pretoria (pop 822,000).
Other important towns: Bloemfontein (230,000); Durban (980,000); East London (190,000); Johannesburg (1,610,000); Kimberley (150,000); Port Elizabeth (651,000); Vereeniging (540,000).
Land use: cultivated 11%; grazing 66%; wooded 4%; uncultivated 19%. Main agricultural products: citrus fruits, wine, maize, pineapples, barley, oats, rye, potatoes, tobacco, groundnuts, cotton, vegetables, fruit. Other activities: fishing, livestock rearing. Mineral resources: gold, diamonds, uranium, silver, asbestos, copper, iron ore, manganese.
Official languages: Afrikaans and English. Many Bantu dialects.
Religion: Predominantly Christian.
Gross National Product: US $ 58,100 million; per capita: US $ 1,750.
Currency: Rand = 100 cents.
Dependencies: the four new, nominally independent states of Bophuthatswana, Ciskei, Transkei and Venda, and the Marion and the Prince Edward Islands in the Indian Ocean.

Bophuthatswana

Designated a Bantustan (Bantu Homeland) in 1971, it has been a nominally independent republic since 6th December 1977. Under the constitution of December 1977, legislative power is exercised by a single-chamber Parliament, with half the members elected by direct universal suffrage, and the other half appointed from among the most influential tribal leaders. Executive power is held by a Government which is answerable to the Parliament.

South Africa: Cape Town

Bophuthatswana is not recognised by the United Nations, nor by any African organization outside South Africa.
It is a large territory in the northern part of the southern African plateau.
Area: 40,330 sq km.
Population: 2,000,000; 99% of the population is Tswana; density: 50 per sq km.
Annual growth rate 3%.
Capital: Mmabatho (pop 10,000).
Other important towns: Mafikeng (240,000).
Land use: Main agricultural products: vegetables, cereals, fruit. Mineral resources: diamonds, vanadium, platinum.
Official language: Tswana.
Religion: Protestant.
Currency: Rand = 100 cents.

Ciskei

Previously a Bantustan, Ciskei has been a nominally independent republic since 4th December 1981. A partially elected Parliament holds legislative power.
Ciskei is not recognised by the United Nations, nor by any African organization outside South Africa.
It is a small territory, south of the River Kei, to the south-east of the South African plateau.
Area: 12,075 sq km.
Population: 950,000; mainly Xhosa; 79 per sq km.
Capital: Bisho (pop 3,000).
Other important towns: Mdantsana (243,000).
Land use: Main agricultural products: vegetables, fruit, cereals.
Official language: Xhosa. English and Afrikaans are also spoken.
Religion: Protestant.
Currency: Rand = 100 cents.

Transkei

Designated a Bantustan in 1963, Transkei has been a nominally independent republic since 26th October 1976. The constitution of October 1976 gives legislative power to a single-chamber Parliament, half of whose members are elected for 5 years by direct universal suffrage of citizens over the age of 25, and the other half appointed from among tribal leaders. Since 30th December 1987 the power has been in the hands of a military junta which has suspended the constitution and dissolved the Parliament.
Transkei is not recognised by the United Nations, nor by any African organization outside South Africa.
It is situated south-east of the Drakensberg mountains, facing the Indian Ocean.
Area: 41,600 sq km.
Population: 2,890,000; mainly Xhosa and Coloureds; 70 per sq km.
Annual growth rate: 2.1%.
Capital: Umtata (pop 50,000).
Land use: Main agricultural products: maize, vegetables, fruit. Other activities: cattle rearing.
Official language: Xhosa. English and Afrikaans are also spoken.
Religion: Protestant.
Currency: Rand = 100 cents.

Venda

Designated a Bantustan in 1973, Venda has been a nominally independent republic since 13th September 1979. A partially elected single-chamber Parliament holds legislative power. The President of the Republic has direct executive power. Venda is not recognised by the United Nations, nor by any African organization outside South Africa.
It is a small territory inside the eastern part of South Africa.
Area: 7 310 sq km.
Population: 550,000; mainly Venda (90%); 63 per sq km.
Annual growth rate: 3.2%.
Capital: Thohoyandou (pop 10,200).
Land use: Main agricultural products: tea, fruit, vegetables.
Official language: CiVenda. English and Afrikaans are also spoken.
Religion: Protestant.
Currency: Rand = 100 cents.

SUDAN

Jumhuriyat ed-Dimuqratiyah es-Sudan

This presidential People's Republic fell under Anglo-Egyptian control after 1899, finally becoming fully independent on 1st January 1956. The 1973 constitution gave executive power to the President of the Republic, who was nominated by the country's only lawful political party, the Sudan Socialist Union, and who chose his own ministers. The single-chamber People's Assembly formed the legislature. Half of its members were elected for 4 years by direct universal suffrage, and represented the Sudan Socialist Union. Following the military coup of 30th June 1989, power passed to the Council of the Revolution whose President is also head of state and of the government.
Sudan is a member of UNO, the OAU, and the Arab League.
Sudan, the largest nation in Africa, borders on the Red Sea. It occupies the vast depression between the Nubian Mountains and the volcanic Jebel Marra range. It is crossed by the Nile and its tributaries. The southern, equatorial region has vast swamps; the central parts are savanna and grassland; and the rest is desert.
Area: 2,510,000 sq km.
Population: 26,250,000; mainly Arab (50%); Nilotic (30%), and Nubian (10%); density: 10 per sq km.
Annual growth rate: 3.8%; birth rate 46‰; death rate 20‰; average life expectancy: 47 years.
Capital: Khartoum (pop 650,000).
Other important towns: Kassala (100,000); Khartoum North (340,000); Omdurman (526,000); Port Sudan (200,000); Wadi Medani (140,000).
Land use: cultivated 7%; grazing 26%; wooded 19%; uncultivated 48%. Main agricultural products: cotton, sugar cane, groundnuts, sorghum, wheat, sesame, dates, bananas, citrus fruits. Other activities: livestock rearing. Mineral resources: chromite, copper, iron ore.
Official language: Arabic. Sudanese and Nilotic dialects widely spoken.
Religion: Animist and Muslim.
Gross National Product: US $ 7,280 million; per capita: US $ 323.
Currency: Sudanese pound = 100 piastre.

SWAZILAND

Swaziland is a monarchy, independent since 6th September 1968, and a member of the Commonwealth of Nations. Formerly a British protectorate, it gained autonomy on 24th April 1967. Under the 1968 constitution, the King holds executive power, and exercises it through the Prime Minister and other ministers. Although these are royal appointments, they are answerable to the two-chamber Parliament. Most members of the Parliament are elected.
Swaziland is a member of UNO, and the OAU.
Swaziland is small nation, occupying a strip of the southern African plateau where it slopes down northwards towards Mozambique.
Area: 17,400 sq km.
Population: 716,000; mainly Swazi (90%); 41 per sq km.
Annual growth rate: 3.2%; birth rate 48‰; death rate 21‰; average life expectancy: 44 years.
Capital: Mbabane (pop 39,000); there are plans to transfer the capital to Lobamba.
Other important towns: Manzini (28,000).
Land use: cultivated 10%; grazing 67%; wooded 6%; uncultivated 17%. Main agricultural products: sugar cane, cotton, tobacco, pineapples, citrus fruits; timber. Other activities: livestock rearing. Mineral resources: asbestos, coal.
Official languages: Swazi and English.
Religion: Protestant and Animist.
Gross National Product: US $ 455 million; per capita: US $ 580.
Currency: Lilangeni = 100 cents.

TANZANIA

Jamhuri ya Mwungano wa Tanzania

Tanzania is a presidential, federal republic, formed on 25th April 1964, through the union of Tanganyika and Zanzibar.
Tanganyika had been a British colony until 9th December 1961, and Zanzibar had been a British protectorate until 10th December 1963. Tanzania has remained a member of the Commonwealth. Both Tanganyika and Zanzibar had been separate members of the Commonwealth after independence. Tanganyika then became a republic on 9th December 1962, and Zanzibar on 12th January 1964.
Tanzania has a single-chamber Parliament. Two thirds of the members are elected by direct universal suffrage from the Tanganyika African National Union, in Tanganyika, and from the Afro-Shirazi Party in Zanzibar. The rest are appointed by the President of the Republic and regional bodies. The President of the Republic, as head of government, holds executive power. He is elected for 5 years by direct universal suffrage, and appoints the various ministers and two vice-presidents. One of these two holds executive power in Zanzibar, with the title of President of Zanzibar, while the other is the leader of Parliament. The islands of Zanzibar and Pemba have considerable administrative and legislative autonomy.
Tanzania is a member of UNO and the OAU.
The country comprises a huge, forested plateau between Lake Victoria and Lake Tanganyika, an often swampy coastal plain, and the islands of Zanzibar and Pemba in the Indian Ocean.
Area: 945,000 sq km in two federal states, Tanganyika and Zanzibar.
Population: 23,990,000; predominantly Black Africans (70%); also Indians and Arabs; density: 25 per sq km.
Annual growth rate: 3.4%; birth rate 33‰; death rate 10‰; average life expectancy: 52 years.
Capital: Dodoma (pop 140,000), although the de facto capital is still Dar es Salaam.
Other important towns: Arusha (55,000); Dar

Morocco: Fès, the old city

Tunisia: The Roman amphitheatre of El Djem

Zimbabwe: The Victoria Falls

es Salaam (760,000); Mbeya (77,000); Moshi (55,000); Mwanza (110,000); Tanga (105,000); Zanzibar (70,000).
Land use: cultivated 6%; grazing 37%; wooded 45%; uncultivated 12%. Main agricultural products: sisal, cotton, groundnuts, coffee, pineapples, copra, sesame, tobacco, bananas, cloves; timber. Other activities: livestock rearing. Mineral resources: gold.
Official language: Swahili. Various Bantu dialects.
Religion: Animist (40%); Muslim (30%); Hindu and Christian.
Gross National Product: US $ 4,400 million; per capita: US $ 200.
Currency: Tanzanian shilling = 100 cents.

TOGO
République Togolaise

Togo is a presidential republic, independent since 27th April 1960, and previously entrusted to French administration by the United Nations. Under the constitution, approved on 30th December 1979, the head of state is the President of the Republic. He appoints and presides over the Government. The legislature is the single-chamber Parliament, whose members all represent the Togolese People's Union.
Togo is a member of UNO and the OAU.
The country is a narrow strip running north to south on the Gulf of Guinea. There are low-lying areas to the north and south, and a plateau in between.
Area: 56,000 sq km.
Population: 2,900,000; Ewe, Kabré tribes; 52 per sq km.
Annual growth rate: 4.1%; birth rate 49‰; death rate 21‰; average life expectancy: 47 years.
Capital: Lomé (pop 400,000).
Other important towns: Atakpamé (27,000); Kpalimé (27,000); Sokodé (48,000).
Land use: cultivated 25%; grazing 4%; wooded 24%; uncultivated 47%. Main agricultural products: cocoa, coffee, palm nuts and palm oil, cotton, groundnuts, citrus fruits, maize, bananas. Mineral resources: phosphates, iron ore.
Official language: French. Sudanese dialects are widely spoken.
Religion: Animist (64%); Catholic (20%); Muslim (11%); Protestant (5%).
Gross National Product: US $ 940 million; per capita: US $ 300.
Currency: CFA franc = 100 centimes.

TUNISIA
Al-Jumhuriya at-Tunusiya

This presidential republic, formerly a French protectorate, has been independent since 20th March 1956, and a republic since 25th July 1957. A single-chamber Parliament constitutes the legislature. Its members are elected every 5 years by direct universal suffrage from the country's only lawful party, the 'Destourien' Socialist Party. Head of state is the President of the Republic, also elected every 5 years by direct universal suffrage. He is also head of government, and appoints the ministers with whom he exercises executive power.
Tunisia is a member of UNO, the OAU, and the Arab League.
The country lies on the Mediterranean, at the northern tip of the continent. In the north, the flattish coast has many coves and inlets;

inland it is hilly and rugged, and the climate is temperate. Towards the centre it is lower, and, in the south, there is flat, desert terrain.
Area: 163,000 sq km.
Population: 7,640,000; mainly Arab or Berber; 49 per sq km.
Annual growth rate: 2.9%; birth rate 37‰; death rate 13‰; average life expectancy: 58 years.
Capital: Tunis (pop 600,000).
Other important towns: Bizerte (94,000); Gabès (92,000); Gafsa (60,000); Qairouan (72,000) Sfax (230,000); Sousse (83,000).
Land use: cultivated 29%; grazing 19%; wooded 3%; uncultivated 49%. Main agricultural products: wheat, barley, olive oil, wine, dates, tobacco, beet, fruit, vegetables. Other activities: fishing, livestock rearing. Mineral resources: oil, phosphates, iron ore.
Official language: Arabic.
Religion: Muslim.
Gross National Product: US $ 8,540 million; per capita: US $ 868.
Currency: Tunisian dinar = 1,000 millimes.

UGANDA
Jamhuri ya Uganda

Independent since 19th October 1962, and a republic since 19th October 1963, Uganda had been a British protectorate since 1894, and remains a member of the Commonwealth of Nations. Executive power is exercised directly by the President of the Republic, who is leader of the majority party. A single-chamber Parliament, partly elected by direct universal suffrage, forms the legislature.
Uganda is a member of UNO and the OAU.
It is an inland nation, situated on a savanna-covered plateau between Lakes Albert and Victoria, and the Ruwenzori and Elgon mountains. The Equator crosses the southern part of the country.
Area: 236,000 sq km.
Population: 13,200,000; mainly Bantu-speaking tribes; then Sudanese, Nilotic and Hamitic peoples; 56 per sq km.
Annual growth rate: 3% birth rate 45‰; death rate 16‰; average life expectancy: 54 years.
Capital: Kampala (pop 460,000).
Other important towns: Entebbe (22,000); Jinja (55,000); Mbale (25,000).
Land use: cultivated 28%; grazing 21%; wooded 24%; uncultivated 27%. Main agricultural products: cotton, coffee, sesame, tea, groundnuts, sugar cane, cassava, maize; timber. Other activities: livestock rearing. Mineral resources: copper.
Official languages: English and Swahili. Bantu and Nilotic dialects.
Religion: Animist (40%); Catholic (28%); Protestant (20%); Muslim (6%).
Gross National Product: US $ 3,000 million; per capita: US $ 200.
Currency: Ugandan shilling = 100 cents.

ZAIRE
République du Zaïre

Formerly the Belgian colony of Belgian Congo, Zaire is now a unitary presidential republic, independent since 30th June 1960. Under the 1979 constitution, head of state is the President of the Republic, and by right, President of the Mouvement Populaire de la Revolution (MPR), the only legally recognized

Zimbabwe/Zambia: The Kariba Dam

The Zimbabwe ancient ruins

party. He is elected for 7 years by direct universal suffrage, and can be re-elected once only. He exercises executive power together with the National Executive Council. The National Legislative Council, presided over by the President, holds legislative power. Its members are elected for 5 years by direct universal suffrage, and all represent the MPR. Zaire is a member of UNO and the OAU.
This enormous nation coincides with much of the Congo River basin, a vast depression surrounded by tablelands. About half of Zaire is covered in equatorial forest. To the west, a narrow corridor gives Zaire access to the Atlantic Ocean.
Area: 2,350,000 sq km.
Population: 29,600,000; mostly Bantu-speaking tribes (65%); then Sudanese, Nilotic, Hamitic and Pigmy peoples; 12 per sq km.
Annual growth rate: 2.3%; birth rate 47‰; death rate 21‰; average life expectancy: 47 years.
Capital: Kinshasa (pop 2,700,000).
Other important towns: Bukavu (180,000); Kananga (600,000); Kikwit (150,000); Kisangani (300,000); Likasi (148,000); Lubumbashi (405,000); Matadi (145,000); Mbandaka (135,000); Mbuji-Mayi (335,000).
Land use: cultivated 3%; grazing 4%; wooded 75%; uncultivated 18%. Main agricultural products: groundnuts, sugar cane, citrus fruits, coffee, cocoa, maize, cassava, sweet potatoes, rice, pineapples. Mineral resources: diamonds, copper, gold, cobalt, manganese, silver, uranium and zinc.
Official language: French. Bantu, Hamitic, Nilotic and Sudanese dialects.
Religion: Animist (45%); Catholic (45%); Protestant (8%); Muslim (2%).
Gross National Product: US $ 5,600 million; per capita: US $ 180.
Currency: Zaire = 100 makuta.

ZAMBIA

Formerly the British protectorate of Northern Rhodesia, Zambia gained autonomy on 1st January 1964, and independence on 24th October 1964. It is now a presidential republic and member of the Commonwealth of Nations. The legislature is a single-chamber Parliament whose members are elected for 5 years by direct universal suffrage, and all represent the United National Independence Party. Head of state, and head of government, is the President of the Republic, who is also elected every 5 years by direct universal suffrage. He exercises executive power together with the vice-president and the ministers he, as head of government, appoints.
Zambia is a member of UNO and the OAU.
Situated inland in central southern tropical Africa, Zambia is formed of a series of plateaux and depressions which constitute the watershed between the Congo and the Zambesi basins.
Area: 752,600 sq km.
Population: 7,270,000; mainly Bantu-speaking tribes (Tonga, Bamba, Ngoni, Lozi etc.), with some Bushman minorities; density: 9 per sq km.
Annual growth rate: 3.5%; birth rate 50‰; death rate 19‰; average life expectancy: 46 years.
Capital: Lusaka (pop 870,000).
Other important towns: Chingola (185,000); Kabwe (120,000); Kitwe (390,000) Luanshya (140,000); Livingstone (Maramba 60,000); Mufulira (160,000); Ndola (280,000).
Land use: cultivated 7%; grazing 46%; wooded 39%; uncultivated 8%. Main agricultural pro-

ducts: maize, groundnuts, cassava, sweet potatoes, cotton, tobacco. Mineral resources: copper, cobalt, lead, zinc.
Official language: English. Bantu dialects also widely spoken.
Religion: Animist (70%); Catholic (20%); Protestant (10%).
Gross National Product: US $ 1,500 million; per capita: US $ 215.
Currency: Kwacha = 100 ngwee.

ZIMBABWE

On 11th November 1965, the politically dominant White minority of the British colony of Southern Rhodesia announced a unilateral declaration of independence, giving the country the name Republic of Rhodesia. Under the multi-racial constitution of 1st June 1979, the country became the Republic of Zimbabwe. It was again a British colony between 11th December 1979 and 18th April 1980, at which time it officially became an independent state, and a member of the Commonwealth of Nations. Head of the government is the President of the Republic who is elected every 5 years by direct universal suffrage. Government, the executive branch, is responsible to the House of Representatives, the legislative branch, also elected by direct universal suffrage.
Zimbabwe is a member of UNO and the OAU.
The country lies just to the north of South Africa, on an inland plateau which slopes towards the Zambesi to the north, and the Limpopo to the south.
Area: 390,580 sq km.
Population: 7,400,000; mainly Bantu-speaking tribes; 19 per sq km.
Annual growth rate: 2.8%; birth rate 48‰; death rate 15‰; average life expectancy: 55 years.
Capital: Harare (pop 660,000).
Other important towns: Bulawayo (400,000); Chinhoyi (30,000); Gweru (80,000); Hwange (35,000); Mutare (75,000); Nyanda (25,000).
Land use: cultivated 7%; grazing 13%; wooded 51%; uncultivated 29%. Main agricultural products: cotton, tobacco, citrus fruits, groundnuts, tea, maize, sugar cane, bananas. Other activities: livestock rearing. Mineral resources: asbestos, chrome, gold, coal, iron ore.
Official language: English. Bantu dialects also spoken.
Religion: Animist (60%); Christian (20%); Muslim.
Gross National Product: US $ 5,300 million; per capita: US $ 600.
Currency: Zimbabwe dollar = 100 cents.

North America

At first glance, the two continental masses of the Americas present numerous similarities: their roughly triangular shape, a vast mountain range of Tertiary origin which stretches along the western side of the continents, climate variation ranging from polar to tropical, a population mainly descendant from European settlers who subjugated the indigenous peoples. A closer examination, however, reveals marked differences between the two Americas. Weather similarity, for example, is only apparent. The North American continent lies almost completely above the Tropic of Cancer, and is consequently dominated by cold and temperate climates. However, the two Americas can be more precisely distinguished in terms of their anthropological and economic features. The northern populations are prevalently of Western European descent and, thanks to intensive industrialisation, have achieved high levels of prosperity. Nevertheless, in the North there continue to be serious social problems. Three regions in the North American continent can be easily distinguished. They correspond to the political division of the three large countries which almost completely occupy the relative land areas.

The northern region, excluding Greenland and the broad Alaskan peninsula, is taken up by Canada. With a land surface of almost 10 million square kilometres, in area it ranks second in the world. Its 26 million inhabitants, concentrated along a narrow southern strip, enjoy a high standard of living thanks to the country's huge agricultural and mineral wealth. These are the elements which characterise this large northern country. The climate in the northernmost regions, with temperatures falling well below zero Celsius, accounts for their being sparsely populated. These very areas, which from a geological standpoint are very ancient, have proved extremely rich in useful minerals such as zinc, uranium, platinum, nickel, iron, copper, not to mention their oil resources which make Canada self-sufficient in terms of energy. The country also has an enormous hydroelectric potential.

North America's central region belongs to the United States of America, which, in terms of natural resources, can consider itself a privileged country. If we exclude Alaska and Hawaii, the United States' total land surface lies in the temperate zone, which explains why there are very few areas which are not settled. There are vast and fertile plains in almost every part of the nation. The United States is bordered by two oceans and has a closely-woven river network which enhances soil fertility. The country's subsoil is rich in raw materials. White colonisation of this part of America, largely from the British Isles but with high percentages of settlers from numerous other European areas, has supplanted the Native American Indian population. Furthermore, it has been able to maximise its human and natural resources to the utmost, turning the country into the world's most developed economy. Its agriculture, which employs only 2.5% of the working population, is undoubtedly the world's most advanced, thanks to intensive mechanisation and to the use of chemical fertilisers. The country's mineral resources (particularly coal, oil, iron, uranium) are huge, and all its industrial sectors are greatly developed. This picture is not without its dark side: the country's wealth is distributed unequally, and minority integration, especially of Blacks but also of Puerto Ricans and Indians, has yet to become a reality.

From south of the Rio Grande in the North to the isthmus of Panama, the continent's southern region narrows to a strip of land no wider than 80 km, facing westward towards an uninterrupted bridge of islands. Geologically, these territories are of recent formation, as is evinced by the numerous volcanoes and the disastrous earthquakes which periodically shake these areas. The climate, which is either hot and humid or torrid, is ill-suited to human settlement. Only in limited areas, like Mexico's *Tierras templadas*, is the climate influenced by altitude and consequently more temperate. Because of certain physical characteristics such as their tropical climate, and anthropological ones, for example Spanish colonisation, together with current levels of socio-economic development, Mexico, and countries of both the isthmus and the Antilles, should perhaps be categorised as Latin American rather than integrally North American. Political instability and socio-economic underdevelopment are the most marked features of almost all these countries. To an often unfavourable natural environment, as well as to historic reasons, have to be added very high rates of population growth, an agriculture conditioned by a lack of local capital and modern technology, poor industrial development, and high levels of foreign interference. Only in recent times has genuine progress been recorded, especially in Mexico, which has abundant mineral and energy resources.

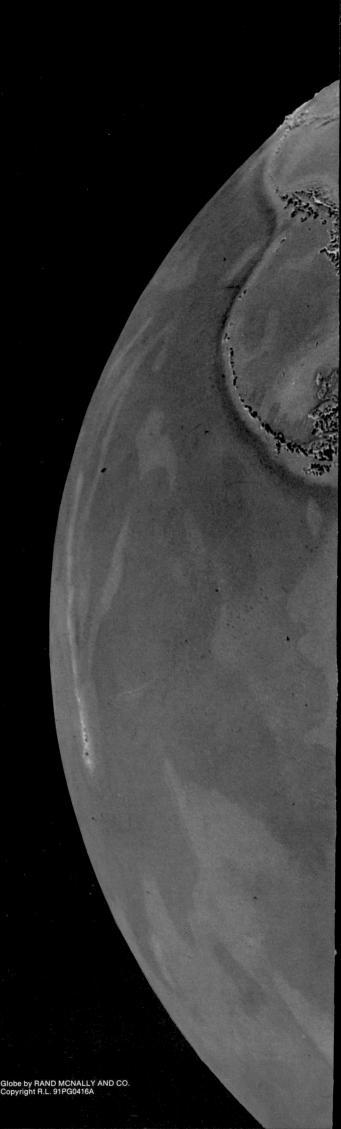

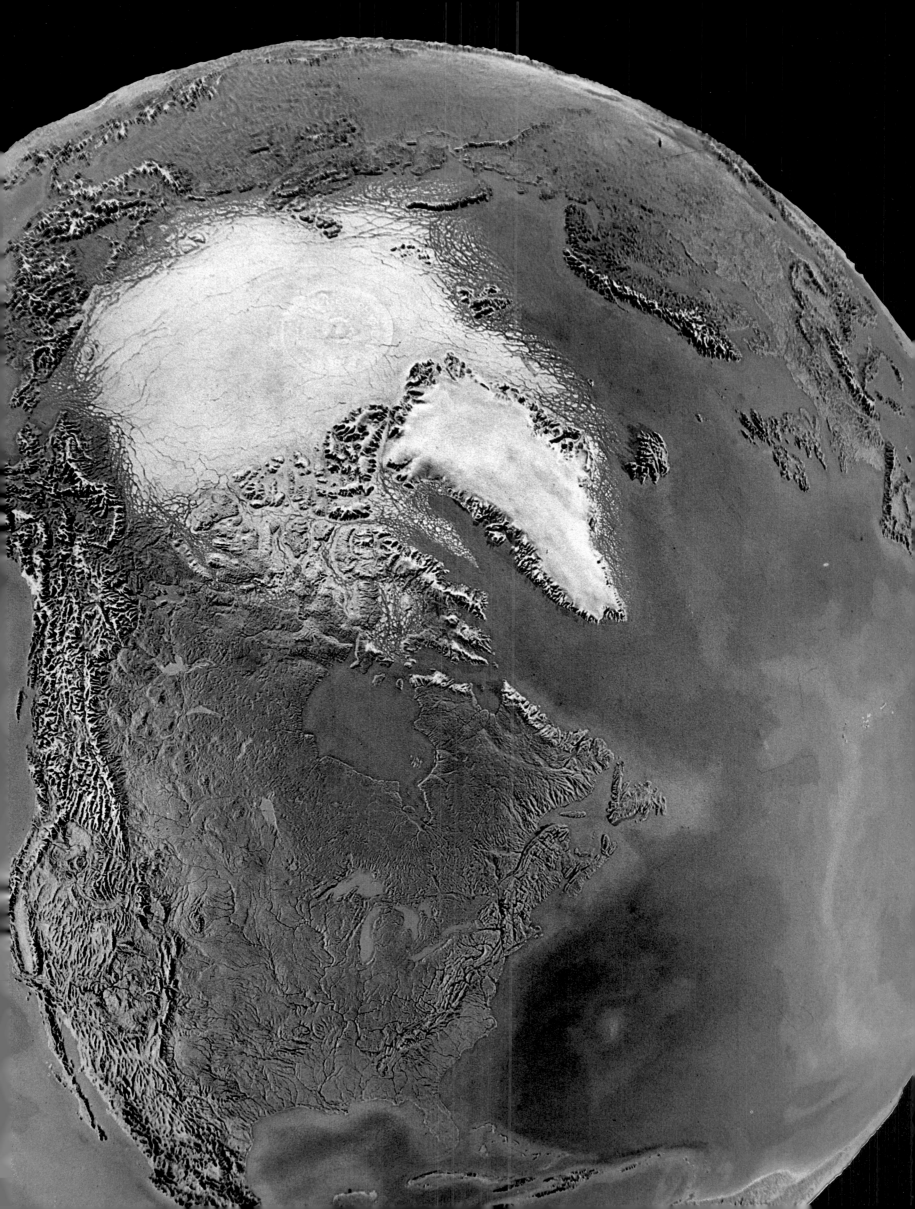

Canada: A coniferous forest

ANGUILLA

Anguilla is a dependent colony located on the island bearing the same name in the Leeward Islands archipelago of the Lesser Antilles.

Anguilla was part of the former British colony of Saint Christopher (or Saint Kitts)-Nevis, and went the way of the other islands, becoming an associate state of Great Britain on 27th February 1967, but seceded from Britain on 17th June of the same year, unilaterally declaring its independence. But, after direct intervention by British troops, the island accepted the status of British dependency, with partial autonomy in internal affairs. On the strength of its 1967 constitution, the British Sovereign is represented by a Commissioner, aided by an elected assembly in charge of defence, foreign affairs and security matters.

Area: 96 sq km.
Population: 6,500; mostly of African descent; 71 per sq km.
Capital: The Valley.
Main agricultural products: fruit, vegetables.
Official language: English.
Religion: Protestant.
Currency: East Caribbean dollar = 100 cents.

ANTIGUA AND BARBUDA

An independent state since 1st November 1981 within the Commonwealth of Nations, Antigua and Barbuda was formerly a British colony and later (since 27th February 1967) an associate state of Great Britain. The head of state is the British Sovereign, represented by a Governor. Legislative power is entrusted to a unicameral Parliament, and the executive

Canada: Niagara Falls

to the Government, which answers to the Parliament.

The state of Antigua and Barbuda is a UNO and OAS member.

Its territory is made up of islands of the same name in the Leeward Islands group, 60 km north of the island of Guadeloupe, and also includes the island of Redonda.

Area: 440 sq km, of which 280 sq km constitute the island of Antigua.
Population: 83,000, mainly people of African descent (95%) and Mulattos (3.5%); density: 170 per sq km.
Annual growth rate: 1.3%; birth rate 20‰; death rate 7‰; average life expectancy: 62 years.
Capital: Saint John's (pop 30,000).
Land use: cultivated 18%; grazing 7%; wooded 16%; uncultivated 59%. Main agricultural products: cotton, vegetables, fruit.
Official language: English.
Religion: Christian.
Currency: East Caribbean dollar = 100 cents.

BAHAMAS

The Commonwealth of the Bahamas

An independent state since 10th July 1973, and a member of the Commonwealth of Nations, the Bahamas' head of state is the British Sovereign, who delegates power to a Governor General. The latter exercises executive power together with the Council of Ministers, which is answerable to the Parliament. Legislative power is entrusted to the Parliament, which consists of two houses: the Senate, whose members are appointed by the Governor General, and a Chamber of Deputies, who are elected to a 5-year term by direct universal suffrage.

The Bahamas is a member of UNO and the OAS.

The territory comprises a coral reef archipelago consisting of 700 islands and islets, and countless rocks extending for over 1,000 km to the north of Cuba, and which are renowned for their mild climate. Among the major islands: New Providence, Grand Bahama, Eleuthera, Andros, Great Abaco.

Area: 13,935 sq km.
Population: 240,000; people of African descent and Mulattos (85%); White (15%); 17 per sq km.
Annual growth rate: 3.6%; birth rate 22‰; death rate 5‰; average life expectancy: 69 years.
Capital: Nassau (pop 135,000).
Land use: cultivated 1.6%; grazing 1%; wooded 31%; uncultivated 66%. Main agricultural products: vegetables, fruit, sugar cane, pineapples, citrus fruit.
Official language: English.
Religion: Christian.
Gross National Product: US $ 1,650 million; per capita: US $ 7,000.
Currency: Bahamian dollar = 100 cents.

BARBADOS

Barbados has been an independent state within the Commonwealth of Nations since 30th November 1966. The head of state is the British Sovereign who delegates power to a Governor General. The latter appoints the Prime Minister and the ministers, who exercise executive power. Legislative power is in the purview of the two houses of Parliament: the Chamber of Deputies, who are elected to a 5-year term by direct universal suffrage, and the Senate, whose members are appointed by the Governor General.

Barbados is a member of UNO and the OAS.

The territory consists of one of the Windward Islands of the Lesser Antilles. It is slightly hilly, and very fertile because of volcanic ash wafted by the wind.

Area: 430 sq km.
Population: 250,000, mostly people of African descent (92%) and the rest Mulattos and Whites; 580 per sq km.
Annual growth rate: 0.6%; birth rate 16‰; death rate 8‰; average life expectancy: 71 years.
Capital: Bridgetown (pop 7,600).
Land use: cultivated 77%; grazing 9%; uncultivated 14%. Main agricultural products: sugar cane, maize, sweet potatoes, rice, cassava, bananas.
Official language: English.
Religion: Anglican (70%).
Gross National Product: US $ 1,300 million; per capita: US $ 5,000.
Currency: Barbadian dollar = 100 cents.

BELIZE

Belize was a former British colonial dependency under the name of British Honduras

Canada/United States: The Great Lakes

until 1973. Administratively autonomous since 1st January 1964, Belize is now an independent state (since 21st September 1981) within the Commonwealth. The head of state is the British Sovereign, represented by a Governor General. Executive power is exercised by the Government, the legislative by the two houses of Parliament: the Chamber of Deputies, who are elected by direct universal suffrage, and the Senate, whose members are appointed by the Governor General. The Government is answerable to the Chamber of Deputies.

Belize is a member of UNO.

Its small, flat and uniform territory faces the Caribbean Sea in the south-eastern sector of the Yucatán peninsula in Central America. Approximately half of the country is covered by equatorial forest.

Area: 22,965 sq km.
Population: 166,500; people of African descent (40%); Mulattos (33%); Amerindians (7%); 7 per sq km.
Annual growth rate: 2.5%; birth rate: 39‰; death rate 6‰.
Capital: Belmopan (pop 5,000).
Other important towns: Belize City (45,000); Orange Walk (9,000); Stan Creek (7,000).
Land use: cultivated 4%; grazing 2%; wooded 44%; uncultivated 50%. Main agricultural products: sugar cane, maize, rice, citrus fruits, bananas, vegetables.
Official language: English.
Religion: Christian.
Gross National Product: US $ 170 million; per capita: US $ 1,020.
Currency: Belize dollar = 100 cents.

BERMUDA ISLANDS

A British colony since 1684, Bermuda is now partly autonomous. It is ruled by a Governor, who exercises his authority by means of an Executive Council and a bicameral Parliament. The latter consists of an Assembly, whose members are elected by direct universal suffrage, and of a Legislative Council, which is appointed by the Governor.

The country is a coral-reef archipelago situated in the Atlantic Ocean, about 1,000 km south-east of New York. It is made up of approximately 360 islets, of which Great Bermuda is the largest.

Area: 55 sq km.
Population: 60,000, mainly Mulattos; 1 per sq km.
Annual growth rate: 0.8%; birth rate 15.5‰; death rate 7.2‰.
Capital: Hamilton (pop 1,700).
Main agricultural products: vegetables, fruit, cotton, tobacco, castor oil.
Official language: English.
Religion: Christian.
Gross National Product: US $ 660 million; per capita: US $ 11,050.
Currency: Bermuda dollar = 100 cents.

BRITISH VIRGIN ISLANDS

The British Virgin Islands is a British colony, ruled by a Governor who is aided in the exercise of his duties by an Executive Council and by a unicameral Parliament, which is partly elective.

The territory consists of the archipelago east of the American Virgin Islands and is made up of 36 islands and numerous rocks, of which only 13 are inhabited. The largest is Tortola.

Area: 155 sq km.
Population: 12,000, mainly people of African descent (66%) and Mulattos (33%); density: 78 per sq km.

Canada: Toronto

Annual growth rate: 2.9%; birth rate 22‰; death rate 7‰; average life expectancy: 53 years.
Capital: Road Town (pop 4,000).
Land use: cultivated 20%; grazing 33%; wooded 7%; uncultivated 40%. Main agricultural products: sugar cane, vegetables, fruit.
Official language: English.
Religion: Protestant.
Currency: US dollar = 100 cents.

CANADA

A federal state and a member of the Commonwealth of Nations, Canada consists of the following federal units (provinces): Newfoundland, Prince Edward Island, Nova Scotia, New Brunswick, Quebec, Ontario, Manitoba, Saskatchewan, Alberta, British Columbia; and of two territories: the Yukon and Northwest Territories. Both the federal units and the territories each have their own executive and legislative bodies. The head of state is the British Sovereign, who delegates authority to a Governor General elected to a 5-year term. Within the federal ambit, legislative power is exercised by the two houses of Parliament: the House of Commons, elected every five years by direct universal suffrage, and the Senate, whose members are appointed by the Governor General as designated by the Prime Minister. Senate members remain in office until the age of 75. The Prime Minister and the Council of Ministers, who are answerable to the Parliament, have executive power.
Canada is a member of UNO, the OECD, the OAS and NATO.
Its territory, which ranks second in the world in terms of surface area, extends almost entirely north of the 49th parallel, and has a generally cold climate. It is rich in lakes and rivers; its coastline is very jagged and dotted with offshore islands. There are five natural regions: to the east the Appalachian Mountains, which have been greatly levelled by erosion; to the west a mountainous region, characterised by two parallel ranges with peaks between 3,000 and 4,000 metres high and with Mount Logan (6,050 metres) as its highest peak; the inland Great Plains region; the hilly area surrounding Hudson Bay which constitutes the Canadian Shield; and lastly, the most highly populated area, the so-called Laurentian region, which is the area surrounding the Great Lakes and extending

Greenland: The port of Umanak

along the middle section of the St Lawrence River.
Area: 9,976,140 sq km, politically and administratively divided into 10 federal units (provinces) and 2 territories.
Population: 26,000,000; 2 per sq km.
Annual growth rate: 0.9%; birth rate 14.8‰; death rate 7.3‰; average life expectancy: 72 years.
Capital: Ottawa (pop 833,000).
Other important towns: Edmonton (560,000); Hamilton (560,000); Montreal (2,940,000); Quebec (607,000); Toronto (3,500,000); Vancouver (1,400,000); Winnipeg (630,000).
Land use: cultivated 4.5%; grazing 3%; wooded 35%; uncultivated 57.5%. Main agricultural products: wheat, barley, oats, potatoes, sugar beet, tobacco, vegetables, fruit; timber. Other activities: fishing, livestock rearing. Mineral resources: coal, oil, nickel, asbestos, uranium, gold, silver, lead, zinc.
Official languages: English and French.
Religions: Catholic (47%) and Protestant (41%).
Gross National Product: US $ 359,000 million; per capita: US $ 14,400.
Currency: Canadian dollar = 100 cents.

CAYMAN ISLANDS

Previously a dependency of the former British colony of Jamaica (which gained independence on 6th August 1962 within the Commonwealth), the Cayman Islands group is now a British colony.
The British Sovereign is represented by a Governor, aided in the exercise of his duties by a partly elected Parliament and by an Executive Council.
The country consists of the part of the Caribbean archipelago 240 km west-northwest of Jamaica. Originally a coral reef, the islands are famous for their sea turtles.
Area: 260 sq km.
Population: 23,400; mostly people of African descent and Mulattos; 90 per sq km.
Annual growth rate: 4.7%; birth rate 17‰; death rate 6‰.
Capital: Georgetown (pop 9,000).
Land use: grazing 8%; wooded 23%. Main agricultural products: cereals, vegetables, fruit. Other activities: fishing.
Official language: English.
Religion: Christian.
Currency: Cayman Islands dollar = 100 cents.

COSTA RICA

República de Costa Rica

A presidential republic, Costa Rica has been independent since 1821. Legislative power is exercised by a unicameral Parliament (Congresso Constitucional), whose members are elected to a 4-year term by direct universal suffrage. The President of the Republic, who is also the head of government, is elected to a 4-year term in office and exercises executive power with the help of ministers whom he appoints.
Costa Rica is a member of UNO, the OAS and the OCAS.
Situated on the Central American isthmus, the country is bordered by both the Pacific and Atlantic Oceans. Its coastlines are flat, hot and humid; while its inland areas are mountainous and have a temperate climate.
Area: 51,100 sq km.
Population: 2,820,000 mainly Whites (80%); followed by Mestizo (15%); people of African descent and Mulattos (4%); Amerindians; 55 per sq km.
Annual growth rate: 2.5%; birth rate 29‰; death rate 4‰; average life expectancy: 70 years.
Capital: San José (pop 280,000).
Other important towns: Alajuela (30,000); Heredia (21,000); Limón (34,000); Puntarenas (30,000).
Land use: cultivated 10%; grazing 45%; wooded 32%; uncultivated 13%. Main agricultural products: rice, sugar cane, maize, coffee, bananas, citrus fruit.
Official language: Spanish.
Religion: Catholic.
Gross National Product: US $ 3,750 million; per capita: US $ 1,410.
Currency: Colón = 100 céntimos.

CUBA

República de Cuba

A Socialist republic, Cuba's constitution, which came into force in 1976, states that the Communist Party has the role of "guiding power of society and state". Legislative

power is in the hands of the National Assembly of Democratic Power, whose members are elected to a 5-year term by the Municipal Assemblies from a single list of candidates drafted by the Communist Party, the only party which is legally recognised. The National Assembly in turn elects the State Council, whose President is also the head of state and of the Council of Ministers. This latter political body has executive power. Cuba claims possession of the island of Navassa (5 sq km) from the United States. Situated between the islands of Jamaica and Hispaniola (or Haiti), the small island of Navassa has a lighthouse and a radiotelegraphy station. It is part of the territory of Guantánamo Bay (111 sq km), and was leased by Cuba in 1903 to the United States, which has an important air and naval base there.
Cuba is both a UNO and Comecon member.
The largest island in the Greater Antilles group, Cuba is situated south of the Tropic of Cancer, is mountainous in the northeastern part of the island and hilly elsewhere, except along the low-lying northern coastline.
Area: 110,920 sq km.
Population: 10,420,000 mainly Whites (70%); then Mulattos (18%) and people of African descent (12%); density: 92 per sq km.
Annual growth rate: 1%; birth rate 15‰; death rate 6‰; average life expectancy: 72 years.
Capital: Havana (pop 2,000,000).
Other important towns: Camagüey (250,000); Holguín (185,000); Matanzas (100,000); Pinar del Rio (118,000); Santa Clara (175,000); Santiago de Cuba (400,000).
Land use: cultivated 30%; grazing 25%; wooded 25%; uncultivated 20%. Main agricultural products: sugar cane, rice, potatoes, tobacco, maize, sweet potatoes.
Official language: Spanish.
Religion: Catholic.
Gross National Product: US $ 11,500 million; per capita: US $ 1,100.
Currency: Cuban peso = 100 centavos.

DOMINICA

Formerly a British colony and later an associate state of Great Britain (since 1st March 1967), Dominica is at present an independent republic within the Commonwealth of Nations (since 3rd November 1978). Executive power is exercised by the Prime Minister and the Government, both answerable to a unicameral Parliament. The latter, elected by direct popular vote, exercises legislative power.
Dominica is both a UNO and OAS member.
The country consists of a mountainous island (which bears the same name) located between Guadeloupe and Martinique, in the Windward Islands group.
Area: 750 sq km.
Population: 87,800, mainly people of African descent (89%) and Mulattos; 116 per sq km.
Annual growth rate: 1.7%; birth rate 21‰; death rate 5‰; average life expectancy: 58 years.
Capital: Roseau (pop 10,000).
Land use: cultivated 23%; grazing 3%; wooded 41%; uncultivated 33%. Main agricultural products: bananas, coconuts, copra, sugar cane, citrus fruit, rice.
Official language: English.
Religion: Christian.
Currency: East Caribbean dollar = 100 cents.

Mexico: The gigantic Tula sculptures

DOMINICAN REPUBLIC

República Dominicana

The Dominican Republic's head of state is the President of the Republic, who is also the head of government. As such, he exercises executive power with the help of ministers whom he appoints. He is elected to a 4-year term in office by direct universal suffrage. Legislative power is exercised by a two-chamber Parliament (Congreso Nacional), consisting of the Senate and the Chamber of Deputies, whose members are elected to a 4-year term by direct universal suffrage.
The Dominican Republic is both a UNO and OAS member.
The country takes up the eastern part of Hispaniola island in the Greater Antilles. It has a rolling land surface, which rises to 3,000 metres, where the climate becomes temperate.
Area: 48,735 sq km.
Population: 6,860,000, mainly Mulattos (60%), then Whites (28%) and people of African descent (11%); density: 141 per sq km.
Annual growth rate: 2.9%; birth rate 42‰; death rate 11‰; average life expectancy: 61 years.
Capital: Santo Domingo (pop 1,410,000).
Other important towns: Barahona (55,000); San Francisco de Macoris (60,000); Santiago de lo Caballeros (210,000); San Pedro de Macoris (65,000).
Land use: cultivated 30%; grazing 43%; wooded 13%; uncultivated 14%. Main agricultural products: sugar cane, bananas, rice, cassava, copra, coffee, cocoa, tobacco; timber. Mineral resources: nickel, gold, silver.
Official language: Spanish.
Religion: Catholic.
Gross National Product: US $ 4,950 million; per capita: US $ 750.
Currency: Dominican peso = 100 centavos.

EL SALVADOR

República de El Salvador

A presidential republic, El Salvador has been independent since 1821. Following the mili-

Mexico: Chichen Itza

Mexico: El Tajin, Zapotec civilisation

tary coup of 18th October 1979, power was taken over by a military junta, which fostered the election of a constituent assembly.
El Salvador is a member of UNO, the OAS and the OCAS.
The country is a tableland suited for tropical crops. It is the smallest of the Central American isthmus countries, and the only one which has solely a Pacific coastline.
Area: 21,041 sq km.
Population: 5,107,000 mainly Mestizos (70%); Amerindians (18%) and Whites (10%); density: 249 per sq km.
Annual growth rate: 1.5%; birth rate 37‰; death rate 10‰; average life expectancy: 63 years.
Capital: San Salvador (pop 500,000).
Other important towns: Nueva San Salvador (52,000); San Miguel (86,000); Santa Ana (135,000).
Land use: cultivated 34%; grazing 29%; wooded 5%; uncultivated 32%. Main agricultural products: sugar cane, maize, cotton, coffee, citrus fruits, bananas.
Official language: Spanish.
Religion: Catholic.
Gross National Product: US $ 3,840 million; per capita: US $ 790.
Currency: Colón = 100 centavos.

GREENLAND
Grønland / Kalaallit Nunaat

Greenland remains a dependent territory of Denmark, but was earlier a Danish county from 5th June 1953, becoming autonomous on 1st May 1979, with its own executive and legislative bodies. Matters of foreign policy and defence are the responsibility of the Copenhagen government. Since 27th April 1951 a territorial defence agreement has been in effect between Denmark and the United States, the latter having had military bases there (such as the one in Thule) since 1941, when Denmark was under German occupation.
The territory consists of the world's largest island, situated between the Arctic and the Atlantic oceans. At least 85% of its area consists of frozen tableland. Only the western coastline, which is warmed by the Gulf Stream, is inhabited.
Area: 2,175,600 sq km, of which only about 341,700 sq km are not covered by glaciers.
Population: 54,600; 0.2 per sq km. Eskimos make up 82% of the population, Europeans 18%.

Annual growth rate: 0.9%.
Capital: Godthåb/Nuuk (pop 11,600).
Official language: Danish; the Eskimos have their own languages.
Religion: Animist and Protestant.
Gross National Product: US $ 430 million; per capita: US $ 8,290.
Currency: Danish krone = 100 øre.

GRENADA

Grenada, an independent state since 7th February 1974, is a Commonwealth member, consisting of the island bearing the same name and of the Southern Grenadines. Formerly a British colony in the Windward Islands group, it became an associate state on 3rd March 1967, with full autonomy in internal affairs. According to the constitution, the head of state is the British Sovereign, who is represented by a Governor General. Legislative power is exercised by a bicameral Parliament, composed of a Chamber of Deputies, elected by direct universal suffrage, and of the Senate, whose members are appointed by the Governor General. Executive power is exercised by the Governor, who is answerable to the Parliament. Following the 13th May 1979 coup, the power was in the hands of the United Movement for social welfare, education and liberation, until the intervention of the USA, on 25th December 1983.
Grenada is a UNO and OAS member.
Its territory, located in the Windward Islands group 150 km north of Trinidad, is mountainous and largely covered with forests.
Area: 345 sq km.
Population: 106,000 mainly people of African descent (53%); and Mulattos (42%); density: 291 per sq km.
Annual growth rate: 0.4%; birth rate 23‰; death rate 7‰; average life expectancy: 69 years.
Capital: Saint George's (pop 8,000).
Land use: cultivated 41%; grazing 6%; wooded 12%; uncultivated 41%. Main agricultural products: bananas, coconuts, sugar cane, cocoa, citrus fruits, cotton.
Official language: English.
Religion: Christian.
Currency: East Caribbean dollar = 100 cents.

GUADELOUPE

Guadeloupe is an Overseas Department of the Republic of France, governed by a Prefect aided by an elected General Council. Guadeloupe is represented in the French Parliament by 2 senators and 4 deputies.
It consists of two adjacent islands, Grande Terre and Basse Terre, which together make up Guadeloupe, and of the Maria Galante, Les Saintes, La Désirade, Saint-Barthélemy islands, and part of Saint-Martin (Sint Maarten in Dutch; the other part of the island belongs to the Netherlands Antilles), which are its dependencies.
Area: 1,704 sq km, including the dependencies.
Population: 328,000, prevalently people of African descent and Mulattos (over 85%); 192 per sq km.
Annual growth rate: 0.5%; birth rate 19‰; death rate 7‰; average life expectancy: 68 years.
Capital: Basse Terre (pop 17,000).
Other important towns: Pointe-à-Pitre (25,000).
Land use: cultivated 25%; grazing 18%; wooded 40%; uncultivated 17%. Main agricultural products: sugar cane, bananas, coffee, cocoa, coconuts, vanilla, fruit.
Official language: French. French Creole is often spoken.
Religion: Catholic.
Currency: French franc = 100 centimes.

GUATEMALA
República de Guatemala

Guatemala is a presidential republic, independent since 1821. By the constitution approved in 1986, legislative power is entrusted to a unicameral Parliament (Congreso), whose members are elected to a 5-year term by direct universal suffrage. Executive power is in the hands of the President of the Republic, in his capacity as head of government, together with his appointed ministers. The President remains in office for five years and is elected by direct universal suffrage. Guatemala claims the territory of Belize, in as much as it was formerly a part of the ancient Capitania del Guatemala when it was under Spanish rule.

United States: The Statue of Liberty

Guatemala is a UNO, OAS and OCAS member.
Its territory, situated on the Central American isthmus, is bordered by both oceans, and its central area is mountainous.
Area: 108,890 sq km.
Population: 8,680,000, mainly Amerindians (55%) and Mestizos (30%); 77 per sq km.
Annual growth rate: 2.9%; birth rate 36‰; death rate 9.5‰; average life expectancy: 59 years.
Capital: Guatemala (pop 1,300,000).
Other important towns: Antigua (20,000); Escuintla (35,000); Mazatenango (40,000); Quetzaltenango (65,000).
Land use: cultivated 17%; grazing 13%; wooded 37%; uncultivated 33%. Main agricultural products: sugar cane, maize, sorghum, grain, bananas, cotton, coffee, sesame, potatoes, beans. Mineral resources: nickel.
Official language: Spanish.
Religion: Catholic.
Gross National Product: US $ 7,280 million; per capita: US $ 900.
Currency: Quetzal = 100 centavos.

HAITI
République d'Haïti

Haiti is a presidential republic, whose President is elected for life by direct universal suffrage. As head of government, the President of the Republic directly exercises executive power with the help of ministers whom he personally appoints. Legislative power is exercised by the National Assembly, whose members are elected to a 6-year term by direct universal suffrage from a single list of candidates drawn up by the Single Party of Revolutionary and Government Action. Since the expulsion of J.C. Duvalier, in 1986, a series of military coups have followed one upon the other, and a new constitution was approved on 29th March 1987.
Haiti is a UNO and OAS member.
The country occupies the western part of the island bearing the same name (also called Hispaniola), in the Greater Antilles. Its territory is the most mountainous of all the archipelago islands; its hot and humid climate

makes for tropical-type vegetation.
Area: 27,750 sq km.
Population: 5,550,000, mainly people of African descent (90%) and Mulattos (9%); 200 per sq km.
Annual growth rate: 1.3%; birth rate 43‰; death rate 17‰; average life expectancy: 53 years.
Capital: Port-au-Prince (pop 750,000).
Other important towns: Cap-Haïtien (65,000); Gonaïves (35,000); Les Cayes (34,000).
Land use: cultivated 32%; grazing 19%; wooded 2%; uncultivated 47%. Main agricultural products: sugar cane, bananas, coffee, sisal, mangoes, maize, cassava, rice, sweet potatoes.
Official language: French.
Religion: Catholic.
Gross National Product: US $ 2,130 million; per capita: US $ 350.
Currency: Gourde = 100 centimes.

HONDURAS
República de Honduras

Honduras is a presidential republic. According to its 1982 constitution, legislative power is administered by a unicameral Parliament (Congreso Nacional), whose members are elected to a 4-year term by direct universal suffrage. Executive power is exercised by the President of the Republic, who is also head of government, and is elected to a 4-year term by direct universal suffrage.
Honduras is a member of UNO, the OAS and the OCAS.
The country's territory lies on the Central American isthmus. Mainly a mountainous country, it is covered with tropical forest.
Area: 112,090 sq km.
Population: 4,800,000, mainly Mestizos (90%), people of African descent (5%), and Amerindians (4%); 39 per sq km.
Annual growth rate: 3.3%; birth rate 41‰; death rate 8‰; average life expectancy: 58 years.
Capital: Tegucigalpa (pop 640,000).
Other important towns: La Ceiba (65,000); Puerto Cortés (42,000); San Pedro Sula (398,000).
Land use: cultivated 16%; grazing 23%; wooded 31%; uncultivated 30%. Main agricultural products: sugar cane, bananas, coffee, coconuts, cotton, tobacco, pineapples, maize, citrus fruits, rice, timber. Mineral resources: lead, zinc, silver.
Official language: Spanish.
Religion: Catholic.
Gross National Product: US $ 3,410 million; per capita: US $ 750.
Currency: Lempira = 100 centavos.

JAMAICA

Jamaica has been an independent state since 6th August 1962 within the Commonwealth of Nations. Head of state is the Sovereign of Great Britain and Northern Ireland, who delegates power to a Governor General. The latter appoints the Prime Minister and the ministers, who exercise executive power. Legislative power is administered by a bicameral Parliament, made up of a Chamber of Deputies, who are elected to a 5-year term by direct universal suffrage, and of the Senate, consisting of members appointed by the Governor General.
Jamaica is a UNO and OAS member.
The country consists of a large island (Jamaica) in the Greater Antilles, which is

Panama: The Panama Canal

United States: The Golden Gate Bridge, San Francisco

United States: Grand Teton mountain

mountainous in the centre and flat along the coastline.
Area: 10,990 sq km.
Population: 2,350,000 mainly people of African descent (76%); followed by Mulattos (15%); Indians, Pakistanis and Chinese; density: 213 per sq km.
Annual growth rate: 1.4%; birth rate 23‰; death rate 5.7‰; average life expectancy: 71 years.
Capital: Kingston (pop 615,000).
Other important towns: May Pen (27,000); Montego Bay (45,000); Spanish Town (40,000).
Land use: cultivated 24%; grazing 19%; wooded 17%; uncultivated 40%. Main agricultural products: sugar cane, bananas, coconut, maize, rice, cassava, sweet potatoes.
Official language: English.
Religion: Protestant. Rastafarian minority.
Gross National Product: US $ 1,970 million; per capita: US $ 870.
Currency: Jamaican dollar = 100 cents.

MARTINIQUE

An Overseas Department of the Republic of France, governed by a Prefect assisted in the exercise of his duties by an elective General Council, Martinique is represented in the French Parliament by 2 senators and 4 deputies.
Martinique occupies the island bearing the same name, of volcanic origin, in the Windward Island group. It is known for its rum and for a disastrous eruption of Mt Pelé.
Area: 1,100 sq km.
Population: 335,000, mainly people of African descent and Mulattos (90%); 296 per sq km.
Annual growth rate: 0.4%; birth rate 19‰; death rate 7‰; average life expectancy: 68 years.
Capital: Fort-de-France (pop 150,000).
Other important towns: Lamentin (25,000); Sainte-Marie (20,000).
Land use: cultivated 18%; grazing 31%; wooded 26%; uncultivated 25%. Main agricultural products: sugar cane, bananas, pineapples, coconuts, sweet potatoes, coffee.
Official language: French.
Religion: Catholic.
Gross National Product: US $ 1,510 million; per capita: US $ 4,640.
Currency: Martinique franc = 100 centimes.

MEXICO

Estados Unidos Mexicanos

Mexico comprises a presidential and federal republic, made up of a Federal District, where the capital is located, and of the following federal states: Aguascalientes, Baja California Norte, Baja California Sur, Campeche, Chiapas, Chihuahua, Coahuila, Colima, Durango, Guanajuato, Guerrero, Hidalgo, Jalisco, México, Michoacán, Morelos, Nayarit, Nuevo León, Oaxaca, Puebla, Querétaro, Quintana Roo, San Luis Potosí, Sinaloa, Sonora, Tabasco, Tamaulipas, Tlaxcala, Veracruz, Yucatán, Zacatecas, each with its own executive and legislative bodies. At the federal level, legislative power is administered by a bicameral Parliament (Congreso de la Unión), composed of a Chamber of Deputies and a Senate, whose members are elected by direct universal suffrage to 3- and 6- year terms respectively. Senate members represent the individual federal states and the Federal District. The President of the Republic, who is also elected to a 6-year term by direct universal suffrage (but is not re-eligible), is also head of government and there-

fore directly exercises executive power with aid of ministers whom he personally appoints. Mexico is a member of UNO, the OAS and ALALC.
Its territory consists of two mountain ranges: the "sierras" which enclose the arid inland tablelands and join in the south in the Southern Sierra Madre, which is dotted from east to west with volcanoes reaching up to 6,000 metres. The long, arid California Peninsula is surrounded by the Pacific, while the broad, flat Yucatán Peninsula extends south-westward between the Gulf of Mexico and the Caribbean Sea. Both are sparsely populated.
Area: 1,972,545 sq km, politically and administratively divided into 31 federal states and 1 federal district.
Population: 82,735,000, mainly Mestizos (55%); Whites (15%); Amerindians (29%); density: 42 per sq km.
Annual growth rate: 2.0%; birth rate 42‰; death rate 9‰; average life expectancy: 66 years.
Capital: Mexico City (pop 18,750,000).
Other important towns: Acapulco de Juarez (425,000); Chihuahua (370,000); Ciudad Juárez (600,000); Cuernavaca (320,000); Guadalajara (2,345,000); León (590,000); Mérida (250,000); Mexicali (350,000); Monterrey (1,923,000); Tijuana (540,000).
Land use: cultivated 12%; grazing 39%; wooded 25%; uncultivated 24%. Main agricultural products: maize, sorghum, grain, sugar cane, citrus fruits, bananas, cotton, potatoes, coffee. Mineral resources: silver, lead, zinc, gold, iron ore, oil.
Official language: Spanish. The Amerindians speak Maya and Nahua languages.
Religion: Catholic.
Gross National Product: US $ 121,000 million; per capita: US $ 1,500.
Currency: Mexican peso = 100 centavos.

MONTSERRAT

Montserrat is a British colony which, in January 1967, preferred not to go along with the other British colonial dependencies of the Antilles and to preserve its status as a colony. The British Sovereign is represented by a Governor, who is aided in the exercise of his powers by an Executive Council and a partly elective unicameral Parliament.
The territory occupies a volcanic island of the same name in the Leeward Islands group, 50 km north of Guadeloupe.
Area: 100 sq km.
Population: 12,000, mainly people of African descent (93%) and Mulattos (6%); 119 per sq km.
Annual growth rate: 2.1%; birth rate 17‰; death rate 13‰.
Capital: Plymouth (pop 3,000).
Land use: cultivated 10%; grazing 10%; wooded 40%; uncultivated 40%. Main agricultural products: cotton, fruit, vegetables.
Official language: English.
Religion: Protestant.
Gross National Product: US $ 20 million, per capita: US $ 1,370.
Currency: East Caribbean dollar = 100 cents.

NETHERLANDS ANTILLES

Nederlandse Antillen

Constitutionally part of the Netherlands and at the same time an autonomous nation, the Netherlands Antilles recognise as their head of state the Dutch Sovereign, who delegates

United States: View of New York

power to a Governor who, together with the Prime Minister and the Ministers, constitute the Government. In matters of foreign affairs, the Government is represented, within the Council of Royal Ministers, by a Minister Plenipotentiary. Legislative powers fall within the purview of the Legislative Assembly (Staten), which is elected to a 4-year term by direct universal suffrage. The Prime Minister and the Ministers are directly answerable to this body.
The Netherlands Antilles are made up of two distinct island groups: Curaçao and Bonaire near the coast of Venezuela; and Sint Eustatius, Saba and part of Sint Maarten (in French Saint-Martin; the other part of the island is included in the French overseas department of Guadeloupe) in the Leeward Islands group. On 1st January 1986, the island of Aruba (193 sq km), which had been part of the Netherlands Antilles, gained autonomy, a first step towards independence which is scheduled to become effective on 1st January 1996.
Area: 800 sq km. (Curaçao: 444 sq km; Bonaire: 288 sq km; Sint Maarten: 34 sq km).
Population: 190,000, people of African descent (75%); Mulattos and Mestizos (20%); 244 per sq km.
Annual growth rate: 0.4%; birth rate 20‰; death rate 5‰; average life expectancy: 62 years.
Capital: Willemstad (pop 100,000).
Land use: cultivated 8%. Main agricultural products: sorghum, peanuts, sweet potatoes, vegetables, maize.
Official language: Dutch.
Religion: Christian.
Gross National Product: US $ 1,100 million; per capita: US $ 4,290.
Currency: Dutch guilder = 100 cents.

NICARAGUA

República de Nicaragua

Nicaragua is a presidential republic. Following the 1979 victory of the Sandinista Front of National Liberation (FSLN), and the end of the Somoza family "dynasty", which had ruled the country for years, all political power passed into the hands of a 5-member government junta. According to the constitution approved on 9th January 1987, the President of the Republic is also the head of the government and exercises the executive power; legislative power is exercised by the

United States: Mount Rushmore (Dakota), and the carved heads of the presidents

National Assembly elected — as well as the President of the Republic — to a 6-year term by direct universal suffrage.
Nicaragua is a member of UNO, the OAS and the OCAS.
It is the largest country of the Central American isthmus and has coastlines on two oceans. Its narrowest and most southern part includes the large Lake Nicaragua.
Area: 130,680 sq km, including inland water.
Population: 3,620,000, mainly Mestizos (70%), then Whites (14%), people of African descent (19%) and Amerindians (14%); 28 per sq km.
Annual growth rate: 3.3%; birth rate 48‰; death rate 14‰; average life expectancy: 56 years.
Capital: Managua (pop 685,000).
Other important towns: Granada (88,000); León (100,000); Masaya (75,000).
Land use: cultivated 10%; grazing 41%; wooded 28%; uncultivated 21%. Main agricultural products: maize, sorghum, rice, cotton, sugar cane, coffee, bananas. Mineral resources: gold, silver, copper.
Official language: Spanish.
Religion: Catholic.
Gross National Product: US $ 2,700 million; per capita: US $ 800.
Currency: Córdoba = 100 centavos.

PANAMA

República de Panama

Panama is a presidential republic. The President of the Republic is also the head of government, in which capacity he directly exercises executive power with the help of ministers whom he personally appoints. Legislative power is exercised by a unicameral Parliament, whose members are elected by direct universal suffrage.
Panama is a member of UNO and the OAS.
Its territory lies along the isthmus that joins Central to South America, and is divided by the Panama Canal that links the two oceans.
Area: 77,080 sq km.
Population: 2,320,000, mainly Mestizos (60%); then Whites (12%) and Amerindians (8%); 20 per sq km.
Annual growth rate: 2.1%; birth rate 24.8‰; death rate 3.8‰; average life expectancy: 70 years.
Capital: Panama City (pop 550,000).
Other important towns: Colón (70,000); David (40,000); La Chorrera (30,000).
Land use: cultivated 8%; grazing 17%; wooded 51%; uncultivated 24%. Main agricultural products: sugar cane, bananas, rice, maize, citrus fruits, coffee.
Official language: Spanish.
Religion: Catholic.
Gross National Product: US $ 4,810 million; per capita: US $ 2,160.
Currency: Balboa = 100 centésimos.

PANAMA CANAL ZONE

Canal Zone

The Canal Zone is a territory about 16 kilometres wide stretching from the Atlantic to the Pacific, which includes the Panama Canal, opened to traffic in 1914. In 1903 the Republic of Panama ceded this territory in perpetuity to the United States of America. The treaty, however, signed in Washington on 7th September 1977 by representatives of both countries, sets 31st December 1999 as the expiration date of the lease. The United States acknowledges that the Republic of Panama has full sovereignty over the territo-

United States: Bryce Canyon

ry, and that, for the duration of the treaty, it "grants the United States the right to administer, operate and efficiently maintain the Panama Canal together with its facilities and installations, to protect and defend it." Administration of the territory is entrusted by the President of the United States to a Governor, who by law is also President of the Panama Canal Company. He remains in office for approximately 4 years and resides in Balboa Heights.
The territory technically consists of a 5-mile zone on each side of the Canal.
Area: 1,430 sq km.
Population: 29,000 (including US Armed Forces); 20 per sq km.
Other important towns: Balboa (6,000); Cristóbal (20,000).
Main agricultural products: fruit and vegetables.
Official language: English.
Religion: Protestant.
Currency: US dollar = 100 cents.

PUERTO RICO
Commonwealth of Puerto Rico / Estado Libre y Asociado de Puerto Rico

Formally an independent state, Puerto Rico is an associate state of the United States of America, represented in the US Parliament by a delegate (Resident Commissioner), who lacks voting rights and is elected every 4

years. Executive power is exercised by a Governor, elected every 4 years by direct universal suffrage. Legislative power is entrusted to a bicameral Parliament, made up of a Chamber of Deputies and a Senate, whose members are also elected to a 4-year term by direct universal suffrage. Puerto Ricans have US citizenship, but cannot vote in US elections unless they reside in the United States.
The territory consists of the smallest and westernmost of the Greater Antilles islands; it has high elevations and hills suited to tropical crops.
Area: 9,103 sq km.
Population: 3,350,000, mainly Whites (80%), and the rest people of African descent and Mulattos; 377 per sq km.
Annual growth rate: 0.2%; birth rate 19.4‰; death rate 7‰; average life expectancy: 72 years.
Capital: San Juan (pop 850,000).
Other important towns: Bayamón (202,000); Caguas (110,000); Carolina (165,000); Mayaguez (100,000); Ponce (180,000).
Land use: cultivated 15%; grazing 37%; wooded 20%; uncultivated 28%. Main agricultural products: sugar cane, bananas, citrus fruit, coffee, coconuts, sweet potatoes.
Official languages: Spanish (97%) and English (2%).
Religion: Catholic.
Gross National Product: US $ 16,380 million; per capita: US $ 4,680.
Currency: US dollar = 100 cents.

SAINT KITTS AND NEVIS
A former associate state of Great Britain (since 27th February 1967), made up of the islands of Saint Kitts, Nevis and Sombrero, St Kitts-Nevis is now an independent state (since 19th September 1983) within the Commonwealth of Nations.
The head of state is the British Sovereign, represented by a Governor, who is assisted in his duties by an elected unicameral Parliament and by an Executive Council. The island of Anguilla, formerly a part of the British ex-colony of Saint Christopher (or Saint Kitts)-Nevis-Anguilla, went the way of the other islands on 27th February 1967. On 17th June of the same year, however, it dissociated itself from the others, unilaterally declaring its dependence. Following direct intervention by British troops, Anguilla accepted the status of semi-autonomous independence (1976 constitution).

United States: Washington - The Capitol

Saint Kitts and Nevis is a member of UNO and the OAS.
The state consists of three volcanic and coral islands located in the Leeward Islands group, 330 km east-south-east of Puerto Rico.
Area: 265 sq km.
Population: 45,000, mainly people of African descent and Mulattos; 167 per sq km.
Annual growth rate: 0.9%; birth rate 21‰; death rate 9‰; average life expectancy: 60 years.
Capital: Basseterre (pop 19,000).
Land use: cultivated 39%; grazing 3%; wooded 17%; uncultivated 41%. Main agricultural products: sugar cane, coconuts, cotton, rice, maize, sweet potatoes.
Official language: English.
Religion: Protestant.
Gross National Product: US $ 50 million; per capita: US $ 920.
Currency: East Caribbean dollar = 100 cents.

SAINT LUCIA
Former British colony and then associate state of Great Britain (since March 1st, 1967), St Lucia is now an independent state (since 22nd February 1979) within the Commonwealth of Nations. Legislative power is entrusted to a unicameral Parliament, whose members are elected by direct universal suffrage.
Saint Lucia is a member of UNO and the

OAS.
Its territory consists of a mountainous island of volcanic origin, 30 km south of Martinique in the Windward Islands group.
Area: 615 sq km.
Population: 145,000, mainly people of African descent and Mulattos (96%); 235 per sq km.
Annual growth rate: 2.0%; birth rate 35‰; death rate 7‰; average life expectancy: 60 years.
Capital: Castries (pop 53,000).
Other important towns: Micoud (8,000); Soufrère (7,000).
Land use: cultivated 28%; grazing 5%; wooded 18%; uncultivated 49%. Main agricultural products: bananas, coconuts, mangoes, sweet potatoes, cassava.
Official language: English. French patois also spoken.
Religion: Catholic.
Gross National Product: US $ 110 million; per capita: US $ 850.
Currency: East Caribbean dollar = 100 cents.

SAINT-PIERRE AND MIQUELON
Saint-Pierre et Miquelon

St-Pierre and Miquelon is a territorial "community" of the Republic of France. Until July 1976 it was a French Overseas Territory. Administered by a Governor, aided in the exercise of his duties by an elected General Council, the country is represented in the French Parliament by 1 senator and 1 deputy. Situated in the group of mountainous islands south of Newfoundland, Canada, it consists of two major and six minor islands.
Area: 240 sq km.
Population: 6,000; density: 25 per sq km.
Capital: Saint-Pierre (pop 5,300).
Official language: French.
Religion: Catholic.
Currency: French franc = 100 centimes.

SAINT VINCENT AND GRENADINES
Formerly a British colony and subsequently an associate state of Great Britain (from 27th October 1969), St Vincent is now an independent state within the Commonwealth of Nations (since 27th October 1979). Legislative power is in the hands of a unicameral parliament, whose members are elected by direct universal suffrage.
The country is a UNO and OAS member.
Situated in the Windward Islands group, 80

THE UNITED STATES OF AMERICA

The table below shows the states of America grouped into nine geographical regions, defined according to natural characteristics and economic activity.

NEW ENGLAND	CAPITAL	POPULATION
Connecticut (Conn.)	Hartford	3,240,000
Maine (Me.)	Augusta	1,200,000
Massachusetts (Mass.)	Boston	5,870,000
New Hampshire (N.H.)	Concord	1,090,000
Rhode Island (R.I.)	Providence	1,000,000
Vermont (Vt.)	Montpellier	560,000
MID-ATLANTIC STATES		
New Jersey (N.J.)	Trenton	7,720,000
New York (N.Y.)	Albany	17,900,000
Pennsylvania (Pa.)	Harrisburg	12,030,000
THE EASTERN STATES		
Delaware (Del.)	Dover	660,000
District of Columbia (D.C.)	Washington	620,000
Florida (Fla.)	Tallahassee	12,380,000
Georgia (Ga.)	Atlanta	6,400,000
Maryland (Md.)	Annapolis	4,640,000
North Carolina (N.C.)	Raleigh	6,530,000
South Carolina (S.C.)	Columbia	3,500,000
Virginia (Va.)	Richmond	5,990,000
West Virginia (W.Va.)	Charleston	1,880,000
THE MID-WEST		
Illinois (Ill.)	Springfield	11,540,000
Indiana (Ind.)	Indianapolis	5,580,000
Michigan (Mich.)	Lansing	9,300,000
Ohio (O.)	Columbus	10,870,000
Wisconsin (Wis.)	Madison	4,860,000

THE PRAIRIE STATES		
Iowa (Ia.)	Des Moines	2,830,000
Kansas (Kans.)	Topeka	2,490,000
Minnesota (Minn.)	Saint Paul	4,310,000
Missouri (Mo.)	Jefferson City	5,140,000
Nebraska (Nebr.)	Lincoln	1,600,000
North Dakota (N.Dak.)	Bismarck	660,000
South Dakota (S.Dak.)	Pierre	720,000
THE SOUTH		
Alabama (Ala.)	Montgomery	4,130,000
Arkansas (Ark.)	Little Rock	2,420,000
Kentucky (Ky.)	Frankfort	3,720,000
Louisiana (La.)	Baton Rouge	4,420,000
Mississippi (Miss.)	Jackson	2,630,000
Oklahoma (Okla.)	Oklahoma City	3,260,000
Tennessee (Tenn.)	Nashville	4,920,000
Texas (Tex.)	Austin	16,780,000
THE ROCKY MOUNTAIN STATES		
Arizona (Ariz.)	Phoenix	3,470,000
Colorado (Colo.)	Denver	3,290,000
Idaho (Ida.)	Boise City	1,000,000
Montana (Mont.)	Helena	800,000
Nevada (Nev.)	Carson City	1,060,000
New Mexico (N.Mex.)	Santa Fe	1,510,000
Utah (Ut.)	Salt Lake City	1,690,000
Wyoming (Wyo.)	Cheyenne	470,000
THE PACIFIC STATES		
Alaska (Alask.)	Juneau	510,000
California (Calif.)	Sacramento	28,170,000
Hawaii (Haw.)	Honolulu	1,090,000
Oregon (Oreg.)	Salem	2,740,000
Washington (Wash.)	Olympia	4,620,000

United States: A missile launching pad at Cape Canaveral

km south of Martinique, its territory consists of Saint Vincent island and the northern Grenadines.
Area: 390 sq km.
Population: 120,000, mostly people of African descent (74%) and Mulattos (19%); 308 per sq km.
Annual growth rate: 2.2%; birth rate 33‰; death rate 10‰; average life expectancy: 59 years.
Capital: Kingstown (pop 29,000).
Land use: cultivated 50%; grazing 6%; wooded 41%; uncultivated 3%. Main agricultural products: bananas, coconuts, copra, mangoes, sugar cane.
Official language: English. French patois also spoken.
Religion: Christian.
Gross National Product: US $ 60 million; per capita: US $ 520.
Currency: East Caribbean dollar = 100 cents.

TRINIDAD AND TOBAGO

Trinidad and Tobago has been a republic since 1st August 1976, and independent since 31st August 1962 within the Commonwealth of Nations. The head of state is the President of the Republic. Executive power is exercised by the Prime Minister, who presides over the Council of Ministers; legislative power is entrusted to a bicameral Parliament. The latter is made up of a Chamber of Deputies, who are elected for five years by direct universal suffrage, and of the Senate, whose members designated by the Prime Minister and by the opposition leader, are appointed to a 5-year term by the President of the Republic.
The country is a member of UNO and the OAS.
Trinidad and Tobago consist of two islands 15 km east of the Venezuelan coast; the climate is suited to tropical crops.
Area: 5,130 sq km.
Population: 1,100,000, mainly people of African descent (40%) and Asiatic Indians (39%); Mulattos (16%); Whites and Chinese; density: 216 per sq km.
Annual growth rate: 2%; birth rate 27‰; death rate 76‰; average life expectancy: 70 years.
Capital: Port of Spain (pop 60,000).
Other important towns: Arima (30,000); San Fernando (33,000).
Land use: cultivated 23%; grazing 2%; wooded 44%; uncultivated 31%. Main agricultural products: sugar cane, coconuts, copra, ba-

United States: A geyser in Yellowstone Park

nanas, coffee, cocoa, rice, maize, cassava. Mineral resources: oil.
Official language: English. Hindi, French and Spanish also spoken.
Religion: Christian, Hindu, Muslim.
Gross National Product: US $ 6,500 million; per capita: US $ 5,300.
Currency: Trinidad and Tobago dollar = 100 cents.

TURKS AND CAICOS ISLANDS

A former dependency of the British ex-colony of Jamaica (independent since 6th August 1962 within the Commonwealth), the two island groups of Turks and Caicos now constitute a British colony. The British Sovereign is represented by a Governor, who is aided in the exercises of his duties by a unicameral Parliament and by an Executive Council which are both partly elective.
The territory is made up of an archipelago of about 30 islands and numerous islets and rocks, 220 km north of Haiti.
Area: 430 sq km.
Population: 10,500 mainly people of African descent (65%) and Mulattos (35%); 24 per sq km.
Annual growth rate: 3.6%; birth rate 27‰; death rate 9‰.
Capital: Cockburn Town (pop 2,500).
Land use: cultivated 2%; uncultivated 98%. Main agricultural products: rice, fruit, vegetables. Other activities: fishing.
Official language: English.
Religion: Protestant.
Currency: US dollar = 100 cents.

UNITED STATES OF AMERICA

The United States comprises a federal and presidential republic, made up of a federal district, the District of Columbia, where the capital is located, and of the following 50 federal states: Alabama, Arizona, Arkansas, California, North Carolina, South Carolina, Colorado, Connecticut, North Dakota, South Dakota, Delaware, Florida, Georgia, Idaho, Illinois, Indiana, Iowa, Kansas, Kentucky, Louisiana, Maine, Maryland, Massachusetts, Michigan, Minnesota, Mississippi, Missouri, Montana, Nebraska, Nevada, New York, New Hampshire, New Jersey, New Mexico, Ohio, Oklahoma, Oregon, Pennsylvania, Rhode Island, Tennessee, Texas, Utah, Vermont, Virginia, West Virginia. Washington, Wisconsin, Wyoming (which together make up the so-called *Conterminal United States*), Alaska (separated from the 48 preceding states, but still a part of the American continent, for which reason the 49 federal states are called the *Continental United States*), Hawaii (comprising the Pacific archipelago which bears the same name). The President of the USA is elected to a 4-year term by an assembly, which in turn is elected by the electoral body through a majority-vote system. The President directly exercises executive power, with the help of the vice-president who is elected together with the President, and substitutes him in case of death or serious impediment. The President is also aided by the Presidential Cabinet and by various offices and councils. Legislative power is exercised by a bicameral Parliament (Congress), which consists of the Chamber of Deputies who are elected to a 2-year term proportional to the number of residents in each federal state, and the Senate, whose members are elected to a 6-year term and represent the individual states on the ratio of 2 per state. A third of the Senate can be re-elected every two years. The federal states, ruled by a Governor and having their own legislative assemblies, are autonomous to a large degree.
The United States is a member of UNO, the OECD, the OAS, ANZUS and NATO.
The country is one of the world's largest and has a most favourable geographic position. Its territory is compact and bordered by two oceans, the Atlantic to the east and the Pacific to the west, and by the Gulf of Mexico to the south. It lies almost entirely in the temperate zone and has many rivers.
The Great Lakes, which constitute important communication routes, are located in the northern part of the country. The United States can be divided into 7 geographic areas: the Atlantic coastal plains; the slightly elevated region of the Appalachian Mountains; the sweeping and fertile central plains, crossed from north to south by the Mississippi River and its tributaries; the semi-arid plateau area between the western mountain ranges; the Rocky Mountain area; the narrow Pacific coast; and the coastal plains of the southern Atlantic coastline and along the

United States: Monument Valley

Gulf of Mexico, covered with perennial sub-tropical vegetation. The territory includes the Alaskan peninsula on the far north-west part of the continent and the Hawaiian Islands in the North Pacific.
Area: 9,363,120 sq km, including 236,230 sq km of inland waters; divided politically and administratively into 50 federal States.
Population: 245,800,000, mainly Whites (76%); followed by people of African descent (10%); Mulattos and Mestizos, Amerindians, Chinese, Japanese, Puerto Ricans, Filipinos; density: 26 per sq km.
Annual growth rate: 0.9%; birth rate 15‰; death rate 9‰; average life expectancy: 70 years.
Capital: Washington D.C. (pop 3,560,000).
Other important towns: Atlanta (2,560,000); Baltimore (2,280,000); Boston (2,760,000); Chicago (8,116,000); Cincinnati (1,690,000); Cleveland (2,760,000); Dallas (3,650,000); Denver (1,850,000); Detroit (4,600,000); Houston (3,600,000); Kansas City (1,330,000); Los Angeles (7,450,000); Miami (1,580,000); Milwaukee (1,400,000); Minneapolis (2,295,000); New York (8,480,000); Philadelphia (4,700,000); Phoenix (1,900,000); Pittsburgh (2,260,000); Saint Louis (2,350,000); San Diego (2,200,000); San Francisco (5,880,000); Seattle (1,750,000).
Land use: cultivated 20.5%; grazing 26%; wooded 28%; uncultivated 25.5%. Main agricultural products: grain, maize, oats, barley, cotton, soya bean, sugar beet, citrus fruit, pineapples, sugar cane, wine, peanuts, tobacco; timber. Other activities: fishing; cattle rearing. Mineral resources: coal, oil, iron ore, copper, lead, gold, phosphates.
Official language: English (79%). Other languages spoken in the United States: Spanish (4%); German (3%); Italian (2%); French (1.5%); Polish (1%) and Yiddish (1%).
Religions: Protestant, Catholic, Jewish.
Gross National Product: US $ 4,166,800 million; per capita: US $ 17,300.
Currency: US dollar = 100 cents.
Dependencies: in Central America: Puerto Rico, the US Virgin Islands and the Panama Canal Zone, the territory of Guantánamo Bay and the island of Navassa, leased to the US in 1903 by Cuba, which now claims the island; in Oceania: the Midways (i.e. Sand Island, Eastern Island and some minor islands for a total of 5 sq km and 2,200 inhabitants.

Although geographically included in the Hawaiian archipelago, these islands are not a part of that federal state, but constitute an important air and naval base, directly administered by the US Ministry of the Navy), Guam, the American Samoas, Wake, Johnston, Howland and Baker Islands, some islands in the Equatorial Sporades (Kingman, Palmyra and Jarvis), the Northern Marianas, Micronesia, the Marshall Islands and Palau. And finally, allotted to the United States, which however has never laid claim to it, is the Antarctic territory which lies between 60° parallel South and longitudes 80°W and 150°W.

VIRGIN ISLANDS OF THE UNITED STATES

The islands are a US dependency. According to the constitution they are considered an unincorporated territory. The inhabitants have US citizenship, but do not have the right to vote in US political elections. Since 1973, they have however been represented in the US Parliament by a delegate without voting rights. Executive power is exercised by the President of the United States, who appoints a Governor for an indeterminate period of time. Since 1971, the latter has been elected by direct universal suffrage. Limited legislative power is exercised by the local Senate, whose members are elected for two years.
The territory is made up of about 60 islands and islets, partly of volcanic and coral origin, 60 km east of Puerto Rico. The main islands are Saint Croix, Saint Thomas and Saint John.
Area: 345 sq km.
Population: 107,000, mainly people of African descent and Mulattos (80%); 340 per sq km.
Annual growth rate: 0.6%; birth rate 21.6‰; death rate 5‰.
Capital: Charlotte Amalie (pop 13,000) on the island of Saint Thomas.
Land use: cultivated 18%; grazing 26%; wooded 6%; uncultivated 50%. Main agricultural products: vegetables, fruit, rice, maize.
Official language: English.
Religion: Protestant.
Currency: US dollar = 100 cents.

United States: Cliff Palace at Mesa Verde

South America

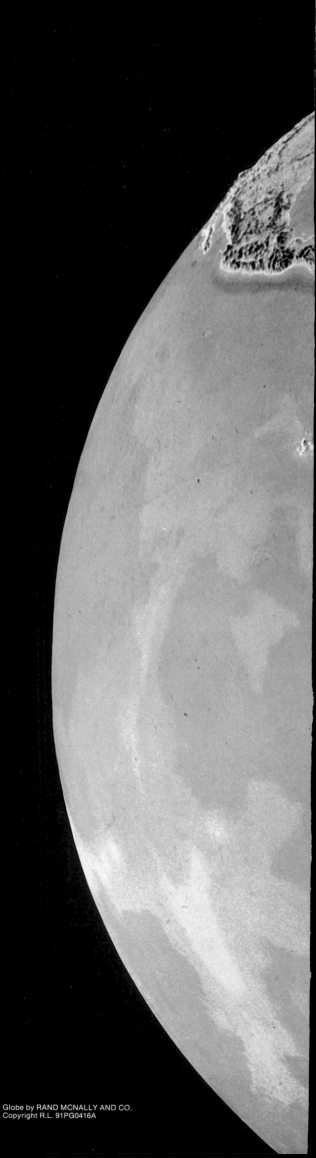

The South American continent, less massive but more compact than North America to which it is connected by the thin isthmus of Central America, stretches in length for over 7,500 kilometres, from the equatorial zone to the sub-polar zone. Such a distribution of land over the latitudes provides for a great variety of climates and landscapes. The Andes ridge constitutes a common element that runs along the western border of the continent from north to south. It is a geologically young ridge, originated during the alpine orogenesis and still settling as demonstrated by the many earthquakes and by the numerous volcanoes. The Andes contribute to differentiate between climates and to restrict the typical tropical characteristics of humidity and heat, so favouring the human settlements on the high highlands.

Because the high ridges of the Andes range lie closer to the western coast, there are great differences in the hydrographic chart on the two sides. West of the mountains the rivers are short, the plains limited, whereas in the east the rivers are among the longest in the world, like the Amazon River, and immense plains stretch out.

Most of the South American states, colonised by south-western Europeans, are in a situation of political instability and socio-economic crisis. The colonisation has also resulted in a racial mixture that during the centuries has deeply changed the ethnic characteristics of South America. Only in small areas less favourable to settlement are the original characteristics preserved, as among the Amazonian Indians or the Aymará of Peru.

The northern part of the continent has two major natural features: the vast Andes range which stretches along the coast, with numerous ridges whose mountains reach above 6,000 metres, their more precipitous slopes inclined towards the west and the Pacific coasts; and the immense Amazon River basin, towards the centre of the continent. In most of the Amazon River basin, crossed by the Equator, the climate is hot and humid, with considerable rainfall all year round. It is the environment of the rain forest, thick and impenetrable, that has only recently been invaded by settlers and crossed by the Trans-Amazon Highway. For some distance either side of the Amazon River there are areas that are alternately drier or wetter: they are the regions of "caatinga" and of "campos", undergrowth and savanna, not suitable for farming. In the Andean zone the altitude determines differences in climate: from the equatorial or temperate climates of the coasts and of the highlands, to the extreme cold of the more elevated regions.

The nations of the Andes are united in the sadly underdeveloped nature of their social and economic structures. Only Venezuela, thanks to its oil income, seems to have improved on this situation. Brazil gives contrasting images: miserable poverty and ostentatious opulence live together in large urban centres: a sign, perhaps, of the imbalance in the exploitation of the natural resources of the country. Chile and Argentina are the most important political entities of the southern sector of the continent. Both are located mostly in the temperate zone, though on opposite sides of the Andes mountains. Chile's territory comprises a thin strip of land no wider than 200 kilometres that extends in length for more than 4,300 kilometres. Argentina occupies part of the vast region that slopes gradually from the Andes towards the Atlantic Ocean, partly made up of large plains like the Pampas. Environmental features of this kind pose different problems to the two states. In Chile level areas suitable for agriculture are very limited, less than 8% of the territory, and are also home to the majority of the population. The northern zone with its arid climate is rich in mineral resources such as nitrates and copper, of which Chile is one of the world's major producers. The southern part is cold and uninhabited. Massive foreign investment has aggravated Chile's economic problems leading to further political instability as in so many South American countries. Similarly, in Argentina vast tracts in the south of the country are practically uninhabited. The economic core of the country is the area of Buenos Aires and the surrounding Pampas. It is in this vast plain that the main economic activities have been developed, where individual cattle ranches may stock more than 50 million cattle (grazing in large open plains) and 30 million sheep, and where in great measure wheat, maize, barley and oats are grown. These enterprises are aimed principally at the export market.

The extreme southern tip of South America is Tierra del Fuego, divided politically between Chile and Argentina. It is a region of austerely harsh terrain, modelled by glaciers. There remain many snowcapped and icy mountains, though generally less than 2,500 metres high, and numerous fjords, which carve through the coastlines leaving precipitous ledges where penguins live.

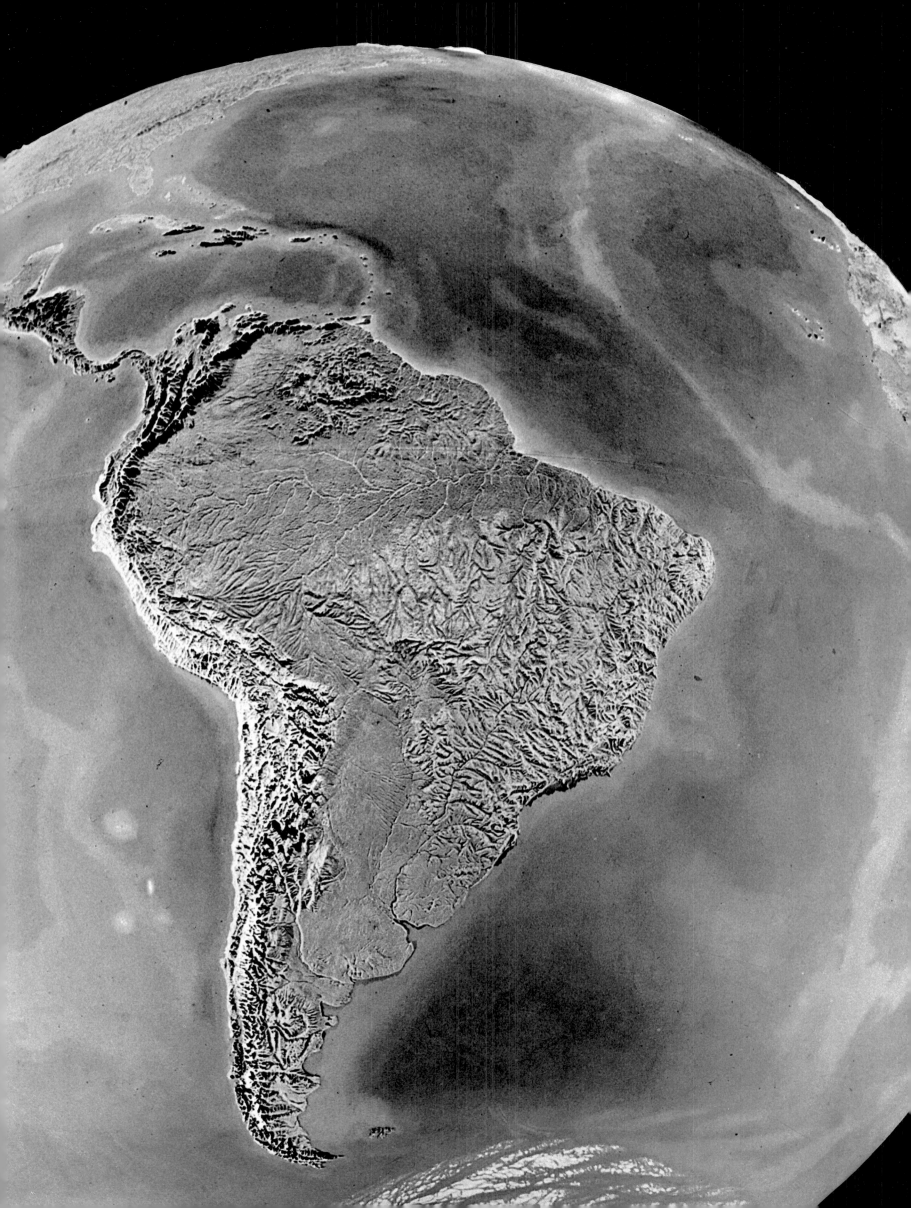

Bolivia/Peru: View of Lake Titicaca

Bolivia: The Cordillera Real, to the north of La Paz

ARGENTINA

República Argentina

Argentina is a federal, presidential republic, formed by a Federal District which hosts the capital, by a National Territory and by the following 22 Federal Units (Provincias): Buenos Aires, Catamarca, Còrdoba, Corrientes, Chaco, Chubut, Entre Ríos, Formosa, Jujuy, La Pampa, La Rioja, Mendoza, Misiones, Neuquèn, Río Negro, Salta, San Juan, San Luis, Santa Cruz, Santa Fe, Santiago del Estero, Tucumán. The National Territory includes the Argentine Tierra del Fuego, and claims to include the following island groups presently administered by Britain: Falkland (Malvinas), South Georgia, South Sandwich Islands, South Orkney Islands, South Shetland Islands; and moreover all the British Antarctic region between 25°W and 74°W and 60°S parallel. According to the constitution of 1853, more than once modified, the executive power is held by the President of the Republic, who is elected together with his vice-president every 6 years by direct universal suffrage, with the collaboration of the Council of Ministers named by him; the legislative power is held by the bicameral Parliament (Congreso), formed by the Senate elected for 9 years, representing the Federal Units and Federal District, and by the Chamber of Deputies elected for 4 years. As a consequence of the military coups of 1966 and 1976, constitutional guarantees were cancelled and a military junta took power. After the military defeat suffered at the hands of Great Britain in warfare over possession of the Falkland Islands, the junta was obliged to restore civilian rule, and in 1983 the constitution was reinstituted.

Argentina is a member of UNO, the OAS and ALALC.

The territory, in South America smaller only than Brazil, occupies most of the continent's southern part. It faces the Atlantic and has geographical regions of varied character: the Pampas, a vast plain between the Colorado and Paraná rivers to the west; the high Andes mountains, including among them Aconcagua (7,021 m) and the chain of Andean foothills; in the north is the Gran Chaco, undulating countryside covered with savanna and forests; in the south Patagonia, an arid stony highland of fierce and constant freezing winds.

Area: 2,766,890 sq km, politically and administratively divided into 22 Federal Units (Provincias).

Population: 32,000,000, mostly Whites (95%) of Spanish and Italian origin; the others are Mestizos and Amerindians; density: 11 per sq km.

Annual growth rate: 1.6%; birth rate 25‰; death rate 9‰; average life expectancy: 70 years.

Capital: Buenos Aires (pop 9,800,000). A new capital is expected to be built near the area of Viedma.

Other important towns: Bahía Blanca (224,000); Còrdoba (985,000); La Plata (570,000); Mar del Plata (415,000); Mendoza (605,000); Rosario (960,000); San Juan (292,000); San Miguel de Tucumán (500,000); Santa Fe (292,000); Viedma (25,000).

Land use: cultivated 13%; grazing 52%; wooded 22%; uncultivated 13%. Main agricultural products: wheat, maize, sorghum, soya bean, sunflowers, citrus fruits, vegetables, fruit, potatoes, tobacco, cotton, dairy products. Other activities: livestock rearing. Mineral resources: coal, oil.

Official language: Spanish.

Religion: Catholic.

Gross National Product: US $ 72,900 million; per capita: US $ 2,360.

Currency: Austral.

BOLIVIA

República Boliviana

Bolivia is a presidential republic. According to the constitution of 1947, many times amended, the executive power is held by the President of the Republic, elected by direct universal suffrage for 4 years; the legislative power is held by the Parliament, bicameral and elective.

Bolivia is a member of UNO, the OAS and ALALC.

The country is landlocked, and divided into two areas: the mountainous west, comprising the arid highlands east of the main Andean chain, on top of which is Lake Titicaca (at 3,812 m), partly in Peru; the flatter, lowland east, comprising plains covered by equatorial forests and savanna, and mostly uninhabited.

Area: 1,098,580 sq km.

Population: 6,740,000; mostly Amerindians (42%) and Mestizos (30%); 5 per sq km.

Annual growth rate: 2.8%; birth rate 44‰; death rate: 16‰; average life expectancy: 50 years.

Capital: La Paz (administrative capital and seat of government, pop 1,030,000) and Sucre (the official capital, pop 89,000).

Other important towns: Cochabamba (330,000); Oruro (184,000); Potosí (117,000); Santa Cruz de la Sierra (460,000).

Land use: cultivated 3%; grazing 25%; wooded 52%; uncultivated 20%. Main agricultural products: potatoes, cassava, maize, sugar cane, bananas, vegetables, fruit. Mineral resources: tin, antimony, copper, lead.

Official languages: Spanish, Quechua (33%); Aymará (21%).

Religion: Catholic.

Gross National Product: US $ 3,540 million; per capita: US $ 540.

Currency: Bolivian peso = 100 Centavos.

Argentina/Brazil: Iguaçu Falls, part of the border between Argentina and Brazil

Argentina: View of the Andes as seen from the town of Mendoza

Argentina: South American gauchos, the cowboys of the Pampas

BRAZIL

República Federativa do Brasil

Brazil is a presidential, federal republic comprising a Federal District, which hosts the capital, and the following Fedel States: Acre, Alagoas, Amazonas, Bahia, Ceará, Espirito Santo, Goiás, Maranhão, Mato Grosso, Mato Grosso do Sul, Minas Gerais, Pará, Paraiba, Paraná, Pernambuco, Piauí, Rio de Janeiro, Rio Grande do Norte, Rio Grande do Sul, Rondonia, Santa Catarina, São Paulo, Sergipe, each of which has its own Government and Legislative Assembly; and furthermore, the following 3 territories: Amapá, Roraima and Fernando de Noronha. In the federal framework the legislative power is given to the bicameral Parliament (Congreso), made up of the Chamber of Deputies and of the Senate, whose members are elected by direct universal suffrage, respectively for 4 and 8 years. The executive power is held by the President of the Republic helped by various ministers. The President, jointly with the vice-president is elected for 5 years by an electoral college comprising members of the Federal Parliament and Legislative Assembly delegates of the various Federal States.
Brazil is a member of UNO, the OAS and ALALC.
The largest country in South America, Brazil can be divided into two principal regions. In the north is Amazonia, the world's largest river basin, crossed by the River Amazon, second longest river in the world, navigable for 3,000 km. This vast equatorial region is covered in thick forest with trees as high as 60 m. In the south is the highland region, generally arid, crossed by the São Francisco, Paraná and Paraguay rivers.
Area: 8,506,671 sq km, political-administrative division into 23 Federal States.
Population: 150,053,000, mostly Whites (53%) then Mestizos and Mulattoes (34%); people of African descent and Amerindians (12%); density: 16 per sq km.
Annual growth rate: 2.2%; birth rate 37‰; death rate 9‰; average life expectancy: 63 years.
Capital: Brasília (pop 1,803,000).
Other important towns: Belém (1,190,000); Belo Horizonte (2,340,000); Curitiba (1,390,000); Porto Alegre (1,370,000); Recife

Bolivia/Peru: Fishing in Lake Titicaca

(1,350,000); Rio de Janeiro (6,020,000); Salvador (2,000,000); São Paulo (10,997,000).
Land use: cultivated 9%; grazing 20%; wooded 66%; uncultivated 5%. Main agricultural products: sugar cane, cassava, cotton, soya bean, coffee, tobacco, citrus fruit, sweet potatoes; timber. Other activities: livestock rearing, fishing. Mineral resources: gold, iron ore, manganese.
Official language: Portuguese.

THE BRAZILIAN STATES

The Brazilian territory is divided into five regions with equally different geographical, economic and population characteristics. This table lists the Brazilian states with their capitals, according to the region to which they belong.

NORTE	
Acre	Río Branco
Amapa (Terr.)	Macapá
Amazonas	Manaus
Pará	Belém
Rondonia	Porto Velho
Roraima (Terr.)	Boa Vista

NORDESTE	
Alagoas	Maceió
Bahia	Salvador
Ceará	Fortaleza
Fernando de Noronha (Terr.)	Remédios
Maranhão	São Luis
Paraiba	João Pessoa
Pernambuco	Recife
Piauì	Teresina
Rio Grande do Norte	Natal
Sergipe	Aracaju

SUDESTE	
Espirito Santo	Vitória
Minas Gerais	Belo Horizonte
Rio de Janeiro	Rio de Janeiro
São Paulo	São Paulo

SUL	
Paraná	Curitiba
Rio Grande do Sul	Porto Alegre
Santa Catarina	Florianopolis

CENTRO-OESTE	
Goiás	Goiánia
Distrito Federal	Brasília
Mato Grosso	Cuiabá
Mato Grosso do Sul	Campo Grande

Religion: Catholic.
Gross National Product: US $ 270,000 million; per capita: US $ 1,950.
Currency: Cruzado = 100 centavos.

CHILE

República de Chile

Chile is a presidential republic. Since the military coup of 11th September 1973, the constitutional guarantees have been suspended, the political parties have been suppressed and full power is in the hands of a nationalist military junta, which uses authoritarian methods. Up to that date the legislative power had been held by the bicameral Parliament (Congreso Nacional), made up of the Senate and of the Chamber of Deputies, whose members were elected by direct universal suffrage, respectively for 3 and 4 years. Executive power was exercised by the President of the Republic, elected for 6 years by direct universal suffrage. At the moment there are profound changes in the political framework of the country, which is gradually returning to democracy.
The country claims the island portion of the Antarctic that is considered British located between 53°W and 90°W of the Greenwich meridian and 60°S parallel. Chile has sovereignty over the islands of Picton, Nueva and Lennox which are situated south-east of Tierra del Fuego.
Chile is a member of UNO, the OAS and ALALC.
Its territory stretches along the coast of the Pacific Ocean on the western side of the Andes for 4,800 km from north to south. The maximum width is only 200 km. Several of the main Andean chain peak at over 6,000 m. Between them and the coast is a ridge of lesser foothills. The climatic conditions are variable: in the north is the Atacama desert, unique to South America; in the centre a temperate area; in the south the climate is always colder and it extends from an area of pine forests to tundra.
Area: 756,625 sq km.
Population: 12,750,000; mostly Mestizos (70%); then Whites (25%) and Amerindians (5%); density: 17 per sq km.
Annual growth rate: 1.7%; birth rate 22‰; mortality rate 6‰; average life expectancy: 67 years.
Capital: Santiago (pop 4,913,000).
Other important towns: Antofagasta (204,000); Concepción (294,000); Puerto Montt (120,000); Temuco (217,000); Valparaiso (278,000); Viña del Mar (297,000).
Land use: cultivated 7%; grazing 16%; wooded 12%; uncultivated 65%. Main agricultural products: sugar beet, potatoes, wine, wheat, barley, fruit, vegetables. Mineral resources: copper, molybdenum, iron ore, nitrates, oil.
Official language: Spanish.
Religion: Catholic (89%).
Gross National Product: US $ 15,000 million, per capita: US $ 1,220.
Currency: Chilean peso = 100 centavos.

COLOMBIA

República de Colombia

Colombia is a presidential republic. The legislative power is held by a bicameral Parliament (Congreso Nacional) made up of the Senate and of the Chamber of Deputies whose members are elected by direct universal suffrage for 4 years. The executive power is held by the President of the Republic who is also head of the government, elected

Brazil: National Congress Buildings, Brasília

by direct universal suffrage for 4 years. The territory of the Colombian province of Guajira is claimed by Venezuela.
Colombia is a member of UNO, the OAS and ALALC.
The country is the only one in South America that faces two oceans; it is characterised by the Andes mountains divided here into three ridges running north and north-east. The two large valleys of the Magdalena and Cauca rivers, which enjoy a favourable climate, are situated between the ridges. The rest of the country is made up of undulating terrain covered by equatorial forest and savanna.
Area: 1,141,748 sq km.
Population: 30,660,000; mostly Mestizos (50%) and Mulattoes (23%) and then Whites (19%); people of African descent (6%) and Amerindians (2%); density: 24 per sq km.
Annual growth rate: 1.8%; birth rate 31‰; mortality rate 9‰; average life expectancy: 63 years.
Capital: Bogotá (pop 4,070,000).
Other important towns: Barranquilla (896,000); Bucaramanga (340,000); Cali (1,323,000); Cartagena (490,000); Cucuta (360,000); Medellín (1,420,000).
Land use: cultivated 6%; grazing 35%; wooded 45%; uncultivated 14%. Main agricultural products: sugar cane, rice, potatoes, maize, cocaine, bananas, cotton, coffee, soya bean, barley, wheat, cocoa; timber. Other activities: cattle rearing. Mineral resources: oil, gold, silver.
Official language: Spanish.
Religion: Catholic.
Gross National Product: US $ 31,250 million; per capita: US $ 1,080.
Currency: Colombian peso = 100 centavos.

ECUADOR

República del Ecuador

Ecuador is a presidential republic. According to the constitution of 1978, the executive power is held by the President of the Republic, elected by direct universal suffrage for 4 years; the legislative power is held by the single-chamber Parliament, elected by direct universal suffrage, for 4 years.
Ecuador officially claims a territory of 174,565 sq km, given to Peru in application of the Rio de Janeiro Protocol of 1942.
Ecuador is a member of UNO, the OAS and ALALC.
The country is situated in the equatorial section

Bolivia: Aymará Indians in their colourful clothes

Brazil: Aerial view of the tropical rain forest of the Amazon

Brazil: View of Rio de Janeiro

of the Andes and faces the Pacific Ocean. Behind the coastal region, low and often forested, is a central, mountainous area, where, between the two Andean ridges, is a large plateau with a temperate climate. To the east undulating countryside slopes gradually towards the Amazonian lowland; it has a rainy climate. Ecuador's territory also includes the Galápagos Islands.
Area: 283,560 sq km, including the Galápagos Islands.
Population: 9,850,000, mostly Amerindians (50%) and Mestizos (40%), then Whites, Blacks and Mulattoes; density: 35 per sq km. Annual growth rate 2.9%; birth rate 37‰, mortality rate 5‰, average life expectancy: 61 years.
Capital: Quito (pop. 1,140,000).
Other important towns: Ambato (122,000); Cuenca (200,000); Esmeraldas (115,000); Guayaquil (1,580,000); Riobamba (150,000).
Land use: cultivated 9%, grazing 18%, wooded 42%, uncultivated 31%. Main agricultural products: sugar cane, potatoes, rice, maize, coffee, cocoa; bananas. Other activities: fishing. Mineral resources: oil.
Official language: Spanish.
Religion: Catholic.
Gross National Product: US $ 10,700 million, per capita: US $ 1,100.
Currency: Sucre = 100 centavos.

FALKLAND ISLANDS
Islas Malvinas

The Falklands constitute a British colony, comprising the islands of the same name, located in the South Atlantic Ocean 500 km off the Argentine coast; it is administered by a Governor who is assisted in his duties by an Executive Council and by a partly elected Legislative Council. Two ex-dependencies of the Falkland Islands, South Georgia (3,755 sq km) and the South Sandwich Islands (335 sq km) are presently an independent British colony. The Falklands are officially claimed by Argentina, which calls them Malvinas, together with South Georgia and the South Sandwich Islands. The Falklands group comprises two major islands, East and West Falkland, and about 200 other small islands. The territory is hilly with low mountains, and has windy coasts with large bays and rocky promontories.
Area: 12,170 sq km.
Population: 1,950.
Annual growth rate: 0.01%; birth rate 13‰; mortality rate: 13‰.

Capital: Port Stanley (pop 1,200).
Main economical resources: fishing, cattle rearing.
Official language: English.
Religion: Protestant and Anglican.
Currency: Falkland pound = 100 pence.

FRENCH GUYANA
Guyane Française

French Guyana is an Overseas Department of the Republic of France (since 19th March 1946), governed by a Prefect assisted in exerting his functions, by an elected general council; it is represented in the French Parliament by 1 Deputy and 1 Senator. Most of the south-western territory is an object of dispute with the bordering Surinam.
The country lies between Surinam and Brazil, and faces the Atlantic Ocean. It is mainly flat, covered by equatorial forest almost up to the coast.
Area: 88,900 sq km.
Population: 92,000; mostly Mulattoes and Asians; 1 per sq km.
Annual growth rate: 3.2%; birth rate 25‰; mortality rate 8‰; average life expectancy: 60 years.
Capital: Cayenne (pop 38,000).
Other important towns: Kourou (7,000); Saint Laurent du Maroni (7,000).
Land use: cultivated 0.05%; grazing 0.07%; wooded 81.9%; uncultivated 18%. Main agricultural products: sugar cane, maize, cassava, rice.
Official language: French.
Religion: Animist and Christian.
Gross National Product: US $ 180 million; per capita: US $ 2,880.
Currency: French franc = 100 centimes.

GUYANA
Cooperative Republic of Guyana

Guyana has been an independent republic since 26th May 1966 and part of the Commonwealth of Nations (republic since 23rd February 1970). The head of state is the President of the Republic, who is elected by the Parliament for 6 years; he nominates the Prime Minister and ministers, who exercise the executive power and are responsible for their actions to the unicameral Parliament (National Assembly). The legislative power is held by Parliament, whose members are elected for 5 years by direct universal suffrage. The eastern region of the territory of

Guyana, up to the River Berbice, is claimed by Surinam.
Guyana is a member of UNO.
The country faces the Atlantic Ocean, and borders on Venezuela, Brazil and Surinam. The terrain is characterised by a series of high plains, covered in forests, that slope gradually towards the coastal plain where the majority of the population lives.
Area: 214,970 sq km.
Population: 750,000; mostly Asian Indians (52%); Blacks and Mulattoes (43%); then Amerindians (4%); Whites and Chinese; density: 4 per sq km.
Annual growth rate: 0%; birth rate 26‰; mortality rate 7‰; average life expectancy: 68 years.
Capital: Georgetown (pop 190,000).
Other important town: Linden (35,000).
Land use: cultivated 2%; grazing 6%; wooded 76%; uncultivated 16%. Main agricultural products: sugar cane, rice, citrus fruit, coconut, coffee, cocoa.
Official language: English.
Religion: Christian.
Gross National Product: US $ 285 million; per capita: US $ 380.
Currency: Guyana dollar = 100 cents.

PARAGUAY
República del Paraguay

Paraguay is a presidential republic. The legislative power is held by the Parliament (Congreso), whose members are elected for 5 years by direct universal suffrage. The State Council has special responsibilities and comprises members nominated by the Government on a co-operative basis. The President of the Republic is head of state who, as head of the government, exercises executive power together with the ministers he appoints.
Paraguay is a member of UNO, the OAS and ALAC.
The landlocked territory is divided into two parts by the river after which the country is named. West of the river stretches the Gran Chaco area covered in prairie and steppe. East of the river lie the last undulating folds of the Mato Grosso stretching in from Brazil and covered in thick forest. Two other rivers, the Pilcomayo and Paraná, determine the borders with Argentina, and in part, with Brazil.
Area: 406,750 sq km.
Population: 4,000,000; almost all Mestizos (91%); 8 per sq km.
Annual growth rate: 2.9%; birth rate 40‰; mortality rate 9‰; average life expectancy: 64 years.
Capital: Asunción (pop 790,000).
Other important towns: Concepción (23,000); Encarnación (27,000); Villarrica (21,000).
Land use: cultivated 5%; grazing 49%; wooded 39%; uncultivated 7%. Main agricultural products: sugar cane, cassava, maize, soya bean, sweet potatoes, cotton, rice, tobacco, wheat. Other activities: cattle rearing.
Official language: Spanish.
Religion: Catholic.
Gross National Product: US $ 3,850 million; per capita: US $ 1,000.
Currency: Guaraní = 100 céntimos.

PERU
República del Perú

Peru is a presidential republic. The head of state is the President of the Republic, elected for 6 years by direct universal suffrage, who, being also the head of the government, holds executive power together with the Prime Minister and the ministers nominated by him. Legislative power is held by the bicameral Parliament (Congreso), elected for 6 years by direct universal suffrage by literate citizens and made up of the Senate and of the Chamber of Deputies.
A territory of 174,565 sq km, given to Peru in compliance with the Rio de Janeiro Protocol of 1942, has been officially claimed by Ecuador since the 1960s.
Peru is a member of UNO, the OAS and ALALC.
The territory, which stretches south of the Equator along the Pacific Coast, is made up of two very different regions. The western region comprises the Andes ranges and the coastal area, and has a temperate but dry climate; the eastern region, the Montana, instead is flat and stretches into the Amazonian lowland: it has high temperatures and considerable rainfall.
Area: 1,285,215 sq km.
Population: 21,790,000, mostly Amerindians

(47%) and Mestizos (33%); density: 17 per sq km.
Annual growth rate: 2.7%; birth rate 34‰; mortality rate 9‰; average life expectancy: 58 years.
Capital: Lima (pop 6,000,000).
Other important towns: Arequipa (590,000); Callao (515,000); Chiclayo (395,000); Cuzco (250,000); Huancayo (200,000); Iquitos (248,000); Piura (297,000); Trujillo (490,000).
Land use: cultivated 3%; grazing 21%; wooded 54%; uncultivated 22%. Main agricultural products: sugar cane, potatoes, maize, cassava, rice, coffee. Mineral resources: oil, copper, silver, iron ore, phosphates. Other activities: fishing.
Official language: Spanish (68%) and Quechua (27%).
Religion: Catholic.
Gross National Product: US $ 21,500 million; per capita: US $ 1,130.
Currency: Sol = 100 centavos.

SURINAM
Republiek van Suriname

An independent republic since 25th November 1975 (it had been a Dutch colony since 1814 and an autonomous state in association with the Netherlands from 1954), Surinam's executive government is in the hands of the Council of Ministers; legislative power is held by the Legislative Assembly (Staten), elected for 4 years by direct universal suffrage and to which the Government is responsible. Following a military coup on 25th February 1980, constitutional guarantees were suspended and power was passed to a military junta. Since 1987 constitutional guarantees have been restored.
Surinam officially claims part of eastern Guyana; in addition a large area of the south-western part of the country is an object of dispute with neighbouring French Guyana.
Surinam is a member of UNO, the OAS and ALALC.
Surinam's territory divides Guyana from French Guyana; it is mountainous in the south, towards Brazil, and flat in the north, towards the Atlantic coast, the only area free of forest.
Area: 163,820 sq km.
Population: 425,000, mostly Asians (35%); Creoles (32%); Indonesians (15%); then Blacks and Amerindians; Europeans; density: 2 per sq km.

Chile: A herd of cattle in southern Chile, the volcanic peak of Osorno in the distance

Peru: An old Inca village

Peru: The fortress at Sacsayhuamán

Venezuela: Oil wells in Lake Maracaibo

Annual growth rate: 2.7%; birth rate 40‰; mortality rate 9‰; average life expectancy: 64 years.
Capital: Paramaribo (pop 67,000).
Other important town: Nieuw Nickerie (34,000).
Land use: cultivated 0.3%; wooded 91%; uncultivated 8%. Main agricultural products: rice, sugar cane, coconut, bananas; timber.
Official language: Dutch.
Religion: Hindu (31%); Christian (20%) and Islam (19%).
Gross National Product: US $ 1,000 million; per capita: US $ 2,430.
Currency: Surinam guilder = 100 cents.

URUGUAY

República Oriental del Uruguay

Uruguay is a presidential republic. According to the constitution of 1967 (suspended between 1973 and 1984 when power was held by a military junta), the head of state is the President of the Republic, who is elected for 5 years by direct universal suffrage and exerts direct executive power with the help of the Council of Ministers. Legislative power is held by the two-chamber Parliament elected for 5 years by direct universal suffrage.
Uruguay is a member of UNO, the OAS and ALALC.
The country, which takes its name from the River Uruguay, marking the border with Argentina, is made up of undulating territory crossed by a network of rivers and covered in savanna grassland. It has an Atlantic coastline.
Area: 175,215 sq km.
Population: 2,980,000, mostly Whites of European descent (90%); density: 16 per sq km.
Annual growth rate: 0.5%; birth rate 18‰; mortality rate 10‰; average life expectancy: 71 years.
Capital: Montevideo (pop 1,300,000).
Other important towns: Mercedes (37,000); Paysandú (75,000); Rivera (56,000); Salto (80,000).

Land use: cultivated 8%; grazing 76%; wooded 4%; uncultivated 12%. Main agricultural products: wheat, maize, barley, rice, sugar beet, potatoes, linen, sunflowers. Other activities: cattle rearing.
Official language: Spanish.
Religion: Catholic.
Gross National Product: US $ 6,000 million; per capita: US $ 1,950.
Currency: Uruguayan peso = 100 centésimos.

VENEZUELA

República de Venezuela

Venezuela is a federal, presidential republic, comprising a Federal District that hosts the capital, two Federal Territories and the following 20 Federal States (Estados): Anzoátegui, Apure, Aragua, Barinas, Bolívar, Carabobo, Cojedes, Falcón, Guárico, Lara, Mérida, Miranda, Monagas, Nueva Esparta, Portuguesa, Sucre, Táchira, Trujillo, Yaracuy, Zulia, each having a Government and Legislative Assembly. In the federal context, the legislative power is held by the bicameral Parliament (Congreso), elected for 5 years by direct universal suffrage and made up of the Senate, formed by representatives of the individual Federal Units and of the Federal Districts and by the ex-Presidents of the Republic, and by the Chamber of Deputies, elected through a proportional system. The President of the Republic is the head of state, who, being also the head of government, exercises direct executive power together with the ministers nominated by him.
Venezuela has territorial claims to the Colombian province of Guajira.
The country is a member of UNO, the OAS and ALALC.
The country has an Atlantic coastline to the north broken, to the west, by the Gulf of Venezuela and the remarkable Lake Maracaibo. Venezuela has three main geographical areas: the Andean mountains to the north-west, some reaching 5,000 m; the partly fertile central flatlands or "llanos"; and the Guiana Highland massif to the south-west.

Area: 912,050 sq km.
Population: 18,750,000, mostly Mestizos and Mulattoes (65%); 20 per sq km.
Annual growth rate: 2.7%; birth rate 28‰; mortality rate 4‰; average life expectancy: 67 years.
Capital: Caracas (pop 3,500,000).
Other important towns: Barquisimeto (741,000); Ciudad Bolívar (268,000); Ciudad Guayana (491,000); Cumaná (254,000); Maracaibo (1,330,000); Maturin (260,000); San Cristóbal (347,000); Valencia (1,180,000).
Land use: cultivated 4%; grazing 19%; wooded 40%; uncultivated 37%. Main agricultural products: maize, rice, sorghum, sugar cane, cassava, coffee, tobacco, cotton, citrus fruit, vegetables; timber. Other activities: cattle rearing, fishing.
Official language: Spanish.
Religion: Catholic.
Gross National Product: US $ 48,000 million; per capita: US $ 2,680.
Currency: Bolívar = 100 céntimos.

Peru: The impressive ruins of Machu Picchu

Oceania

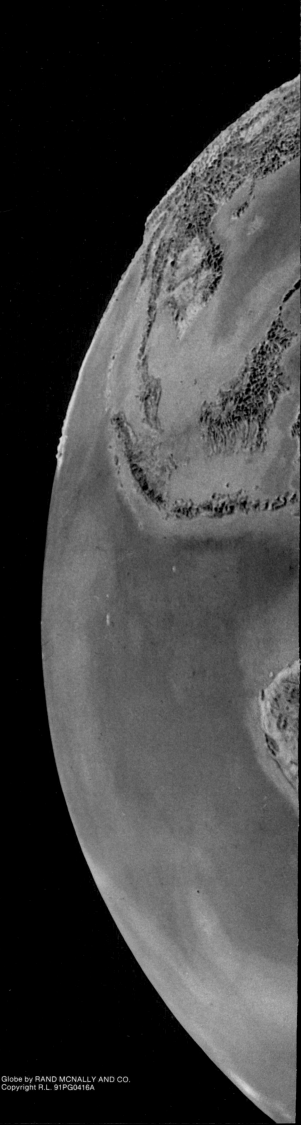

The name Oceania refers to the smallest of the continents and the last to become known to the West. It includes two very different geographical areas. On one hand there is Australia, a huge island nearly as big as the USA, and on the other four smaller islands and a myriad tiny islands. There are also enormous climatic and geological differences between the two areas. Australia is geologically extremely old, for the most part levelled by erosion, while the Pacific islands are of relatively recent origin. In some of these, like New Guinea and New Zealand, there are mountain chains of the same geological period as the Alps, while the smallest islands are of volcanic origin. On the ocean bed there are numerous trenches, such as the Kermadec Trench. There are also various ridges, such as the Hawaiian Ridge and the East Pacific Ridge, that rise to form chains of islands. A great number of islands have been built by the activity of tiny warm-water organisms like coral, which live in the tropical belt where the water maintains a temperature of 25°C. They are responsible for the existence of coral islands and atolls and also coastal barriers like the Great Barrier Reef, which extends for 2,000 km along the eastern coast of Australia. Most of the islands of Oceania, with the exception of Australia, have a hot/humid climate. Only Tasmania and New Zealand, because of their latitude, enjoy a temperate climate.

The continent of Australia is predominately arid, with a maximum annual rainfall of 250 mm. A large part of the enormous Australian plain is within the tropical high pressure belt and is therefore covered by desert and scrub. Only along the eastern coast are there mountain chains, which, however, never rise above 2,000 metres. The white population, the whole of which emigrated from the late 18th century onwards, is more than 15 million and is mostly distributed along the east coast where the climate is less arid. The original ancient inhabitants, the Aborigines, unable to oppose the advance of the Europeans, retreated in general to the less hospitable, desert areas. They have been progressively integrated into the European culture and only a small number continue to follow their original way of life, characterised by extreme technological backwardness in contrast to an elaborate social organisation and a rich mythology. The basis of the Australian economy and exports depended for a long time on the rearing of livestock and extensive cultivation of cereals. Recently, however, there has been an increase in the industrial and in particular in the mining sectors. In fact there are many important mineral resources: gold, iron, coal and zinc, plus huge reserves of oil. The Australian economy is rapidly developing, as is evidenced by the country's capacity to absorb large numbers of immigrants every year.

The islands of Oceania, outside Australia, are divided into three groups: Melanesia, named after the dark skin colour of the inhabitants, includes all the islands from New Guinea to Fiji. New Guinea, the second largest island in Oceania is crossed by a ridge of mountains of the Tertiary Period, reaching a height of over 5,000 m. Heavy rainfall and high temperatures typical of equatorial areas have produced a dense rain forest which covers the whole island. These physical characteristics have contributed to the preservation of groups of extremely primitive people in the interior of the island. Most of the population of New Guinea is Melanesian, the Papuans forming the most homogeneous group. The other islands of Melanesia are also mountainous and covered in dense forest, but are of volcanic origin. Micronesia is the group of nearly 1,500 volcanic and coral islands, most of them small. It extends from the north-east of Melanesia and includes the northern archipelagoes such as the Marianas and Caroline Islands. The population of this area is today the most diverse, being a mix of Polynesians and Melanesians. Polynesia, the most easterly group, extends from New Zealand to Hawaii. The ancestors of present-day Polynesians emigrated in fragile dugout raft-style canoes to populate the most far-flung islands like Easter Island.

The New Zealand archipelago is distinguished by its latitude, climate and terrain. Situated in the temperate zone it has a marine climate with high rainfall. A ridge of mountains runs the length of the islands. Most of the population is of British descent while the Maoris, the ancient inhabitants, of whom there are nearly 300,000 present, risk becoming extinct over the next few decades. The basic economic activity is livestock farming, most of which is sheep rearing. The products, meat, wool and cheese, are exported on a wide scale.

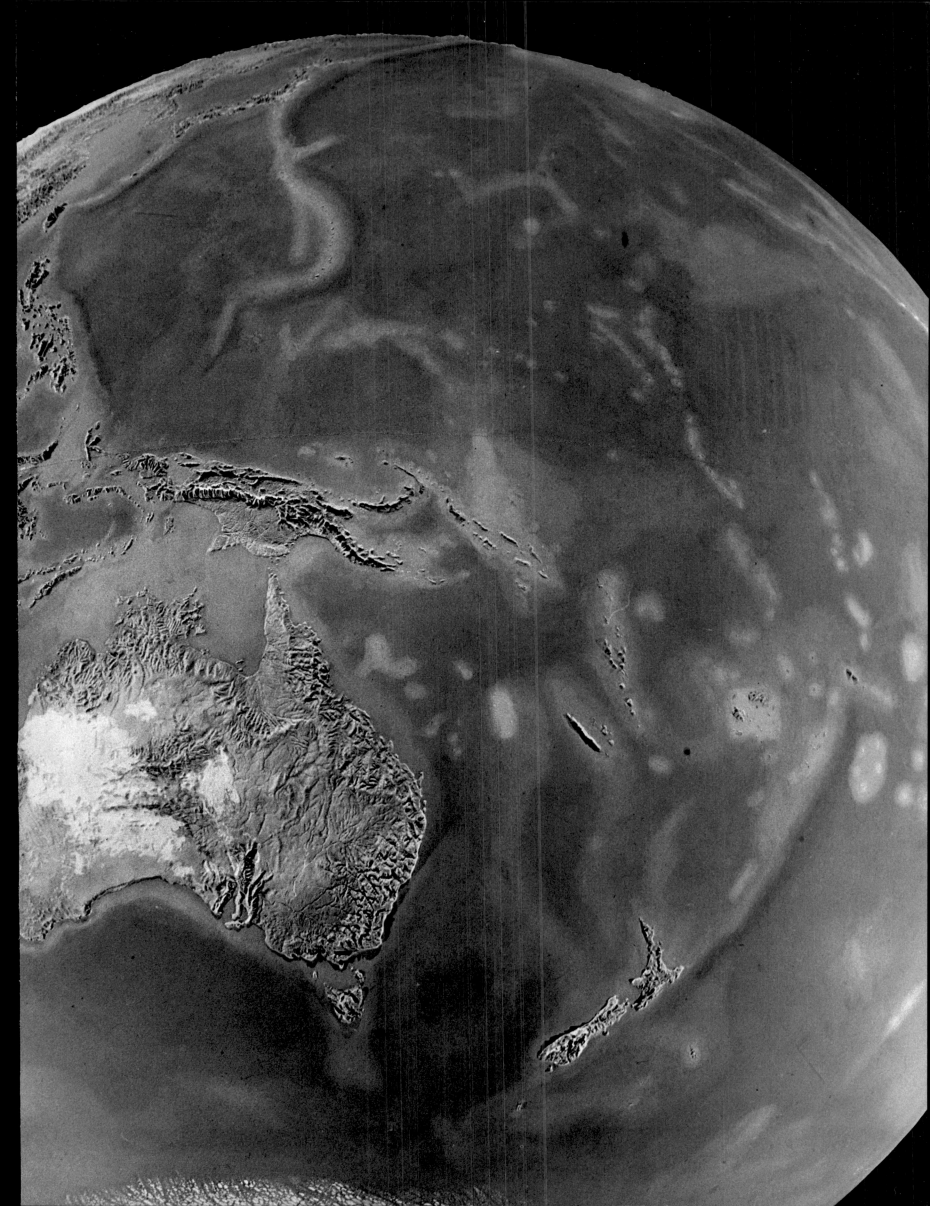

Polynesia: Traditional boats

AMERICAN SAMOA

The five islands and two atolls of American Samoa comprise a United States dependency, defined in the constitution as an Unincorporated Territory, largely autonomous in internal matters. They are administered by the Ministry of Internal Affairs of the United States of America and fall under the jurisdiction of a Governor, responsible to the bicameral Parliament (Fono/Legislature), which comprises a Chamber of Deputies, elected by direct universal suffrage, and the Senate, whose members are elected by the chief Samoans.

The territory is made up of the more easterly islands of Samoa in Polynesia; the largest is Tutuila, seat of the capital, Pago Pago.
Area: 197 sq km.
Population: 38,000, mostly Polynesian.
Capital: Pago Pago (pop 3,100) on Tutuila Island, but the seat of government is on Fagatogo.
Land use: cultivated 40%; wooded 50%; uncultivated 10%. Main agricultural products: coconuts, copra, bananas.
Official languages: Samoan and English.
Religion: Protestant, Catholic.
Gross National Product: US $ 180 million; per capita: US $ 5,480.
Currency: US dollar = 100 cents.

Australia: Ayer's Rock

AUSTRALIA
Commonwealth of Australia

Australia is a federal state, and a member of the Commonwealth of Nations, comprising 6 Federated States (Southern Australia, Western Australia, South New Wales, Queensland, Tasmania, Victoria), one Territory (Northern Territory) and a Federal District that hosts the capital. The head of state is the Sovereign of Great Britain, whose authority is delegated through a Governor General appointed by the British Government. Legislative power is held by the Federal Parliament, constituted by the Governor General, by the Chamber of Deputies, elected for 3 years by direct universal suffrage, and by the Senate, made up of 76 members elected for 6 years, also by direct universal suffrage. Executive power is exercised by the Federal Executive Council under the Presidency of the Governor General. Each of the 6 Federated States is administered by a Governor and an elected Parliament.

Australia is a member of UNO, the OECD and ANZUS.

Australia is situated in the southern hemisphere between the Pacific and the Indian Oceans. It includes all of the continental part of Oceania and the island of Tasmania. The territory is quite uniform. Along the eastern and south-eastern coasts there is the Great Dividing Range of mountains; west of this extends a low grassland which becomes more arid until it transforms itself into vast sandy desert plains which continues up to the coasts of the Indian Ocean. The only forests (eucalyptus) are in the north. Many lakes such as Lake Eyre show the effects of irregular rainfall. There are only two important rivers. The offshore Great Barrier Reef extends to the east and to the north parallel to the coast.
Area: 7,685,000 sq km, politically and administratively divided into 6 Federated States, plus 1 Territory and the Federal District.
Population: 16,470,000 mostly Whites; only 1% approx. are Aborigine; 2 per sq km.
Annual growth rate: 1.5%; birth rate 15‰; death rate 7.5‰; average life expectancy: 74 years.
Capital: Canberra (pop 300,000).
Other important towns: Adelaide (930); Brisbane (1,170,000); Darwin (68,000); Hobart (170,000); Melbourne (2,940,000); Newcastle (416,000); Perth (1,030,000); Sydney (3,430,000).
Land use: cultivated 6%; grazing 57%; wooded 14%; uncultivated 23%. Main agricultural products: wheat, barley, sugar cane, wine, vegetables, wool, fruit; timber. Other activities: livestock rearing. Mineral resources: bauxite, iron ore, lead, gold, oil.
Official language: English.
Religion: Protestant.
Gross National Product: US $ 161,400 million; per capita: US $ 10,100.
Currency: Australian dollar = 100 cents.
Dependencies: Norfolk Island, Macquarie Islands; the Coral Sea Islands Territory, the Ashmore and Cartier Islands; Cocos, Christmas, Heard and McDonald Islands; Australian Antarctic Territory.

COOK ISLANDS

The Cook Islands are partly dependent on New Zealand but have had complete internal autonomy since 4th August 1965. New Zealand remains in charge of its defence and foreign policy. The head of state is the same as that of New Zealand, that is the Sovereign of Great Britain; a Resident Commissioner represents both the Sovereign and the New Zealand Government; he is assisted in his functions by a Legislative Assembly and by one Executive Cabinet and is responsible to the Legislative Assembly.

The territory, in Polynesia, consists of 8

Australia: Merino sheep

principal islands of which two are of volcanic origins and the other coral. Rarotonga is the largest.
Area: 235 sq km.
Population: 18,000 mostly Polynesian; 76 per sq km.
Capital: Avarua, on the island of Rarotonga.
Main agricultural products: coconuts, fruit, vegetables.
Official language: English.
Religion: Protestant.
Gross National Product: US $ 20 million; per capita: US $ 1,360.
Currency: New Zealand dollar = 100 cents.

FIJI
Matanitu ko Viti

Fiji has been an independent state since 10th October 1970 (previously it was a British colony). It was part of the Commonwealth of Nations until 16th October 1987. Following the military coup of 6th October 1987 the constitution was suspended.
Fiji is a member of UNO.

The territory consists of about 320 islands of which 105 are inhabited, in the extreme south-east of Melanesia. Viti Levu and Vanua Levu, which constitute 87% of all the territory, are mountainous, of volcanic origin and protected by a coral barrier.
Area: 18,270 sq km.
Population: 745,000, mostly Asian Indians (48%) and Fijians (46%); then Polynesians, Chinese and Melanesians; density: 40 per sq km.
Annual growth rate: 2%; birth rate 28‰; death rate 4‰; average life expectancy: 70 years.
Capital: Suva (pop 70,000).
Land use: cultivated 13%; grazing 3%; wooded 65%; uncultivated 19%. Main agricultural products: sugar cane, coconuts, rice, maize, cocoa.
Official languages: English and Fijian.
Religion: Hindu (45%); Christian and Islamic.
Gross National Product: US $ 1,280 million; per capita: US $ 1,710.
Currency: Fijian dollar = 100 cents.

FRENCH POLYNESIA
Polynésie Française

French Polynesia is an Overseas Territory of the Republic of France, partly autonomous,

administered by a Governor, who is assisted in exercising his functions by a Government Council, elected and presided over by him, and by a Territorial Assembly, whose members are elected for 5 years by direct universal suffrage; it is represented in the French Parliament by 1 Senator and 2 Deputies.

Its territory is constituted by five groups of islands: the Society Islands, Marquesa Islands, Tubuai Islands, Tuamotu Islands and Gambier Islands. Except for the Tuamotus, which are atolls, all the other islands are volcanic, very high, with peaks and valleys covered by tropical vegetation, most of them with coral barriers and lagoons.

Area: 4,000 sq km; administratively divided into 4 sections: Society Islands, Marquesas, Tubuais, Tuamotus.
Population: 160,000, mostly Polynesian; 40 per sq km.
Annual growth rate: 2.6%.
Capital: Papeete (65,000).
Land use: cultivated 20.5%; grazing 5.5%; wooded 31%; uncultivated 43%. Main agricultural products: coconuts, copra, sugar cane, vegetables.
Official language: French.
Religion: Christian.
Currency: CFP franc = 100 centimes.

GUAM

Guam is a dependency of the United States of America as, according to the constitution, an Unincorporated Territory, and allowed considerable autonomy in internal affairs. The territory, corresponding to the island of the same name, is the largest and the most southerly of the Mariana Islands; since 1949 it has been dependent on the United States' Ministry of Internal Affairs (from 1889 to 1949 it was subject to the authority of the Naval Office). It is now presided over by a Governor, elected for 4 years, who administers with the assistance of the Guam Legislature, elected for 2 years by direct universal suffrage by permanent residents; these are United States citizens for all practical purposes, but they do not have the right to vote in a US federal election. Guam is represented in the United States House of Representatives by 1 Delegate elected every 2 years.

The territory consists of the main island of the Marianas in the western Pacific, which is considered a most important strategic location. The north is terraced and cultivated, the south is hilly and pastoral.
Area: 550 sq km.
Population: 130,000, mostly Micronesian; 236 per sq km.
Annual growth rate: 2.2%.
Capital: Agana (pop 4,800).
Land use: cultivated 22%; grazing 15%; wooded 18%; uncultivated 45%. Main agricultural products: pineapples, bananas, maize, rice, sweet potatoes.
Official language: English.
Religion: Christian.
Gross National Product: US $ 740 million; per capita: US $ 7,010.
Currency: US dollar = 100 cents.

KIRIBATI

Republic of Kiribati

Once a British colony as the Gilbert Islands, Kiribati has been an independent republic since 12th July 1979, and a member of the Commonwealth of Nations. The legislative power is held by a unicameral Parliament,

Australia: The coast near Port Campbell

whose members are elected by direct universal suffrage.
Area: 850 sq km.
Population: 68 200, mostly Micronesian and Polynesian; 80 per sq km.
Annual growth rate: 1.9%.
Capital: Bairiki (2,100), on the island of Tarawa.
Land use: cultivated 50%; wooded 3%; uncultivated 47%. Main agricultural products: coconuts, copra, fruit, vegetables.
Official language: English and Gilbertese.
Religion: Christian.
Gross National Product: US $ 50 million; per capita: US $ 770.
Currency: Australian dollar = 100 cents.

MARSHALL ISLANDS

The Marshall Islands form a semi-independent republic, constituted in 1986 following the break-up of the Trust Territory of the Pacific Islands, entrusted to the United States by UNO in 1947. It enjoys complete administrative autonomy, but its defence and foreign policy are the responsibility of the United States.

It comprises an archipelago of atolls, made up of two long arcs, Ratak and Ralik, in Micronesia. The largest of the atolls is Kwajalein, the most famous is Bikini.
Area: 180 sq km.
Population: 42,000, mostly Micronesian.
Capital: Jaluit, in the Majuro Atoll.
Main agricultural products: coconuts, copra, vegetables, fruit.
Official language: English.
Religion: Christian.
Currency: US dollar = 100 cents.

MICRONESIA

Federated States of Micronesia

Micronesia forms a semi-independent state, constituted in 1986 following the break-up of the Trust Territory of the Pacific Islands, entrusted by UNO to the United States in 1947. Its defence and foreign policy are the responsibility of the United States.

The territory comprises the eastern Caroline Islands in Micronesia: the islands are mostly coralline, the major ones are Ponape and Truk.
Area: 720 sq km.
Population: 100,000, mostly Micronesian.
Capital: Kolonia, on Ponape island.
Main agricultural products: coconuts, copra, vegetables, fruit.
Official language: English.
Religion: Christian.
Currency: US dollar = 100 cents.

MIDWAY ISLANDS

A United States dependency, administered directly by the Ministry of the Navy, Midway Islands is the site of an important naval air base.

The territory comprises Midway Island and 3 other little islands at the extreme north-west of the Hawaiian islands.
Area: 5 sq km.
Population: 2,500, mostly Polynesian.
Main agricultural products: vegetables, fruit.
Official language: English.
Religion: Christian.
Currency: US dollar = 100 cents.

NAURU

Republic of Nauru / Naoero

Once a fiduciary administrative territory entrusted in 1947 by UNO to Australia, Nauru is now an independent republic (from 31st

Australia: Sydney and its harbour

January 1968) and a member of the Commonwealth of Nations, comprising a single atoll. Legislative power is held by a unicameral Parliament whose members are elected by direct universal suffrage for 3 years. Executive power is held by the President of the Republic, who exercises his functions with the help of the Council of Ministers and is responsible to Parliament.

Nauru is a small coral island in Micronesia, comprising a thin and fertile coastal strip surrounding an internal plateau.
Area: 21.5 sq km.
Population: 7,300, mostly Polynesian; 339 per sq km.
Capital: Yaren.
Main agricultural products: vegetables, fruit.
Official language: English (8%) and Nauruan (52%).
Religion: Protestant.
Currency: Australian dollar = 100 cents.

NEW CALEDONIA

Nouvelle Calédonie

New Caledonia is an Overseas Territory of the Republic of France, partly autonomous, administered by a Governor, who is assisted in exercising his functions by an elected Territorial Assembly and by an Executive Council. New Caledonia is represented in the French Parliament by 2 Senators and 2 Deputies.

Its territory includes various islands and the large island of the same name, located south-west of Melanesia.

The island is mountainous, of volcanic origin, bordered by a coral barrier and partly covered in forest.
Area: 19,060 sq km.
Population: 165,000, mostly Melanesian (45%); then European and Polynesian.
Annual growth rate: 1.3%.
Capital: Nouméa (pop 75,000).
Land use: cultivated 0.5%; grazing 8%; wooded 51%; uncultivated 40,5%. Main agricultural products: coconuts, copra, maize, coffee, sweet potatoes.
Official language: French.
Religion: Christian.
Gross National Product: US $ 1,100 million; per capita: US $ 7,830.
Currency: CFP franc = 100 centimes.

NEW ZEALAND

Dominion of New Zealand

An independent state, New Zealand has been a member of the Commonwealth of Nations since 1931. The head of state is the Sovereign of Great Britain who delegates authority through a Governor General appointed by the Government. He exercises his executive power through the Prime Minister and the Executive Council. The legislative power is held by the House of Representatives, whose members are elected for 3 years by direct universal suffrage.

New Zealand is a member of UNO, the OECD and ANZUS.

It is separated from Australia by the Tasman Sea and is surrounded by the Pacific Ocean; the New Zealand archipelago is formed by two large islands: North Island has many mountains, some of them volcanic; South Island is crossed by the Southern Alps, also high mountains, but is rich in fields and pasture lands.
Area: 268,675 sq km.
Population: 3 350,000, mostly Whites of European origin; 12 per sq km.
Annual growth rate: 0.7%; birth rate 18‰; death rate 8‰; average life expectancy: 73 years.

Capital: Wellington (pop 350,000).
Other important towns: Auckland (840,000); Christchurch (300,000); Dunedin (106,000); Hamilton (103,000); Invercargill (52,000); Napier (52,000); New Plymouth (48,000).
Land use: cultivated 2%; grazing 52%; wooded 27%; uncultivated 19%. Main agricultural products: wheat, potatoes, tobacco, vegetables, fruit. Other activities: cattle rearing. Mineral resources: coal, gold.
Official language: English.
Religions: Anglican, Presbyterian and Catholic.
Gross National Product: US $ 25,900 million; per capita: US $ 7,850.
Currency: New Zealand dollar = 100 cents.
Dependencies: Cook Islands; Tokelau Islands; Niue Atoll; the Ross Dependency (in Antarctica).

NIUE

Niue Islands

Niue is a New Zealand dependency comprising an atoll of the same name, which has complete internal autonomy in free association with New Zealand, who is responsible for foreign policy and defence and provides any necessary economic assistance. It is administered by a Resident Commissioner, who represents the Sovereign of Great Britain and the Government of Wellington. The Commissioner is assisted in exercising his functions by a local legislative and executive body.

The atoll geographically belongs to the Cook Islands.
Area: 260 sq km.
Population: 2,400, mostly Polynesian; 15 per sq km.
Capital: Alofi.
Main agricultural products: coconuts, copra, bananas, fruit, vegetables.
Official language: English, but Niuan is normally spoken.
Religion: Christian.
Currency: New Zealand dollar = 100 cents.

NORTHERN MARIANAS

Commonwealth of the Northern Mariana Islands

The Northern Marianas are a territory in the western Pacific comprising the islands of the same name but excluding Guam. The country is a Commonwealth of the United States of America (from 1st January 1978). The inhabitants of the Northern Mariana Islands are United States citizens (from 3rd November 1986) and enjoy considerable autonomy in their internal affairs (defence and foreign policy are handled by the United States). Head of state is the Governor, who is assisted in exercising his functions by an Executive Council and by an elected bicameral Parliament.

The territory consists of 14 islands in Micronesia, the northern ones originally volcanic, the others coral atolls. The largest are Saipan, Tinian and Rota.
Area: 477 sq km.
Population: 21,900, mostly Micronesian.
Capital: Garapan, on Saipan island.
Main agricultural products: coconuts, copra, rice, fruit, vegetables.
Official languages: English and Chamorro.
Religion: Catholic.
Currency: US dollar = 100 cents.

Melanesia: A village in the Fiji islands

A coral island in Oceania

PALAU

Republic of Palau / Republic of Belau

Palau is a semi-independent republic, constituted in 1986 following the break-up of the Trust Territory of the Pacific Islands, entrusted by UNO to the United States in 1947. The state, which corresponds to the Palau archipelago, enjoys complete autonomy, but its defence and foreign policy are handled by the United States.
The territory comprises the island of Palau in the western Pacific, east of the Philippines.
Area: 485 sq km.
Population: 14,700, mostly Micronesian.
Capital: Koror (pop 7,600).
Main agricultural products: coconuts, fruit, vegetables.
Official language: English.
Religion: Christian.
Currency: US dollar = 100 cents.

PAPUA NEW GUINEA

Papua New Guinea is an independent state (from September 1975, but since 1st December 1973 it has gained internal autonomy), and a member of the Commonwealth of Nations. It comprises the ex-Australian Territory of Papua and the ex-Australian Trust Territory of New Guinea, mandated in 1946 by UNO to Australia and administered jointly with Papua. The head of state is the Sovereign of Great Britain who delegates authority through a Governor General appointed by the Government. Legislative power is held by the unicameral Parliament (House of Assembly), whose members are elected for 4 years by direct universal suffrage. Executive power is held by the Government, presided over by the Prime Minister, who is responsible to the Parliament.
Papua New Guinea is a member of UNO.
The territory comprises eastern New Guinea, the Bismarck archipelago and the northern Solomon Islands. It is crossed by the Bismarck Mountains with perennial snowy summits. The flat and hilly areas that stretch down to the coasts are covered by equatorial vegetation.
Area: 462,840 sq km.
Population: 3,560,000, mostly Papuan, then Malaysian, Melanesian and Chinese; density: 7 per sq km.
Annual growth rate: 2.3%; birth rate 45%; death rate 16‰; average life expectancy: 51 years.
Capital: Port Moresby (pop 152,000).
Other important towns: Goroka (19,000); Lae (61,700); Madang (21,000); Rabaul (15,000); Wewak (20,000).
Land use: cultivated 0.8%; grazing 0.2%; wooded 83%; uncultivated 16%. Main agricultural products: cocoa, copra, bananas, sugar cane, sweet potatoes, tea, coffee.
Official language: English. Many native dialects spoken; also Pidgin English.
Religion: Christian.
Gross National Product: US $ 2,410 million, per capita: US $ 670.
Currency: Kina = 100 toae.

PITCAIRN ISLANDS

A British colony administered by the Governor of the Fiji Islands until its independence in October 1970, the Pitcairn Islands have since been administered by a British High Commissioner in New Zealand, assisted in exercising its functions by a Council (Island Council) composed of 10 members only partly elected.
The territory comprises Pitcairn Island (inhabited by the descendants of the mutineers of the *Bounty*) and three uninhabited atolls in the southern extreme of Polynesia.
Area: 37 sq km.
Population: 70; 2 per sq km.
Main town: Adamstown.
Main agricultural products: fruit, vegetables.
Official language: English.
Religion: Christian.
Currency: UK £ Sterling = 100 pence.
Dependencies: the uninhabited islands of Ducie, Henderson, Oeno.

SOLOMON ISLANDS

The Solomon Islands has been a British protectorate since 1893, autonomous since 2nd January 1976, and now is an independent state (since 7th July 1978), and a member of the Commonwealth of Nations. Legislative power is held by a unicameral Parliament, whose members are elected by direct universal suffrage.
The Solomon Island is a member of UNO.
The country comprises a large group of islands in Melanesia, some of which are of coralline origin, others volcanic.
Area: 27,550 sq km.
Population: 301,000; mostly Melanesian, then Polynesian; Micronesian, Chinese and European.
Annual growth rate: 3.5%; birth rate 41‰; death rate 10‰.
Capital: Honiara (31,000), on Guadacanal Island.
Land use: cultivated 2%; grazing 1%; wooded 93%; uncultivated 4%. Main agricultural products: coconuts, copra, sweet potatoes, rice, cocoa.
Official language: English.
Religion: Protestant.
Gross National Product: US $ 100 million; per capita: US $ 360.
Currency: Solomon dollar = 100 cents.

TOKELAU ISLANDS

Tokelau has been an island dependency of New Zealand since 11th February 1926, but

Polynesia: Easter Island

was formally annexed to New Zealand on 1st January 1949. It is administered by a Governor General, who represents the Sovereign of Great Britain and the Government of Wellington.
The country is a group of coral islands north of Samoa in Polynesia.
Area: 10 sq km.
Population: 1,600, mostly Polynesian.
Capital: Fakaofo.
Main agricultural products: coconuts, copra, bananas.
Official language: English, but Tokelauan is commonly spoken.
Religion: Christian.
Currency: New Zealand dollar = 100 cents.

TONGA

Once a British Protectorate Tonga is now an independent state (from 4th June 1970), ruled by a monarchy in which the royal heritage is through the male or female line; it is a member of the Commonwealth of Nations. The Sovereign exercises executive power through a Privy Council, which he nominates, and legislative power through the Legislative Assembly, formed of members of the Privy Council, of Governors of Ha'apai and of Vava'u, and of a certain number of Deputies (as few as two thirds) elected for 3 years by universal direct suffrage.
Tonga comprises some 150 islands and islets to the east of the deep-sea Tonga Trench; there are 3 major islands groups, all subject to volcanic activity.
Area: 700 sq km.
Population: 100,000, mostly Polynesian; 143 per sq km.
Capital: Nukualofa (29,000).
Land use: cultivated 79%; grazing 6%; wooded 12%; uncultivated 3%. Main agricultural products: coconuts, copra, sweet potatoes, bananas.
Official language: Tongan and English.
Religion: Protestant.
Gross National Product: US $ 50 million; per capita: US $ 520.
Currency: Pa'anga = 100 seniti.

TUVALU

As the Ellice Islands, Tuvalu was a British colony administered jointly with the Gilbert Islands (now Kiribati) until October 1975, when the Ellice Islands became the separate colony of Tuvalu. They are now an independent state (since 1st October 1978) and member of the Commonwealth of Nations. The legislative power is held by a unicameral Parliament whose members are elected by direct universal suffrage.
Tuvalu is a group of 9 atolls south of Kiribati, in Micronesia, the most important of which is Fanafuti.
Area: 25 sq km.
Population: 9,000, mostly Polynesian.
Capital: Vaiaku (pop 3,000).
Main agricultural products: coconuts, copra, vegetables.
Official language: Tuvaluan and English.
Religion: Protestant.
Gross National Product: US $ 4 million; per capita: US $ 570.
Currency: Australian dollar = 100 cents.

VANUATU

Ripablik blong Vanuatu

Previously jointly held by France and Britain (from 1906), Vanuatu has been an independent state since 30th July 1980, constituted as a parliamentary republic, and a member of the Commonwealth of Nations. Legislative power is held by a unicameral Parliament, whose members are elected by direct universal suffrage.
Vanuatu is a member of UNO.
It is constituted by approx. 40 volcanic and coral islands, in Micronesia. The most important are Espiritu Santo, Maéwo, Pentecoste, Malakula, Éfaté and Eromanga, in part covered by forests.
Area: 14,765 sq km.
Population: 150,000, mostly Melanesian.
Annual growth rate: 3.1%.
Capital: Port-Vila (pop 15,000), on the island of Éfaté.
Land use: cultivated 6%; grazing 2%; wooded 1%; uncultivated 91%. Main agricultural products: coconuts, copra, cocoa, coffee.
Official languages: English, French, Bislama.
Religion: Christian and Animist.
Gross National Product: US $ 60 million; per capita: US $ 530.
Currency: Vatu.

WALLIS AND FUTUNA

Wallis et Futuna

Previously a French Protectorate under the control of the Commissioner of New Caledonia, Wallis and Futuna is now (since 22th December 1959) a French Overseas Territory, ruled by a Governor and represented in the French Parliament by 1 Senator and 1 Deputy.
The territory comprises the Wallis Islands including Uvéa and the Hoorn Islands with Futuna and Alofi, north-east of Fiji. The islands are hilly and covered in dense forest.
Area: 255 sq km.
Population: 12,500, mostly Polynesian.
Capital: Mata-Utu.
Main agricultural products: coconuts, copra, cassava, bananas.
Official language: French.
Religion: Catholic.
Currency: French franc = 100 centimes.

WESTERN SAMOA

Samoa i Sisifo

Once a territory mandated in administrative trust to New Zealand by UNO, Western Samoa is now an independent state (from 1st January 1962), member of the Commonwealth of Nations.
The present head of state, who holds a lifetime post (while the next will be elected by the Parliament for 5 years), exercises his executive power through the Prime Minister and the ministers nominated by him based on the suggestions of the Prime Minister. The legislative power is held by the Legislative Assembly, whose members are elected for 3 years, mostly by the chiefs of the several Samoan tribes.
Western Samoan is a member of UNO.
The territory occupies the larger part of the island of Samoa situated in western Polynesia. There are two larger islands, Savai'i and Upolu, which are of volcanic origin, mountainous and half covered by forests. There are also two minor islands.
Area: 2,840 sq km.
Population: 162,000, mostly Polynesian (90%); 55 per sq km.
Annual growth rate: 0.6%; birth rate 37‰; death rate 7‰; average life expectancy: 63 years.
Capital: Apia (35,000).
Land use: cultivated 42%; grazing 0.5%; wooded 47%; uncultivated 10.5%. Main agricultural products: coconuts, copra, cocoa, bananas.
Official languages: Samoan and English.
Religion: Protestant.
Currency: Tala = 100 sene.

The Polar Regions

The Arctic and the Antarctic are grouped together because of their geographical position, both being at latitudes within the Arctic Circles, and because of their constantly low temperatures. It must be remembered however that while Antarctica is a true continent covered with ice, the Arctic, though it includes the northern extremities of Canada, Alaska and Siberia, and the whole of Greenland, is for the most part an ice-cap floating on the Arctic Ocean. The temperatures are extremely low, with a monthly average varying from +1.5°C to —30°C. Even in the period when the Sun does not set, because it never rises more than 23° 30' above the horizon effective thermal energy is very limited owing to the inclination of the Sun's rays.

The surface of the ice-cap, which reaches a thickness of 4 kilometres, is not regular. Winds and currents compress and fracture the ice creating crevasses of varying dimensions. In the summer period the ice-cap breaks up into numerous fragments and diminishes in size. Vegetation typical of tundra areas develops in the most southerly areas where the Arctic peoples live: the Eskimos in Greenland and Alaska, the Samoyeds and Chukchi in Siberia, and the Lapps in Scandinavia.

The Antarctic ice lies on a base of solid rock, which is a real continent, bigger than Europe. Some 90% of the ice in the world is found in Antarctica. The enormous cap of ice, formed by snow deposited over millennia, has an average thickness of 2,000-2,500 metres. Huge glaciers, hundreds of metres long, extend from the centre of the continent to the ocean. There are several mountains of over 4,000 metres in height, the highest being the Vinson Massif.

The climate is more severe than that of the Arctic. Average temperatures vary from —25°C to —60°C, but in the highland inland areas winter temperatures of below —80°C have been recorded. This is due to the limited amount of heat from the Sun and the considerable dispersal of heat caused by reflection from the snow on the ice-cap. In the very few areas not covered by snow and ice, called the 'dry valleys', higher temperatures have been recorded, probably resulting from volcanic activity in the areas.

The Arctic Region

The Arctic is the name used to refer to the vast area which includes all the territories and waters north of the Arctic Circle. Spitsbergen/Svalbard and Jan Mayen islands (Norwegian) and Novaya Zemlya and Franz Josef Land/Zemlya Frantsa Josifa (Soviet) are in Europe, while in Asia are Severnaya Zemlya, the New Siberian Islands and Wrangel Island, all of which are Soviet territories. In North America are the groups of islands to the north of Canada: Queen Elizabeth Islands, Baffin Island, Ellesmere Island etc. (Canadian) and Greenland (ex-Danish).

The Antarctic Region

This name refers to the enormous expanse of the Antarctic continent, which is permanently covered by a thick layer of ice, together with the islands which surround it in the south Atlantic, Indian and Pacific Oceans.

Part of this immense area has been claimed by various states, but at the end of the International Geophysical Year, on 1st De-

cember 1959, 12 countries (Argentina, Australia, Belgium, Chile, France, Great Britain, Japan, New Zealand, Norway, South Africa, USA, and USSR - Poland also joined in 1977) signed the Antarctic Treaty, and agreed to freeze until 1991 the various territorial claims and controversies about sovereignty until the resources of this huge area are better known. They also agreed to complete denuclearization of the area, including a ban on the depositing of nuclear waste.

According to the treaty the 'Ice Continent' should be under a sort of international supervision and all territory below the 60° latitude may not belong to any country. Nevertheless some of the countries who signed the treaty have not renounced their claim to specific areas of the Antarctic.

Norway claims sovereignty of the area between longitudes 20°W and 45°F and also of Peter Island (250 sq km) in the south-east Pacific and Bouvet Island (60 sq km) in the south Atlantic. The area between 45°E and 160°E, apart from Terre Adélie, which is claimed by France, is normally considered

Australian and called Australian Antarctic Territory. The Macquarie Islands (175 sq km) in the south-west Pacific and Heard and Macdonald Islands (together 260 sq km) in the southern Indian Ocean also belong to Australia.

As well as Terre Adélie between 136°E and 142°E also belonging to France are the Kerguelen Islands (6,230 sq km), the Crozet group (475 sq km), Amsterdam Island (65 sq km) and Saint Paul Island (7 sq km) in the southern Indian Ocean. Together they are called French Austral and Antarctic Territories (Terres Australes et Antarctiques Françaises).

New Zealand claims sovereignty over the area between 160°W and 150°W, calling it the Ross Dependency.

Immediately east of this area, between longitudes 150°W and 80°W is the area normally considered to belong to the USA, though they have never claimed sovereignty.

Great Britain considers British Antarctic Territory as hers. It includes the South Shetland Islands, the South Orkney Islands and the

part of the continent between longitudes 20°W and 80°W.

Finally Chile and Argentina claim the areas between longitudes 53°W and 90°W and between 25°W and 74°W respectively.

Useful Information

The geographical maps are numbered 1–57. The diagrammatic subject maps have roman numerals.

The index is in alphabetical order. The number given in heavy type gives the page number of the relevant map. The letter and number following the page number correspond to numbers printed in red above and to the side of each map. Imaginary lines drawn between this letter and figure will meet at the place-name being sought.

Glossary of Geographical and Geological Terms

Artesian well – A deep, narrow well sunk into an artesian basin and producing a continuous stream of water at the surface. The water is forced upwards because the outlet of the well is below the level of the water's source.

Atmosphere, Air – The envelope of mixed gases that surrounds the Earth, up to a height of some 300 miles (about 480 km). It consists of about 78% nitrogen and about 21% oxygen. Argon, carbon dioxide, helium, and some other gases make up the remaining 1%. Often, the atmosphere also contains water vapour. The atmosphere is tasteless, odourless, and colourless. Its characteristics vary at different altitudes. For this reason it is usually described as having four layers—the troposphere, stratosphere, ionosphere, and exosphere.

Atmospheric pressure – The pressure of the atmosphere on the surface of the Earth as a result of its weight of about 6,000 million million tons. The average atmospheric pressure at sea level is 14.7 pounds per sq inch (1,033 g per sq cm). Atmospheric pressure decreases with altitude.

Bayou – A marshy creek found in flat country, especially a creek along the lower reaches of the Mississippi River in the United States.

Bedrock – Solid, unweathered rock lying beneath the soil and subsoil with which most of the Earth is covered.

Bore – A wall of foaming water that travels at speed up a river. It occurs when a tidal wave enters an estuary and breaks as it proceeds up river.

Boulder clay – Thick clay with stones of all sizes formed of rock that has been crushed and deposited by glaciers and ice sheets.

Caledonian – Term used to describe ancient mountain ranges that run through western Scandinavia, Scotland, and north-western Ireland. The term also describes the Silurian-Devonian Periods when these mountains were being formed.

Chalk – A white, fine-grained type of limestone, easily broken. It is made up mainly of shells and skeletons of tiny animals. Most of it was formed during the Cretaceous Period, which began about 135 million years ago.

Clay – A type of smooth, slightly oily earth. It is fine-textured and consists of sedimentary rock. When wet, it turns into slippery, sticky mud. Many clays have a large content of mineral fragments.

Col – A high pass in the mountains; a saddle-like gap between two peaks or across a ridge. It is formed when two corries (glacier-formed, half-moon depressions at the head of mountain valleys) eat into opposite sides of a ridge and meet.

Cold desert – (i) A term for the polar regions and tundra, where plant life is limited or non-existent because of snow and ice. (ii) A high inland plateau such as the Gobi Desert, in Asia, whose altitude and distance from the sea make it very cold and dry.

Continental shelf – Shelf round the coasts of the continents. It slopes gently, and is covered by shallow water. Its approximate edge is at the depth of 100 fathoms (about 600 ft or 182 m). In places, the shelf extends outwards from the shore for several hundred miles. Beyond the continental shelf is the continental slope.

Coral reef – A ridge of rock in the sea that is composed chiefly of the skeletons of small animals called *reef-building coral polyps*. The upper part of such reefs is usually at or near the surface. Coral reefs occur only in warm seas.

Current – (i) The upward movement of an air mass. (ii) The distinct flow of water in the channel of a river or stream. (iii) The driving force of an ocean. Ocean currents are caused by the wind and the rotation of the Earth, and flow both in deep and in shallow waters. They may be warm or cold, and have a marked influence on climate.

Delta – A fan-shaped area of land where a river enters a body of standing water. It is built up from alluvial material carried by the river and deposited at its mouth. It is named after *celta* (D), the fourth letter of the Greek alphabet, but not all deltas have this triangular shape. In time, a delta becomes criss-crossed by a network of small channels.

Doldrums – A low-pressure belt round the equator with light surface winds or calms. The doldrums are hot and often wet. Sailing ships avoided them because of the danger of being becalmed.

Fold, Folding – The bending of rock strata, usually molten strata, by pressures beneath the Earth's crust. Folding usually takes place along lines of weakness.

Geest – An area of heath-covered coarse sand and gravel, found in the northern lowlands of Germany and neighbouring regions of Poland, the Netherlands, and Denmark.

Geyser – A hot spring that periodically throws steam and hot water up into the air with explosive force. Geysers are common in the north island of New Zealand, in Iceland, and in Yellowstone National Park in the United States.

Glacier – A very slow-moving river of ice that creeps down a valley from a snowfield above the snow line. It moves under the influence of gravity.

Karst – A rugged type of landscape made up of barren limestone, such as occurs in north-western Yugoslavia, the northern Pennines in England, and the Yucatan region of Mexico. Its main features are dry valleys, sinkholes, caverns, and underground streams.

Limestone – A sedimentary rock consisting of at least 50% calcium carbonate ($CaCO_3$). Some types of limestone formed from the hard remains of tiny sea creatures. Others formed when minerals held in solution were deposited as the water evaporated.

Llanos – A Spanish term meaning 'level lands'; specifically the huge tropical grasslands of the Orinoco basin, in Venezuela and Colombia.

Loess – Fine, clinging, yellowish dust that has been deposited as a soil by the wind. It comes from deserts and from areas that were once covered by ice sheets. Loess soils are highly-valued for agriculture because they are fertile and well-drained.

Maelstrom – (i) A whirlpool. (ii) A powerful current that sweeps between two of the Lofoten Islands off the north-western coast of Norway.

Magma – Molten rock at a very high temperature and pressure lying under the surface of the Earth. Igneous rocks are formed from magma. Magma loses much of its water and gas when thrown out by volcanoes as *lava*.

Magnetic Pole – One of two poles of the Earth's magnetic field to which the free-swinging magnetic needle of a compass points. The North magnetic Pole is near Prince of Wales Island, in northern Canada. The South magnetic Pole is in Wilkes Land, in Antarctica. The magnetic poles are not true N and S. The North magnetic Pole is about 1,000 miles (1,600 km) from the North Pole; the South magnetic Pole about 1,500 miles (2,400 km) from the South Pole.

Metamorphic rock – One of the three main kinds of rocks that makes up the Earth's crust. Originally igneous or sedimentary rock, it has been metamorphosed (transformed) by pressure, heat, and chemical action.

Moraine – Large quantities of rock debris carried along and deposited by a glacier. The material deposited at either side is called a *lateral moraine*; that at the bottom of the valley forming the glacier's course, a *ground moraine*; and that at the melting front of the glacier, a *terminal moraine*.

Permafrost – Subsoil and bedrock that is permanently frozen, as in polar regions. Even though the topsoil may thaw temporarily, the permafrost sometimes goes down as far as 2,000 ft (610 m).

Plateau – A large, level area of land that, generally, rises above the surrounding land. It may have been formed by the upward thrusting of a plain, or by layers of hard rock resisting denudation. Some plateaux, however, lie between higher fold mountain ranges. Plateaux of this type are described as *intermontane*.

Polder – A term used in the Netherlands to describe a stretch of land, at or below sea level, that has been reclaimed from the sea by the building of dykes.

Sediment – Material that has been carried by wind, water, or ice and eventually deposited. Hence *sedimentary rock* is a type of rock made up of sediments that have been laid down in layers and compacted or cemented together.

Sierra – A Spanish term for a mountain range with jagged, saw-like peaks.

Silt – Fine muddy soil that is carried by rivers and streams and deposited as sediment in lakes, deltas, and river valleys.

Steppe – Temperate grassland, as a rule level and treeless. Specifically, steppes are found in the mid-latitudes of Europe and Asia. They correspond to the *prairies* of North America and the *pampas* of South America.

Strait, Straits – A narrow stretch of water that connects two larger bodies of water.

Taiga – Coniferous forests in the high latitudes of the Northern Hemisphere. Tundra lies to the north and steppes to the south.

Trade winds – Fresh, dry, steady winds that blow from high pressure areas in subtropical regions towards the low pressure region of the equator. In the Northern Hemisphere they blow from the NE and in the Southern Hemisphere from the SE. The trade wind belts vary a little in latitude during the course of the year.

Tundra – A treeless Arctic plain that has no corresponding region in the Southern Hemisphere. It lies between the northern polar ice and the northern coniferous forests. Part of the ground is frozen throughout the year and much is waterlogged. Vegetation is made up mostly of sparse grasses, mosses, and lichens.

Veld – A Dutch term meaning 'field'. In South Africa it refers to open grassland.

Volcano – An opening in the Earth's crust through which magma is forced up to the surface. The magma that flows out is called *lava*. As the volcanic materials pile up around the vent, a typical conical hill is formed. An *active* volcano is one that erupts regularly; an *extinct* volcano is one that has not erupted since the beginning of recorded history, and is consequently regarded as dead; a *dormant* volcano is one that has been quiet for a long period but may still be active.

Wadi – An Arabic term for a steep-sided stream bed in a desert.

Index to the maps of the British Isles

A

Abbeyfeale 7 B4
Abbeyleix 7 D4
Aberaeron 5 B4
Aberchirder 6 F3
Aberdare 5 C5
Aberdeen 6 FG3
Aberfeldy 6 E4
Abergavenny 5 CD5
Abertillery 5 CD5
Aberystwyth 5 B4
Abingdon 5 EF5
Achill 7 B3
Achill Head 7 A2-3
Achill Island 7 A3
Achnasheen 6 CD3
Airdrie 6 E5
Aldeburgh 5 H4
Aldershot 5 F5
Alloa 6 E4
Almondsbury 5 D5
Alness 6 D3
Alnwick 5 E1
Alston 5 D2
Altnaharra 6 D2
Alton 5 E5
Altrincham 5 D3
Amlwch 5 B3
Am Uaimh 7 E3
Andover 5 E5
Anglesey 5 B3
Annan 6 E5
Antrim 7 E2
Antrim, Mountains of 7 E1-2
Appleby-in-Westmorland 5 D2
Aran Island 7 C2
Aran Islands 7 B3
Arbroath 6 F4
Ardavasar 6 BC3
Ardee 7 E3
Ardnamurchan, Point of 6 B4
Ardrossan 6 D5
Ards 7 F2
Arisaig 6 C4
Arklow 7 EF4
Armagh 7 E2
Arran 6 C5
Ashbourne 5 E3
Ashford 5 GH5
Athboy 7 E3
Athery 7 C3
Athlone 7 D3
Athy 7 E4
Auchterarder 6 E4
Auchtermuchty 6 E4
Aughnacloy 7 D2
Aviemore 6 E3
Avon, Country 5 D5
Avon, River 5 E4
Axminster 5 D6
Aylesbury 5 EF5
Ayr 6 D5
Ayre, Point of 5 B2

B

Bailieborough 7 DE3
Balallan 6 B2
Balbriggan 7 EF3
Ballachulish, North 6 CD4
Ballaghaderreen 7 C3
Ballater 6 EF3
Ballina 7 C4

Ballina 7 BC2
Ballinasloe 7 C3
Ballinrobe 7 BC3
Ballybunion 7 B4
Ballycastle 7 EF1
Ballyclare 7 E2
Ballyhaunis 7 C3
Ballymena 7 E2
Ballymoney 7 E1
Ballymote 7 C2
Ballynahinch 7 EF2
Ballyshannon 7 C2
Baltasound 6 a
Baltimore 7 B5
Banagher 7 D3
Banbridge 7 E2
Banbury 5 E4
Banchory 6 F3
Bandon 7 C5
Banff 6 F3
Bangor 7 F2
Bangor 5 BC3
Bann 7 E2
Bantry 7 B5
Bantry Bay 7 B5
Bardsey Island 5 B4
Barmouth 5 B4
Barnard Castle 5 E2
Barnsley 5 E3
Barnstaple 5 BC5
Barra 6 A4
Barrhead 6 D5
Barrow 7 E4
Barrow-in-Furness 5 C2
Barry 5 C5
Barton-upon-Humber 5 F3
Barvas 6 B2
Basildon 5 G5
Basingstoke 5 E5
Bath 5 D5
Bathgate 6 E5
Beachy Head 5 G6
Beauly 6 D3
Beaumaris 5 BC3
Beccles 5 H4
Bedale 5 E2
Bedford 5 F4
Bedfordshire 5 F4
Bedworth 5 E4
Belfast 7 E2
Belfast, County 7 EF2
Belfast Lough 7 F2
Bellingham 5 D1
Belmullet 7 B2
Belper 5 E3
Belturbet 7 D2
Benbecula 6 AB3
Ben Dearg 6 D3
Ben Hope 6 D2
Ben Lawers 6 D4
Ben Macdhui 6 E3
Ben More 6 D4
Ben More Assynt 6 D2
Ben Nevis 6 CD4
Berkshire 5 EF5
Berwick-upon-Tweed 6 FG5
Berwick-upon-Tweed 5 E1
Betws-y-Coed 5 C3
Beverley 5 F3
Bexhill 5 G6
Bideford 5 B6
Biggar 6 E5
Birkenhead 5 C3
Birmingham 5 E4
Birr 7 D3
Bishop Auckland 5 DE2
Bishop's Stortford 5 G5
Blackburn 5 D3
Blackpool 5 C3
Blackwater, River 7 C4

Blackwater, River 7 E3
Blackwater, River 7 E2
Blair Atholl 6 E4
Blairgowrie 6 E4
Blandford Forum 5 DE6
Bletchley 5 F4
Bloody Foreland 7 C1
Blyth 5 E1
Bodmin 5 B6
Bognor Regis 5 F6
Bolton 5 D3
Bonarbridge 6 D3
Bo'ness 6 E4
Borders 6 EF5
Borth 5 B4
Boston 5 FG3
Bournemouth 5 DE6
Boyle 7 C2
Boyne 7 E3
Brackley 5 E4
Bradford 5 DE3
Bradford-on-Avon 5 D5
Brae 6 a
Braemar 6 E4
Braintree 5 G5
Brandon Mountain 7 A4
Bray 7 E3
Brechin 6 F4
Brecon 5 C5
Brecon Beacons 5 C5
Brentwood 5 G5
Bridgend 5 C5
Bridgford, West 5 EF4
Bridgnorth 5 D4
Bridgwater 5 CD5
Bridlington 5 FG2
Bridport 5 D6
Brighton 5 FG6
Bristol 5 D5
Bristol Channel 5 BC5
Brixham 5 C6
Broadford 6 BC3
Broad Law 6 E5
Brodick 6 C5
Bromsgrove 5 D4
Brora 6 E2
Brora, River 6 D2
Brosna 7 D3
Brown Willy 5 B6
Buckhaven 6 EF4
Buckie 6 EF3
Buckingham 5 EF5
Buckinghamshire 5 EF5
Bude 5 B6
Builth Wells 5 C4
Bunclody 7 E4
Buncrana 7 D1
Bundoran 7 C2
Bungay 5 H4
Burghead 6 E3
Burnley 5 D3
Burton 5 E3
Burton-upon-Trent 5 E4
Bury 5 D3
Bury Saint Edmunds 5 GH4
Bute 6 C5
Buttevant 7 C4
Butt of Lewis 6 B2

C

Cader Idris 5 C4
Caernarfon 5 B3
Caernarfon Bay 5 B3
Caerphilly 5 C5
Cahersiveen 7 A5
Cahir 7 D4
Cahore Point 7 EF4

Cairngorm Mountains 6 E3
Caldy Island 5 B5
Caledonian Canal 6 D3
Calf of Man 5 AB2
Callan 7 D4
Callander 6 D4
Cam 5 G4
Camborne 5 aB
Camborne 5 A6
Cambrian Mountains 5 C3-4
Cambridge 5 G4
Cambridgeshire 5 FG4
Campbeltown 6 C5
Cannich 6 D3
Cannock 5 D4
Canterbury 5 H5
Capel Curig 5 C3
Cape Wrath 6 C2
Cardiff 5 CD5
Cardigan 5 B4
Cardigan Bay 5 B4
Cardonagh 7 DE1
Carlisle 5 CD2
Carlow 7 E4
Carloway 6 AB2
Carmarthen 5 B5
Carn Eige 6 CD3
Carnoustie 6 F4
Carnsore Point 7 EF4
Carrauntoohill 7 B4
Carrickfergus 7 F2
Carrickmacross 7 E2
Carrick-on-Shannon 7 CD3
Carrick-on-Sur 7 D4
Cashel 7 D4
Castlebay 6 A4
Castleblayney 7 DE2
Castle Douglas 6 E6
Castleford 5 EF3
Castleisland 7 B4
Castlerea 7 C3
Castletown 6 E2
Castletown 5 B2
Castletown Bearhaven 7 AB5
Cavan 7 D3
Cavan, Country 7 D2
Ceanannus Mor 7 D3
Central 6 D4
Chatham 5 G5
Chelmsford 5 G5
Cheltenham 5 DE5
Chepstow 5 D5
Cheshire 5 D3
Cheshunt 5 G5
Chester 5 CD3
Chesterfield 5 E3
Chester-le-Street 5 E2
Cheviot Hills 5 DE1
Cheviot, the 5 DE1
Chichester 5 F6
Chigwell 5 G5
Chilterns 5 F5
Chippenham 5 DE5
Chipping Norton 5 E5
Chorley 5 D3
Christchrch 5 E6
Cirencester 5 DE5
Clachan 6 A3
Clacton-on-Sea 5 H5
Clara 7 D3
Clare 7 BC4
Clare Island 7 A3
Claremorris 7 B3
Clear Island 7 B5
Cleat 6 F2
Cleethorpes 5 G3
Cleveland 5 E2
Clew Bay 7 B3

Clifden 7 B3
Clisham 6 B2-3
Clogher Head 7 EF3
Clonakilty 7 C5
Clondalkin 7 E3
Clonmel 7 D4
Clovelly 5 B5
Clwyd 5 C3
Clyde 6 E5
Clyde, Firth of 6 CD5
Coalville 5 E4
Coatbridge 6 DE5
Cockermouth 5 C2
Colchester 5 GH5
Coldstream 6 F5
Coleraine 7 E1
Coll 6 B4
Collooney 7 C2
Colonsay 6 B4
Colwyn Bay 5 C3
Congleton 5 DE3
Consett 5 E2
Conwy 5 C3
Cooktown 7 E2
Corby 5 F4
Cork 7 C5
Cork, Country 7 C4
Cornwall 5 B6
Cornwall 5 aB
Cotswolds 5 DE4-5
Coupar Angus 6 EF4
Coventry 5 E4
Cowdenbeath 6 E4
Cowes 5 E6
Craigavon 7 E2
Craighouse 6 B5
Craignure 6 C4
Crawley 5 F5
Crewe 5 D3
Crianlarich 6 D4
Crieff 6 E4
Cromarty 6 DE3
Cromer 5 H4
Cross Fell 5 D2
Crowborough 5 G5
Cumbernauld 6 E5
Cumbria 5 CD2
Cumbrian, Mountains 5 CD2
Cumnock 6 D5
Cupar 6 EF4

D

Daingean 7 D3
Dalkeith 6 EF5
Dalmally 6 CD4
Darlington 5 E2
Dartford 5 G5
Dartmoor 5 BC6
Dartmouth 5 C6
Dawlish 5 C6
Deal 5 H5
Dee 5 D3
Dee 6 F3
Denbigh 5 C3
Derby 5 E4
Derbyshire 5 E3
Dereham, East 5 GH4
Derg 7 D2
Derryveagh Mountains 7 C2
Derwent 5 F3
Devizes 5 E5
Devon 5 C6
Dewsbury 5 E3
Didcot 5 E5
Dingle Bay 7 A4

Dingwall 6 D3
Diss 5 H4
Dolgellau 5 C4
Don 6 F3
Doncaster 5 EF3
Donegal 7 CD2
Donegal, Country 7 D2
Donegal Bay 7 C2
Dorchester 5 D6
Dornoch 6 DE3
Dornoch Firth 6 E3
Dorset 5 D6
Douglas 5 B2
Dover 5 H5
Dover, Strait of 5 H5-6
Down 7 F2
Downham Market 5 G4
Downpatrick 7 F2
Driffield 5 F2-3
Drogheda 7 E3
Droichead Nua 7 E3
Droitwich 5 D4
Dublin 7 E3
Dudley 5 D4
Dumbarton 6 D5
Dumfries 6 E5
Dumfries and Galloway 6 D5
Dunbar 6 F4
Dunblane 6 D4
Duncansby Head 6 F2
Dundalk 7 E2
Dundalk Bay 7 E3
Dundee 6 EF4
Dundrum 7 F2
Dunfermline 6 E4
Dungannon 7 E2
Dungannon, Country 7 DE2
Dungarvan 7 D4
Dunkeld 6 E4
Dunkery Beacon 5 C5
Dun Laoghaire 7 EF3
Dunmanway 7 BC5
Dunnet Head 6 E2
Dunoon 6 CD5
Duns 6 F5
Dunstable 5 F4-5
Dunvegan 6 B3
Durham 5 E2
Durham, Country 5 D-E2
Durness 6 D2
Dursey Head 7 A5
Dursley 5 D5
Dyfed 5 B4-5

E

Earn 6 E4
Eastbourne 5 G6
East Grinstead 5 FG5
East Kilbride 6 D5
Eastleigh 5 E6
East Retford 5 F3
Ebbw Vale 5 CD5
Eday 6 F1
Eden 5 D2
Edenderry 7 DE3
Edinburgh 6 EF4-5
Eigg 6 B4
Elgin 6 E3
Ellesmere 5 D4
Ellesmere Port 5 CD3
Ellon 6 FG3
Ely 5 G4
English Channel 5 DG6
Ennis 7 C4
Enniscorthy 7 E4
Ennistimon 7 B4

Epping **5** G5
Epsom **5** F5
Erne **7** C2
Errigal **7** C1
Erris Head **7** A2
Essex **5** G5
Evesham **5** E4
Exe **5** C6
Exeter **5** C6
Exmoor **5** C5
Exmouth **5** C6
Eyemouth **6** FG5

F

Fair Head **7** EF1
Fakenham **5** GH4
Falkirk **6** DE4-5
Falmouth **5** AB6
Falmouth **5** aB
Fareham **5** E6
Fermanagh **7** D2
Farnborough **5** EF5
Faversham **5** GH5
Feale **7** B4
Felixstowe **5** H5
Fens, The **5** FG4
Fergus **7** BC4
Fermoy **7** C4
Fetlar **6** a
Ffestiniog **5** C4
Fife **6** EF4
Fife Ness **6** F4
Filey **5** F2
Finn **7** D2
Firth of Forth **6** EF4
Firth of Lorn **6** BC4
Firth of Tay **6** EF4
Fishguard **5** A4
Flamborough Head **5** FG2
Fleetwood **5** C3
Flint **5** C3
Folkestone **5** GH5
Forfar **6** F4
Forres **6** E3
Forsinard **6** E2
Fort Augustus **6** D3
Forth **6** D4
Fortrose **6** D3
Fort William **6** C4
Foulness Island **5** GH5
Fowey **5** B6
Foyle **7** D2
Foynes **7** BC4
Fraserburgh **6** FG3
Frome **5** D5

G

Gainsborough **5** F3
Gairloch **6** C3
Galashiels **6** EF5
Galston **6** D5
Galty Mountains **7** CD4
Galtymore **7** C4
Galway **7** B3
Galway, Country **7** BC3
Galway Bay **7** B3
Gatehouse of Fleet **6** D6
Gateshead **5** E2
Giggleswick **5** D2
Gigha Island **6** C5
Gillingham **5** G5
Girvan **6** CD5
Glamorgan, Mid **5** C5
Glamorgan, South **5** C5
Glamorgan, West **5** C5
Glasgow **6** D5
Glas Maol **6** E4
Glastonbury **5** D5
Glengarriff **7** B5
Glenluce **6** D6
Glenrothes **6** E4
Glenties **7** C2
Gloucester **5** D5
Gloucestershire **5** D5
Golspie **6** E3
Goole **5** F3
Gorey **7** E4
Gort **7** C3
Gosport **5** E6
Grafham Water **5** F4
Gramisdale **6** A3
Grampian **6** EF3
Grampian Mountains **6** DE4
Granard **7** D3
Grand Canal **7** D3
Grand Union Canal **5** EF4
Grangemouth **6** DE4
Grantham **5** F4
Grantown-on-Spey **6** E3

Great Malvern **5** D4
Great Ouse **5** G4
Great Yarmouth **5** H4
Greenock **6** CD5
Greenore Point **7** EF4
Greystones **7** EF3
Grimsby **5** FG3
Guildford **5** F5
Gweedore **7** Cl
Gwent **5** CD5
Gwynedd **5** BC3

H

Haddington **6** F5
Halifax **5** DE3
Halkirk **6** E2
Halstead **5** G5
Haltwhistle **5** D2
Hamilton **6** DE5
Hampshire **5** E5
Harlech **5** B4
Harlow **5** G5
Harris **6** B3
Harrogate **5** E3
Hartlepool **5** EF2
Hartland Point **5** B5
Harwich **5** H5
Haslemere **5** F5
Hastings **5** G6
Havant **5** F6
Haverfordwest **5** A5
Haverhill **5** G4
Hawes **5** D2
Hawick **6** F5
Haywards Heath **5** F5
Hebrides **6** B3-4
Hebrides, Outer **6** A2-3
Hebrides, Sea of the **6** AB3-4
Helensburgh **6** D4
Helmsdale **6** E2
Helston **5** aB
Helston **5** A6
Hemel Hempstead **5** F5
Henley-on-Thames **5** EF5
Hereford **5** D4
Hereford and Worcester **5** D4
Herne Bay **5** H5
Hertford **5** FG5
Hertfordshire **5** F5
Hexham **5** D2
Heysham **5** D2-3
Highland **6** BD3
Highlands, North West **6** CD3
High Willhays **5** C6
High Wycombe **5** F5
Hillsborough **7** EF2
Hillswick **6** a
Hinckley **5** E4
Hitchin **5** F5
Holmfirth **5** DE3
Holsworthy **5** B6
Holyhead **5** B3
Holy Island **5** E1
Holy Island **5** B3
Hook Head **7** E4
Horncastle **5** FG3
Hornsea **5** FG3
Horsham **5** F5
Hoswick **6** a
Hove **5** F6
Hoy **6** E2
Huddersfield **5** E3
Hugh Town **5** aA
Humber **5** F3
Humberside **5** F3
Hunstanton **5** G4
Huntingdon **5** FG4
Huntly **6** F3
Hythe **5** H5

I

Ilfracombe **5** B5
Ilkley **5** E3
Immingham **5** F3
Inchnadamph **6** D2
Inner **6** B4-5
Inishbofin **7** A3
Insch **6** F3
Inveraray **6** C4
Inverbervie **6** FG4
Invergarry **6** D3
Inverness **6** DE3
Inverurie **6** F3
Ipswich **5** H4
Irish Sea **7** F3
Irvine **6** D5
Irvinestown **7** D2
Islay **6** B5

J

Jedburgh **6** F5
John o'Groats **6** EF2
Johnstone **6** D5
Jura **6** C4
Jura, Sound of **6** C4-5

K

Kanturk **7** C4
Keepe Hill **7** C4
Keighley **5** DE3
Keith **6** F3
Kelso **6** F5
Kendal **5** D2
Kenmare **7** B5
Kent **5** G5
Kerry **7** B5
Kerry, Mountains of **7** AB5
Keswick **5** CD2
Kettering **5** F4
Kidderminster **5** D4
Kildare **7** E3
Kiltoom **7** C3
Kilkee **7** B4
Kilkenny **7** D4
Killala **7** B2
Killaloe **7** C4
Killarney **7** B4
Killin **6** D4
Killorglin **7** B4
Killybegs **7** C2
Kilmallock **7** C4
Kilmarnock **6** D5
Kilrush **7** B4
King's Lynn **5** G4
Kingston upon Hull **5** FG3
Kingussie **6** DE3
Kinlochleven **6** CD4
Kinnairds Head **6** FG3
Kinross **6** E4
Kinsale **7** C5
Kirkcaldy **6** EF4
Kirkconnel **6** DE5
Kirkintilloch **6** D5
Kirkudbright **6** DE6
Kirkwall **6** F2
Kirriemuir **6** EF4
Knaresborough **5** E2
Kyle of Lochalsh **6** C3

L

Lairg **6** D2
Lake District **5** CD2
Lampeter **5** B4
Lanark **6** E5
Lancashire **5** D3
Lancaster **5** D2
Land's End **5** aB
Land's End **5** A6
Langholm **6** EF5
Largs **6** CD5
Laois **7** D4
Larne **7** F2
Larne, Country **7** EF2
Launceston **5** B6
Laurencekirk **6** F4
Lavagh More **7** CD2
Leamington **5** E4
Leeds **5** E3
Leeds and Liverpool Canal **5** DE3
Leek **5** E3
Leicester **5** EF4
Leicestershire **5** EF4
Leighton Buzzard **5** F5
Leitrim **7** CD2
Leominster **5** D4
Lerwick **6** a
Letchworth **5** FG4-5
Letterkenny **7** D2
Lewes **5** G6
Lewis **6** B2
Lichfield **5** E4
Liffey **5** E3
Lifford **7** D2
Limavady **7** DE1
Limavady, Country **7** DE2
Limerick **7** C4
Limerick, Country **7** BC4
Lincoln **5** F3
Lincolnshire **5** FG3
Lisburn **7** EF2
Lisburn, Country **7** E2
Liskeard **5** B6
Lismore **7** D4
Listowel **7** B4
Little Ouse **5** G4
Liverpool **5** C3

Liverpool Bay **5** C3
Lizard Point **5** aB
Lizard Point **5** AB7
Llandovery **5** C4
Llandrindod Wells **5** C4
Llandudno **5** BC3
Llandybie **5** BC5
Llanelli **5** B5
Llangollen **5** C4
Llanidloes **5** C4
Lochaline **6** C4
Loch Awe **6** C4
Lochboisdale **6** A3
Loch Earn **6** D4
Lochearnhead **6** D4
Loch Fyne **6** C4-5
Lochgilphead **6** C4
Lochinver **6** C2
Loch Katrine **6** D4
Loch Ken **6** D5
Loch Leven **6** E4
Loch Linnhe **6** C4
Loch Lomond **6** D4
Lochmaddy **6** A3
Loch Maree **6** C3
Loch Ness **6** D3
Loch Rannoch **6** D4
Loch Shiel **6** C4
Loch Shin **6** D2
Loch Tay **6** DE4
London **5** G5
Londonderry **7** D1
Londonderry, Country **7** D2
Long Eaton **5** E4
Longford **7** D3
Loop Head **7** AB4
Lossiemouth **6** EF3
Lothian **6** EF5
Lough Allen **7** C2
Lough Arrow **7** C2
Loughborough **5** EF4
Lough Conn **7** B2
Lough Corrib **7** B3
Lough Derg **7** C3-4
Lough Foyle **7** D1
Lough Mask **7** B3
Lough Neagh **7** E2
Loughrea **7** C3
Lough Ree **7** D3
Lough Sheelin **7** D3
Lough Swilly **7** D1
Louth **5** G3
Louth **7** E3
Lower Lough Erne **7** D2
Lowestoft **5** H4
Luce Bay **6** D6
Ludlow **5** D4
Lugnaquillia Mountain **7** E4
Lundy **5** B5
Lurgan **7** E2
Luton **5** F5
Lybster **6** E2
Lydd **5** GH6
Lyme Bay **5** D6
Lyme Regis **5** CD6
Lymington **5** E6
Lynton **5** C5
Lytham Saint Annes **5** CD3

M

Mablethorpe **5** G3
Macclesfield **5** DE3
Macduff **6** F3
Macroom **7** C5
Maghera **7** E2
Magherafelt **7** E2
Maidenhead **5** EF5
Maidstone **5** G5
Mainland **6** E1
Mainland **6** a
Mal Bay **7** B4
Maldon **5** G5
Malin Head **7** D1
Mallaig **6** BC3
Mallow **7** C4
Malton **5** F2
Man, Isle of **5** B2
Mansfield **5** EF3
March **5** G4
Margate **5** H5
Market Drayton **5** D4
Market Harborough **5** EF4
Market Rasen **5** F3
Market Weighton **5** F3
Marlborough **5** E5
Maryport **5** C2
Matlock **5** E3
Maybole **6** D5
Maynooth **7** E3
Mayo **7** B3
Meath **7** E3

Medway **5** G5
Melrose **6** F5
Melton Mowbray **5** F4
Melvich **6** E2
Merrick **6** D5
Mersey **5** D3
Merseyside **5** CD3
Merthyr Tydfil **5** C5
Middleham **5** DE2
Middlesbrough **5** EF2
Middleton **7** E2
Midlands, West **5** DE4
Mickleton **7** C5
Mid Yell **6** a
Mildenhall **5** G4
Milford Haven **5** B5
Millom **5** C2
Milport **6** C5
Miltown **7** B4
Minch, Little **6** B3
Minch, The **6** BC2-3
Minehead **5** C5
Mitchelstown **7** CD4
Mizen Head **7** AB5
Moate **7** D3
Moffat **5** E5
Mold **5** C3
Monadhliath Mountains **6** D3
Monaghan **7** D2
Monaghan, Country **7** DE2
Monasterevin **7** DE3
Moneymore **7** E2
Monmouth **5** D5
Montgomery **5** C4
Montrose **6** F4
Moray Firth **6** E3
Morecambe **5** D2
Morecambe Bay **5** CD2-3
Morpeth **5** E1
Motherwell **6** E5
Mountmellick **7** D3
Mountrath **7** D3-4
Mount's Bay **5** aB
Mount's Bay **5** A6-7
Mourne **7** D2
Mourne Mountains **7** E2
Moville **7** D1
Moy **7** B2
Mull **6** B4
Mullingar **7** D3
Mull of Galloway **6** D6
Mull of Kintyre **6** C5
Musselburgh **6** EF5
Mweelrea **7** B3

N

Naas **7** E3
Nairn **6** E3
Nantwich **5** D3
Narberth **5** B5
Neath **5** C5
Nenagh **7** C4
Nephin **7** B2
Newark-on-Trent **5** F3
Newbury **5** E5
Newcastle **7** F2
Newcastle-under-Lyme **5** DE3
Newcastle-upon-Tyne **5** EF2
Newcastle West **7** BC4
New Galloway **6** D5
Newhaven **5** G6
Newmarket **5** G4
Newport **5** D5
Newport **5** E6
Newport **7** B3
Newport-on-Tay **6** F4
Newquay **5** A6
Newquay **5** aB
New Ross **7** E4
Newry **7** E2
Newry and Mourne **7** E2
Newton Abbot **5** C6
Newtonmore **6** D3
Newton Stewart **6** D6
Newtown **5** C4
Newtownabbey **7** E2
Newtownabbey, Country **7** EF2
Newtownards **7** F2
Newtown Saint Boswell **6** F5
Nidd **5** E2
Nith **6** E5
Nore **7** D4
Norfolk **5** GH4
Northallerton **5** E2
Northampton **5** F4
Northamptonshire **5** EF4
North Berwick **6** F4
North Channel **6** C5-6
North Down **7** F2
North Downs **5** FG5

North Sunderland **5** E1
Northumberland **5** DE1
North Walsham **5** H4
Nort York Moors **5** EF2
Norwich **5** H4
Nottingham **5** EF3-4
Nottinghamshire **5** EF3
Nuneaton **5** E4

O

Oakham **5** F4
Oban **6** C4
Offaly **7** D3
Okehampton **5** C6
Oldham **5** DE3
Old Head of Kinsale **7** CD5
Omagh **7** D2
Orkney Islands **6** F1-2
Ormskirk **5** CD3
Oswestry **5** C4
Ouse **5** E3
Overbister **6** F1
Oxford **5** E5
Oxfordshire **5** E5

P

Padstow **5** AB6
Paignton **5** C6
Paisley **6** D5
Passage West **7** C5
Peebles **6** E5
Peel **5** B2
Pembroke **5** B5
Pennines **5** DE2-4
Penrith **5** D2
Pentland Firth **6** EF2
Penzance **5** aB
Penzance **5** A6
Perth **6** E4
Peterborough **5** FG4
Peterhead **6** FG3
Peterlee **5** E2
Petersfield **5** F5
Pickering **5** F2
Plynlimon **5** C4
Plymouth **5** BC6
Pontypool **5** D5
Pitlochry **6** E4
Pontypridd **5** C5
Poole **5** DE6
Portadown **7** E2
Portarlington **6** D3
Port Askaig **6** B5
Port Ellen **6** B5
Port Glasgow **6** D5
Porthcawl **5** C5
Portland, Isle of **5** D6
Port Laoise **7** D3
Portmahomack **6** E3
Portree **6** B3
Portrush **7** E1
Portsmouth **5** EF6
Portsoy **6** F3
Portstewart **7** E1
Port Talbot **5** BC5
Portumna **7** C3
Powys **5** C4
Prestatyn **5** C3
Preston **5** D3
Prestwick **6** D5
Pwllheli **5** B4

R

Raasay **6** BC3
Ramsey **5** B2
Ramsey Island **5** A5
Ramsgate **5** H5
Rathdrum **7** EF4
Rathlin **7** E1
Rath Luirc **7** C4
Reading **5** E5
Redcar **5** F2
Redditch **5** DE4
Redruth **5** aB
Reigate **5** F5
Rhum **6** B4
Rhyl **5** C3
Ribble **5** D3
Richmond **5** E2
Ringwood **5** E6
Ripon **5** E2
Rochdale **5** DE3
Rochester **5** G5
Ronas Hill **6** a
Roscommon **7** C3
Roscrea **7** D4

Rosehearty 6 F3
Rossan Point 7 BC2
Rosslare 7 E4
Ross-on-Wye 5 D5
Rothbury 5 E1
Rotherham 5 EF3
Rothes 6 E3
Rothesay 6 C5
Rousay 6 E1
Rugby 5 E4
Rushden 5 F4
Ruthin 5 C3
Ryde 5 EF6
Rye 5 G6

S

Saffron Walden 5 G4-5
Saint Abb's Head 6 FG5
Saint Albans 5 F5
Saint Andrews 6 F4
Saint Austell 5 B6
Saint Bee's Head 6 BC2
Saint David's Head 5 A5
Saint George's Channel 7
    EF4-5
Saint Helens 5 D3
Saint Ives 5 aB
Saint Ives 5 A6
Saint Martin's 5 aA
Saint Mary's 5 aA
Saint Neots 5 F4
Salcombe 5 BC6
Salford 5 D3
Salisbury 5 DE5
Saltash 5 B6
Sanday 6 F1
Sandown 5 EF6
Sandringham 5 G4
Sawel Mountain 7 DE2
Saxmundham 5 H4
Scafell Pikes 5 C2
Scalloway 6 a
Scalpay 6 C3
Scarborough 5 F2
Scarinish 6 B4
Scilly, Isles of 5 aA
Scourie 6 C2
Scunthorpe 5 F3
Seaham 5 E2

Selby 5 F3
Selkirk 6 EF5
Sevenoaks 5 G5
Severn 5 D4
Shaftesbury 5 DE6
Shannon, River 7 B4
Shannon, River 7 C3
Shapinsay 6 F1
Sheffield 5 EF3
Sheppey, Isle of 5 GH5
Shepton Mallet 5 D5
Sheringham 5 H4
Shetland Isles 6 a
Shrewsbury 5 D4
Sidmouth 5 CD6
Sittingbourne 5 G5
Sixmilebridge 7 C4
Skegness 5 G3
Skibbereen 7 B5
Skipton 5 DE3
Skokholm Island 5 A5
Skomer Island 5 A5
Skye 6 B3
Slaney 7 E4
Sleaford 5 F3
Slea Head 7 A4
Slieve Donard 7 EF2
Sligo 7 C2
Slough 5 F5
Slyne Head 7 A3
Snaefell 5 B2
Snowdon 5 BC3
Solihull 5 E4
Solway Firth 6 E6
Solway Firth 5 C2
Somerset 5 C5
Southampton 5 E6
South Downs 5 F6
Southend-on-Sea 5 GH5
Southern Uplands 6 DF5
South Esk 6 EF4
South Molton 5 C5
Southport 5 C3
South Ronaldsay 6 F2
Southwold 5 H4
Spalding 5 F4
Spennymoor 5 E2
Sperrin Mountains 7 DE2
Spey 6 E3
Spurn Head 5 G3
Stafford 5 DE4
Staffordshire 5 DE4
Staines 5 F5

Stamford 5 F4
Start Point 5 C6
Stevenage 5 FG5
Stewarton 6 D5
Stirling 6 DE4
Stockport 5 DE3
Stockton-on-Tees 5 E2
Stoke-on-Trent 5 DE3-4
Stonehaven 6 FG4
Stornoway 6 B2
Stowmarket 5 H4
Stow-on-the-Wold 5 E5
Stour, River 5 G4-5
Stour, River 5 D6
Strabane 7 D2
Strangford Lough 7 F2
Stranraer 6 C6
Stratford-upon-Avon 5 E4
Strathclyde 5 C4
Strathy Point 6 D2
Stromness 6 E2
Stronsay 6 F1
Stroud 5 D5
Suck 7 C3
Sudbury 5 G4
Sunderland 5 EF2
Suffolk 5 GH4
Sumburgh Head 6 a
Surrey 5 F5
Sussex, East 5 G6
Sussex, West 5 F6
Sutton-in-Ashifield 5 EF3
Swadlincote 5 E4
Swaffham 5 G4
Swale 5 E2
Swanage 5 E6
Swansea 5 B5
Swindon 5 E5
Swinford 7 C3
Swords 7 E3

T

Tain 6 D3
Tamar 5 B6
Tamworth 5 E4
Tarbert (Outer Hebrides)
    6 B3
Tarbert (Strathclyde) 6 C5
Taunton 5 CD5

Tavistock 5 BC6
Taw 5 C6
Tay 6 E4
Tees 5 E2
Teifi 5 B4
Teignmouth 5 C6
Telford 5 D4
Templemore 7 D4
Test 5 E5
Tetbury 5 DE5
Teviot 6 F5
Tewkesbury 5 D5
Thames, River 5 E5
Thames, River 5 G5
Thetford 5 G4
Thirsk 5 E2
Thomastown 7 DE4
Thornhill 6 E5
Thurles 7 CD4
Thurso 6 E2
Tilbury 5 G5
Tipperary 7 C4
Tipperary, Country 7 CD4
Tiree 6 AB4
Tiverton 5 C6
Tobercurry 7 C2
Tobermory 6 B4
Tonbridge 5 G5
Tongue 6 D2
Torbay 5 C6
Torridon 6 C3
Totnes 5 C6
Towcester 5 E4
Tralee 7 B4
Tramore 7 D4
Trent, River 5 E4
Trent, River 5 F3
Tresco 5 aA
Trim 7 E3
Troon 6 D5
Trowbridge 5 DE5
Truro 5 aB
Truro 5 AB6
Tuam 7 C3
Tullamore 7 D3
Tullow 7 E4
Tunbridge Wells 5 G5
Turriff 6 F3
Tyne 5 DE2
Tyne and Wear 5 E1-2
Tynemouth 5 E1
Tywi 5 C5
Tywyn 5 B4

U

Uig 6 B3
Uist, North 6 AB3
Uist, South 6 A3
Ullapool 6 CD3
Ullswater 5 D2
Ulverston 5 CD2
Unshin 7 C2
Unst 6 a
Upper Lough Erne 7 D2
Ure 5 E2

V

Valencia Island 7 A5
Ventnor 5 E6
Vyrnwy, Lake 5 C4

W

Wakefield 5 E3
Wallingford 5 E5
Walls 6 a
Walney, Isle of 5 C2
Walsall 5 E4
Warley 5 E4
Warminster 5 DE5
Warrenpoint 7 E2
Warrington 5 D3
Warwick 5 E4
Warwickshire 5 E4
Wash, The 5 G4
Waterford 7 DE4
Waterford, Country 7 D4
Watford 5 F5
Waveney 5 H4
Wellingborough 5 F4
Wellington 5 CD6
Wells 5 D5
Wells-next-the-Sea 5 G4
Welshpool 5 C4
Welwyn Garden City 5 F5
West Bromwich 5 E4
Western Isles 6 AB3
Westmeath 7 D3
Weston-super-Mare 5 CD5
Westport 7 B3
Wexford 7 E4

Weymouth 5 D6
Whalsay 6 a
Wharfe 5 E3
Whernside 5 D2
Whitby 5 F2
Whitehaven 5 C2
Whithorn 6 D6
Whitstable 5 H5
Whittlesey 5 F4
Wick 6 EF2
Wicklow, County 7 E3
Wicklow 7 EF3
Wicklow Head 7 F4
Wicklow Mountains 7
    E3-4
Widnes 5 D3
Wigan 5 D3
Wight, Isle of 5 EF6
Wigtown 6 D6
Wiltshire 5 DE5
Winchester 5 E5
Windermere 5 CD2
Windermere 5 D2
Windsor 5 F5
Winsford 5 D3
Wisbech 5 FG4
Witham 5 G5
Witham, River 5 F3
Withernsea 5 G3
Witney 5 E5
Woking 5 F5
Wolverhampton 5 D4
Woodbridge 5 H4
Woodstock 5 E5
Worcester 5 DE4
Workington 5 C2
Worksop 5 E3
Worthing 5 F6
Wrexham 5 C3
Wye 5 D4-5
Wymondham 5 GH4

Y

Yare 5 H4
Yell 6 a
Yeouil 5 D6
York 5 EF2-3
Yorkshire, North 5 EF2
Yorkshire, South 5 E3
Yorkshire, West 5 E3

General index to the maps

A

Aa 16 M 8
Aachen 13 AB 3
Aarau 13 C 5
Aare 12 B 5
Abaco, Gran-, 48 D 1
Abadan 28 L 5
Abadeh 28 N 5
Abadla 37 D 3
Abaetetuba 52 H 2
Abagach Jasak 31 I 2
Abakaliki 39 F 4
Abakan 22 I 4
Abancay 52 C 4
Abashiri 32 F 3
Abau 55 H 2
Abaya, Lake 38 D 5
Abbai 35 G 4
Abbeville 11 F 1
Abbi Addi 38 C 5
Abbottabad 29 F 5
Abd el-Kuri 38 F 5
Abdulino 24 G 8
Abe, Lake 38 D 5
Abéché 37 I 7
Abel 56 a
Abelbodh 37 D 6
Abeltoft 17 D 8
Abengourou 39 D 4
Abenra 17 C 9
Abeokuta 39 E 4
Abercorn 40 E 4
Aberdeen (Scotland) 4 E 3
Aberdeen (USA, Wash.) 46 B 3
Aberdeen (USA, S. Dak.) 46 G 3
Aberystwyth 4 D 5
Abetone, P.dell'-18 C 2
Abez 22 F 3
Abha 38 D 4
Abibe, Serrania de-51 A 2
Abidjan 39 D 4
Abilene 46 G 6
Abinsk 25 E 3
Abinsi 39 F 4
Abiquas Puts 41 B 4
Abisko 17 H 2
Abitibi 44 O 5-6
Abo (Finland) 17 L 6
Abo (Nigeria) 39 F 4
Abomey 39 E 4
Abong-Mbang 39 G 5
Abou Deïa 37 H 7
Abrantes (Brazil) 52 L 4
Abrantes (Portugal) 9 B 4
Abra Pampa 53 C 1
Abri 37 M 5
Abruzzi 19 DE 3
Abu 30 B 4
Abu al Abyadh 29 B 7
Abu Arish 38 D 4
Abu-Dara, Ras 38 C 3
Abu Dhabi 29 B 7
Abu Dis 37 M 6
Abu-Dulù 37 M 6
Abufari 52 E 3
Abu Gabra 37 L 7
Abu-Hadriya 28 L 7
Abu Haraz 37 M 6
Abu Hashim 38 B 5
Abuja 39 F 4
Abu Kemal 28 F 3
Abu Mad, Ras 38 C 3
Abu Markha 38 C 2
Abumombasi 40 C 2
Abunà 52 D 3
Abunà 52 D 3
Abuna Josef 38 C 5
Abu Qurqas 37 M 4
Abu-Salama 28 C 7
Abu Shagara, Ras 38 C 3
Abu Simbel 37 L 5
Abu Tabari 37 L 6
Abu Zenima 28 B 6
Aby 16 I 4
Abyei 40 D 1
Abyj 22 P 3
Abyn 17 I 4
Acajutlà 47 G 5
Acaoua 37 EF 6-7
Acapulco de Juàrez 47 E 4
Acarà 52 H 2
Acaraù 52 I 2
Acarigua 51 C 2
Acca 37 D 6
Accra 39 D 4

Acha, General 53 D 4
Achaguas 51 C 2
Achaia 20 E 8
Achak Gompa 31 F 4
Achegour 37 G 6
Acheloos 20 E 8
Achill 3 A 4
Achi Tagh 31 E 2
Achourat 37 D 5
Ackar 51 D 2
Acklins 48 E 2
Acinsk 22 I 4
Acireale 19 E 6
Acomayo 52 C 4
Aconcagua 53 B 3
Acorizal 52 F 4
Acqui Terme 19 B 2
Acre (Brazil) 52 CD 3-4
Acre (Brazil) 52 D 4
Acri 19 F 5
Ada 39 E 4
Adado, Ras 38 E 5
Adaja 8 D 3
Adak 22 T 4
Adals-Liden 17 G 5
Adam (Oman) 29 C 7
Adamaua 35 E 5
Adamello Mt. 18 C 1
Adams 46 B 3
Adam's Peak 30 D 7
Adana 28 C 2
Adar 37 EF 7
Adarama 37 C 4
Adare, Cape 57 A 2
Adavale 55 G 5
Adda (Sudan) 40 C 1
Adda, River (Italy) 18 B 1
Addia 37 G 7
Addis Ababa 38 C 6
Ad-Diwaniya 28 H 5
Adelaide (Australia) 55 F 6
Adelaide (Antarctica) 57 O 3
Adelaide River 55 E 2
Adélie-Coast 57 C 3
Adelsberg 21 B 5
Ademuz 9 F 3
Aden 38 E 5
Aden, Gulf of 38 E 5
Adenau 13 B 3
Adi 34 H 5
Adis 34 H 5
Adige 18 C 1-2
Adigrat 38 C 5
Adimi 22 O 5
Adi Qualà 38 C 5
Adi Ugri 38 C 5
Adiyaman 28 E 2
Adjerar 37 F 5
Adjud 21 H 4
Admer 37 F 5
Admiralty 45 N 5
Admiralty G. 55 D 2
Admirality Inlet 44 N 1
Ado-Ekití 39 F 4
Adok 40 E 1
Adonara 34 F 6
Adoni 30 C 5
Adouda 37 F 6
Adour 10 E 5
Adra (India) 30 E 4
Adra (Spain) 9 E 5
Adrano 19 E 6
Adrar (Algeria) 37 D 4
Adrar (Mauritania) 35 B 3
Adrar, M.t (Algeria) 37 F 5
Adrar des Iforas 35 D 4
Adrar Makteïr 37 BC 5-6
Adrar-Sot-Tuf 37 A 5
Adria 19 CD 2
Adrianopoli 20 H 7
Adriatic Sea 18 DG 2-4
Adula 18 B 1
Adulab 38 C 3
Aduwa 38 C 5
Adyca 22 O 3
Adz'vavom 24 L 1
Aéré 37 B 6
Aerö 16 D 9
Afdem 38 D 5
Afdera 38 D 5
Affollé 37 C 6
Afghanistan 27 I 6
Aflou 37 E 3
Afognak 45 H 5
Afta 17 G 6
Afweina, El- 38 E 6
Afyon 2 O 8
Agadem 37 G 6
Agadès 37 F 6
Agadir 37 C 3

Agadir Tissint 37 C 4
Agan 37 B 6
Agano 32 E 4
Agaro 38 C 6
Agartala 27 b 11
Agata 22 I 3
Agbandi 39 E 4
Agboville 39 D 4
Agde 11 G 5
Agedir, Ras 37 G 3
Agen 11 F 4
Agepsta, Gora 25 F 4
Agha-Jari 28 M 5
Aghéila, El- 37 H 3
Aglagal 37 E 4
Agmar 37 B 4
Agogna 18 B 2
Agoladeï 37 H 6
Agordat 38 C 4
Agordo 19 D 1
Agout 10 G 5
Agra 30 C 3
Agri 18 F 4
Agrigento 19 D 6
Agrihan 54 E 3
Agrinion 21 E 8
Agua Clara 52 G 6
Aguada 53 C 2
Aguadilla 48 F 3
Aguanaval 47 D 2-3
Aguarico 52 B 2
Aguascalientes 47 D 3
Agudos 52 H 6
Agueda 9 B 3
Agueda 8 C 3
Aguelhok 37 F 6
Aguel el-Melah 37 C 5
Aguilar de Campo 9 D 2
Aguilas 9 F 5
Aguja, p.ta de- 52 A 3
Agulà 38 C 5
Agulhas, Cape 35 F 9
Agung, M.t 34 E 6
Ahaggar 35 D 3
Ahanfous 37 E 5
Ahar 25 I 6
Ahé 54 N 6
Ahenet 37 E 4-5
Ahkaf 38 E 4
Ahlainen 17 I 6
Ahlat 25 G 6
Ahmadabad (India) 30 B 4
Ahmadabab, (Iran) 28 I 2
Ahmar, Al-, Ras 38 D 4
Ahmedabad 30 B 4
Ahmednagar 30 B 5
Ahmeyine 37 B 5
Ahome 47 C 2
Ahrweiler 13 B 3
Ahtopol 21 H 6
Ahuachapan 47 G 5
Ahus 17 F 9
Ahvaz 28 L 5
Ahwaz 38 E 1
Ahwar 38 E 5
Aigurance 11 F 3
Ai hun 32 C 2
Aijal 33 A 2
Aikawa 32 E 4
Aileron 55 E 4
Ailigas 16 N 2
Ailingtapalap, Islands 54 G 4
Aim 22 O 4
Aimis vesi 23 G 3
Aimorés, Sierra d. 52 I 5
Ain 10 H 3-4
Ainan-Rasnir 28 N 3
Ainazi 17 M 8
Ain Ben-Tili 37 C 4
Ain Cheikr 37 E 5
Ain el-Gazal 37 I 5
Ain el-Hadjadj 37 F 4
Ain el-Kiyeh 37 L 6
Ain el-Murr 37 I 5
Ain Galakka 37 H 6
Ain Guettara 37 E 4
Ain Madhi 37 E 3
Ain Sefra 37 D 3
Ainsworth 46 G 4
Ain Taïba 37 F 3
Ain Tikki'dine 37 E 4
A n Zalak 28 G 2
Aïoun Abd-el-Malek 37 C 5
Aïoun el-Atrouss 37 C 6
Aïr 37 F 6
Aire 11 G 3
Airuk 1 T 6
Aisch 12 D 4
Aisne 10 GH 2
Aitana, Sierra de- 8 F 4

Aitutaki 54 M 6
Aiviekste 23 F 6
Aix 11 H 5
Aixe-sur-Vienne 11 F 4
Aix-les-Bains 11 H 4
Aizpute 17 I 8
Ajäbshähr 28 H 2
Ajaccio 11 a
Ajaccio, Gulf of- 11 a
Ajaguz 22 H 5
Ajaju 51 B 3
Ajan 22 O 4
Ajana 55 A 5
Ajdabiya 37 I 3
Ajdabul 22 F 4
Ajigin 39 G 3
Ajmer 30 B 3
Ajoewa 51 E 3
Akabli 37 E 4
Akacomoékrou 39 D 4
Akasa 39 F 5
Akdagmadeni 25 C 6
Akelo, M 18 B 4
Akernes 17 B 7
Akershus 17 D 6-7
Aketi 40 C 2
Akhadar, Gebel 26 H 7
Akhalkalaki 25 G 5
Akhaltsikhe 25 G 5
Akhaura 27 b 11
Akhisar 21 H 8
Akhmim 37 M 4
Aki 32 D 5
Akimiski 44 O 5
Akita 32 F 4
Akkeshi 32 F 3
Akko 28 C 2
Aklavik 43 F 3
Aknïste 23 E 6
Akobo 40 E 1
Akola 30 C 4
Akonolinga 39 G 5
Akosu (Aksu) 31 C 2
Akpatok 44 R 3
Akra 17 B 7
Akreïdil 37 A 6
Akritas, Cape 20 E 9
Akron (USA, Colorado) 46 F 4
Akron (USA, Ohio) 46 L 4
Aksa 22 M 4
Aksaray 25 C 6
Aksenovo Zilovskoe 22 M 4
Aksu (Akosu) 31 C 2
Aksuat 22 F 4
Akta 22 Q 3
Aktau 25 N 1
Aktse 17 H 3
Aktyubinsk 22 E 4
Akure 39 F 4
Akureyri 17 S 12
Akuse 39 E 4
Akyab 33 A 2
Alabama 46 I 6
Alaçam 25 C 5
Alacam 20 I 8
Alaéos 9 D 3
Alagoas 52 L 3
Alagoinhas 52 L 4
Alagon 8 C 3
Alai 22 G 6
Alajia 28 C 3
Alaji 38 C 5
Alakamisy 41 C 8
Ala Kul 22 H 5
Alamogordo 46 E 6
Alamos 47 C 2
Aland Is. 16 HI 6
Alanya 28 B 2
Alapaevsk 24 M 6
Alaska 45 H 3
Alaska, Gulf of 45 IL 5
Alaska, Peninsula 45 FG 5
Alaska, Range 45 HI 4
Alasehir 21 I 8
Alastaro 17 L 6
Ala Tau 26 LM 5
Alatyr' 24 CD 7
Alausi 52 B 2
Alaveteli 17 L 5
Alavieska 17 M 4
Alazeja 22 Q 2-3
Al 'Aziziya 28 H 4
Alba 19 B 2
Albacete 9 F 4
Al-Badana 28 F 5
Alba de Tormes 9 D 3
Alban, Alpi 21 D 6
Albani, Monti 18 D 4

Albania 21 E 6-7
Albano 19 D 4
Albany (Australia) 55 B 6
Albany (USA, New York) 46 N 4
Albany (USA, Oregon) 46 B 4
Albany 44 N 5
Albarracin 9 F 3
Al Batan 28 GH 5-6
Al Batin 28 I 6
Albemarle, p.ta 52 a
Albenga 19 B 3
Alberche 8 D 3
Alberga 55 E 5
Alberta 44 FG 5
Albia 46 H 4
Albina 51 F 2
Albina, p.ta 41 A 2
Albion 46 D 4
Albo, M 18 B 4
Alborg 17 C 8
Albuquerque 46 E 5
Al-Burgan 28 L 6
Alburquerque 9 C 4
Albury 55 H 7
Alcala de Chisbert 9 G 3
Alcala de Henares 9 E 3
Alcamo 19 D 6
Alcañiz 9 F 3
Alcántara (Brazil) 52 I 2
Alcántara (Spain) 9 C 4
Alcaraz 9 E 4
Alcaraz, Sierra de 8 E 4
Alcarria, La- 8 EF 3
Alcazar de S. Juan 9 E 4
Alcira 9 F 4
Alcorisa 9 F 3
Alcoutim 9 C 5
Alcoy 9 F 4
Alcudia 9 H 4
Alcudia 9 D 4
Alcudia, Valle de- 9 D 4
Aldabra 36 H 6
Aldama 47 E 3
Aldan 22 N O 3-4
Aldan 24 D 8
A efä 38 C 5
A eg 37 B 6
A egrete 52 F 7
Aléançon 11 F 2
A eknagnik 45 FG 5
Aleksandrija 25 B 1
Aleksandrov 22 G 3
Aleksandrovka 25 E 2
Aleksandrovsk 24 I 5
Aleksandrow 13 H 2
Aleksandroysk 22 P 4
Alekseevka (Sowiet Union, Kasachstan) 29 F 1
Alekseevka (Sowiet Union, Obscij Syrt) 24 F 8
Alekseevskoe 25 D 1
Aleksin 23 M 7
Alemania 53 C 2
Alemguer 52 G 2
Aleppo 28 D 2
Alès 11 G 4
Alessandria 19 B 2
Alexander I. 57 O 2
Aleutian Islands 22 SU 4
Alexander 41 B 4
Alexander Arch. 45 M 5
Alexandre 41 A 2
Alexandria (Australia) 55 F 3
Alexandria (Agypt) 37 L 3
Alexandria (South Africa) 41 D 5
Alexandria (USA) 46 H 6
Alexandrupolis 21 G 7
Alfambra 9 F 3
Alfatar 21 H 6
Alfeios 20 E 9
Alferovskaja 24 C 4
Alföld 20 DE 4
Alford 4 E 3
Alfot bre 17 A 6
Alfredo, Principe- 45 P 2
Algard 17 A 7
Algarrobo del Aguila 53 C 4
Algarve 8 B 5
Algeciras 9 D 5
Algemesi 9 F 4
Algeria 36 D 2
Alghar 37 F 4
Alghero 19 B 4
Algiers 37 E 2
Algoa 41 D 5

Al-Hafar 28 I 6
Al-Haql 28 C 6
Al Hasa 38 E 2
Al-Himeida 28 C 6
Alhus 17 B 6
Aliakmon 20 F 7
Alicante, Gulf of 9 FG 4-5
Alice, p.ta dell'- 19 F 5
Alicedale 41 D 5
Alice Springs 55 E 4
Alicudi 18 E 5
Aligarh 30 C 3
'Ali Gharbi 28 I 4
Alijo 9 C 3
Ali Khel 29 E 5
Aliluchalin 32 B 1
Alima 35 E 6
Alindao 40 C 1
Alingsas 17 E 8
Aliwal North 41 D 5
Al-Jahrak 28 I 6
Aljat 25 L 5-6
Al-Jauf 28 E 6
Alje Zur 9 B 5
Aljustrel 9 B 5
Al-Kadhimain 28 GH 4
Al Khamis 28 D 6
Al Khasab 29 C 6
Alkmaar 15 G 2
Al-Kufa 28 H 4
Al-Kuwait 28 I 6
Al-Labbe 38 D 2
Allada 39 E 4
Allahabad 30 D 3
Allajkha 22 P 2
Allariz 9 C 2
Allegheny 42 MN 6
Allen (Norway) 16 L 2
Allen (Ireland) 3 B 4
Allende 47 D 2
Allenstein 13 I 2
Allentown 46 M 4
Aller 12 C 2
Alleppey 30 C 7
Alliance 46 F 4
Allier 10 G 3
Alloa 4 E 3
Alma-Ata 22 G 5
Al-Machmi 28 G 5
Almadén 9 D 4
Almansa 9 F 4
Almanzor 8 D 3
Almanzora 8 EF 5
Almar 9 D 3
Almazan 9 E 3
Almeida 9 C 3
Almelo 15 H 2
Almenara 8 E 4
Almendralejo 9 C 4
Almeria 9 E 5
Almeria, Gulf of 8 E 5
Almodov 9 B 5
Almonte 8 CD 4
Almonte 9 C 5
Almunécar 9 E 5
Almunia de D.a Godina, La- 9 F 3
Al-Muwailik 28 C 7
Almvik 17 G 8
Alnwich 4 F 4
Alor 27 Q 10
Alora 9 D 5
Alor Star 33 C 5
Alpena 46 L 3
Alpenvorland 12 CE 4-5
Alpujarras, Las- 9 E 5
Al-Qaim 28 F 3
Al Qarah 28 F 6
Al Qathma 38 D 3
Al Qufar 28 F 7
Al-Qurna 28 I 5
Al-Qusaiba 28 G 7
Al Quwara 28 G 7
Alsace 11 I 2-3
Alsen (Denmark) 16 C 9
Alsen (Sweden) 16 E 4
Alstera 17 G 8
Alta 17 L 2
Alta Gracia (Argentina) 53 D 3
Altagracia (Venezuela) 51 B 1
Altai 26 MN 4-5
Altamachi 52 D 5
Altamaha 46 L 6
Altamira 52 G 2
Altamura 19 F 4
Altan Bulak 31 H 1
Altar 47 B 1
Altdorf 19 B 1

Altenburg 13 E 3
Altin Tag 26 MN 6
Altmühl 12 D 4
Alto Alentejo 9 C 4
Alto Douro 9 C 3
Alto Madeira 50 D 4
Altona 13 C2
Altoona 46 M 4
Altun Köprü 28 H 3
Alturas 46 B 4
Aluise 41 E 3
Aluksne 23 E 6
Alula 38 F 5
Al-'Ula 28 E 7
Alung Gangri 31 C 4
Al Uqba 28 H 6
Alus 28 G 3
Aluta 40 D 3
Alvdalen 17 F 6
Alvernia 11 G 4
Alvros 17 F 5
Alvsborg 17 E 7-8
Alvsby 17 I 4
Alytus 17 M 9
Ama Dablam 26 P 17
Amadi 40 E 1
Amadjuak 44 Q 3
Amager 17 E 9
Amagete 39 F 4
Amakusa 32 D 5
Amal 17 E 7
Amalfi 51 A 2
Amami-Islands 32 C 6
Amamula 40 D 3
Amanbai 52 F 6
Amangel'dy 29 D 1
Amapa 51 F 3
Amapari 51 F 3
Amar 39 G 4
Amara (Iraq) 28 I 5
Amarante 52 I 3
Amarillo 46 F 5
Amasra 25 B 5
Amasya 25 C 5
Amataura 52 D 2
Amazon 50 D 3-4
Amazonas, Rio 52 FG 2
Ambala 30 C 2
Ambalavao 41 c 8
Ambam 39 G 5
Ambanja 41 c 6
Ambarcik 22 R 3
Ambasi 55 H 1
Ambato 52 B 2
Ambatolampy 41 c 7
Ambatomainty 41 c 7
Ambatondrazaka 41 c 7
Ambelau 34 G 5
Amberg 13 D-E 4
Ambergris Cay 47 G 4
Ambérieu 11 H 4
Ambert 11 G 4
Ambigol 37 M 5
Ambilope 41 c 6
Amble 13 F 4
Ambleve 14 G 3
Ambo 52 B 2
Amboasary 41 c 7
Ambodifototra 41 c 7
Ambohibe 41 b 8
Ambohimahasoa 41 c 8
Ambon 34 G 5
Ambongo 35 H 7
Ambovombe 41 c 9
Amboyna 34 D 3
Ambre, Cape d'- 41 c 6
Ambriz 40 A 4
Amchitka 22 S 4
Am Dam 37 I 7
Am Djéress 37 I 6
Amedeo 55 E 4
Ameland 14 G 2
Americus 46 L 6
Amery Eisschelf 57 F 3
Am et Timan 37 I 7
Amga 22 O 3
Amgu 32 E 2
Amguid 37 F 4
Amgun 22 O 4
Amhara (Ethiopia) 38 C 5
Amherst 33 B 3
Amiata, M. 18 C 3
Amiens 11 G 2
Aminuis 41 B 3
Amli 17 C 7
Amlia 22 T 4
Amlwch 13 D 5
Amman 28 C 5
Ammemurgil 31 EF 3
Ammer 16 F 5
Ammersee 12 D 4
Amorgos 20 G 9
Amot 17 G 6
Amöy 17 E 3
Ampana 34 F 5
Ampanihy 41 b 8
Ampato 52 C 5
Amper 12 D 4
Amrawati 30 C 4
Amrum 12 C 1
Amsach Mellet 37 G 4-5

Amsterdam (Netherlands) 15 G 2
Amudarya 22 EG 5-6
Amul 28 N 2
Amundsensee (Antarctica) 57 Qq 2-3
Amundsen Mt. (Antarctic) 57 d 3
Amundsen Bay (Antarctic) 57 g 3
Amundsen (Canada) 42 GH 2-3
Amuntai 34 E 5
Amur 22 NO 4
Amur 22 NO 4-5
Amurang 34 F 4
Amurzet 32 D 2
Amuzunzag 37 B 5
'Ana 28 F 3
Anaa 54 N 6
Anabalava 41 c 6
Anabar 22 LM 2-3
Anaconda 46 D 3
Anadyr 22 S 3
Anadyr Gulf of 22 T 3
Analfi 20 G 9
Ana-hög 16 E 5
Anagni 19 D 4
Anaimudi 30 D 6
'Anaiza 38 D 2
Anajas 52 H 2
Anaklia 25 F 4
Anamur 28 B 2
Anamur, Cape 28 B 2
Anantapur 30 C 6
Anantnag 30 C 2
Anapa 25 D 3
Anapolis 52 H 5
Anapu 52 G 2
Anar 29 C 5
Anarak 29 B 5
Anardarra 29 D 5
Anatahan 54 E 3
Anatuya 53 D 2
Anaua 51 D 3
Anauac 42 I 8
Anching 31 L 4
Anchorage 45 I 4
Anco 52 C 4
Ancona 19 DE 3
Anconchel 9 C 4
Ancud 53 B 5
Andalgala 53 C 2
Andalusia 9 CE 5
Andaman Islands 33 A 4
Andaman, Little 33 A 4
Andaman, Middle 33 A 4
Andaman, North 33 A 4
Andaman Sea 33 B 4-5
Andaman, South 33 A 4
Andanga 24 C 5
Andarai 52 I 4
Andelys, Les- 11 F 2
Andéramboukane 37 E 6
Anderma 22 F 3
Anderson 44 D 2
Andes, Los- 53 B 3
Andevoranto 41 c 7
Andilamena 41 c 7
Andizan 22 G 5
Andkhui 29 E 4
Andoga 23 M 5
Andoma 23 M 4
Andörja 17 G 2
Andorra 9 G 2
Andorra la Vella 9 G 2
Andöy 17 F 2
Andreas, Cape 28 C 3
Andreanof Islands 22 T 4
Andréba 36 H 7
Andria 19 EF 4
Andringitra 35 H 8
Androka 41 b 8
Andros (Greece) 20 G 9
Andros l. 48 D 1
Androth 30 B 6
Ands 16 G 2
Andujar 9 D 4
Anegada 48 G 3
Aneho 39 E 4
Anelo 53 C 4
Anemomilos, Cape 20 G 10
Aneto, Pico de 8 G 2
Angamos 53 B 1
Angangchi 31 M 1
Angara 22 L 4
Angareb 38 C 5
Angarsk, N. 22 L 4
Angarsk, V. 22 M 4
Angattu 22 S 4
Angel de la Guarda 47 B 2
Angelholm 17 E 8
Angenong 31 E 4
Angerman, f. 16 G 5
Angermünde 13 E 2
Angers 11 E 3
Anges 16 L 3
Angesö 16 I 5
Angkor 33 C 4
Anglesey 3 D 5
Angmagssalik 44 Z 2
Angol 53 B 4
Angola 36 EF 7
Angoulême 11 F 4

Angouma 39 G 5
Angoumois 11 F 4
Angra da Heroismo 37 a
Angra de Cintra 37 A 5
Angra dos Reis 52 I 6
Angra Pequenna 41 B 4
Angras Juntas 41 B 4
Anguilla 48 G 3
Anholt 16 D 8
Anhsi 31 F 2
Anhui 31 L 4
Aniak 45 G 4
Anicuns 52 H 5
Anie 9 F 2
Aniene 18 D 3-4
Animkog 17 E 7
Aniwa Bay 32 F 2
Anjar 30 B 4
Anjou 11 E 3
Anjouan 41 b 6
Anjozorobe 41 c 7
Anju 31 N 3
An kang 31 H 4
Ankara 25 B 6
Ankaratra 35 H 7
Ankasakasa 41 b 7
Ankavandra 41 c 7
Ankazobe 41 c 7
An Khe 33 D 4
Anklam 13 E 2
Ankoro 40 D 4
Anlu 31 I 4
Ann 17 E 5
Ann, Cape 57 G 3
Annaba 37 F 2
Annai 51 E 3
An-Najaf 28 H 4
Annam 26 O 8
Annan 3 E 4
Annapolis 46 M 5
Annapurna 30 D 3
An-Nasiriya 28 I 5
Annecy 11 I 4
Anniston 46 J 5
Annuello 55 G 6
Anod, Las 38 E 6
Anoritôq 44 W 3
Anou Mellen 37 E 6
An pei 31 J 2
Ansab 28 H 6
Ansbach 13 D 4
An shum 31 H 5
An shan 31 M 2
Anson, Bay 55 E 2
Ansongo 37 E 6
Antabamba 52 C 4
Antakya 51 A 2
Antalaha 41 d 6
Antalya 28 A 2
Antalya, Gulf of 28 A 2
Antananarivo 41 C 7
Antanimora 41 c 8
Antelat 37 I 3
Antequera 9 D 5
Antiatlas 37 C 3-4
Antibes, Cape d'- 10 I 5
Antibes 11 I 5
Anticosti 44 S 6
Antifer, Cape d'- 11 F 2
An tig 31 H 3
Antigua 48 G 3
Antikithira 20 F 10
Anti Lebanon 28 D 2-3
Antilles, Greater 48 CF 2-3
Antilles, Lesser 48 FG 3-4
Antimilos 20 G 9
Antioquia 51 A 2
Antipodes Islands 57 A 5
Antofagasta 53 B 1
Antofagasta de la Sierra 53 C 2
Antong 31 N 3
Antonibe 41 c 7
Antonina 52 H 7
Antonio Ennes 41 F 2
Antonio Joao 52 F 6
Antony Lagoon 55 F 3
Antsal 25 I 4
Antsalova 41 b 7
Antsenavolo 41 c 8
Antsira 41 C 7
Antsirabe 41 C 7
Antsiranana 41 C6
An tu 31 N 2
An tung 31 M 2
Antwerpen 15 G 3
Anufrievo 23 N 4
Anundsjö 16 H 5
Anuradhapura 30 D 7
Anvers 57 O 3
Anvik 45 F 4
Anzero Sudz, 22 H 4
Anzio 19 D 4
Aoiz 9 F 2
Aomori 32 F 3
Aosta 19 A 2
Aosta, Valle d'- 19 A 2
Aouchich 37 B 5
Aouderas 37 F 6
Aouinet Legraa 37 C 4
Aouker 37 B 6
Aoulef In Rhar 37 E 4
Aozi 37 H 5
Apa 52 F 6
Apalachee Bay 46 L 7

Apalachicola 46 I 7
Apam 39 D 4
Aparri 34 F 1
Apataki 54 N 6
Apatin 21 D 5
Apeldoorn 15 G 2
Apennines, Central 18 DE 3-4
Apennines, Northern 18 AB 2-3
Apennin, Southern 18 EF 4-5
Aperé 52 G 2
Api 30 D 2, 34 G 6
Apiapianom 26 m 13
Aplao 52 C 5
Apo 34 G 3
Apollonia 37 I 3
Apolo 52 D 4
Apolyont, L. 20 I 7
Apostolovo 25 B 2
Appalachi 43 MN 5-6
Appelbo 17 E 6
Appin 55 d 11
Appleby 4 E 4
Apremont 11 H 2
Aprica 18 C 1
Aprilia 19 D 4
Apseron 1 S 7
Apt 11 H 5
Apuka 22 R 3
Apure 49 CD 3
Apurimac 52 C 4
Aputajuitsok 44 V 3
Aq Kuprak 29 E 4
Aqsu 31 C 2
Aqua Boa 52 I 5
Aquila, L'- 19 D 3
Aquin 48 E 3
Aquiperta 52 F 2
Ara 27 d 13
Arabi 28 HI 5
Arabia 26 GH 7-8
Arabian Sea 26 I 8
Ara Bulak 31 F 1
Aracau 52 L 4
Aracati 52 L 2
Araçatuba 52 G 6
Aracena, Serra de- 8 C 5
Arachthos 20 E 8
Aracruz 52 I 5
Araçuai 52 I 5
Arad (Iran) 2 R 8
Arad (Romania) 21 E 4
Arada 37 I 7
Aradal 17 E 5
Aradzhargalanta Khid 31 L 1
Araf 37 E 4
Arafura Sea 26 n 14-15
Aragats 25 H 5
Aragon 8 F 2
Aragon 9 FG 2-4
Aragua 51 D 1
Araguacema 52 H 3
Araguaia 50 E 5
Araguari 52 H 5
Araich, El- 37 C 2
Arakan Yoma 26 N 7-8
Araks 26 G 6
Aral Sea 22 EF 5
Aral'sk 22 F 5
Aramac 55 H 4
Aran In. 1 B 5
Aranda de Duero 9 E 3
Arang 30 D 4
Arani 52 D 5
Aranjuez 9 E 3
Aranyaprathet 33 C 4
Aranuane 37 D 6
Arapkir 25 E 6
Araracuara 52 C 2
Ararangua 52 H 7
Ararapira 52 H 7
Araraquara 52 H 6
Araras 52 G 3
Ararat (Australia) 55 G 7
Aratané 37 C 6
Arauca 51 B 2
Aravalli Ranger 26 L 7
Araxa 52 H 5
Arbai Khere 31 G 1
Arbela 25 G 3
Arber 12 A 3
Arboga 17 F 7
Arbra 17 G 6
Arbroath 4 E 3
Arc, River 10 I 4
Archena 9 F 4
Archidona 52 B 2
Arco (USA) 46 D 4
Arcos 9 E 3
Arctic Ocean, 56 OP 1
Arda 20 GH 7
Ar-Rachidiya 37 D 3
Ardacan 38 F 1
Ardahan 25 G 5
Ardal (Iran) 28 M 5
Ardal (Norway) 17 B 6
Ardatov 24 D 7

Ardebil 28 L 1
Ardeevo 23 M 3
Ardelan 28 I 3
Ardennes 14 G 3-4
Arderin 3 C 5
Ardila 8 C 4
Ardilan 1 R 8-9
Ardim 24 C 8
Ardistan 28 N 4
Ardjuno 26 m 13
Ardmore 46 G 6
Ards 4 D 4
Ardzim 24 F 6
Are 17 E 5
Arebi 40 D 2
Arecibo 48 F 3
Areia Branca 52 L 2
Arenal 17 C 7
Arends 34 D 6
Arequipa 52 C 5
Areskutan 16 E 5
Arévalo 9 D 3
Arezzo 19 CD 3
Arfak 26 R 10
Arga 8 F 2
Argao 34 F 2
Arga-Sala 22 LM 3
Arga Tag 26 M 6
Argens 10 I 5
Argentan 11 E 2
Argenteuil 11 G 2
Argentat 11 F 4
Argentera, Pizzo- 18 A 2
Argentina 50 D 6-7
Argentino 53 B 7
Argenton 11 F 3
Arges 20 GH 5
Arghanadab 29 E 5
Argianak 28 L 4
Argolis 20 F 9
Argolischer Gulf of 20 F 9
Argonne 10 H 2
Argos 21 F 9
Argostolion 21 E 8
Argun 22 MN 4
Argunovo 24 C 5
Arhavi 25 F 5
Arhus 17 D 8
Ariab 38 C 4
Ariari 51 B 3
Aribinda 39 D 3
Arica (Chile) 52 C 5
Arica (Colombia) 52 C 2
Arica, G.v. (Chile) 49 C 5
Aridh, El- 38 E 2-3
Ariege 10 F 5
Ariesul 20 F 4
Arima 52 E 3
Arinda 51 E 3
Arinos 52 F 4
Aripuana 52 EF 3-4
Arish, El- 38 B 1
Arizaro, Salar de- 53 C 1
Arizona (Argentina) 53 C 4
Arizona (USA) 46 D 6
Arjas 24 D 9
Arjenovsk 25 G 1
Arjona 51 B 1
Arjuvarre 16 M 2
Arka 22 P 3
Arkansas 46 H 5-6
Arkansas 42 L 6
Arkavi 25 F 8
Arkhangelsk 23 O 2
Arkhangel'skoe 24 I 7
Arkhara 32 D 2
Arklow 4 C 5
Arkona 12 E 1
Arkonam 30 C 6
Arkull' 24 F 6
Arlanza 9 E 2
Arlanzon 9 DE 2
Arlberg 12 D 5
Arles 11 H 5
Arli 37 E 6
Armagh 4 C 4
Armançon 10 GH 3
Armavir 25 F 3
Armenia (Colombia) 52 B 2
Armenia 25 GI 5-6
Armidale 55 I 6
Arnar 16 Q 12
Arnes 17 D 6
Arnhem 15 G 3
Arnhem, Cape 55 F 2
Arnhem Land 55 EF 2
Arno 18 C 3
Arnöy 16 I 1
Aroche 9 C 5
Arona 19 B 2
Arorae 54 H 5
Arpaçay 25 G 5
Ar-Ragati 38 E 2
Arrah 30 E 3
Ar-Ras 38 D 2
Arran 4 D 4
Arranmore 4 B 4
Ar-Rachidiya 37 D 3
Ar-Ras 38 D 2
Arrecifal 51 C 3
Arrecife 37 B 4
Arrojado 52 H 4
Arronches 9 L 4

Arroux 10 H 3
Arsinjan 38 F 2
Arsk 24 E 6
Arsuz 28 C 2
Arta (Greece) 21 E 8
Artá (Spain) 9 H 4
Artëmovsk 22 I 4
Artëmovskij 24 N 5
Arten 31 O 2
Arti 24 L 6
Artigas 53 E 3
Artington 41 D 4
Artjärvi 17 N 6
Artois 11 FG 1
Artvin 25 F 5
Aru-Islands 34 H 6
Arua 40 E 2
Aruab 41 B 4
Aruana 52 G 4
Arumatéua 52 H 2
Arusha 40 F 3
Arussi 38 CD 6
Aruti 52 D 2
Aruwimi 35 F 5
Arvidsjaur 17 H 4
Arvika 17 E 7
Arwala 34 G 6
Arys 22 F 5
Aryta 22 N 3
Arzamas 2 Q 4
Arzew 37 D 2
Arzua 9/ B 2
Asa (Denmark) 17 D 8
Asa (Soviet Union) 24 I 7
Asaba 39 F 4
As'adabad 28 L 3
Asafo 39 D 4
Asahi 32 F 3
Asahigawa 32 F 3
Asaki 27 c 13
Asansol 30 E 4
Asapas 28 N 5
Asar 17 S 13
Asarna 17 F 5
Asase 32 F 2
Asäyr 38 F 5
Ascension, Baia de la- 47 G 4
Ascension 36 B 6
Aschaffenburg 13 C 4
Aschersleben 13 D 3
Ascoli Piceno 19 D 3
Ascope 52 B 3
Ase 25 E 4
Asele 17 G 4
Asen 17 E 6
Ashanti 39 D 4
Ashau-Hannek 37 M 6
Ashburton 55 B 4
Asheville 46 L 5
Ashland (USA, Oregon) 46 B 4
Ashland (USA, Wisconsin) 46 H 3
Ashraf, Bir- 38 D 1
Ash-Shaab 38 D 5
Ashur 28 G 3
Ashuriya 28 G 5
Asiago 19 C 2
Asida 38 E 5
Asia Minor 1 NP 8
Asinara 18 AB 4
Asinara, G.of 18 B 4
Asino 22 H 4
Asir 27 G 8
Asita 28 G 2
Ask 28 N 3
Aska 16 MN 3
Askersund 17 F 7
Askhabad 22 E 6
Askino 24 I 6
Askja 17 I 12
Asköy 17 A 6
Asmara 38 C 4
Asosa 38 B 5
Aspromonte 18 EF 5
Assa 20 C 6
Assab 38 D 5
Assaba 37 B 6
As-Safa 38 E 2
As-Salman 28 H 5
Assam 33 A 1
Assaré 52 L 3
Asselar 37 E 6
Assen 15 H 2
Assiniboine, 44 L 6
Assinie 39 D 4
As Sirr 38 D 2
Assis 52 G 6
Assisi 19 D 3
Assodé 37 F 6
As-Summan 38 DE 2
Astaf'evo 23 N 4
Astara 25 L 6
Asti 19 B 2
Astillero 52 D 4
Astin Tag 31 BD 3
Astipalaia 20 H 9
Astorga 9 C 2
Astoria 46 B 3
Astradamovka 24 D 7
Astrakhan 25 I 2
Astrida 40 D 3
Astrolabio 54 E 5
Astudillo 9 D 2
Asturien 9 CD 2

Asuncion (Paraguay) **52** F 7
Asuncion (Mariana Island) **54** E 3
Asuncion, La- (Venezuela) **51** D 1
Aswan **37** M 5
Asyut **37** M 4
Atacama, Salar de- **53** C 1
Atacama **49** D 6
Atafu **54** I 5
Atak Hapchiga **31** E 4
Atakora **39** E 3
Atakpamé **39** E 4
Atalaya **52** C 4
Atami **27** d 13
Atamisqui **53** D 2
Atapupu **34** F 6
Atar **37** B 5
Atasus **29** F 2
Atasuskyi **22** G 5
Atauro **34** G 6
Atbara **38** B 4
Atbara **35** G 4
Atbasar **29** E 1
Atchison **46** G 5
Atebubu **39** D 4
Ateca **9** F 3
Atfif **37** M 4
Athabasca **44** G 5
Athabasca, Lake **44** H 4
Athens **21** F 9
Athens **46** L 6
Athi **40** F 3
Athiemé **39** E 4
Athy **4** C 5
Ati **37** H 7
Atico **52** C 5
Atienza **9** E 3
Atiquipa **52** C 5
Atiu **54** M 6
Atka **22** T 4
Atkarsk **24** C 9
Atlanta **46** L 6
Atlantic City **46** O 5
Atlantic Ocean, **1** CD 3-8
Atlasova **22** Q 4
Atlin **44** C 4
Atlöy **16** A 6
Atna **17** D 6
Atouat **26** O 8
Atoya de Alvarez **47** D 4
Atran **16** E 8
Atranos **20** I 8
Atrato **49** C 3
Atrek **1** ST 8
Atsap **41** A 3
Atsugi **27** d 13
At-Ta'labiya **38** D 2
Attar **37** F 3
Attawapiskat **44** N 5
Attersee **12** E 5
Attika **20** F 8
Attopeu **33** D 4
Attow, Ben- **3** D 3
Attu **22** S 4
Atuel **53** C 4
Atvidaberg **17** G 7
Aube **10** H 2
Aubin **11** G 4
Aubusson **11** G 4
Auch **11** F 5
Auckland, Town **55** g 13
Auckland, Islands **57** a 4
Aude **10** G 5
Audierne **11** C 2
Audincourt **11** I 3
Aue **13** C 2
Auenat, Geb el-, Mt. **35** F 3
Augsburg **13** D 4
Augusta (Australia) **55** B 6
Augusta (Italy) **19** E 6
Augusta (USA, Maine) **46** O 4
Augusta (USA, S. Carolina) **46** L 6
Augustine **45** H 5
Augustow **13** L 2
Augustus, M.^t **55** B 4
Aui **37** H 5
Auktsjaur **17** H 4
Aumale **37** E 2
Auncanquilcha **52** D 6
Aunis **11** E 3
Aurangabad **30** C 5
Auray **11** D 3
Aurès **37** F 2
Aurillac **11** G 4
Auronzo **19** D 1
Aurora, Town **46** I 4
Aurora, I. **54** G 6
Aurskog **17** D 7
Aurukun **55** G 2
Aurunci **18** D 4
Aussig **21** B 2
Aust Agder **17** BC 7
Austin (USA, Nevada) **46** C 5
Austin (USA, Texas) **46** G 6
Austin **55** B 5
Austral. Alpen **54** E 8
Austral. Downs **55** F 4
Australia **55**
Australia, South- **55** EF 5
Australia, West- **55** BD 4-5
Australia Bight, Great, **55** DE 6
Austria **13** DG 4-5
Austria, Lower **13** FG 4
Austria, Upper **13** EF 4
Autlan **47** D 4
Autun **11** H 3
Auvergne **11** G 4
Auxerre **11** G 3
Auxi **11** G 1
Auzat **11** F 5
Avalon, Peninsula **44** U 6
Avarsin **25** I 6
Avasaxa **16** L 3
Ave **9** B 3
Aveh **28** L 3
Aveiro (Brazil) **52** F 2
Aveiro (Portugal) **9** B 3
Avellaneda **53** E 3
Avellino **19** E 4
Averöy, Is. **16** B 5
Aversa **19** DE 4
Aves **48** G 3
Avesta **17** G 6
Aveyron **10** FG 4
Avezzano **19** D 3
Avia Terai **53** D 2
Avignon **11** H 5
Avila **9** D 3
Aviles **9** C 2
Avion **8** B 2
Avola **19** E 6
Avon **3** EF 5-6
Avranches **11** E 2
Awanui **55** g 13
Awe, Town **39** F 4
Awe, L. **3** D 3
Awash **38** D 5
Awdegle **38** D 7
Awsa **38** D 5
Awjila **37** I 4
Axar **16** T 11
Axel Heiberg **42** LM 1-2
Axim **39** D 5
Axum **38** C 5
Ayabaca **52** B 2
Ayacucho (Argentina) **53** E 4
Ayacucho (Peru) **52** C 4
Ayaghkun **31** D 3
Ayamonte **9** C 5
Ayancik **25** C 5
Ayapel **51** A 2
Ayas (Turkey) **28** C 2
Ayaviri **52** C 4
Aydin **21** H 9
Aydos **28** C 2
Ayerbe **9** F 2
Aygues **10** H 4
Aylesbury **4** F 6
Ayon **27** i 16
Ayora **9** F 4
Ayr (Australia) **55** H 3
Ayr (United Kingdom) **13** D 4
Ayutthaya **33** C 4
Ayvacik **21** H 8
Ayvalik **21** H 8
Azaouad **35** C 4
Azaouak **35** D 4
Azauak **37** E 6
Azbine **37** F 6
Azefal **37** AB 5
Azemmour **37** C 3
Azennezal **37** E 5
Azerbaijan **25** HL 5
Azigui **37** E 6
Azizia, El- **37** G 3
Azogues **52** B 2
Azores **37** a
Azov **25** F 2
Azov, Sea of **25** CE 2-3
Azovy **24** O 2
Azrou **37** C 3
Azuaga **9** D 4
Azuero, Pen. **48** C 5
Azul **53** E 4
Azum **37** I 7
Az-Zubair **28** I 5
Azzurro **26** OP 6-7

B

Ba **39** D 3
Baa **34** F 7
Ba'albek **28** D 4
Baba **20** I 9
Baba, Cape **20** H 8
Babadag, **21** I 5
Babahoyo **52** B 2
Babar **34** G 6
Bab el Mandeb **35** H 4
Babeltuap **54** D 4
Babi **25** I 6
Babia Gora **12** HI 4
Babimbi **39** G 5
Babo **34** H 5
Babol **28** N 2
Babouda **40** A 1
Babulsar **28** N 2
Babuskin **24** B 5
Babylon **28** H 4
Babuyan-Islands **26** Q 8
Bacabal **52** F 3
Bacan Islands **34** G 5
Bacau **21** H 4
Bäccegel Halde **16** I 2
Back **44** IL 2
Bac Kan **33** D 2
Backa Palanka **21** D 5
Bäckerfors **17** E 7
Bac Lieu **33** D 5
Bacolod **34** F 2
Bacuit **34** E 2
Bada **39** C 4
Badagri **39** E 4
Badajos **52** H 2
Badajoz **9** C 4
Badalona **9** H 3
Bad Ems **13** BC 3
Baden **38** C 4
Baden-Baden **13** BC 4
Baden-Wurttemberg **13** C 4-5
Badi'a **38** E 3
Badin **29** E 7
Bad Ischl **13** E 5
Badon **37** B 7
Badoumbe **37** B 7
Badr **38** D 4
Badra **28** H 4
Baduen **38** E 6
Badulla **30** D 7
Baena **9** D 5
Baeza **9** E 5
Bafang **39** G 4
Baffin Bay **42** NO 2
Baffin Island **44** OR 1-4
Bafing **37** B 7
Bafoulabé **37** B 7
Bafq **29** C 5
Bafra **25** C 5
Bafuka **40** D 2
Bafwabaka **40** D 2
Bafwaboli **40** D 2
Bafwasende **40** D 2
Bagadza **22** M 3
Bagalkot **30** C 5
Bagamayo **40** F 4
Bagan Siapiapi **34** B 4
Bagata **40** B 3
Bagé **53** F 3
Bagede **17** F 4
Baghashwa **38** F 5
Baghdad **28** H 4
Bagherhat **27** a 11
Bagheria **19** D 5
Bagirpasa Dagi **25** F 6
Bagnères d. Luchon **11** F 5
Bagoé **37** C 7
Bagou **39** E 3
Bagué **39** D 3
Baguezane **37** F 6
Baguio **34** F 1
Baguirmi **37** H 7
Bahadurabat **30** E 3
Bahama **48** DE 1-2
Bahar Dar **38** C 5
Bahawalpur **29** F 6
Bahia State **52** IL 4-5
Bahia, Islas de la- **47** G 4
Bahia Blanca Town **53** D 4
Bahia Blanca **53** DE 4
Bahia de Caraquez **52** A 2
Bahia Grande **53** C 7
Bahia Honda **48** C 2
Bahia Laura **53** C 6
Bahia Negra **52** F 6
Bahia Salvador **52** L 4
Bahraich **30** D 3
Bahrain **28** L 4
Bahrain, Island **26** H 7
Bahramabad **29** C 5
Bahram Chah **29** C 5
Bahr as-Safi **38** E 4
Bahrein **27** H 7
Bahr el' Arab **35** F 4-5
Bahr el-Ghazal **40** DE 1
Bahr el-Jebel **40** E 1
Bahr es Zeraf **40** E 1
Bahr Oulou **37** I 7-8
Bahr Salamar **37** HI 7
Bai **31** C 2
Baia Mare **21** F 4
Bailesti **21** F 5
Bailey **54** E 2
Bailundo **40** B 5
Baing **34** F 7
Bairnsdale **55** b 8
Baise **10** F 5
Baito **26** R 7
Baiwala **39** B 4
Baiyadh **38** E 3
Baiyuda **37** M 6
Baja **21** D 4
Baja, Punta **46** C 7
Bajan-Aul **22** G 4
Bajibo **39** E 4
Bajkit **22** I 3
Bajmak **22** E 4
Bajram-Ali **29** D 4
Bajtugan **24** G 7
Bajungtintjir **34** B 5
Bakana **29** G 3
Bakary **40** D 1
Bakau **34** E 4
Bakel **37** B 7
Baker, Town **46** C 4
Baker, Island **54** I 4
Baker, Lake **44** L 3
Baker, M^t. **46** B 3
Baker River **53** B 6
Bakersfield **46** C 5
Bakharden **29** C 4
Bakhta **22** H 3
Bakka **16** U 11
Bakkagerdhi **17** V 12
Bakola **40** B 2
Bakony Forest **20** CD 4
Bakote **40** C 4
Baksaj **25** M 2
Baku **29** A 3
Bakundi **39** G 4
Bakungan **34** A 4
Balabac **34** E 3
Balabri **39** F 5
Balad **38** E 7
Balad Sinjar **28** F 2
Balagannoe **22** P 4
Balaghat **30** D 4
Balaguer **9** G 3
Balaklava **25** B 3
Balakleja **25** D 1
Balakovo **24** D 8
Balambangan **34** E 3
Balangan **34** E 5
Balasore **30** E 4
Balassagyarmat **21** D 3
Balat **37** L 4
Balaton, L. **20** C 4
Balboa **48** C 5
Balcarce **53** E 4
Balcik **21** I 6
Bald Head **55** B 7
Baldo, M. **18** C 2
Bale **38** CD 6
Balearic Islands **8** GH 3-4
Baleia **52** L 5
Bali **34** DE 6
Balkesr **21** H 8
Balikpapan **34** E 5
Balkan, Central **20** G 6
Balkan, Eastern **20** H 6
Balkan, Western **20** FH 6
Balkasino **29** E 1
Balkh **29** E 4
Balkhan, Gran- **1** S 8
Balkhash **22** G 5
Balkhash, Lake **22** G 5
Balladonia **55** C 6
Ballarat **55** G 7
Ballard **55** C 5
Ballater **4** E 3
Ballenas, Bahia **47** B 2
Balleny Islands **57** a 3
Ballina **4** B 4
Ballinasloe **4** B 5
Ballon **10** I 3
Ballycastle **4** C 4
Balmaceda **53** B 6
Balovale **36** I 7
Balranald **55** G 6
Balsan Tumen **31** I 1
Balsas **52** B 3
Balsas, Rio (Brazil) **52** H 3
Balsas, Rio (Mexico) **47** DE 4
Balsas, Rio das- **52** H 4
Balstad **17** E 2
Balta **21** I 4
Baltic Sea **16** FI 7-9
Baltimore **46** M 5
Baltit **29** F 4
Baluchistan **29** DE 5-6
Balvi **23** F 6
Balygyian **22** Q 3
Bam (Iran) **29** C 6
Bam (South Africa) **40** B 1
Bama **39** G 3
Bamako **37** C 7
Bamba **37** D 6
Bambari **40** C 1
Bambe **41** F 3
Bamberg **13** D 4
Bambili **40** D 2
Bamenda **39** G 4
Baminghi **40** B 1
Bamingui **40** C 1
Bamni **27** b 11
Bampur **29** D 6
Bampur **29** CD 6
Banaga **39** F 3
Banalia **40** D 2
Banamba **37** C 7
Banana **40** A 4
Bananal, Island **52** G 4
Banas, Ras **35** G 3
Banas, River **30** BC 3-4
Banat **21** E 5
Banbury **4** F 5
Banda **30** D 3
Bandama **35** C 5
Bandar **30** D 5
Bändär Abbas **29** C 6
Bandar Maharani **33** C 6
Bändär Nasiri **28** L 5
Bandar Pählavi **28** L 2
Bandar Seri Begawan **34** D 4
Bändär Shah **28** N 2
Banda Sea **34** G 6
Bandawe **40** E 5
Bandeira, Pico de- **49** FG 6
Bandera **53** D 2
Banderas **47** C 3
Bandiagara **37** D 7
Band-i-Baba **29** D 4-5
Band-i-Mushki **29** C 6
Band-i-Qir **28** L 5
Bandirma **21** H 7
Bandon **4** B 6
Bandra **30** B 5
Bandundu **40** B 3
Bandung **34** C 6
Baneza, La- **9** D 2
Banff **4** E 3
Banfora **39** D 3
Bangala **40** B 2
Bangandou **40** B 2
Bangassi **37** C 7
Bangassou **40** C 2
Banggi **34** E 3
Bangka **34** C 5
Bangkalan **34** D 6
Bangko **34** B 5
Bangkok **27** O 8
Bangla-Desh **27** MN 7
Bangor (United Kingdom) **4** D 5
Bangor (USA, Maine) **46** O 4
Bangoran **40** BC 1
Bangued **34** F 1
Bangui (Philippines) **34** F 1
Bangui (South Africa) **40** B 2
Bangweulu, Lake **40** D 5
Ban Hat Yai **33** C 5
Bani **35** C 4
Bania **40** B 2
Banjaluca **21** C 5
Baniyas **28** C 3
Banja **21** H 6
Banjarmasin **34** D 5
Banjul **37** A 7
Banjuwangi **34** D 6
Banket **41** E 2
Banks I. (Australia) **55** G 2
Banks I. (Canada) **44** EF 1
Banks Peninsula **55** g 14
Banks Strait **55** b 9
Ban Mae ariang **33** B 3
Ban Me Thuot **33** D 4
Bann **3** C 4
Bannu **29** F 5
Bantry **4** B 6
Bantry Bay **3** B 6
Banyo **39** G 4
Banzare Coast **57** c 3
Baoulé **37** C 7
Baq'a **38** D 2
Baqeir, El- **37** M 6
Ba'quba **28** H 4
Baquedano **53** C 1
Bar (Yugoslavia) **21** D 6
Bar (Soviet Union) **21** H 3
Bara (Mali) **37** E 6
Bara (Molucca) **34** G 5
Bara (Sudan) **37** M 7
Baracoa **48** E 2
Barahona **48** E 3
Baraka (Congo) **40** D 3
Baraka (Sudan) **37** L 7
Barail **33** A 1
Baran **30** C 3
Barankwa **38** B 5
Baranof **45** M 5
Baranovici **23** F 8
Barao do Melgaço **52** F 5
Barate **34** F 6
Barawe **38** D 7
Barbaca **51** C 3
Barbacena **52** I 6
Barbacoas **51** A 3
Barbados **50** E 2
Barbastro **9** G 2
Barberton **41** E 4
Barbezieux **11** E 4
Barbuda **48** G 3
Barca **35** G 4
Barcaldine **55** H 4
Barce **37** I 3
Barcellona Pozzo di Gotto **19** E 5
Barcelona (Spain) **9** H 3
Barcelona (Venezuela) **51** D 1
Barcelonnette **11** I 4
Barcelos (Brazil) **52** E 2
Barcelos (Spain) **9** B 3
Barci **37** I 7
Barcoo, The **55** G 4
Barcs **21** C 4
Barda **24** H 6
Bardaï **37** H 5
Bardenas, Las- **8** F 2-3
Bardera **38** D 7
Bardia **37** L 3
Bardsey **4** D 5
Bardu **16** H 2
Barduk **28** H 2
Bareilly **30** C 3
Barents Sea **22** CD 2
Barentù **38** C 4
Barfleur **11** E 2
Barfleur, P.te de- **11** E 2
Bargal **38** F 5
Barguzin **22** L 4
Bahr el-Djebel **35** G 5
Barka, El- **37** C 4
Barkha **31** C 4
Barkly **54** D 6
Barkly West **41** C 4
Bar Kol **31** E 2
Bari **19** F 4
Baridi **38** C 3
Barikhane **33** C 3
Bariku **38** F 2
Barinas **51** B 2
Baringa **40** C 2
Baripada **30** E 4
Barisal **30** F 4
Barito **34** D 5
Bârlad River **20** H 5
Bar-le-Duc **11** H 2
Barlee **55** B 5
Barletta **19** F 4
Barmer **30** B 3
Barnaul **22** H 4
Barnastaple **4** D 6
Barnastaple Bay **4** D 6
Baro **39** F 4
Baro **38** B 6
Baroda **30** B 4
Baroghil - Pass **29** F 4
Barquisimeto **51** C 1
Barra da Estiva **52** I 4
Barra Islands **4** C 3
Barra, P.ta da- **41** F 3
Barraba **55** I 6
Barracao do Barreto **52** F 3
Barrackpore **30** E 4
Barra da Estiva **52** I 4
Barra do S. Manuel **52** F 3
Barra Falsa, P.ta da **41** F 3
Barrancas **51** D 2
Barrancos **9** C 4
Barranquilla **51** B 1
Barreiras **52** I 4
Barreirinhas **52** I 2
Barreiros **52** L 3
Barren Grounds **42** GI 3
Barretos **52** H 6
Barro **51** D 3
Barron **46** H 3
Barros, Tierra de- **9** C 4
Barrow (Alaska) **43** D 2
Barrow (United Kingdom) **4** E 4
Barrow **3** C 5
Barrow, Island **55** B 4
Barrow, P.^t **45** G 2
Barrow Strait **44** L 1
Barrow Creek **55** E 4
Barrowon **55** H 5
Barry **4** E 6
Bars **28** M 5
Barsaloi **40** F 2
Barsi **30** C 5
Bar-sur-Aube **11** H 2
Bar-sur-Seine **11** H 2
Barta, **17** I 8
Bartica **51** E 2
Bartin **25** B 5
Bartolomeu Dias **41** F 3
Bartoszyce **4** I 1
Barua **39** G 4
Barumun **34** B 4
Barun **26** q 17
Barum **26** q 17
Barung **26** m 13
Baruntse **26** p 17
Barus **34** A 4
Barwaha **30** C 4
Barya **40** B 1
Barycz **12** G 3
Basaki **28** M 5
Basankusu **40** B 2
Baschiria **24** I 7-8
Basco **31** M 6
Basel **13** B 5
Basento **18** F 4
Bashar **39** G 4
Bashi -Strait **31** M 6
Bash Qurghan **31** E 3
Basht **28** M 5
Basidu **29** C 6
Basilan Island **34** F 3
Basilicata **19** EF 4
Basim **30** C 4
Basingstoke **4** F 6
Basirhat **27** a 11
Baskale **28** G 1
Baskuncak **25** I 1
Basoko **40** C 2
Basongo **40** C 3
Basque Provinces **9** E 2
Basra **2** R 9
Bass-Strait **54** E 8
Bassac **33** D 4
Bassam **39** D 4
Bassan da India **36** H 8
Bassano **44** G 5
Bassano del Grappa **19** C 2
Bassar **39** E 4
Bassas da India **41** F 3
Bassas de Pedro **30** B 6
Bassa Sinoe **39** C 4
Bassein **33** H 3
Basse Terre **48** G 3
Bassikounou **37** C 6
Bassila **39** E 4
Basso **35** F 4
Basso Alentejo **9** BC 4-5
Bastak **38** F 2
Bastelica **11** a
Basti **30** D 3
Bastia (France) **11** a
Bastia (Italy) **18** B 3
Bastogne **15** G 3

Bastuträsk 17 H 4
Bata 39 F 5
Batajsk 25 F 2
Batala 30 C 2
Batam 27 hi 16
Batan 26 Q 7
Batangaf 40 B 1
Batangas 34 F 2
Batanta 34 H 5
Batavia 34 C 6
Bâte 40 B 1
Bath 4 E 6
Batha 37 H 7
Bathurst (Australia) 55 H 6
Bathurst (Canada) 44 R 6
Bathurst 44 D 1
Bathurst, Island Australia) 55 E 2
Bathurst, Island (Canada) 44 IL 1
Bathurst Inlet 44 H 2
Batiè 38 D 5
Batna 37 F 2
Batoka 41 D 2
Batonne 55 H 5
Baton Rouge 46 H 7
Battambang 33 C 4
Batticaloa 30 D 7
Battle 44 G 5
Battlefields 41 D 2
Battle Harbour 44 T 5
Batu 34 E 5
Batu Island 34 A 5
Batuata 34 F 6
Batumi 25 F 5
Batunga 40 C 1
Baturadja 34 B 5
Batutiban 34 D 4
Baubau 34 F 6
Bauchi 39 F 3
Baudh 30 D 4
Baudo 51 A 2
Baudouinville 40 D 4
Baugé 11 E 3
Baul, El- 51 C 2
Bauld 44 T 5
Bauru 52 H 6
Baus 52 G 5
Bauska 17 M 8
Bautzen 13 F 3
Bavaria 13 D 4
Bavarian Forest 12 E 4
Bavreuth 13 D 4
Bawdwin 33 B 2
Bawean 34 D 6
Bayanga 40 B 2
Bayan Gol 31 H 2
Bayan Hara Uula 26 N 6
Bayan Hongor 31 H 1
Bayan Khashiatu 31 H 1
Bayan Ondur 31 F 2
Bayan Ula 31 F 1
Bayard 10 I 4
Bay Bay 34 F 2
Bayburt 25 F 5
Bayeux 11 E 2
Baykal, Lake 22 L 4
Bayombon 34 F 1
Bayona 9 B 2
Bayonne 11 E 5
Baza 9 E 5
Bazar-djuzi 25 I 5
Beachport 55 F 7
Beachy H. 3 G 6
Beaconsfield 4 C 4
Bear Island 22 R 2
Bear Lake, Great 44 EF 2
Béarn 11 E 5
Beata 48 E 3
Beatrice 46 G 4
Beauce 10 FG 2-3
Beaufort (Malaya) 34 E 3
Beaufort (USA, South Carolina) 46 L 6
Beaufort See 45 IN 3
Beaufort West 41 C 8
Beaumont (USA) 46 H 6
Beaumont (Zealand) 55 f 15
Beaune 11 H 3
Beauvais 11 G 2
Beaver 44 G 5
Beawar 30 B 3
Bebedouro 52 H 6
Becej 21 E 5
Bechuanaland 41 C 4
Bedanga 37 H 7
Bédarieux 11 H 5
Bedford 13 F 5
Bedlington 4 F 4
Bedourie 55 F 7
Beeville 46 G 7
Beeskow 13 F 2
Befandriana 41 b 8
Befotaka 41 c 6
Bega 55 H 7
Begar, El- 37 B 5
Begna 16 C 6
Béhar 37 D 3
Behbehan 28 M 5
Beheloka 41 b 7
Behenjavilo 41 b 7
Beiarn 17 F 3

Beida, El- 37 I 3
Beidoa 38 D 7
Beiga 39 D 3
Beila 38 F 6
Beilul 38 D 5
Beins 21 F 4
Beira (Somalia) 38 E 6
Beira Alta 9. BC 3
Beira Baixa 9 C 3-4
Beira Litor 9 B 3-4
Beirut 28 C 4
Beitstad 17 D 4
Béja (Tunisia) 37 F 2
Beja (Portugal) 9 C 4
Bejaïa 37 E 2
Béjar 9 D 3
Békéscsaba 21 E 4
Bekipay 41 c 7
Beoodoka 41 c 7
Bela (India) 30 D 3
Bela (Pakistan) 29 E 6
Belaberim 37 G 6
Bela Crkva 21 E 5
Belaja 1 ST 4-5
Belaja Glina 25 F 2
Belasica Planina 20 F 3
Bela Vista (Brazil) 52 F 6
Bela Vista (Mozambique) 41 E 4
Belcher Islands 44 P 4
Belchite 9 F 3
Belebej 24 H 7
Belém 9 B 4
Belém Para 52 H 2
Belén 48 C 5
Belet Uen 38 E 7
Belfast (Norther Ireland) 4 D 4
Belfast (South Africa) 41 E 4
Belfort 11 I 3
Belgaum 30 B 5
Belgium 15 FG 3-4
Belgorod 2 P 5
Belgorod-Dnestrovskij 21 L 4
Belgrade 21 E 5
Belgrano, General- 53 E 4
Belice 18 D 6
Beliki 25 C 1
Belingwe 41 D 3
Belinju 34 C 5
Belize (Angola) 40 A 3
Belize 47 G 4
Beljanica 20 E 5
Bell Pen. 44 D 5
Bella Coola 44 D 5
Bellac S. Junien 11 F 3
Bellary 30 C 5
Bella Vista 52 F 7
Belle Ile 10 D 3
Belle Isle 44 T 5
Belle Isle, Str.of 44 T 5
Belleville (Canada) 44 P 7
Belleville (USA) 46 I 5
Belley 11 H 4
Bellingham 46 B 3
Bellingshausensee 57 P 2-3
Bellinzona 19 B 1
Bello, Porto 8 C 2
Bellona 54 F 6
Bellsund 56 a
Belle Ville 53 D 3
Belmont 41 C 4
Belmonte (Brazil, Bahia) 52 L 5
Belmonte (Brazil, Paraiba) 52 L 3
Belmonte (Spain) 9 E 4
Belmopan 47 G 4
Belo 41 b 7
Beloe Oz. 23 M 4
Beloha 41 b 9
Belo Horizonte 52 I 5
Belomorsk 23 L 2
Beloola 55 G 5
Beloomut 31 H 1
Beloretsk 24 L 8
Belozersk 23 M 4
Belt, Great 16 D 9
Belt, Little 16 CD 9
Bel'tsy 21 H 4
Belukha 26 M 4
Beluran 34 E 3
Belyj 23 I 7
Bermaraha 41 bc 7
Bemarivol 41 c 7
Bembe 40 A 4
Bemuti 34 H 5
Bena Dibele 40 C 3
Benadir 35 H 5
Ben Améra 37 B 5
Benavente 9 D 2
Benbecula 4 C 3
Bend 46 B 4
Bende 39 F 4
Bendery 21 I 4
Bendigo 55 G 7
Bendu 39 B 4
Besna Kobila 20 F 6
Besni 28 D 2
Besparmak 20 H 9
Benevento 19 E 4
Bengal 30 EF 4
Bengal, Bay of 26 MN 8
Ben Gardane 37 G 3
Benghazi 37 I 3
Bengkulu 34 B 5

Bengo 40 A 4
Benguela 40 A 5
Ben Guerir 37 C 3
Benha 37 M 3
Beni 52 D 5
Beni Abbès 37 D 3
Benicarlò 9 G 3
Bénima 40 C 1
Benin (State) 36 D 4-5
Benin, River 39 F 4
Benin, Bight of 39 E 4
Benin-City 39 F 4
Benisa 9 G 4
Beni Suef 37 M 4
Benjamin Constant 52 D 2
Ben More 3 D 3
Benoni 41 D 4
Benoue 39 G 4
Bensane 39 B 3
Bensheim 13 C 4
Benteng 34 F 6
Benty 39 B 4
Benue 35 DE 5
Benwee Head 4 B 4
Beo 34 G 4
Béoumi 39 C 4
Barakit 27 i 16
Beraru 26 n 14
Berat 20 D 7
Berati 21 D 7
Barau 34 E 4
Berber 38 B 4
Berbera 38 E 5
Berchtesgaden 13 E 5
Berck 11 F 1
Berdicev 21 I 3
Berdjansk 25 D 2
Bereby 39 C 5
Beregovo 21 F 3
Berenike 37 M 5
Berestovo 25 D 2
Berettyvo 20 E 4
Berezina 23 G 7-8
Berëznici 24 I 5
Berezno 21 H 2
Berezovka (Ukraine) 25 A 2
Berëzovka (Kasachstan) 24 C 8
Berëzovo 24 O 3
Berëzovskij 24 M 6
Berg 17 G 2
Berga (Spain) 9 G 2
Berga (Sweden) 17 G 8
Bergama 21 H 8
Bergamasque A. 18 BC 1-2
Bergamo 19 BC 2
Bergedorf 13 D 2
Bergerac 11 F 4
Bergkvara 17 G 8
Bergö 17 I 5
Bergsfjord 17 I 1
Berguent 37 D 3
Bergvik 17 G 6
Bergville 41 D 4
Berhampore 30 E 4
Berhampur 30 D 5
Beri 40 A 2
Berim 39 G 4
Bering Sea 22 RU 3-4
Bering Strait 45 E 3-4
Berislav 25 B 2
Berkelev 46 B 5
Berlevag 16 O 1
Berlin, East 13 E 2
Berlin, West 13 E 2
Berlino (Australia) 55 F 5
Bermeja, p.ta 53 D 5
Bermejo, Rio 53 C 2
Bermuda Is. 43 O 6
Bern 19 A 21
Bernasconi 53 D 4
Berneray 4 C 3
Bernese A. 18 A 1
Bernesga 9 D 2
Bernina 18 B 1
Bernina, Passo 18 C 1
Bernoub, El- 37 E 3
Bero 41 A 2
Beroroha 41 c 8
Berounka 20 AB 3
Berre, Le 11 H 5
Berry 11 FG 3
Bertoua 39 G 5
Berwich upon Tweed 4 F 4
Berzosa, La- 8 CD 3
Besalampy 41 b 7
Besançon 11 I 3
Besed' 23 HI 8
Beskids 12 HIL 4
Beskids, East 12 IL 4
Beskids, West 12 HI 4
Beslan 25 H 4
Bessarabia 21 HI 3-4
Besseroudi 37 D 4
Besson 10 G 4
Bessëges 11 H 4
Betanzos 9 B 2
Bétaré Oya 39 G 4

Beteina 37 B 4
Bethal 41 D 4
Bethanie 41 B 4
Bethel 45 F 4
Bethlehem 41 D 4
Béthune 11 F 1
Béthune, River 11 F 2
Betou 40 B 2
Bet Park dala 22 FG 5
Betsiboka 35 H 7
Bettiah 30 D 3
Betwa 30 C 3-4
Beurfou 37 H 6
Beveland 15 F 3
Bevensen 13 D 2
Beveridge 54 L 7
Beyin 39 D 4
Beyla 39 C 4
Beypazari 25 5
Beysehir 28 A 2
Beysehir Lake 28 A 2
Bezetsk 23 M 6
Bezitsa 23 L 8
Bezvodnoe 24 C 8
Bhadgaon 30 E 3
Bhadrak 30 E 4
Bhagalpur 30 E 3
Bhamo 33 B 2
Bhan, Ben- 4 D 3
Bhandara 30 C 4
Bharatpur 30 C 3
Bhatiapara Ghat 27 a 11
Bhatinda 30 BC 2
Bhatpara 27 a 11
Bhavnagar 30 B 4
Bhilsa 30 C 4
Bhima 30 BC 5
Bhopal 30 C 4
Bhor 30 B 5
Bhote Kosi 26 p 17
Bhubaneswar 30 E 4
Bhuj 30 A 4
Bhusawal 30 C 4
Bhutan 26 N 7
Biach 37 A 6
Biafra, Bight of 39 F 5
Biak 34 I 5
Biala Podlaska 13 L 2
Bialowicza 13 L 2
Bialystok 13 L 2
Biar Mezara, El- 37 A 5
Biaro 34 G 4
Biarritz 11 E 5
Bias 11 F 4
Bia Uoraba 38 D 6
Biban 38 B 2
Bibemé 40 A 1
Biberach 13 CD 4
Bibi 41 A 2
Bibiani 39 D 4
Bibirevo 23 I 6
Bida 39 F 4
Bidar 30 C 5
Bideford 4 D 6
Biel 19 A 1
Bielefeld 13 C 2-3
Bielsk 13 L 2
Bielsko-Biala 13 H 4
Bienboa 33 D 4
Bierzo, El- 9 C 2
Biesco 53 B 7
Biesiesfontein 41 B 5
Bifermo 18 E 4
Biga 21 H 7
Bigadiç 21 H 8
Biggeluobbal 17 L 2
Big Horn 46 E 3-4
Bignona 39 A 3
Big River 44 H 5
Bihac 21 B 5
Bihar 26 M 7
Bihor 20 F 4
Bija 22 H 4
Bijapur 30 C 5
Bijar 28 I 3
Bijeljina 21 D 5
Bijelo Polje 21 D 6
Bijistan 29 C 5
Bijsk 22 H 4
Bikaner 30 B 3
Bikar 54 H 3
Bikie 40 A 3
Bikin 22 O 5
Bikini 54 G 4
Bilaspur 30 D 4
Bilauk Taung 33 B 4
Bilbao 9 E 2
Bilbao, Ria de- 8 E 2
Bilgoraj 13 L 3
Bili 40 D 2
Biliran 34 E 2
Biljamor 24 E 6
Biljarsk 24 F 7
Billet 38 D 7
Billings 46 E 3
Billiton 34 C 5
Bilma 37 G 6
Bimbéreké 39 E 3
Bimbila 39 E 4
Binala Soounga 37 I 6
Bindals 16 F 3
Binder 40 A 1
Bindjai 34 A 4
Bindo 40 B 1

Bingen 13 B 4
Binghamton 46 M 4
Bingöl 25 F 6
Bingöl Dagi 25 F 6
Binh Dinh 33 D 4
Binji 39 E 3
Binongko 34 F 6
Bintan 34 B 4
Bintuhan 34 B 5
Bintuln 34 D 4
Bio 40 B 2
Biobio 53 B 4
Biocia 38 C 4
Bioko 39 F 5
Bir 30 C 5
Bira 32 D 2
Bir Abu Gawa 28 B 7
Bir-Abu Gharadig 37 L 3
Bir al Mashi 28 C 6
Bir-Amran 37 C 5
Bir el-'Anz 28 C 7
Bir el-Gareb 37 A 5
Bir-el-Gidami 28 B 7
Bir el-Hadjaj 37 D 4
Bir el-Mers 37 B 4
Bir-el-Uaar 37 G 5
Bir es Sof 37 F 3
Bir es-Suweir 28 C 6
Bir Fadhil 38 F 3
Bir Fajr 28 F 6
Birganj 30 E 3
Bir Ghardäia 37 F 3
Bir Ghenduz 37 A 5
Bir Halfala 37 M 5
Bir Hirmas 28 D 6
Biriljussy 22 I 4
Birimgan 55 H 4
Biriri 39 G 3
Birjand 29 C 5
Birket Fatmé 37 H 7
Birket Qarum 37 M 4
Birkot 29 F 4
Bîrlad 21 H 4
Birmingham (United Kingdom) 13 F 5
Birmingham (USA, Alabama) 46 I 6
Bir Murr (Libyan Desert) 37 M 5
Bir Murr (Sinai) 28 B 6
Bir Natrum 36 F 4
Birni (Chad) 37 H 7
Birni (Niger) 39 E 3
Birnin (Gwari 39 F 3
Birni-N-'Konni 37 F 7
Birobidzan 22 O 5
Bir-Ould-Brini 37 D 4
Bir-Qiseib 28 B 6
Birr 4 C 5
Bir Samit 28 G 5
Birsk 22 E 4
Bir Sultan 37 L 6
Bir Terfawi 37 L 5
Birti 37 M 8
Birzai 17 M 8
Bir Zerir 37 G 3
Bisbee 46 E 6
Biscarrosse, Étang de-11 E 4
Biscay, Bay of 8 EF 1-2
Biscoe 57 O 3
Biscra 37 F 3
Biserovo 24 G 5
Bisert' 24 L 6
Bisha 38 D 4
Bisheh Daraz 28 I é
Biscay, Bay of 11 DE 4-5
Bisling 34 G 3
Bismarck, Town 46 F 3
Bismarck, Archipelago 54 E 5
Bissagos-Islands 39 A 3
Bissandougou 39 C 4
Bissau 39 A 3
Bissigu 39 E 3
Bissikrima 39 B 3
Bistrita 21 G 4
Bistrita, River 20 H 4
Bitche 11 I 2
Bitola 21 E 7
Bitterfeld 13 E 3
Bitterfontein 36 E 9
Biu 39 G 3
Biwa, Lake 32 E 4
Bizana 41 D 5
Bizerte 37 F 2
Bjala 21 G 6
Bjelasnica 20 D 6
Bjelasnica Planina 20 D 6
Bjeljani 21 D 6
Bjelland 17 F 3
Bjellanes 17 F 3
Bjelovar 21 C 5
Björk, M.t 16 G 3
Björkö (Finland) 17 I 5
Björkö (Sweden) 17 H 7
Björne 17 A 6
Björneborg 17 I 6
Bjosna 16 A 6
Bjungn 17 C 5
Bjuröklubb 16 I 4

Bla 17 F 4
Blackall 55 H 4
Blackfoot 46 D 4
Black Forest 12 BC 4-5
Black Hills, M.t 46 F 4
Black River 33 CD 2
Black Rock 57 N 4
Black Sea 1 NQ 6-7
Blacktown 55 I 10
Black Volta 35 C 4-5
Blackwater 3 BC 5
Blafjäll 16 T 12
Blagovescensk 22 N 4
Blair Atholl 4 E 3
Blairgowrie 4 E 3
Blais 11 F 3
Blamannen 16 H 2
Blambangan 26 m 13
Blanc, Cape 37 A 5
Blanc, Le- 11 F 3
Blanca Peak 46 E 5
Blanche 55 F 5
Blanco, Cape 46 B 4
Blancs 9 H 3
Blanda 16 S 12
Blandford 13 E 6
Blanquilla, La- 51 D 1
Blanquillo 53 E 3
Blantyre 41 E 2
Blattnicksele 17 G 4
Blavet 10 D 3
Blekinge 17 F 8
Bleia 16 B 6
Blenheim 55 G 14
Blieron 39 C 5
Bloemfontein 41 D 4
Bloemhof 41 D 4
Blonie 13 I 2
Bloody Foreland 4 B 4
Bloomington 46 I 4
Blora 34 D 5
Bloumet 37 F 5
Blouwberg 41 D 3
Blue (Jamaica) 48 I 3
Blue, M.t. (USA, Oregon) 46 C 3-4
Blue, Mt. (USA, Maine) 46 N 4
Blue Nile 35 G 4
Bluefields 48 C 4
Bluff (New Zealand) 55 f 15
Bluff (USA, Utah) 46 E 5
Blumenau 52 H 7
Blumenthal 13 C 2
Blyth 4 F 4
Bö 17 F 2
Boac 34 F 2
Boa Vista (Cape Verde) 39 a
Boa Vista (Brazil) 52 G 2
Bobandana 40 D 3
Bobbili 30 D 5
Bobo Dioubasso 39 D 3
Bobr 12 F 3
Bobrinets 25 B 1
Bobrujsk 23 G 8
Boca do Acre 52 D 3
Boca do Capana 52 E 3
Bocairente 9 F 4
Bocalia 37 H 6
Bocaranga 40 B 1
Bocas del Toro 48 C 5
Bocay 48 B 4
Bocca Serriola 18 D 3
Bochnia 13 I 3
Bocholt 13 B 2
Bochum 13 B 2
Boco de Jari 52 G 2
Bocoyna 47 C 2
Bod 13 F 3
Böda 17 G 8
Boda 17 G 5
Bodajobo 22 M 4
Bode 12 D 3
Bodele 37 H 6
Boden 17 I 4
Bodéra 40 B 1
Bodjonegoro 34 D 6
Bodö 17 F 3
Bodrum 21 H 9
Bodsjö 17 F 5
Bodva 20 E 3
Boedo 9 D 2
Boën 11 G 4
Boende 40 C 3
Boffa 39 B 3
Bogar 37 I 6
Bogazliyau 25 C 6
Boodo Úla 31 D 2
Boghari 37 E 2
Boghé 37 B 6
Bogol-Magno 38 D 7
Bogor 34 C 6
Bogoroditsk 23 N 8
Bogorodsk 24 I H 8
Bogorodskoe 24 F 6
Bogota 51 B 3
Bogou 39 E 3
Bogucar 25 F 1
Bohemia 20 AB 3
Bohemian Forest 12 E 4
Bohol 34 F 3
Bohotleh Neih 38 E 6
Bohov 25 F 1
Bohus 17 D 8
Boiana 21 D 7
Boila 41 F 2

Bois, dos- 52 H 5
Boise 46 C 4
Bojarka 22 I 2
Bojnurd 29 C 4
Bokala 40 B 3
Bokan Sukhai 31 G 2
Bokani 39 F 4
Bokatola 40 B 3
Boké 39 B 3
Bokn 16 A 7
Boko Songo 40 A 3
Bokoro 37 H 7
Boksburg 41 D 4
Bol 37 G 7
Bolama 39 A 3
Bolan-Pass 29 E 6
Bolbec 11 F 2
Bole (Ghana) 39 D 4
Bolé (Mali) 37 C 7
Bolenge 40 B 3
Boleslawiec 13 F 3
Bolgrad 21 I 5
Bolivar (Argentina) 53 D 4
Bolivar (Colombia) 51 A 3
Bolivia 50 D 5
Bolkhov 23 LM 8
Bollnäs 17 G 6
Bolobo 40 B 3
Bologna 19 C 2
Bologoe 23 L 6
Bolomba 40 B 2
Bolon 32 E 2
Bolotovskoe 24 N 5
Bolsena, Lake 18 CD 3
Bolshevik-Island 22 IL 2
Bolsiuka 25 F 1
Bol'soe-Zabolot'e 23 M 4
Bolton 4 E 5
Bolu 25 A 5
Bolzano 19 C 1
Boma 40 A 4
Bomassa 40 B 2
Bomba (Libya) 37 I 3
Bombala 55 H 7
Bombay 30 B 5
Bomlo, Town 17 A 7
Bomlo, Island 1 A 7
Bomili 40 D 2
Bom Jardim 52 C 3
Bom Jesus 52 I 3
Bomnak 22 N 4
Bomokandi 40 D 2
Bomu 40 C 1
Bon, Cape 37 G 2
Bonaflé 39 C 4
Bonaire 51 C 1
Bonaké 39 C 4
Bonavista 44 U 6
Bonavista Bay 44 U 6
Bondo 40 C 2
Bondoukou 39 D 4
Bone 34 F 5
Bone, Gulf of 34 F 5
Bonga 38 C 6
Bongabong 34 F 2
Bongadanga 40 C 2
Bongo 40 B 3
Bongor 37 H 7
Bonifacio 11 a
Bonifacio, Str. of 18 B 4
Bonin 27 S 7
Bonn 13 B 3
Bonnétab 11 F 2
Bonneval 11 F 2
Bonny 39 F 5
Bontang 34 E 4
Bonthain 34 E 6
Bonthe 39 B 4
Bookaloo 55 F 6
Boothia, Gulf of 44 MN 1
Boothia Peninsula 44 M 1
Booué 40 A 3
Bophutatswana 41 CD 3-4
Boporo 39 B 4
Bor (Soviet Union) 23 I 5
Borama 38 D 5
Borana 38 CD 7
Boras 17 E 8
Borazjan 28 M 6
Borbonese 11 G 3
Bordas Blancas 53 C 4
Bordeaux 11 E 4
Borden Peninsula 44 O 1
Bordö 3 a
Borè 37 D 6
Borga (Finland) 17 M 6
Borga (Sweden) 16 F 4
Borgarnes 17 R 12
Borge 17 E 2
Borgholm 17 G 8
Borgo Pass 20 G 4
Borgou 39 E 3-4
Borgsiä 17 G 5
Borkum 12 B 2
Borislav 21 F 3
Borisov 23 G 7
Borisovka 29 E 3
Borko 37 H 6
Borkum 12 B 2
Borlänge 17 F 6
Borlu 21 I 8
Borma 24 F 7
Bormida 18 B 2
Borneo 26 P 9-10
Bornholm 16 F 9
Bor Nor 31 I 1
Bornu 39 FG 3
Borodino 23 L 7
Borodino 54 D 2
Boro Khoro Ula 31 C 2
Boromo 39 D 3
Boron 39 C 4
Borotou 39 C 4
Borovici 23 I 5
Borroloola 55 F 3
Bor Safaga 28 C 7
Borsava 20 F 3
Borskoe 24 F 8
Borujerd 28 L 4
Borzja 22 M 4
Borzonu 25 G 5
Borzya 32 A 1
Bosa 19 B 4
Bosaso 38 E 5
Bosna 20 D 5
Bosnek 34 I 5
Bosnia 21 CD 5
Bosobolo 40 B 2
Bosporus 20 I 7
Bossakala 40 B 1
Bossekopp 17 L 2
Bosso 37 G 7
Boston (United Kingdom) 4 F 5
Boston (USA) 46 N 4
Boston Mts. 46 H 5
Bosut 20 D 5
Botany 55 e 10
Botany Bay 55 e 11
Botea 17 G 5
Botasani 21 H 4
Bothnia, Gulf of 16 HM 4-6
Botou 39 E 3
Botswana 36 F 8
Botte Donato 18 F 5
Botucatu 52 H 6
Boua 40 A 2
Bouala 40 B 1
Bouali 40 A 3
Bou Barour 37 E 3
Bou Bernous 37 D 4
Boubout 37 D 4
Boucau 11 E 5
Bouda 40 B 2
Bou Denib 37 D 3
Boudoum 37 G 7
Bouel-jad 37 C 3
Boungainville 54 F 5
Bougara 37 B 6
Bougouni 37 C 7
Bou Guema 37 E 4
Bou Guerba 37 B 5
Boui Dieri 37 A 6
Bouka 40 B 1
Boulal 37 C 6
Boulder (Australia) 55 C 6
Boulder (USA) 46 E 4
Boulé Bani 37 C 7
Boulia 55 F 4
Boullong 37 H 7
Boulogne 11 F 1
Boulon 37 B 7
Boumba, Town 37 E 7
Boumba, River 40 AB 2
Boumo 40 B 1
Bouna 39 D 4
Bountou 37 B 7
Bounty 54 I 9
Bourbonne 11 H 3
Bourem 37 D 6
Bourg 11 E 4
Bourg en Bresse 11 H 3
Bourges 11 G 3
Bourget 11 H 4
Bourke 55 H 6
Bournemouth 4 F 6
Bou Saada 37 E 2
Bousso 37 H 7
Boutlimit 37 B 6
Bouvet 57 i 4
Bouza 37 F 7
Bowen 55 H 3
Bowling Green 46 I 5
Bowman 57 d 3
Boyle 4 B 5
Boyne River 3 C 5
Boyoma Falls 35 F 6
Boz Dag 20 HI 8
Bözö 27 e 13
Bozoum 40 B 1
Bozscakul' 22 G 4
Bra 19 A 2
Braas 17 F 8
Brabant 14 G 3
Brabante 57 O 3
Bracciano 19 D 3
Bracciano, Lake 18 CD 3
Bracebridge 44 P 6
Brach 37 G 4
Bräcke 17 F 5
Bradano 18 F 4
Bradelon, M^t. 20 E 8
Bradford (United Kingdom) 4 F 5
Bradford (USA) 46 M 4
Braga 9 B 3
Bragalnica 20 F 7
Bragança (Brazil) 52 H 2
Braganza (Portugal) 9 C 3
Brahmanbaria 30 F 4
Brahmaputra 31 DE 5
Brakna 37 B 6
Braich-y-Pwll 4 D 5
Bràila 21 H 5
Brämö 17 G 5
Bramsche 13 B 2
Branchville 46 L 6
Branco, Cape 52 L 3
Branco, Rio- 49 D 3
Brandberg 41 A 3
Brandenburg 13 E 2
Brandon 44 L 6
Braniewo 13 H 1
Bransfield Strait 57 On 3
Bransk 13 L 2
Brantas 26 m 13
Brantford 44 O 7
Brantôme 11 F 4
Brasile 49 F 5
Brasilia 52 H 5
Braslav 23 F 7
Brasov 21 G 5
Brass 39 F 5
Bratislava 21 C 3
Bratsk 22 L 4
Braunau 13 E 4
Brava 39 a
Bravo del Norte 47 C 1
Brazil 50 DF 4-5
Brazos 46 G 6
Brazzaville 40 A 3
Breko 21 D 5
Brda 12 G 2
Brdy 20 A 3
Breaza 20 F 4
Brechin 4 E 3
Brecon 4 E 6
Breda 15 G 3
Bredasdorf 41 B 5
Bredy 24 M 8
Bregenz 13 CD 5
Brei 17 A 5
Breida 16 Q 12
Brejo 52 I 2
Brekke 17 A 6
Bremanger 16 A 6
Bremen 13 C 2
Bremerhaven 13 C 2
Brenner 18 C 1
Brenta 18 C 2
Brescia 19 C 2
Bresle 11 F 1-2
Bressay 3 F 1
Brest (France) 11 C 2
Brest (Ukraine) 21 F 1
Bretcu 21 H 4
Breteuil 11 G 2
Brevoort 44 S 3
Brewarrina 55 H 5
Brewton 46 I 6
Breyten 41 E 4
Brezina 37 E 3
Bria 40 C 1
Briançon 11 I 4
Bridgend 4 E 6
Bridgeport 46 O 4
Bridgetown 51 E 1
Bridgwater 4 E 6
Bridlington 4 F 4
Brie 10 G 2
Brieg 13 G 3
Briey 6 A 4
Brig 13 AB 1
Bright 55 H 7
Brighton (Australia) 55 b 8
Brighton, (United Kingdom) 13 F 6
Brighton (Tasmania) 55 b 9
Brignogan 11 C 2
Brignoles 11 I 5
Brihuega 9 E 3
Brijnagar 30 C 4
Brindisi 19 G 4
Brinje 21 B 5
Brintbodar 17 F 6
Brioude 11 G 4
Brisbane 55 I 5
Bristol 4 E 6
Bristol Bay 45 FG 5
Bristol Channel 13 DE 6
Bristol, Island. 57 M 4
Brittany 11 DE 2-3
Britstown 41 C 5
Brive 11 F 4
Brno 21 C 3
Broach 30 B 4
Broad Arrow 55 C 6
Broad Law 3 E 4
Brochet 44 I 4
Brocken 12 D 3
Brocks 42 DE 3
Brod 21 E 7
Brodeur Peninsula 44 N 1
Broken Hill (Australia) 55 G 6
Brönderslev 17 C 8
Bronnitsy 23 N 7
Brönnöysund 17 D 4
Bronte 19 E 6
Brooke's Point 34 E 3
Broom 4 D 3
Broome 55 C 3
Brora 4 DE 2
Brotas de Macaubas 52 I 4
Brownsville 46 G 7
Brownsweg 51 E 3
Brownwood 46 G 6
Bruck 13 F 5
Bruck 13 G 4
Brügge 15 F 3
Brukkaros 41 B 4
Brumado 52 I 4
Brunei 34 D 3
Brunswick (West Germany) 13 D 2
Brunswick (USA) 46 L 6
Brunswick Bay 55 C 3
Brunswick, Peninsula 53 B 7
Bruny 55 B 9
Brurskank 16 E 4
Brus 21 E 6
Brusenets 24 B 4
Brussels 15 G 3
Bryansk 23 L 8
Brzeg 13 G 3
Brzeziny 13 H 3
Bua 37 L 7
Buayan 34 G 3
Buba 39 AB 3
Bubijan 28 L 6
Bubye 41 E 3
Bucaramanga 51 B 2
Buchanan 39 B 4
Bucharest 21 H 5
Buchloe 13 D 4
Bucikha 24 C 5
Budapest 21 D 4
Bud Bud 38 E 7
Buddyri 23 I 2
Budhardalur 17 R 12
Büdingen 13 C 3
Budjala 40 B 2
Buea 39 F 5
Buech 11 H 4
Buema 37 F 5
Buenaventura 51 A 3
Buena Vista 51 C 1
Buenos Aires 53 E 3
Buenos Aires, Lake 53 B 6
Buerat el-Hsun 37 H 3
Buffalo (USA, Sout Dakota) 46 F 3
Buffalo (USA, New York) 46 M 4
Bug (Poland) 13 I 2
Bug (Ukraine) 20 IL 3
Bugar 31 C 2
Bugsuk 34 E 3
Bugul'ma 24 G 7
Buguruslau 24 G 8
Bugutu 31 G 1
Buhain 31 F 3
Buhusi 24 H 4
Buie 21 A 5
Buinsk 24 E 7
Buis-le-Baronnies 11 H 4
Bujaga 22 N 4
Bujalance 9 D 5
Bujnaksk 25 I 4
Bujumbura 40 D 3
Bukakata 40 E 3
Bukama 40 D 4
Bukhara 29 D 4
Bükk 20 E 3
Bukittingi 34 B 5
Bukoba 40 E 3
Bukovina 21 GH 3-4
Bukuru 39 F 4
Bula 34 H 5
Bulacan 34 F 2
Bulagan 31 G 1
Bulagan 31 E 1
Bulan 27 h 16-17
Bulanovo 24 H 8
Bulaq 37 M 4
Bulawayo 41 D 3
Buldan 21 I 8
Bulgar Dagi 1 O 8
Bulgaria 21 FH 6
Bulhar 38 D 5
Bu'l Khair 28 M 6
Buli Serani 34 G 4
Buller 55 g 14
Bulli 55 d 11
Bulloo 55 G 5
Bulo Burti 38 E 7
Bululundu 40 B 4
Bulun 27 Q 2
Bulungula 40 C 3
Bulun Tokhoi 31 D 1
Bumba 40 C 2
Bumbuli 40 C 3
Buna 40 F 2
Bunbury 55 B 6
Buncrana 4 C 4
Bundaberg 55 I 4
Bundi 30 C 3
Bundooma 55 E 4
Bunol 9 F 4
Bunsuru 39 F 3
Buntok 34 D 5
Buol 34 F 4
Buolkalakh 22 M 2
Bur, El- 38 E 7
Bur 54 D 4
Bura 40 G 3
Buraevo 24 H 7
Burajba 38 D 2
Buraida 38 D 2
Buraimi 29 C 7
Buram 37 L 7
Buran 38 E 5
Burao 38 E 6
Bur-Berde 38 D 7
Burchun 31 D 1
Burdekin 55 H 4
Burdwan 30 E 4
Burea 17 I 4
Bureba, La- 8 E 2
Bureja 32 D 2
Bureja, River 22 NO 4-5
Burela 9 C 2
Burg 13 D 1
Burgas 21 H 6
Burgas, G. of 20 H 6
Burgenland 13 G 5
Burgersdorf 41 D 5
Burgos 9 E 2
Burgsvik 17 H 8
Burgundy 11 H 3
Burhanpur 30 C 4
Burketown 55 F 3
Burki 30 E 3
Burkina 36 CD 4
Burias 34 F 2
Buriè 38 C 5
Burli 24 M 8
Burlington (USA, Iowa) 46 H 4
Burlington (USA, Col.) 46 F 5
Burma 27 N 7
Burmantovo 24 M 4
Burnell 55 I 5
Burnie 55 b 9
Burnley 4 E 5
Burnt Creek 43 O 4
Burray 4 E 2
Burriana 9 F 4
Burruyacu 53 D 2
Bursa 21 I 7
Burton 4 F 5
Burträsk 17 I 4
Buru 34 G 5
Buru-Bajtal 22 G 5
Burum 38 E 5
Burundi 36 FG 6
Burunurt 31 I 1
Burutu 39 F 4
Burwell 46 G 4
Buryat A.S.S.R. 22 LM 4
Bury S. Edmunds 4 G 5
Busa 39 E 3
Busaci 22 E 5
Busan 31 N 3
Busanga 34 F 2
Busanovo 22 E 2
Bushir 28 M 6
Bushmanland 41 B 4
Busk 21 G 3
Buskerud 17 C 6
Busi 41 E 2-3
Busie 39 D 3
Businga 40 C 2
Busira 40 BC 3
Bussaco 9 B 3
Bussola 35 F 9
Busto Arsizio 19 B 2
Buta 40 C 2
Butan 34 F 2
Butare 40 D 3
Bute 9 D 5
Butiaba 40 E 2
Butte 46 D 3
Butterworth 41 D 5
Butt of Lewis 4 C 2
Butuan 34 G 3
Butung 34 F 5
Buvu 40 F 4
Buyo 39 C 4
Büyükada 21 I 7
Büyük Agri D, 25 G 6
Buzaci, Peninsula 25 M 3
Buzançais 11 F 3
Buzau 21 H 5
Buzias 21 E 5
Buzirayombo 40 E 3
Buzovjazy 24 H 7
Buzuluk 24 G 8
Byakar Dzong 30 F 3
Bydalen 17 E 5
Bydgoszcz 13 G 2
Bygdea 17 I 4
Byknov 23 H 8
Bykovo 25 H 1
Bylot 44 P 1
Byrka 32 A 1
Byrock 55 H 6
Byron B. 44 T 5
Byron 54 F 7
Byrranga Mountains 22 IL 2
Bystra 20 D 3
Bystraja 22 Q 4
Bystrice n.P. 7 K 1
Bystritsa 20 G 3
Bytantaj 22 NO 3
Bytom 13 H 3
Bytow 13 G 1
Bzema 37 I 5
Bzura 12 H 2

C

Caala 40 B 5
Caatbridge 4 E 4
Caazapa 52 F 7
Cabanaluan 34 F 1
Cabanes 9 G 3
Cabeza del Buey 9 D 4
Cabezas 52 E 5
Cabinas 51 B 1
Cabinda 40 A 4
Cabiri 40 A 4
Cabo Pantoja 52 B 2
Cabo Raso 53 C 5
Cabot Str. 44 T 6
Cabrera 8 C 2
Cabriel 8 F 4
Cabruta 51 C 2
Cacak 21 E 6
Caccamo 19 DE 6
Caceres (Brazil) 52 F 5
Caceres (Colombia) 51 A 2
Caceres (Spain) 9 C 4
Caceu 39 A 3
Cachoeira 52 L 4
Cachoeiro de Itapemirim 52 I 6
Cachuela Esperanza 52 D 4
Cacolo 40 B 5
Caconda 41 B 1
Cadereyta 47 E 2
Cadibona, Colle di- 18 B 2
Cadillac 46 I 4
Cadiz 9 C 5
Cadiz, Gulf of 8 C 5
Cadui 51 D 2
Caen 11 E 2
Caernarvon 4 D 5
Caernarvon Bay 4 D 5
Caesarea 28 C 4
Caetité 52 I 4
Cafayate 53 C 2
Cafu 41 B 2
Cagayan 34 F 3
Cagda 22 O 4
Cagliari 19 B 5
Cagliari, G. of 18 B 5
Cagodosca 23 LM 5
Cahors 11 F 4
Càibarien 48 D 2
Caico 52 L 3
Caicos 48 E 2
Caicos Passage 48 E 2
Caihengula 46 C 4
Cailloma 52 C 5
Cairari 52 H 2
Cairns 55 H 3
Cairo (Egitto) 37 M 3
Cairo (USA) 46 I 5
Cajabamba 52 B 3
Cajamarca 52 B 3
Cajanda 22 M 3
Cajdakh 22 O 3
Calabar 39 F 5
Calabozo 51 C 2
Calabria 18 F 5
Cala Burras, p^ta. de 9 D 5
Calafat 21 F 6
Calah 28 G 2
Calais 11 F 1
Calama (Brazil) 52 E 3
Calama (Chile) 52 D 6
Calamar 51 B 1
Calang 34 A 4
Calapan 34 F 2
Calarasi 21 H 5
Calasparra 9 F 4
Calat 25 G 5
Calatafimi 19 D 6
Calatayua 9 F 3
Calatrava 39 F 5
Calatrava, Campo de- 8 E 4
Calayan 31 M 6
Calbayog 34 F 2
Calchaqui 53 D 2
Calcutta 30 E 4
Caldera 53 B 2
Caledon 41 B 5
Caledonian Can 3 D 3
Calella 9 H 3
Calenzana 11 a
Calgary 44 G 5
Cali 51 A 3
Caliente 46 D 5
California 46 BC 4-6
California, Gulf of 42 H 7
California, Lower 43 H 6-7
Calimanu 20 G 4
Calitzdorf 41 C 5
Callabonna 55 G 5
Callao 52 B 4
Callis 38 E 6
Caloton 55 e 10
Caltagirone 19 DE 6
Caltanissetta 19 D 6
Calundo 41 B 2
Calvi 11 a
Calvi, M^t. 18 B 3
Calvinia 41 B 5
Cama 51 A 2
Camabatela 40 B 4
Camacupa 40 B 5
Camagüey 48 D 2
Camana 52 C 5
Camarat 10 I 5
Camargo 47 E 2
Camaron 47 H 4
Camarones (Argentina) 53 C 5
Camarones (Chile) 52 D 5
Camau 33 C 5
Ca Mau, Cape 33 C 5
Cambay 30 B 4
Cambay, Gulf of 30 B 4
Cambo 40 B 4

Cambrai 11 G 1
Cambrian Mountains 3 E 5
Cambridge 4 F 5
Cambodia 27 O 8
Camden (USA, Ark.) 46 H 6
Camden (USA, New Jersey) 46 N 5
Camden Bay 45 L 2
Camena 20 F 5
Cameron 46 H 7
Cameroon 36 E 5
Cameroons Mount 35 DE 5
Camerota 19 E 4
Cameta 52 H 2
Camiguin 34 F 1
Caminha 9 B 3
Camlibere 25 B 5
Camocim 52 I 2
Camooweal 55 F 3
Camorta 33 A 5
Campana (Argentina) 53 E 3
Campana P.ta 18 DE 4
Campanella P.ta 18 DE 4
Campania 19 E 4
Campbell 57 a 4
Campbelltown 55 d 11
Campbeltown 55 b 9
Campeche 47 F 4
Campeche, Banco de- 47 FG 3
Campeche, G. of 47 EF 3-4
Campidano 18 B 5
Campina (Brazil) 52 E 2
Campina Grande 52 L 3
Campina, La- 8 D 5
Campinas 52 H 6
Campo (Cameroun) 39 F 5
Campo 39 G 5
Campobasso 19 E 4
Campo de Criptana 9 E 4
Campo de Montiel 9 E 4
Campo Gallo 53 D 2
Campo Grande 52 G 6
Campos 52 I 6
Campos, Tierra de- 8 D 2
Canada 43 GO 3-4
Canadian 46 F 5
Canakkale 20 H 7
Canal Zone 43 N 9
Canama 52 C 3
Cananea 47 B 1
Canary Islands 37 AB 4
Canavieras 52 L 5
Canberra 55 H 7
Candala 38 E 5
Candarli 21 H 8
Candelaria (Bolivia) 52 F 5
Candelaria (USA, Nev.) 46 C 5
Candelaro 18 E 4
Cândre 21 F 5
Canelos 52 B 2
Canete 9 F 3
Canga 9 B 2
Cangamba 41 B 1
Cangombè 41 B 1
Canhoca 40 A 4
Canicatti 19 DE 6
Canigou 10 G 5
Canin 1 Q 2
Canindé 52 H 2
Canindé (Ceara) 52 L 2
Canna 3 C 3
Cannanore 30 C 6
Cannel, Pass- 42 HI 5
Cannes 11 I 5
Canoas, p.ta 47 A 2
Canon City 46 E 5
Canta 10 G 4
Cantabrian Mts. 8 DE 2
Canterbury 4 G 6
Canterbury B. 55 G 14
Canton (China) 31 I 6
Canton (USA, Ohio) 46 L 4
Canton (Polynesia) 54 I 5
Canuma 52 F 2
Cao Bang 33 D 2
Capaccio 19 E 4
Capaev 25 M 2
Capaevo 29 B 1
Capanaparo 51 C 2
Capatariba 51 B 1
Cap Breton I. 44 ST 6
Cape Coast 39 D 4
Cape Girardeau 46 I 5
Capelongo 41 B 1
Capenda Comulemba 40 B 4
Cape Province 41 BC 4-5
Cape Town 41 B 5
Cape Verde, Islands 39 a
Cape York 55 G 2
Cape York Peninsula 55 G 2
Cap-Haïtien 48 E 3
Capim 52 H 2
Capitari 52 E 3
Capiz 34 F 2
Capoudia 37 G 2
Cappanda 22 M 3
Caprara 18 E 3
Caprera 18 B 4
Capri 18 E 4
Caprivi Strip 41 C 2
Caprobo 52 L 3

Capua 19 DE 4
Capul 20 G 4
Caquengue 40 C 5
Caqueta 49 C 3-4
Cara 22 MN 3-4
Carabane 37 A 7
Carabaya, Andes de- 52 CD 4
Caracal 21 G 5
Caracarai 51 D 3
Caracas 51 C 1
Caracol 52 I 3
Caracorum 27 O 5
Carahue 53 B 4
Caras 20 E 5
Caratasca 47 H 4
Caratinga 52 I 5
Carauari 52 D 2
Caravaca 9 F 4
Caravelas 52 L 5
Carballo 9 B 2
Carbo 47 B 2
Carboneras 9 F 5
Carcajou 44 F 4
Carcans 11 E 4
Carças, River 52 G 5
Carcassonne 11 G 5
Cardenas 48 C 2
Çardi 21 I 8
Cardiel 53 B 6
Cardiff 4 E 6
Cardigan 4 D 5
Cardigan Bay 3 D 5
Cardzhou 29 D 4
Carei 21 F 4
Carentan 11 E 2
Carev 55 C 5
Careysburg 39 B 4
Carhaix 11 D 2
Carhue 53 D 4
Caria 21 HI 9
Cariango 40 B 5
Cariati 19 F 5
Caribbean Sea 48 CF 3-4
Caribou, Mt. 44 FG 4
Carin 38 E 5
Carinhanha 52 H 4-5
Carinthia 13 EF 5
Carlingford (Ireland) 4 C 4
Carlisle 4 E 4
Carlitte 11 F 5
Carlota, La- 53 D 3
Carlow 4 C 5
Carlsbad 46 F 6
Carmarthen 4 D 6
Carmarthen Bay 3 D 6
Carmel Head 4 D 5
Carmen (Bolivia) 52 D 4
Carmen (Mexico) 47 F 4
Carmen 47 B 2
Carmen de Patagones 53 D 5
Carmmn, El- 51 A 2
Carmona 9 D 5
Carnarvon 41 C 5
Carnarvon 55 A 4
Carnegie 55 C 5
Carn Eige 3 D 3
Carnero, Punta 53 B 4
Carnic Alps 18 D 1
Carnot 40 B 1
Carnotville 39 E 4
Carnsore Pass 3 C 5
Carolina 52 H 3
Carolina, La- 9 E 4
Carolina (Micronesia) 54 EG 4
Carolina (Polynesia) 54 M 5
Caroni 51 D 2-3
Carpathians 20 DG 3-4
Carpathians, Eastern 20 FH 3-4
Carpathians, Little 20 C 3
Carpathians Western 20 DE 3
Carpentariagolf 55 FG 2
Carpentras 11 H 4
Carpi 19 C 2
Carrantuohill 3 AB 6
Carrara 19 C 2
Carrick 4 C 5
Carrillo Puerto 47 G 4
Carrion 9 D 2
Carrizal Bajo 53 B 2
Carrizozo 46 E 6
Carrocal 52 F 3
Carsamba 25 D 5
Carson City 46 C 5
Carstensz 54 D 3
Cartagena (Colombia) 51 A 1
Cartagena (Spain) 9 F 5
Cartago 48 C 5
Carteret 11 E 2
Carter Fell 3 E 4
Cartier 55 C 2
Cartwright 44 T 5
Caruaru 52 L 3
Carupano 51 D 1
Carvoeiro (Portugal) 9 B 4
Casablanca 37 C 3
Casale Monferrato 19 B 2
Casamance 37 A 7
Casa Nova Sento Sé 52 I 3

Casar 35 G 4
Cäsarea 28 C 4
Casas Grandes 47 C 1
Casas Ibanez 9 F 4
Cascais 9 B 4
Cascavel 52 L 2
Caserta 19 E 4
Casiguran 34 F 1
Casilda 53 D 3
Casiquiare 49 D 3
Casma 52 B 3
Caspe 9 F 3
Caspian Depression 29 AB 2
Caspian Sea 1 RS 6-8
Cassano 19 DE 4
Casteljaloux 11 F 4
Castellamare, G. of 18 D 5
Castellamare del Golfo 19 D 5
Castellammare di Stabia 19 DE 4
Castelli 53
Castellon de la Plana 9 F 4
Castelo Branco 9 C 4
Castelvetrano 19 D 6
Castile, New 9 DE 3-4
Castile, Old 9 DE 2-3
Castres 11 G 5
Castries 48 G 4
Castro (Brazil) 52 H 6
Castro (Chile) 53 B 5
Castrogeriz 9 D 2
Castro Urdiales 9 E 2
Castrovillari 19 F 5
Catacaos 52 A 3
Çatak 28 F 2
Çatalao 52 H 5
Çatalca 21 I 7
Çatal D. 20 I 8
Catalonia 9 GH 2-3
Catamarca 53 C 2
Catanduanes 34 F 2
Catania 19 E 6
Catania, G. of 18 E 6
Catara 41 A 1
Catbalogan 34 F 2
Catena delle Cascate 42 G 5
Catentin 11 E 2
Catina 21 D 6
Catingas 50 EF 4
Cato 54 F 6
Catoche 47 G 3
Catria 19 D 3
Catrimani 51 D 3
Catwick 33 D 4
Cauca 50 C 3
Caucaya 52 C 2
Caucasus 25 FI 4-5
Cauguenes 53 B 4
Çaukiri 25 B 5
Caungula 40 B 4
Caura 51 D 2
Causy 23 G 8
Cauterets 11 E 5
Cauto 48 D 2
Caux 10 F 2
Cavado 8 B 3
Cavally 39 C -5
Cavan 4 C 5
Caviana 52 G 2
Cavite 34 F 2
Cavour, Canal 12 B 2
Caxias 52 I 2
Caxias do Sul 52 G 7
Caxito 40 A 4
Cayambe 52 B 2
Cayenne 51 F 3
Cayman, Grand 48 C 3
Cayman Islands 48 C 3
Cayman, Little 48 CD 3
Cayes, Les- 48 E 3
Cayeux sur M. 11 F 1
Cayo Arenas 47 F 3
Cayo Nuevo 47 F 3
Cayo Romano 48 D 2
Cays 55 I 3
Cazaux, Étang de- 11 E 4
Cazin 21 B 5
Cazma 20 C 5
Cazombo 40 C 5
Cazorla 9 E 5
Cea, 9 D 2
Ceara (Fortaleza) 52 L 2
Ceara 52 L 2-3
Ceboksari 24 D 6
Cebollera 8 E 3
Cebu 34 F 2
Cecina 19 C 3
Cedar Creek 46 F 3
Cedar Key, 46 L 7
Cedar Rapids 46 H 4
Cedros 47 A 2
Ceduna 55 E 6
Cefalonia 20 E 8
Cefalù 19 E 5
Cegléd 13 I 3
Ceglie Messapico 19 F 4
Ceiba, La- 51 B 2
Cekmagus 24 H 7
Cekunda 22 O 4
Celaya 47 D 3
Celebes 34 EF 5

Celebes Sea 34 F 4
Celeken 1 S 8
Celica 53 B 2
Celje 21 B 4
Celkar 22 E 5
Celkar L. of 22 F 5
Celle 13 D 2
Celorico da Beira 9 C 3
Celtic Sea 12 BC 6
Cemerna Planina 20 E 6
Cemernica 20 C 5
Cenis, M¹. 18 A 2
Cento 19 C 2
Central African Republic 36 EF 5
Central Siberian Plateau 22 IM 3
Centrali 26 o 14
Ceram 34 G 5
Ceram Sea 34 A 5
Cercal 9 B 5
Cereales 53 D 4
Ceremkhovo 22 L 4
Cerepanovo 22 H 4
Cerepanovo 22 L 3
Cerepövets 23 M 5
Ceres (Argentina) 53 D 2
Cerevkovo 24 C 4
Cerignola 19 E 4
Çerikli 25 B 6
Çerikov 23 H 8
Cerkassy 25 B 1
Cerkessk 25 G 3
Çermik 28 E 1
Cerna 20 F 5
Cernavoda 21 I 5
Cernigov 21 L 2
Cernuska 24 H 6
Cernye Brat'ja 22 Q 5
Cerralvo 47 C 3
Cerrik 21 D 7
Cerro Aguas Blancas 53 C 2
Cerro Calaveras 47 CD 3
Cerro Chanaro 51 D 2
Cerro de Pasco 52 B 4
Cerro del Toro 53 C 2
Cerro Kamuk 48 C 5
Cerro Mercedario 53 B 3
Cerro Murallon 53 B 6
Cerro Pular 53 C 1
Cerro Roraima 51 D 2
Cerros de Araracuara 52 C 1-2
Cerro S. Lorenzo 53 B 6
Cerro S. Valentin 50 C 8
Cerros Turumiquire 51 D 1
Cerro Triangulo 47 C 3
Certkovo 25 F 1
Cervantes 23 F 8
Cervati 18 E 4
Cerven' 23 G 8
Cervera 9 G 3
Cervia 19 D 2
Cerviato 19 E 4
Cervione 11 a
Cesena 19 D 2
Cesis 17 M 8
Ceské Budejovice 13 F 4
Çesme 21 H 8
Cestos 39 C 4
Cetinje 21 D 6
Cetraro 19 EF 5
Ceuta 37 C 2
Ceva 19 B 2
Cevennes 10 GH 4
Ceyhan 28 D 2
Ceyhan 28 CD 2
Ceylanpinar 28 E 2
Ceylon 27 M 9
Chabubrun 31 F 4
Chachapovas 52 B 3
Chaco 52 E 6
Chad 36 EF 4
Chad, Lake 37 G 7
Chadam 22 I 4
Chadron 46 F 4
Chafe 39 F 3
Chagai 29 D 6
Chahar 31 IL 1-2
Chähar Deh 29 E 5
Chah Bahar 29 D 6
Chaibasa 30 E 4
Chaiya 33 B 5
Chak-Chak 40 D 1
Chakhansur 29 D 5
Cha la ping 31 F 4
Chalkidike 21 F 7
Challans 11 E 3
Challapata 52 D 5
Challis 46 D 4
Chalna 27 a 11
Châlons-sur-Marne 11 H 2
Chalon-sur-Saône 11 H 3
Chaman 29 F 5
Chamarun 28 L 3
Chamba (India) 30 C 2
Chamba (Tanzania) 40 F 5

Chambal 30 C 3-4
Chamberlain 46 G 4
Chambéry 11 H 4
Chambezi 40 E 5
Chamdo 31 F 4
Chamical 53 C 3
Chamlang 26 pq 17
Chamonix 11 I 4
Champagne 11 GH 2-3
Champlain 46 N 4
Champua 30 E 4
Chanaral 53 B 2
Chanarcillo 53 B 2
Chancay 52 B 4
Chancay 52 B 3
Chanchiang 27 P 7
Chanda 30 C 5
Chandernagor 30 E 4
Chandpur 27 b 11
Changane 41 E 3-4
Chang chou 32 A 5
Chang ling 31 M 2
Changma 31 F 3
Chang pai Shanmo 31 N 2
Chang pao 31 I 2
Changri 26 p 17
Changsha 31 I 5
Chang shan 27 f 15
Chang Tang 31 CE 4
Changte 31 L 5
Changtse 26 p 16
Changtu 31 F 4
Changyeh 31 G 3
Chanhua 31 F 4
Channel Islands 11 D 2
Chantenay 11 E 3
Chanthaburi 33 C 4
Chantrey Inlet 44 L 2
Chao an 31 L 6
Chaonde 41 G 1
Chaotung 31 G 5
Chapala 47 D 3
Chapra 30 D 3
Chapéu 52 H 4
Charana 52 D 5
Charchan 31 D 3
Charcot 57 o 2
Charente 10 E 4
Charikar 29 E 4-5
Charité La- 11 G 3
Charkov 25 D 1
Charleroi 15 G 3
Charles (Canada) 43 P 4
Charles (USA) 46 M 5
Charles (Canada) 44 Q 3
Charles Towers 55 H 3
Charleston (USA, South Car.) 46 M 6
Charleston (USA, West Virg.) 46 L 5
Charleville (Australia) 55 H 5
Charleville (France) 11 H 2
Charlotte 46 L 5
Charlotte Harbor, 46 L 7
Charlottenberg 17 E 7
Charlottenburg 51 F 2
Charlottetown 44 I 6
Charlotte Waters 55 F 5
Charlton 44 P 5
Charolles 11 H 3
Charray 29 B 6
Chartres 11 F 2
Chartreuse 10 H 4
Chascomus 53 E 4
Chasie 41 C 2
Chasong 31 N 2
Chasseral 10 I 3
Chasseron 10 I 3
Châteaubriant 11 E 3
Château Chinon 11 G 3
Châteaurenault 11 F 3
Châteauroux 11 G 3
Château Thierry 11 G 2
Châtellerault 11 F 3
Châtillon-sur-Seine 11 H 3
Châtre, La- 11 G 3
Chattahoochee 42 M 6
Chattanooga 46 I 5
Chaukan Pass 33 B 1
Chaumont 11 H 2
Chaun 37 C 2
Chauny 11 G 2
Chauvigny 11 F 3
Chaux-de-Fonds, La- 13 B 5
Chaves (Brazil) 52 H 2
Chaves (Portugal) 9 C 3
Chaya 31 F 5
Che chiang 31 L 5
Chechon 31 N 3
Checiny 13 I 3
Chef-Boutonne 11 E 3
Chefoo 31 M 3
Chegutu 41 E 2
Cheiron, M¹. 11 I 5
Cheli 31 G 6
Chelm 13 L 3
Chelmno 13 H 2

Chelmos 20 F 8-9
Chelmsford 4 G 6
Chelmza 13 H 2
Cheltenham 4 E 6
Chelva 9 F 4
Chelyabinsk 24 M 7
Chemnitz 13 E 3
Chenachane 37 D 4
Chenan 31 H 4
Chengan 31 H 5
Cheng chiang 31 G 6
Cheng chou 31 I 4
Cheng hsien 31 I 5
Chenghwa 31 D 1
Cheng kou 31 H 4
Chengte 31 L 2
Chengto 31 F 4
Chengtu 31 G 4
Chen hsi 31 E 2
Chen hsien 31 I 5
Chen pa 31 H 4
Chenyuan 31 H 5
Chenyüan 31 G 6
Cheonan 31 N 3
Cheongjin 31 N 2
Cheo Reo 33 D 4
Chepén 52 B 3
Chepes 53 C 3
Chepo 48 D 5
Cher 10 FG 3
Cherbourg 11 E 2
Cheri 37 G 7
Cherken 31 D 3
Chereppe 52 B 3
Cherskiy Ranger 22 P 3
Cherta 9 G 3
Chesapeake Bay 42 N 6
Chester 4 E 5
Chesterfield 54 F 6
Chesterfield Inlet 44 M 3
Cheviot Hills 3 E 4
Cheyenne 46 F 4
Cheyenne, River 46 EF 4
Chhatarpur 30 C 4
Chhindwara 30 C 4
Chiahsing 31 M 4
Chiai 31 M 6
Chiamussu 31 O 1
Chian 31 IL 5
Chianghsi 31 L 5
Chiang Khan 33 C 3
Chiang ling 31 I 4
Chiang Men 27 f 15
Chiang su 31 M 4
Chiani 18 D 3
Chianje 41 A 2
Chianti, Monti del- 18 C 3
Chi ao 27 f 15
Chiaohsien 31 M 3
Chiavari 19 B 2
Chiba 27 e 13
Chibemba 41 A 2
Chibia 41 A 2
Chibuta 40 A 5
Chibuto 41 E 3
Chicago 46 I 4
Chicapa 40 C 4
Chichagof 45 M 5
Chichester 4 F 6
Chiclayo 52 B 3
Chico 53 C 5-6
Chicomda 41 A 1
Chicomo 41 E 3
Chicoutimi 44 Q 6
Chidambaram 30 C 6
Chiehshih 31 L 6
Chiemsee 12 E 5
Chienchuan 31 F 5
Chieng chaung 31 G 5
Chiengi 40 D 4
Chieng Mai 33 B 3
Chien ko 31 H 4
Chien li 31 I 5
Chienning 31 L 5
Chienou 31 L 5
Chien shan 27 f 15
Chienshih 31 H 4
Chiente 31 L 5
Chienti 18 D 3
Chiese 18 C 2
Chieti 19 E 3
Chigasaki 27 d 13
Chignik 45 G 5
Chigubo 41 E 3
Chih chiang 31 H 5
Chihfeng 31 L 2
Chihsien 31 I 3
Chihuahua 47 C 2
Chijumutu 22 N 4
Chikura 27 d 13
Chikwa, Lake 41 F 2
Chikwawa 41 E 2
Chilas 29 F 4
Chilca 52 B 4
Childress 46 F 6
Chile 50 CD 6-7
Chilecito 53 C 2
Chilin 31 N 2
Chillagoe 55 G 3
Chillan 53 B 4
Chiloé 53 B 5
Chilpancingo 47 E 4
Chiltern Hills 3 F 6
Chilubula 40 E 5
Chilung 31 M 5

Chiman 51 A 2
Chimbai 29 C 3
Chimborazo 49 BC 4
Chimbote 52 B 3
Chimkent 29 E 3
Chin 31 I 3
China 27 NP 6
Chinan 31 L 3
Chinandega 48 B 4
Chincha Alta 52 B 4
Chincheng 31 I 3
Chinchilla de M. Aragon 9 F 4
Chinchon 9 E 3
Chin chou 31 M 2
Chindamani 31 F 1
Chinde 41 F 2
Chindio 41 F 2
Chindwin 33 B 1
Chinga 41 F 2
Ching chi 27 g 15
Ching chiang 31 L 5
Ching hai 31 EG 3
Chingho 31 C 2
Chingiu 31 N 3
Chingkou 31 L 4
Ching ku 31 G 6
Ching ning 31 H 3
Chingola 40 D 5
Ching peng 31 L 2
Chingtai 31 G 3
Chingtao 31 M 3
Chingte 31 L 4
Chinh tung 31 G 6
Chingune 41 E 3
Chingyang 31 H 3
Chingyüan 31 H 3
Chinhoyi 41 E 2
Chinhsien (China, Kwangsi) 31 H 6
Chinhsien (China, Liaoning) 31 M 3
Chinhsien (China, Shensi) 31 I 3
Chinhua 31 L 5
Chining (China, Shensi) 31 I 2
Chining (China, Schantung) 31 L 3
Chin Ling Shan 31 M 4
Chinon 11 F 3
Chinsura 27 a 11
Chinta 31 F 2
Chintai 31 I 2
Chioggia 19 D 2
Chios 20 H 8
Chios, Island 20 GH 8
Chipana 52 C 6
Chipata 41 E 1
Chipawa 41 D 1
Chiquian 52 B 4
Chinquinquira 51 B 2
Chiquita, Mar- 53 D 3
Chira (Tsehleh) 31 C 3
Chiriguana 51 B 2
Chirikof 35 G 5
Chirripo 42 M 9
Chirumuco 47 D 4
Chi shih Shan mo 31 F 4
Chisimario 36 H 6
Chita 22 M 4
Chitaldroog 30 C 6
Chitor 30 B 4
Chitre 48 C 5
Chittagong 30 F 4
Chittoor 30 C 6
Chiu chiang (China, Kiangsi) 31 L 5
Chiu chiang (China, Kwangtung) 31 I 6
Chiu chüan 31 F 3
Chiumbe 40 C 4
Chiupei 31 G 6
Chivasso 19 A 2
Chivay 52 C 5
Chivilcoy 53 D 3
Chivinde 40 E 5
Choapa 53 B 3
Choapan 47 E 4
Choconta 51 B 2
Chodziez 19 G 2
Choele-Choel 53 C 4
Choiren 31 N 1
Choiseul 54 F 5
Choinice 13 G 2
Cholatse 26 p 17
Cholet 11 E 3
Cholomon 20 F 7
Chomo Lonzo 26 q 17
Chomo Lungma 31 D 5
Chonan (Japan) 27 e 13
Chonchiana 31 D 3
Chondwe 41 D 1
Chonos, Archip. de los- 53 B 5-6
Cho Oyu 26 p 16
Cho Polu 26 pq 17
Chorrera, La- 52 C 2
Chorzow 13 H 3
Chosan 31 N 2
Choshi 32 F 4
Chos Malal 53 B 4
Choszczno 13 F 2
Chou Shan 31 M 4

Choutsun 31 L 3
Chowie 31 M 1
Choybalsan 31 I 1
Christchurch 55 g 14
Christensen, M¹. 57 g 3
Christian 44 R 1
Christianshab 44 U 2
Christmas (Java) 26 I 13
Christmas (Polynesia) 54 M 4
Chrudim 21 B 3
Chu 27 f 14-15
Chuadanga 27 a 11
Chuan chou 31 L 5-6
Chuangho 31 M 3
Chüan hsien 31 I 5
Chubb Crater 44 Q 3
Chubut 53 BC 5
Chüchiang 31 I 6
Chüching 31 G 5
Chuguchak 31 CE 1
Chü hsien (China, Chekiang) 31 L 5
Chü hsien (China, Schantung) 31 L 3
Chukchi Pen. 22 RS 3
Chukhung 26 p 17
Chuma 52 D 5
Chumphon 33 B 4
Chuncheon 31 N 3
Chungan 31 L 5
Chung ching 31 H 5
Chung hsiang 31 I 4
Chung hsien 31 H 4
Chungju 31 N 3
Chungpu 31 H 3
Chung shan 31 H 6
Chung tien 31 F 5
Chungwei 31 H 3
Chunquibamba 52 C 5
Chur 19 B 1
Churchill 44 M 4
Churchill 44 IL 4
Churchill Park 44 E 4
Churuguara 51 C 1
Chuska Pass 46 E 5
Chüyen 31 G 2
Cicevac 21 E 6
Ciechanow 13 I 2
Ciénaga 51 B 1
Cienfuegos 48 C 2
Cies 9 B 2
Cieszyn 19 H 4
Cieza 9 F 4
Cigirin 25 B 1
Cikaevo 22 S 3
Cikhaleva 22 P 2
Cilacap 34 C 6
Cilo Dag 1 Q 8
Cima d'Asta 18 C 1
Cima Dodici 18 C 2
Cimarron 46 G 5
Cimini, Monti- 18 CD 3
Cimkent 22 F 5
Cimone 18 C 2
Cîmpina 21 G 5
Cîmpulung 21 G 4
Cinca 9 G 8
Cincer 20 C 6
Cincinnati 46 L 5
Cinco Villas, Las- 9 F 2-3
Çine 21 I 9
Cinto 18 B 3
Ciobe 41 C 2
Ciotat, La- 11 H 5
Cir 25 FG 1
Circeo, Cape 19 D 4
Circeo, M¹. 18 D 4
Circle 45 L 3
Cirebon 34 C 6
Cirkavo 24 C 8
Ciron 11 E 4
Cirpan 21 G 6
Cisa, La- 18 B 2
Ciscaucasia 1 PQ 6-7
Ciskei 41 D 5
Cismy 24 H 7
Cistopol' 24 F 7
Citlaltepetl 47 E 4
Città di Castello 19 D 3
Città di Pieve 19 D 3
Cittanova 19 F 5
City 46 H 3
Ciucas 20 G 5
Ciudad Bolivar 51 D 2
Ciudadela 9 H 4
Ciudad Garcia 47 D 3
Ciudad Juarez 47 C 1
Ciudad Real 9 E 4
Ciudad Rodrigo 9 C 3
Ciudad Victoria 47 E 3
Civitavecchia 19 C 3
Civray 11 F 3
Cizre 28 G 2
Ckalov 24 H 9
Clain 10 F 3
Clamecy 11 G 3
Clanwilliam 41 B 5
Clare 4 A 5
Clarence (Australia) 55 I 5
Clarence (Antarctica) 57 n 3
Clarence 53 B 7
Clarion 47 B 4
Clark Lake 45 H 4
Clarksburg 46 L 5

Clarksville 46 I 5
Claro 52 G 5
Clear 4 B 6
Cles 19 C 1
Cleveland 46 L 4
Cleveland Hills 3 F 4
Clermont-Ferrand 11 G 4
Clifden 4 A 5
Clifton 46 E 6
Clinton 44 E 5
Clipperton 42 I 8
Clisham 3 C 2
Clisson 11 E 3
Clonakilty 4 B 6
Cloncurry 55 G 4
Cloncurry, River 55 G 3
Clonmel 4 C 5
Clorinda 53 E 2
Cloud Peak 46 E 4
Clovis 46 F 6
Cluj 21 F 4
Cluny 11 H 3
Clutha 55 f 15
Clyde 3 DE 4
Cna 20 G 1
Cnang hua 31 M 6
Coa 8 C 3
Coari 52 E 2
Coari 52 DE 2-3
Coast Range 42 FG 4
Coats 44 O 3
Coatzacoalcos 47 F 4
Coban 47 F 4
Cobar 55 H 6
Cobh 4 B 6
Cobija 52 D 4
Coburg 13 D 3
Coburg Peninsula 55 E 2
Coca, La- 52 B 2
Coca, Pizzo di- 18 B 1
Cocachacra 52 C 5
Cocama 52 C 4
Cochabamba 52 D 5
Cochin 30 C 7
Cochinchina 27 o 8
Cochrame 44 O 6
Cocos 43 M 9
Cod 44 R 7
Cod 44 S 4
Codajas 52 E 2
Codima 20 L 4
Codo 52 I 2
Coen 55 G 2
Coeur d'Alene 46 C 3
Coffeyville 46 G 5
Coghinas, Fl. 18 B 4
Cognac 11 E 4
Coiba 48 C 5
Coimbatur 30 D 6
Coimbra 9 B 3
Coin 9 D 5
Colbeck Archipelago 57 f 3
Colby 46 F 5
Colcha 52 D 6
Colchester 4 G 6
Coldfoot 45 H 3
Coleman 55 G 2
Colemerik 28 G 2
Colesberg 41 D 5
Colfax 46 C 3
Colico 19 B 1
Coligny 41 D 4
Colima 47 D 4
Colima, Nevado de-, M¹. 47 D 4
Colima 42 I 8
Coll 3 C 3
Collie 55 B 6
Collier Bay 55 C 3
Colline Metallifere 18 C 3
Collo 37 F 2
Collooney 13 B 4
Colmar 11 I 2
Colmenar Viejo 9 E 3
Cologne 13 B 3
Colombia 50 C 3
Colombo 30 C 7
Colon 48 D 5
Colona 55 E 6
Colonia (Uruguay) 53 E 3
Colonne, Cape 18 F 5
Colonnel Oviedo 52 F 7
Colonsay 3 C 3
Colorado 46 G 6
Colorado, Little 46 DE 5-6
Colorado Plateau 46 D 5
Colorado, (State U.S.A.) 46 EF 5
Colorado Springs 46 F 5
Columbia 46 I 5
Columbia, British 44 DE 4-5
Columbia, 46 BC 3
Columbia, Mount 44 F 5
Columbus (USA, Georgia) 46 L 6
Columbus (USA, Ohio) 46 L 5
Colusa 46 B 5
Colville 46 C 3
Colville 45 H 3
Colville, Lake 44 D 2
Colwyn 4 E 5
Coma 22 LM 3-4
Comacchio 19 D 2
Comayagua 47 G 5

Comburg 11 E 2
Comilla 30 F 4
Comillas 9 D 2
Comino Cape 18 BC 4
Comitan 47 F 4
Commercy 11 H 2
Committee Bay 44 N 2
Como 19 B 2
Como, L. of 18 B 1-2
Comodoro Rivadavia 53 C 6
Comoé 35 C 5
Comorin, Cape 30 C 7
Comoros 41 bc 6
Compagnijesdrif 41 C 5
Compiègne 11 G 2
Conakry 39 B 4
Conceiça 52 F 3
Conceiçao 41 F 2
Conceiçao do Araguaia 52 H 3
Concepcion (Bolivia) 52 E 5
Concepcion (Chile) 53 B 4
Concepcion (Paraguay) 52 F 6
Concepcion, Punta (Mexico) 47 B 2
Concepcion del Oro 47 D 3
Conches 11 F 2
Conchos, R. 47 C 2
Concord 46 N 4
Concordia (Argentina) 53 E 3
Concordia (USA) 46 G 5
Concurbion, Ria de- 8 B 2
Conda, 1 V 3-4
Condamine 55 H 5
Condeuba 52 I 5
Condobolin 55 H 6
Conesa, General- 53 D 5
Confuso 52 F 6
Congo 36 E 5-6
Conil 9 C 5
Conn 3 B 4
Connacht 4 B 4-5
Connacht 3 B 5
Connecticut 46 NO 4
Conquista 52 D 4
Constance 21 I 5
Constance, Lake 12 C 5
Constantine 37 F 2
Constitucion 53 B 4
Contamana 52 C 3
Contas das- 52 IL 4
Conway 46 H 5
Coober Pedy 55 E 5
Cooch Behar 30 E 3
Cook 53 B 7
Cook 44 D 6
Cook 54 LM 6-7
Cook, M¹. 55 g 14
Cookstrasse 55 g 14
Cook Inlet 45 H 4-5
Cooktown 55 H 3
Coonamble 55 H 6
Coopers Creek 55 G 5
Cootamundra 55 H 6
Copenhagen 17 E 9
Copetonas 53 D 4
Copiapo 53 B 2
Copparo 19 D 2
Copper 45 F 2
Coppermine 44 F 2
Coquimbo 53 B 2
Coração de Jesus 52 I 5
Coracora 52 C 5
Cora Divh 30 B 6
Coral Harbour 44 O 3
Corato 19 F 4
Corbach 13 C 3
Corbeil 11 G 2
Corbières 10 G 5
Corcovado 53 B 5
Corcubion 9 B 2
Cordillera, Eastern 49 CD 5
Cordillera Central 49 C 3-4
Cordillera, Western 49 C 3
Cordoba (Argentina) 53 D 3
Cordoba (Spain) 9 D 5
Cordoba (Brazil) 52 I 5
Cordova (Alaska) 45 I 4
Coria 9 C 3
Corinth 21 F 9
Corinth, G. of 20 F 8
Corinto (Brazil) 52 I 5
Corinto (Nicaragua) 43 M 8
Cork 4 B 6
Cork Harbour 4 B 6
Corleone 19 D 6
Cor u 31 H 3
Cornimont 11 I 3
Corno, M¹. 18 D 3
Cornwall 3 D 6
Cornwallis 44 L 1
Coro 51 C 1
Coroata 52 I 2
Coroca 41 A 2
Corocoro 52 D 5
Coroico 52 D 5
Coromandel 55 h 13
Coromandel Coast 30 D 5-6

Corondo 48 C 5
Coronation G. 44 G 2
Coronation 57 N 3
Coronel 50 C 7
Coronie 51 E 2
Coropuna 49 C 5
Corpus Christi 46 G 7
Corpus Christi 42 L 7
Corque 52 D 5
Corral 53 B 4
Corral de Almaguer 9 E 4
Corralitos 47 C 1
Corrane 41 F 2
Corrente 52 H 4
Corrib 3 B 5
Corrientes 52 F 7
Corrientes (Argentina) 53 E 4
Corrientes (Colombia) 51 A 2
Corrientes (Mexico) 47 C 3
Corrientes 52 B 2
Corse, C. 18 B 3
Corsica 18 B 3-4
Corte 11 a
Cortina d'Ampezzo 19 D 1
Cortona 19 C 3
Coruche 9 B 4
Çorum 25 C 5
Corumba 52 F 5
Coruna, La- 9 B 2
Corvo 37 a
Corwin 45 F 3
Coseguina 48 B 4
Cosenza 19 EF 5
Cosne 11 G 3
Costa d'Avorio 39 CD 5
Costa Murmana 1 P 2
Costarica 43 M 8-9
Cotabato 34 F 3
Cotagaita 52 D 6
Cotonou 39 E 4
Cotopaxi 52 B 2
Côte d'Or, M¹. 10 H 3
Cotswold Hills 3 E 6
Cottbus 13 F 3
Cotter 57 A 2
Cottian Alps 18 A 2
Cottica 51 F 3
Cotulla 46 G 7
Couman 57 a 2
Council Bluffs 46 G 4
Courantyne 51 E 3
Courland 17 LM 8
Cours 11 H 3
Coursan 11 G 5
Coutances 11 E 2
Coutrai 15 C 4
Coventry 4 F 5
Cov Iha 9 C 3
Covington (USA, Kentucky) 46 L 5
Covington (USA, Virg.) 46 M 5
Cowal 55 H 6
Cowan 55 C 6
Coxim 52 G 5
Cox's Bazar 33 A 2
Cozumel 47 G 3
Cradock 41 D 5
Crag 46 E 5
Craig Habour 45 N 5
Craova 21 F 5
Craplândia 52 H 3
Crater 46 E 4
Crateus 52 I 3
Crato 52 I 3
Crawford 46 F 4
Crema 19 BC 2
Cremona 19 BC 2
Cres 21 B 5
Crescent City 46 B 4
Cresco 46 H 4
Crete 21 G 10
Crete, Sea of 21 FG 9-10
Cretin 26 o 14
Creus, Golf of 9 G 2
Creuse 10 F 3
Creusot, Le- 11 H 3
Cricomola 48 C 5
Crimea 25 BC 3
Cristobal, punta 52 a
Crisul Albo 20 E 4
Crisul Negru 20 E 4
Crisul Repede 20 E 4
Crixas Açu 52 G 4
Crna 20 E 7
Crnomelj 21 B 5
Crocodile 41 D 3
Croatia 21 BC 5
Cromarty 4 D 3
Cromwell 55 f 15
Cronulla 55 e 11
Crookston 46 G 3
Cross 39 F 4-5
Crosse, La- 46 H 4
Cross Fell 3 E 4
Crotone 19 F 5
Croydon (Australia) 55 G 3
Croydon (United Kingdom) 4 F 6
Cruces, Las- 47 C 2
Cruz, La- 51 A 3

Cruz 48 D 3
Cruz Alta 52 G 7
Cruz del Eje 53 D 3
Cruzeiro do Sul 52 C 3
Cruzen 57 r 2
Csepel 21 D 4
Csepreg 21 C 4
Csongrad 21 E 4
Csovanyos 20 D 4
Cu 29 F 3
Cua 35 E 6
Cuando 35 EF 7
Cuangar 41 B 2
Cuango 40 B 4
Cuango 40 B 5
Cua Rao 33 C 3
Cuatro Ojos 52 E 5
Cuba 43 MN 7
Cubango 35 EF 7
Cucalon, Serra de- 9 F 3
Cucuta 51 B 2
Cuddapah 30 C 6
Cudgewa 55 H 7
Cudillero 9 C 2
Cudovo 23 H 5
Cudskoe L. (L. Peipus) 23 F 5
Cue 55 B 5
Cüili 22 F 5
Cuenca (Ecuador) 52 B 2
Cuenca (Spain) 9 E 3
Cuenca, Serrania de- 8 EF 3-4
Cuernavaca 47 E 4
Cuero 46 G 7
Cugus 1 Q 7
Cuiaba 52 F 5
Cuikci 22 T 3
Cuillin Hills 4 C 3
Cuio 40 A 5
Cuito 35 EF 7
Cuito Cuanavale 41 B 2
Cuiuni 52 E 2
Culakivka 25 B 2
Culgoa 54 E 7
Culiacan 47 C 3
Culion 34 F 2
Cullinan 41 D 4
Culman 22 N 4
Culuene 52 G 4
Culym 22 HI 4
Cuma, B. de- 52 I 2
Cumana 51 D 1
Cumberland 46 M 5
Cumberland Gulf of 44 RS 2-3
Cumberland Plateau (USA) 46 IL 5
Cumberland Peninsula 44 RS 2
Cumbre, La- p. 49 D 7
Cumbrian. Mt. 12 E 4
Cumerna 20 H 6
Cumikan 22 O 4
Cumina 49 E 4
Cumuraxatiba 52 L 5
Cuna 22 I 4
Cunani 51 F 3
Cunco 53 B 4
Cunene 41 B 1
Cunene 35 E 7
Cuneo 19 A 2
Cuni Cingrau 25 M 4
Cunjamba 41 C 2
Cunnamula 55 H 5
Cunnbjorns 42 ST 3
Cunojar 22 I 4
Cuprija 21 E 6
Curaçao 51 C 1
Curapca 22 O 3
Curapiqui 52 F 3
Curdistan 26 FG 6
Curiapo 51 D 2
Curico 53 B 3
Curicuriari 52 D 2
Curitiba 52 H 7
Curralinho 52 G 2
Curtis I. (Australia) 55 I 4
Curtis I. (New Zealand) 54 I 8
Curua 52 G 3
Curuça 52 E 3
Curuça 52 H 2
Cururupù Cuatia 52 F 7
Curvelo 52 I 5
Curzola 20 C 6
Cusco 52 C 4
Cusovaja 1 T 4
Cusovo 24 I 5
Cutata 40 B 5
Cuttack 30 E 4
Cuvo 40 A 5
Cuxhaven 13 C 2
Cuy, El- 53 C 4
Cuyuni 51 DE 2
Cuyutlan 47 D 4
Cvrsnica 20 C 6
Cyclades 21 G 9
Cypress Hills 44 GH 6
Cyprus 20 8-9
Cyrenaica 37 I 3-5
Cyrene 37 I 3
Czaplinek 13 G 2
Czarnkow 13 G 2
Czechoslovakia 21 AF 3
Czersk 13 G 2
Czestochowa 13 M 3

D

Dab, El- 38 E 6
Dabakala 39 D 4
Dabarò 38 E 6
Dabbag 38 C 2
Dabib 37 L 7
Dabola 39 B 3
Daboya 39 D 4
Dabrowa 19 H 3
Dabrowa Tarn 19 I 3
Dabu 55 G 1
Dabus 38 B 5-6
Dabuza 23 L 7
Dacca 30 F 4
Dachstein 18 E 5
Dadabad 28 L 4
Dadu 29 E 6
Daet 34 F 2
Daegu 31 N 3
Daejeon 31 N 3
Dafina 39 D 3
Dagabur 38 D 6
Dagana 37 A 6
Dagebüll 19 C 1
Dagestan 25 I 5-6
Dagruca Dagi 25 B 5
Dagu-bayazit 25 G 6
Dagupan 34 F 1
Dahana 38 E 2
Dahanu 30 B 4
Daheua, ed- 37 I 4
Dahlak Islands 38 D 4
Dai 40 B 1
Dailiman 28 L 2
Daimiel 9 E 4
Dair 37 M 7
Daka 39 D 4
Dakala 37 E 7
Dakar 37 A 7
Dakingari 39 E 3
Dalan 31 G 2
Dalat 33 D 4
Dalfors 17 F 6
Dalhart 46 F 5
Dalias 9 E 5
Dalj 21 D 5
Dall 45 N 5
Dallas 46 G 6
Dallol Bosso 37 E 7
Dalma 29 B 7
Dalmaj, Lake 28 H 4
Dalmatia 21 BD 5-5
Dalmatovo 24 N 6
Daloa 39 C 4
Dalrymple 54 E 7
Daltonganj 30 D 4
Dalupiri 34 F 1
Dalvik 17 S 12
Daly 55 H 6
Daly Waters 55 E 3
Dam (Saudi Arabia) 38 D 3
Dam (Surinam) 51 F 3
Daman 30 B 4
Damanhur 37 M 3
Damar Island 34 G 6
Damara (Central
 African Republic) 40 B 1
Damara (South Africa) 35 E 8
Damascus 28 D 4
Damba 40 B 4
Dambovit 20 G 5
Dambuki 22 N 4
Damergou 37 F 7
Damghan 29 B 4
Damietta 37 M 3
Damodar 27 a 11
Damoh 30 C 4
Dampier Archipelago 55 B 4
Dampier Land 55 C 3
Damraou 37 H 7
Danai 34 B 4
Danane 39 C 4
Da Narg 33 D 4
Dana Parma 38 D 7
Danao 34 F 2
Dancalia 35 H 4
Dande, Punta 40 A 4
Danesi 56 a
Dangbae 39 E 4
Danger 54 L 6
Danghila 38 C 5
Dangriga 47 F 5
Danilaka 24 I 2
Danilov 23 O 5
Dankassa 39 E 3
Dankov 23 N 8
Dannebrogs 44 Z 2
Danube 20 AL 3-6
Danville (USA, Illinois)
 46 I 4
Danville (USA, Virginia)
 46 M 5
Dao 34 F 2
Dapha-Bum 33 B 1
Dapitan 34 F 3
Dapsang 30 C 1
Dara 37 L 7
Darab 38 F 2
Dar Adrar 37 B 5
Dar al Hamra 28 D 7
Darasun 22 M 4
Daraw 37 M 5
Darazo 39 G 3
Dar Banda 35 EF 5
Darbenai 17 I 8

Darbhanga 30 E 3
Darbi 31 E 1
Dardanelles 20 GH 7
Dar eb Humr 37 L 7
Dar el-Beida (Casablanca)
 37 C 3
Darende 25 D 6
Dar es Salaam 40 F 4
Darfung 38 B 5
Dar Fur 35 F 4
Dargai 29 F 5
Dargaville 55 g 13
Dargol 37 E 7
Dar Hamar 37 L 7
Dar Hamid 37 LM 7
Darién, G. of 42 N 9
Dariganga 31 I 1
Darjeeling 30 E 3
Dar Kibet 37 HI 7
Darling River 55 G 6
Darling Range 54 B 8
Darlington 13 F 4
Darlowo 13 G 1
Dàrmanesti 21 H 4
Darmstadt 13 C 4
Darnley, Cape 57 F 3
Dar Nuba 37 LM 7
Daroca 9 F 3
Daror 38 D 6
Daror 38 EF 5
Dar Ould 37 C 3
Dar Rounga 37 IF 8
Dart 57 R 2
Dart, Cape 3 E 6
Dartmoor Forest 3 DE 6
Dartmouth 4 E 6
Daru 55 G 1
Darun 28 M 4
Dar Urrti 37 L 6
Darvaz 2 T 7
Darwin (Australia) 55 E 2
Darwin (USA) 52 a
Daryacheh Nämäkzar
 29 D 5
Darya yl Namak 28 M 3
Dar Zaghawa 37 I 6
Dásht 29 D 6
Dashtiari 29 D 6
Dásht-i-Kävir, 29 BC 5
Dásht-i-Lut 29 C 5
Dásht-i-Margo 29 D 5
Datia 30 C 3
Datu, Cape 34 C 4
Dauphiné 11 HI 4
Daugavgriva 17 M 8
Daugavpils 23 F 7
Daule 52 B 2
Daulet Yar 29 E 5
Dauqa 38 D 4
Daura (Iraq) 28 H 4
Daura (Nigeria) 39 F 3
Daurskoe 22 I 4
Dauzot 25 G 5
Davangere 30 C 6
Davao 34 G 3
Davao, Gulf of 34 G 3
Davenport 46 H 4
David 48 C 7
Davidson Mt. 44 B 2
Davik 17 A 6
Davissee 57 E 3
Davis Strai 44 ST 2
Davos 19 BC 1
Dawari 39 G 4
Dawson, Canal 44 B 3
Dawson, (Australia) 55 H 4
Dawson, Island 53 B 7
Dawson Ra. 44 B 3
Dawson Creek 44 E 4
Dax 11 E 5
Dayton 46 L 5
Daytona Beach 46 L 7
De Aar 41 C 5
Deakin 55 D 6
Dead Sea 28 C 5
Dean Funes 53 D 3
Dease Strait 44 H 2
Debaba 38 D 4
Debar 21 E 7
Debba, El- 37 M 6
Debessy 24 G 6
Debiso 39 D 4
Deblin 13 I 3
Debra Markos 38 C 5
Debra Tabor 38 C 5
Debrecen 21 E 4
Decatur (USA, Illinois)
 46 I 5
Decatur (USA, Alabama)
 46 I 6
Decazeville 11 G 4
Deccan 30 C 6-5
Decize 11 GM 43
Dedougou 39 D 3
Dee (United Kingdom) 13 E 5
Dee (Scotland) 12 D 4
Dee (Wales) 12 E 5
Deep Bay 27 f 15
Deering 55 D 4
Defferrari 53 E 4
Degema 39 F 5
Degerhamn 17 G 8
De Grey 55 C 4
Dehane 39 G 5
Deh Bid 29 B 5
Dehibat 37 G 3

Dehine, Hassi- 37 F 5
Dehra Dun 30 C 2
Deim Zubeir 40 D 1
Deir-ez-Zor 28 F 3
Deir-Shemeyil 28 D 3
Dej 21 F 4
Dekese 40 C 3
Delaware 46 M 5
Delaware Bay 46 M 5
Delft 15 G 3
Delgada, Punta
 (Argentina) 53 D 5
Delgada, Punta (Azores)
 37 a
Delhi 30 C 3
Dell 16 G 6
Delli Abbas 28 H 3
Dellys 37 E 2
Delmenhorst 13 BC 2
Delos 20 G 9
De Long 22 Q 2
De Long-Strait 22 ST 2-3
Del Rio 46 F 7
Delta 37 M 3
Dema 24 H 8
Demak 34 D 6
Demawend 26 H 6
Demba 40 C 4
Dembidolo 38 B 6
Demchok 31 B 4
Demeni 51 D 3
Demidov 23 H 7
Deming 46 E 6
Demjamskoe 22 F 4
Demjansk 23 I 6
Demmin 19 E 2
Dempo 34 B 5
Denain le Cateau 11 G 1
Denchin 31 F 4
Dendang 34 C 5
Denezkin Kamen 1 T 3
Dengdeng 39 G 4
Den Helder 15 G 2
Denia 9 G 4
Deniliquin 55 G 7
Denis 39 F 5
Denison 46 G 6
Denisovka 24 H 1
Denizli 20 I 9
Denmark 17 CE 8-9
Denmark Str. 42 HS3
Denpasar 34 E 6
Dent du Midi, Mt. 10 I 3
D'Entrecasteux Island 54 F 5
D'Entrecasteux Point 55 B 6
Denver 46 F 5
Deogarh 30 D 4
Depressione Caspica
 1 RS 6
Dera Ghazi Khan 29 F 5
Dera Ismail Khan 29 F 5
Derbent 25 L 4
Derby 13 F 5
Dere, El- 38 E 7
Dereham 13 G 5
Dereva 23 L 5
Derg, L. 12 B 5
Derj 37 G 3
Derna 37 I 3
Dernieres 46 H 7
Derudeb 38 C 4
Derven 21 F 6
Dervent 12 F 4-5
Derventa 21 C 5
Derzavinskoe 22 F 4
Desaguadero (Argentina)
 53 C 3
Desaguadero (Bolivia)
 52 D 5
Deseado 53 C 6
Desengano 53 C 6
Deset 17 D 6
Des Moines 46 H 4
Desna 1 O 5
Desolacion 53 B 7
De Soto 46 H 5
Desventuradas 50 BC 6
De Trechter 26 m 13
Detroit 46 I 4
Deva 21 E 3
Devenport (Tasmania)
 55 b 9
Devenport (New Zealand)
 55 g 13
Deventer 15 H 2
Deveron 3 E 3
Devin 21 G 7
Devoli 20 E 7
Dévon 12 DE 6
Devon Island 43 M 2
Devonport (United
 Kingdom) 4 D 6
Devrekáni 25 B 5
Dey Dey 55 E 5
Dezful 28 L 4
Dezginze 21 I 4
Dezhnëv, Cape 22 T 3
Dhaba 28 C 7
Dhahran 28 M 7
Dhala 38 D 5
Dhaleswari 27 ab 11

Dhamar 38 D 5
Dhamtari 30 D 4
Dhankuta 30 E 3
Dhar 30 C 4
Dhariya 38 D 3
Dhar Oualata 37 C 6
Dharwar 30 C 5
Dhasan 37 M 7
Dhat al Haggi 28 D 6
Dhaulagiri 30 D 3
Dhond 30 B 5
Dhoraji 30 B 4
Dhufar 38 F 4
Dhula 38 E 5
Dhulia 30 B 4
Dhurma 38 E 3
Dia 20 G 10
Diaha 37 B 4
Diala 37 C 7
Dialafara 37 B 7
Dialakoto 37 B 7
Diale 1 QR 8-9
Diamantina 55 G 4
Diamantino 52 F 4
Diamond Harbour 27 A 11
Diankabo 37 D 7
Diani 39 B 4
Diari 39 D 4
Dibah 29 C 6
Dibaya 40 C 4
Dibdi 29 C 6
Dibella 37 G 6
Dibra 21 E 7
Dibrugarh 33 A 1
Dickinson 46 F 3
Dickson 33 C 6
Dider 37 F 4
Die 11 H 4
Diebougoa 39 D 3
Diéfoula 39 D 3
Diele 46 H 3
Dien Bien phu 33 C 2
Dieppe 11 F 2
Dif 40 G 2
Digba 40 D 2
Digby 44 R 7
Digermul 16 N 1
Digiuma 38 D 7
Digne 11 I 4
Digoin 11 G 3
Digos 34 G 3
Digul 54 DE 5
Dijon 11 H 3
Dikanka 25 C 1
Dikoudou 40 A 3
Dikson 22 H 2
Dikti Ori 20 G 10
Dikwa 39 G 3
Dilam 38 E 3
Dilaram 29 D 5
Dili 34 G 6
Dillingham 45 G 5
Dilman 28 H 1
Dilolo 40 C 5
Diltawa 28 H 4
Dima 41 C 2
Dimapur 33 A 1
Dimbokro 39 D 4
Dinagat 34 G 2-3
Dinajpur 30 E 3
Dinan 11 D 2
Dinangourou 37 D 7
Dinant 15 G 3
Dinapore 30 E 3
Dinara 20 C 5
Dinaric Alps 20 C 5-6
Dindigul 30 C 6
Dingboche 26 p 17
Dingle 4 A 5
Dingle Bay 3 A 5
Dinguiraye 39 B 3
Dinsor 38 D 7
Diouloulà 37 A 7
Dioura 37 C 7
Diourbel 37 A 7
Dipolog 34 F 3
Dir 29 F 4
Dire Dawa 38 D 6
Dirfis 20 F 8
Dirranbandi 55 H 5
Dirri 38 E 7
Dirschkeim 17 H 9
Disappointment, L. 55
 C 4
Dishna 37 M 4
Disko Bugt 44 U 2
Disko 46 U 2
Disna 23 G 7
Diss 4 G 5
Ditràu 21 G 4
Diu 30 B 4
Divenskij 23 GH 5
Dives 11 E 2
Divci 21 L 5
Dividal 17 H 2
Divnoe 25 G 3
Divrigi 25 E 6
Dixcove 39 D 5
Dixon Entrance 44 C 5
Diyarbakir 28 F 2
Dizak 29 D 6
Dize 28 G 2
Dizful 2 R 9

Dja 35 E 5
Djadjidouna 37 F 7
Djado 37 G 5
Djailolo 34 G 4
Djakarta 34 C 6
Djakovica 21 E 6
Djamba 39 G 4
Djambala 40 A 3
Djambi 34 B 5
Djanet 37 G 5
Djelfa 37 E 3
Djéma 40 D 1
Djemaa 36 D 5
Djemadja 34 C 4
Djember 34 D 6
Djenné 37 D 7
Djerem 39 G 4
Djernih 27 h 16
Djevdjelija 21 F 7
Dja 40 C 1
Djibo 39 D 3
Djibouti, (State) 38 D 5
Djibouti (City) 38 D 5
Djidjelli 37 F 2
Djombo 40 C 2
Djorat 25 L 5
Djougou 39 E 4
Dj Telerheta 37 F 5
Djugu 40 E 2
Djungkulon 26 I 13
Djupivogur 17 U 12
Djurdjevac 21 C 4
Djursland 17 D 8
Dmitra 23 M 6
Dmitrovsk-Orlovskij 23 L 8
Dnepr-Bug Canal 20 G 1
Dneprodzerzinsk 25 C 1
Dnepropetrovsk 25 C 1
Dnestr 20 FL 3-4
Dnjepr 1 O 4-6
Dno 23 GH 6
Doba 40 B 1
Dobané 40 C 1
Dobbiaco 18 D 1
Doblas 53 D 4
Dobo 34 H 6
Dobrianka 21 L 1
Dobruja 21 HI 5-6
Doce 52 I 5
Dodge City 46 F 5
Dodici, Cima 18 C 2
Dodo 39 G 4
Dodoma 40 F 4
Dogondoutchi 37 E 7
Doha 38 F 2
Dohazari 27 c 11
Doi Inthanon 33 B 3
Doksitsy 23 F 7
Dokuy 39 D 3
Dol 11 E 2
Dôle 11 H 3
Dolgelley 4 E 5
Dolgoe 21 F 3
Dolgoscel'e 23 P 1
Dolianova 19 B 5
Dolina 21 G 3
Dolinsk 22 P 5
Dolinskaia 25 B 1
Dollart 13 B 5
Dolleman 57 n 2
Dolo (Ethiopia) 38 D 7
Dolok 26 n 14
Dolomites 18 C 1
Dolores 53 E 4
Dolphin and Union Str.
 44 FG 2
Dombas 17 C 5
Dombe Grande 40 A 5
Dombovar 21 D 4
Dome 33 B 4
Domesnäs 16 L 8
Domfront 11 E 2
Dominica 48 G 3
Dominica Rep. 50 CD 2
Dömitz 13 D 2
Domnarvet 17 F 6
Domo 38 E 6
Domo Gouaira 40 B 1
Domonovo 23 E 8
Dompa 37 D 6
Dompierre-sur-Besbre
 11 G 3
Don (United Kingdom) 3 F 5
Don (Scotland) 3 E 3
Don, (Soviet Union) 2
Donald Station 44 F 5
Don Benito 9 D 4
Donde 40 F 4
Dondo 40 A 4
Dondra Head 30 D 7
Donegal 4 B 4
Donegal Bay 3 B 4
Dones, Los- 53 C 1
Donets 1 PQ 5-6
Donetsk 25 D 2
Donfar, El- 38 E 5
Donga 39 G 4

Dongarra 55 A 5
Dongba 31 C 5
Donggala 34 E 5
Dong hoi 33 D 3
Dongo (Chad) 40 B 1
Dongo (The Congo) 40 B 2
Dongola 37 M 6
Dongou 40 B 2
Dongur 38 C 5
Dongwe 41 CD 1
Dönna 16 E 3
Donnybrook 41 D 4
Doorn 41 B 5
Dopori 40 C 2
Dora 55 C 4
Dora Baltea 18 A 2
Doral 31 D 2
Dora Riparia 18 A 2
Dorchester 4 E 6
Dorchoi 21 H 4
Dordogne 10 F 4
Dordrecht (Netherlands)
 15 G 3
Dordrecht (South Africa) 41
 D 5
Dore 10 G 4
Dores de Indaia 52 H 5
Dori 39 D 3
Dorbirn 13 C 5
Dornoch 4 D 3
Dornoch Firth 3 E 3
Dorogobuz 23 I 7
Dorotea 17 G 4
Dorsale Obscij 1 RS 5
Dortmund 13 B 3
Dos Bahias, Cape 53 C 5
Dospot 20 FG 7
Dossor 25 N 2
Dothan 46 I 6
Douai 11 G 1
Douala 39 F 5
Doubs 10 I 3
Doué 39 C 4
Douentza 37 D 6
Douglas (United Kingdom) 4
 D 4
Douglas (South Africa)
 41 C 4
Douglas (USA) 46 E 6
Douglas 57 f 3
Dougoula 37 C 7
Douma Kaba 40 C 1
Doumé 39 G 5
Douna 37 C 7
Dourados 52 F 6
Douro 9 B 3
Dover (United Kingdom)
 4 G 6
Dover (South Africa) 41 D 4
Dover (USA) 46 M 5
Dover-Foxcroft 46 O 3
Dover, Strait of 14 E 3
Dovrefjell 16 C 5
Downpatrick 4 D 4
Downs 3 FG 6
Doyung 31 F 4
Draa, W. 37 C 3-4
Drac 10 HI 4
Draguignan 11 I 5
Drakensberge 35 FG 8
Drama 21 G 7
Drammen 17 D 7
Drams 17 D 7
Dranga Jökull 16 Q 11
Drava 20 AD 4-5
Drawsko 13 F 2
Dre 31 E 4
Dreihernspitze 13 CD 1
Dresden 13 E 3
Dreux 11 F 2
Drewin 39 C 5
Drin 20 DE 6
Drin, G. of 20 D 7
Drina 20 D 5
Dröbak 17 D 7
Drobin 13 I 2
Drogheda 4 C 5
Drôme 10 H 4
Dronne 10 F 4
Drubeta-Turnu Severin
 21 F 5
Druja 23 F 7
Drvar 21 C 5
Drweca 12 H 2
Drigalski 57 E 3
Drisdale 55 D 2-3
Dschang 39 F 4
Dschubaland 36 H 5-6
Dubawnt 44 I 3
Dubbo 55 H 6
Dubica 21 C 5
Dubienka 19 L 3
Dubisa 16 L 9
Dublin 4 C 5
Dublin Bay 4 CD 5
Dubna 23 F 6
Dubno 21 G 2
Du Bois 46 M 4
Dubovka 25 H 1
Dubreka 39 B 4
Dubrovka 21 D 6
Dubrovnik 21 D 6
Dubuque 46 H 4
Duca di Gloucester 54 N 7
Duchess Dajarra 55 F 4
Duchi 39 G 3

Ducie 54 P 7
Ducodde 17 F 9
Dudinka 22 H 3
Dudley 4 E 5
Dudo 38 F 6
Duenas 9 D 3
Duero 8 CE 3
Duff 54 G 5
Dufile 40 E 2
Dugebüll 13 C 1
Dugi Otok 21 B 5
Duglha 26 p 17
Dugur 25 G 5
Duhak 29 C 5
Duisburg 13 B 3
Duivelskloof 41 E 3
Duk Fadiat 40 E 1
Dukhovscina 23 I 7
Duku 39 G 3
Dulawan 34 F 3
Dulce 48 C 5
Dulce 53 D 2
Dülmen 13 B 3
Dulovka 23 G 6
Dulut 46 H 3
Dumaguete 34 F 3
Dumanli 20 H 8
Dumanti D. 1 P 7
Dumaran 34 E 2
Dumaring 34 E 4
Dumbier 20 D 3
Dumfries 4 E 4
Dunaföldvar 21 D 4
Dunaj 31 O 2
Dunajec 12 I 4
Dunbar 4 E 4
Duncansby Head 3 E 2
Dundaga 17 L 8
Dundalk 4 C 4
Dundalk B. 3 C 5
Dundas 55 C 6
Dundas Harbour 44 OP 1
Dundee 4 E 3
Dundeli 16 F 3
Dunder 38 B 5
Dund Gobi 31 H 1
Dundrusana 40 C 2
Dunedin 55 g 15
Dunga 40 D 2
Dungarvan 4 C 5
Dungas 37 F 7
Dungu 40 D 2
Dungunab 38 C 3
Dünkerque 11 G 1
Dunkwa 39 D 4
Dunmore Head 3 A 5
Duns 4 E 4
Duque de Bragança 40 B 4
Duque de York, Island 53 A 7
Durack 55 D 3
Durance 10 H 5
Durango (Mexico) 47 D 3
Durango (Spain) 9 E 2
Durango (USA) 46 E 5
Durazno 53 E 3
Düren 13 B 3
Durban 36 G 9
Durbo 38 F 5
Durch, Las- 38 E 5
Durg 30 D 4
Durge Nur 31 E 1
Durmitor 20 D 6
Durrës 21 D 7
Durrës, G. of 20 D 7
Dusanbe 22 F 6
Dusseldorf 13 B 3
Dutck 22 U 4
Dutovo 24 I 3
Duwadami 38 D 3
Dverberg 17 F 2
Dvina 23 G 7
Dvina Bay 23 NO 2
Dvina, Northern 1 QS 3
Dwarka 30 A 4
Dyer Plateau 57 O 2
Dyer 44 S 2
Dyje 20 BC 3
Dyke Lake 44 R 5
Dykh-tau 25 G 4
Dymer 21 L 2
Dyngjufjöll 16 T 12
Dzabhan 31 EF 1
Dzadagad 31 H 2
Dzag Somon 31 F 1
Dzagtu Tsetsei 31 H 2
Dzalinda 22 N 4
Dzambul 29 F 3
Dzamyn Ude 31 I 2
Dzankoj 25 C 3
Dzaoudzi (Mamoudzou) 41 c 6
Dzebrail 25 I 6
Dzekemde 22 N 4
Dzerzinsk 23 F 8
Dzesi 31 I 2
Dzetygara 22 F 4
Dzez-Kazgan 22 F 5
Dzhida 22 L 4
Dzhizak 29 E 3
Dzhugdzhur Ranger 22 OP 4
Dzialoszyce 13 I 3
Dzizak 22 F 5

Dzonglu 26 p 17
Dzubga 25 E 3
Dzungaria 31 CD 2
Dzun Mod 31 H 1
Dzusaly 29 D 2

E
Eagle 44 T 5
Earn 4 E 3
East 4 G 5
Eastbourne 4 G 6
East China Sea 26 Q 6-7
East London 41 D 5
Eastmain 44 PQ 5
East Siberian Sea 22 QU 2
Eau Claire 46 H 4
Eauripik 54 E 4
Ebbe 12 B 3
Eberswalde 13 EF 2
Ebi Nor 31 C 1-2
Ebola 40 C 2
Eboli 19 E 4
Ebolowa 39 G 5
Ebro 8 EF 2-3
Eccles 4 E 5
Ech-Cheliff 37 E 2
Echuca 55 G 7
Ecija 9 D 5
Eckernförde 13 C 1
Ecuador 50 C 4
Ed 17 G 5
Edd 38 D 5
Ed Dab'a 37 L 3
Ed Damer 38 B 4
Ed-Diwan 37 M 5
Ed Dueim 37 M 7
Ed Dzong 31 E 4
Edéa 39 G 5
Edefors 17 I 3
Eden 3 E 4
Edenburg 41 D 4
Eder 12 C 3
Ederengen Nuru 31 F 2
Edessa 21 F 7
Edfu 37 M 5
Edge 56 a
Edinburgh 4 E 4
Edina 39 B 4
Edirne 21 H 7
Edith Ronne 57 NO 1
Edjeleh 37 F 4
Edmonton 44 F 5
Edmundston 44 R 6
Edo 27 d 13
Edoardo VII 57 G 3
Edremit 21 H 8
Edremit, G. of 20 H 8
Edri 37 G 4
Edsele 17 G 5
Edsel Ford Ra. 57 rS 2
Efate 54 G 6
Efoulen 39 G 5
Efremov 23 N 8
Ega 8 E 2
Egadi Is. 18 CD 5-6
Egam 38 C 4
Eger 21 A 2
Egeröy 17 A 7
Egersund 17 B 7
Egito 40 A 5
Eglinton 45 P 1
Egmont 55 g 13
Egmont Mt. 55 g 13
Egorévsk 23 N 7
Egridir 1 O 8
Eguéi 37 H 6
Egyn 31 G 1
Egypt 36 FG 3
Eiao 54 N 5
Eid 17 B 6
Eide 17 B 6
Eide 17 B 5
Eidsvold 55 I 5
Eifel 14 H 3
Eigg 3 C 3
Eightsküste 57 Pp 2
Eil 38 E 6
Eilat 28 C 6
Einasleigh 55 G 3
Einasleigh 55 G 3
Einbeck 13 CD 3
Eindhoven 15 G 3
Eirunepe 52 C 3
Eisenhut 19 E 5
Eja, 1 PQ 6
Ejby 5 E 1
Eisk 25 E 2
Ejutla 47 E 4
Ekenäs 17 L 7
Eksjo 17 F 8
Ekträsk 17 H 4
Ekwan 44 O 5
Elabuga 24 G 7
El Aiun 37 B 4
El-'Aqaba 28 C 6
El-'Arish 28 B 5
Eiâzig 25 E 6
Elba 18 C 3
El-Bab 28 D 2
Elbasan 21 E 7
Elbe 12 CE 2-3
Elbert 42 I 6

Elbeuf 11 F 2
Elbistan 28 D 1
Elblag 13 H 1
El-Boulaïda 37 E 2
Elbrus 25 G 4
Elburz 1 S 8
Elche 9 F 4
Elche de la Sierra 9 E 4
Elda Logna 17 D 6
Eldama 40 F 2
El-Djouf 37 C 5-6
Eldorado 47 C 3
El Dorado 51 D 2
Eldoret 40 F 2
Ele 51 B 2
Elephant 57 n 3
Elets 23 N 8
Eleuthera 48 D 1
El Ghurdaga 28 B 7
El Ismalia 28 B 5
Elista 25 H 2
Elizabeth 46 O 4
Elizabeth, Cape 45 H 5
Elizavety 22 P 4
El-Kerak 28 C 5
El-Khalil 28 C 5
El-Kharga 36 G 3
El'khotovo 25 H 4
Elkhovka 24 F 8
Elko 46 C 4
Elku kaln 17 M 8
Ellesmere 42 MN 1-2
Ellice 54 H 5
Elliot 41 D 5
Elliotdale 41 D 5
Elliston 55 F 6
Ellore 30 D 5
Ellsworthland 57 oQ 2
Ellwangen 13 D 4
Elm 12 D 2
El Manteco 51 D 2
El Matartya 28 A 5
El-Mekhili 37 I 3
Elmina 39 D 4
Elmira 46 M 4
Elmshorn 13 C 2
El-Nebq 28 D 3
Elnja 23 I 7
Elota 47 C 3
Elphinstone 33 B 4
El-Qantara 28 B 5
Elsa 18 C 3
El'sk 21 I 2
Elster 12 E 3
El Tigre 51 D 2
El'ton 25 I 1
El'tsi 23 I 6
Elvas 9 C 4
Elvend 1 R 9
Elverum 17 D 6
Elvira 44 G 1
El-Wak 40 G 2
Ely 46 D 5
Ema 17 F 8
Eman 16 FG 8
Emanzelinsk 24 M 7
Emba 23 E 3
Emba 1 ST 6
Embarcación 53 D 1
Embu 40 F 3
Emden 13 B 2
Emerald 55 H 4
Emerson 44 L 6
Emetsk 23 O 3
Emi Koussi 37 H 6
Emilia Romagna 19 BC 2
Emine, Cape 20 H 6
Emmaste 17 L 7
Emmen 15 H 1
Emmerich 13 B 3
Empangeni 41 E 4
Empoli 19 C 3
Emporia 46 G 5
Ems 23 H 1
Ena 23 H 1
Enakievo 25 E 1
Enard 4 C 2
Enare 17 N 2
Encantada, La 47 A 1
Encanto, El- 52 C 2
Encarnacion 52 F 7
Encontrados 51 B 2
Ende 34 F 6
Enderby Land 57 gG 2-3
Endicott Mt. 45 HI 3
Engadin 7b E 2
Engan 17 F 3
Engano, Cape 34 F 1
Engeles 24 D 9
Engeöy 17 F 3
Enggano 34 B 6
Englehart 44 P 6
English 44 M 5
Elglish Bahar 30 E 3
English Channel 14 CE 3-4
Enid 46 G 5
Enipeus 20 F 8
Eniwetok 54 G 3
Enjuka 22 N 4
Enkeldoorn 41 E 2
Enköping 17 G 7

Enna 19 E 6
Ennadai 44 I 3
Ennedi 35 F 4
Ennis 4 B 5
Enniscorthy 4 C 5
Enniskillen 4 C 4
Ennistimon 4 B 5
Enns 12 F 4
Enontekiö 17 L 2
Enos 20 E 8
Enotaevka 25 I 2
Enschede 15 H 2
Ensenada 47 A 1
Enshih 31 H 4
Entebbe 40 E 2
Entre Rios (Brazil) 52 G 3
Entre Rios (Argentina) 49 E 6-7
Enugu 39 F 4
Enz 12 C 4
Epéna 40 B 2
Epernay 11 G 2
Ephesos 21 H 9
Epila 9 F 3
Epinal 11 I 2
Epirus 21 E 8
Epitacio, Presidente 52 G 6
Epukiro, Wadi 41 C 3
Epukiro 41 B 3
Equatorial Guinea 36 E 5
Era 19 C 2
Eralé 51 F 3
Erba, Gebel- 35 G 3
Erbaa 25 D 5
Erbeskopf 12 B 4
Erbil 28 G 2
Ercis 25 G 6
Erciyas Dagi 25 C 6
Erdek 21 H 7
Erdek, Gulf of 20 H 7
Erdeni Mandal 31 G 1
Erdeni Tsogtu 31 G 1
Erdi 37 I 6
Erdre 11 E 3
Erebus 57 a 2
Erechim 52 G 7
Erederickton 44 R 6
Erei, Mt. 18 E 6
Erema 22 L 3
Eremeevka 24 I 3
Erentsab 31 L 1
Erfoud 37 D 3
Erfurt 13 D 3
Erg d'Admer, des. 37 F 5
Erg el-Ahmar, des. 37 D 5
Ergene 20 H 7
Ergeni, Colli 1 Q 6
Erg er Raoui, des. 37 D 4
Ergu Khara 31 G 2
Erichi 37 H 6
Ericht 13 D 3
Erie 46 L 4
Erie Lake 42 M 5
Erigavo 38 E 5
Erimanthos 20 E 8-9
Erin Dabasu 31 I 2
Eritrea 36 GH 4
Erkhau-boro 25 H 2
Erki 25 H 2
Erlangen 13 D 4
Erlau 21 E 4
Ermakovo 22 H 3
Ermenak 28 B 2
Erne 3 BC 4
Erne Lower, Lake 3 C 4
Erne Upper, Lake 3 C 4
Erode 30 D 6
Erofe Pavloivic 22 N 4
Eromanga 55 G 5
Eromanga 54 G 6
Eropol 22 R 3
Er-Raqqah 28 E 3
Er Rih 38 C 4
Erris H. 3 A 4
Er-Roseire 38 B 5
Ertarskij 24 O 6
Ertom 24 D 3
Ertvagöy 17 C 5
Erx Amar 37 A 5
Eryen Khabirga 31 C 2
Erzgebirge 12 E 3
Erzincau 25 E 6
Erzurum 25 F 6
Esahi 32 F 3
Esbjerg 17 C 9
Escada 52 L 3
Escalon 47 D 2
Escalona 9 D 3
Escanaba 46 I 3
Escaut 11 G 1
Eschwege 13 CD 3
Escocesa, Bay 48 F 3
Escuinapa 47 C 3
Escuintla 47 F 5
Eséka 39 G 5
Esfahan 28 M 4
Eshowe 41 E 4
Esin-Shobak 28 C 5
Esin-Shuweiref 37 G 4
Esino 18 D 3
Esk, North- 3 E 3
Esk, South- 3 E 3
Eskilstuma 17 G 7
Eskimo 44 M 3
Eski Mossul 28 G 2
Eskisehir 2 O 8

Esla 8 D 3
Esmeralda 51 C 3
Esmeraldas 52 B 1
Eso 21 B 5
Espada, Punta 48 F 3
Espanola 52 a
Espartel 35 C 2
Esperance 55 C 6
Esperanza 53 B 7
Espichel 8 B 4
Espinho 9 B 3
Espirito Santo 52 I 5-6
Esplanada 52 L 4
Espluga 9 G 3
Esquel 53 B 5
Essaouira 37 C 3
Essaauira 2 D 9
Essej 22 L 3
Essen 13 B 3
Essequibo 49 E 3
Essojila 23 I 4
Essonne 10 G 2
Es-Suweida 28 D 4
Estaca de Bares,P.ta de 9 C 2
Estacado, Llano- 42 I 6
Estados, I. de los 53 D 7
Estância 52 L 4
Estcourt 41 D 4
Este 19 C 2
Estei 48 B 4
Estela 9 E 2
Esterias 39 F 5
Esterel, L'- 10 I 5
Estevan 44 I 6
Estonia 23 EF 5
Esztergom 39 D 4
Etah 43 N 2
Étaples 11 F 1
Etawah 30 C 3
Etea 52 D 4
Etelia 37 E 6
Ethiopia 36 GH 5
Etna 16 C 6
Etna 18 E 6
Etnedal 17 C 6
Etoile 40 D 5
Etolin Strait 45 EF 4-5
Etosha Pan 41 B 2
Etoumbi 40 A 2
Etowa 30 C 4
Etrepole 21 F 6
Etsin 31 G 2
Et-Tafilah 28 C 5
Et-Tih 28 BC 5
Et-Tor 28 B 6
Eu 11 F 1
Eua 54 I 7
Euboea 20 FG 8
Euboea, G. of 20 F 8
Eucla 55 D 6
Euganei, Mt. 18 C 2
Eugene 46 B 4
Eugenia, punta 47 A 2
Eulda 13 C 3
Eumbes 52 L 2
Eunda 41 A 2
Euphrates 1 PR 8-9
Eure 10 F 2
Eureka (USA, Cal.) 46 B 4
Eureka (USA, Nev.) 46 C 5
Europa, Picos de- 8 D 2
Europa Island 36 H 8
Europa, Punta de- 9 D 5
Eurotas 20 F 9
Eutin 13 D 1
Evans 44 P 5
Evans, Mt. 46 E 5
Evans Strait 44 O 3
Evanston 46 D 4
Evansville 46 I 5
Everard 55 E 6
Everest 26 M 7
Evje 17 B 7
Evo 17 M 6
Évora 9 C 4
Evreux 11 F 2
Ewe 4 D 3
Exeter 4 E 6
Exmoor 3 E 6
Exmouth 4 E 6
Exmouth Gulf 55 A 4
Exuma, Grand 48 D 2
Exuma Island 48 D 2
Eyasi Lake 40 EF 3
Eye 4 C 4
Eyenes 17 G 2
Eyja 16 S 11
Eyrarbakki 17 R 13
Eyre 55 D 6
Eyre Peninsula 55 F 6
Eyre 55 F 5
Ez-Zarqa' 28 D 4
Ez Zibane 37 F 3
Ezuga 24 C 2

F
Fabriano 19 D 3
Fada 37 I 6
Fada-N'Gourma 39 E 3
Faenza 19 D 2
Faeroe Islands 3 a
Fagan 54 E 3
Fagelsjö 17 F 6
Faghibin 35 C 4
Fagita 34 H 5
Faiaka 54 H 6
Faial 37 a
Faid 28 F 7
Faifo 33 D 3
Faiki 39 F 3
Fair 3 F 2
Fairbanks 45 I 4
Fairfield 55 d 10
Fairlie 55 g 14
Faiyum, El- 37 M 4
Faizabad (Afghanistan) 29 F 4
Faizabad (India) 30 D 3
Fakaoko 54 I 5
Fakarava 54 N 6
Fak Fak 34 H 5
Fakse 17 E 9
Falaba 39 B 4
Falaise 11 E 2
Falakron Oros 20 G 7
Falam 33 A 2
Falcone, Pta. d. 18 AB 4
Falea 37 B 7
Faleme 37 B 7
Falkenberg 17 E 8
Falkland Is. 53 E 7
Falkland, East 53 E 7
Falkland, West 53 D 7
Falkland Sound 53 E 7
Falköping 17 E 7
Fällahiyeh 28 L 5
Fall River 42 I 5
Falls, Grand 44 T 6
Falmouth (Jamaica) 48 D 3
Falmouth (United Kingdom) 4 D 6
False Bay 35 E 9
Falso 48 E 3
Falster 16 E 9
Falsterbo 17 E 9
Falterona, Mt. 18 CD 3
Falun 17 F 6
Famagusta 28 B 3
Fangataufa 54 N 7
Fanning 54 M 4
Fano 19 D 3
Fanos 20 D 8
Fao 28 L 6
Fara 39 D 3
Faradje 40 D 2
Farafangana 41 c 8
Farah 29 D 5
Farak 37 F 6
Farako 37 C 7
Faramana 39 D 3
Faranah 39 B 3
Faras 37 M 5
Farasan Islands 36 G 4
Faregh, Wadi 37 I 3
Farèna 37 C 7
Farewell 55 g 14
Farewell, C. 44 w 4
Fargo 46 G 3
Faridpur 27 a 11
Fârila 17 F 6
Farim 39 A 3
Farina 55 F 6
Farmington 46 E 5
Faro (Brazil) 52 F 2
Faro (Portugal) 9 C 5
Faro, Punta del- 18 E 5
Farö 16 H 8
Färras 16 F 3
Farrukhabad 30 C 3
Fars 26 H 7
Farsala 21 F 8
Farsan 38 D 4
Farshiut 37 M 4
Farsi 29 D 5
Farsund 17 B 7
Fartak 38 F 4
Farur 29 B 6
Fasa 29 B 6
Fasano 19 F 4
Fasher, El- 37 L 7
Fassangouni 39 C 4
Fastov 21 I 2
Fataki 40 D 3
Fathabad 29 C 6
Fatu Hiva 54 O 6
Faucilles 11 HI 2-3
Fauresmith 41 C 4
Fauske 17 F 3
Faux Cap 41 c 9
Favara 19 D 6
Favignana 18 CD 6
Fawn 44 N 5
Faxa floi 16 Q 12
Faya 37 H 6
Fayala 40 B 3

Fayetteville (USA, Arkansas) 46 H 5
Fayetteville (USA, North Carolina) 46 M 5
Fayid 28 B 5
Fazhi 37 G 6
Fazughil 38 B 5
Fear 46 M 6
Fécamp 11 F 2
Federal District of Brasilia 52 H 5
Fedje 17 A 6
Fehmarn I. 12 D 1
Fehmarn Belt 12 D 1
Feira de S. Ana 52 L 4
Feiran 28 B 6
Feiring 17 D 6
Fejö 17 D 9
Feldberg 12 C 5
Felsengerbirge (Rocky Mountains) 42 Gl 4-6
Feltre 19 C 1-2
Femö 17 D 9
Femundi 16 E 5
Fen 31 I 3
Fenaket 21 I 9
Fénérive 41 c 7
Fengchen 31 I 2
Feng chied 31 H 4
Feng hsiang 31 H 4
Feng hsien 31 H 4
Feng huang 31 H 5
Fengyang 31 L 4
Fenice 54 I 5
Fenny 27 b 11
Fenoarivo 41 c 7
Fens 16 A 6
Fenyang 31 I 3
Feodosija 25 C 3
Ferfer 38 E 6
Fergana 29 F 3
Fergusson 55 I 1
Feriano 37 F 2
Ferkéssédougou 39 C 4
Ferlo 37 AB 6
Fermo 19 D 3
Fermoselle 9 CD 3
Fermoy 4 B 5
Fernandina 52 a
Fernando de Noronha 49 G 11
Fernand Vaz 39 F 6
Ferrara 19 C 2
Ferreira 52 H 2
Ferret 11 E 4
Ferro 37 A 4
Ferrol, El- 9 B 2
Ferros 52 I 5
Ferté-St. Aubin, la- 11 F 3
Fès 37 D 3
Feshi 40 B 4
Festyag 17 F 3
Fetesti 21 H 5
Fetisovo 29 B 3
Fetlar 3 F 1
Fianarantsoa 41 c 8
Fichtelgebirge 12 DE 3
Fidenza 19 B 2
Fife Ness 3 E 3
Figeac 11 F 4
Figeholm 17 G 8
Figi 54 H 6
Figueira da Foz 9 B 3
Figueras 9 H 2
Figuig 37 D 3
Fil, Ras el- 37 I 7
Filabres, Sierra de los- 9 E
Filey 4 F 4
Filiatra 20 E 9
Filicudi 18 E 5
Filingué 37 E 7
Filipou 51 F 3
Filyos Çayi 25 B 5
Fimi 35 E 6
Findhorn 3 E 3
Finisterre 8 B 2
Finke 55 E 5
Finland 17 MN 2-6
Finland, Gulf of 23 EG 5
Finlay 44 E 4
Finlay Forks 44 E 4
Finmark 17 LN 1-2
Finspang 17 F 7
Finsteraar Horn 19 AB 1
Finsterwalde 13 E 3
Firdaus 29 C 5
Firminy 11 H 4
Firth of Clyde 3 D 4
Firth of Forth 3 E 3
Firth of Lorne 3 D 3
Firth of Tay 3 E 3
Firuzkuh 28 N 3
Fish 41 B 3
Fisher Strait 44 O 3
Fishguard 4 D 5
Fishwater 41 B 5
Fismes 11 G 2
Fitero 9 F 2
Fitjar 17 A 7
Fitzory 55 HI 4
Fitzroy 55 C 3
Fitzroy-Crossing 55 D 3
Fiume 21 B 5
Fiume Giallo 31 HI 2-3
Fjällsjö 17 G 5

Fjät 17 E 5-6
Fjord Röykenv 17 D 6
Flakstad 17 E 2
Flakstadöy 17 EF 2-3
Flam 17 B 6
Flamborough H. 3 F 4
Flaming 12 E 2-3
Flanders 15 F 3
Flandria 40 B 3
Flannan 4 C 2
Flasjön 16 G 4
Flaten 17 C 7
Flattery (Australia) 55 H 2
Flattery (USA) 44 D 6
Flekkefjord 17 B 7
Flensburg 13 C 1
Flers 11 E 2
Fleurance 11 F 5
Flinders Island 55 b 8
Flinders Ra. 55 F 6
Flinders Reefs 55 H 3
Flint 46 L 4
Flint (River) 46 L 6
Flint (Pacific Ocean) 54 M 6
Flisa 17 E 6
Flix 9 G 3
Florac 11 G 4
Florence (USA, Arizona) 46 D 6
Florence (USA, South Carolina) 46 M 6
Florence 19 C 3
Florencia 51 A 3
Flôres 52 L 3
Flores, Las 53 E 4
Flores Sea 34 EF 6
Flores (Azores) 37 a
Flores (Indonesia) 34 F 6
Floriano 52 I 3
Florianopolis 52 H 7
Florida (Argentina) 53 E 3
Florida, 42 M 7
Florida Keys 46 L 8
Florida Str. 46 L 8
Floridia 19 E 6
Floriana 21 E 7
Florö 17 A 6
Fluberg 17 D 6
Flumendosa 18 B 5
Flushing 15 F 3
Fluvia 9 H 2
Fly 54 E 5
Flyng Fish, Cape 57 Q 2
Foca 21 D 6
Foça 21 H 8
Fochi 37 H 6
Focsani 21 H 5
Fogaha, El- 37 H 4
Foggia 19 EF 4
Fogo 39 a
Föhr 12 C 1
Foià 9 B 5
Foix 11 F 5
Folden 16 F 3
Folegandros 20 G 9
Folgefonn 17 B 6
Folgo 16 B 6-7
Folkestone 4 G 6
Foligno 19 D 3
Follonica 19 C 3
Fominskaja 24 E 2
Fondi 19 D 4
Fongen 16 D 5
Fonsagrada 9 C 2
Fonseca, Gulf of 47 G 5
Fontainebleau 11 G 2
Fonte Boa 52 D 2
Foping 31 H 4
Förberg 17 G 4
Forcados 39 F 4
Förd 17 A 6
Fordlândia 52 F 2
Forécariah 39 B 4
Forel, M¹. 44 Z 2
Forelhögna 17 D 5
Forfar 4 E 3
Forges-les-Eaux 11 F 2
Forli 19 C 2
Formentera 8 G 4
Formentor 8 H 4
Formia 19 D 4
Formiga 52 H 6
Formosa (Argentina) 53 E 2
Formosa (Brazil) 52 H 5
Formosa 31 LM 5-6
Formosa (Taiwan), I. 26 Q 7
Formosa Strait 26 PQ 7
Fornœs 16 D 8
Fornäs 17 H 3
Forssa 17 L 6
Forst 13 F 3
Forsyth 46 E 3
Fort Archambault 40 B 1
Fort Beaufort 41 D 5
Forto Chimo 44 R 4
Fort Chipewyan 44 G 4
Fort Crampel 40 B 1

Fort Dauphin 41 c 9
Fort-de-France 48 G 4
Forte de Possel 40 B 1
Fort Dodge 46 H 4
Forte Mac-Mahon 37 E 4
Fortescue 55 B 4
Fortezza (Franzensteste) 7 E 4
Fort Flatters 37 F 4
Fort Frances 44 M 6
Fort Frances Lake 44 D 3
Fort George 44 P 5
Fort George (Australia) 55 H 2
Fort George (River) 44 PQ 5
Fort Good Hope 44 CD 2
Fort Hall 40 F 3
Fort Hawley 46 E 3
Fortin Avalos Sanchez 52 E 6
Fortin Ayacucho 52 F 2
Fortin Ballivian 52 E 6
Fortin Johnston 41 F 1
Fortin Miribel 37 E 4
Fort Motylinski 37 F 5
Fort Myers 46 L 7
Fort Nelson 44 E 4
Fort Norman 44 D 2
Fort Portal 40 E 2
Fort Pradié 37 H 7
Fort Providence 44 F 3
Fort Reliance 44 H 3
Fort Resolution 44 G 3
Fort Rietfontein 41 C 3
Fort Rixon 41 D 3
Fort Rousset 40 B 3
Fort Saint-John 44 E 4
Fort Sanderman 29 E 5
Fort Scott 46 H 5
Fort Selkirk 44 B 3
Fort Sevcenko 22 E 5
Fort Severn 44 N 4
Fort Simpson 44 E 3
Fort Smith (Canada) 44 G 4
Fort Smith (USA) 46 H 5
Fort Vermilion 44 F 4
Fort Wayne 46 K 5
Fort William (Canada) 44 N 6
Fort William (Scotland) 4 D 3
Fort Worth 46 G 6
Fort Yukon 45 I 3
Fos 11 H 5
Foskros 17 E 5
Fossa Planet 54 F 5
Fouchou 31 L 5 ·
Fougères 11 E 2
Foula 3 F 1
Fouladougou 37 C 7
Fouliang 31 L 5
Fouling 31 H 5
Foulpointe 41 c 7
Foulwind 55 g 14
Foumban 39 G 4
Foum-el-Hassane 37 C 4
Foum Tatahouine 37 G 3
Foundiougne 37 A 7
Founing 31 L 4
Fouping 31 I 3
Fourmies 11 G 1
Fouyang 31 L 4
Foveaux Str. 55 f 15
Fowlers Bay 55 E 6
Foxe Basin 44 P 2
Foxe Pen. 44 P 2-3
Foxen 17 D 7
Foyle 3 C 4
Foz do Breu 52 C 3
Foz do Cunene 41 A 2
Foz do Embira 52 C 3
Foz do Iguaçu 52 G 7
Foz do Jordao 52 C 3
Foz do Riozinho 52 C 3
Franca 52 H 6
Francavilla Fontana 19 FG 4
France 11 FH 2-5
Francesco Giuseppe 42 ST 2
Franceville 40 A 3
Franche Comté 11 HI 3
Francia, Sierra de- 9 C 3
Francistown 41 D 3
Franconia 13 D 4
Franconian Jura 12 D 4
Frankfort (Suoth Africa) 41 D 4
Frankfort (USA) 46 L 5
Frankfurt (East Germany) 13 F 2
Frankfurt (West Germany) 13 C 3
Franklin 41 D 5
Franklin B. 44 E 1
Franklin, Mt. (Canada) 42 G 3
Franklin, Mt. (USA) 46 E 6
Franklin Str. 44 L 1

Franö 17 G 5
Franzfontein 41 B 3
Franz Josef Land 22 DF 1-2
Frascati 19 D 4
Fraser, (Austr.) 55 I 5
Fraser I. 55 I 5
Fraser, (USA) 43 G 4
Fraserburgh 4 F 3
Frech 28 H 5
Fredericia 17 C 9
Frederikshavn 17 D 8
Frederikshab 44 U 3
Fredrika 17 H 4
Fredrikstad 17 D 7
Freels 44 U 6
Freeman 56 a
Freetown 39 B 4
Freiberg 13 E 3
Freiburg 13 BC 5
Freising 13 D 4
Freistadt 13 F 4
Freital 13 E 3
Fréjus 18 A 2
Frejus 11 I 5
Fremantle 55 B 6
French Guiana 50 E 3
Fresko 39 C 4
Fresno 46 C 5
Frew River 55 F 4
Frias (Argentina) 53 C 2
Frias (Spain) 9 E 2
Friaul 18 D 1-2
Friedberg 7 K 3
Fribourg 19 E 3
Friedrichshafen 13 C 5
Friedland 13 E 2
Friesach 13 F 5
Frisian Is. East 13 B 2
Frisian Is., North 12 C 1
Frisian Is., West 13 A 2
Friesland 14 GH 2
Friesland West 15 GH 2
Frio (Sout Africa) 41 A 2
Frio (Brazil) 52 I 6
Frisia 14 GH 2
Frisone 14 GH 2
Frisone 18 C 1
Friuli-Venezia Giulia 19 D 1
Froan, Islands 17 C 4
Frobischer Bay 44 RS 3
Frohnleiten 7 I 3
Frolovo 23 L 8
Frome (United Kingdom) 4 E 6
Frome, L. (Australia) 55 G 6
Fronteira 9 C 4
Front Range 42 I 5-6
Frosinone 19 D 4
Frostviken 17 F 4
Fröya 16 C 5
Frunze 22 G 5
Fruska Gora 20 D 5
Fu 31 L 5
Fuchien 31 L 5
Fuchin 31 O 1
Fucino, Conca del- 19 D 3-4
Fud, El- 38 D 6
Fuente de Cantos 9 C 4
Fuerte, Rio del- 47 C 2
Fuerte General Roca 53 C 4
Fuerteventura 37 B 4
Fuglö 3 a
Fuglöy 17 E 3
Fuji 26 R 6
Fujian 27 d 13
Fukien 32 E 4
Fukuoka 32 D 5
Fukushima 32 F 4
Fukuyama 32 D 5
Fulda 13 C 3
Fulda, R. 12 C 3
Fumaiolo 18 D 3
Fumel 11 F 4
Funabashi 27 d 13
Funafuti 54 H 5
Funchal 37 A 3
Fundao 9 C 3
Fundy, Bay of 44 R 7
Fung 27 g 15
Funil 52 C 3
Furg 38 G 2
Furillen 17 H 8
Furmanovka 29 F 3
Furmanovo 25 L 1
Furneaux Group 55 b 9
Furnes 15 F 3
Fürstenfeld 13 G 5
Fürth 13 E 4
Fürth 13 D 4
Fusa 27 e 13
Fushih 31 H 3
Fushun 31 M 2
Fu sung 31 N 2
Futa, La 18 C 2
Futa Gialon 35 B 4
Futtsu 27 d 13
Fuyü 31 N 1
Fuyuan 32 D 2
Fyn 16 CD 9
Fyres 16 B 7
Fyresvatn 17 B 7

G

Gabela 36 E 7
Gabes 37 G 3
Gabès, Gulf of 37 G 3
Gabin 13 H 2
Gabon 39 FG 5
Gaborone 41 D 3
Gabras 37 L 7
Gabrat-Sa'id 37 M 6
Gabrehor 38 D 6
Gach Saran 28 M 5
Gadabi 38 C 5
Gadam 39 G 3
Gadames 37 F 3
Gadag 30 C 5
Gador, Sierra de 8 E 5
Gaeta 19 D 4
Gaeta, G. of 18 D 4
Gafdos 20 G 10
Gaffra 37 F 3
Gagnoa 39 C 4
Gagouli 39 D 4
Gagra 25 F 4
Gail 12 E 5
Gaillac 11 F 5
Gaitaler Alps 18 D 1
Gairdner 55 F 6
Gairlock 4 D 3
Gaizina kaln 23 F 6
Gajny 24 H 4
Gajsin 21 I 3
Gal, El- 38 F 5
Galana 34 G 4
Galapago Is. 49 B 4
Galashiels 4 E 4
Galati 21 H 5
Galauag 34 F 2
Galbraith 55 G 3
Galdhopiggen 16 B 6
Galela 34 G 4
Galera, Punta (Chile) 53 B 5
Galera, Punta (Ecuador) 52 A 1
Galic 21 G 3
Galicia 9 C 2
Galite 37 F 2
Galhak 38 B 5
Gallabat 38 C 5
Galladi 38 E 6
Galle 30 D 7
Gallego 8 F 2-3
Gallinas, p.ta 51 B 1
Gallipoli 19 F 4-5
Gallup 46 E 5
Galloway Rhinns-of- 3 D 4
Gallur 9 F 3
Gallura 18 B 4
Galty 3 B 5
Galveston 46 H 7
Galvez 53 D 3
Gam 33 D 2
Gama 53 D/5
Gambaga 39 D/3
Gambela 38 B 6
Gambell 45 D 4
Gambia 37 AB 7
Gambia, River 35 B 4
Gambier 54 O 7
Gamboma 40 B 3
Gambos 41 A 1
Gamkunoro 34 G 4
Gamou 37 B 7
Gamsungi 34 G 4
Gamtoos 41 C 5
Gan 32 AB 1
Ganatcha 37 F 7
Gandak 38 DE 3
Gandia 9 F 4
Ganedidalem 34 G 5
Ganga 30 C 3
Gangan (Argentina) 53 C 5
Gangan (Iran) 29 C 6
Gangara 37 F 7
Gangas de Narcea 9 C 2
Ganges, River 26 M 7
Ganges, Mouths of the 30 EF 4
Gangtok 30 E 3
Ganiadje 40 A 1
Gannet Peak 46 E 4
Gans 35 E 8
Ganta 39 C 4
Gantara 37 E 3
Gao 37 D 6
Gaoua 39 D 3
Gaouar 37 G 3
Gaouy 39 D 4
Gap 11 H 4
Gara 41 C 2
Garad 38 E 6
Garanhuns 52 L 3
Gard 16 G 4
Garda, L. of 18 C 2
Gardanne 11 H 5
Gardelegen 13 D 2
Garden City 46 F 5
Gardez 29 E 5
Gardhar 17 R 12
Gardik 16 F 4
Gardiner 46 D 4

Gardner (Hawaii) 54 L 2
Gardner (Phoenix-Islands) 54 I 5
Garesnica 21 C 5
Garet el-Djenoun 37 F 5
Gargano 18 E 4
Gargano, Testa del- 18 F 4
Gargouna 37 E 6
Gari 24 N 5
Garian 37 G 3
Garian 35 E 2
Garies 41 B 5
Garigliano 18 D 4
Garissa 40 F 3
Galway 3 B 5
Garm 29 F 4
Garmisch 13 D 5
Gärmsar 28 N 3
Garoe 38 F 6
Garondoli 39 G 3
Garonne 10 EF 4
Garoua 39 G 4
Garry L. 42 IL 3
Gartempe 10 F 3
Gartok 31 C 4
Garub 41 B 4
Garut 34 C 6
Gary 46 I 4
Garzon 51 A 3
Gasbi, El- 7 F 3
Gascony 11 EF 5
Gascoyne 54 B 7
Gashun 31 F 3
Gashun Nor 31 G 2
Gaspé 43 O 5
Gaspé, Pen. 44 R 6
Gasper 46 E 4
Gastre 53 C 5
Gata, Cape (Cyprus) 28 B 3
Gata, C. de- (Spain) 8 E 5
Gata, Sierra de- 8 C 3
Gâtaya 21 E 5
Gatcina 23 H 5
Gateshead 4 F 4
Gâtine, Hauteurs de la- 10 E 3
Gatrun, el- 37 G 4
Gatun, el- 37 M 6
Gaubon 37 H 5
Gaucin 9 D 5
Gaud-i-Zirreh 29 D 6
Gaufield 55 b 8
Gauhati 33 A 1
Gauja 16 M 8
Gauko Otavi 41 H 2
Gauri Sangar 31 D 5
Gauss berg 57 e 3
Gausta 16 C 7
Gave de Pau 10 E 5
Gave d'Oloron 10 E 5
Gävle 17 G 6
Gavleborg 17 G 6
Gawler 54 D 8
Gaxsjö 17 F 5
Gaya (India) 30 E 4
Gaya (Niger) 39 E 3
Gaya (Nigeria) 39 F 3
Gayéri 39 E 3
Gaza (Central African Republic) 40 B 2
Gaza (Mozambique) 41 E 3
Gazi 40 C 2
Gaziantep 2 P 8
Gazipasa 28 B 2
Gdansk 17 H 1
Gdansk Bay 17 H 1
Gdov 23 F 5
Gdynia 13 H 1
Geba 39 B 3
Gedaref 38 C 5
Gediz 20 H 8
Gedser Odde 16 DE 9
Geelong 55 a 8
Geelvink Chan. 55 A 5
Geh 29 D 6
Geidam 39 G 3
Geili, El- 37 M 6
Gela 19 E 6
Gela, G. of 18 DE 6
Geladi 38 E 6
Gelda 38 C 5
Gelendzik 25 E 3
Gelibolu 21 H 7
Gemas 33 C 6
Gemerek 25 D 6
Gemlik G. of 20 I 7
Gemiyan 25 C 5
Gen 22 P 3
Geneina, El- 37 I 7
General Alvear 53 C 3
Geneva 11 I 3
Geneva, L. of 10 I 3
Genevad 17 E 8
Genévre, M.¹ 10 I 4
Genicesk 25 C 2
Genil 8 DE 5
Gennale 38 D 7
Gennargentu 19 B 4-5
Genoa 19 B 2
Genoa, Gulf of 19 B 2-3
Genovesa 52 a
Gent 15 F 3
Gente Hermosa 54 I 6
Genteng 34 C 6
Genthin 13 DE 2

Geographe B. 55 B 6
Geographe Chan. 55 A 4
Geokcaj 25 I 5
George, 41 C 5
George, River 42 O 4
George's 55 d 10-11
Georgetown (Gambia) 37 B 7
Georgetown (Guyana) 51 E 2
Georgetown (Cayman-Is.) 48 C 3
Georgetown (USA) 46 M 6
George-V.-Coast 57 Bb 3
George VI-Sound 57 O 3-2
Georgia (USSR) 25 GH 5
Georgia, Reg. (USA) 46 L 6
Georgia, Str. of 44 E 6
Georgia, South 57 m 4
Georgiana 42 MN 5
Georgievsk 25 G 3
Georgin 55 F 4
Gera 13 E 3
Geraldton 55 A 5
Gerania 20 F 8
Gerede 25 B 5
Gereif, El- 37 M 6
Gérgal 9 E 5
Gerid, Shott el- 35 D 2
Gerlachovka 20 E 3
Germany 13 BE 2-4
Germiston 41 D 4
Gerona 9 H 3
Gers 10 F 5
Gertsa 21 H 3
Gerze 25 C 5
Getafe 9 E 3
Geteina, El- 37 M 7
Gevas 28 G 1
Gessjö 17 E 5
Geyik D. 28 B 2
Ghabatel Arab 40 D 1
Ghaidat al-Mahra 38 F 4
Ghail (Saudi Arabia) 38 E 3
Ghail (Yemen) 38 D 4
Ghana 36 C 5
Ghandpur 30 F 4
Ghardaia 37 E 3
Ghat 37 G 4
Ghats, Eastern 26 LM 8
Ghats, Western 26 L 8
Ghaza 28 C 1
Ghazal, Bahr el- 35 EG 4-5
Ghaziabad 30 C 3
Ghazipur 30 D 3
Ghazni 29 E 5
Ghir 37 C 3
Ghisonaccia 11 a
Ghubbat al Qamar 38 F 4
Giamda 31 E 4
Giamna 26 L 7
Giannutri 18 C 3
Giara 22 M 4
Giarre 19 E 6
Gibara 48 D 2
Gibeon 36 E 8
Gibraltar 9 D 5
Gibraltar, Str. of 8 D 5
Gibsonwüste 55 CD 4
Gide 16 H 5
Gien 11 G 3
Giessen 13 C 3
Gifu 32 E 4
Gigantes, Llano de los- 47 D 2
Giggiga 38 D 6
Giglio 18 C 3
Güela 8 E 4
Gijon 9 D 2
Gila 42 H 6
Gila Bend 46 D 6
Gila Des. 46 D 6
Gilan 28 L 2
Gilbert, River 55 G 3
Gilbert, Islands 54 H 4-5
Gilbués 52 H 3
Gilden 16 C 8
Gilehdar 38 F 2
Gilgil 40 F 3
Gilgit 29 F 4
Giljuj 22 N 4
Gimli 44 L 5
Gimma 38 C 6
Gindi 39 F 3
Gingoog 34 G 3
Ginzo de Limia 9 C 2
Giohar 38 E 7
Gioia, G. of 18 E 5
Gioiosa Ionica 19 F 5
Giona 20 F 8
Gioura 20 G 8
Giovi Pass 18 B 2
Girardot 51 B 3
Giresun 25 E 5
Giri 40 B 2
Giridih 30 E 4
Girishk 29 D 5
Giromagny 11 I 3
Gironde 10 E 4
Girvan 4 D 4
Girvin 46 F 6
Gisborne 55 h 13
Gislaved 17 E 8
Giuiuelo 9 D 3
Giur 40 D 1

Giurgiu 21 G 6
Giusanbourg 51 F 3
Givors 11 H 4
Giza, El- 37 M 4
Gjamys, Gora 25 I 5
Gjegnalund 16 A 6
Gjirokastër 21 E 7
Gjovdal 17 C 7
Gjøvik 17 D 6
Gladstone (Western, Australia) 55 A 5
Gladstone (Australia, Queensland) 55 I 4
Gladstone (Canada) 44 L 5
Glafs Fjord 16 E 7
Glama 16 D 6
Glama Jökull 16 Q 12
Glamorgan 3 E 6
Glan 34 G 3
Glan, Lake 16 F 7
Glasgow, (USA) 46 E 3
Glasgow (United Kingdom) 4 D 3-4
Glauchau 13 E 3
Glava 17 E 7
Glendive 46 F 3
Glenfield 55 d 10
Glenhope 55 g 14
Glen Innes 55 I 5
Glen More 4 D 3
Glenmorgan 55 H 5
Glenora 44 C 4
Glenties 4 B 4
Glenwood Springs 46 E 5
Glina 20 BC 5
Glittertind 16 C 6
Gliwice 13 H 3
Globe 46 D 6
Glogow 13 G 3
Gloria 52 L 3
Glorieuses, Iles- 41 c 6
Glossa, C. 20 D 7
Glotovo 24 E 5
Gloucester 4 E 6
Gossen 17 B 5
Glubokoe 23 F 7
Glusitsa, Bol'saja- 24 F 8
Gmunden 13 EF 5
Gnarp 17 G 6
Gnivan' 21 I 3
Gnjilane 21 E 6
Goa 30 B 5
Goodenough 57 c 3
Goagib 41 B 4
Goatpara 30 F 3
Goba (Ethiopia) 38 D 6
Goba (Mozambique) 41 E 4
Gobabis 41 B 3
Gober 37 F 7
Gobi 31 HI 2
Goce Delcev 21 F 7
Gochas 41 B 3
Gocong 33 D 4
Godavari 26 LM 8
Goddo 51 E 3
Goddua 37 G 4
Godeanu 21 F 5
Goderich 44 O 7
Godhavn 44 U 2
Godhdalir 17 S 12
Gödöllő 21 D 4
Godthab 44 U 3
Gogan 28 H 2
Goggiam 36 G 4
Gogra 30 D 3
Gogrial 40 D 1
Goi 27 e 13
Goiana 52 L 3
Goiania 52 H 5
Goianinha 52 L 3
Goias, Town 52 G 5
Goias, State 52 H 3-5
Goila 39 G 4
Gojam 36 G 4
Gök 1 O 8
Gökbel 20 I 9
Gokcal 1 R 7
Goksü 25 G 6
Gol 17 C 6
Golaghat 33 A 1
Gol'cikha 22 H 2
Goldap 13 L 1
Goldberg 13 DE 2
Gold Coast 39 DE 5
Goléa, El- 37 E 3
Golerum 30 D 6
Golija Planina 20 E 6
Golo 18 B 3
Goloe 25 E 1
Golosa, Pena- 8 F 3
Golovanevsk 25 A 1
Goma 40 D 3
Gomba 39 E 3
Gombe 39 G 3
Gomel' 23 H 8
Gomera 37 A 4
Gomez Palacio 47 D 2
Gomo Selung 31 D 4
Gonaïves 48 E 3
Gonam, River 22 NO 4
Gonâve 48 E 3
Gondar 38 C 6
Gondia 30 D 4
Gondokoro 40 E 2
Gondvana 26 LM 7
Gönen 21 H 7
Gönen 20 H 7

Gongola 39 G 3
Goodenough 55 I 1
Good Hope, Cape of 41 B 5
Goondwindi 55 I 5
Gooty 30 C 5
Gor 16 E 6
Gorakhpur 30 D 3
Goran, El- 38 D 6
Gorazde 21 D 6
Gordino 24 G 5
Gordium 25 AB 6
Gordon Dows 55 D 3
Goré (Chad) 40 B 1
Gore (Ethiopia) 38 C 6
Gorgol 37 B 6
Gorgona 18 B 3
Gori 25 H 5
Gorizia 19 D 2
Gorjanci 20 B 5
Gorka 24 D 3
Gorki 23 H 7
Gorki (Niznij-Novgorod) 24 B 6
Gorlice 13 I 4
Görlitz 13 F 3
Gorlovka 25 E 1
Gornalunga 18 E 6
Gornyj Tikic 20 L 3
Goro (New Zealand) 55 f 15
Gorodets 24 B 6
Gorodisce 25 E 1
Gorodok 23 GH 7
Gorontalo 34 F 4
Gorori 39 G 4
Gorouol 39 E 3
Gorrahei 38 D 6
Gort 4 B 5
Goryn' 21 H 2
Gorzow Wielk. 13 F 2
Gosainthan 31 D 5
Gospic 21 B 5
Gosport 4 F 6
Gossen 17 B 5
Gossinga 40 D 1
Gota 16 E 8
Gotaland, 17 EF 8
Göteborg 17 D 8
Gotha 13 D 3
Gothem 17 H 8
Gotska Sancö 16 H 7
Göttingen 13 C 3
Gottwaldov 21 C 3
Gouande 39 E 3
Goubere 40 E 1
Gough 36 C 9
Gougoufema 37 E 7
Goulburn 55 H 6
Goulfeï 37 H 7
Goulimine 37 B 4
Goumbou 37 C 6
Gounda 40 C 1
Goundi 40 B 1
Gouradi 37 H 6
Gourao 37 D 6
Gourara 37 E 4
Gouré 37 G 7
Gouritz 35 F 9
Gouro 37 I 6
Goverla 20 G 3
Goya 52 F 7
Goz Beïda 37 I 7
Goz Regeb 38 C 4
Gozo 18 DE 6
Graaff Reinet 41 C 5
Grabbevsk 25 G 2
Grabtovy 22 G 4
Gracac 21 B 5
Gracanica 21 D 5
Gracias a Dios, Puerto Cabo- 48 C 4
Gracias a Dios 48 C 3
Graciosa (Canarias Is.) 37 B 4
Graciosa (Azores) 37 a
Gradaus 52 G 3
Graddis 17 F 3
Gradizsk 25 B 1
Grado (Italy) 19 D 2
Grado (Spain) 9 C 2
Grafton 55 I 5
Graham, I. 44 C 5
Graha Land 57 On 3
Graham, Mts. 46 E 6
Graham Bell, I. 22 F 1
Grahamstall 41 D 5
Graian Alps 19 A 2
Graiba 37 G 3
Grain Coast 39 BC 4-5
Grajau 52 H 3
Gramat 11 F 4
Grampian Mts. 3 DE 3
Granada (Nicaragua) 48 B 4
Granada (Spain) 9 E 5
Grand Bahama 48 D 1
Grand Bahama Bank 48 D 1-2
Grand Bank 44 T 6
Gran Canaria 26 P 6
Gran Canaria 37 A 4
Gran Chaco 49 DE 6
Grand Canal 13 C 5
Grand Canal (China) 31 L 3
Grand Canyon 46 D 5
Grand Cayman 48 C 3
Grand Cess 39 C 5

Grande, R. (Nicaragua) 48 BC 4
Grande, Riv. (Brazil, Minas Geiras) 52 GH 5-6
Grande R. (Brazil, Bahia) 52 I 4
Grande, R. (USA) 46 EG 5-7
Grande Comore 41 B 6
Grande de Santiago, R. 47 CD 3
Grand Forks 46 G 3
Grand-Island 46 G 4
Grand Junction 46 E 5
Grand Lahou 39 D 4
Grand Morin 10 G 2
Grand Popo 39 E 4
Grand Rapids 46 I 4
Grand River 46 E 5
Grängesberg 17 F 6
Grangeville 46 C 3
Granite Peak 46 D 3
Granitola, Cape 18 D 6
Gran Karru 35 F 9
Gran Malvina 53 D 7
Gränna 17 F 7
Gran Nama 35 E 8
Granö 17 H 4
Gran Paradiso 18 A 2
Gran Sandy 55 I 5
Gran Sasso d'Italia 18 DE 3
Grant, Land 43 MN 1
Grantham 4 F 5
Granvik 17 L 4
Granville (Australia) 55 e 10
Granville (France) 11 E 2
Gran Wollongong 55 I 6
Grao Mogol 52 I 5
Graon 11 E 3
Grappa, Mt. 18 CD 2
Graret el Merba 37 H 3
Graskop 41 E 3
Gras Kop, Mt. 41 C 4
Grasse 11 I 5
Grassö 16 H 6
Grave, Pte de- 10 E 4
Gravelines 11 G 1
Gravina di Puglia 19 EF 4
Graz 13 F 5
Great Barrier I. 55 h 13
Great Barrier Reef 55 GH 2-3
Great Basin 42 H 5-6
Great Bear Lake 44 EF 2
Great Bernera 4 C 2
Great Britain 3 FH 3-5
Great Detached Reef 55 G 2
Great Dividing Range 54 E 7-8
Great Eastern Erg 35 CD 2-3
Great Falls, 46 D 3
Great Fish, River 41 D 5
Great Kei, 41 D 5
Great Namaland 41 B 4
Great Salt Lake 46 D 4
Great Slave Lake 44 FG 3
Great S. Bernard 18 A 2
Great Wall, The 31 IL 1
Great Western Erg 35 CD 2-3
Great Whale 44 P 5
Great Yarmouth 4 G 5
Grebbestad 17 D 7
Greece 21 EG 7-9
Green 46 E 4
Green Bay 46 I 4
Greenland 43 Q 2-3
Greenock 4 D 4
Greenough 55 B 5
Green River 46 I 5
Greensboro 46 M 5
Greenville (USA, Mississippi) 46 H 6
Greenville (USA, South Carolina) 46 L 6
Greenville (USA, Texas) 46 G 6
Greenwich 4 G 6
Greenwille 39 C 4
Gregory 55 F 3
Gregory Salt L. 55 D 4
Greifswald 13 E 2
Greiz 13 E 3
Greko, Cape 28 B 3
Grena 17 D 8
Grenada 46 I 6
Grenada, Islands 48 G 4
Grenoble 11 H 4
Gresik 34 D 6
Grey Range 55 G 5
Greytown (Nicaragua) 48 C 4
Greytown (South Africa) 41 E 4
Griba 20 D 7
Grieff 4 E 3
Griffith 55 H 6
Grigoriopol 21 I 4
Grijalva 47 F 4
Grim 55 a 9
Grimes 54 E 5
Grimma 13 E 3
Grimsby 4 F 5
Grimsey, I. 17 S 11
Grimshaw 44 F 4
Grimstad 17 C 7
Griquatown 41 C 4

Gris Nez 14 E 3
Griva (Soviet Union, Komi) 24 F 4
Griva (Soviet Union lettland) 23 F 7
Grizim 37 D 4
Grjazavets 23 D 5
Grmec Planina 21 C 5
Grobina 17 I 8
Grodekovo 31 O 2
Grodro 23 D 8
Groix 10 D 3
Gromer 4 G 5
Gron Fjeld 16 F 4
Groningen 15 H 2
Groote Eylandt 55 F 2
Grootfontein (Namibia) 41 B 4
Grootfontein (Namibia) 41 B 2
Groot Winter Berg 41 D 5
Grossa 21 B 6
Grosse Arabische Wüste (Rub al-Khali) 38 EF 3
Grosseto 19 C 3
Grossevichi 32 E 2
Grossvenediger 12 E 5
Grotli 17 B 5
Gröto 17 H 1
Groumania 39 D 4
Groznyy 25 H 4
Grudziadz 13 H 2
Grue 17 E 6
Grundorn 41 B 4
Gruzino 23 H 5
Grythyttan 17 F 7
Grytöy 17 G 2
Grytten 17 B 5
Guacaraje 52 E 4
Guadalajara (Mexico) 47 D 3
Guadalajara (Spain) 9 E 3
Guadalcanal (Spain) 9 D 5
Guadalcanal (Salomon Is.) 54 FG 5
Guacalete 8 D 5
Guacalhorce 8 D 5
Guacalimar 8 E 4
Guacalmena 9 E 4
Guacalope 8 F 3
Guacalquivir 8 CE 5
Guaceloupe Island 50 D 2
Guadalupe 9 D 4
Guadalupe 42 GH 7
Guadalupe, Sierra de- 8 D 4
Guadarrama, Puerto de- 8 D 3
Guadarrama, Sierra de- 8 DE 3
Guadiana 8 CD 4
Guadiato 8 D 4-5
Guadiela 9 E 3
Guadix 9 E 5
Guania 51 C 3
Guajara-Mirim 52 D 4
Guajira 49 C 2
Guala 39 C 4
Gualaquiza 52 B 2
Gualeguaychu 53 E 3
Guallatiri 52 D 5
Guam 54 E 3
Guama 52 H 2
Guanabacoa 48 C 2
Guanabara 52 C 4
Guanahani 48 E 2
Guanajuato 47 D 3
Guanare 51 C 2
Guanarito 51 C 2
Guane 48 C 2
Guantanamo 48 D 2
Guaoé 51 A 3
Guaooré 49 D 5
Guaqui 52 D 5
Guara 39 F 4
Guara, Sierra de- 8 F 2
Guaranda 52 B 2
Guarapuava 52 F 7
Guardia Sanframondi 19 E 4
Guardo 9 D 2
Guarico 51 C 2
Guarnacevi 47 C 2
Guasipati 51 D 2
Guastalla 19 C 2
Guatemala 43 L 8
Guaviare 49 C 3
Guaxupé 52 H 6
Guayabero 51 B 3
Guayamas 47 B 2
Guayaquil 52 B 2
Guayaquil, Gulf of 52 A 2
Gucakha 24 I 5
Gubba 38 C 5
Gubdor 24 I 4
Guben 13 F 3
Guble 25 B 5
Gudar, Sierra de- 8 F 3
Gudbrands 17 CD 6
Gudermes 25 I 4
Gudhjem 17 F 9
Guduk 28 N 3
Gudur 30 C 5
Gudziunai 17 L 9
Guéchédou 39 C 4

Gueleba 39 C 4
Guémar 37 F 3
Guer 11 D 3
Guerche, La- 11 E 3
Guercif 37 D 3
Guéret 11 G 3
Guernsey 4 E 2
Guerrara 37 E 3
Guettara, El- 37 D 5
Guguan 54 E 3
Guiana 50 E 3
Guiglo 39 C 4
Guildford 4 F 6
Guilherme Capelo 40 A 4
Guimaraes, 52 I 2
Guimaras 34 F 2
Guinea 36 BC 4-5
Guinea-Bissau 36 B 4
Guinea, Gulf of 35 CD 5-6
Guinea, Equatorial 36 E 5
Guinguinéo 37 A 7
Guinou 40 C 1
Guirel 37 C 6
Gujan 11 E 4
Gujarat 26 IL 7
Gujiba 39 G 3
Gujranwala 30 B 2
Gujur 29 C 5
Gulbarga 30 C 5
Gulbi 39 F 3
Gullabo 17 F 8
Gullera 9 F 4
Gulpaigan 28 M 4
Gulu 40 E 2
Gumel 39 F 3
Gumishan 28 N 2
Gummersbach 13 B 3
Gummi 39 F 3
Gumti 30 D 3
Gumurgina 21 G 7
Gümüsane 25 E 5
Guna 30 C 4
Güney 21 I 8
Gunnison 46 E 5
Guntur 30 D 5
Gunung 34 A 4
Gurban Sayhan 31 G 2
Guardaspur 30 C 2
Gurev 25 M 2
Gurgieia 52 I 3
Guriev 22 I 3
Gurla Mandhata 31 C 4
Guromer 28 H 2
Gürün 25 D 6
Gurupa 52 G 2
Gurupi 52 H 2
Guru-Sikhar 30 B 3
Gusau 39 F 3
Gusev 17 L 9
Gusiatin 21 H 3
Güstrow 13 E 2
Gutersloh 13 C 3
Guthrie 46 G 5
Guayana 50 DE 2
Guyenne 11 EG 4
Guzar 29 E 4
Gwaai 41 D 2
Gwada 12 G 2
Gwadar 29 D 6
Gwadi 41 D 3
Gwalior (Lashkar) 30 C 3
Gwanda 41 D 3
Gwangju 31 N 3
Gweru 41 D 2
Gwona 39 G 4
Gyachung Kang 26 p 16
Gyangtse 31 D 5
Gydan 26 TU 3
Gydan Peninsula 22 GH 2
Gympie 55 I 5
Gyöngyös 21 D 4
Györ 21 C 4
Gypsumville 44 L 5
Gyula 21 E 4
Gzatsk 23 L 7

H

Haapajärvi 17 M 5
Haapavesi 17 M 4
Haapsalu 17 L 7
Haakon VII.- Land 56 a
Haardt 12 BC 4
Haarlem 15 G 2
Hab 29 E 6
Habaswein 40 G 2
Habbaniya 28 G 4
Habbaniya, Lake 28 G 4
Haboro 32 F 3
Hacha 37 H 6
Hachijo 32 E 5
Hachinohe 32 F 3
Hachioji 32 E 4
Hacking 55 e 11
Hadarba 38 C 3
Hadd 29 C 7
Hadda 38 C 3
Haddar 38 E 3
Haddington 4 E 4
Hadejia 39 G 3
Hadejia, River 39 FG 3
Haderslev 17 C 9
Haditha 28 G 3

Hadibu 38 F 5
Hadiya 38 C 2
Hadjar, Hassi el- 37 E 3
Hadsel 17 F 2
Hadslöya 17 F 2
Haeju 31 N 3
Hafert el-Jebbi 37 B 4
Hafsto 17 B 6
Häft Kel 28 L 5
Hafun 38 F 5
Hagari 30 C 5-6
Hagemeister 45 F 5
Hagen 13 I 2
Hagerstown 46 M 5
Häggenas 17 F 5
Hagi 32 D 5
Hagion Oros 20 FG 7
Hagira, El- 37 F 3
Haguenau 11 I 2
Hahot 21 C 4
Haid 40 E 1
Haifa 28 C 4
Haig 55 D 6
Haikang 31 I 6
Hail 28 F 7
Haiya 38 C 4
Hai yang 31 M 3
Hajar 38 E 5
Hajara 38 D 2
Hajdúböszörmény 21 E 4
Hakodate 32 F 3
Halabja 28 H 3
Halaib 38 C 3
Halanneso 20 G 8
Halba 28 C 4
Halberstadt 13 D 3
Halde Field 16 I 2
Halden 16 D 7
Halditstjokko 17 I 2
Halfa 37 LM 5
Hali 21 E 4
Halifax (Canada) 44 S 7
Halifax (United Kingdom) 4 F 5
Halima 37 L 3
Haliri 29 C 6
Hall I. (Alaska) 45 D 4
Hall I. (Caroline Is.) 54 F 4
Hall 44 R 3
Halland Kristjanstad 17 EF 8-9
Hallat'Ammar 28 D 6
Halle 13 D 3
Hallefors 17 F 7
Hallingdal 17 C 6
Hallingdals 16 C 6
Hallingskarv 16 B 6
Hall's Creek 55 D 3
Halmahera 34 G 4
Halmstad 17 E 8
Halsa 17 C 5
Haltalen 17 D 5
Hama 2 P 8
Hamada, El- 37 DE 3
Hamada d'Issaouan 37 F 4
Hamada el Hamra 37 G 4
Hamada el Haricha 37 D 5
Hamadan 28 L 3
Hamamatsu 32 E 5
Hamar 17 D 6
Hamata 37 M 5
Hamborn 13 B 3
Hamburg (West Germany) 13 D 2
Hamburg (South Africa) 41 D 5
Hamdall 37 B 7
Hämeenlinna 17 M 46
Hamelin Pool 55 A 5
Halmen 13 C 2
Hamersley 55 B 4
Hamersley Range 55 B 4
Ha mi 31 E 2
Hamilton (Australia) 55 G 7
Hamilton (Canada) 44 P 7
Hamilton (United Kingdom) 4 D 4
Hamilton (New Zealand) 55 h 13
Hamilton (USA, Montana) 46 D 3
Hamilton, River (Canada) 44 S 5
Hamilton Inlet 44 T 5
Hamina (Fredrikshamn) 23 F 4
Hamm 13 B C 3
Hammam, El- 37 L 3

Hammamet 37 G 2
Hammamet, Gulf of 37 G 2
Hammami 37 B 5
Hammar, Lake 28 I 5
Hammerfest 17 L 1
Hammeröy 17 F 2
Hamoyet 38 C 4
Hamra, El- 37 F 3
Hamra, Saguia el- 35 B 3
Hamre 17 H 1
Hamun-i-Jaz Murian 29 C 6
Hamun-i-Mashkel 29 D 6
Hamun-i-Sabari 29 D 5
Hamurre, El- 38 E 6
Han 31 HI 4
Hanau 13 C 3
Hanceville 44 E 5
Hanchou 31 I 5
Handa 4 D 2
Handeni 40 F 4
Hangana 37 H 6
Hangay 31 F 1
Hang chou 31 M 4
Hangö 17 L 7
Hango 16 L 7
Hangöudde 16 L 7
Hangshan 31 I 6
Hanha 41 A 1
Han Hai 26 MO 5-6
Hank, El- 37 C 5
Hänkasalmi 17 N 5
Hanko 17 L 7
Hannibal 46 H 5
Hanno 27 d 13
Hanö Bay 16 F 8-9
Hanoi 33 D 2
Hanover 13 CD 2
Hanover, Island 53 A 7
Hanstholm 16 C 8
Hantelo 31 L 1
Hantsville 46 G 6
Hao 54 O 6
Haouach 37 I 6
Haoul 37 F 3
Haouz 37 C 3
Haparanda 17 M 4
Hara 40 G 3
Hara Irtish 31 D 1
Harak 38 C 2
Haram 17 B 5
Hara Nor 31 F 3
Hara Nur 31 E 1
Harar 38 D 6
Harardera 38 E 7
Härauabad 28 L 2
Hara Usa Nur 31 E 1
Harazé 37 H 7
Harbin 31 N 1
Harbo 39 F 3
Harburg 13 C 2
Hardang 17 B 6
Hardanger Fjell 16 B 6-7
Harding 41 D 5
Hare 17 E 7
Hareidland 16 A 5
Haret Zueia 37 I 5
Hargeisa 38 D 6
Harghita Mts. 20 G 4
Hari (Afghanistan) 29 DE 4-5
Hari (Sumatra) 34 B 5
Härjehagna 16 E 6
Harju 17 N 6
Hårlau 21 H 4
Harlingen 15 G 2
Harlösa 17 E 9
Harmanger 17 G 6
Harnosand 17 G 5
Haro 9 E 2
Harold Byrd, Monti- 57 R 1
Haroy 17 B 5
Harper 39 C 5
Harput 25 E 6
Harran 28 E 2
Harrisburg 46 M 4
Harrismith 41 D 4
Harstad 17 G 2
Harsyssel 17 C 8
Hartberg 3 F 5
Harteig 17 B 6
Hartford 46 N 4
Hartkiölen 17 E 4
Hartland Point 13 D 6
Harare 41 E 2
Hartola 17 N 6
Hartso 17 G 7
Harudj el-Aswad 37 H 4
Harut, 29 D 5
Harvasstua 17 F 4
Harvey 46 B 5
Harwich 4 G 6
Harz 12 D 3
Hasankak 25 F 6
Hasan Kuli 29 B 4
Hasantu 31 H 2
Hasdo 30 D 4
Hase 12 B 2
Hasi 20 H 7
Hasi Dogma 37 B 4
Hasi Dumus 37 B 5
Hasiheisa 38 B 5
Hasi Ma ata Al-lah 37 A 5
Hasi Tirakli 37 B 4
Haskovo 21 G 7

Hassan 30 C 6
Hassela 17 G 5
Hasselfors 17 F 7
Hassi Aflisses 37 E 4
Hassi el-Khenig 37 E 4
Hassi Inifel 37 E 4
Hassi Messaud 37 F 3
Hassi Msegguem 37 E 4
Hassi Rimel 37 E 3
Hassi Tartrat 37 F 3
Hastings (United Kindgom) 4 G 6
Hastings (New Zealand) 55 h 13
Hastings (USA, Nebraska) 46 G 4
Hateg 21 F 5
Hathras 30 C 3
Hatia 27 b 11
Hatiba 38 C 3
Ha-Tien 33 C 4
Hatinh 33 D 3
Hatteras 46 M 5
Hattfjelldal 17 E 4
Hattiesburg 46 I 6
Hatun Bulak 31 H 2
Hauberg 57 o 2
Haugesund 17 A 7
Haukipudas 17 M 4
Haura 38 E 5
Hauran 1 Q 9
Hausa 38 C 2
Hauta 38 E 3
Havana 48 C 2
Havel 12 E 2
Havelberg 12 D 2
Haverö 17 F 5
Havre (Brazil) 52 C 3
Havre (USA, Mont.) 46 E 3
Havre, Le- 11 F 2
Hawaii (Sandwich) 54 IM 2-3
Hawick 4 E 4
Hay (Australia) 55 G 6
Hay, Riv. (Australia) 55 F 4
Hay (Canada) 44 F 3-4
Haydarpasa 21 I 7
Haymet 34 L 7
Hay River 44 F 3
Hays 46 G 5
Hazard Hills 44 M 2-3
Hazaribagh 30 E 4
Hazelton 44 D 4
Healdsburg 46 B 5
Heany 41 D 3
Hearst 57 O 3
Hebeke, El- 38 D 2
Hebrides 4 C 2-3
Hebrides, Sea of the 4 C 3
Hebron (Canada) 44 S 4
Hebron (Israel) 28 B 1
Hecate Strait 44 C 5
Hedal 17 C 6
Hede 17 E 5
Hedemora 17 G 6
Hedmark 17 D 5-6
Heerenveen 15 G 2
Heerlen 15 G 3
Hegyalja 20 E 3
Hei 31 G 3
Heide 13 C 1
Heidelberg 13 C 4
Heilbronn 13 C 4
Heiligenstadt 13 CD 3
Heilung Chiang 31 NO 1
Heim 17 C 5
Hoa binh 33 D 2
Heinola 17 N 6
Hejaz 37 I 3
Hekla 16 S 13
Helena (USA, Ark.) 46 H 6
Helena (USA, Mont.) 46 D 3
Helgea 16 F 8
Helgun 17 G 5
Heligoland 13 BC 1
Helikon 20 F 8
Hellenthal 13 B 3
Hellin 9 F 4
Hellville 41 c 6
Helmond 15 G 3
Helmsdale 4 E 2
Helsingfors 17 M 6
Helsinki 17 M 6
Helwan 37 M 4
Hemne 17 C 5
Hemnes 17 E 3
Hemsedal 17 C 6
Hemsö 17 H 5
Henares 9 E 3
Hendaye 11 E 5
Henderson (Antarctica) 57 E 3
Henderson (Polynesia) 54 P 7
Hendeyan 28 L 5
Heng chun 31 M 6
Hengelo 15 H 2
Heng hsien 31 H 6
Heng Men 27 f 15
Heng Shan 26 P 7
Hengyang 31 I 5
Henrietta Maria, Cape 44 O 4
Hentey 31 H 1
Henzada 33 B 3
Heppner 46 C 3
Hola 40 G 3
Holar 17 S 12
Heras, Colonia Las- 53 C 6

Herat 29 D 5
Hérault 10 G 5
Herberton 55 H 3
Herby 13 H 3
Herdubreidh, Mt. 17 T 12
Héréhérétué, Island 54 N 6
Herentals 15 G 3
Herford 13 C 2
Herki 28 H 2
Hermosillo 47 B 2
Hernandarias 52 G 7
Hernad, 20 E 3
Herning 17 C 8
Heröy 17 E 4
Herrera del Duque 9 D 4
Herrero, Punta 47 G 4
Hers, 11 F 5
Hersfeld 13 C 3
Hertford 4 F 6
Hertogenbosch, 's- 15 G 3
Hervas 9 D 3
Hervey 55 I 5
Hervey Bay 55 I 5
Hervey, Island 54 LM 6-7
Herzegovina 21 CD 6
Hessen 13 C 3-4
Heungnam 31 N 3
Hiamma, Mt. 45 H 4
Hida 21 F 4
Hierro, I. 37 A 4
High Atlas 35 C 2
High Willhays, Mt. 4 E 6
Highwood, Mt. 46 D 3
Hiiumaa 23 D 5
Hijar 9 F 3
Hilal, Ras el-, c. 37 I 3
Hildesheim 13 C-D 2
Hilla 28 H 4
Hillesöy 17 H 2
Hillsboro 46 E 6
Hilversum 15 G 2
Himalaya 26 LN 6-7
Himanka 17 L 4
Himeji 32 D 5
Himmerland 17 C 8
Hindubagh 29 E 5
Hindu Kush, Mt. 26 IL 6
Hindupur 30 C 6
Hingol, 29 E 6
Hingol 30 C 5
Hingshanchen 31 O 1
Hinis 25 F 6
Hinlopen, Strait 56 a
Hinnöy, Mt. 17 F 2
Hinojosa del Duque 9 D 4
Hirosaki 32 F 3
Hiroshima 32 D 5
Hîrsova 21 H 5
Hirtshals 16 C 8
Hiruga, Mt. 27 d 13
Hisar 28 M 6
Hissar 30 C 3
Hitoyoshi 32 D 5
Hitra, Island 16 C 5
Hiva Oa, Island 54 N 5
Hjälmaren, L. 17 FG 7
Hjelle 17 B 7
Hjelmeland 17 B 7
Hjelmsöy 17 M 1
Hjorring 17 C 8
Ho 39 E 4
Hoa binh 33 D 2
Hoachanas 41 B 3
Hobart 55 b 9
Hobbs, Coast 57 r 2
Hobdo (Jargalant) 31 E 1
Hobdo, River 31 E 1
Hobi, Island 32 B 6
Hobsogol 31 F 1
Hobya 38 E 6
Hochgolling 12 EF 5
Hochschwab, Mt. 13 F 5
Hochuan 31 H 4
Hodeida 38 D 5
Hodh 37 C 6
Hodmezövasarhely 21 E 4
Hoerwong 31 N 2
Hof (Iceland) 17 T 13
Hof (West Germany) 13 D 3
Ho fei 31 L 4
Hofmeyr 41 D 5
Hofraten-Nahas 40 C 1
Hofs Jökull 16 S 12
Hofteren 17 A 6
Hofuf 38 E 2
Hoganäs 17 E 8
Höggi, Mt. 16 D 5
Hogheden 17 G 3
Högtuvbre, Mt. 16 E 3
Hohe Acht 12 B 3
Hohe Rhon 13 CD 3
Hohes Venn, Mt. 14 H 3
Hohe Tauern 12 E 5
Hohsien 31 I 6
Hojo 27 d 13
Hokang 31 O 1
Hokitika 55 g 14
Hokkaido, Islands 32 F 3
Hola 40 G 3
Holar 17 S 12
Holbäk 17 D 9

Holdich 53 C 6
Holdrege 46 G 4
Holguin 48 D 2
Holic 21 C 3
Holland 14 G 2
Hollandia 54 E 5
Hollick Kenyon, Mts. 57 Q 2
Hollywood 46 C 6
Holmavik 17 R 12
Holmes Reefs, Island 55 H 3
Holmestrana 17 D 7
Holmö 17 I 5
Holmö, Island 16 I 5
Holmsund 17 I 5
Holon 28 C 5
Holsatia 41 A 3
Holstebro 17 C 8
Holstensborg 44 U 2
Holyhead 4 D 5
Holyhead, Cape 3 D 5
Holzminden 13 C 3
Homalin 33 B 2
Hombori 37 D 6
Home Bay 44 R 2
Homestead 46 L 7
Hommel, Mt. 16 D 5
Homs (Libya) 37 G 3
Homs (Syria) 2 P 9
Hon 37 H 4
Honan, 31 IL 4
Honda 51 B 2
Hondeklip 41 B 5
Hondo, Island 32 DE 3-4
Honduras 43 M 8
Honduras, Gulf of 47 G 4
Hönefoss 17 D 6
Höng Kong 31 I 6
Hong Kong, Island 27 g 15
Hongor Obo 31 G 2
Hongu 26 p 17
Hongu Khola 26 p 17
Honhom 47 G 3
Hon Khoi 33 D 4
Honolulu 54 M 2
Hon Quan 33 D 4
Honshu, Island 32 DE 3-4
Hoogly, Island 30 E 4
Hoopstad 41 D 4
Hoorn 15 G 2
Hopa 25 F 5
Hope 44 E 6
Hope, Ben-, Mt. 3 D 2
Hope, Pt. 45 E 3
Hopedale 44 S 4
Ho pei, 31 IL 3
Hope Mine 41 B 3
Hopetoun 55 C 6
Hopkins, Lake 55 E 4
Hopu 31 H 6
Horcajo del Minas 9 D 4
Hordaland, 17 AB 6
Hordio 38 F 5
Hormuz 38 G 2
Hormuz, Strait of 29 C 6
Horn 13 F 4
Horn, Cape (Chile) 49 D 9
Horn C. (Iceland) 16 V 12
Horn Avan, 16 GH 3
Hörnefors 17 H 5
Hornisgrinde, Mt. 18 C 4
Hornsburg 55 e 10
Hornsland 17 G 6
Horqueta 52 F 6
Horsens 17 C 9
Horseshoe 55 B 5
Horsham 4 F 6
Hortens, fj. 17 D 4
Horyn, 20 GH 2-3
Hosanna 38 C 6
Hosap 28 G 1
Hoshab 29 D 6
Hoshangabad 30 C 4
Hoshihmiao 31 L 1
Hoste, Island 53 C 7
Hotagen 17 F 5
Hotagen, River 16 F 5
Hotien 31 B 3
Hotseh 31 L 3
Hotsin 31 I 3
Hot Springs 46 H 6
Hou, 33 C 2-3
Houlton 46 O 3
Houma 46 H 7
Hourtin Etang d' 11 E 4
Houston 46 G 7
Hovden 17 B 7
Howar 37 I-L 6
Howard, L. 44 H 3
Howe, Cape 55 C 8
Howland, Island 54 I 4
Howrah 30 E 4
Hoy, Island 3 E 2
Hoya 13 C 2
Höylandet 17 D 4
Hoyüan 31 I 6
Hozat 25 E 6
Hradec Kralové 21 B 2
Hranice 21 C 3
Hron, 20 D 3
Hsi, 27 f 15
Hsiao 30 C 3
Hsiaho 31 G 3
Hsiamen 31 L 6
Hsiangshan, Island 27 f 15
Hsiang tan 31 I 5
Hsiangyang 31 I 4

Hsiang yün 31 G 5
Hsiao Hsingan Shan, Mt. 32 C 1-2
Hsiapu 31 M 5
Hsiating 31 L 3
Hsichang 31 G 5
Hsi hsiang 27 f 15
Hsi ku 31 G 4
Hsi lung 31 H 6
Hsin chu 31 M 6
Hsing hsing hsia 31 F 2
Hsingi 31 H 5
Hsing tai 31 I 3
Hsin hailien 31 L 4
Hsin hsu 27 g 15
Hsin hui ku chih 27 f 15
Hsin i 31 I 6
Hsi ning 31 G 3
Hsi ning, River 31 G 3
Hsin Kao, Mt. 31 M 6
Hsin tang 27 f 14
Hsin ti 31 I 5
Hsin tsao 27 f 14
Hsipaw 33 B 2
Hsiwuchumuchin 31 L 2
Hsuan cheng 31 L 4
Hsü chang 31 I 4
Hsüchou 31 L 4
Hsü pu 31 I 5
Hsü wen 31 I 6
Hsü yung 31 H 5
Huacho 52 B 4
Huai ho, 26 P 6
Huaitara 52 B 4
Huai yang 31 I 4
Huai yin 31 L 4
Huajuapan 47 E 4
Hua lien 31 M 6
Huallaga 52 B 3
Huallanca 52 B 3
Huambo (Nova-Lisboa) 40 B 5
Huancabamba 52 B 3
Huancané 52 D 5
Huancavelica 52 C 4
Huancayo 52 B 4
Huang (Yellow River) 31 L 3
Huang chuang 31 L 4
Huang Hai 31 M 3
Huang ho 26 NP 6
Huang pu 27 f 14
Huang yuan 31 G 3
Huanta 52 C 4
Huantze Hu 31 L 4
Huanuco 52 B 3
Huaras 52 B 3
Huarmey 52 B 4
Huarusib 41 A 2
Huascaran, Mt. 49 C 4
Huasco 53 B 2
Hua ti 27 f 15
Hubli 30 C 5
Huddersfield 4 F 5
Hudiksvall 17 G 6
Hudson Bay 44 MO 3-4
Hudson, River 46 N 4
Hudson 57 p 2
Hudson Strait 44 QR 3
Hué 33 D 3
Huebra 9 C 3
Huecu, El- 53 B 4
Huejutla 47 E 3
Huelva 9 CM45
Huelva 9 C 5
Huelva 9 C 5
Huércal Overa 9 F 5
Huesca 9 F 2
Huetamo 47 D 4
Huete 9 E 3
Hughenden 55 G 4
Hugija, Islands 38 E 2
Huh-Hoto 31 I 2
Huichon 31 N 2
Huila 41 A 1
Huila, Nevado del-, Mt. 51 A 3
Hui li 31 G 5
Huimin 31 L 3
Huisne 10 F 2
Hui tse 31 G 5
Huiyang 31 I 6
Hu kou 31 L 5
Hu lan 31 N 1
Hu lin 31 O 1
Hull 44 P 6
Hull, Islands (Phoenix Is.) 54 I 5
Hull, Island (Maria - Is.) 54 M 7
Hull, Mt. 46 B 5
Hultsfred 17 F 8
Hulun (Hailar) 31 L 1
Huma 22 N 4
Humahuaca 53 C 1
Humaita 52 E 3
Humansdorf 41 C 5
Humber 3 F 5
Humberto de Campos 52 I 2
Humboldt, River 46 C 4
Humboldt, Mt. 54 G 7
Hu men, Town 27 f 15
Hu Men, Bay 27 f 15
Humphrey Point 45 L 3
Huna floi 16 R 12
Hunan 31 I 5

Hun chun 31 O 2
Hundujia 47 E 4
Hungarian Plain 20 DE4
Hungary 21 CE3-4
Hungerford 55 G 5
Hung shui 31 H 5
Hunö 17 a
Hunsruck 12 B4
Hunte 12 C 2
Huntingdon 4 F 5
Huntington 46 L 5
Huntly 4 E 3
Hunza 29 F 4
Huon, Gulf of 26 o 14
Hu pei 31 I 4
Hurghada 28 B 7
Hurhu Uula, Mt. 31 G 2
Hurmuk 29 D 6
Huron 46 G 4
Huron, Lake 42 M5
Hurson 11 H 2
Hursville 55 e 10
Hurungi 17 L 3
Husavik 17 T 11
Hu shan 27 f 15
Husi 21 I 4
Huskvarna 17 F 8
Husum 13 C1
Hutchinson (South Africa) 41 C 5
Hutchinson (USA, Kansas) 46 G 5
Hu tiao Men 27 f 15
Hütola 23 G 4
Hu tou 31 O 1
Hutt 55 h 14
Hüttinen 17 L 7
Hu tu tao 31 M2
Huy 15 G 3
Hvar 20 C 6
Hvamms, fj. 16 Q 12
Hvammur 17 S 12
Hvita 16 R 12
Hvitar Vatn 16 S 12
Hwange 41 D2
Hwei chang 31 L5
Hydarabad 30 C 5
Hyderabad 29 E 6
Hyères 11 I 5
Hyères Islands 10 I 5
Hyndman Peak, Mt. 46 D 4
Hyrynsalmi 23 G 2

I

Iaco 52 D 3-4
Ialomita 20 G 5
Iasi 21 I 4
Iauaretê 51 C3
Iavelo 38 C 7
Ib 30 D 4
Iba 34 F 1
Ibadan 39 E 4
Ibagué 51 A 3
Ibar 20 E 6
Ibarra 52 B 1
Ibatuba 52 I 6
Ibba 40 D 1
Ibdakane 37 E 6
Ibembo 40 C 2
Ibi 39 F 4
Ibicui 52 F 7
Ibiza 9 G 4
Ibiza, I. 9 G 4
Ibo 40 G 5
Ibonma 34 H 5
Iboziva 40 E 3
Ibresi 24 D 7
Ibusuki 32 C 5
Ica (Perù) 52 B 4
Ica (Soviet Union) 22 Q 4
Ica, Rio 52 D 2
Icana, Rio 51 C 3
Icatù, Rio 52 I 4
Ice Cape 45 F 2
Ice Fjord 56 a
Iceland 2 BC2-3
Icera 22 L 4
Ichang 31 I 4
Ichikawa 27 d 13
Ichinomiya 27 e 13
Ichun 31 I 5
Ichuna 52 C 5
Ida 20 G 10
Idah 39 F 4
Idaho 46 CD 3-4
Idaho Falls 46 D 4
Iddan 38 E 6
Idehan 37 G 4
Iderlin 31 F 1
Idhra 21 F9
Idhra, I. 20 F9
Idi 34 A 3
Idice 18 C 2
Idiofa 40 B 3
Idlib 28 D 3
Idria 18 DE 1
Idris 38 B 5
Idritsa 23 G 6
Idunda 40 E 4
Iebbi Suma 37 H 5
Ieper 15 F 3
Ierapetra 21 G 10
Iesi 19 D 3
Iet 38 D 7

Ifakara 40 F 4
Iférouane 37 F 6
Ifetesene, Mt. 37 E 4
Iffley 55 G 3
Ifon 39 F 4
Igan 34 D 4
Iganga 40 E 2
Igangan 39 E 4
Igarka 22 H 3
Igatimi 52 F 6
Igdir 25 GH 6
Ighil Izane 37 E 2
Iglesias 19 AB 5
Igli 37 C 3
Igloolik 44 O 2
Iglovia 21 E 3
Ignatovka 24 D 8
Igneada, Cape 20 I 7
Iguacu, Cataratas del 49 E 6
Iguacu, R 49 E 6
Iguala 47 E 4
Igualdade 52 D 2
Iguape 52 H 6
Iguatemi 52 G 6
Iguatu 52 L 3
Iguéla 39 F 6
Iguidi, des. 35 C 3
Igula 40 E 4
Igumira 40 E 4
Igusi 41 D 2
Igwavuma 41 E 4
Ihosy 41 c 8
Ihsien 31 M 2
Ii 16 MN 4
Iisaku 23 F 5
Iisalmi 17 N 5
Ijang, Mt. 26 m 13
Ijebu Ode 39 E 4
Ijsselmeer 14 G 2
Ik 24 GH 7
Ikaalinen 17 L 6
Ikaria 20 H 9
Ikateq 44 Z 2
Ikela 40 C 3
Ikelemba 40 B 2
Ikermiut 44 W 3
Iki, Island 32 C 5
Ikopa 41 c 7
Ikuri Shan, Mt. 32 BC 1
Ikutha 40 F 3
Ikwa 20 G 2
Ila 40 C 5
Ilafok 37 C3
Ilagan 34 F 1
'Ilam 28 I 4
Ilamane, Mt. 37 F 5
Ilan (China) 31 N 1
Ilan (Taiwan) 31 M 6
Ilanskij 22 I 4
Ilbunga 55 F 5
Ilck 1 ST 5-6
Ilm à la Crosse 44 H 4
Ilcanda Mare 21 F 4
Ilebo 40 C 3
Ile de France 11 FG 2
Iller 12 D 5
Ilesha 39 E 4
Ilet 24 E 6
Ilfracombe 4 D 6
Ilgaz Dagi, Mt. 1 O 7
Ilgaz (Kochisar) 25 B 5
Ilhavo 9 B 3
Ilhéus 52 L 4
Ili 22 G 5
Ili, River 22 G 5
Iliamma 45 H 5
Ilic 29 E 3
Il'ic 22 F 5
Iligan 34 F 3
Ilim 22 L 4
Ilimsk 22 L 4
Ilinsk 23 L 5
Il'inskoe 24 H 5
Ill 10 I 2
Illampu, Mt. 49 D 5
Illapel 53 B 3
Iller 12 D 5
Illimani, Mt. 49 D 5
Illinois 46 I 4-5
Illinois, River 46 H 4
Illo 39 E 3
Ilmen, L. 23 H 5
Iloilo 34 F 2
Ilolo 40 F 4
Ilorin 39 E 4
Ilovlja 25 H 1
Ilwaki 34 G 6
Ima 22 M 4
Iman 31 O 1
Iman, River 31 P 1
Imandra, Lake 23 HI 1
Imba 27 e 13
Imbituba 52 H 7
Imbros 20 G 7
Imese 40 B 2
Imettos 20 F 9
Imja Khola 26 p 17
Imola 18 C 2
Imongo 36 E 6
Imperia 19 B 3
Impfondo 40 B 2
Imphal 33 A 2
Ina 12 F 2
In Afellahlah 37 F 5
Inagua, Gr.-, Island 48 E 2
In-Allarene 37 F 6

In-Amandaouiss 37 E 6
In Amenas 37 F 4
In-Amguel 37 F 5
Inari 17 N 2
Inari, Lake 17 N 2
In Azar 37 F 4
In Azaraf 37 E 6
In Azaua 37 G 4
In Belbel 37 E 4
Ince Burun, Pt. 25 C 4
Incesu 25 C 6
Incheon 31 N 3
Incoronata, I. 21 B 6
Indaal 13 C 4
Indal 17 G 5
Indals 16 G 5
Indaw 33 A 2
Inderagiri 34 B 5
Inderborskij 29 B 2
Inderöy 17 D 5
Indi 38 C 5
India 27 L N 7
Indian Lake 44 L 4
Indiana 46 I 4-5
Indianapolis 46 I 5
Indigirka 22 P 2-3
Indochina 26 NO 8
Indonesia 27 OR 10
Indore 30 C 4
Indramaju, Town 34 C 6
Indramaju, Cape 26 1 13
Indrapura 34 B 5
Indravati 30 D 5
Indre 10 F 3
Indura 23 D 8
Indus 26 IL 7
Indus Mouths of the 29 E 7
Inebolu 25 B 5
In Eker 37 F 5
Inés, Mt.53 C 6
In Ezzane 37 G 5
In-Gall 37 F 6
Ingham 55 H 3
Ingleburn 55 d 11
Ingolstadt 13 D E 4
Ingöy 17 M 1
Ingria 1 N 4
Ingrid Christensen, Coust 57 F 2-3
In Guezzam 37 F 6
Inhambane 41 F 3
Inhaminga 41 F 2
Inharrime 41 F 3
Inifeg 37 D 4
Ining 31 C 2
Inirida 51 C 3
Inishbofin, Island 4 A 5
Inishowen Pen. 4 C 4
Inishturk, Island 4 A 5
Inja 22 P 4
Injune 55 H 5
Inkonane 41 D 3
Inn 12 E 4
Innamincka 55 G 5
Inner Sound, Strait 3 C 3
Innichen 19 D 1
Innisfail 55 H 3
Innsbruck 19 D 5
Innvik 17 B 6
Inongo 40 B 3
I-n-Ouzzal 37 E 5
In Rhar 37 E 6
In Rhellal el-Foukani 37 E 4
In Salah 37 E 4
Insar 24 C 8
I-n-Tiraouine 37 E 5
Intutu 52 C 3
Inubò, K. 27 e 13
Inveraray 4 D 3
Invercargill 55 f 15
Inverell 55 I 5
Inverness 4 D 3
Inverurie 4 E 3
Inverway 55 E 3
Inyanga, Town 41 E 2
Inyanga, Mt. 35 G 7
Inza 24 D 8
Inzia 40 B 4
In Zizé 37 E 5
Ioannina 21 E 8
Iola 46 G 5
Ioniam Is. 20 DE 8
Ioniam Sea 18 F 5-6
Ios 20 G 9
Ioullemeddene 37 DE 6
Iowa 46 H 4
Ipatovo 25 G 3
Ipel 20 D 3
Ipiales 51 A 3
Ipiranga 52 D 2
Ipin 31 G 5
Ipoh 27 NO 9
Ippa 20 I 1
Ippy 40 C 1
Ipsala 21 H 7
Ipswich (Australia) 55 I 5
Ipswich (United Kingdom) 4 G 5
Ipu 52 I 2
'Iqba 38 D 3
Iquique 52 C 6
Iquitos 52 C 3
Irak-Ajemi 1 RS 9
Iraklia, Island 20 G 9
Iraklion 21 G 10

Iran 2 RT 8-10
Iran, Mt. 26 P 9
Irapa 51 D 1
Irapuato 47 D 3
Iraq 2 QR 8-9
'Iraq (Soltanabad) 28 L 3
Irawadmündungen 33 AB 3
Irazu 48 C 4
Irbit 24 N 6
Irbensund 16 IL 8
Irebu 40 B 3
Ireland 4 BC 4-5
Ireland, Northern 4 C 4
Iremel Mt. 24 L 7
Irena 40 B 1
Ireng 51 E 3
Irgalem 38 C 6
Irgiz, Town 22 F 5
Irgiz, Bol'soj.- 24 DF 8-9
Irgiz, Malvj.- 24 E 8
Irgiz, River 1 U 5-6
Iri 31 N 3
Irian, West- 34 H 5
Iriklinskij 24 L 9
Iringa 40 F 4
Iriomote, Island 32 B 7
Iriona 47 D 4
Iriri, Rio- 52 G 2
Irish Sea 3 DE 5
Irkutsk 22 L 4
Irmak 25 B 5-6
Iro, Island 37 H 7
Iroise 11 C 2
Iron Gate 20 F 5
Iron Knob 55 F 6
Iron Range 55 G 2
Irpen 20 IL 2
Irrawaddy 26 N 7
Irrawaddy, Mouths of the 33 AB 3
Irsa 20 I 2
Irsha 23 L 4
Irtys 22 FH 3-5
Irumu 40 D 2
Irun 9 F 2
Irva 24 EF 3
Is 28 G 4
Isa 39 F 3
Isabel, Cape 26 o 14
Isabela, Cape 48 E 3
Isabela, Island 49 A 4
Isabena 9 G 2
Isafjördur 17 Q 11
Isangi 40 C 2
Isar 12 E 4
Isarco 18 C 1
Isavarre, Mt. 17 I 2
Isaxagene 37 E 6
Ischia 18 D 4
Ise, Bay 32 E 5
Ise, fj. 16 D 9
Isel 13 E 5
Iseo, L. d'- 18 C 2
Isére 10 HI 4
Iserlohn 13 B 3
Isernia 19 DE 4
Iset 1 UV 4
Ishâhiye 28 D 2
Ishan 31 H 6
Ishigaki, Island 32 B 7
Ishinomaki 32 F 4
Ishkashim 29 F 4
Ishqanan 38 F 2
Isik Dagi 25 B 5
Isim, Town 22 F 4
Isim, River 2 VZ 4-5
Isimbaj 24 I 8
Isiolo 40 F 2
Iskâr 20 G 6
Iskenderun Gulf of 28 D 2
Iskilip 25 C 5
Iskininskij 29 B 2
Iskuras, Mt. 16 M 2
Isla 3 E 3
Islambad 29 F 5
Island, Lake 44 LM 5
Island, North 55 g 13
Island, South 55 g 14-15
Islandia 52 B 3
Islay, Island 3 C 4
Isle, Lake 10 F 4
Isna 37 M 4
Isoanala 41 c 8
Isojoki 17 L 5
Isoka 40 E 5
Isonzo 18 D 2
Isparta 2 O 8
Ispikan 29 D 6
Ispir 25 F 5
Israel 28 C 4-5
Isriyah 28 D 3
Issa 24 C 8
Issalane 37 F 5
Issano 48 E 3
Isseye 37 D 7
Issia 37 C 4
Issik Kul, Island 22 G 5
Issoire 11 F 3
Issoudun 11 F 3
Istanbul 21 I 7
Istmina 51 A 2
Isthumus Perry, Mt. 52 a
Istomina 24 B 3

Istranca Mts. 20 HI 7
Istria 21 AB 5
Isuela 9 F 3
Ita 52 F 7
Itabira 52 I 5
Itabuna 52 I 4
Itaccunas 52 G 3
Itachen. Island 44 G 2
Itacoai 52 C 3
Itacoatiara 52 F 2
Itaguatins 52 H 3
Itaituba 52 F 2
Itajai 52 H 7
Itajui 52 H 4
Italia, Mt. 53 C 7
Italy 2 H-L 6-8
Itamarandiba 52 I 5
Itambé, Pico de- 49 F 5
Itampolo 41 b 8
Itapaci 52 H 5
Itapecuru Mirim 52 I 2
Itaperuna 52 I 6
Itapeva 52 H 6
Itapicuru 52 L 4
Itaretana 52 L 3
Itatiaia, Mt. 49 F 6
Itaunas 52 L 5
Itbayat, Island 31 M 6
Ite 52 C 5
Ithaka 20 E 8
Itiquira 52 G 5
Itiso 40 F 4
Itlar 25 N 6
Ito 27 d 13
Itobe 39 F 4
Itoko 40 C 3
Itonamas 49 D 5
Itu (Brazil) 52 H 6
Itu (China) 31 L 3
Itui, Rio 52 C 3
Ituiutaba 52 H 5
Itula 40 D 3
Itumpiara 52 H 5
Ituri 40 D 2
Iturup, Island 22 P 5
Itwad 38 D 4
Itzehoe 13 C 2
Iubdc 38 C 6
Ivai 52 G 6
Ivanec 21 C 4
Ivangrad 21 D 6
Ivanhoe 55 G 5
Ivaniegrad 21 C 5
Ivanic-Krankovsk 21 G 3
Ivancvka 24 G 8
Ivancvo 21 G 1
Ivancvsk 24 L 7
Ivanscica, Mt. 20 BC 4
Ivatsevici 23 E 8
Ivdel 22 F 3
Ive 23 E 8
Ivina 23 L 4
Ivinheima 52 G 6
Ivory Coast 39 CD 5
Ivrea 19 A 2
Iwamizawa 32 F 3
Iwanai 32 F 3
Iwo 36 D 5
Iwungu 40 E 4
Ixopo 41 E 5
Iyang 31 I 5
Izabal 47 E 4
Izad Khast 28 N 5
Izberbas 25 I 4
Izevsk 22 E 4
Izileg 37 F 5
Izium 25 D 1
Izmail 21 I 6
Izmir, Town 21 H 8
Izmir, Gulf of 20 H 8
Izmit 21 I 7
Iznik, L. 20 I 7
Iztapa 47 E 4
Izucar 47 E 4

J

Jaala 17 N 6
Jabal at-Tuwaiq 38 E 2-3
Jabalon 8 E 4
Jabalpur 30 C 4
Jabal Shammar 38 CD 2
Jablanza 20 E 7
Jabrin 38 E 3
Jabrin Island 28 M 7
Jaca 9 F 2
Jacaré 52 I 4
Jacaretinga 52 F 3
Jacarézinho 52 G 6
Jachal 53 C 3
Jacitara 52 D 2
Jack 44 L 5
Jackson (USA, Kent.) 46 L 5
Jackson (USA, Mich.) 46 L 4
Jackson (USA, Missis.) 46 H 6
Jackson (USA, Tenn.) 46 I 5
Jackson, Mt. 46 D 4
Jacksonville 46 L 6
Jacktown 39 C 4

Jacmel 48 E 3
Jacobina 52 I 4
Jacqueville 39 D 4
Jacui 52 I 4
Jacunda 52 G 2
Jäderensrev 17 A 7
Jadrin 24 D 7
Jaén (Perù) 52 B 3
Jaén (Spain) 9 E 5
Jafar 38 E 2
Jaffa 28 C 4
Jaffna 30 D 7
Jafura 38 EF 2-3
Jagdalpur 30 D 5
Jäggevarre, Mt. 16 I 2
Jagharu 31 F 3
Jaghbub 37 I 4
Jagst 12 C 4
Jagtial 30 C 5
Jaguarao 53 F 3
Jaguariaiva 52 H 6
Jaguaribe 49 G 4
Jahrum 29 B 6
Jaigarth 30 B 5
Jaipur 30 C 3
Jaisalmer 30 B 3
Jajabiriri 39 G 3
Jajce 21 C 5
Jakalswater 41 B 3
Jäkkvik 17 G 3
Jakobstad 17 L 5
Jakora 41 c 8
Jakovaara 23 H 3
Jaksa 24 I 4
Jalalabad 29 F 5
Jalapa Enriquez 47 E 4
Jalasjärvi 17 L 5
Jal'ciki 24 D 7
Jaldak 29 E 5
Jalgaon 30 C 4
Jaliba 28 I 5
Jalla 39 F 4
Jalna 30 C 5
Jalon 8 F 3
Jalpaiguri 30 E 3
Jalpan 47 E 3
Jalpukh 20 I 4
Jalu 36 F 3
Jaluit, Island 54 G 4
Jam 38 F 2
Jamaica 48 D 3, 50 C 2
Jamal-Bariz, Mt. 29 C 6
Jamalpur 30 E 3
Jaman Tau, Mt. 26 I 4
Jamanxim 52 F 3
Jamari 52 E 3
Jambe 34 H 5
Jambol 21 H 6
Jamdena, Island 34 H 6
James 46 G 3
James Bay 44 OP 5
Jamestown 46 G 3
Jamiltepec 47 E 4
Jamklandi 30 C 5
Jammu 30 B 2
Jamnagar 30 B 4
Jamno, Island 19 F 1
Jämsä 17 M 6
Jamshedpur 30 E 4
Jamsk 22 Q 4
Jämtland 17 EF 5
Jamursba 26 n 14
Jan 28 N 7
Jana 22 O 2-3
Janauba 52 I 5
Janaul 24 H 6
Jandaq 29 B 5
Jangyeon 31 N 3
Janjira 30 B 5
Janow 13 L 3
Jansenville 41 C 5
Janskij 22 O 3
Jantra 20 G 6
Januaria 52 I 5
Jaoho 32 D 2
Jaora 30 C 4
Japarana 52 E 4
Japan 27 RS 5-6
Japan, Sea of 32 DE 3-4
Japen 34 I 5
Japura 50 D 4
Jaragua 52 H 5
Jarama 8 E 3
Jaramillo 53 C 6
Jaransk 24 D 6
Jardim 52 F 6
Jardines de la Reina 48 D 2
Jarensk 24 E 3
Jari 49 E 3-4
Jarkino 22 I 4
Jarocin 13 G 3
Jaroslaw 13 L 3
Jartsevo (Soviet Union, Krasnojarsk) 22 I 3
Jartsevo (Soviet Union, Smolensk) 23 I 7
Jaru 52 E 4
Jaruapuca 52 D 2
Jarvis, Island 54 L 5
Järvso 17 G 6
Jask 29 C 6
Jasnur 24 E 6
Jáson, Pen. 57 n 3
Jassan 28 H 4

Jastolda **20** GH 1
Jastrebac, Mt. **20** E 6
Jaszbereny **21** D 4
Jata, Island **39** A 3
Jatai **52** G 5
Jatapu **52** F 2
Jath **30** C 5
Jativa **9** F 4
Jatobal **52** H 2
Jatuarana **52** E 3
Jau, Town **52** H 6
Jau, Rio. **52** E 2
Jauja **52** B 4
Jaula, La- **53** C 3
Jaunjelgava **17** M 8
Jaunpur **30** D 3
Jauru, Rio. (Rio Paraguai) **52** F 5
Jauru, Rio. (Rio Taquari) **52** G 5
Java **27** OP 10
Java sea **26** OP 10
Javalambre, Mt. **8** F 3
Javorice **12** F 4
Javorie, Mt. **20** D 3
Javorina, Mt. **20** C 3
Javornik, Mt. Czechoslovakia) **20** D 3
Javornik, Mt. (Yugoslavia, Bosna) **20** D 5
Javornik, Mt. (Yugoslavia, Croatia) **20** D 5
Jawf, El- **37** I 5
Jawhar **30** B 5
Jazira **28** FG 3
Jazirat. an-Naman **28** C 7
Jebba **39** E 4
Jebel Aneiza, Mt. **28** E 4
Jebel-ed-Druyz **28** D 4
Jebel el-Kar **37** L 6
Jebel el Uweienat **37** L 5
Jebel es-Soda **37** GH 4
Jebel Gharib **37** M 4
Jebel Marra **37** I 7
Jebel Umm Selit **37** L 8
Jeberos **52** B 3
Jefferson City **46** H 5
Jega **39** E 3
Jeju **31** N 4
Jeui **52** F 6
Jejustrasse **31** N 4
Jekabpils **16** M 8
Jelenia Gora **13** F 3
Jelgava **17** L 8
Jena **13** D 3
Jenapur **30** E 4
Jenipapo **52** E 3
Jenisej, River **26** M 3
Jenisej, Gulf of **22** H 2
Jenkins **46** L 5
Jequié **52** I 4
Jeonju **31** N 3
Jequitinhonha **49** FG 5
Jeremie **48** E 3
Jeremoabo **52** L 3
Jerez de la Frontiera **9** C 5
Jerez de los Caballeros **9** C 4
Jericho **55** H 4
Jersey City **46** N 4
Jerusalem **28** C 5
Jessore **27** a 11
Jestro **38** D 6
Jesus Maria, Boca- **47** E 3
Jetpur **30** B 4
Jevnaker **17** D 6
Jeypore **30** D 5
Jezira, El- **37** I 4
Jhang Maghiana **29** F 5
Jhansi **30** C 3
Jhelum, Stadt **29** F 5
Jhelum, River **29** F 5
Jhunijhunu **30** C 3
Ji, Island **23** G 2
Jia **20** F 5-6
Jiachan **31** C 4
Jibhalanta **31** F 1
Jibòu **21** F 4
Jidali **38** E 5
Jidbaleh **38** E 6
Jidda **38** C 3
Jihlava **21** B 3
Jijia **20** H 4
Jijiga **38** D 6
Jiloca **8** F 3
Jimbolia **21** E 5
Jiménez **47** E 3
Jimma **38** C 6
Jinja **40** E 2
Jinnampo **31** N 3
Jipijapa **52** A 2
Jirau **52** E 3
Jirgalanta (Hobdo) **31** E 1
Jisr Diyala **28** H 4
Jitin **23** G 8
Jiu **20** F 5
Jizan **38** D 4
Joacaba **52** G 7
Joaima **52** I 5
Joanico **52** D 2
Joanna Spring **55** C 4
Joao Pessoa (Paraiba) **52** M 3
Jodhpur **30** B 3
Joensuu **23** G 3
Joerg Plateau **57** O 2
Joesjö **17** F 4
Jofane **41** E 3
Joffreville **41** c 6
Jogle, Mt. **16** B 7
Jogykarta **34** D 6
Johanna **41** b 6
Johannesburg **41** D 4
John Day **46** C 4
Johnson City **46** L 5
Johnston, **54** L 3
Joho **31** L 2
Johore, Strait of **27** h 16
Johore, River **27** hi 16
Johore Bahru **33** C 6
Joigny **11** G 3
Joinville (Brazil) **52** H 7
Joinville (France) **11** H 2
Joinville, Island **57** n 3
Jokijärvi **17** O 4
Jokkmokk **17** H 3
Jökulsa **16** S 12
Jökulsa **16** U 12
Jökulsa a Fjöllum **16** T 12
Jones, Strait of **42** M 2
Jönesboro **46** H 5
Jong **39** B 4
Jongka Dzong **31** D 5
Jönköping Town **17** F 8
Jönkoping **17** EF 8
Jöplin **46** H 5
Jordan **28** CD 4-5
Jordan, River **28** C 4
Jordet **17** E 6
Jörhat **33** A 1
Jörn **17** I 4
Jorullo **47** D 4
José de Amacuro **51** D 2
Joseph-Bonaparte-Golf **54** C 6
Jostedals Brä, Mt. **16** B 6
Jotunheimen **16** C 6
17 C 6
Jousta **17** N 6
Joutsenvesi, Island **23** G 3
Joya, La- **52** CM45
Juan de Fuca, Strait of **44** D 6
Juan de Nova **41** G 2
Juan Fernandez, Island **50** BC 7
Juan-Gulbene **23** F 6
Juarez **53** E 4
Juaso **39** D 4
Juazeiro **52** I 3
Juazeiro do Norte **52** L 3
Juba (Iraq) **28** G 4
Juba (Somalia) **35** H 5
Juba (Sudan) **40** E 2
Jubail **28** L 7
Jubba **28** F 6
Jucar **8** EF 3-4
Juchipila **47** D 3
Juchitan **47** E 4
Judenburg **13** F 5
Judoma **22** OP 3-4
Judoma Krestovsk **22** OP 3
Jug **24** CD 4-5
Jugan **1** Z 3-4
Juigalpa **48** B 4
Juir **35** F 5
Juiz de Fora **52** I 6
Jujuv **53** C 1
Jukhuov **23** L 7
Jula **24** C 3
Juli **52** D 5
Juliaca **52** C 5
Julian Alps **20** B 4-5
Julianehab **44** V 3
Jullundur **30** C 2
Jum **24** H 5
Jumaguzino **24** I 8
Jumaima **38** D 2
Jumet **15** G 3
Jumilla **9** F 4
Jumin **29** C 5
Jumna **30** C 2-3
Junagadh **30** B 4
Junak **21** H 6
Junan **31** I 4
Jundiai **52** H 6
Juneau **42** F 4
Juneda **9** G 3
Jungfrau **18** AB 1
Jung kiang **31** H 5
Junin (Argentina B. Aires) **53** D 3
Junin (Argentina Mendoza) **53** C 3
Junin (Perù) **52** B 4
Junin de los Andes **53** B 4
Junosuando **17** L 3
Junsele **17** G 5
Junta, La- **46** F 5
Jupagua **52** I 4
Jur **22** O 4
Jura, Island **3** D 3
Jura gebirge **10** HI 3-4
Jura Krakowska **12** H 3
Juribej **22** G 2
Jurijuzan, Town **24** L 7
Jurjuzan River **24** IK 7
Jurkovo **24** B 5
Juroma **24** C 2
Jurua **52** CD 2-3
Juruena **52** F 4
Jurva **17** L 5
Juskozero **23** I 2
Jutai **52** D 2-3
Juterborg **13** E 3
Jutigalpa **47** G 5
Jutland **17** C 8-9
Juventud, I. de la **48** C 2
Juwain **29** D 5
Jyona **9** F 4
Jyväskylä **17** M 5

K

K 2, Mt. **26** L 6
Kaahka **29** C 4
Kaapmuiden **41** E 4
Kab, El- **37** E 4
Kabaena **34** F 6
Kabaisa **28** G 4
Kabale **40** E 3
Kabalo **40** D 4
Kabambare **40** D 3
Kaban'e **25** E 1
Kabba **39** F 4
Kabilcevaz **28** F 1
Kabinda **40** C 4
Kabompo **41** C 1
Kabongo **40** D 4
Kabul **29** E 5
Kabunda **40** D 5
Kabwe **41** D 1
Kacanik **21** E 6
Kacanovo **23** F 6
Kacheliba **40** F 2
Ka cheng tzu **31** D 2
Kachia **39** F 4
Kachiyama **27** d 13
Kaçkar Dagi, Mt. **25** F 5
Kacuga **22** L 4
Kadé **39** B 3
Kadei **40** AB 2
Kadero, Mt. **37** M 7
Kadial **37** D 7
Kadinhani **25** B 6
Kadjang **34** F 6
Kadjema **40** D 1
Kadnikov **23** O 5
Kadoma **41** D 2
Kadugli **37** M 7
Kaduna, Town **39** F 3
Kaduna, River **9** F 3-4
Kaedi **37** B 6
Kaesong **31** N 3
Kaf **28** D 5
Kaffa **38** C 6
Kafia Kingi **40** C 1
Kafu, River **40** E 2
Kafue, Town **41** D 2
Kafue **35** F 7
Kafulwe **40** D 4
Kagal'nitskaja **25** F 2
Kagan **29** D 4
Kagao **39** D 4
Kagen, Island **17** I 2
Kagera, Island **35** G 6
Kagizman **25** G 5
Kagoshima **32** D 5
Kagul **21** I 5
Kahafa **28** L 7
Kahaifiya **38** D 2
Kahajan **34** D 5
Kahperàsvaara, Mt. **16** I 2
Kai Islands **34** H 6
Kaifeng **31** I 4
Kaikoura, Mt. **55** g 14
Kai lu **31** M 2
Kai lung **31** M 2
Kaimanawa, Mt. **55** h 13
Kai Mouth **41** D 5
Kainunn selkä **23** G 2
Kairouan **37** G 2
Kaiserslautern **13** BC 4
Kai yüng **31** M 2
Kaj **24** G 5
Kajaani (Kajana) **17** N 4
Kajan **34** E 4
Kajana (Kajaani) **17** N 4
Kajtum **16** H 3
Kajuadi, Island **34** F 6
Kaka (South Africa) **40** D 1
Kaka (Sudan) **37** M 7
Kakamari **40** F 2
Kakamas **41** C 4
Kakerli **24** D 7
Kakinada **30** D 5
Kakoulima, Mt. **39** B 4
Kal River **29** CD 5
Kala **40** E 4
Kala, El- **37** F 2
Kala **16** M 4-5
Kalabakan **34** E 4
Kaladan **33** A 2
Kalahari, des. **35** F 8
Kalakan **22** M 4
Kalamai **21** F 9
Kalamazoo **46** I 4
Kalamba **40** C 4
Kalambaka **21** E 8
Kalao, Island **34** F 6
Kala Otlak **31** E 3
Kalaotoa, Island **34** F 6
Kalecik (Kalaycik) **25** B 5
Kalehe **40** D 3
Kalemie **40** D 4
Kalewa **33** A 2
Kalfafell **17** T 13
Kalfafellsstad **17** U 12
Kalgalaksa **23** L 2
Kalgon (Wan chuan) **31** I 2
Kalgoorlie **55** C 6
Kali **38** D 4
Kalianda **34** C 6
Kaliakra, C. **20** I 6
Kalimantan **34** DE 5
Kalimnos **20** H 9
Kalimpong **30** E 3
Kalinin **23** L 6
Kaliningrad **17** I 9
Kalinniki **24** H 7
Kalinovskaja **25** H 4
Kalispell **46** D 3
Kalisz **13** G 3
Kaliua **40** E 4
Kalix **16** IL 3
Kaljazin **23** M 6
Kalkfeld **41** B 3
Kalkfontein **36** F 8
Kalkrand **41** B 3
Kall **17** E 5
Kallfonn **17** C 5
Källvik **17** G 8
Kalmar **17** G 8
Kalmykovo **22** E 5
Kalna **30** E 4
Kalocsa **21** D 4
Kalomo **41** D 2
Kalpeni, Island **30** B 6
Kalta **25** C 2
Kaluga **23** M 7
Kalundborg **17** D 9
Kalvarija **17** L 9
Kalyan **30** B 5
Kama, Town **40** D 3
Kama, River **24** GI 5-7
Kama Res **24** HI 5
Kamaishi **32** F 4
Kamakura **27** d 13
Kamar **25** D 2
Kamaran **38** D 4
Kamba **40** C 3
Kambia **39** B 4
Kambove **40** D 5
Kamchatka **22** QR 4
Kamcija **20** H 6
Kamelik **24** E 8
Kamenets-Podolskij **21** H 3
Kamenjak, Cape **20** A 5
Kamen' Kasirskij **21** G 2
Kamennik, Mt. **23** I 6
Kamennogsk **23** G 4
Kamensk **23** M 1
Kamenskoe **22** R 3
Kamensk Sakhtynskij **25** F 1
Kamensk-Uralskij **24** M 6
Kamenz **13** F 3
Kamesnica, Mt. **20** C 6
Kamienna, River **12** I 3
Kamil **25** C 5
Kamina **40** C 4
Kam Kent **33** C 3
Kamlin **38** B 4
Kamloops **44** E 5
Kamogawa **27** e 13
Kamp **12** I 7
Kampala **40** E 2
Kampar **34** B 4
Kampot **33** C 4
Kamptee **30** C 4
Kamysin **25** H 1
Kan, River (China, Inner Mongolia) **32** B 1-2
Kan, River (China, Kiangsi) **31** IL 5
Kanaaupscow **44** PQ 5
Kanadej **24** D 8
Kanaga, Island **22** T 4
Kananga **40** C 4
Kanas **24** D 7
Kanazawa **32** E 4
Kanchenjunga, Mt. **26** MN 7
Kanchindu **41** D 2
Kanchipuram **39** C 6
Kanchumiao **31** L 1
Kancossa **37** B 6
Kandagaç **29** C 2
Kandalaksa **23** I 1
Kandalaksa Bay **23** IL 1
Kandale **40** B 4
Kandavu, Island **54** H 6
Kandi **39** E 3
Kandy **30** D 7
Kanem **35** E 4
Kanev **25** A 1
Kanevskaja **25** E 2
Kanga **40** E 4
Kangaba **37** C 7
Kangal **25** D 6
Kangâmiut **44** U 2
Kangan **28** N 7
Kangar **33** C 5
Kangare **37** C 7
Kangasniem **17** N 6
Kängavär **28** I 3
Kangdu, Mt. **31** E 5
Kangkar Chemaran **27** i 16
Kangkar Pulai **27** h 16
Kangta **31** F 4
Kangtega, Mt. **26** p 17
Kang ting **31** G 4
Känguruhinsel **55** F 7
Kaniapiskau, River **44** R 4
Kaniapiskau Lake **44** R 5
Kanin **22** E 3
Kaninabad **22** G 5
Kankan **39** C 3
Kannus **17** L 5
Kano (Mali) **37** D 6
Kano (Nigeria) **39** F 3
Kanpur **30** D 3
Kanq **41** C 3
Kansanshi **40** D 5
Kansas **46** FG 5
Kansas, River **42** L 6
Kansas City **46** H 5
Kansu **31** FG 3
Kantang **33** B 5
Kantemirovka **25** E 1
Kantse **27** O 6
Kan tzu **31** G 4
Kanye **41** D 3
Kanzi, Cape **40** F 4
Kao an **31** L 5
Kaohsiung **27** Q 7
Kaoko Veld **41** A 2-3
Kaolack **37** A 7
Kao lai **31** F 3
Kaomba, Mt. **35** F 7
Kao yao **31** I 6
Kao yu **31** L 4
Kapa **31** C 3
Kapanga (Zaire, Katanga) **40** C 4
Kapanga (Zaire, Kinshasa) **40** B 4
Kapeh **40** E 2
Kapela **20** B 5
Kapidagi **20** H 7
Kapingamarangi, Islands **54** F 4
Kapiskau **44** O 5
Kapit **34** D 4
Kapoeta **40** E 2
Kapos **20** D 4
Kaposvar **21** C 4
Kappelshamn **17** H 8
Kapsukas **17** L 9
Kapuas **34** CD 5
Kapustin Jar **29** A 2
Kara **22** F 3
Kara Bil, Mt. **29** D 4
Kara Bogaz **29** B 3
Kara Bogaz-Gol **22** E 5
Karabutak **29** D 2
Karacabey **21** I 7
Karachi **29** E 7
Karaçukur **25** C 5
Karadong, Ruinen **31** C 3
Karaga (Ghana) **39** D 4
Karaga (Soviet Union) **22** R 4
Karaganda **22** G 5
Karagin Island **22** R 4
Karakhoto **31** G 2
Karakorum **26** L 6
Karaköse **25** G 6
Karakul **22** G 6
Karakul'skoe **24** N 7
Karakum **22** E 6
Karakütüt **28** D 2
Karala **17** F 4
Karaman **28** B 2
Karaman, Mt. **20** I 8
Karamürsel **21** I 7
Karapinar **28** B 2
Karas, Mt. **35** E 8
Karasburg **41** B 4
Kara Sea **22** FG 2
Kara Strait **22** E 2
Karasjok **17** M 2
Karasu **28** G 1
Kara Su **1** RS 8-9
Karatas **28** C 2
Karatau **1** S 7
Kara Tjube **22** E 5
Karaul **22** H 2
Karaugan **25** G 5
Karbala **28** H 4
Karböle **17** F 5
Karcag **21** E 4
Karé **37** H 7
Kareima **37** M 6
Karelia **23** HL 1-4
Karema **40** E 4
Karesuando **17** L 2
Karet **37** C 5
Karganrud **28** L 2
Kargat **22** H 4
Kargopol **23** N 4
Kariba, Lake **41** D 2
Karibib **41** B 3
Karijoki **17** I 5
Karikal **30** C 6
Karimata Island **34** C 5
Karimun **27** h 16
Karin **38** E 5
Karisimbi, Mt. **35** F 6
Karitind, Mt. **16** B 5
Karjaa **17** L 6
Karjalan Selka **23** G 3
Karkaralinsk **29** G 2
Kärkha **1** R 9
Karlö **17** M 4
Karlovac **21** B 5
Karlovka **24** E 9
Karlovo **21** G 6
Karlovy Vary **13** E 3
Karlsbäck **17** H 5
Karlshamm **17** F 8
Karlskoga **17** F 7
Karlskrona **17** F 8
Karlsruhe **13** C 4
Karlstad **17** E 7
Karluk **45** H 5
Karma Changri **26** q 16
Karmöy Islands **16** A 7
Karnafuli Res. **27** c 11
Karnak, El- **37** M 4
Karnali **30** D 3
Karnobat **21** H 6
Karonga **40** E 4
Karorga **36** G 6
Karosa **34** E 5
Karou **37** E 6
Karpathos **20** H 10
Karst **20** AB 5
Karpinsk **24** LM 5
Karpo, P. **26** q 16
Karpogory **24** C 3
Kars **25** G 5
Karsakpaj **29** E 2
Karsava **23** F 6
Karshi **29** E 4
Karsi **22** F 6
Karstula **17** M 5
Karsun **24** D 7
Karthago **37** G 2
Kartajol' **24** G 2
Kartaly **22** F 4
Kartun **31** O 1
Karufa **34** H 5
Karumba **55** G 3
Karun **28** LM 5
Karungu **40** E 3
Karwar **30** B 6
Kasai **36** F 6
Kasak **25** M 3
Kasama **40** E 5
Kasanga **40** E 4
Kasar, Cape **38** C 4
Kasba **44** I 3
Cascade Range **46** B 3-4
Kascitu **41** D 1
Kasempa **41** D 1
Kasenga (Congo) **40** D 5
Kasenga Tanzania **40** E 3
Kasenve **40** E 2
Kashan **28** M 4
Kashgar **31** B 3
Kashmar **29** C 4
Kashmir **27** L 6
Kashmor **29** E 6
Kasin **23** M 6
Kasindi **40** D 3
Kasira **23** N 7
Kasirota, Islands **34** G 5
Kasko **16** I 5
Kasli **24** M 7
Kaslo **44** F 6
Käsmu **17** M 7
Kasongo **40** D 3
Kasos **20** H 10
Kassala **38** C 4
Kassandra **20** F 7
Kassel **13** C 3
Kastamonu **25** B 5
Kastoria **21** E 7
Kasur **29** F 5
Kaswein **38** F 4
Kata **22** L 4
Kataba **41** D 2
Katagum **39** G 3
Katakai **27** e 13
Katako Kombe **40** C 3
Katanga (Shaba) **36** F 6-7
Katanich **40** E 1
Katannie **55** B 6
Katanning **55** B 6
Katchall, Island **33** A 5
Katerini **21** F 7
Kates Needle, Mt. **44** C 4
Katha **33** B 2
Katherine **55** E 2
Kathiawar **26** IL 7
Kathkin, Mt. **35** FG 9
Katihar **30** E 3
Katiola **39** C 4
Katla **16** S 13
Katmandu **30** E 3
Katowice **13** H 3
Katrineholm **17** F 7
Katshabala **40** C 3
Katsina Town **39** F 3
Katsina, River **39** G 4
Katsina Ala **39** G 4
Katsuura **27** e 13
Katta Kurgan **29** E 4
Kattegat **16** D 8
Katthammarsvik **17** H 8
Katumba **40** D 4
Katumbi **40** E 5
Katwa **27** a 11
Katyn **23** H 7
Katyryk **22** I 2
Katzenbuckel, Mt. **12** C 4
Kauai, **54** M 2
Kauai, Island **54** M 2
Kauar **37** G 6
Kaukau Veld **41** C 2-3
Kaukura, Island **54** N 6
Kaunas **17** L 9
Kaura-Namoda **39** F 3

Kautokeino 17 L 2
Kavacha 27 V 3
Kavala 21 G 7
Kavar 28 N 6
Kavaratti, Island 30 B 6
Kävir, W. 1 ST 9
Kawa 37 M 7
Kawagoe 27 d 13
Kawaguchi 27 d 13
Kawasaki 27 d 13
Kawlin 33 B 2
Kay, Island 57 a 2
Kaya 39 D 3
Kayak 45 L 5
Kayambi 40 E 4
Kayes 37 B 7
Kayoyo 40 C 5
Kayseri 2 P 8
Kaza 23 M 4
Kazace 22 O 2
Kazakh 25 H 5
Kazakhstan 25 LN 1
Kazan 27 H 4
Kazandzik 29 C 4
Kazarka 24 EF 6-7
Kazatin 21 I 3
Kazbek, Mt. 25 H 4
Kaz Dagi (Ida), Mt. 20 H 8
Kazerun 28 M 6
Kaztalovka 29 A 2
Kazym 1 V 3
Kazyn 22 FG 3
K. Christian IX Land 43 R 3
K. Christian X Land 43 S 2
Ké 40 B 1
Kea 20 G 9
Kebili 37 F 3
Kebkabiya 37 I 7
Kebnekaise, 16 H 3
Kech 29 D 6
Kechika 44 D 4
Kecskemet 21 D 4
Kedainiai 17 L 9
Kediri 34 D 6
Kèdougou 37 B 7
Keele 44 D 3
Keetmanshoop 41 B 4
Kef, El- 37 F 2
Kefalit, Cape 20 D 8
Kefallinia 20 E 8
Keffi 39 F 4
Keflavik 17 Q 12
Kehsi Mansam 33 B 2
Keil 20 A 2
Keila 17 M 7
Keitele 16 N 5
Kel 22 N 3
Kelafo 38 D 6
Keldur 17 S 13
Kellé 37 G 7
Keller 12 C 3
Kellett, Cape 44 D 1
Kelolokan 34 E 4
Kelso 41 E 5
Keltie, Cape 57 C 3
Kem 23 L 2
Kem, River 23 IL 2
Kema 23 M 4
Ke Macina 37 C 7
Kemah 25 E 6
Kembla, Mt. 55 d 11
Kemerovo 22 H 4
Kemi 17 M 4
Kemi, River 17 NO 3
Kemiö 17 L 6
Kemper 14 G 3
Kemp, Land 57 G 3
Kempsey 55 I 6
Kempten 13 D 5
Ken 30 CD 3-4
Kenadza 37 D 3
Kenai 45 H 4
Kenai Pen. 45 HI 4-5
Kendal 4 E 4
Kendari 34 F 5
Kendawangan 34 D 5
Kendrapara 30 E 4
Kene 22 T 3
Kenema 39 B 4
Keng-Tung 33 B 2
Kenhardt 41 C 4
Kénitra 37 C 3
Kenmare 4 B 6
Kenne, Cape 16 N 6
Kennedy Channel 43 O 1
Kennicott 45 L 4
Kenogami 44 N 5
Kenora 44 M 5
Kenscela 37 F 2
Kent 39 B 4
Kent Pen. 44 H 2
Kent, co. 3 G 6
Kentei, Mt. 31 H 1
Kentu 39 G 4
Kentucky 46 IL 5
Kenya 36 G 5
Kenya, Mt. 35 G 6
Keokuk 46 H 4
Kepno 13 G 3
Keramian, Islands 26 m 13
Kerang 55 G 7
Kerangani, Mt. 40 F 2
Kerbo 22 L 3
Kerc 25 D 3
Kerc Strait of 25 D 3

Kercemja 24 G 4
Keren 38 C 4
Keret' 23 I 1
Kergu 17 M 7
Kerico 40 F 2
Kerintji, Mt. 34 B 5
Keriya (Yütien) 31 C 3
Keriya, Fl. 31 C 3
Kerki 29 E 4
Kerkyra 21 D 8
Kermadec, Island 54 I 7-8
Kerma-en-Nuzl 37 M 6
Kerman 29 C 5
Kermanshah 2 R 9
Kerme, Gulf of. 21 H 9
Kermine 29 E 3
Kérouane 39 C 4
Kerrville 46 G 6
Kesten'ga 23 H 2
Kestilä 17 N 4
Ket 22 HI 4
Keta 39 E 4
Ketapang 34 D 5
Ketchikan 45 N 5
Kete Krachi 39 E 4
Ketoj, Island 22 Q 5
Keton 32 F 2
Ketrzyn 13 I 1
Key West, Island 43 M 7
K. Frederik VIII. Land 43 S 2
Khabarikha 24 G 2
Khaburah 29 C 7
Khadasan 31 G 1
Khadkhal 31 G 1
Khaibar 38 C 2
Khairpur 29 E 6
Khajar 31 E 3
Khajrjuzovo 22 Q 4
Khalka 31 L 1
Khalturin 24 E 5
Kham 26 NO 6
Khamba Dzong 31 D 5
Khamis Mushait 38 D 4
Khamsara 22 I 4
Khamseh 28 IL 2-3
Khan 41 B 3
Khanabad (Afganistan) 29 E 4
Khanabad (Iran) 28 L 4
Khana Nor. Island 31 E 2
Khanaqin 28 H 3
Khandak, El- 37 M 6
Khandwa 30 C 4
Khaneh, Lake 28 N 4
Khangayn Nuruu, Mt. 31 F 1
Khanglasy 24 M 3
Khania 21 G 10
Khania, B. of 20 F 10
Kharjangda 22 P 4
Khanka, Lake 22 O 5
Khanpur 29 F 6
Khantaj 22 O 3
Khan Tengri, Mt. 31 C 2
Khanty Mansijsk 22 F 3
Khanu 29 C 6
Khanzi 41 C 3
Khanzira, Cape 38 E 5
Khao Chum Thong 3 C 5
Kharabali 29 A 2
Kharagpur 30 E 4
Kharampur 22 G 3
Khara Tala 22 Q 3
Kharg, Island 28 M 6
Kharga, El- 37 M 4
Kharimkota, Island 22 Q 5
Kharm 28 H 5
Kharma 37 H 6
Kharma, River 37 I 6
Kharnemskaja 24 D 3
Kharovsk 23 N 5
Kharstan 22 P 2
Kharetaphu, Mt. 26 pq 16
Khartoum 38 B 4
Khasav Jurt 25 I 4
Khash 29 D 5
Khashm el Girba 38 C 5
Khasi Hills 30 F 3
Khatanga 22 L 2
Khatan Kai 29 E 6
Khatyn 22 S 3
Khaulan 38 D 4
Khes 41 C 4
Khenachich, El-37 D 5
Khenachiche 37 D 5
Khenifra 37 C 3
Kherlen 31 I 1
Kherson 25 B 2
Kheta 22 IL 2-3
Khetinsiring 31 E 4
Khettamia 37 D 4
Khiav 25 I 6
Khibiny, Mt. 1 O 2
Khingan Mts., Great 31 LM 1-2
Khingan Mounts, Little 32 C 1-2
Khirgis Nur, I 31 E 1
Khisitori 32 F 2
Khislavici 23 I 7
Khitug Undur 31 G 1
Khiva 27 I 5
Khlebnavolok 23 H 1
Khmel'nitskij 21 H 3
Khodorov 21 G 3

Khoi 25 H 6
Khoimqk 32 F 2
Khol'epenici 23 G 8
Kholm 23 H 6
Kholmogory 23 O 2
Kholmsk 22 P 5
Kholm Zirkovskij 23 I 7
Khomas, Mt. 41 B 3
Khombole 37 A 7
Khongor 31 I 1
Khon Kaen 33 C 3
Khor 32 E 2
Khor ad Dhuwaihin 38 F 3
Khorassan 26 H 6
Khorat 33 C 3
Khoreh, Las- 38 E 5
Khorinsty 22 N 3
Khormali 31 D 1
Khorog 29 F 4
Khorol 25 B 1
Khorrämabad 28 L 4
Khorramshähr 28 L 5
Khotan 31 B 3
Khotan, River 31 C 3
Khotin 21 H 3
Khouribga 37 C 3
Khubsugui Dalay, I. 31 F 1
Khuff 38 C 3
Khuis 41 C 4
Khuiseb 41 B 3
Khu Khan 33 C 4
Khulna 21 E 4
Khumbila, Mt. 26 p 17
Khumbu 26 p 17
Khur 29 C 5
Khurma 38 D 3
Khurmuj 28 M 6
Khurremabad 28 M 2
Khurs 38 D 3
Khushab 29 F 5
Khust 21 F 3
Khuzdar 29 E 6
Khuzistan 1 RS 9
Khvalynsk 24 E 8
Khvorostjanka 24 E 8
Khyber, P. 29 F 5
Kiahuen 31 I 3
Kialing 31 H 4
Kiambi 40 D 4
Kibaya 40 F 4
Kiboga 40 E 2
Kibreck, Ben-, Mt. 12 D 2
Kibungu 40 E 3
Kibwesa 40 D 4
Kibwezi 40 F 3
Kichi Kichi 37 H 6
Kidal 37 E 6
Kidatu 40 F 4
Kidira 37 B 7
Kielce 13 I 3
Kiel 13 D 1
Kiel Bay 13 D 1
Kiel Canal 13 CD 1-2
Kien ping 31 L 2
Kierinki 17 M 3
Kiev 2 O 5
Kievka 29 F 1
Kiffa 37 B 6
Kifri 28 H 3
Kigali 40 E 3
Kigi 25 F 6
Kigoma 40 D 3
Kih sien 31 I 3
Kikinda 21 E 5
Kikondja 40 D 4
Kikvit 40 B 4
Kila 39 F 3
Kilbasan 28 B 2
Kilbrennan 4 D 4
Kilbuck Mts. 45 F 4
Kildare 4 C 4
Kilembe 40 E 2
Kilija 21 I 5
Kilimane 41 F 2
Kilimanjaro 35 G 6
Kilimatinde 40 E 4
Kilis 28 D 2
Kilive 40 D 5
Kiljazi 25 L 5
Kilkenny 4 C 5
Killala 4 B 4
Killini 20 F 9
Killybegs 4 B 4
Kilmarnock 4 D 4
Kil'mez' 24 F 6
Kil'mez', River 24 FG 6
Kilo 40 E 2
Kilosa 40 F 4
Kilrush 4 B 5
Kiltan, Island 30 B 6
Kilwa 36 F 6
Kilwa Kisiwani 40 F 4
Kilwa Kivinje 40 F 4
Kimali 40 E 3
Kimaros, Cape 20 F 10
Kimasozero 23 H 2
Kimball Mts. 45 I 4
Kimberley 41 C 4
Kimberley, Distrikt 55 D 3
Kimbla 55 F 6
Kimi 21 G 8
Kimito 17 L 6
Kimpese 40 A 4

Kinabaly, Mt. 34 E 3
Kinak 45 F 4
Kinchassa 40 B 2
Kinda 40 C 4
Kindia 39 B 3
Kindu 40 D 3
Kinel', River 24 FG 8
Kinel'-Cerkassy 24 F 8
King Chiang Saen 33 C 2
King City 46 B 5
King frederik-VI-Küste 44 W 2
King George Island 57 n 3
King Island 55 a 8
Kingisepp 23 G 5
King Leopold Range 55 D 3
Kingman 46 D 5
Kingman, Reef 54 L 4
Kingoonya 55 F 6
Kings, Island 33 B 4
Kingsbridge 4 E 6
Kingscote 55 F 7
Kingscourt 4 C 5
King's-Lynn 4 G 5
King Sound 55 C 3
Kings Peak, 46 D 4
Kingston (Australia) 55 F 7
Kingston (Canada) 46 M 4
Kingston (Jamaica) 48 D 3
Kingston (New Zealand) 55 f 15
Kingston (USA) 46 N 4
Kingston upon Hull 4 F 5
Kingstown (Ireland) 4 C 5
Kingstown (Lesser Antilles) 51 D 1
Kingussie 4 E 3
Kingwa 44 P 3
King William, Island 44 L 2
King Williams Town 41 D 5
Kinhu, Island 16 L 7
Kinnaird's Head 3 F 3
Kinnekulle 17 E 7
Kinsale 4 B 6
Kinshasa 40 B 3
Kintampo 39 D 4
Kintyre 3 D 4
Kintyre, Islands 4 D 4
Kioga, Island 35 G 5
Kio ling 20 H 7
Kiparissia, G. of 21 E 9
Kipembawe 40 E 4
Kipili 40 E 4
Kipini 40 G 3
Kira Panagia 20 F 8
Kirdimi 37 H 6
Kirensk 22 L 4
Kirgizia 22 G 5
Kiri (Congo) 40 B 3
Kiri (Mali) 37 D 7
Kiri (Sudan) 38 B 5
Kirikkale 25 B 6
Kirin (Ethiopia) 38 B 6
Kirillov 23 N 5
Kirisi 23 I 5
Kirit 38 E 6
Kirkagaç 21 H 8
Kirkcaldy 4 E 3
Kirkenes 17 O 2
Kirkjubajarklaustur 17 S 13
Kirkuk 2 Q 8
Kirkwall 4 E 2
Kirov (Vjatka) 24 E 5
Kirovabad 25 I 5
Kirovo 24 O 7
Kirovograd 25 B 1
Kirovsk 23 I 1
Kirsanov 24 G 9
Kirsehir 25 C 6
Kirtachi 37 E 7
Kirthar, Mt. 26 I 7
Kiruna 17 I 3
Kirura 34 H 5
Kirzac 23 N 6
Kisangari 40 D 2
Kisar, Island 34 G 6
Kisarazu 27 d 13
Kischinev 21 I 4
Kisii 40 E 3
Kisiju 40 F 4
Kisinëv 21 I 4
K ska, Island 22 S 4
Kiskars 17 I 7
Kiskunfélegyh 21 D 4
Kiskunhalas 21 D 4
Kislovodsk 25 G 4
Kissidougou 39 B 4
Kissu, J, Mt.- 37 L 5
Kisumu 40 E 3
Kisurra 28 H 5
Kiswere 40 F 4
Kita 37 C 7
Kitajaur 17 I 3
Kitakyushu 32 D 5
Kitale 40 F 2
Kitchu 31 N 2
Kitega 40 E 3
Kitgum 40 E 2
Kitlairon 20 F 8
Kithira 21 F 9
Kithnos 20 G 9
Kitinen 16 N 3
Kittila 17 M 3
Kitunda 40 F 4
Kitwa 40 D 4

Kiu lung 31 G 5
Kivu 36 F 6
Kivu, Lake 40 D 3
Kiyozumi, Mt. 27 e 13
Kizel 24 I 5
Kizi irmak 25 BE 5-6
Kizi 'skoe 24 L 8
Kiziramuyaga 40 E 3
Kizi jar 25 I 4
Kizljar 25 I 4
Kizyl Arvat 29 C 4
Kizyl Atrek 29 B 4
Kjäkan 17 I 2
Kjakhla 22 L 4
Kjanda 23 N 2
Kjerringöy 17 F 3
Kjmgoke 16 N 6
Kjölhaug, Mt. 16 DE 5
Kjun Tas, Mt. 22 O 3
Kjustendil 21 F 6
K. Karles-Land 56 a
Klabat, Mt. 34 G 4
Kladovo 23 N 4
Klagenfurt 13 F 5
Klaipeda 23 C 7
Klamath 46 B 4
Klamath Falls 46 B 4
Klar 16 E 6
Klawer 36 E 9
Kleinkaras 41 B 4
Klekovaca, Mt. 20 C 5
Klerksdorp 41 D 4
Klescevo 23 N 3
Klenja 23 I 8
Klimovici 23 H 8
Klintehamm 17 H 8
Klintsy 23 I 8
Klippan 17 E 8
Klippladt 41 C 5
Kljazma 1 PQ 4
Klinovec 12 E 3
Klin 23 M 6
Klöfsjö 17 F 5
Klötze 13 D 2
Knin 21 C 5
Knittelfeld 13 F 5
Knjaginino 24 C 7
Knockboy, Mt. 13 B 6
Knox, Costa- 57 d 3
Knoxville 46 L 5
Knud Rasmussen-Land 43 OP 2
Knüll 12 C 3
Knutshöltind, Mt. 16 C 6
Koala 39 D 3
Kobbe Kum 31 D 1
Kobe 32 E 5
Kobjaj 22 N 3
Koblenz 13 B 3
Koboòa 23 L 5
Kobra 24 F 4
Kobra River 24 F 5
Kobrin 23 E 8
Kobroör 34 H 6
Kobuk 45 G 3
Koca 20 H 7-8
Kocabas 20 H 7
Kocani 21 F 7
Ko Chang, Island 33 C 4
Kocher 12 C 4
Kochi 32 D 5
Kodala 30 D 5
Kodiak 45 H 5
Kodina 23 N 3
Kodjar 29 A 2
Kodok 38 B 6
Koffiefontein 41 C 4
Kofiau, Island 34 G 5
Koforidua 39 D 4
Kofu 32 E 4
Kogaluk 44 P 4
Kogaran 55 e 10
Kogil'nik 20 I 4
Koh-i-Baba, Mt. 29 E 5
Kohima 33 A 1
Kohsan 29 D 5
Koida 23 P 1
Koip, Gora-, Mt. 24 L 3
Koja 23 N 3
Köje Do, Island 31 N 4
Kokand 22 G 5
Kokcetav 22 F 4
Kokemäki 17 L 6
Koko Nor, Island 26 N 6
Koko Shilin, Mt. 31 DE 3
Koko Tangla, Mt. 31 DE 4
Kckpekty 22 H 5
Kcksenga 24 B 4
Kcksoak 44 R 4
Kcla, Island 34 H 6
Kcla Peninsula 1 OP 2
Kclaka 34 F 5
Kclan 31 I 3
Kolar 30 C 6
Kolari 17 L 3
Kolda 37 B 7
Kolding 17 C 9
Kole (Zaire, Kasai) 40 C 3
Kole (Zaire, Haut) 40 D 3
Kolenets 23 N 5

Kolesovo 22 Q 2
Kolgolema 23 I 4
Kolguev, Island 1 R 2
Kolhapur 30 B 5
Kolin 21 D 5
Kolita 39 C 3
Kolki 21 G 2
Kolman 37 E 7
Köln 13 B 3
Kolobrzeg 13 F 1
Kologriv 24 C 5
Kologue 38 B 6
Kolojar 24 D 8
Kolomna 23 N 7
Kolomyja 21 G 3
Kolona 37 C 7
Kolokan 39 D 3
Kolorua 55 h 13
Kolp 23 LM 5
Kolpacovo 22 Q 4
Kolpasevo 22 H 4
Kolpino 23 H 5
Kolpny 23 M 8
Kolubara 20 E 5
Kolva 24 IL 4
Kolyk 17 M 1
Kolyma 22 PR 3
Kolymagebirge 22 QR 3
Kolymsk 22 Q 3
Komadougou 35 DE 4
Komagfjord 17 L 1
Komandorskiye Islands 22 R 4
Komarno 21 D 4
Komati 41 E 4
Komatipoort 41 E 4
Kombe 40 C 3
Komodo, Island 34 E 6
Komonos, Mt. 39 D 4
Komotit, Bir- 38 C 4
Komsomolets, Island 22 I 1
Komsomolsk 22 O 4
Konakovo 23 M 6
Konda 22 F 3-4
Kondangan 34 E 5
Kondapsk 23 H 2
Kondinskoe 22 F 3
Kondoa 40 F 3
Kondopoga 23 L 3
Koner 26 p 17
Kong 39 D 4
Kongolo 40 D 4
Kongor 40 E 1
Kongs, -Fj. 17 O 1
Kongsberg 17 C 7
Kongsmo 17 E 4
Kongswinger 17 D 6
Koniechol 13 H 3
Königin-Maud-Kette 57 R-a 1
Königin-Maud-Land 57 iH 2
Konin 13 H 2
Konjuh Planina 21 D 5
Könkäma 16 I 2
Konkaure 39 B 3
Konkobiri 39 E 3
Konne, Island 16 N 5
Konosa 2 Q 3
Konotop 2 O 5
Konskie 13 I 3
Konstantinovka 25 D 1
Konstantinovskij 25 F 2
Kontagora 39 F 3
Kontiha 39 G 4
Kontora 25 G 2
Kontum 30 E 3
Konya 2 O 8
Konza 40 F 3
Konzakovskij Kamen, Mt. 1 T 4
Kooloonong 55 G 6
Kooper 1 Q 5-6
Kootjeskolk 41 C 5
Kopaonik 20 E 6
Kopejsk 24 M 7
Kopet Dagh, Mt. 1 T 8
Koporskij 23 G 5
Kopparberg 17 EF 6
Koprivnica 21 C 4
Kopro 22 M 4
Korab 20 E 7
Korallensee 54 EF 6
Korana 20 B 5
Koratong 40 E 1
Korcë 21 E 7
Korcula 20 C 6
Kordofan 36 FG 4
Korea Bay 31 M 3
Korea, North- 27 Q 5-6
Korea Strait 31 N 4
Korea, South 27 Q 6
Korepino 24 I 4
Korhogo 39 C 4
Korfu 21 D 8
Korfu, Channel 21 E 8
Köris, Mt. 20 C 4
Koriyama 32 F 4
Korkstad 41 D 5
Kormakiti, Cape 28 B 3
Körmend 21 C 4
Kornat 20 B 6
Korneevka 24 E 9
Koror 34 H 3

Körös, Fl. 20 E 4
Korosten' 21 I 2
Koro Toro 37 H 6
Korpilombolo 17 L 3
Korpo 17 I 6
Korsakov 32 F 2
Korsnäs 17 I 5
Korsör 17 D 9
Korsun-Sevcenk 25 A 1
Korti 37 M 6
Kortkeros 24 F 4
Kortrijk 15 F 2
Korvalsk 23 L 4
Koryak Ranger 22 RS 3-4
Kos 20 H 9
Kosa 24 H 5
Kosaka 32 F 3
Koscagyl 29 B 2
Koscian 19 G 2-3
Kosciusko, Mt. 54 E 8
Kos Dagi, Mt. 25 BC 5
Köse Dagi, Mt. 25 G 6
Koseong 31 N 3
Koshan 31 N 1
Koshigaya 27 d 13
Kosi 30 E 3
Kosice 21 E 3
Kos'javom 24 L 1
Kosjerici 21 D 5
Koslan 24 E 3
Kosòng 31 N 3
Kostajnica 21 C 5
Kosti 37 M 7
Kostrzyn 12 F 2
Kos, Yu 24 L 1-2
Koszalin 13 G 1
Köszeg 13 G 5
Kota Agung 34 B 6
Kotabaharu 34 D 5
Kotabaru (Indonesia) 34 E 5
Kota Baru (New Guinea)
  26 o 14
Kota Bharu 33 C 5
Kotabumi 34 B 5
Kotabuna 34 F 4
Kotah 30 C 3
Kota Kinabalu 34 E 3
Kota Kota 40 E 5
Kotelnic 24 E 5
Kotelny Island 22 OP 2
Köthen 13 D 3
Kotien 13 D 3
Kotik, Mt. 31 D 2
Kotka 23 F 4
Kotlas 24 D 4
Kotly 23 G 5
Koton Karifi 39 F 4
Kotor 21 D 6
Kotor, B.of 20 D 6
Kotri 29 E 6
Kotto 35 F 5
Kotuj 22 IL 2-3
Kotzebue 45 F 3
Kouango 40 B 1
Kouango River 40 C 1
Koudougou 39 D 3
Koufonisi 20 H 10
Kouga 40 C 1
Koulen 33 C 4
Koulikoro 37 C 7
Kouloa 37 G 7
Koumbia 39 B 3
Koundé 40 A 1
Koundou 39 B 4
Kouonkan 39 C 4
Kouroulé 37 C 7
Kouroussa 39 C 3
Kousseri 37 H 7
Koutiala 37 C 7
Kova 22 L 4
Kovel' 21 G 2
Kovno 17 L 9
Kowal 13 H 2
Kowloon 31 I 6
Koyuk 45 F 4
Koyukuk 45 G 3
Kozaki 27 e 13
Kozan 28 G 2
Kozane 21 E 7
Kozar 21 C 5
Kozara Planina, Mt. 20 C 5
Kozel'sk 23 L 7
Kozenivkovo 22 M 2
Kozhikode 30 C 6
Kozienice 13 I 3
Kozim-Iz, Mt. 24 M L 3
Koz'modem'jansk 24 D 6
Koz'mogorodskoe 24 C 2
Kozva 24 I 2
Kra 33 B 4
Kra, Isthmus of 26 N 8
Krabi 33 B 5
Krafy 39 D 4
Kragerö 17 C 7
Kragujevac 21 E 5
Krajina 21 C 5
Krapivna 23 M 8
Krasavino 24 D 4
Krasino 22 E 2
Krasivoe 2 V 5
Krasnaja Poljana 25 F 4

Krasnij-Jar 25 L 2
Krasnik 13 L 3
Krasnoarmeisk 25 G 2
Krasnoarmeisk (Yalta) 25 C 3
Krasnoborsk 24 C 4
Krasnodar 25 E 3
Krasnodonetskdja 25 F 1
Krasnoe 23 H 7
Krasnograd 25 C 1
Krasnokamsk 24 H 5
Krasnoslobodsk 24 C 7
Krasnoturinsk 24 M 5
Krasnoufimsk 24 I 6
Krasnouralsk 24 M 5
Krasnousol'skij 24 I 8
Krasnovisersk 24 I 4
Krasnovodsk 27 H 6
Krasnoyarsk 23 I 4
Krasnye-Baki 24 C 6
Krasnyi Cikoj 22 L 4
Krasnyj Kholm 23 M 6
Krasny-Yar 29 A 2
Krastianstad 16 F 8-9
Kratié 33 D 4
Kratovo 21 F 6
Krawang, Cape 26 I 13
Krefeld 13 B 3
Kreider, Le- 37 D 3
Kremencug 25 B 1
Kremenetz 21 G 2
Krems 13 F 4
Krepinskaia 25 E 2
Krestjakh 22 M 3
Krest-Khal'dzaj 22 O 3
Kresttsy 23 I 5
Kretinga 17 I 9
Kreuzberg. 18 D 3
Kribi 39 F 5
Kriegern 6 I 3
Krinichna 25 E 1-2
Krios, Cape 20 F 10
Krishna 30 BC 5
Krishnagar 30 E 4
Kristiansand 17 B 7
Kristiansund 17 B 7
Kristiinankaupunki 17 I 5
Kristineham 17 E 7
Krivaja 21 D 5
Krivoy Rog 25 B 2
Krk 20 B 5
Kroksjö 17 H 4
Krokvik 17 H 2
Kromy 23 L 8
Kronoberg 17 EF 8
Kronstadt, Island 23 G 4-5
Kroonstad 41 D 4
Kropotkin (Soviet Union,
  Krasnodar) 25 F 3
Kropotkin (Soviet Union,
  Irkutsk) 22 M 4
Krotovka 24 F 8
Krsko 21 B 5
Kr-Sulin 25 F 2
Krüger National Park 41 E 3
Krugersdorp 41 D 4
Krui 34 B 6
Krumlov, C. 13 F 4
Krung Thep 27 O 8
Krusevac 21 E 6
Krusevo 21 E 7
Krustpils 23 E 6
Krzna 12 L 2-3
Ksabi 37 D 3
Ksaib, El- 37 C 5
Ksar-Kebir, El 37 C 2
Ksar Torchane 37 B 5
Kuala Dungun 33 C 6
Kualakapuas 34 D 5
Kualakurun 34 D 5
Kuala Lipis 33 C 6
Kuala Lumpur 33 C 6
Kualamandjual 34 D 5
Kuala Selangor 33 C 6
Kuala Trengganu 33 C 5
Kuandang 34 F 4
Kuang hsi Chuang 31 HI 6
Kuang hau 31 I 4
Kuang nan 31 H 6
Kuangsi 26 O 7
Kuangtung 31 IL 6
Kuang yüan 31 H 4
Kuan hsien 31 H 4
Kuan lan 27 g 15
Kuantan 33 C 6
Kuarvekods, Mt. 16 M 2
Kuba 25 L 5
Kuban 25 DF 3-4
Kubas 41 B 3
Kubbum 37 I 7
Kubena 23 ON-45K
Kubenskoe 23 NO 4-5
Kublichi 23 G 7
Kucha 31 C 2
Ku chen 27 f 15
Ku ching (China) 27 f 15
Kuching (Malaysia) 34 D 4
Kudat 34 E 3
Kuddalore 30 C 6
Kudus 34 D 6
Kurgan Tjube 29 E 4
Kurgievo 23 I 2
Kuria Muria, Island 26 H 8
Kuril Islands 22 PQ 5
Kuril'sk, Island 22 P 5
Kurinskij, Cape 29 A 4
Kur'ja 24 I 4
Kurkijoki 23 G 4

Kueite 31 G 3
Kueiyang 31 H 5
Kuen Lun, Mt. 26 MN 6
Kufi 39 F 3
Kufra Oasis 37 I 5
Kufstein 13 E 5
Kuhaifiya 28 G 7
Kuhak 29 D 6
Kuh-i-Aliabad, Mt. 28 M 3
Kuh-i-Alijuq, Mt. 28 M 5
Kuh-i-Angaran, Mt. 29 D 5
Kuh-i-Bampust, Mt. 29 D 6
Kuh-i-Bul, Mt. 28 N 5
Kuh-i-Chah-i-Chäshmmh,
  Mt. 28 I 3
Kuh-i-Furgun, Mt. 29 C 6
Kuh-i-Hazar, Mt. 28 N 7
Kuh-i-Karan, Mt. 29 D 5
Kuh-i-Khabr, Mt. 38 G 2
Kuh-i-Lalehzar, Mt. 29 C 6
Kuh-i-Sängan, Mt. 29 D 5
Kuhistak 29 C 6
Kuhistan 29 BC 5
Kuh-i-Surkh, Mt. 29 C 4
Kuhmo 23 G 2
Kuhtelysvaara 23 H 3
Kui 41 C 4
Kuito 40 B 5
Kuiu 45 N 5
Kuivaniemi 17 M 4
Kujawy 12 H 2
Kuji 32 F 3
Kuju 34 G 5
Kük 29 F 2
Kuka Usus 31 F 3
Kukawa 39 G 3
Kuk-i-Dinar, Mt. 1 S 9
Kukong 41 C 3
Kukuj 23 I 5
Kukup 27 h 16
Kula (Yugoslavia) 21 D 5
Kula (Turkey) 21 I 8
Kulady 22 N 2
Kulaly, Island 29 B 3
Kulay, Island 1 RS 6-7
Kuldiga 17 L 8
Kulema 24 G 2
Kuliab 22 F 6
Kuliai 17 I 9
Kullen 16 E 8
Kulmasa 39 D 4
Kuloj 24 B 2
Kult 16 F 4
Kultala 17 N 2
Kulu 25 B 6
Kulunda 22 G 4
Kulyab 29 E 4
Kum 31 D 2
Kuma 25 GI 3
Kumamoto 32 D 5
Kumanovo 21 E 6
Kumara 22 N 4
Kumasi 39 D 4
Kumba 39 F 5
Kumbakonam 30 D 6
Kumi 40 E 2
Kümingin 16 N 4
Kumla 17 F 7
Kumo 16 L 6
Kunashiri, Island 32 G 3
Kunasir, Island 22 P 5
Kunda 23 F 5
Kung chu ling 31 M 2
Künges, 31 C 2
Kung ho 31 G 3
Kungrad 2 T 7
Kungsäter 17 E 8
Kungsbacka 17 E 8
Kungur 24 I 6
Kungur, Mt. 31 B 3
Kung Veld 41 BC 2
Kunie, Island 54 G 7
Kun ming 31 G 5
Kunna 16 E 3
Kunovat 24 OP 2
Kuolajärvi 23 G 1
Kuopio 17 N 5
Kuorevesi 17 M 6
Kuortane 17 L 5
Kupa 20 BC 5
Kupang 34 F 7
Kupjansk 25 D 1
Kupjansk Uzlovoj 25 D 1
Kuplandeevy 22 G 4
Kupreanof, Cape 45 G 5
Kupreanof, Island 45 N 5
Kura 25 GL 5-6
Kurajalung, Mt. 31 D 4
Kura Soak 55 D 3
Kure, Island 54 I 2
Kurejka 22 HI 3
Kurgan 22 F 4.

Kurla (Kuerhlei) 31 D 2
Kurmuk 38 B 5
Kurmys 24 D 7
Kurnak Dagi, Mt. 25 B 5
Kurnool 30 C 5
Kursk 2 P 5
Kurskiy Z. 16 I 9
Kursu 17 O 3
Kuru 40 D 1
Kurug Tagh, Mt. 31 D 2
Kuruman 41 C 4
Kurume 32 D 5
Kurumkan 22 M 4
Kurunegala 30 D 7
Kuruslu 37 M 5
Kusa 24 L 7
Kusadasi 21 H 8
Kusadasi, Gulf of 20 H 9
Kusaie, Island 54 G 4
Kusan, Mt. 34 E 5
Kushan 31 M 3
Kushiro 32 F 3
Kushka 29 D 4
Kushtia 2 a 11
Ku shui 31 E 2
Kuskokwin 45 F 5
Kuskokwin 45 G 4
Küstala 17 M 3
Kustanaj 22 F 4
Kusva 24 L 5
Kuta 21 F 6
Kutaisi 25 G 4
Kutaradja 34 A 3
Kut-al-Hai 28 H 4
Kut-al-Imara 28 H 4
Kutaradja 34 A 3
Kutatjane 34 A 4
Kutch, Gulf of 30 A 4
Kutch, Rann of- 30 AB 4
Kutkova 23 N 4
Kutno 13 H 2
Kutu 40 B 3
Kutum 37 I 7
Kutun Nor 31 L 1
Kuttivara 23 I 3
Kutu 40 B 3
Kuu yang 31 I 2
Ku yuan 31 H 3
Kuzmovka 22 I 3
Kuznetsk 24 D 8
Kuzreka 23 L 1
Kvalö, Island 16 H 1
Kvaloy Island 16 L 1
Kvalöy Nord, Island 17 H 1
Kvanang, Fj. 16 I 1
Kvarner 18 B 2
Kvas 17 J 3
Kvigtind, Mt. 17 E 4
Kvikkiokk 17 G 3
Kvikne (Norway Hedmark) 17
  D 5
Kvikne (Norway Opland) 17
  C 6
Kviteseid 17 C 7
Kwa 40 B 3
Kwajalein, Island 54 G 4
Kwamouth 40 B 3
Kwekwe 41 D 2
Kwenge 40 B 4
Kwidzyn 13 H 2
Kwilu 35 E 6
Kwanza 35 E 6
Kyabé 40 B 1
Kyaikto 33 B 3
Kyangin 33 B 3
Kyaring 31 F 4
Kyaukpyu 33 A 3
Kyaukse 33 B 2
Kyber, P. 26 L 6
Kyffhäuser 12 D 3
Kyll 12 B 4
Kymi 17 N 6
Kyoga, Lake 40 E 2
Kyoto 32 E 4
Kyparissischer G. 21 E 9
Kyritz 13 E 2
Kyron 16 L 5
Kystalym 22 N 3
Kystovka 22 G 4
Kyushu 32 D 5
Kyyvesi 16 N 6
Kyzyl 22 I 4
Kyzylkum 22 F 5
Kzyl Kija 29 F 3
Kzyl-Orda 22 F 5

Lac 40 G 2
Laccadive Islands 30 B 6
La Ceiba 47 G 4
Lachtan 55 G 6
Lacin 25 I 6
La Coruña 9 B 2
Ladis (Iran) 29 D 6
Ladismith 41 C 5
Ladva 23 L 4
Lady Newnes, B. 57 A 2
Ladysmith 41 D 4
Lafaiete, Conselheiro-52 I 6
Lafia 39 F 4
Lag 16 C 5
Lagan 16 E 8
Lagen 16 C 7
Laghouat 37 E 3
Lagoa 9 B 5
Lagos (Nigeria) 39 E 4
Lagos (Portugal) 9 B 5
Lagos, Los- 53 B 5
Lagosa 40 D 4
La Gouletta 37 G 2
Lagrange 55 C 3
Lahat 34 B 5
Lahej 38 D 5
Lahewa 34 A 4
Lahn 12 BC 3
Laholm 17 E 8
Lahore 29 F 5
Lahr 13 B 4
Lahti 17 M 6
Laï 40 B 1
L'Aia 15 G 2-3
L'Aigle 11 F 2
Laihia 17 L 5
Laihka 33 B 2
Laila 38 E 3
Laingsburg 41 C 5
Lainio 17 L 3
Lainio 16 IL 2-3
Lairi 37 H 7
Lais 34 B 5
Lais 16 G 4
Laisvall 17 G 3
Laja 24 I 1
Lajasti 24 H 7
Lajes 52 G 7
Lajes 52 L 3
Lakat Datu 34 E 4
Lakaträsk 17 I 3
Lak Boggal 40 F 2
Lak Bor 40 F 2
Lake Charles 46 H 6
Lake-Harbour 44 R 3
Lakeland 46 L 7
Lakeport 46 B 5
Lakeview 46 B 4
Lakhnau 30 D 3
Lakonia, Gulf of 20 F 9
Lakse, Fj. 16 N 1
Lali 28 L 4
Lalitpur 30 C 4
Lalorica 20 F 3
Lal'sk 24 D 4
Lambaréné 40 A 3
Lamberts Bay 41 B 5
Lambro 18 B 2
Lamenajve, Mt. 16 H 3
Lamia 21 F 8
Lamon 37 L 6
Lamotrek, Island 54 E 4
Lampasas 46 G 6
Lampedusa, Island 37 G 2
Lampeter 4 D 5
Lampung, Bay 26 I 13
Lamu 40 F 2
Lan, Island 27 f 15
Lanai, Island 54 M 2
Lanak-P. 31 B 4
Lancashire 5 F 3
Lancaster 4 E 4
Lancaster Sound 44 NO 1
Lanchou 31 G 3
Lanciano 19 E 3
Landau 13 D 4
Landegode 17 F 3
Lander 46 E 4
Landes 46 B 5
Landes, Les- 10 E 4-5
Landes d. Lanvaux 11 D 3
Landi Khana 29 F 5
Landi Muammed Amin
  Khan 29 D 5
Landö 16 E 5
Land's End 3 D 6
Landshut 13 D 4
Langa 17 C 8
Langanes 17 U 11
Lang chung 31 H 4
Langdon 46 G 3
Lange Berge 41 B 5
Langeland, Island 16 D 9
Langhe 18 B 2
Langholm 4 E 4
Lang Jökull 16 R 12
Langkaw 33 B 5
Langon 11 E 4
Langöy, Island 17 F 2
Langres 11 H 3
Langres, Plateau de
  10 H 3

Langsa 34 A 4
Langsele 17 F 4
Lang Suan 33 B 5
Languedoc 11 FH 4-5
Lannilis 11 C 2
Lansing 46 L 4
Lan tsang 31 F 6
Lanusei 19 B 5
Lan Yu, Island 31 M 6
Lanzarote, Island 37 B 4
Lanzo Torinese 19 A 2
Laoag 34 F 1
Laoha 31 LM 2
Laohokou 31 I 4
Lao Kay 33 C 2
Laon 11 G 2
Laos 27 O 7-8
Lapa 52 H 7
La Perouse Strait 32 F 2
Lapinlahti 23 F 3
Lappi 17 MO 3
Lappland 17 IN 2-3
Lâpseki 21 H 7
Laptev Sea 22 MO 2
Laptev Strait 22 P 2
Lapuan 16 L 5
Lapuseni Mts. 20 FG 4
Lar 29 B 6
Lara, La 39 G 5
Laramate 52 C 4
Laramie 46 E 4
Larap 34 F 2
Larat, Island 34 H 6
Larch. 44 Q 4
Lärdal 17 B 6
Laredo 46 G 7
Lares 52 C 4
Larino 19 E 4
Larisa 21 F 8
Laristan 29 BC 6
Larjak 22 H 3
Larkana 29 E 6
Larnaka 28 B 3
Larne 4 D 4
Larouco, Mt. 8 C 3
Larsa 28 H 5
Lars Christensen, Coast-
  57 f 2-3
Larsen-Eisschelf 57 O 3
Larvik 17 D 7
Lasdared 38 E 5
Lashio 33 B 2
Lashkar 30 C 3
Lasi 34 F 6
Laskhi Sarai 30 E 3
Läsö, Island 16 D 8
La Spezia 19 B 2-3
La Spezia, Gulf of 18 BC 2-3
Las Qoray 38 E 5
Lastoursville 40 A 3
Lastovo 21 C 6
Latacunga 52 B 2
Latakia 28 B 3
Lätasena 16 L 2
Latina 19 D 4
Latiri 40 D 1
Latitpur 30 C 4
Latium 19 CD 3-4
Latse Dzong 31 D 5
Latvia 23 CF 6
Lau (Nigeria) 39 G 4
Lau (Sudan) 40 E 1
Lau, River 40 E 1
Lau, Island 54 I 6
Lauchanstein 21 C 6
Launceston 55 b 9
La Union 47 D 4
Laura 55 C 3
Lauria 19 EF 4
Laurie, Island 57 N 3
Lauro 18 E 6
Lauro Müller 52 H 7
Lausanne 19 A 1
Laut, Island 34 E 5
Lauta 39 D 3
Laval 11 E 2
Lavangen 17 G 2
Lavansaari, Island 23 F 4-5
La Vela 55 C 1
Laverton 55 C 5
Laviisa 17 N 6
Lavongai, Island 26 o 14
Lavras do Sul 53 F 3
Lawers, Ben-, Mt. 3 D 3
Lawlers 55 C 5
Lawton 46 G 6
Lawu, Gunung-, Mt. 34 D 6
Lay 11 E 3
Laysan, Island 54 I 2
Lea 3 F 6
Lead 46 F 4
Leadville 46 E 5
Leaf 44 Q 4
Leahy, Cape 57 q 2
Lealtà, Island 54 G 6-7
Lealui 41 C 2
Leba 13 G 1
Lebak 34 F 3
Lebam 27 i 16
Lebanon 28 CD 3-4
Lebanon, Mouts 28 CD 3-4
Lébba 37 I 4
Lebedjan' 23 N 8
Lebesby 17 N 1

L

Labbiar 37 C 4
Labé 39 B 3
Labe, River 12 CF 1-3
Labinsk 25 F 3
Labouheyre 11 E 4
Labrador 43 N P 4
Labrea 52 E 3
Labuan 34 E 3
Labunan 34 C 6
Labur, Mt. 40 F 2
Lac 24 H 3

Lebjaze 24 E 6
Lebombo Mountains 41 E 3
Lebrija 9 C 5
Lebu 53 B 4
Lecce 19 FG 4
Lecco 19 B 2
Lech 12 D 4
Lechemti 38 C 6
Lectoure 11 F 5
Leçzna 13 L 3
Leczyca 13 H 2-3
Leda 12 B 2
Ledesma 9 CD 3
Leeds 4 F 5
Leer 13 B 2
Lees Ferry 46 D 5
Leesi 17 M 7
Leeuwarden 15 G 2
Leeuwin, Cape 55 B 6
Lefkas 21 E 8
Lefkas Island 20 E 8
Lefkas, Mt. 20 FG 10
Lefroy 55 C 6
Legaspi 34 F 2
Leghorn 19 C 3
Legnica 13 G 3
Leh, Stadt 30 C 2
Leh, River 14 G 3
Lehcevo 21 F 6
Lehe 37 B 6
Lehrte 13 C-D 2
Lehututu 41 C 3
Lei 31 I 5
Leiah 4 F 5
Leicester 4 F 5
Leichharde 55 F 3
Leichou, M.-I. 31 HI 6
Leiden 15 G 2
Leie 14 F 3
Leine 12 C 2
Leinster 3 C 5
Leinster, Mt. 3 C 5
Leipo 31 K 5
Leipzig 13 E 3
Leira 17 R 12
Leiria 9 B 4
Leirvik 17 A 7
Leith 4 E 4
Leitha Geb. 12 G 5
Leka, Town 17 D 4
Leka, Island 16 D 4
Lekki 39 E 4
Lekop 27 h 16
Lelle 17 M 7
Le Maire Strait 53 CD 7
Lembeni 40 F 3
Lemdiyya 37 E 2
Lemnos 20 G 8
Lempiiälä 17 L 6
Lemva 24 M 1-2
Lemvig 17 C 8
Lena 22 LN 2-4
Lendery 23 H 3
Lengua de Vaca, Pt. 53 B 3
Lengyeltoti 21 C 4
Lenin, Peak- 29 F 4
Leninabad 22,F 5
Leninakan 25 G 5
Leningrad 23 H 5
Leningradskaja 25 E 2
Leninogorsk 22 H 4
Leninsk 25 H 1
Leninsk Kuznetskij 22 H 4
Leninskoe 22 O 5
Lenkoran' 25 L 6
Lens 11 G 1
Lensvik 17 C 5
Lentiira 23 G 2
Lentini 19 E 6
Léo 39 D 3
Leoben 13 F 5
Léon (France) 11 E 5
Leon (Mexico) 47 D 3
Leon (Nicaragua) 48 B 4
Leon (Spain) 9 D 2
Leone, Mt. 18 B 1
Lepold-Küste 57 M 2
Lepanto 21 E 8
Lepel' 23 G 7
Lepini, Mts. 18 D 4
Lepontine A. 18 B 1
Lepsa 23 O 3
Lepsy 22 G 5
Leptis Magna 37 G 3
Lequeitio 9 E 2
Leri 39 F 4
Lérida 9 G 3
Lerma 47 E 3-4
Leros 20 H 9
Lerwick 4 F 1
Lesbos 20 GH 9
Lésima, Mt. 18 B 2
Lesina, L. of 19 E 3-4
Lesjaskog 17 C 5
Leskovac 21 E 6
Leslie 46 H 5
Lesna 20 F 1
Lesogorsk 32 F 2
Lesotho 36 F 8
Lesozavodsk 22 O 5
Lesozavodskij 24 E 5
Lesparre 11 E 4
Lessebo 17 F 8

Lesser Slave Lake 44 F 4
Lessini, Mts. 18 C 2
Lestijarvi 17 M 5
Lesukonskoe 24 D 2
Leszno 13 G 3
Lethbridge 44 G 6
Leti Island 34 G 6
Leticia 52 D 2
Letka, Town 24 E 5
Letka, River 24 EF 5
Leusi 22 F 4
Levanger 17 D 5
Levanzo 18 D 5
Levasi 25 I 4
Levick, Mt. 57 a 2
Levico 19 C 2
Levie 11 a
Levroux 11 F 3
Lewes 4 G 6
Lewis, Island 3 C 2
Lewiston 46 C 3
Lewistown 46 E 3
Lexington 46 L 5
Leyre 10 E 4
Leyte, Island 34 F 2
Leza 23 O 5
Lezajsk 13 L 3
Lhasa 31 E 5
Lho 26 p 16
Lhotse, Mt. 26 p 17
Lhuntse Dzong 31 E 5
Liandambia 40 C 5
Lianga 34 G 3
Liao 31 M 2
Liaocheng 31 L 3
Liao ning 31 MN 2
Liao tung, Gulf of- 31 M 2-3
Liao tung, Pen. 31 M 2-3
Liao yuan 31 M 2
Liard 44 CE 3-4
Liard River 44 D 4
Libebe 41 C 2
Libenge 40 B 2
Liberal (Brazil) 52 E 3
Liberal (USA) 46 F 5
Liberec 13 F 3
Liberia, State 36 BC 5
Liberia, Town 48 B 4
Libertad, La- 47 F 4
Liborta 41 C 1
Libourne 11 E 4
Libreville 39 F 5
Libya 36 EF 3
Libyan Desert 37 IL 4-5
Licata 19 D 6
Li chi 27 f 15
Li chiang 31 G 5
Lichtenfels 44 U 3
Licosa, Pt. 18 E 4
Lid' 23 L 5
Lida 23 E 8
Liddes 7b B 2
Lidkoping 17 E 7
Liège 15 G 3
Lieksa 23 G 3
Lien hsien 31 I 6
Lien hua 31 I 5
Lienz 13 E 5
Liepàja 23 C 6
Lier 15 G 3
Liévin 11 G 1
Liezen 13 F 5
Lifan 31 G 4
Lifford 4 C 4
Lifu, Island 54 G 7
Ligonha 41 F 2
Ligua, La- 53 B 3
Liguria 19 AB 2-3
Ligurian Sea 18 AB 3
Lihou Reefs, Island 55 I 3
Li hsien 31 I 5
Li hua 31 G 4
Likasi 40 D 5
Likati 40 C 2
Likiep, Island 54 G 3
Likimi 40 C 2
Likoma 40 E 5
Likouala-Mossaka 40 B 2-3
Lilibeo, Cape 18 D 6
Li ling 31 I 5
Lille 11 G 1
Lillehammer 17 D 6
Lillesand 17 C 7
Lillhärdal 17 F 6
Lilongwe 41 E 1
Liloy 34 F 3
Lim, River 20 D 6
Lim, Fj. 16 C 8
Lima (Paraguay) 52 F 6
Lima (Peru) 52 B 4
Lima (USA) 46 L 4
Limassol 28 B 3
Limay 53 C 4
Limbang 34 E 4
Limbara, Mt. 18 B 4
Limbazi 17 M 8
Limbdi 30 B 4
Limbiri 40 C 2
Limerick 4 B 5
Limia 8 B 3
Liminka 17 M 4
Limmen Bigt 55 F 3
Limoges 11 F 4
Limousin 11 F 4

Limoux 11 G 5
Limpopo 35 G 8
Limsk 23 O 4
Lina, Town 38 D 2
Lina, River 16 I 3
Linard, Piz- 18 B 1
Linares (Chile) 53 B 4
Linares (Mexico) 47 E 3
Linares (Spain) 9 E 4
Linaro, Cape 18 C 3-4
Linas, Mt. 98 B 5
Lin chuan 31 L 5
Lincoln (Argentina) 53 D 3
Lincoln (United Kingdom) 4 F 5
Lincoln (USA) 46 G 4
Lindau 13 C 5
Lindesberg 17 F 7
Lindesnes, Island 16 B 7
Lindi, Town 40 F 4
Lindi, River 40 D 2
Lindja 22 MN 3
Lindsay 44 P 7
Linea, La- 9 D 5
Linesöy 17 C 4
Lin feng 31 I 3
Lingakok 31 D 5
Lingayen 34 F 1
Lingayen, Gulf of 34 F 1
Ling cheng 31 I 3
Lingeh 29 B 6
Lingen 13 B 2
Lingga Island 34 B 5
Ling ling 31 I 5
Ling ting Yang 27 f 15
Lingtren, Mt. 26 p 16
Linguere 37 A 6
Lin yün 31 H 6
Lin hai 31 M 5
Lin ho 31 H 2
Lin hsi 31 L 2
Lin hsia 31 G 3
Lin i 31 L 3
Linju 31 I 4
Linkoping 17 F 7
Lin kou 31 O 1
Linn, Mt. 46 B 4
Linnbe 4 D 3
Linosa 18 D 7
Lin pien 31 M 6
Lins 52 H 6
Linsäll 17 E 5
Linz 13 F 4
Licn, Gulf of 10 GH 5
Liczno 23 H 7
Lipari Island 18 E 5
Liperi 23 G 3
Lipetsk 23 N 8
Li ping 31 H 5
Lipno 13 H 2
Lipovets 21 I 3
Lipovka 24 E 8
Lippe 13 C 3
Lippstadt 13 C 3
Lira 40 E 2
Liranga 40 B 3
Liri 18 D 4
Liria 9 F 4
Lisala 40 C 2
Lisavetivka 25 D 2
Lisbon 9 B 4
Lisbune, Cape 45 E 3
Li shih 31 I 3
Li shui 31 I 5
Lismore 55 I 5
Lisieux 11 F 2
Lissinga 40 C 5
Lister, Fj. 17 B 7
Lit 17 F 5
Lith 38 D 3
Lithuania 23 DE 7
Litomerice 13 F 3
Litoral 9 B 3
Litovko 22 O 5
Little America 57 Tt 2
Little Rock 46 H 6
Little S. Bernard 18 A 2
Litto 9 E 4
Livenza 18 D 2
Live Oak 46 L 6
Liverpool (Australia) 55 I 6
Liverpool (Canada) 44 S 7
Liverpool (United Kingdom) 4 E 5
Liverpool Bay 4 DE 5
Liverpool, Mt. 55 F 2
Livingston, Island 57 On 3
Livingston 46 D 3
Livingstone (Maramba) 41 D 2
Livingstonia 40 E 5
Livno 21 C 6
Livny 23 M 8
Lvo 17 N 4
Lvonia 23 EF 5-6
Livramento 53 E 3
Livundo 39 G 5
Liwale 40 F 4
Liwiec 13 IL 2

Lizard Point 3 D 7
Lizerorta, Cape 17 I 8
Ljadova 20 I 3
Ljapin 24 M 2-3
Ljora 17 E 6
Ljuban' (URSS, Leningr.) 23 H 5
Ljuban' (URSS, Russia) Bianca) 27 G 8
Ljubim 23 O 5
Ljubisnja, Mt. 21 D 6
Ljubljana 21 B 4
Ljuboten, Mt. 20 E 6
Ljubuski 21 C 6
Ljuca Ongokton 22 L 3
Ljudinovo 23 L 8
Ljurgan, Town 17 H 8
Ljungan, River 16 EG 5
Ljusman 16 G 6
Ljusne 17 G 6
Ljusnedal 17 E 5
Llagostera 9 H 3
Llama 52 B 3
Llancanelo 53 C 4
Llanes 9 D 2
Llanos 49 CD 3
Llanos de Urgel 8 G 3
Llanquihue 53 B 5
Llata 52 B 3
Llerena 9 C 4
Llobregat 8 G 3
Llorena, Pt. 48 C 5
Lluchmayor 9 H 4
Llullaillaco, Mt. 53 C 1
Loa 52 D 6
Loango 40 A 3
Loangue 40 B 4
Lobaye 40 B 2
Lobito 40 A 5
Lobos, 53 E 4
Lobos, Punta de- 52 C 6
Lobos, Cape 47 B 2
Lobos, Island 49 B 4
Locarno 19 B 1
Lo chang 31 I 5
Loches 11 F 3
Lochou Men, 27 f 15
Locle, Le- 13 A 1
Locmine 11 D 3
Locri 19 F 5
Lodejnoe Pole 23 I 4
Lodève 11 G 5
Lodingen 17 F 2
Lodja 40 C 3
Lodji 34 G 5
Lodosa 9 E 2
Lodwar 40 F 2
Lodz 13 H 3
Logaceva 23 I 7
Logan, Mt. 44 B 3
Logansport 46 I 4
Logaskino 22 Q 2
Lögde 16 H 5
Logon 39 G 3
Logouale 39 C 4
Logovaraka 23 H 2
Logrono 9 E 2
Logrosan 9 D 4
Loting 31 I 6
Lohardaga 30 D 4
Lohou 39 C 4
Loikaw 33 B 3
Loing 10 G 2-3
Loir 10 G 2-3
Loire 10 EG 3
Loja (Ecuador) 52 B 2
Loja (Spain) 9 D 5
Loje 40 A 4
Lojma 24 E 4
Lokako 40 C 3
Lokalahti 17 I 6
Lokandu 40 D 3
Loko (Nigeria) 39 F 4
Loko (Central African Republic) 40 B 2
Lokoja 39 F 4
Lokojanov 24 C 7
Lokolama 40 B 3
Lokolo 40 C 3
Lokoro 40 BC 3
Loks 44 S 3
Lokurakwa 40 F 2
Lol 40 D 1
Lolland 16 D 9
Lolung chung 31 F 4
Lom, Town 21 F 6
Lom, River 39 g 14
Loma, Pt. 46 C 6
Loma Alta, Mt. 46 G 7
Lomas. River 52 C 5
Lomas de Zamora 53 E 3
Loma Tina, Mt. 48 E 3
Lombardy 19 BC 1-2
Lomblen, Island 34 F 6
Lombok, Island 34 E 6
Lombovoz 24 M 3
Lomé 39 E 4
Lomela, Town 40 C 3
Lomela, River 40 C 3

Lomié 39 G 5
Lomnica 20 G 3
Lomond 3 D 3
Lomonosov 23 G 5
Lomsak 33 C 3
Lomza 13 L 2
Londo Hills, Mt. 40 F 5
London (United Kingdom) 4 FG 6
London (Canada) 44 O 7
Londonderry 4 C 4
Londonderry, Island 53 B 7
Londrina 52 G 6
Longa, Town 41 B 1
Longa, River 40 A 5
Longa, Island 4 D 3
Long Beach 46 C 6
Longdor, Gora- 22 M 4
Long-Eaton 4 F 5
Longiram 34 E 4
Long Island, Island 46 O 4
Longledju 34 E 4
Longlac 44 N 5
Long Range 44 T 5-6
Longtown 4 E 4
Longwai 34 E 4
Longwy 11 H 2
Long Xuyen 33 D 4
Lonigo 19 C 2
Lons-le-Saunier 11 H 3
Lookout 44 N 5
Lookout, Cape 46 M 6
Looma 39 B 4
Loop Head 3 B 5
Lopatin 21 G 2
Lopatina, Mt. 22 P 4
Lopatino 24 C 8
Lopatka, Cape 22 Q 4
Lopei 31 O 1
Lop Nor 31 E 2
Lopez, Cape 35 D 6
Lopsen'ga 23 N 2
Loputa 40 C 4
Lopydino 24 G 4
Lora, La- 8 DE 2
Loralai 29 E 5
Lora, La- 8 DE 2
Lorca 9 F 5
Lord Howe, Island 54 F 8
Lorena 52 H 6
Lorestan 28 IL 4
Lorient 11 D 3
Lorraine 11 HI 2
Los 17 F 6
Los Angeles (USA) 46 C 6
Los Angeles (Chile) 53 B 4
Losap, Island 54 F 4
Loshan 31 G 5
Loshult 17 F 8
Losombo 40 B 2
Losombo 40 C 3
Losova, Mt. 20 G 4
Lossiemouth 4 E 3
Lot 10 FG 4-5
Lota 53 B 4
Lotagipi Swamp 40 EF 2
Lotaki 23 H 8
Lothlekane Well 41 D 3
Lotten, Mt. 57 L 2
Lotumbe 40 B 3
Loudéac 11 D 2
Loudima 40 A 3
Louga 37 A 6
Louisa 34 D 3
Louisiana 46 H 6
Louis Trichardt 41 D 3
Louisville 46 I 5
Loulé 9 B 5
Lourdes 11 F 5
Lourenço Marques 41 E 4
Louriçal 9 B 3
Louta 37 D 7
Louth 4 F 5
Lövanger 17 I 4
Lovat' 23 H 6-7
Lovcen, Mt. 20 D 6
Lovec 21 G 6
Lovelock 46 C 4
Lovere 19 C 2
Lovoi 40 D 4
Lövstabr 17 G 6
Low, Cape 44 N 3
Lowa 40 D 3
Lowa, River 40 D 3
Lowell 46 N 4
Löwen 15 G 3
Lower 55 g 14
Lower, Pen. 42 M 5
Lower Post 44 D 4
Lower Saxony 13 BD 2
Lowestoft 4 G 5
Lowicz 19 H 2
Lowlands 3 DE 3-4
Lo yang 31 I 4
Loyoro 40 E 2
Lozère 10 G 4
Loznica 21 D 5
Lozovaja 25 D 1
Lozva 1 U 3-4

Lualaba 35 F 6
Luambala 41 F 1
Luanda 40 A 4
Luando 40 B 5
Luanginga 41 C 1
Luang Prabang 27 O 8
Luangua 35 G 7
Luangwa 40 E 5
Luanshya 36 F 7
Luapula 40 D 5
Luarca 9 C 2
Luau 40 C 5
Lubanas, Island 23 F 6
Lubango 41 A 1
Lubartow 4 L 3
Lübeck Bay 13 DE 1
Lübben 13 E 3
Lubbock 46 F 6
Lübeck 13 D 2
Lubefu 40 C 3
Lubilash 40 C 4
Lubksikaping 34 B 4
Lublin 4 L 3
Lubudi 40 CD 4-5
Lubuklinggau 34 B 5
Lubumbashi 40 D 5
Lubutu 40 D 3
Lucania 19 E 4
Lucca 19 C 3
Luce B. 4 D 4
Lucena (Philippines) 34 F 2
Lucena (Spain) 9 D 5
Lucena 21 D 3
Lucerne 13 C 5
Lucerne, L. of 12 C 5
Lucero 47 C 1
Luchenza 41 F 2
Lucie 51 E 3
Lucin 46 D 4
Luckenwalde 13 E 2
Lucki 40 D 3
Luçon 11 E 3
Lucrecia, Cape 48 D 2
Lucusse 40 C 5
Lü-da 31 M 3
Lüderitz 41 B 4
Lüderitz, B. 35 E 8
Ludhiana 30 C 2
Luditz 61 I 3
Ludvika 17 F 6
Ludwigsburg 13 CD 4
Ludwigshafen 13 BC 4
Ludwigslust 13 D 2
Ludza 23 F 6
Luebo 40 C 4
Luémbe 40 C 4
Luena (Angola) 40 BC 5
Luena (Zambia) 40 E 5
Luena, River 41 C 1
Luenha 41 E 2
Luepa 48 G 5
Lueta 40 C 4
Lufira 40 D 4-5
Luga 23 G 5
Luga, River 23 GH 5
Lugano 19 B 2
Lugano, Lake 18 B 1-2
Lugela 41 F 2
Lugenda 35 G 7
Lugh Ganane 38 D 7
Lugnaquilla, Mt. 3 C 5
Lugo (Spain) 9 C 2
Lugoj 21 E 5
Lugovoi 29 F 3
Luhaiya 38 D 4
Luhit 33 B 1
Luhsien 31 H 5
Lui 40 B 4
Luiana 41 C 2
Luiana, River 40 B 4
Luiggi, Ingeniero- 53 D 4
Luilaka 40 C 3
Luishia 40 D 5
Luisiade, Islands 54 F 6
Lujan 53 C 3
Lukafu 40 D 5
Lukashi 40 CD 4
Lukaskashi 41 E 1
Lukenie 40 C 3
Lukolela 40 B 3
Lukuga 35 F 6
Lukula 40 A 4
Lulea 17 L 4
Lulea, River 16 F 3
Lüleburgaz 21 H 7
Luleio 41 F 1
Lulonga 40 B 2
Lulua 35 F 6
Lu lung 31 L 3
Lumadjang 34 D 6
Lumbala 41 C 1
Lumbira 40 E 4
Lumnets 23 F 8
Lumparland 17 I 6
Lumut 33 C 6
Lund 17 E 9
Lunda 35 EF 6
Lundankia 24 D 4
Lundi 41 E 3
Lunding 3 A 1
Lundy, Island 3 D 6
Lune 4 E 5
Lüneburg 13 CD 2
Lunéville 11 I 2
Lung 31 H 1
Lunga 40 C 5

Lung chen 32 C 2
Lung chi 31 L 6
Lung chiang 31 H 5
Lung chow 31 H 6
Lung hsi 31 G 4
Lung hua 27 f 15
Lung kang 27 g 15
Lung kiang (Tsitsihar) 31 M 1
Lungheh 33 A 2
Lung ling 31 F 6
Lung ming 31 H 6
Lung shan 27 f 15
Lunguebung 35 F 7
Lung yen 31 L 5
Luni 30 B 3
Luninets 21 H 1
Luofu 40 D 3
Luozi 40 A 3
Lu pei 31 M 2
Lupin 31 L 1
Lure, Mts. 10 H 4
Luribay 52 D 5
Lurin 52 B 4
Lurio 41 G 1
Lurio, River 35 G 7
Luristan 1 R 9
Luros 20 E 8
Luröy 17 E 3
Lusaka 41 D 2
Lusambo 40 C 3
Lusatia 12 EF 3
Lusatian Mts. 20 B 2
Lu shan 31 I 4
Lushoto 40 F 3
Luster 17 B 6
Lu tien 31 G 5
Lutful 24 F 6
Luton 4 F 6
Lutpul 24 F 6
Lutsk 21 G 2
Lützow-Holmbukta, B. 57 H 3
Luvua 40 D 4
Luwegu 40 F 4
Luxembourg 15 H 4
Luxembourg, State 15 GH 4
Luze 24 DE 4-5
Luzern 19 C 1
Luzki 23 F 7
Luznice 20 B 3
Luzon 34 F 1
Lvov 21 G 3
Iyakhov Islands 22 P 2
Lyallpur 29 F 5
Lybster 4 E 2
Lyck 13 L 2
Lycksele 17 H 4
Lydenburg 41 E 4
Lydia 21 HI 8
Lyme Bay 3 E 6
Lyna 12 I 1
Lynchburg 46 M 5
Lyngen 17 I 2
Lynn Lake 43 I 4
Lyons 55 B 4
Lysahora 20 D 3
Lysaja Gora 23 F 7
Lyse, Fj. 17 B 7
Lysekil 17 D 7
Lysica, Mt. 12 I 3
Lyskovo 24 C 6-7
Lysogory 12 I 3
Lys'va 22 E 4
Lysvik 17 E 4
Lysye Gory 24 C 9
Lyubytino 23 I 5

M

Ma 31 F 4
Ma'an 28 C 5
Maan Selkä 17 O 3
Ma'arret en Na'man 28 D 3
Maas 14 G 3
Maastricht 15 G 3
Mababe Flats 41 C 2
Mabenga 40 B 3
Mabote 41 E 3
Mabrouk (Mali) 37 D 6
Mabrouk (Mauritania) 37 B 5
Mabrous 37 G 5
Mabruk 37 H 4
Maca 52 C 2
Macaé 52 I 6
Macane 41 E 3
Macapa 52 G 2
Macas 52 B 2
Macao 31 I 3
Macau 52 L 3
Macauba 52 G 4
Macaubas 52 I 4
Maccio 52 L 3
Maccio, Pt. 52 L 2
Macclesfield 4 E 5
Mac Dermitt 46 C 4
Macdhui, Ben-, Mt. 3 E 3
Macdonell Ranges 55 E 4
Macedonia 21 EF 7
Macenta 39 B 4
Mac Grath 45 G 4
Machakos 40 F 3
Machala 52 B 2
Machallie, Island 55 G 4
Machichaco, Cape 8 E 2

Machiques 51 B 1
Macia 41 E 4
Macina 35 C 4
Mackay 55 H 4
Mackenna, Vicuna- 53 D 3
Mackenzie Bay (Canada) 44 B 1-2
Mackenzie, Bay of Antarctica 57 F 3
Mackenzie, Mts. 44 CD 3
Mackenzie, River 44 BE 2-3
Maclear 41 D 5
Macmillan 44 C 3
Macobesa 41 C 2
Macomer 19 B 4
Mâcon (France) 11 H 3
Macon (USA) 46 L 6
Macquarie, River 54 E 8
Macquarie, Island 57 B 4
Macujer 51 B 2
Macvalanana 41 c 7
Madaba 40 F 4
Madadi 37 I 6
Madagascar 36 H 7-8
Madahiyat 38 E 2
Madain Salih 28 D 7
Madama 37 G 5
Madao 37 F 7
Madariaga, General- 53 E 4
Madaripur 27 b 11
Maddalena, La- 19 BC 4
Maddalena Island 18 B 4
Madeira Islands 37 A 3
Madeira, Rio 52 F 2
Madenassa Veld 41 D 2
Madhar 38 C 2
Madhumali 27 a 11
Madhupur 30 E 4
Madimba 40 B 3
Madiq, El- 37 M 5
Madison 46 I 4
Madium 34 D 6
Madjene 34 E 5
Madjngo 39 G 5
Madonie, Le- 18 DE 6
Madra Dagi, Mt. 20 H 8
Madras 30 D 6
Madre de Dios 52 C 4
Madre de Dios, Islands 53 A 7
Madre de Dios, Rio 49 CD 5
Madrid 9 E 3
Madrid, La- 53 C 2
Madridejos 9 E 4
Madrona, Serra- 8 D 4
Madukani 40 F 3
Madura, Island 34 D 6
Madura, Strait 26 m 13
Madurai 30 C 7
Madvar, Mt. 28 M 5
Maebashi 32 E 4
Maella 9 G 3
Maestrazgo, El- 9 F 3
Mafate 39 G 3
Mafaza 38 B 5
Mafia, Island 40 G 4
Mafikeng 41 D 4
Mafra 9 B 4
Magadan 22 Q 4
Magadi 40 F 3
Magalo 38 D 6
Magangue 51 B 2
Magara 28 B 2
Magaria 37 F 7
Magas 29 D 6
Magburaka 39 B 4
Magci 22 P 4
Magdagaci 22 N 4
Magdala 38 C 5
Magdalena 52 E 4
Magdalena, Bay 47 B 3
Magdalena, River 50 C 3
Magdalena Island (Canada) 44 S 6
Magdalena Island (Chile) 53 B 5
Magdalena, Rio 47 B 1
Magdeburg 13 DE 2
Magelang 34 D 6
Magellan, Strait of 53 BC 7
Mageröy 16 M 1
Maggie's Spring 55 E 5
Maggiore, Lake 18 B 1-2
Magilev Podol'skij 21 H 3
Magina, Sierra- 8 E 5
Maglie 19 G 4
Magnitogorsk 22 E 4
Magnolia 46 H 7
Magra 18 B 2
Magro 9 F 4
Maguarinho, Cape 52 H 2
Magude 41 E 3
Magumeri 39 G 3
Magwe 33 A 2
Mähabad 28 H 2
Mahabo 41 b 8
Mahagi 40 E 2
Mahail 38 D 4
Mahajanga 41 C 7
Mahalapye 41 D 3

Mahallat Bala 28 M 4
Mahaly 41 c 8
Mahanadi 26 M 7
Mahanje 40 F 5
Mahanoro 41 c 7
Mahara, El- 37 A 6
Maharuga 37 G 4
Mahatsinjo 41 c 7
Mahavavy 41 c 7
Mahdia 37 G 2
Mahé 30 D 6
Mahebourg 41 a
Mahenge 40 F 4
Mahi 30 B 4
Mahlabatini 41 E 4
Mahmudabad 28 N 2
Mahon (Upper Volta) 39 C 3
Mahon (Spain) 9 I 4
Maicuru 51 F 3-4
Maidan 28 H 3
Maidan-i-Naftun 28 L 5
Maiduguri 39 G 3
Maiella, La- 19 DE 3
Maikain 29 G 1
Maimana 29 D 4
Main 12 C 4-5
Mainalon, Mt. 20 F 9
Mai-Ndombe, Lake 40 B 3
Maine 46 O 3-4
Maine Turenna 11 EF 2-3
Mainland, Island 3 F 1
Main Strait 27 hi 16
Maintenon 11 F 2
Maintirano 41 b 7
Mainz 13 C 4
Maio, Island 39 a
Maipu 53 E 4
Maipuco 52 B 2
Maipures 51 C 2
Maiquetia 51 C 1
Maira 18 A 2
Mairi 52 I 4
Maisi, Pt. 48 E 2
Maisur 30 C 6
Mait 38 E 5
Maintencillo 53 B 3
Maitland 55 I 6
Maitne 37 B 4
Maitsang 31 G 4
Maja 22 O 3-4
Majari 52 C 2
Majerten 38 EF 5-6
Majevica Planina, Mt. 20 D 5
Maji 38 C 6
Majma'a 38 E 2
Majoli 51 E 3
Maju, Island 34 G 4
Makabana 40 A 3
Makal 22 E 5
Makala 40 D 2
Makale 38 C 5
Makandjia 40 B 2
Makanya 40 F 3
Makarib 24 E 3
Makarikari Salt Pan 41 D 3
Makarov 22 P 5
Makassar 34 E 6
Makeevka 25 DE 1
Makemo, Island 54 N 6
Makeni 39 B 4
Makhac Kala 25 I 4
Makharadze 25 F 5
Makhmud 25 H 3
Makin, Island 54 H 4
Makinda 36 G 6
Makinnon Road 40 F 3
Makna, Mt. 37 E 3
Maknassy 37 F 3
Mako 21 E 4
Makokou 39 G 5
Makongga, Mt. 34 F 5
Makoua 40 B 3
Maksamaa 17 L 5
Makstog 39 D 6
Maku 25 H 6
Makumbako 40 E 4
Makumbi 40 C 4
Makurdi 39 F 4
Mal 37 B 6
Mala 17 H 4
Mala, Pt. 48 D 5
Malabar Coast 30 B 6
Malabo 39 F 5
Maladeta, Mt. 8 G 2
Malaga 9 D 5
Malagarasi 40 E 4
Malaimbandy 41 b 8
Malaita, Island 54 G 5
Malaja Visera 23 I 5
Malaja Viska 25 A 1
Malakal 37 M 8
Malakka 33 C 6
Malakka Strait of 34 B 4
Malang 34 D 6
Malange 40 B 4
Malangen, Fj. 16 G 2
Malanville 39 E 3
Malanka 55 E 2
Mälaren L. 16 G 7
Malargüe 53 C 4
Malatya 2 P 8
Malawi 36 G 7

Malay Peninsula 26 NO 9
Malaya 27 O 9
Malaybalay 34 G 3
Malayer 28 L 3
Malawi, Lake (Nyasa) 35 G 7
Malazgirt 25 G 6
Malbork 13 H 1
Malchin 13 E 2
Malden, Island 54 M 5
Maldonado 53 E 3
Male 27 L 9
Maleas, C. 20 F 9
Malediven 27 L 9-10
Malegaon 30 B 4
Malekula, Island 54 G 6
Malela 40 A 4
Malème 37 A 7
Malese, Pen.- 33 BC 5-6
Malha 37 L 6
Malheur Lake 46 C 4
Mali 40 D 3
Mali, River 33 B 1
Mali Çikes, Berg. 21 D 7
Malili 37 B 6
Malin Ead 3 C 4
Malinau 34 E 4
Malindi (Kenia) 40 G 3
Malindi (Rhodesia) 41 D 2
Malinovo 23 M 8
Malko Tårnovo 21 H 6
Mallawi 37 M 4
Mallorca 9 H 4
Mallow 4 B 5
Mallowa Well 55 C 4
Malmberget 17 I 3
Mâlmédy 15 G 3
Malmö 17 E 9
Malmyz (Khabarovsk)) 22 O 5
Malmyz (Kirov) 24 F 6
Maloca 51 E 3
Maloclap 54 H 4
Malojaroslavets 23 M 7
Malongwe 40 E 4
Malpelo, Island 50 B 3
Malström 19 E 3
Malta 19 E 7
Maltahöhe 36 E 8
Malung 17 E 6
Malvan 30 B 5
Malye Karmakuly 22 E 2
Malyj Tastakh 22 O 3
Malyj Uzen' 25 L 1
Mama 22 M 4
Mamadys 24 F 7
Mamanguape 52 L 3
Mambasa 40 D 2
Mamberamo 26 no 14
Mambére 40 B 1
Mambone 41 E 3
Mamfe 39 F 4
Mamon 25 F 1
Mamoré 49 D 5
Mamykan 22 N 3
Mamykovo 24 F 7
Man 36 C 5
Man, Island 3 D 4
Mana (French. Guiana) 51 F 2
Mana (Sumatra) 34 B 5
Mana, Rio 51 F 3
Manacapuru 52 E 2
Manacor 9 H 4
Manado 34 F 4
Managua 48 B 4
Managua, Island 48 B 4
Manakara 41 c 8
Manama 38 E 2
Manama Doha 27 g 7
Manakara 41 c 7
Mananjary 41 c 8
Manantenina 41 c 8
Manar, Jebel-, 26 G 8
Manas 31 D 2
Manas, River 31 D 1-2
Manaus 52 E 2
Manavgat 28 E 2
Mancha, La- 9 E 4
Manchester 4 F 5
Manchom 40 E 1
Manchuria 31 MO 1
Mancora 52 A 2
Manda 40 E 5
Mandal 17 B 7
Mandalay 33 B 2
Mandalaya, G. of 20 H 9
Mandal Gobi 31 H 1
Mändali 28 H 4
Mandals 16 B 7
Mandan 46 F 3
Mandasawu, Mt. 34 F 6
Mandasor 30 C 4
Mande 40 CM44
Mandeb, Bab el- 38 D 5
Mandi 30 C 2
Manding 37 C 7
Mandinga 51 A 2
Mandioli, Island 34 G 5

Mandla 30 D 4
Mandronarivo 41 c 8
Mandungu 40 C 2
Manduria 19 F 4
Manera 41 b 8
Manfalut 37 M 4
Manfredonia 19 F 4
Manfredonia, Gulf of 18 F 4
Manga 37 G 6-7
Mangai 40 B 3
Mangaia, Island 54 M 7
Mangalia 21 I 6
Mangalore 30 B 6
Mangareva, Island 54 O 7
Mangany, Mt. 26 NO 5
Mangaung 40 C 1
Mangawe, Pt. 47 D 4
Manguali 41 E 3
Mangueira, Lake of 53 F 3
Mangyslak Pen. 25 MN 3-4
Mani (China) 31 D 4
Mani (Colombia) 51 B 3
Mania 41 c 7
Manicoré 50 D 4
Manifold, Cape 55 I 4
Manihi, Island 54 N 6
Manihiki, Island 54 L 6
Manikuagan, River 44 R 5-6
Manila 34 F 2
Maniniam 39 C 3
Manipur 33 A 2
Manisa 21 H 8
Manistee 46 I 4
Manitoba 44 IM 4
Manitoba, Island 44 L 5
Manitoulin 44 O 6
Manizales 51 A 2
Mänjil 28 L 2
Mankarga 39 D 3
Mankato 46 H 4
Mankono 39 C 4
Mankoya 41 C 1
Manly 55 e 10
Manmad 30 B 4
Mannar, Gulf of 30 C 7
Mannheim 13 C 4
Mano 39 B 4
Mano, River 39 B 4
Manokwari 34 H 5
Manombo 41 b 8
Manono 40 D 4
Manosque 11 H 5
Manresa 9 G 3
Mans, Le- 11 G 3
Mansel 44 OP 3
Mansfield (Australia) 55 H 7
Mansfield (United Kingdom) 4 F 5
Mansfield (USA) 46 L 4
Manso 39 D 4
Manso-ou 52 G 5
Mansura, El- 37 M 3
Mantaro 52 B 4
Mantecal 51 C 2
Mantes 37 E 6
Manthani 30 C 5
Manti 46 D 5
Mantiouga 37 C 6
Mänttä 17 M 5
Mantua 19 C 2
Manu 52 C 4
Manuel Antonio 52 F 4
Manuel Benavides 47 D 2
Manuelzinho 52 G 3
Manui, Island 34 F 5
Manuk, River 26 I 13
Manuk, Island 34 H 6
Manus, Island 26 o 14
Manyas, Lake 20 H 7
Manyc 2 O 5
Manyc, Eastern 25 GH 3
Manyoni 40 E 4
Manyuki 40 F 2
Manzai 29 F 5
Manzanares 9 E 4
Manzanillo (Cuba) 48 D 2
Manzanillo (Mexico) 47 D 4
Mao 37 H 7
Mao ming 31 I 6
Mao mu 31 F 2
Mapaga 34 E 5
Mapai 41 E 3
Mapastepec 47 F 4
Mapien 31 G 5
Mapire 48 P 5
Maple Creek 44 H 5
Mapuera 52 F 2
Maputo 41 E 4
Maqdam, Cape 38 C 4
Maqna 28 C 6
Maquela do Zombo 40 B 4
Maquinchao 53 C 5
Mar 31 E 4
Mara 40 EF 3
Maraa 52 D 2
Maraba 52 H 3
Maraca, Island 51 F 3
Maracaibo 51 B 1

Maracaibo, Lake 51 B 2
Maracav 51 C 1
Marada 37 H 4
Maradi 37 F 7
Maradu 39 F 3
Maragheh 28 I 2
Marajó, Baia de 52 H 2
Marojo, Ilha 52 GH 2
Marakanata 51 E 3
Marakend 25 H 6
Maralbashi 31 B 3
Marali 40 B 1
Maralinga 55 E 6
Maramba (Livingstone) 41 D 2
Maramba (Tanzania) 40 F 3
Maran 28 L 3
Marangandu 40 F 4-5
Maranguape 52 L 2
Maranhao (Sao Luis) 52 I 2
Maranhao, R. 52 H 4
Maranoa 55 H 5
Maranon, Rio- 52 B 2-3
Marari 52 D 3
Maras, 28 D 2
Marau 52 L 4
Maravilha 52 D 3
Marble Bar 55 B 4
Marburg 13 C 4
Marcali 21 C 4
Marcelino 52 D 2
Marche (Italy) 19 D 3
Marche (Belgium) 15 G 3
Marche (France) 11 FG 3
Marchena 9 D 5
Marchena, Island 52 a
Marcillat 11 G 3
Marcus, Island 54 F 2
Mar de Plata 53 E 4
Mardin 28 F 2
Mare, Island 54 G 7
Marechal Deodoro 52 L 3
Maree, Island 3 D 3
Maremma 18 C 3
Marettimo 18 CD 6
Marfa 46 F 6
Margarita, Island 51 D 1
Margate 4 G 6
Margeride, La-, Mt. 10 G 4
Maria, Sierra de- 9 E 5
Maria, Island 54 M 7
Marie-Byrd-Land 57 R 1-2
Mariager, Fj. 17 D 8
Mariampole 17 L 9
Marianao 48 C 2
Marianen Groben 54 E 3
Marianne, Island 54 E 3
Mariato, Pt. 42 M 9
Maria van Diemen, Cape 55 g 12
Marib 38 D 4
Maribo 16 D 9
Maribor 21 B 4
Maridi 40 D 2
Marié 52 D 2
Marie Galante, Island 48 G 3
Mariehamn 17 H 6
Mariental 41 B 3
Mariestad 17 E 7
Marietta 46 L 5
Mariinsk 22 H 4
Marilia 52 G 6
Marinarivo 41 c 7
Maringa 40 C 2
Maringhat 27 a 12
Marion 46 I 4
Marion Reef 55 I 3
Maripa (Brazil) 51 C 2
Maripa (Venezuela) 51 C 2
Maritime A. 18 A 2
Maritsa 20 H 7
Mariveles 34 F 2
Marjata 27 a 12
Markha 26 P 3
Markham, Albert-, 57 B 1
Markham, 57 B 1
Markovsk 24 D 1
Markuet 40 F 2
Marlborough (Australia) 55 H 4
Marlborough (Guyana) 51 E 2
Marmande 11 F 4
Marmara 21 H 7
Marmara Island 20 H 7
Marmara, Sea of 20 HI 7
Marmarica 37 I 3
Marmaris 21 I 9
Marmatjakko, 17 H 2
Marmolada 18 CD 1
Marne River 10 GH 2-3
Maroa 51 C 3
Maroantsétra 41 c 7
Maroba 52 L 5
Marokau, Island 54 N 6
Marolambo 41 c 8
Maromandia 41 c 6
Marondera 41 D 3
Maroni 51 F 2
Maros 34 E 6
Marotandrano 41 c 7

Marotiri 54 N 7
Maroua 37 G 7
Marovoay 41 c 7
Marquesado 53 C 3
Marquesas, Islands 54 NO 5
Marquette 46 I 3
Marquise 11 F 1
Marra, Mt. 35 F 4
Marrakech 1 E 9
Marrargiu, Cape 18 AB 4
Marrawah 55 a49
Marre 55 F 5
Marroqui, Pt. 8 D 5
Marsa 37 A 6
Marsabit 40 F 2
Marsabit, Mt. 40 F 2
Marsa el Brega 37 H 3
Marsa el-Mreisa 37 L 3
Marsa Fanoidig 38 C 3
Marsala 19 CD 6
Marseille 11 H 5
Mars Fjelt, Mt. 16 F 4
Marsh, Islands 46 H 7
Marshall (Liberia) 39 B 4
Marshall (USA) 46 G 4
Marshall, Island 54 GH 3
Marshall Creek 55 F 4
Marstrand 17 D 8
Martaban 33 B 3
Martaban, Gulf of 33 B 3
Martigny 19 A 1
Martigues 11 H 5
Martin Pen. 57 q 2
Martina Franca 19 F 4
Martinique 50 D 2
Martin Vaz, Island 50 H 6
Martos 9 D 5
Martre, La-, Island 44 F 3
Martuk 29 C 1
Marud 34 D 4
Maràf 38 D 6
Maràim 52 L 4
Marun 28 L 5
Maràtea, Island 54 O 7
Marvas 38 F 1
Marvejols 11 G 4
Marwar 30 B 3
Marx 24 D 9
Mary 22 F 6
Maryland (Liberia) 39 C 5
Maryland (USA) 46 M 5
Maryoorough 55 I 5
Marysvale 46 D 3
Maryville 46 H 4
Marzafal 37 D 6
Masafa 41 D 1
Mas Afuera, Island 49 B 7
Masamba 34 F 5
Masan 31 N 3
Masbate 34 F 2
Masbate, Island 34 F 2
Mascarene, Island 41 a
Mascat 27 H 7
Masela, Island 34 G 6
Maseru 41 D 5
Mashhad (Corassan) 29 C 4
Mashhad (Esfahan) 28 M 4
Mashi 41 C 2
Mashkel 29 D 6
Mashona 41 DE 2
Masibi 41 E 4
Masindi 40 E 2
Masindi Port 40 E 2
Masira 27 H 7
Masisea 52 C 3
Masisi 40 D 3
Masjid-i-Solaiman 28 L 5
Mask 3 B 5
Mason City 46 H 4
Masovia 12 IL 2
Masöy 17 M 1
Masqat 29 C 7
Massa 19 BC 3
Massaca 41 B 2
Massachussets 46 N 4
Massakori 37 H 7
Massa Marittima 19 C 3
Massangena 41 E 3
Massawa 38 C 4
Massenya 37 H 7
Masset 44 C 5
Massiac 11 G 4
Massif Central 10 G 4
Masson, Island 57 E 3
Massu, Mt. 34 F 4
Masterton 55 h 14
Mastura 38 C 3
Masuria 13 IL 2
Masvingo 41 E 3
Masyaf 28 D 3
Matabele 35 FG 7
Matadi 40 A 4
Matagalpa 48 B 4
Matagorda Bay 46 G 7
Matam 37 B 6
Matamoros 47 E 2
Matancita 47 B 2
Matandu 40 F 4
Matang 31 G 4
Matankari 37 E 7
Matanzas 48 C 2
Matapan, Cape 20 F 9
Matara 30 D 7
Mataram 34 E 6
Mataro 9 H 3

Matata 55 h 13
Matatiele 41 D 5
Mategua 52 E 4
Matehuala 47 D 3
Matera 19 F 4
Materkovsk 24 E 6
Matese 18 E 4
Mateur 37 F 2
Matha 11 E 4
Mathura 30 C 3
Mati (Philippines) 34 G 3
Mati 20 D 7
Matiacuali 39 E 3
Matla 27 a 12
Matlabas 41 D 3
Mato Grosso 52 F 5
Mato Grosso, Plateau of 49 E 5
Matra 21 DE 4
Matra, Mts. 20 DE 4
Matrah 29 C 7
Matruh 37 L 3
Matsang 31 C 4-5
Matsena 39 G 3
Matsudo 27 d 13
Matsue 32 D 4
Matsumae 32 F 3
Matsumoto 32 E 4
Matsuyama 32 D 5
Mattagami 44 O 6
Matterhorn 18 A 2
Matthew, I. 54 H7
Matua 34 D 5
Matua, Island 22 Q 5
Matun 29 E 5
Maturin 51 D 2
Matveeyka 24 G 8
Maua 41 F 1
Ma-ubin 33 B 3
Maués 52 F 2
Maués, Rio 52 F 2
Maug, Island 54 I 3
Maugyslak, pen. 25 M 3
Maui, Island 54 M 2
Maul 37 G 6
Mauléon 11 E 5
Maumere 34 F 6
Maun 41 C 2
Mauna Kea, Mt. 54 M 3
Maungdaw 33 A 2
Maunoir 44 E 2
Mau Ranipur 30 C 3
Maures, M.ts des- 10 I 5
Mauriac 11 G 4
Maurice 55 E 5
Mauritania 36 BC 4
Mauritius 41 a
Maurs 11 G 4
Mavas 16 G 3
Mavinga 41 C 2
Mawambi 40 D 2
Mawkmai 33 B 2
Mawlu 33 B 2
Mayagnana Passage 48 E 2
Mayaguana 48 E 2
Mayagüez 48 F 3
Mayagüez 48 F 3
Mayaki 37 F 7
Mayenne 10 E 3
Maykop 25 F 3
Mayo 47 C 2
Mayotte 41 c 6
Mayoumba 40 A 3
Maysville 46 L 5
Mayum, Pass 31 C 4
Mayung 27 f 14
Mazabuka 41 D 2
Mazagan 37 C 3
Mazamet 11 G 5
Mazan 53 C 2
Mazanderam 28 M 2
Mazara del Vallo 19 D 6
Mazar-i-Sharif 29 E 4
Mazarron 9 F 5
Mazarron, Puerto 9 F 5
Mazatlan 47 C 3
Mazdak 31 D 3
Mazeikiai 17 L 8
Mazirbe 16 L 8
Mazoe 41 E 2
Mbabane 41 E 4
M'bahiakro 39 D 4
M'bala 40 C 1
Mbale 40 E 2
M'Balmayo 39 G 5
Mbam 39 G 4
Mbandaka 40 B 2
Mbanga 39 F 5
Mbanza-Congo 40 A 4
Mbarara 40 E 3
M'Bari 40 C 1
M'Bari, River 40 C 1
Mbassaï 40 B 1
Mbemkuru 40 F 4
Mbére 40 A 1
Mbeya 40 E 4
M'Bomou 40 C 2
Mbout 37 B 6
M'Bres 40 B 1
M'Bridge 40 A 4
Mbulamua 40 E 2
Mc Clintock Island 22 E 1
Mc Clure Strait 45 PQ 1
Mc Cook 46 F 4
Mc Kinley, Mts. 45 H 4
M'Clintock Channel 44 PL 1

Mc Mundo, Strait 57 a 2
Mc Robertson, Land 57 f 2
Mealy, Mt. 44 T 5
Mearim 52 I 3
Mecca 38 C 3
Mechelin 15 G 3
Mechems 37 C 4
Mecklenburg 12 DE 2
Mecklenburg - Pomerania 13 DE 2
Mecsek 20 D 4
Medan 34 A 4
Medanosa, Pt. 53 C 6
Medellin 51 A 2
Medenin 37 G 3
Mederdra 37 A 6
Medford 43 G 5
Medias 21 G 4
Medicine Hat 44 G 5
Medina 38 C 3
Medina del Campo 9 D 3
Medina Sidonia 9 D 5
Mediterranean Sea 1 FO 8-9
Mediwa 34 H 5
Medjana 24 C 7
Medjerda, River 37 F 2
Mednogorsk 29 C 1
Médoc 10 E 4
Meduno 10 E 3
Medveditsa, River (Wolga) 23 LM 6
Medveditsa, River (Don) 25 G 1
Medvednica, Mt. 20 C 5
Medvezegorsk 23 L 3
Medyn 23 L 7
Meekalharra 55 B 5
Meerut 30 C 3
Mega (Ethiopia) 38 C 7
Mega (Indonesia) 34 H 5
Megara 21 F 8
Meghna, River 27 b 11
Mehadia 21 F 5
Meherpur 27 a 11
Mehkar 30 C 4
Mehsana 30 B 4
Meiapa, Mt. 34 E 4
Meidi 38 D 4
Meidoua, El- 37 A 5
Meidougau 40 A 1
Mei hsien 31 L 6
Meiktila 33 B 2
Meimet 28 M 4
Meiningen 13 D 3
Meio 52 H 4
Meishan 31 G 4
Meissen 13 E 3
Meissner, Mt. 12 CD 3
Mejillones 53 B 1
Meknés 37 C 3
Meko 39 E 4
Mekong 26 O 8
Mekran 29 CD 6
Mekrou 39 E 3
Melanesia 54 DH 4-6
Melbourne 55 a 8
Melbourne Island 44 I 2
Mele, Cape 18 B 3
Melekess 24 E 7
Meleuz 24 H 8
Melfi (Chad) 37 H 7
Melfi (Italy) 19 E 4
Melghir, Shott- 35 D 2
Melilla 37 D 2
Melitopol' 25 C 2
Melito Porto Salvo 19 EF 6
Melito Porto Salvo, Pt. 18 EF 6
Melk 13 F 4
Melk Fjeld, Mt. 16 F 3
Mella 18 C 2
Mellanga 37 I 6
Melle 11 E 3
Mellem 37 L 8
Mellerud 17 E 7
Melnik (Bulgaria) 21 F 7
Melnik (Czechoslovakia) 21 B 2
Melnikovo 23 G 4
Melo 53 F 3
Melouprey 33 D 4
Melöy 37 F 2
Melsetter 41 E 2
Meltaus 17 M 3
Melton 13 F 5
Melun 11 G 2
Melut 38 B 5
Melville, Bay of 42 O 2
Melville, Cape 55 G 2
Melville, Canal 42 HI 2
Melville Islands (Australia) 55 E 2
Melville Island (Canada) 42 HI 2
Melville, Lake. 44 ST 5
Melville Mts. 44 E 2
Melville Pen. 44 NO 2
Memba 41 G 1
Membij 28 D 2
Memboro 34 E 6
Memmingen 13 D 5
Memphis 46 I 6
Mena-al-Ahmadi 28 L 6
Ménaka 37 E 6
Menakeb, El- 37 D 4

Menan 26 NO 8
Mena, Wadi. 28 D 6
Menderes 21 HI 9
Medif 37 G 3
Meyanburg 13 E 2
Mendocino, Cape 46 B 4
Mendong Gomba 31 D 4
Mendoza 53 C 3
Menfi 19 D 6
Menfi 36 E 3
Menggala 34 C 5
Mengibar 9 E 5
Meng mao 31 F 6
Meng ting 31 F 6
Meng tsu 31 G 6
Menindee 55 G 6
Menkong 31 F 5
Menongue 41 B 1
Menor, Mar- 9 F 5
Menor, Mt. 8 F 5
Menorca 8 HI 3-4
Menzelinsk 24 G 7
Menzies 55 C 5
Meppel 15 H 2
Meppen 13 B 2
Meraker 17 D 5
Merano 19 C 1
Merauke 55 G 1
Merauke River 55 G 1
Merayer, El- 37 C 5
Merbabu, Mt. 26 m 13
Merca 36 H 5
Mercara 30 C 6
Merced, La- 52 B 4
Mercedario 53 BC 3
Mercedes (Argentina, Buenos Aires) 53 E 3
Mercedes (Argentina, San Luis) 53 C 3
Mercedes (Bolivia) 52 D 4
Mercedes (Uruguay) 53 E 3
Merceditas 53 B 2
Mercoya 37 C 7
Mercy, Cape 44 S 3
Merdinik 25 C 5
Merg, El- 37 I 3
Merga 37 L 4
Mergui 33 B 4
Mergui - Arcipelago 33 B 4
Merhagno, Pt. 38 F 5
Mérida (Mexico) 47 G 3
Mérida (Spain) 9 C 4
Mérida (Venezuela) 51 B 2
Meridian 46 I 4
Meriharvia 17 I 6
Merin, Islands 34 H 4
Merir, Islands 34 H 4
Merket Bazar 31 B 3
Merkine 17 M 9
Meroe, Island 38 B 4
Merowe 37 M 6
Merredin 55 B 6
Mersa Fatma 38 D 5
Merseburg 13 D 3
Mersey 3 E 5
Mersin 28 C 2
Mersing 33 C 6
Mersin Galgalo 38 E 6
Merthyr Tydfil 4 E 6
Mértola 9 C 5
Meru 40 F 2
Meru, Mt. 40 F 3
Merume Mountains, Mt. 51 DE 2
Mervane 28 G 2
Merv 29 D 4
Merzifon 25 C 5
Merzig 13 B 6
Mesa 46 D 6
Mesa, La- 51 B 3
Mesagne 19 FG 4
Mesamir 37 C 4
Mescovsk 23 L 7
Meshra er-Req 40 D 1
Meskene 28 E 2
Mesolongion 21 E 8
Mesopotamia 28 FG 2-3
Messema 20 E 9
Messenischer Golf 20 EF 9
Messina (Italy) 19 E 5
Messina (South Africa) 41 E 3
Messina, Str. of 19 E 5-6
Messini 21 E 9
Messinia. G. of 20 EF 9
Messira 37 A 7
Mestghanem 37 E 2
Mestre 19 D 2
Mesurado, Cape 39 B 4
Meta, La- 18 DE 4
Meta, Rio 51 C 3
Metarica 40 F 5
Metauro 18 D 3
Metemma 38 C 5
Methven 55 g 14
Metlili 37 F 3
Metz 11 I 2
Meulaboh 34 A 4
Meureudu 34 A 3
Meurthe 10 I 2
Mexiana, Island 52 H 1
Mexicali 47 A 1

Mexico 47 E 4
Mexico, Gulf of 42 LM 7
Mexiko, State 43 IL 7-8
Meyenburg 13 E 2
Meyadin 28 F 3
Mezen' 24 C 2
Mezen', River 24 CF 2-3
Mezen Gulf 23 P 1
Mézéne, Mt. 10 H 4
Mézières 11 H 2
Mezötur 28 I 2
Mezvodnoe 25 B 3
Mgla 24 C 1
Mhow 30 C 4
Miaj 34 H 5
Miajadas 9 D 4
Miami 43 M 7
Miandan 39 BC 3-4
Mianeh 28 I 2
Miary 41 c 8
Miass, River 24 MO 6-7
Miass 24 M 7
Mica 41 E 3
Micay 51 A 3
Michigan 46 IL 3-4
Michigan, Lake 42 M 5
Michikamau Lake, 44 S 5
Middelburg 41 D 5
Middle Atlas 37 CD 3
Middlesbrough 4 F 4
Middleton 55 G 4
Midi, Canal du- 10 FG 5
Midi, Pic du- 10 E 5
Midland 46 F 6
Midnapore 30 E 4
Midway, Islands 54 I 2
Midye 21 I 7
Midzor, Mt. 20 F 6
Miedzyrzec 13 L 3
Mielec 13 I 3
Mienga 41 C 2
Mieng ning 31 G 5
Mien ning 31 G 6
Miesso 38 D 6
Mijeres 8 F 3-4
Mijess 1 UV 4
Mikhajlov 23 N 7
Mikhajlovskij 27 L 4
Mikhlaf 38 D 4
Mikkeli 23 F 4
Mik ndani 40 G 5
Mik holt 17 Q 12
Mikonos 20 G 9
Mikronesien 54 EH 3-5
Milan 46 H 4
Milás 21 H 9
Mildura 55 G 6
Miles 55 I 6
Milesa 37 H 7
Miles City 46 E 3
Miletos 21 H 9
Miletto 18 E 4
Milford 4 D 6
Milford Haven 4 D 6
Mili, Island (Antarctica) 57 d 3
Mili, Island (Marshall Islands) 54 H 4
Miling 55 B 6
Milh, Lake 28 G 4
Milk 46 E 3
Mill, Island 44 P 3
Millau 11 G 4
Mille Isole 56 a
Millen 46 L 6
Millerovo 25 F 1
Millom 4 E 4
Millto 21 H 9
Milnor 46 G 3
Milo 31 G 6
Milos 20 G 9
Milparinka 55 F 5
Milwaukee 46 I 4
Mimbu 33 A 2
Mir 31 G 5
Mira, Mt. 35 C 4
Mirab 29 C 6
Mirami, Islands 32 D 6
Miramiiwo, Islands 54 E 2
Minas (Spain) 9 C 5
Minas (Uruguay) 53 E 3
Minas Gerais 52 HI 5
Minas Novas 52 I 5
Minato 27 d 13
Minch 3 C 3
Min chin 31 G 3
Minchinabad 29 F 5
Mincio 18 C 2
Mindanao, Island 34 FG 3
Mindelo, Islands 39 a
Minden 13 G 2
Mindoro, Island 34 F 2
Mineral'nye Vody 25 G 3
Mingan (Canada) 44 S 5
Ming an (China, Pang kiang) 31 I 2
Mingary 55 G 6
Minglanilla 9 F 4
Mingoyo 40 F 5
Ming shui 31 F 2
Ming-Taka-Pass 29 F 4
Mingulay, Island 4 C 3
Minho 26 O 6-7
Minhsien 31 G 4

Minicoy, Island 30 A 7
Minigwall, Island 55 C 5
Minija 16 I 9
Minioglobo 40 D 1
Ministra, Serra- 8 E 3
Min'jar 24 I 7
Minkébé 39 G 5
Minna 39 F 4
Minneapolis 46 H 4
Minnesota 46 G 3-4
Minnesota, State 43 L 5
Minnipa 55 F 6
Mino 9 BC 2-3
Minot 46 F 3
Min Shan, Mt. 26 O 6
Minsin 33 B 1
Minsk 23 F 8
Minto Inlet 44 F 1
Minya, El- 37 M 4
Minya Konka, Mt. 26 O 7
Miquelon 44 T 6
Mir 37 G 7
Mira (Portugal) 9 B 3
Mira (Spain) 9 F 4
Miradeh 28 I 2
Mirador 52 I 3
Miraj 30 B 5
Mirana 52 C 2
Miranda 52 F 6
Mirande 11 F 5
Mirandela 9 C 3
Mirecourt 11 I 2
Mirgorod 25 B 1
Miri 34 D 4
Mirim, Islands 50 E 7
Mirim, Lagoa- 53 F 3
Miroc Planina, Mt. 20 F 5
Mirs Bay 27 g 15
Mirtu 31 F 3
Mirzapur 30 D 3
Misaki 27 d 13
Misal 38 E 3
Misamis 34 F 3
Misawa 32 F 3
Mishagua 52 C 4
Miskino 24 O 7
Miskolc 21 E 3
Misoöl 34 GH 5
Missina 37 C 7
Mississippi Delta 46 HI 7
Mississippi, River 42 L 6
Mississippi, State 46 HI 6
Missoula 46 D 3
Missouri, Little- 46 F 3
Missouri, Pl. du Coteau du- 46 EF 3
Missouri 42 L 5
Mistassini, Lake 44 Q 5
Mistelbach 13 G 4
Mistretta 19 E 5-6
Misurata 37 H 3
Mitava 17 L 8
Mitchell (Australia) 55 H 5
Mitchell (USA) 46 G 4
Mitchell, Mt. 42 M 6
Mitchell River 55 G 3
Mitilino 21 H 8
Mito 32 F 4
Mitre 39 F 5
Mitre, General- 53 D 2
Mitrovica (Kosovska) 21 E 6
Mitrovica (Stremska) 21 D 5
Mitu 51 B 3
Mittweida 13 E 3
Miyako, Island 32 C 7
Miyandoab 28 I 2
Miyazaki 32 D 5
Miyazu 32 E 4
Miyun 31 L 2
Mizda 37 G 3
Mizen Head, Cape 3 B 6
Mizque 52 D 5
Mizusawa 32 F 4
Mjölby 17 F 7
Mjösa 16 D 6
Mkalama 40 E 3
Mkalinju 40 F 4
Mkangira 40 F 4
Mlahi 40 F 5
Mlange, Mt. 35 G 7
Mljet 20 C 6
Mluluca 41 F 1
Mo (Norway Hedmark) 17 D 6
Mo (Norway Hordaland) 17 A 6
Mo (Norway Nordland) 17 F 3
Mo (Norway Telemark) 17 B 7
Mo (Sweden) 17 H 5
Moa, Island 34 G 6
Moab 46 E 5
Moakhali 30 F 4
Moamba 41 E 4
Mobara 27 e 13
Mobaye 40 C 2
Moberly 46 H 5
Mobile 46 I 6
Mobridge 46 F 3
Mobutu Sese Seko, Lake 40 E 2
Moçambique 41 G 2
Mochudi 41 D 3
Mocimboa da Praia 40 G 5
Mocoa 51 A 3

Moctezuma 47 C 2
Moctezuma, Rio 47 E 3
Mocuba 41 F 2
Modane 11 I 4
Modder 41 CD 4
Modena 19 C 2
Modhràvellir 17 S 12
Modlin 13 I 2
Mo Duc 33 D 4
Moelv 17 D 6
Moffat 4 E 4
Mogadishu 38 E 7
Mogandjo 40 C 2
Mogaung 33 B 1
Mogen 17 B 6
Mogilëv 23 H 8
Mogincual 41 G 2
Mogoca 22 M 4
Mogoi 34 H 5
Mogok 33 B 2
Mogpo 31 N 4
Moguer 9 C 5
Mohacs 21 D 5
Mohéli, Island 41 b 6
Mohemba 40 D 3
Mohican, Cape 45 E 4
Mohn, Cape 56 a
Moho 22 N 4
Mohoro 40 F 4
Moia 40 D 2
Mointy 22 G 5
Môisaküla 17 M 7
Moisie 44 R 5
Moisie, River 44 R 5
Moissac 11 F 4
Moissala 40 B 1
Moitaco 51 D 2
Moïto 37 H 7
Mojacar 9 F 5
Mojave Des. 46 CD 5-6
Moji 32 D 5
Mojo, Island 34 E 6
Mojos, Llanos de- 52 E 4
Mokha 38 D 5
Mokiang 31 G 6
Mokra Planina, Mt. 20 E 6
Mokrinsk 25 L 1
Moksa 1 Q 5
Moksan 24 C 8
Mokwangu 35 F 5
Mola di Bari 19 F 4
Molat 20 B 5
Moldavia 2 N 6
Molde 17 B 5
Molde, Fj. 17 B 5
Moldova 20 H 4
Molepolole 41 D 3
Molfetta 19 F 4
Moliro 40 E 4
Molise 19 E 4
Mölla 17 F 2
Molledo 9 D 2
Mollendo 52 C 5
Mölndal 17 E 8
Molodecno 23 F 7
Mologa 23 LM 5-6
Molokai, Island 54 M 2
Moloma 24 DE 5
Molopo 35 F 8
Molu, Island 34 H 6
Moluccas 26 Q 9-10
Molucca Sea 34 FG 4-5
Moma (Zaire) 40 C 3
Moma (Mozambique) 41 F 2
Momba 40 E 4
Mombasa 40 F 3
Mombetsu 32 F 3
Momboyo 40 BC 3
Mominabad 30 C 5
Mompono 40 C 2
Mompos 51 B 2
Mön 16 E 9
Mona Passage 48 F 3
Monaco, State 11 I 5
Monadhliath Mounts, 4 D 3
Monastir 37 G 2
Moncada 9 F 4
Moncalvo, Mt. 8 C 2
Moncao 52 H 2
Mon Cay 33 D 2
Moncayo, Mt. 8 F 3
Monchique 9 B 5
Monchique, Sierra de- 8 B 5
Monclova 47 D 2
Mondego, Cape 8 B 3
Mondego 8 BC 3
Mondimbi 40 C 3
Mondombe 40 C 3
Mondonedo 9 C 2
Mondovì 19 A 2
Monegros, Los- 8 FG 3
Monegros, Sierra de los- 9 F 3
Monferrato 18 AB 2
Monforte di Lemos 9 C 2
Mongalla 40 E 1
Monghsal 33 B 2
Monghyr 30 E 3
Mongo 37 H 7
Mongolia 27 NP 5
Mongolia, Inner- 31 GL 1-2
Mongonu 39 G 3

Mongu 41 C 2
Monhuaçu 52 I 6
Monim, Rio 52 I 2
Monkoto 40 C 3
Mono 39 E 4
Monopoli 19 F 4
Monor 21 D 4
Monreal del Campo 9 F 3
Monroe 46 H 6
Monrovia 39 B 4
Mons 15 F 3
Mönsteras 17 G 8
Montagu 57 M 4
Montague 45 I 4-5
Montalto, Mt. 18 EF 5
Montana 46 DE 3
Montana, La- 49 C 4-5
Montargis 11 G 3
Montauban 11 F 5
Montbard 11 H 3
Montbél 11 I 3
Mont Blanc 10 I 4
Montbrison 11 H 4
Mont de Marsan 11 E 5
Monte Azul 52 I 5
Monte Caseros 53 E 3
Montecristo 18 BC 3
Monte Croce, Pass 18 D 1
Montefrio 9 D 5
Montélimar 11 H 4
Montemor a Novo 9 B 4
Montemuro, Mt. 8 C 3
Montenegro, Mt. 21 D 6
Montepulciano 19 C 3
Monterey 46 B 5
Monteria 51 A 2
Monteros 53 C 2
Monterrey 47 D 2
Montes Claros 52 I 5
Monteverde (Angola) 40 B 4
Montevideo 53 E 3
Montevideu 52 E 2
Montfort 11 E 2
Mont Gambier 55 a 8
Montgomery 46 I 6
Montgomery Peak, 46 C 5
Montijo (Portugal) 9 B 4
Montijo (Spain) 9 C 4
Montilla 9 D 5
Mont Laurier 44 P 6
Montluçon 11 G 3
Montmédy 11 H 2
Montmorillon 11 F 3
Montoro 9 D 5
Montpelier (USA, Idaho) 46 D 4
Montpelier (USA, Vermont) 46 N 4
Montpelier 11 G 5
Montpon 11 F 4
Montreal 44 Q 6
Montrose 4 E 3
Montseny, Sierra del- 8 H 3
Montserrado 39 B 4
Montserrat, Island 48 G 3
Montserrat, Mt. 8 G 3
Monviso, Mt. 18 A 2
Monwya 35 B 2
Monza 19 B 2
Monzon 9 G 3
Moora 55 B 6
Moore, Bay 57 a 2
Moore, Island 55 B 5
Moose, River 44 O 5
Moose Factory 44 O 5
Moose Jaw 44 H 5
Moosonee 43 M 4
Mopihaa, Island 54 M 6
Mopti 37 D 7
Moquegua 52 C 5
Mora (Camerun) 39 G 3
Mora (Spain) 9 E 4
Moraca 20 D 6
Moradabad 30 C 3
Morafenobe 41 b 7
Moramanga 41 c 7
Morané, Island 54 O 7
Morant, Pt. 48 D 3
Morar, Island 4 D 3
Morastrand 17 F 6
Moratuwa 30 C 7
Morava 20 C 3
Morava, Southern 20 EF 6
Morava, West. 20 E 6
Moravia 21 C 3
Moravian Hts 20 BC 3
Morawhanna 51 E 2
Moray Firth 3 E 3
Mörbylänga 17 G 8
Morcenx 11 E 4
Möre 17 BC 5
More, Ben-, Mt. 3 D 2
Moreda 9 E 5
Moree 55 H 5
Morelia 47 D 4
Morella 9 F 3
Morelos 47 C 2
Morena, Sierra- 8 CE 4-5
Moresby 44 C 5
Moreton 55 G 2
Moreton Island 55 I 5
Morfu 28 B 3
Morgano 55 F 6
Morgans 55 C 5

Mori (Nigeria) 39 E 4
Morioka 32 F 4
Morkorka 22 LM 3
Mörkret 17 E 6
Morlaix 11 D 2
Mornington 55 F 3
Moroc 23 F 8
Morocco 36 C 2-3
Morogoro 40 F 4
Morohe 55 H 1
Morokwen 41 C 4
Morombe 41 b 8
Morona, Rio 52 B 2
Morondava 41 b 8
Moron de la Frontera 9 D 5
Moroni 41 b 6
Morotai 34 G 4
Moroto 40 E 2
Morova 20 E 5
Morozovsk 25 F 1
Morrinhos 52 H 5
Morris Jesup, Cape. 43 R 1
Morroqul, Pt. 9 D 5
Morrumbene 41 F 3
Mors 17 C 8
Mörsvikbotn 17 F 3
Mortain 11 E 2
Mortara 19 B 2
Mortcha 37 HI 6-7
Morte, V. della- 42 H 6
Mortes, R. das- 49 E 5
Morto, Gulf 1 S 6
Morven, Mt. 3 C 2
Morvi 30 B 4
Morzhovoi 45 F 6
Morzovets 23 P 1
Mös 16 C 7
Mosal'sk 23 L 7
Moscow 23 M 7
Mosel 12 B 3
Moselle 10 I 2
Moshi 40 F 3
Mosjöen 17 E 4
Moskenesöy, Island 16 E 2
Moskosel 17 H 4
Moskva 23 MN 7
Moslavacka, Mt. 20 C 5
Mosor Planina, Mt. 20 C 6
Mosquero 46 F 5
Mosquitos, G. de los- 48 C 4
Moss 17 D 7
Mossaka 40 B 3
Mosselbaai 41 C 5
Mossoro 52 L 3
Mossuril 41 G 1
Most 21 A 2
Mostar 21 C 6
Mostardas 53 F 3
Mosti 24 E 8
Mösting, Cape 44 W 2
Mostki 25 E 1
Mosty 23 E 8
Mosul 2 Q 8
Mota 38 C 5
Motaba 40 B 2
Motilla del Palancar 9 F 4
Mototomari 32 F 2
Motoundoù 40 B 2
Motril 9 E 5
Motu Motu 55 H 1
Motuoca, Porto do- 52 H 2
Mouasskar 37 F 2
Moudjéria 37 B 6
Mou hsien 31 G 4
Mouila 40 B 4
Mouileh-Matallah, Hassi- 37 F 4
Mouka 40 C 1
Moulay Idriss 37 C 3
Moulins 11 G 3
Moulouya 37 D 3
Moulmein 33 B 3
Mount Cathbert 55 F 3
Mount Darwin 41 E 2
Mount Eba 55 F 6
Mount Hampden 41 E 2
Mount Isa 55 F 4
Mount Magnet 55 B 5
Mount Morgan 55 I 4
Mount Royal 55 I 6
Mount Selinda 41 E 3
Mount Vernon (USA, Illinois) 46 I 5
Mount Vernon (USA, Washington) 46 B 3
Moura (Brazil) 52 E 3
Moura (Portugal) 9 C 4
Mourao 9 C 4
Mourdiah 37 C 7
Mourne Mts. 3 C 4
Mourrah 37 I 7
Mourucuya 52 F 7
Mousgoum 37 H 7
Mousson 11 I 2
Moussoro 37 H 7
Moutamba 40 A 3
Moutier 13 B 5
Moûtiers 11 I 4
Mouydir 37 E 4-5
Moy 3 B 4
Moyamba 39 B 4
Moyobamba 52 B 3
Mozaisk 37 N 7
Mozambique 36 G 7-8
Mozambique Channel 35 GH 7-8

Mozarsk 25 H 3
Mozdok 25 H 4
Mozyr 21 I 1
Mpal 37 A 6
Mpanta 40 D 5
Mpika 40 E 5
Mpimbi 41 F 2
Mporokoso 40 E 4
Mpulungu 40 E 4
Mpwapwa 40 F 4
M'Rair 37 F 3
Msalu 41 F 5
Msesia 40 E 4
Msta 23 L 6
Mstislavl' 23 H 7-8
Msus, Zauiet- 37 I 3
Mtsensk 23 M 8
Mtwara 40 G 5
Muambo 40 G 5
Muang Chiang Rai 33 B 3
Muang Lampang 33 B 3
Muang Nan 33 C 3
Muang Payao 33 B 3
Muang Phrae 33 C
Muang Ubon 33 C 3
Muaraaman 34 B 5
Muaradua 34 B 5
Muaraenim 34 B 5
Muarakaman 34 B 5
Muarasabak 34 B 5
Muaratebo 34 B 5
Muaratewe 34 D 5
Muatienvo 40 B 5
Mubarraz 38 E 2
Mubende 40 E 2
Mucajai, Rio 51 D 3
Muchanes 52 D 5
Mucinga, Mt. 35 G 7
Muck 4 C 3
Mucojo 40 G 5
Mucula 40 A 4
Mucumburi 41 FG 1
Mucuri, Rio 52 I 5
Mudanya 21 I 7
Mudug 38 E 6
Muglad, El- 37 L 7
Mughaira 38 C 2
Mugia 9 B 2
Mugla 21 I 9
Muglad, El- 37 L 7
Mugodzary Mountains 26 H 5
Muharraq 38 F 2
Muhembo 41 C 2
Muhinga 40 E 3
Mühlausen 13 D 3
Mühldorf 13 E 4
Muhu, Island 17 L 7
Muhà-Vain, Island 16 L 7
Muilrea, Mt. 12 B 5
Mui Ron, Cape 33 D 3
Muizenberg 41 B 5
Muja 22 M 4
Mujnak 29 C 3
Mukacëvo 21 F 3
Mukah 34 D 4
Mukalla 38 E 5
Mukdahan 33 C 3
Mukden 31 M 2
Mukhluja 22 M 3
Mukhol 25 G 4
Mukombelm 41 C 2
Mukomuko 34 B 5
Mukry 29 C 2
Muleba 12 E 3
Mulemua 41 C 2
Muleng 31 O 2
Muleng 31 O 1
Mulhacén, Mt. 8 E 5
Mulhouse 11 I 3
Muli 31 G 5
Mull, Island 3 C 3
Mullen 46 F 4
Mullewa 55 B 5
Mullingar 4 C 5
Mulobesi 36 F 7
Mulondo 41 B 2
Mulowa 40 C 5
Multan 29 F 5
Mulumba 41 D 2
Mumra 29 A 2
Mun 33 C 3
Muna, Mt. 1 N 4
Muna, River 22 MN 3
Muna, Island 34 F 6
Muncie 46 I 4
Mund 28 MN 6-7
Mundawindi 55 C 4
Münden 13 C 3
Mund Rud 38 F 2
Mungaiyat, Gebel-, Mt. 40 D 1
Mungari 41 E 2
Mungbere 40 D 2
Mungindi 55 H 5
Munhango 40 B 5
Muni 39 FG 5
Munich 13 D 4
Munkhu Haan 31 I 1
Munku Sardyk, Mt. 26 N 4
Muns 4 B 5
Muns, Mt. 16 F 4
Munster (Ireland) 12 BC 5
Munster (West Germany) 13 B 2-3
Muntelui-Mare, Mt. 21 F 4

Muntenia 21 GH 5
Muntok 34 C 5
Muong Lai 33 C 2
Muong Ou Neue 33 C 2
Muong sing 33 C 2
Muong Son 33 C 2
Muoni 16 L 2-3
Muonio 17 L 3
Mupele 40 D 2
Mur 21 C 4
Muramvia 40 D 3
Murasi 24 E 5
Murat 1 PQ 8
Muratbasi Dagi, Mt. 25 G 6
Murchison 55 B 5
Murcia 9 F 4
Mure-d'Isere, La- 11 H 4
Muren 31 G 1
Murgab Fl. 29 F 4
Murgab (Tadzhikistan) 29 F 4
Murgab (Turkmeniya) 29 D 4
Murge, Le- 18 F 4
Murghab 29 DE 4
Muri 39 FG 4
Murjek 17 I 3
Murjo, Mt. 26 m 13
Muro Lucano 19 E 4
Muroran 32 F 3
Muros 9 B 2
Muros, Ria de- 8 B 2
Murrat 37 M 5
Murray 55 GH 6-7
Murro di Porco, C. 18 EF 6
Murrua 41 F 2
Murrumbidgee 55 H 6
Murtoa 55 G 7
Murukta 22 L 3
Murupu 51 D 3
Mururoa, Island 54 N 7
Murwara 30 D 4
Murwillumbah 55 I 5
Murzuq 37 G 4
Mus 25 F 6
Musa 16 L 8
Musaia 39 B 4
Musala, Mt. 20 F 6
Musa Qala 29 D 5
Musciani 40 B 3
Muscat 38 F 3
Musgrave 55 G 2
Musgrave Ranges 55 E 5
Mushairib, Cape 38 F 3
Mushie 40 B 3
Musi 34 B 5
Muskengon 46 I 4
Muskogee 46 G 5
Musmar 38 C 4
Musoma 40 E 3
Mussar 38 C 4
Mussà-ali, Mt. 38 D 5
Musselshell 46 E 3
Mussendi 40 B 5
Mussomeli 19 D 6
Mustag Ata, Mt. 31 B 3
Mustahil 38 D 6
Mustimiye 28 D 2
Mustjala 17 L 7
Mustvee 33 F 5
Muswellbrook 55 I 6
Mutan 31 N 1-2
Mutanchiang 31 N 2
Mutano 41 E 2
Mutarara 41 E 2
Mutare 41 E 2
Mutinyane 41 C 2
Mutis, Mt. 34 F 6
Mutnyj Materik 24 C 2
Mutombo Mukulu 40 C 4
Mutoraj 22 L 3
Muttaburra 55 G 4
Mutum Biu 39 G 4
Muxima 40 A 4
Muyaga 40 E 3
Muyumba 40 D 4
Muyunkum 29 EF 3
Muzart 31 C 2
Muzart River 31 C 2
Muzi 24 O 2
Muztag, Mt. 31 C 3
Muztagh, Mt. 31 C 3
Mvadhi 39 G 5
Mvera 41 F 1
Mverluf 41 C 2
Mvolo 40 D 1
Mwanza (Zaire) 40 D 4
Mwanza (Tanzania) 40 E 3
Mwelrea, Mt. 4 B 5
Mwenga (Zaire) 40 D 3
Mwenga (Zambia) 41 D 2
Mweru, Lake 40 D 4
Mwinga 33 A 3
Mwinga 41 F 2
Myaungmya 33 A 3
Mycenae 21 F 9
Myingyan 33 B 2
Myitkyina 33 B 1
Mymensingh 30 F 4
Myoung 39 G 5
Myrria 37 F 7
Mysen 17 D 7
Myskino 23 N 6
Mysia 21 H 8
Mys Meganom, Pt. 25 C 3
Myssjö 17 E 5
My Tho 33 D 4
Myvatn, Island 16 T 12

N

Naâma 37 D 3
Naab 12 E 4
Nabadwip Nadia 27 a 11
Nabereznye Celny 24 G 7
Nablus 28 C 4
Naboomspruit 41 D 3
Nabou 39 C 3
Nabq 28 C 6
Nacala 41 G 1
Nacaome 47 G 5
Nacarôa 41 F 1
Nachod 21 C 2
Nacimiento 47 D 2
Nacogdoche 46 H 6
Nadi 37 M 6
Nadiad 30 B 4
Nadoporoje 23 N 5
Nadvoitsy 23 L 3
Nadym 22 G 3
Nafada 39 G 3
Nafpaktos 21 E 8
Nâft-i-Shah 28 H 3
Nâft Khaneh 28 H 3
Naft Safid 28 L 5
Nafud 26 FG 7
Naga 34 F 2
Naga Hills 35 AB 1
Nagano 32 E 4
Nagaoka 32 E 4
Nagapattinam 30 C 6
Nagasaki 32 C 5
Nagaur 30 B 3
Nagchhu Dzong 31 E 4
Nagercoil 30 C 7
Nago 27 d 13
Nagornyj 22 N 4
Nagove 23 H 6
Nagoya 32 E 4
Nagpur 30 C 4
Nagrong 31 C 4
Nagykanizsa 21 C 4
Nagykörös 21 D 4
Naha 32 C 6
Nahe 12 B 4
Nahr Umr 28 I 5
Nahud, En- 37 L 7
Naï-Acha 37 H 7
Naibändan 29 C 5
Naichi 31 E 3
Nain (Canada) 44 S 4
Nain (Iran) 28 N 4
Naini tal 30 C 3
Naira, Island 34 G 5
Nairo 32 F 2
Nairobi 40 F 3
Nairôto 40 F 5
Naivasha 40 F 3
Najin 31 O 2
Nakazza 37 I 6
Nakha 25 I 5
Nakhicevan 25 H 6
Nakhl 28 B 6
Nakhon Mubarak 38 C 3
Nakhon Pathom 33 C 4
Nakhon Ratchasima 33 C 3
Nakhon Sawan 33 C 3
Nakhon Si Thammarat 33 C 5
Nakskov 17 D 9
Nakuru 40 F 3
Nal'cik 25 G 4
Nalut 37 G 3
Namacunde 41 B 2
Namak, Lake 29 B 5
Namakzar, Lake 29 C 5
Namangan 22 G 5
Namasagali 40 E 2
Nambanje 40 F 4
Nambour 55 I 5
Namcha Barwa, Mt. 31 F 5
Namche Bazar 26 p 17
Nam Dinh 33 D 2
Namib, Desert 35 E 7-8
Namibe 35 E 7
Namibe 41 A 2
Namibia 36 E 8
Namiza 32 E 4
Namlea 34 G 5
Namling Dzong 31 D 5
Namoi 55 H 6
Namorona 41 c 8
Nampa 17 N 3
Nampala 37 C 6
Nampula 41 F 2
Namsen 16 E 4
Namsos 17 D 4
Nam Tso 26 N 6-7
Namtsy 22 N 3
Namtu 33 B 2
Namuli, Mt. 41 F 2
Namur 15 G 3
Namuruputh 40 F 2
Namutoni 41 B 2
Namwala 41 D 2
Nan 33 C 3
Nana 40 B 1
Nana 35 E 5
Nanaimo 44 D 6
Nana Kru 39 C 5
Nanam 31 N 2
Nan chang 31 L 5
Nan cheng (China, Chiang hsi) 31 L 5

Nan cheng (China, Shen hsi) 31 H 4
Nanking 27 P 6
Nan chung 31 H 4
Nancorainza 52 E 6
Nancy 11 I 2
Nanda Devi, Mt. 30 CD 2
Nander 30 C 5
Nandgaon 30 D 4
Nandidroog, Mt. 30 C 6
Nandurbar 30 B 4
Nadyal 30 C 5
Nanfio, Island 21 G 9
Nang 26 p 17
Nanga Eboko 39 G 5
Nanga Parbat 29 F 4
Nangatajap 34 D 5
Nangchien 31 F 4
Nangis 11 G 2
Nan hai 31 I 6
Nan hsiung 31 I 5
Nan hu 31 E 3
Nanning 31 H 6
Nan ping 31 L 5
Nansen, Mt. 57 t 1
Nanshan, Island 34 E 2
Nan Shan (China, Chiang hai), Mt. 26 NO 6
Nan Shan (China, Hu nan), Mt. 26 P 7
Nantes 11 E 3
Nan tien 31 M 5
Nantua 11 H 3
Nantucket, Island 46 O 4
Nan tung 31 M 4
Nanumea, Island 54 H 5
Nanunque 52 I 5
Nan yang 31 I 4
Naouri, Mt. 39 D 3
Napassoq 44 U 3
Nape 33 D 3
Napier 55 h 13
Napier, Mt. 57 G 3
Naples 19 DE 4
Naples, G. of 18 DE 4
Napo, Rio 52 BC 2
Napuka, Island 54 N 6
Napuli 41 F 1
Naqira 28 L 7
Naquel Huapi, Island 49 c 8
Nara, Canal 29 E 6
Naracorte 55 G 7
Narayanganj 27 b 11
Narbada 26 L 7
Narbonne 11 G 5
Narenta 21 CD 6
Narew 18 IM 2
Narita 27 c 13
Narjan 28 L 3
Narjan Mar 22 E 3
Narni 19 D 3
Narodnaya, Mount 22 F 3
Naro Fominsk 23 M 7
Narok 40 F 3
Näröy 17 D 4
Narpio 17 I 5
Narraben 55 e 10
Narrabri 55 H 6
Narran, Island 55 H 5
Narrogin 55 B 6
Narrouwana 55 F 4
Narsinghpur (India, Madhya Pradesh) 30 C 4
Narsinghpur (India, Orissa) 30 E 4
Narva 23 G 5
Narva, Bay of 23 FG 5
Narvik 17 G 2
Naryn 22 G 5
Naryskino 23 L 8
Näs (Sweden, Alvsborg) 17 E 8
Nas (Sweden, Jämtland) 17 F 5
Nas (Sweden, Kopparberg) 17 F 6
Nasca 52 C 4
Nase 32 C 6
Nashville 46 I 5
Nasi, Island 16 L 6
Nasian 39 D 4
Nasice 21 D 5
Nasik 30 B 5
Nasir 38 B 6
Naskaupi 44 S 4-5
Nassarawa 39 F 4
Nassau 48 D 1
Nassau, Island 54 L 6
Nasser, Lake 37 M 5
Nässjö 17 F 8
Nastapoka Islands 44 P 4
Nasva 23 H 6
Nata 48 C 5
Natagaima 51 A 3
Natal (Brazil, Acre) 52 C 3
Natal (Brazil, Rio Grande del Nord) 52 L 3
Natal (Sumatra) 34 A 4
Natal, Prov. 36 G 8
Natale, Islands 54 M 4
Natara 22 N 3
Natchez 46 H 6
Natitingou 39 E 3
Natividade 52 H 4
Nätra 17 H 5
Natron, Lake 40 F 3

Natuna Islands 34 C 4
Naturaliste, C. 55 A 6
Natushquan 44 S 5
Naumburg 13 D 3
Naurai 38 B 3
Nauari 51 F 3
Nauplion 21 F 9
Nauplia 21 F 9
Nauru 54 G 5
Nauta 52 C 2
Nautla 47 E 3
Navahermosa 9 D 4
Navalcarnero 9 D 3
Navalmoral de la Mata 9 D 4
Navarin, Cape 22 S 3
Navarino, Island 53 C 7
Navarre 9 C 2
Navia 9 C 2
Navlja 23 L 8
Navrongo 39 D 3
Nawalia 40 E 5
Nayoro 32 F 3
Nazaré (Brazil) 52 L 4
Nazaré (Portugal) 9 B 4
Nazaret 38 C 6
Nazareth 28 C 4
Nazas, Rio 47 CD 2
Nazilli 21 I 9
Nazla, El- 37 M 4
Ndanga 41 E 3
Ndasegera, Mt. 40 F 3
Ndélé 40 C 1
Ndembesi 40 E 3
N'diago 37 A 6
N'Djamena 37 H 7
N'Djolé 40 A 3
Ndola 36 F 7
Nea 16 D 5
Neagh, Island 3 C 4
Neapolis 21 F 9
Near Islands 22 S 4
Nebi 40 E 2
Nebit Dag 29 B 4
Nebraska, 46 FG 4
Nebrodi, Mts. 18 E 5-6
Nechi 51 B 2
Neckar 12 C 4
Necker, Island 54 L 2
Necochea 53 E 4
Nedong Dzong 31 E 5
Nedre Soppero 17 I 2
Needle, Mt. 46 E 4
Neeperlt 15 G 3
Nee Soon 27 h 16
Neftu 37 F 3
Negara 34 D 6
Neged 26 G 7
Negelli 38 C 6
Negoiu 20 G 5
Negotin 21 F 5
Negrais, Cape 33 A 3
Negrita 48 C 4
Negro, Pt. 56 a
Negro, Rio (Bolivia) 52 D 4
Negro, Rio (Brazil) 49 D 4
Negro, Rio (Uruguay) 49 E 7
Negros, Island 34 F 2-3
Negru Voda 21 I 6
Neh 29 D 5
Neikura 17 M 2
Neisse, River 12 F 3
Neitsas 41 B 2
Neiva 51 A 3
Neiva 1 UV 4
Neja 24 B 5
Nejd 26 G 7
Nekaaskarv, Mt. 16 D 5
Neksö 17 F 9
Nelby 37 B 6
Nel'kan 22 O 4
Nellur 30 C 6
Nel'ma 32 E 2
Nelson, Mt. 55 g 14
Nelson, River 44 L 4
Nelson Head, 44 E 1
Nelson House St. 44 L 4
Néma 37 C 6
Neman 23 D 7
Nemira, Mt. 20 H 4
Nemuro 32 G 3
Nen chiang 32 C 2
Nen Chiang 31 M 1
Nene 3 F 5
Nengonengo, Island 54 N 6
Neosho 46 G 5
Nepa 22 L 4
Nepa River 22 L 4
Nepal State 27 M 7
Nephin, Mt. 3 B 4
Nera, River (Italy) 18 D 3
Nera, River (Romania) 20 E 5
Nérac 11 F 4
Nerchinskij Zavod 32 A 1
Néré 37 C 6
Nerekhta 23 O 6
Neri, Mt. (Afrika) 35 F 9
Neri, Mt. (USA) 42 I 5
Neries 17 M 9
Neris 16 M 9
Nerja 9 E 5
Neroj 22 I 4
Nerusa 23 L 8
Nerva 9 C 5

Nes' 24 C 1
Nesebar 21 H 6
Nesken 22 T 3
Nesöy, Island 16 E 3
Ness, Island 3 D 3
Nesseby 17 O 1
Nesviz 23 F 8
Netherlands 15 FH 2-3
Nétia 41 F 1
Neto 19 F 5
Nettilling L. 44 Q 2
Netze 12 FG 2
Neu-Bistritz 21 B 3
Neubritannien, Island 54 EF 5
Neuchâtel 18 A 1
Neuchâtel, L. de 19 A 1
Neue Hebriden, Islands 54 GH 6
Neuenhaus 13 B 2
Neuenglad kette 54 F 7
Neuenhaus 13 B 2
Neu-Hebriden-Groben 54 G 6-7
Neuir and, Island 54 F 5
Neukaledonien, Islands 54 G 7
Neumarkt 21 G 4
Neumünster 13 Dl 2
Neunkirchen 13 G 5
Neuquén 53 C 4
Neuquén, Rio 53 C 4
Neusüdwales 55 GH 6
Neusiedler, Lake 13 G 5
Neustadt 13 C 2
Neustralitz 12 E 2
Neu Ulm 13 D 4
Neuwied 13 B 3
Neva 17 F 6
Neva, River 23 H 5
Nevada 46 C 4-5
Nevada, Sierra- 8 E 5
Nevel' 23 GH 6
Nevel'sk 22 P 5
Nevers 11 G 3
Neves, Island 48 G 3
Nevis, Ben-, Mt. 3 D 3
Nevosi, Mt. 54 D 5
Nevsehir 25 C 6
New Amsterdam 51 E 2
Newark 46 N 4
Newark, Island 44 S 4
Newata 40 F 5
New Bedford 46 O 4
New Bern 46 M 5
New Brunswick 44 R 6
New Castile 9 DE 3-4
Newcastle (Australia) 55 I 6
Newcastle (Ireland) 4 B 5
Newcastle (South Africa) 41 E 4
Newcastle u.-Tyne 4 F 4
Newcastle Waters 55 E 3
Newdegate 55 B 6
New Delhi 30 C 3
New England 41 D 5
Newenham, Cape 45 F 5
Newfoundland 44 TU 6
New Guinea 54 DE 5
New Hampshire 46 N 4
Newhaven (United Kingdom) 4 G 6
New Haven (USA) 46 N 4
New Jersey 46 O 4
New Mexico 46 EF 6
New Norfolk 55 b 9
New Orleans 46 I 7
New Plymouth 55 g 13
Newport (United Kingdom) 13 E 6
Newport (USA) 46 B 4
Newry 4 C 4
New Siberia 22 PQ 2
New Siberian Islands 22 OF 2
Newton, Mt. 56 a
Newton-Stewart 4 D 4
Newtown 39 D 4
New York 46 N 4
New York, State 46 MN 4
New Zealand 55 h 14
New Zealand, Alps 55 fg 14
Nez 11 F 1
Ngabang 34 C 4
N'Gambé 39 C 4
Ngami 41 C 3
Ngami Pfanne 41 C 3
N'Gantchou 40 B 3
N'Gaoundere 39 G 4
Ngara 41 E 1
Ngathaing-gyaung 33 B 3
Ngiva 41 B 2
Ngoiba 39 G 5
Ngoko, River 40 B 2
Ngongo 40 E 4
Ngoring Nor 31 F 4
Ngorongoro, 40 F 3
Ngounie 40 A 3
N'Gcuri 37 H 7
N'Guigmi 37 G 7
N'Guila 39 G 5
Ngunze 40 A 5
Nguru 40 F 4
Nhamacurre 41 F 2
Nhamunda, Rio 52 F 2

Nhapala 41 E 3
Nha Trang 33 D 4
Niafadié 39 C 4
Niafounké 37 D 6
Niagara Falls 42 N 5
Niagassola 37 C 7
Niako 39 C 3
Niamey 37 E 7
Nianfors 17 G 6
Niangara 40 D 2
Nianing 37 A 7
Niago 39 D 3
Nias, Island 34 A 4
Nica 17 I 8
Nicaragua 48 BC 4
Nicaragua, Lake 48 BC 4
Nicastro 19 EF 5
Nice 11 F 5
Nicobar, Great 33 A 5
Nicobar, Islands 33 A 5
Nicobar, Little 33 A 5
Nico Pérez 53 E 3
Nicopoli 21 G 6
Nicosia (Italy) 19 E 6
Nicosia (Cyprus) 28 B 3
Nicoya Pen. 48 B 4-5
Nida 18 I 3
Nidelv 16 C 7
Nidzica 13 I 2
Nied 10 I 2
Nieddu, Mt. 18 B 4
Niegos, Mt. 20 D 6
Niellim 40 D 1
Niemba 40 D 4
Nienburg 13 C 2
Nienoport 15 F 3
Nieuwe Nickerie 51 E 2
Nieuwoudtville 41 B 5
Nieve, Serra de la 9 D 5
Nigaluk 45 H 2
Nigde 28 C 2
Niger 35 CD 4-5
Nigeria 36 DE 4
Nightcaps 55 f 15
Niigata 32 E 4
Niihau, Island 54 L 2
Nihao, Island 54 L 2
Nijar 9 E 5
Nijmegen 15 G 3
Nike 39 F 4
Nikolaev 25 B 2
Nikolaevsk 22 P 4
Nikolaevskij 25 H 1
Nikol'sk 24 C 5
Nikopol (Bulgaria) 21 G 6
Nikopol' (Soviet Union) 25 C 2
Niksar 25 D 5
Niksic 21 D 6
Nikulino 23 I 5
Nila, Island. 34 G 6
Nil'dino 24 N 3
Nile 35 G 2-4
Nimach 30 C 4
Nimai 33 B 1
Nimba, Mt. 35 C 5
Nîmes 11 H 5
Nimule 40 E 2
Nin 21 B 5
Ningan 31 N 2
Ning chin 31 F 5
Ningerh 31 G 6
Ning hsia 31 FH 2-3
Ning kwo 31 L 4
Ning po 31 M 5
Ning te 31 L 5
Ning tu 31 L 5
Ning wu 31 I 3
Ninh Dinh 33 D 2
Ninigo, Island 54 E 5
Niniveh 28 G 2
Ninomiya 27 d 13
Niobrara 46 F 4
Nioki 39 D 4
Nioro (Mali) 37 C 6
Nioro (Senegal) 37 A 7
Niort 11 E 3
Nipe 48 D 2
Nipigon 44 MN 6
Niquelandia 52 H 4
Niriz, Lake 29 B 6
Niriz, City 29 B 6
Nirmal 30 C 5
Nis 21 E 6
Nisa 9 C 4
Nisab 38 E 5
Nisava 20 F 6
Nishapur 29 C 4
Nisiros 20 H 9
Nissan 16 E 8
Nissan, Island 54 F 5
Nisser 16 C 7
Nissila 16 N 5
Nissum, Fj. 17 C 8
Niteroi 52 I 6
Nith 3 E 4
Nitra 21 D 3
Nitra, River 20 D 3
Nitsa 24 NO 6
Niut, Mt. 34 C 4

Nivernais 11 G 3
Nivsera 24 FG 3-4
Ni wan Men 27 f 15
Niya Bazar 31 C 3
Niyaok 38 B 5
Nizam 30 C 5
Nizamabad 30 C 5
Nizhe-Kolymsk 27 U 3
Nizhne Tambovskoe 32 E 1
Nizh Shakhtama 32 A 1
Nizip 28 D 2
Nizne-Angarsk 22 L 4
Nizne Udinsk 22 I 4
Nizni Tagil 22 E 4
Niznjaja Pesa 24 D 1
Niznjaja Tojma 24 C 3
Njaksimvol 24 M 3
Njavve 17 H 3
Njoko 41 C 2
Njukenitsa 24 D 4
Njuvcim 24 F 4
Nkanta, Mt. 40 E 5
Nkata Bay 40 E 5
Nkolayoub 39 G 5
Nkongsamba 39 F 5
Nkoranza 39 D 4
Noakhali 27 b 11
Noalejo 9 E 5
Noatak 45 G 3
Nobére 39 D 3
Nobo 34 F 6
Nofilia, En- 37 H 3
Nogajly 22 E 5
Nogajsk 25 D 2
Nogal 38 E 6
Nogent-le-Rotrou 11 F 2
Noginsk (Soviet Union, Moscow) 23 N 7
Noginsk (Soviet Union, Krasnojarsk) 22 I 3
Nogliki 22 P 4
Nogoya 53 E 3
Noho 31 M 1
Noire, Mounts 10 G 5
Noires, Mounts 10 D 2
Noirmoutier, Island 11 D 3
Nojima, Cape 27 d 13
Nokhoch, Mt. 29 D 6
Nokhtujsk 22 M 3-4
Nok Kundi 29 D 6
Nokola 23 N 4
Nokunau, Island 54 H 5
Nola (Italy) 19 E 4
Nola (Central African Republic) 40 B 2
Nolloth, Pt. 41 B 4
Nomoi, Island 54 F 4
Nomtsas 41 B 3
Nonni 26 Q 5
Nonoai 52 G 7
Nonouti, Island 54 H 5
Nootka 44 D 6
Noqui 40 A 4
Nora 17 F 7
Norasen 25 H 6
Nor Bajazet 25 H 5
Nordall 17 B 5
Norden 13 B 2
Nordenham 13 C 2
Norderney 12 C 2
Nord Fjord 16 A 6
Nordfok, fj. 17 F 3
Nordhausen 13 D 3
Nordinsel 55 g 13
Nordringa 17 H 5
Nordkanal 3 CD 4
Nord, Cape (Iceland) 16 Q 11
Nord, Cape (Norway) 16 M 1
Nord Cape (New Zealand) 55 g 12
Nordkynn 16 NO 1
Nordland 17 EF 4-5
Nordli 17 E 4
Nordmark 17 E 7
Nordreisa 17 I 2
Nordsjona 17 E 3
Nordstrand 13 C 1
Nordstrand, I. 12 C 1
Nordtrondelag 17 DE 4-5
Nordterritorium 55 EF 3-4
Nordvik 27 P 2
Nordwestkap 55 A 4
Nore 17 C 6
Nore, River 3 C 5
Noret 17 F 6
Norfolk (Nebraska) 46 G 4
Norfolk (Virginia) 46 M 5
Norfolk, co. 3 G 5
Norfolk, Island 54 G 7
Norilks 22 H 3
Norman 55 G 3
Normanby, I. 55 I 1
Normandy 11 EF 2
Normanton 55 G 3
Norman Wells 44 D 2
Nornalup 55 B 6
Norquinco 53 B 5
Norra 17 F 4
Norrbotten 17 GL 3
Norrby 17 F 4
Nörresundby 17 C 8
Norrfjärden 17 I 4
Norrkoping 17 G 7

Norrland 17 FI 3-5
Norrsundet 17 G 6
Norrtälje 17 H 7
Norsjo 17 H 4
Norsjo-S. 16 C 7
Norsk 22 N 4
North Channel 4 B 5
North Foreland 3 G 6
Northam 55 B 6
Northampton 4 F 5
North Bay 44 P 6
North Cape 34 G 4
North, Cape (Canada) 44 S 6
North Canadian 46 F 5
North Carolina 46 LM 5
Northcliffe 55 B 6
North Dakota 46 FG 3
Northeast Land 56 a
Northeim 13 C 3
Northern Ireland 4 C 4
North Frisian I.ª 16 BC 9
North Horr 40 F 2
North Platte 46 F 4
North Platte, River 46 E 4
North Rhine-Westphalia 13 BC 3
North Sea 1 G 4-5
North Sound, I. 4 E 2
North Sunderland 4 F 4
Northwest Territories 44 DM 3
North York Moors 4 F 4
Norton Sound 45 F 4
Norway 17 CL 1-6
Norwegian Sea 1 FH 1-3
Norwick 4 G 5
Noshiro 32 F 3
Nosob 35 EF 8
Nosseman 55 C 6
Nosy Bé, Island 41 c 6
Nosy Milsio, Island 41 c 6
Notec 12 H 2
Noto 19 E 6
Noto, Gulf of 18 E 6
Noto Peninsula 32 E 4
Notre Dame Bay 44 T 6
Notre Dame Mts. 44 R 6
Nottaway 45 P 5
Nottingham 4 F 5
Nottingham, Island 44 P 3
Notwani 41 D 3
Nouadhibou 37 A 5
Nouakchott 37 A 6
Nouatja 39 E 4
Nouchas 41 B 3
Noun 39 G 5
Novaci 21 F 5
Nova Cruz 52 L 3
Nova Friburgo 52 I 6
Nova Gaia 40 B 5
Nova Iorque 52 I 3
Novaja Kazanka 22 D 5
Novaja Odessa 25 A 2
Nova Lusitania 41 E 2
Novara 19 B 2
Nova Roma 52 H 4
Nova Sagres 34 G 6
Nova Scotia 44 RS 7
Nova Sofala 41 E 3
Nova Soure 52 L 4
Nova Trento 52 H 7
Novauzensk 29 A 1
Nova Venécia 52 I 5
Novaya Zemlya 22 E 2
Nové Mesto 21 C 3
Novgorod 23 H 5
Novi 21 B 5
Novi, Bosanski- 21 C 5
Novi-Burasy 24 D 8
Novi Ligure 19 B 2
Novi Pazar (Bulgaria) 21 H 6
Novi Pazar (Yugoslavia) 21 E 6
Novi Sad 21 D 5
Novo Aleksandrovskaja 25 F 3
Novobogatinskoe 22 E 5
Novocerkassk 25 F 2
Novoel'nja 23 E 8
Novograd Volynskij 21 H 2
Novogrudok 23 E 8
Novo Kazalinsk 29 D 2
Novokuznetsk 22 H 4
Novo Mesto 21 B 5
Novomoskovsk 23 N 7
Novonazyvoevka 22 G 4
Novonikol'skoe 25 H 1
Novo Orsk 24 L 9
Novo Pskov 25 E 1
Novorossijsk 25 D 3
Novorossiskij 29 C 1
Novorzey 23 G 6
Novoselé 23 G 5
Novo Sergievka 24 G 8
Novosibirsk 22 H 4
Novosil' 23 M 8
Novosokol'niki 23 H 6
Novo Traitskoe 25 F 3
Novo Ukrainka 25 A 1
Novozybkov 23 H 8
Novy Bydzov 21 B 2
Novyj Bug 25 B 2
Novyj Port 22 G 2

Novyj Salty 24 G 7
Novyj Torial 24 E 6
Nowe 13 H 2
Nowra 55 I 6
Nowy Sacz 13 I 4
Noya 9 B 2
Noyon 11 G 2
Nsawam 39 D 4
N'Tima 40 E 2
Ntoroko 40 E 2
Nuanetsi 41 E 3
Nuang chiao 27 f 15
Nubia 35 FG 3
Nubian Desert 37 M 5
Nueva Gerona 48 C 2
Nueva Lubeca 53 B 5
Nueva Poblacion 53 D 2
Nueva San Salvador 47 G 5
Nueve de Julio 53 D 4
Nuevo Laredo 47 E 2
Nuhurowa, Island 34 H 6
Nui, Island 54 H 5
Nuku Hiva, Island 54 N 5
Nukus 22 E 5
Nukutjut, Island 34 H 6
Nulato 45 G 4
Nullarborebene 55 D 6
Numan 39 G 4
Numancia 9 E 3
Nun 39 F 5
Nungan 31 N 2
Nunivak 45 E 5
Nunligran 22 T 3
Nuoro 19 B 4
Nuosi 17 M 5
Nup 26 p 16
Nupeba 52 H 4
Nuppivarre, Mt. 16 L 2
Nuppval, Mt. 16 F 6
Nuptse, Mt. 26 p 17
Nura 29 EF 1-2
Nurakita, Island 54 H 6
Nuralu 28 M 3
Nuremberg 13 D 4
Nurmes 23 G 3
Nurmo 17 L 5
Nurri 19 B 5
Nusaybin 28 F 2
Nushagak 45 G 5
Nushki 29 E 6
Nutrias 51 C 2
Nuweveld, Mt. 35 F 9
Nyahanga 40 E 3
Nyala 37 I 7
Ny Alesund 56 a
Nyama 41 D 1
Nyaming 37 C 7
Nyamlell 40 D 1
Nyanga 40 A 3
Nyanga, River 40 A 3
Nyangage 40 E 3
Nyanje 41 E 1
Nyanza Lac 40 D 3
Nyasa, Lake (Malawi) 35 G 7
Nyatakara 40 E 3
Nyborg 17 D 9
Nybro 17 G 8
Nyda 22 G 3
Nyenchen Tangla, Mt. 31 DE 4
Nyeri 40 F 3
Nyggenas 17 a
Nyhem 17 F 5
Nyiel 40 E 1
Nyiregyhaza 21 E 4
Nyiru, Mt. 40 F 2
Nykarleby 17 L 5
Nyköbing (Falster, Island) 17 D 9
Nyköbing (Mors, Island) 17 C 8
Nyköping 17 G 7
Nyland 17 MN 6
Nylstroom 41 D 3
Nymindegab 17 C 9
Nynäshamn 17 G 7
Nyngan 55 H 6
Nyong 39 G 5
Nyons 11 H 4
Nysa 13 G 3
Nysa, River 12 F 3
Nysätra 17 I 4
Nytva 24 H 6
N'Zèrekore 39 C 4
Nzeto 40 A 4
Nzoia 40 E 2

O

Oahu, Island 54 M 2
Oakland 46 B 5
Oami 27 e 13
Oas 41 A 2
Oassara 52 E 4
Oates, Coast 57 aB 2
Oaxaca 47 E 4
Ob 22 FH 3-5
Ob, Gulf of 22 G 2-3
Oban 4 D 3
Obcuga 23 G 7
Obeh 29 D 5
Obeid, El- 37 M 7
Obertin 21 G 3

Obidos 52 F 2
Obihiro 32 F 3
Obilnoe 25 H 2
Obkeik, Mt. 38 C 3
Oblivskaja 25 G 1
Obluce 22 O 5
Obo 40 D 1
Obock 38 D 5
Oborniki 13 G 2
Obotu Khural 31 G 2
Obra 12 F 2
Obrocnaja 24 E 4
Obscij Syrt 24 FH 8-9
Obubra 39 F 4
Ocakov 25 A 2
Ocana 51 B 2
Ocean, Cape 45 L 5
Oceano, Island 54 G 5
Ocer 24 H 6
Ochi, Mt. 20 G 8
Ocmulgee 46 L 6
Ocoa, Bay of 48 E 3
Ocos 47 F 5
Ocotal 48 B 4
Oda, Mt. 38 C 3
Odaiya, El- 37 L 7
Oddi 17 R 13
Oddur 38 D 7
Odemira 9 B 5
Odemis 21 H 8
Odenburg 13 G 5
Odense 17 D 9
Odense, River 17 CD 9
Odenwald 12 C 4
Oder 12 F 2
Odessa 25 A 2
Odiel 8 C 5
Odienné 39 C 4
Odosnur 24 D 6
Odowara 27 d 13
Odra 12 FH 2-3
Odweina 38 D 6
Odzak 21 C 5
Odzi 41 E 2
Oeiras 52 I 3
Oeno, Island 54 O 7
Ofanto 19 E 4
Ofot, Fj. 16 G 2
Ogaden 35 H 5
Ogaki 32 E 4
Ogbomosho 39 E 4
Ogden 46 D 4
Ogdensburg 46 M 4
Oglio 18 BC 2
Ognon 10 HI 3
Ogoja 39 F 4
Ogosta 20 F 6
Ogoué (Ogooué) 35 DE 6
Ogre 16 M 8
Ogulin 21 B 5
Ogurcinsk, Island 1 S 8
Ohanet 37 F 4
Ohara 27 e 13
Ohio, River 42 M 5-6
Ohio, State 46 L 4-5
Ohre 12 D 2
Ohre 12 EF 3
Ohrid 21 E 7
Ohrid Lake 20 E 7
Oiapoque 51 F 3
Oise 10 G 2
Oituz Pass 20 H 4
Oja de Agua 53 D 2
Ojat' 23 IL 4
Ojinaga 47 D 2
Ojos del Salado 53 C 2
Ojun-Kjuël 22 O 3
Oka, (Angara) 22 L 4
Oka, (Volga) 1 PQ 4
Okahandja 41 B 3
Okano 39 G 5
Okatevsk 24 E 5
Okaukuejo 41 B 3
Okavango Swamps 41 C 2
Okayama 32 D 5
Okeechobee 46 L 7
Okha (India) 30 A 4
Okha (Soviet Union) 22 P 4
Okhansk 24 H 6
Okhota 26 S 3
Okhotsk 22 P 4
Okhotsk, Sea of 22 PQ 4-5
Okhotski Perevoz 29 O 3
Okhvat 23 I 6
Oki-Islands 32 D 4
Okinawa-Islands 32 C 6
Okino, I. 32 D 7
Okino Erabu, Island 32 C 6
Okken 17 E 4
Oklahoma 46 G 5
Oklahoma City 46 G 5
Oknitsa 20 H 3
Okolovo 23 F 7
Okombahe 41 B 3
Okondja 40 A 3
Okpara 39 E 4
Okpara, River 39 E 4
Okre 20 A 2
Okstinder, Mt. 16 F 4
Okussi 34 F 6
Okussi-Ambeno 34 F 6
Okwa 41 C 3
Okwa River 39 F 4
Okwoga 39 F 4
Oland 16 G 8

Olanga 23 H 1
Olavarria 53 D 4
Olbia 19 B 4
Olbia, Gulf of 18 B 4
Oldenburg 13 C 2
Oldenburg 13 D 1
Old Castile 9 DE 2-3
Old Fort Confidence 44 F 2
Old Tati 41 D 3
Olej 22 QR 3
Olekma 22 MN 3-4
Olëkminsk 22 N 3
Olema 24 D 2
Olen 17 A 7
Olenëk 22 M 3
Olenëk, River 22 MN 2-3
Olenino, 23 I 6
Olevsk 21 H 2
Olga 22 O 5
Olga, Strait 56 a
Olgopol' 21 I 3
Olhao 9 C 5
Olifants River 41 E 3
Olimpus, Mount (Greece) 20 F 7
Olimpus, Mount (USA) 46 B 3
Olita 17 M 9
Oliva 37 B 4
Oliveira dos Brejinhos 52 I 4
Ollague 52 D 6
Olmedo 9 D 3
Olmos 52 B 3
Olomouc 21 C 3
Olona 18 B 2
Olonets 21 I 2
Olonk, River 23 I 4
Olonne, Les Sables d'- 11 E 3
Oloron S. Marie 11 E 5
Olot 9 H 2
Olovjannaja 22 M 4
Olsztyn 13 I 2
Olt 20 G 4-6
Olten 13 AB 1
Oltenia 21 F 5
Oltenizza 21 H 5
Oltu 25 F 5
Oluklu 25 G 5
Olym, River 23 N 8
Olympia 46 B 3
Olyutorskiy, Cape 22 S 4
Om 26 L 4
Om Ager 38 C 5
Omaha 46 G 4
Omaheke 41 BC 2-3
Omakhta 22 O 4
Omarkud 38 D 4
Omarura 41 B 3
Omatako, Mt. 41 B 3
Ombrone 19 C 3
Omdurman 37 M 6
Ome 27 d 13
Omein 38 D 6
Omigawa 27 e 13
Omitara 41 B 3
Omiya 27 d 13
Omo, 35 G 5
Omoj 22 NO 2-3
Omolon 22 QR 3
Omsk 22 G 4
Omul, Mt. 20 G 5
Omulew 13 I 2
Omura 32 B 5
Omuramba 41 B 2
Omuta 32 D 5
Omuntninsk 24 G 5
Omvane 39 G 5
Ona 22 I 4
Onda 23 IL 3
Ondangua 41 B 2
Ondava 20 E 3
Ondozero 23 I 3
Onega, Town 23 N 3
Onegabai 22 MN 2-3
Onega, River 23 N 3-4
Onega, G. of 23 M 2
Onega Lake 23 LM 3-4
Onekotan, Island 22 Q 5
Ongerup 55 B 6
Ongoin 31 G 1
Ongole 30 D 5
Onilahy 41 b 8
Onitska 39 F 4
Onkhor 38 E 5
Onomichi 32 D 5
Onon 31 I 1
Ons, Island 9 B 2
Onslow 55 B 4
Ontananga 41 B 2
Ontario, Lake 18 B 2
Ontario, State 44 MP 5-6
Ontonagon 46 I 3
Ontong Java, Island 54 F 5
Oodnadatte 55 F 5
Ooldea 55 E 6
Oomaru 55 g 15
Ootacamund 30 D 6

Opala 40 C 3
Oparino 24 E 5
Opastija 21 B 5
Opava 21 C 3
Opdal 17 C 5
Opinaka 44 PQ 5
Opobo 39 F 5
Opocka 23 G 6
Opole 13 H 3
Oporto 9 B 3
Opparinna 55 E 5
Opto, Island 23 G 2
Opua 55 g 13
Oqair 38 F 2
Oradea 21 E 4
Orafa Jökull, Mt. 16 T 12
Oran (Algeria) 37 D 2
Oran (Argentina) 53 D 1
Oran, G. of 8 F 6
Orange (Australia) 55 H 6
Orange (France) 11 H 4
Orange (River) 35 EF 8-9
Orange (Stait) 41 D 4
Orango, Island 39 A 3
Oranjefontein 41 D 3
Oranjemond 41 B 4
Orastie 21 F 5
Orava 20 D 3
Orba 37 I 6
Orbetello 19 C 3
Orbigo 9 D 2
Orbost 55 b 8
Orcera 9 E 4
Orcia 18 C 3
Orco 18 A 2
Ord 55 D 3
Ordabaj 22 G 4
Ordos 26 O 6
Ord Peak, Mt. 46 E 6
Ordu 25 D 5
Ordubad 25 H 5
Ordzonikidze 25 H 4
Ore 17 F 6
Ore, River 16 H 4-5
Orealla 51 E 2
Orebro 17 F 7
Oredez 23 H 5
Oregon 46 BC 4
Oregon Inlet, Strait 46 M 5
Orekhov 25 C 2
Orekhovo-Zuevo 23 N 7
Orël 23 LM 8
Orellana 52 B 3
Orenburg 27 H 4
Orense 9 C 2
Orerk 17 F 7
Oré Vendou 37 D 6
Orfani 21 F 7
Orgeev 21 I 4
Orhaneli 21 I 8
Orient Dal 16 E 6
Orih, Island 23 G 3
Orihuela 9 F 4
Orinoco 49 D 3
Oriolo 19 F 4
Orissa 26 M 7
Oristano 19 B 5
Oristano, Gulf of 18 AB 5
Orivesi 17 M 6
Orizaba 47 E 4
Orjen, Mt. 20 D 6
Orkhon 31 G 1
Orklo 16 CD 5
Orlando 46 L 7
Orléanais 11 FG 3
Orléans 11 F 3
Orm, Cape 17 G 4
Ormara 29 D 6
Ormea 19 AB 2
Ormoc 34 F 2
Ormus, Strait 26 H 7 29 C 6
Ornain 11 H 2
Orne 10 E 2
Ornö, Island 16 H 7
Ornsköldsvik 17 H 5
Oro, El- 47 C 2
Orocué 51 B 3
Orolik 22 P 3
Orontes (River) 11 H 4
Oroquieta 34 F 6
Orosh 21 D 7
Oroshaza 21 E 4
Orosi 48 B 4
Oroville 46 C 3
Oroya, La- 52 B 4
Orrefors 17 F 8
Orsa 23 H 7
Orsanka 24 D 6
Orsi, Island 22 R 2
Orsk 9 T 5
Orsta 17 B 5
Orsted 17 D 8
Orta, Lake 18 B 2
Ortega 51 A 3
Ortegal, Cape 8 B 2
Ortigueira 9 C 2
Ortles 18 C 1
Orton 17 D 7
Orträsk 17 H 4
Oruro 52 D 5
Orust, Island 16 D 7

Orvieto 19 D 3
Osa 24 H 6
Osa, Pen. 48 C 5
Osaka 32 E 5
Osage, 46 H 5
Osan 20 G 6
Osarca, Mt. 20 H 4
Osby 17 E 8
Oschersleben 13 D 2
Osen 17 D 4
Osětrovo 22 L 4
Osh 29 F 3
Oshamambe 32 F 3
O Shima, Island 32 E 5
Oshkosh 46 I 4
Oshogbo 39 E 4
Oshwe 40 B 3
Osijek 21 D 5
Osimo 19 D 3
Osipovici 23 G 8
Oskarshamm 17 G 8
Oskarsström 17 E 8
Oskaba 22 L 3
Oslo 17 D 7
Osmancik 25 C 5
Osmaniye 28 D 2
Osnabrück 13 BC 2
Osnaburgh House 44 M 5
Oso 40 D 3
Osogovska Planina, Mt. 20 F 6
Osorno 53 B 5
Osprey Reef, Island 55 H 2
Ossa 20 F 8
Ossjö, Island 16 E 6
Oste 13 C 2
Ostend 15 F 3
Oster 21 L 2
Osterdal 17 D 5-6
Ostergotland 17 F 7-8
Osterö 17 a
Osterö, Island 3 a
Osterode 13 D 3
Osteröy 17 A 6
Ostersund 17 F 5
Osthammar 17 H 6
Ostiglia 19 C 2
Ostfriesland 13 D 2
Ostrau 21 D 3
Ostrava 21 D 3
Ostrog 21 H 2
Ostroleka 13 I 2
Ostrov, Island 21 C 3-4
Ostrow 13 IL 2
Ostrowiec 13 I 3
Ostrow Wielkopolski 13 GH 3
Ostrzeszow 13 GH 3
Ostula 47 D 4
Osum 20 E 7
Osuna 9 D 5
Otaki 27 e 13
Otar 29 G 3
Otaru 32 F 3
Otava 12 E 4
Otaval 20 AB 3
Otavalo 52 B 1
Otavi 41 B 2
Oteren 17 H 2
Oti 39 E 4
Otish Mt. 44 Q 5
Otiwarongo 41 B 3
Otjihaiavara 41 B 3
Otoineppu 32 F 3
Otra 16 B 7
Otranto 19 G 4
Otranto, Str. of 18 G 4
Otscher 12 F 5
Otsu 32 E 4
Ottawa 44 P 6
Ottawa, River 42 N 5
Ottawa, Island 44 O 4
Otterndorf 13 C 2
Otteröy 17 D 4
Otteröy, Island 17 B 5
Otuquis 52 F 5
Otusco 52 B 3
Otway, Cape 55 a 8
Otztaler Alps 13 D 5
Ouachita 46 H 6
Ouadane 37 B 5
Ouadda 40 C 1
Ouagadougou 39 D 3
Ouahigouya 39 D 3
Ouahran (Oran) 37 D 2
Ouaka 40 C 1
Ouakara 39 D 3
Oualadji, El- 37 D 6
Oualata 37 C 6
Ouallen 37 E 5
Ouanda Djalé 40 C 1
Ouango 40 C 2
Ouantonou 40 B 1
Ouaran, West 35 C 3
Ouargala 37 I 6
Ouarsénis, Massif de- 37 F 2
Oudtshoorn 41 C 5
Oued, El- 37 F 3
Ouessant, Island 10 C 2
Ouessat, El- 37 B 5
Ouesso 40 B 2

Ouezzane 37 C 3
Ouidah 39 E 4
Oujaf 37 C 6
Oujda 37 D 3
Oujeft 37 B 5
Oulainen 17 M 4
Ouled-Djellal 37 F 3
Oulu 17 M 4
Oulu, River. 16 M 4
Oulu, Lake 16 N 4
Oum Chalouba 37 I 6
Oum el-Adam 37 I 6
Oum el-Asel 37 C 5
Oum er-Rbia 37 C 3
Oum Hadjer 37 H 7
Ounas 16 M 3
Ounas, Selkä 16 LM 3
Ounianga 37 I 6
Ounianga Kebir 37 I 6
Ounianga Sérir 37 I 6
Ounissauï Tarouska 37 G 6
Ouola 37 C 7
Ouosseboubou-Banibara 37 C 7
Oupu 22 N 4
Ourarèn 37 F 6
Ourarène 37 F 6
Ouricuri 52 I 3
Ouro Fino 52 F 4
Ourthe 14 G 3
Ouse (Norfolk), 3 G 5
Ouse (York), 3 F 4-5
Oust, Island 10 D 3
Outakoski 17 N 2
Outardes 44 R 5-6
Outjo 41 B 3
Ouyen 55 G 7
Ovalle 53 B 3
Ovambo 35 E 7
Ovambre, Cape 9 D 2
Ovansjö 17 G 6
Ovar 9 B 3
Overlulea 17 I 4
Overtornea 17 L 3
Oviedo 9 D 2
Ovikst, Mt. 16 E 5
Ovinisce 23 M 5
Ovruc 21 I 2
Owens 46 C 3
Owensboro 46 I 5
Owen Sound 44 O 7
Owen Stanley, Mt. 26 o 14
Owerri 39 F 4
Owyhee, River 46 C 4
Oxelösund 17 G 7
Oxford House 44 L 5
Oxford Tottenham 4 F 6
Oxley 55 G 6
Oyapock 49 E 3
Oye 17 B 5
Oyem 39 G 5
Oyer 17 D 6
Oyer, Island 16 D 7
Oymyakon 22 P 3
Ozark Plateau 42 L 6
Ozerki 24 C 9
Ozërnoe 22 Q 4
Ozëry 23 N 7
Ozery 21 H 2
Ozieri 19 B 4
Ozogino 22 P 3
Ozorkow 13 H 3
Ozren, Mt. 20 E 6
Ozu 37 H 5
Ozurgeti 25 FGM45

P

Pää, Island 1 O 2
Paan 31 F 5
Paarl 41 B 5
Pabianice 13 H 3
Pacasmayo 52 B 3
Pachino 19 E 6
Pachu 31 B 3
Pachuca 47 E 3
Pa chung 31 H 4
Pacocha 52 C 5
Padang 34 B 5
Padang Sidimpuan 34 A 4
Padasjoki 17 M 6
Paderborn 13 C 3
Padilla 52 E 5
Padma 27 b 11
Padrao, Pt. 40 A 4
Padre Island 46 G 7
Padstow 4 D 6
Padua 19 CD 2
Paducah 46 I 5
Pafos 28 B 3
Pafuri 41 E 3
Pagadjan 34 F 3
Pagalu 39 F 6
Paget, Mt. 49 G 9
Paglia 18 CD 3
Pag 20 B 5
Pahang 33 C 6
Paicheng 31 C 2
Paico 52 C 4
Paide 17 M 7
Paiho 31 I 4
Paijanne 16 M 6
Pailung 31 G 4

Paimion 17 L 6
Paimpol 11 D 2
Painan 34 B 5
Paise 31 H 6
Paisha 27 f 14
Paisley 4 D 4
Paita 52 A 2
Paittas Jarvi 16 H 3
Paiyü 31 F 4
Pai yung, Mt. 27 g 15
Paiz do Vinho 8 BC 3
Pajala 17 D 3
Paj Er, Mt. 24 NO 1
Pajeu 52 L 3
Pak 31 H 6
Pakanbaru 34 B 4
Paki 39 F 3
Pakir 20 H 8
Pakistan 27 IL 6-7
Pak-Lay 33 C 3
Pakokku 33 B 2
Pakrac 21 C 5
Paks 21 D 4
Paksane 33 C 3
Pakse 33 D 3
Palabuhan, B. 26 I 13
Palafrugell 9 H 3
Palamcottah 30 C 7
Palana 22 R 4
Palanan 34 F 1
Palangan 34 F 1
Palangir 28 I 4
Palanka 21 E 5
Palanpur 30 B 4
Palarye 41 D 3
Palatinate 13 BC 4
Palatinate, Upper 12 DE 4
Palau-Islands 54 D 4
Palawan, Islands 34 E 2-3
Paldiski 17 M 7
Paleleh 34 F 4
Palembang 34 B 5
Palencia 9 D 2
Palenque 47 F 4
Palermo 19 DE 5
Palermo Gulf of 18 D 5
Palestina 53 C 1
Palestine 46 G 6
Paletwa 33 A 2
Palghat 30 D 6
Pali 30 B 3
Palimé 39 E 4
Palinuro, Cape 18 E 5
Palk Strait 30 C 6-7
Palla Road 41 D 3
Pallastunturi, Mt. 16 L 2
Palling miao 31 I 2
Palliser, Cape 55 h 14
Palma 9 H 4
Palma, Bay 8 H 4
Palma, La- 51 A 2
Palma, La-, Island 37 A 4
Palma, Rio da- 52 H 4
Palmares 52 L 3
Palmas 52 G 7
Palmas, Las- 37 A 4
Palmeira das Indios 52 L 3
Palmeirinhas, Pt. 40 A 4
Palmer -Arch. 57 O 3
Palmer, Cape 57 p 2
Palmerston, Island 54 L 6
Palmerston North 55 h 14
Palmerville 55 G 3
Palmi 19 E 5
Palmira 51 A 3
Palmira, Island 54 L 4
Palmyras Point 30 E 4
Palm Springs 46 C 6
Palopo 34 F 5
Palos, Cape 8 F 5
Pältas, Mt. 17 I 2
Palu (Indonesia) 34 E 5
Palu (Turkey) 25 E 6
Pa lung 31 F 3
Pama 39 E 3
Pamekasan 34 D 6
Pamiers 11 F 5
Pamir, River 29 F 4
Pamir, Mt. 26 L 6
Pamlico Sound 46 M 5
Pampilhosa 9 B 3
Pamplona (Colombia) 51 B 2
Pamplona (Spain) 9 F 2
Pana 23 LM 1
Panaitan, Island 26 I 13
Panama 48 D 5
Panama Canal Zone 48 C 5
Panama, Gulf of 48 D 5
Panama,Isthmus 42 MN 9
Panama, State 43 MN 9
Panapie 51 F 3
Panarea 18 E 5
Panaro 18 C 2
Panav, Island 34 F 2
Panbult 41 E 4
Pancevo 21 E 5
Pandan 34 F 2
Pandharpur 30 C 5
Pandurucan 34 F 2
Panevezys 17 M 9
Panga 40 D 2
Pangala 40 A 3
Pangani 40 F 4
Pangani, River 40 F 3
Pangeon, Mt. 20 FG 7
Pangiab 26 L 6
Pangkalan Berandan 34 A 4
Pangkalanbuun 34 D 5
Pangkalpinang 34 C 5
Pang kiang 31 I 2
Pangnirtung 44 RS 2
Pang pei 31 I 2
Pangrango, Mt. 26 I 13
Panguitch 46 D 5
Pan hsien 31 G 5
Panipat 30 C 3
Panjgur 29 D 6
Panjim 30 B 5
Panozero 23 I 2
Pantar, Island 34 F 6
Pantelleria 18 CD 6
Panuco 47 E 3
Panzi 40 B 4
Pao 52 D 3
Pao an 27 f 15
Pao ching 31 O 1
Pao de Acucar 52 L 3
Paola 19 E 5
Paoleh 31 I 3
Paoshan 31 F 5
Paoshan (Yünnan) 31 F 5
Pao ting 31 L 3
Pao tou 31 I 2
Paouignan 39 E 4
Pa Yu, Mt. 31 H 3
Papa 21 C 4
Papagaio 52 F 4
Papar 34 E 3
Papas, C. 20 E 8
Papasquiaro 47 C 3
Papa Stour, Island 4 F 1
Papa Westray, Island 4 E 2
Paposo 53 B 2
Papua New Guinea 26 o 14
Papuagulf 54 E 5
Papuk 20 C 5
Papun 33 B 3
Para (Belém) 52 H 2
Para, State 52 G 2-3
Paracatu 52 H 5
Parachilna 55 F 6
Paracuru 52 L 2
Paragua, La- 51 D 2
Paragua 52 E 4-5
Paraguana Pen. 49 D 2
Paraguay 50 DE 6
Paraguay, Rio 49 E 5-6
Parahoue 39 E 4
Paraiba (Joao Pessoa) 52 M 3
Paraiba, Rio 49 F 6
Paraiba, State 52 L 3
Parakou 39 E 4
Paramaribo 51 E 2
Paramonga 52 B 4
Paramusir, Island 22 Q 4
Parana (Argentina) 53 D 3
Parana (Brazil) 52 H 4
Parana, Rio 49 DE 6-7
Parana, State 52 GH 6-7
Paranagua 52 H 7
Paranaiba 52 G 5
Paranaiba, Rio 49 F 5
Paranapanema, Rio 49 EF 6
Paraopeba 52 H 5
Parapirim 52 I 4
Parapiti 52 E 5
Paratoa 55 F 6
Parbati 30 C 3-4
Parbhani 30 C 5
Pachim 13 D 2
Pardo (Bahia) 52 IL 5
Pardo (Mato Grosso) 52 G 6
Pardubice 21 B 2
Parece Vela, Island 54 D 2
Paren 22 R 3
Parepare 34 E 5
Paria, Gulf of 51 D 1
Pariaman 34 B 5
Parida, Island 48 C 5
Parigi (Indonesia) 34 F 5
Parika 51 E 2
Parinas, Pt. 52 A 2
Parintins 52 F 2
Paris (France) 11 G 2
Paris, (USA, Tenn.) 46 I 5
Paris (USA, Texas) 46 G 6
Parjuman 29 D 5
Parkano 17 L 5
Parkes 55 H 6
Parlakimedi 30 D 5
Parma 19 BC 2
Parnagua 52 I 4
Parnaiba 52 I 2
Parnaiba, Rio 52 I 2
Parnassos 20 F 8
Parnassus 55 g 14
Parnon 20 F 9
Pärnu 17 M 7
Pärnu, River 16 M 7
Paros 20 G 9
Paroo 55 B 5
Paroo, River 55 H 5
Paroumba 37 B 7
Parramatta 55 I 6
Parras 47 D 2
Parrett 3 E 6
Parry, Cape 44 E 1
Parry, Island (Canada) 42 HI 2
Parry, Island (Oceania) 54 E 2
Parson 46 G 5
Parte Fjeld, Mt. 16 G 3
Partenkirchen 13 D 5
Parthenay 11 E 3
Paru 52 G 2
Parvatipuram 30 D 5
Pas, The- 44 I 5
Pasa 23 IL 4-5
Pasak 33 C 3-4
Pasangkaju 34 E 5
Pascani 21 H 4
Pasewalk 13 F 2
Pasija 24 L 5
Pasing 13 D 4
Pasir 34 E 5
Pasleka 12 H-I 1
Pasley, Cape 55 C 6
Pasman 20 B 5-6
Pasni 29 D 6
Paso, El- 46 E 6
Paso de Indios 53 C 5
Paso Robles 46 B 5
Passau 13 E 4
Passo de Camaragibe 52 L 3
Passo Fundo 52 G 7
Passos 52 H 6
Pastaza 52 B 2
Pastaza, Rio 52 B 2
Pasto 51 A 3
Pasubio 18 C 2
Pasul-Prislop, Mt. 20 G 4
Pasuruan 34 D 6
Patagonia Pampas 49 D 7-8
Patagonica, Cord- 49 C 8-9
Patan (India) 30 B 4
Patan (Nepal) 30 E 3
Patas 52 B 3
Patchewollock 55 G 7
Pategi 39 F 4
Paternò 19 E 6
Paternoster, Island 34 E 6
Pathiu 33 B 4
Pati 34 D 6
Patia 51 A 3
Patiala 30 C 2
Patience Well 55 D 4
Patillos 52 C 6
Patjitan 34 D 6
Patmo, Island 20 H 9
Patna 30 E 3
Pato 51 C 3
Patos 52 L 3
Patos, Lagoa dos- 53 F 3
Patos de Minas 52 H 5
Patras 21 E 8
Patras, Gulf of 20 E 8
Patrick, Pr.-, Island 42 GH 2
Patrick, Pt. 4 D 4
Patrocinio 52 H 5
Pattani 33 C 5
Patti 19 E 5
Patti, Gulf of 18 E 5
Patuakhali 27 b 11
Patuca, Pt. 47 H 4
Patuca, Rio 47 H 4-5
Patuha, Mt. 26 I 13
Patuleme 21 F 5
Pau 11 E 5
Paucartambo 52 C 4
Pau dos Ferros 52 L 3
Pauillac 11 E 4
Pauini 52 D 3
Paulding, Bay 57 c 3
Paulistana 52 I 3
Paulpietersburg 41 E 4
Paumotu (Tuamotu), Island 54 NO 6-7
Paungde 33 B 3
Pauraitepui 51 D 3
Paurito 52 E 5
Pauträsk 17 G 4
Pavia 19 B 2
Pavilosta 17 I 8
Pavlodar 22 G 4
Pavlof 45 F 5
Pavullo nel Frignano 19 C 2
Paxoi 20 E 8
Payen 31 N 1
Paylovskaja 25 E 2
Payne Bay 44 R 3
Payo Obispo 47 G 4
Paysandu 53 E 3
Paz, La- (Argentina) 53 E 3
Paz, La- (Bolivia) 52 D 5
Paz, La- (Mexico) 47 B 3
Pazardzik 21 FG 6-7
Pazarköy 21 H 8
Peace 44 F 4
Peace River 44 F 4
Peack, Cape 57 e 3
Peak 3, Mt. 26 q 17
Peak 4, Mt. 26 q 17
Peak 38, Mt. 26 p 17
Pearston 41 C 5
Peary, Land of 42 QS 1
Pebas 52 C 2
Pébo 40 B 1
Pec 21 E 6
Pecenga 2 O 2
Pecgora 24 C 2
Pechino 31 L 3
Pecora 24 I 2
Pecora, River 2 ST 2-5
Pecos 46 F 6
Pecos, River 46 F 6
Pécs 21 D 4
Pedemonte 42 MN 6
Pedernales 52 A 1
Pedra Azul 52 I 5
Pedro II 52 I 2
Pedro Afonso 52 H 3
Pedroches, Los- 9 D 4
Pedrogao Grande 9 B 4
Pedro Luro 53 D 4
Pedroso, El- 9 D 5
Peebinga 55 G 6
Peedee 46 M 6
Peel 4 D 4
Peel, River 44 BC 2
Peene 12 E 2
Pegu 33 B 3
Pegu Yoma 33 B 2-3
Peh 31 I 6
Pehcevo 21 F 7
Pehuajo 53 D 4
Pei 27 f 15
Peian 31 N 1
Peihai 31 H 6
Peio 51 F 3
Peipan 31 GH 5
Peipuss, Lake 23 F 5
Pei Shan 31 GH 3
Peita 31 F 3
Peitz 13 F 3
Peixe 52 G 6
Pek 20 E 5
Pekalongan 34 C 6
Pekan 33 C 6
Peking 31 L 3
Pelagie, Islands 37 G 2
Peleaga, Mt. 20 F 5
Peleng, Island 34 F 5
Pelion 20 F 8
Peljesac 20 C 6
Pelkosenniemi 17 N 3
Pella 41 B 4
Pellegrino, Mt. 18 D 5
Pello 17 M 3
Pellworm 12 C 1
Pelly 44 C 3
Peloponnesos 20 EF 9
Pelotas 53 F 3
Pelvoux 10 I 4
Pelym 24 N 5
Pelym, River 24 N 4-5
Pemalang 34 C 6
Pematangsiantar 34 A 4
Pemba (Mozambique) 40 G 5
Pemba (Tanzania) 40 FG 4
Pembroke (Canada) 44 P 6
Peombroke (United Kingdom) 4 D 6
Pembuang 34 D 5
Pen, Island 45 HI 4
Pena, Sierra de la- 8 F 2
Penafiel (Portugal) 9 B 3
Penafiel (Spain) 9 E 3
Penalara, Mt. 8 E 3
Penamacor 9 C 3
Penandjung, Bay 26 I 14
Pena Nevada, Mt. 47 E 3
Penaranca de Brac 9 D 3
Penarroya Pueblonuevo 9 D 4
Penas, Gulf of - (Chile) 53 B 6
Penas, Gulf of - (Spain) 8 D 2
Pendembu 39 B 4
Pendzikent 29 E 4
Penedo 52 L 4
Peneios 20 E 9
Penganga 30 C 4-5
Peng chia, Island 31 M 5
Penghu, Island 31 L 6
Peng lai 31 M 3
Peng shui 31 H 5
Peniche 9 B 4
Penida, Island 34 E 6
Penki 31 M 2
Penmarch, P.te de- 10 C 3
Pennabilli 19 CD 3
Penner 30 C 6
Pennick, B. 57 a 3
Pennine A. 18 A 1-2
Pennines 3 EF 4-5
Pennino, Mt 18 D 3
Pennsylvania 46 M 4
Penong 55 E 6
Pensacola 46 I 6
Pentecoste, Island 54 G 6
Penteleu, Mt. 20 H 5
Pentland 55 H 4
Pentland Firth 3 E 2
Penungah 31 E 3
Penza 2 R 5
Penzance 4 D 6
Penzina, Gulf of 22 R 3
Penzina 22 R 3
Penzino 22 R 3
Peoria 46 I 4
Pepel 36 B 5
Pequena, Bay 47 B 2
Pequerra 41 F 2
Pequiri 52 FG 5
Perabumulin 34 B 5
Perche 11 F 2
Perdido, Mt 10 E 5
Perecop, Strait of 1 O 6
Pereginsko 21 G 3
Peregrebnoe 24 O 3
Pereira 51 A 3
Pereirinha 52 F 3
Perejaslavka 32 E 2
Perelik, Mt. 20 G 7
Peremysl' 23 M 7
Pereslavl'-Zalesskij 23 N 6
Perez, Island 47 G 3
Pergamino 53 D 3
Perhon 16 L 5
Peribonka, 44 Q 5
Perigord 10 F 4
Périgueux 11 F 4
Peristeri, Mt. 20 E 8
Perlas, Islands de las 48 D 5
Perlas, Lag. de las- 48 C 4
Perleberg 13 D 2
Perm 22 E 4
Pernambuco 52 L 3
Perpignan 11 G 5
Perry River 44 I 2
Persepolis 28 N 5
Persian Gulf 26 GH 7
Perslakhata 23 N 3
Perth (Australia) 55 B 6
Perth (Scotland) 4 E 3
Perthus, Le- 8 H 2
Pertuis Breton 11 E 3
Pertuis Salernes 11 H 5
Peru 50 C 4-5
Perugia 19 D 3
Peruibe 52 H 6
Pervomajsk 25 A 1
Pervomajskoe 23 G 4
Pervouralsk 24 L 6
Pesa 24 E 1
Pesaro 19 D 3
Pescadores, Islands 31 L 6
Pescara 19 E 3
Pescara River 18 DE 3
Peschici 19 F 3-4
Peschiera 19 C 2
Pescia 19 C 2-3
Peskehaure, Island 16 G 3
Pesocnyj 23 H 4
Peso da Regua 9 C 3
Pesqueira 52 L 3
Petaihari 34 D 5
Petas, Las- 52 E 5
Petas, Rio 52 F 5
Peterborough (Australia) 55 F 6
Peterborough (United Kingdom) 4 F 5
Peterhead 4 F 3
Peter Pond Lake 44 G 4
Petersburg 46 M 5
Peterson, Mt. 57 P 2
Pethang Ringmo 26 q 16
Pethangtse, Mt. 26 q 17
Petit François 51 F 3
Petkula 17 N 3
Peto 47 G 3
Petraskoe 25 G 3
Petric 21 F 7
Petrinja 21 C 5
Petrodvorets 23 G 5
Petrokrepost' 23 H 5
Petrolandia 52 L 3
Petropavlovsk (Kamchatskiy) 22 Q 4
Petropavlovsk (Kazakhistan) 22 F 4
Petropolis 52 I 6
Petrovac 21 C 5
Petrova Gora, Mt. 20 B 5
Petrovo 25 B 1
Petrovsk 22 L 4
Petrovka 25 E 1
Petrozavodsk 23 L 4
Petrun 24 M 1
Petrusburg 41 D 4
Petseri 23 F 6
Pevek 22 S 3
Peyrehorade 11 E 5
Peza 24 CE 2
Pezenas 11 G 5
Phalodi 30 B 3
Phaltan 30 B 5
Phangnga 33 B 5
Pfaffenhofen 13 D 4
Pfan Rang 33 D 4
Phan Ri 33 D 4
Pfan Thiet 33 D 4
Pforzheim 13 C 4
Phatthalung 33 C 5
Phet Buri 33 B 4
Phetchabun 33 C 3
Philadelphia 46 M 5
Pfilippinen 26 Q 8-9
Phitsanulok 33 C 3
Phnompenh 33 C 4
Phoenix 46 D 6
Phongdo 31 E 4
Phuket 33 B 5
Phu Lang Thuong 33 D 2
Phu Luang, Mt 33 C 3
Phu Quoc, Island 33 C 4
Piacenza 19 BC 2
Piacoa 51 D 2
Piai, Cape 27 h 16
Piandz 29 EF 4
Pianosa 18 BC 3
Piata 52 I 4
Piatra Neamt 21 H 4
Piatra Semenicului, Mt. 20 F 5
Piaui, Rio 52 I 3
Piaui, State 52 I 2-3
Piave 18 D 2
Piazza Armerina 19 E 6
Pibor Post 40 E 1
Pica 52 D 6
Picardy 11 FG 1-2
Pichan 31 E 2
Pichieh 31 H 5
Pichilemu 53 B 3
Piciti 52 E 5
Pico, General- 53 D 4
Pico, Island 37 a
Pico de Itambé 52 I 5
Picos 52 I 3
Picton 55 g 14
Piduratalagala 30 D 7
Piedmont 19 AB 2
Piedras, R. de las- 52 C 4
Piela, Island 16 N 5
Pielavesi 17 N 5
Pielimen 23 G 3
Pienaarsriver 41 D 4
Pierre (France Guiana) 51 F 3
Pierre (USA) 46 F 4
Pietarsaari 17 L 5
Pietermaritzburg 41 E 4
Pietersburg 41 D 3
Pietro I, Island 57 p 3
Pietrosul, Mt. 20 G 4
Pihtipudas 17 M 5
Piketberg 41 B 5
Pikiutdleq 44 W 2
Pikiv 21 I 3
Pikou 31 H 4
Pikonunda 40 B 2
Pik Pobedy 22 G 5
Pikuj, Mt. 21 F 3
Pila 13 G 2
Pilar 52 F 7
Pilar do Sol 52 H 6
Pilat 10 H 4
Pilatus 18 AB 1
Pilcaniyeu 53 B 5
Pilcomayo 49 D 6
Pilis, Mt 20 D 4
Piltene 17 I 8
Pimenta 52 F 2
Pinaki, Island 54 O 6
Pinang (George Town) 33 C 5
Pinar, Sierra- 8 D 5
Pinar del Rio 48 C 2
Pinatubo, Mt. 34 F 1
Pinczow 13 I 3
Pinda 41 A 2
Pindus 20 E 8
Pine Island Bay 57 Q 2
Pine Bluff 46 H 6
Pine Creek 55 E 2
Pinedo, General- 53 D 2
Pinega 24 B 2
Pinega, River 24 BD 2-3
Pinerolo 19 A 2
Ping 33 BC 3
Pinga 40 D 3
Ping chiang 31 N 1
Ping chüan 31 L 2
Ping liang 31 H 3
Ping lo (Kan su) 31 H 3
Ping lo (Kuangsi) 31 I 6
Ping shan 27 g 15
Ping ting 31 I 3
Ping tung 31 M 6
Pingwu 31 G 4
Pinheiro 52 H 2
Pinhel 9 C 3
Pin hsien 31 H 3
Pini, Island 34 A 4
Pinsa 39 D 3
Pinsk 21 H 1
Pinta, Island 52 a
Pintado, El- 53 D 2
Piombino 19 C 3
Pioner Island 22 I 1-2
Piotrkow 13 H 3
Pipinas, Las- 53 E 4
Piracicaba 52 H 6
Piracuruca 52 I 2
Piraeus 21 F 9
Pir 'Ali 28 L 4
Pirané 53 E 2
Piranhas 52 E 3
Piranhas, Rio das- 52 L 3
Pirano 21 A 5
Pirapora 50 F 5
Pirat 25 E 6
Pires do Rios 52 H 5
Pirgos 21 E 9
Pirin Planina, Mt. 20 F 7
Pirmasens 13 BC 4
Pirot 21 F 6
Pirtikkylä 17 I 5
Piru 34 G 5
Pisa 19 C 3
Pisagua 52 C 5
Pisanino 18 C 2
Pisco 52 B 4
Pisek 21 B 3
Pishan 31 B 3
Piskin Lora 29 E 5-6
Pisticci 19 F 4
Pistoia 19 C 3
Pisuerga 9 D 2-3
Pita 39 B 3
Pitcairn, Island 54 O 7

Pite 17 I 4
Pitea 16 HI 4
Pitesti 21 G 5
Pithiviers 11 G 2
Pitljar 24 OP 2
Pito 51 A 2
Piton des Neiges, Mt. 41 a
Pitsani 41 D 4
Pitt, River 46 B 4
Pitt, Island 44 D 5
Pittsburgh 46 M 4
Pi tzà wo 31 M 3
Piura 52 A 3
Pixaria, Mt. 20 F 8
Pizma, River 24 DE 6
Pjalitsa 23 N 1
Pjalitsa, River 23 N 1
P'jana, River 24 C 7
Pjasina, River 22 HI 2
Pjatikhatki 25 B 1
Piasencia 9 C 3
Plast 24 M 7
Plastun 31 P 2
Plata, La- 53 E 3
Plata, Rio de la- 49 E 7
Platani 18 D 6
Platen, Cape 56 a
Platte 42 L 5
Plauen 13 DE 3
Playas 52 A 2
Plenty, Bay of- 55 h 3
Plesca Mare 20 F 4
Pleven 21 G 6
Plevlja 21 D 6
Pliva 21 C 5
Pljussa 23 G 5
Plock 13 H 2
Ploiesti 21 G 5
Plotemais 21 E 7
Plougasnou 11 D 2
Plovidiv 21 G 6
Plumas, Las- 53 C 5
Plumtree 41 D 3
Plunge 17 I 9
Plymouth (United Kingdom)
    4 D 6
Plymouth (USA) 46 M 5
Plynlimon, Mt. 3 E 5
Plzen 21 A 3
Podetta 19 D 2
Po 18 AD 2
Poai 31 I 3
Pobé 39 E 4
Pobedi, Peak 26 M 5
Pobedino 22 P 5
Pocatello 46 D 4
Pocep 23 I 8
Pochutla 47 E 4
Pocinki 24 C 7
Pocinok 23 I 7
Pocone 52 F 5
Podcere 24 I 3
Podgajtsy 21 G 3
Podkamennaja Tuoguska
    22 I 3
Podolia 20 GI 3
Podol'sk 23 M 7
Podor 37 B 6
Podosinovets13 24 D 4
Podporoz'e 23 L 4
Poel 13 D 1-2
Poggibonsi 19 C 3
Pogost 23 O 3
Pogradeec 21 E 7
Poh 34 F 5
Po Hai, Gulf of 31 L 3
Pohang 31 N 3
Pohorje, Mt. 20 B 4
Poiana, Mt. 20 G 4
Poimro 51 F 3
Poinsett, Cape 57 D 3
Pointe Noire 40 A 3
Point Lay 45 F 3
Poitiers 11 F 3
Poitou 11 EF 3
Pojarkovo 22 N 5
Pokalaroo 55 H 5
Pokca 24 I 3
Pokhara 30 D 3
Pokka 17 M 2
Poko 40 D 2
Pokor 39 G 4
Pokotu 31 M 1
Pokrov 23 N 7
Pola 23 HI 5-6
Poland 13 FL 2-3
Poleang 34 F 5
Poles'e 20 GH 2
Polesine 18 C 2
Polevskoj 24 M 6
Poli 31 O 1
Policastro, Gulf of 18 E 4-5
Polina Osipenko 22 O 4
Polinesia 54 LO 3-7
Polist' 23 H 5-6
Poljani 24 F 6
Pollensa 9 H 4
Pollica 19 E 4
Pollino 18 F 5
Polmak 17 O 1
Polnovat 22 F 3
Pologi 25 D 2
Polonnoe 21 H 2
Polotan, Island 34 F 2
Polotsk 23 G 7

Poltava 25 C 1
Poltsamaa 16 N 7
Poluj 24 P 1
Polur 31 C 3
Pomabamba 52 B 3
Pombal 9 B 4
Pomerania 3 FG 1-2
Pomeranian Bay 12 F 1
Pomona 41 B 4
Pomona, Island 3 E 2
Pomozdino 24 H 3
Ponape, Island 54 F 4
Ponce 48 F 3
Pondicherry 30 C 6
Pondo 41 D 5
Pongo, River 40 D 1
Ponnadyar 30 C 6
Ponoj 23 O 1
Ponoj, River 23 LO 1
Ponorogo 34 D 6
Pons 9 G 3
Ponta Grossa 52 G 7
Pontal 52 I 3
Ponta Pora 50 E 6
Ponte do Lima 9 B 3
Ponte Nova 52 I 6
Pontevedra 9 B 2
Pontevedra, Ria de- 8 B 2
Pontianak 34 C 5
Pontici, Mts.- 25 BF 5
Pontine Is. 19 D 4
Pontivy 11 D 2
Pont S. Esprit 11 H 4
Ponza 18 D 4
Poole 4 F 6
Pool Malebo 40 B 3
Poopo, Lake 52 D 5
Popadia, Mt. 20 G 3
Popayan 51 A 3
Pope 17 I 8
Popel'nja 21 I 3
Popigaj 22 LM 2
Poplar Bluff 46 H 5
Popocatépetl Mt 42 L 8
Popokabaka 40 B 4
Poprad 20 E 3
Porbandar 30 A 4
Porcupine 45 I 3
Pori 17 I 6
Porjus 17 H 3
Porkha 31 C 4
Porkhov 23 G 6
Poronajsk 22 P 5
Porosozero 23 I 3
Porpoise, Bay 57 c 3
Porqyerolles, Island 11 I 5
Porsanger, fj. 16 M 1
Porsanger 17 M 1
Port Adelaide 55 F 6
Port Albert 55 b 8
Portalegre 9 C 4
Portales 46 F 6
Port Alfred 41 D 5
Port Arthur (USA) 46 H 7
Port Augusta 55 F 6
Port-au-Prince 48 E 3
Port-aux-Basques 44 T 6
Port Beaufort 41 C 5
Port Bell 40 E 2
Port Balir 33 A 4
Port Bou 9 G 2
Port Burwell 44 S 3
Port Davey 55 b 9
Port Douglas 55 H 3
Portel 52 G 2
Port Elizabeth 41 D 5
Port Gentil 39 F 6
Port Hacking 55 e 11
Port Harcourt 39 F 5
Port Harrison 44 P 4
Port Hedland 55 B 4
Port Herald 41 F 2
Port Hurd 55 E 2
Port Huron 46 L 4
Port Kembla 55 d 11
Portland (Australia) 55
    G 7
Portland (United Kingdom)
    4 E 6
Portland (Maine) 46 N 4
Portland (Oregon) 46 B 3
Portland, Cape 16 S 13
Portland, Punta 48 D 3
Portland, Billof 3 E 6
Port Lincoln 55 F 6
Port Lokko 39 B 4
Port Louis 41 a
Port Maria 48 D 3
Port Moresby 54 E 5
Port Natal 36 G 9
Port Nelson 44 M 4
Port Said 37 M 3
Porto Acre 52 C 3
Porto Alegre 53 F 3
Porto Amboim 40 A 5
Porto de Moz 52 G 2
Porto Esperança 52 F 5
Portoferraio 19 BC 3
Port onSpain 51 D 1
Porto Grande 51 F 3
Portogruaro 19 D 2
Pôrto Nacional 52 H 4
Porto Novo 39 E 4

Porto Real 9 C 5
Porto Recanati 19 DE 3
Port Orford 46 B 4
Porto Santo 37 A 3
Pôrto Seguro 52 L 5
Porto S. Giorgio 19 DE 3
Porto Torres 19 B 4
Porto Vecchio 11 a
Portoveiejo 52 A 2
Port Phillip, B. 55 a 8
Port Pirie 55 F 6
Port Radium 43 H 3
Portree 4 C 3
Port Roper, Bay 55 F 2
Portrusk 4 C 4
Port Saint Johns 41 D 5
Port-Saint-Louis 11 H 5
Port Shepstone 41 E 5
Portsmouth (United
    Kingdom) 4 F 6
Portsmouth (New
    Hampshire) 46 N 4
Portsmouth (Virginia)
    46 M 5
Port Stanley 53 E 7
Port Sudan 38 C 4
Portugal 9 BC 3-5
Portugalete 9 E 2
Port Vendres 11 G 5
Port Weld 33 C 6
Porvoo 17 M 6
Posadas (Argentina) 53 E 2
Posco 52 G 3
Poso 34 F 5
Posse 52 H 4
Post 46 F 6
Postmasburg 41 C 4
Potchefstroom 41 D 4
Potgietersrust 41 D 3
Poti 25 F 4
Poti, Rio 52 I 2-3
Potiskum 39 G 3
Poto 52 C 4
Potomac 42 N 6
Potosi 52 D 5
Potrerillos 47 G 4
Potsdam 13 E 2
Pouso Alegre (Mato
    Grosso) 52 F 4
Pouso Alegre (Minas
    Gerais) 52 H 6
Poved 23 L 6
Povenets 23 L 3
Povoa de Varzim 9 B 3
Povungnituk 44 P 4
Powder 46 E 4
Powell Creek 55 E 3
Poxim 52 L 4
Poyang 31 L 5
Poyang Hu, Island 31 L 5
Poylen, Mt. 20 D 5
Pozarevac 21 E 5
Pozeg 24 H 4
Pozega 21 C 5
Pozerevitsy 23 G 6
Poznan 13 G 2
Pozo Hondo 53 D 2
Pozzuoli 19 DE 4
Pra 39 D 4
Prachin Buri 33 C 4
Prachuap Khiri Khan 33 B 4
Prado 52 L 5
Prague 13 F 3
Prai 33 C 5
Praia 39 a
Prainha 52 G 2
Prairie, Gr.- 44 F 4
Prairies, Coteau des-
    46 G 3-4
Prampram 39 E 4
Pran Buri 33 B 4
Pràsto 17 E 9
Prasu 39 D 4
Pratas, Island 31 L 6
Prato 19 C 3
Pratomagno 18 C 3
Predeal Pass 20 G 5
Pregolia 16 I 9
Prenj Planina, Mt. 20 C 6
Preparis, Island 33 A 4
Prerov 21 C 3

Prilep 21 E 7
Priluka 21 I 3
Primorsko-Akhtarsk 25 E 2
Prince Albert 44 H 5
Prince Albert I. (Canada)
    44 S 6
Prince Edward I. (South
    Africa) 57 H 5
Prince George 44 E 5
Prince Regent Inlet, Strait
    44 M 1
Prince Rupert 44 D 5
Principe 39 F 5
Pr. Albert S.a 44 F 1
Pr. Albert B.ge 57 B 2
Pr. Albert Pen. 44 FG 1
Pr. Charles Island (Canada)
    44 P 2
Pr. Charles Mt. 57 f 2
Principe da Beira 52 E 4
Prince of Wales, Cape 45 E 3
Prince of Wales Island
    (Alaska) 45 N 5-6
Prince of Wales Island
    (Australia) 55 G 2
Prince of Wales Island
    (Canada) 44 L 1
Prince of Wales Strait 44 F 1
Prince Harald Coast -57 H 2
Prinz Olaf Coast 57 g 3
Princess Astrid Coast
    57 il 2
Princess Martha Coast
    57 li 2
Princess Ragnhitd Coast
    57 hH 2
Pringles, Coronel- 53 D 4
Prinsen, Island 34 C 6
Prinzapolca 48 C 4
Priozersk 23 H 4
Pripyat 32 MO 5
Pripyat Marsches 20 HI 1-2
Pristina 21 E 6
Pritzwalk 13 DE 2
Privas 11 H 4
Privol'noe 22 Q 4
Prizren 21 E 6
Prjaza 23 I 4
Prienai 17 M 9
Prieska 41 C 4
Proclamation, Island 57 G 3
Progreso 47 G 3
Prokopievsk 22 H 4
Prokuplje 21 E 6
Proletarij 21 H 5
Proletarskaja 25 F 2
Prome 33 B 3
Promina, Mt. 20 BC 6
Pronja 23 H 7-8
Propria 52 L 4
Prorva 29 B 2
Proserpine 55 H 4
Prosna 18 H 3
Prostejov 21 C 3
Proston 55 I 5
Provence 11 HI 5
Providence 46 O 4
Providence Channel 48 D 1
Providence, Island 35 H 6
Providencia, Island 48 C 4
Providenija 22 T 3
Provins 11 G 2
Provo 46 D 4
Prozor 21 C 6
Prt 20 GI 3-5
Prutz 7 D 3
Prypec 20 H 1-2
Prypet 20 G 2
Pryz, Bay 57 F 3
Przedborz 13 H 3
Przemysl 13 L 4
Psara, Island 21 G 8
Pskov 23 G 6
Pskov, L. 23 FG 5-6
Psunj Planina, Mt. 20 C 5
Ptic' 21 I 1
Ptic', River 23 FG 8
Ptuj 21 B 4
Puca Curo 52 B 2
Pucallpa 52 C 3
Pucaurco 52 C 2
Puck 13 H 1
Pudasjärvi 17 N 4
Pudoz 38 M 4
Puebla 47 E 4
Puebla de Alcocer 9 D 4
Puebla de Caramin 9 B 2
Puebla de Don Fadrique,
    La- 9 E 5
Puebla de Guzman 9 C 5
Puebla de Montalban, La-
    9 D 4
Pueblo 46 F 5
Pueblo Hundido 53 B 2
Puedpa 48 G 5
Pueches 53 C 4
Puente, El- 52 E 5
Puente Genil 9 D 5
Puerto Aisen 53 B 6
Puerto América 52 B 2
Puerto Artur 47 G 2
Puerto Ayacucho 51 C 2
Puerto Barrios 47 G 4
Puerto Berrio 51 B 2

Puerto Cabello 51 C 1
Puerto Cabezas 48 C 4
Puerto Cabo Gracias a Dios
    48 C 4
Puerto Cabras 37 B 4
Puerto Caneco 52 F 4
Puerto Carreno 51 C 2
Puerto Casado13 52 F 6
Puerto Chico 52 a
Puerto Coig 53 C 7
Puerto Colombia 51 B 1
Puerto Cortes (Costa Rica)
    48 C 5
Puerto Cortés (Honduras)
    47 G 4
Puerto de Libertad 47 B 2
Puerto de Lobos 47 B 1
Puerto de S. Maria 9 C 5
Puerto Esperidiao 52 F 5
Puerto Estrella 51 B 1
Puerto Franco 52 H 3
Puerto Guaira 52 G 6
Puerto Guarani 52 F 6
Puerto Heath 52 D 4
Puerto Isabel 52 F 5
Puerto Limon (Colombia)
    51 B 3
Puerto Limon (Costa Rica)
    48 C 5
Puertollano 9 D 4
Puerto Lobos 53 C 5
Puerto Madryn 53 C 5
Puerto Maldonado 52 D 4
Puerto Melendez 52 B 2
Puerto Montt 53 B 5
Puerto Murtinho 52 F 6
Puerto Natales 53 B 7
Puerto Paez 51 C 2
Puerto Patillos 52 C 6
Puerto Penasco 47 B 1
Puerto Plata 48 E 3
Puerto Princesa 34 E 3
Puerto Rico 50 D 2
Puerto Suarez 52 F 5
Puerto Velho 52 E 3
Puerto Wilches 51 B 2
Puerto Yessup 52 C 4
Pugacev 24 E 8-9
Puget Theniers 11 I 5
Puhos, Island 17 O 4
Puigcerda 9 G 2
Puigmal, Mt. 9 H 2
Puig Mayor, Mt. 8 H 4
Puka 28 B 6
Pukapuka, Island 54 O 6
Pukarua, Island 54 O 6
Pukcheong 31 N 2
Pula 21 A 5
Pulai, River 27 h 16
Pulai, Mt. 27 h 16
Pulap, Island 54 E 4
Pulaumadjang 34 D 4
Pulo Anna, Island 54 D 4
Pulog, Mt. 26 Q 8
Pultusk 13 I 2
Pu lun tai 31 E 3
Pumori, Mt. 26 p 16
Puna 52 D 15
Pune 30 B 5
Punggol, Cape 27 i 16
Pungsan 31 N 2
Pungutaran Islands 34 F 3
Puno 52 C 4
Punta Arenas 53 B 7
Punta Colorada 53 B 2
Punta Prieta 47 B 2
Puntarenas 48 C 5
Puolanka 17 N 4
Pupuya, Nevado-, Mt. 52
    D 4
Puquios 53 C 2
Pur 22 G 3
Puri 30 E 5
Purikkala 23 G 4
Purnea 30 E 3
Purnema 23 M 2
Puruktjau 34 D 5
Purulia 30 E 4
Purus, Rio 52 CE 3
Purwakarta 34 C 6
Purwokerto 34 C 6
Pusa 23 F 6
Pusula 17 M 6
Pursat 33 C 4
Puruktjau 34 D 5
Pursur 27 a 11
Putao 33 B 1
Pu tien 31 L 5
Putignano 19 F 4
Puturana Mountains 22
    IL 3
Puttalam 30 C 7
Putussibau 34 D 4
Puula-Vesi, Island 16 N 6
Puumala 23 G 4
Puy, Le 11 H 4
Puy de Dôme, Mt. 10 G 4
Puy de Dôme, Mt. 10 G 4
Pweto 40 D 4
Pwllheli 4 D 5
Pyapon 33 B 3
Piatigorsk 25 G 3
Pyeongyang 31 N 3
Pyhä 16 M 4-5
Pyhäjoki 17 M 4
Pyhat, Mt. 17 N 3

Pykäsellä, Island 23 G 3
Pyramid, Mt. 44 D 4
Pyrenees 8 FH 2
Pyrzyce 13 F 2
Pyscug 24 C 5
Pyssa 24 E 2
Pyoesa 17 M 9

Q

Qacentina 37 F 2
Qadhima 38 C 3
Qain 29 C 5
Qais, Island 29 B 6
Qala Niaz Khan 29 D 4-5
Qala Bist 29 D 5
Qal'a Shahar 29 E 4
Qal'a Sikar 28 I 5
Qal'a Sulik 28 I 5
Qal'at al-Muladhar 28 D 7
Qal'at Knamis Akhada
    28 D 6
Qandahar 29 E 5
Qara Aghach 28 I 2
Qara Su 28 LM 3
Qarghaliq 31 B 3
Qars, El- 37 L 4
Qasr Al-Haiyaniyn 28 G 6
Qasr Farafra 37 L 4
Qasr-i-Shirin 28 H 3
Qatar 38 F 2
Qatif 28 L 7
Qattara, El- 37 L 3
Qazvin 28 L 2
Qelti el-Khudeira 37 L 6
Qena 37 M 4
Qena 28 B 7
Qirab 28 L 4
Qishm, Island 29 C 6
Qishn 38 F 4
Qizil qaya 28 I 2
Qizil Uzun 1 R 8
Qnaa 28 F 7
Qomul 31 E 2
Quakenbrück 13 B 2
Qualidia 37 C 3
Quang Ngai 33 D 3
Quang tri 33 D 3
Qu'Appelle 44 I 5
Quatsino 44 D 5
Quchan 29 C 4
Quebec, Town 44 Q 6
Quebec 44 PR 4-6
Quebrachal, El- 53 D 2
Queensland 55 GH 4
Queenstown (South Africa)
    41 D 5
Queenstown (Tasmania)
    55 b 9
Quelimane 41 F 2
Quelpart 31 N 4
Quelpart, Island 26 Q 6
Queen Alexandra Ra.
    57 aB 1
Queen Charlotte Islands
    44 C 5
Queen Charlotte Sd. 44 D 5
Queen Mary Coast 57 E 3
Queretaro 47 D 3
Quessa 39 D 3
Quetta 29 E 5
Quezaltenango 47 F 5
Quezon City 27 Q 8
Quiaca, La- 53 C 1
Quibala 40 A 5
Quibdo 51 A 2
Quicia 52 L 4
Quieimadas 52 L 4
Quiepe, Island 52 L 4
Quilan, Cape 53 B 5
Quillabamba 52 C 4
Quillagua 52 D 6
Quillan 11 G 5
Quillota 53 B 3
Quilon 30 C 7
Quilpie 55 G 5
Quimili 53 D 2
Quimper 11 C 3
Quincy 46 H 5
Quines 53 C 3
Qui Nhon 33 D 4
Quinto 9 F 3
Quirimbo 40 A 5
Quissanga 40 F 5
Quissico 41 E 3
Quitaro 51 E 3
Quito 52 B 2
Quitasueno 48 C 4
Quixada 52 L 2
Qul'an, Ras. 38 C 3
Qulanaldi 30 C 1
Qal'a Shargat 28 G 3
Quliabab 28 L 3
Qum 28 M 3
Qunduz 29 E 4
Qunfida 38 D 4
Quoram 38 C 5
Qusai 38 F 5
Quseir, El- 37 M 4
Qushgakh 28 M 3
Qusuriya 38 D 3
Qutuf 38 F 3
Quwar 28 G 2

R

Raahe 17 M 4
Raasay Sound, Strait 3 C 3
Rab 21 B 4
Raba 34 E 6
Raba, River 20 C 4
Raba, Riv (Poland) 12 I 4
Raba, (Saudi Arabia) 38 D 3
Rabai 40 F 3
Rabat (Marocco) 37 C 3
Rabat (Sumatra) 34 B 5
Rabaul 26 o 14
Rabca 20 C 4
Rabigh 38 C 3
Race, Cape 44 U 6
Rachel, 12 E 4
Rachgoun 37 D 2
Raciborz 13 GH 3
Racine 46 I 4
Radan, Mt. 20 E 6
Radauti 21 G 4
Radhanpur 30 B 4
Raditsa 23 L 8
Radom 13 I 3
Radomka, River 12 I 3
Radomsko 13 H 3
Radöy Oster, Fj. 17 A 6
Radzymin 13 I 2
Radzyn 13 L 3
Rae Bareli 30 D 3
Rafaela 53 D 3
Rafah 28 C 5
Rafaï 40 C 1
Raga 40 D 1
Raggo 17 O 1
Raguba 37 H 4
Raguli 25 G 3
Ragusa 19 E 6
Raha 34 F 5
Rahad, 38 B 5
Rahaeng 33 B 3
Rahbur 29 C 6
Rahden 13 C 2
Raheita 38 D 5
Rahgird 28 M 3
Raichur 30 C 5
Raigarh 30 D 4
Raimangal 27 a 12
Rainier, Mt. 42 G 5
Raipur 30 D 4
Raiyan 27 G 8
Rajahmundry 30 D 5
Rajang, River 34 D 4
Rajkot 30 B 4
Rajshahi 30 E 4
Rakan, Cape 38 F 2
Rakisvaara, Mt. 17 I 2
Rakops 41 C 3
Rakvere 23 F 5
Rakwach 40 E 2
Raleigh 46 M 5
Raleigh Bay 46 M 6
Ralik, Island 54 GH 3-4
Rallapuïa 37 B 5
Ram 31 F 4
Rama 21 C 6
Ramadi 28 G 4
Ramah 44 S 4
Ramansdrift 41 B 4
Ramartina 41 c 7
Ramathlabama 41 CD 4
Rämen 17 F 6
Ramenskoe 23 N 7
Rameswaram 30 C 7
Ramhaill 17 G 6
Ram Hormuz 28 L 5
Râmnicul 20 H 5
Râmnicu Valcea 21 G 5
Ramntigar 30 D 3
Ramohira 41 c 8
Ramoutsa 41 D 3
Rampur 30 C 3
Ramree, Island 33 A 3
Ramsey 4 D 4
Ramsjö 17 F 5
Ramvik 17 G 5
Ran, Fj. 16 E 3
Ranaghal 27 a 11
Rancagua 53 B 3
Ranchi 30 E 4
Randers 17 C 8
Rands 17 C 6
Rands, River 16 D 6
Rands Fjord 17 D 6
Rands Fjord, Fj. 17 D 6
Randwick 55 e 10
Ranm 16 I 3
Rangamati 27 e 11
Ranges 46 G 6
Rangiora 55 g 14
Rangiroa, Island 54 N 6
Rangitikei, River 55 h 13
Rangoon 33 B 3
Ranibennur 30 C 6
Rankine 55 F 3
Rann 26 IL 7
Rannock, 4 D 3
Ranomafana 41 c 8
Ranong 33 B 5
Rantabe 41 c 7
Rantemario 34 F 5
Raoul, Island 54 I 7
Rapa, Island 54 N 7
Rapid City 46 F 4
Räpina 23 F 5

Rapiu, Pt. 26 pq 16
Rapla 17 M 4
Rapti 30 D 3
Raroia, Island 54 N 6
Raratonga, Island 54 M 7
Rasa, I. 54 L 2
Ras Abu Soma, Cape 28 C 7
Ras al-Badi'a, Cape 28 L 7
Ras al-Hadd, Cape 26 H 7
Ras al-Mish'ab, Cape 28 L 6
Ras Bahrgan, Cape 28 L 5
Ras Barabakh, Cape 28 L 7
Raseiniai 17 L 9
Rasha 39 D 2
Ras-el-Ma 37 D 6
Rashad 37 M 7
Rashid 38 C 5
Rasht 28 L 2
Ras Koh, Mt. 29 E 6
Ras Mahrash, Cape 28 C 7
Ras Muari, Cape 29 E 7
Ras Muhammad, Cape 28 C 7
Raso, Cape 51 G 3
Rason, 55 C 5
Rassua, Island 22 Q 5
Ras Tanura, Cape 28 L 7
Rastegaissa, Mt. 16 MN 1
Rastovitsa 20 I 3
Rasu Mt. 18 B 4
Ras 'Ubid, Cape 28 C 7
Ratak, Island 54 GH 3-4
Rätan 17 F 5
Rathenow 13 DE 2
Rath Gia 33 D 4
Ratnagiri 30 B 5
Ratlam 30 C 4
Raton 46 F 5
Rättvik 17 F 6
Raub 33 C 6
Rauberg, Mt. 17 BC 6
Raudan, 16 N 3
Raufarhofn 17 U 11
Raukumara, Mt. 55 h 13
Rauli 17 F 4
Rauma 17 I 6
Raung, Gunung-, Mt. 34 D 6
Rauscha 6 L 2
Rautas 16 H 2
Rauworavi, Mt. 16 L 2
Ravansar 28 I 3
Ravenna 19 D 2
Ravensthorpe 55 C 6
Ravenswood 55 H 4
Ravi 29 F 5
Rawalpindi 29 F 5
Rawa Mazowiecka 19 I 3
Rawicz 13 G 3
Rawka, Mt. 20 F 3
Rawlinna 55 D 6
Rawlins 46 E 4
Rawson 53 C 5
Ray, Mt. 45 H 3
Rayong 33 C 4
Razan 28 L 3
Razgrad 21 H 6
Razvil'noe 25 F 2
Re, Bay del- 56 a
Ré, Island de 10 E 3
Reading (United Kingdom 4 F 6
Reading (USA) 46 M 4
Ream 33 C 4
Reata 47 D 2
Reboly 23 H 3
Recherche, Arch. of the 55 C 6
Recife 52 L 3
Recitsa 20 I 1
Reconquista 53 E 2
Recuay 52 B 3
Red Bluff 46 B 4
Red Deer 44 G 5
Red Deer, River 44 G 5
Redding 46 B 4
Rede 4 F 4
Redeyef 37 F 3
Red Lake, 46 GH 3
Redon 11 D 3
Redondela 9 B 2
Redondo 9 C 4
Red River, (N. Dakota, Minnesota) 46 G 3
Red River, (Texas) 46 G 6
Red River (Vietnam) 33 CD 2
Red Sea 26 FG 7-8
Redruth 4 D 6
Red Tower P. 20 G 5
Red Volta 39 D 3
Ree 3 B 5
Regba 37 B 6
Regbat 37 C 4
Reg el Aftout 37 D 4
Regen 12 E 4
Regensburg 13 DE 4
Reggan 37 D 4
Reggio Calabria 19 EF 5
Reggio Emilia 19 C 2
Reghinuls-Sasesc 21 G 4
Regima, El- 37 I 3
Regîna 44 I 5
Registan 29 DE 5
Registro de Araguaia 52 G 5
Regnitz 12 D 4
Regone 41 F 2

Regueibat 37 BC 4-5
Rehar 30 D 4
Rehoboth (Damara Land) 41 B 3
Rehoboth (Ovamboland) 41 A 2
Rehsja-egg, Mt. 17 C 6
Reibell 37 E 2
Reï Bouba 40 A 1
Reichenbach 13 DE 3
Reims 11 H 2
Reindeer 44 I 4
Reinosa 9 D 2
Reinöy, Island 17 H 2
Rejal al-Mà 38 D 4
Reks, Mt. 16 B 6
Remanso 52 I 3
Rembang 34 D 6
Rempang, Island 27 i 17
Remscheid 13 B 3
Renca 33 C 3
Rendal Sölen, Mt. 17 D 6
Rengat 34 B 5
Reni 21 I 5
Renigunta 30 C 6
Renk 37 M 7
Renmark 55 G 6
Rennebu 17 C 5
Rennell, Island 54 G 6
Rennes 11 E 2
Reno 18 C 2
Reo 34 F 6
Reo, Island 54 O 6
Requena (Peru) 52 C 2-3
Requena (Spain) 9 F 4
Resende 9 C 3
Reschen-P. 18 C 1
Resistencia 53 E 2
Resita 21 E 5
Resolution (Canada) 44 RS 3
Retalhuleu 47 F 5
Retamito 53 C 3
Rethel 11 H 2
Réunion 41 a
Reus 9 G 3
Reuss 19 B 1
Reut 20 HI 3-4
Reutlingen 13 C 4
Revda 24 L 6
Revel 11 F 5
Reventazon 52 A 3
Revillagigedo Islands 47 B 4
Revoil Beni Unif 37 D 3
Rewa 30 D 4
Rewari 30 C 3
Reyes (Bolivia) 52 D 4
Reyes (Mexico) 47 D 3
Reykjahlidh 17 T 12
Reykjanes 16 Q 13
Reykjavik 17 R 12
Reynivellir 17 R 12
Rez 24 M 6
Rezaiyeh 28 H 2
Rezekne 23 F 6
Rezvaja 20 H 7
Rhaetian Alps 12 CD 5
Rhaetic Alps 18 BC 1
Rhat 37 H 6
Rhatangarh 30 B 3
Rheine 13 B 2
Rhergo 37 D 6
Rheydt 13 B 3
Rhine 10 F 2
Rhine (USA) 46 C 5
Rhineland 13 B 3
Rhinelander 46 I 3
Rhodes 21 I 9
Rhodes I. 20 I 1
Rhodesia-Zimbabwe 36 FG 7
Rhodopen 20 FG 6-7
Rhön 12 CD 3
Rhondda 4 E 6
Rhône 10 HI 3 5
Rhun 3 C 3
Riad (Riyadh) 38 E 3
Riau Islands 34 B 4
Ribadeo 9 C 2
Ribagorza 9 G 2
Ribatejo 9 B 4
Ribaue 41 F 1
Ribbenesöy, Island 16 H 1
Ribble 3 F 5
Ribe 17 C 9
Ribeirao Prêto 52 H 6
Ribeiro Gonçalves 52 H 3
Ribera 19 D 6
Riberalta 52 D 4
Richard Black Coast 57 n 2
Richards,Island 44 C 2
Richelieu 11 F 3
Richfield 46 D 5
Richmond (Australia) 55 G 4
Richmond (South Africa) 41 C 5
Richmond (USA) 46 M 5
Richtersveld 41 B 4
Riesa 13 E 3
Rietfontein 41 C 4
Rieti 19 D 3
Rifst'angi 17 T 11
Riga 17 M 8

Riga, Gulf of 23 D 5-6
Rigi, Mt. 18 C 5
Rigolet 44 T 5
Rijeka 21 B 5
Rikkavesi 23 G 3
Rila 21 F 6
Rille 10 F 2
Rima 39 F 3
Rimar, Mt. 16 S 12
Rimarska Sobota 21 E 3
Rimatara, Island 54 M 7
Rimava 20 DE 3
Rimini 19 D 2
Rimouski 44 R 6
Rindal 17 C 5
Rindja, Island 34 E 6
Rindjam, Mt. 34 E 6
Ringebu 17 D 6
Ringervil e 39 D 4
Ringköbing 17 C 8
Ringnes, Island 42 I 2
Ringvassöy, Island 16 H 2
Rinnes, Ben-, Mt. 4 E 3
Rio Apaporis 49 C 3
Riobamba 52 B 2
Rio Brilhante 52 G 6
Rio Caguan 51 B 3
Rio Catrimani 51 D 3
Rio Chico 51 C 1
Rio Claro 52 H 6
Rio Colorado 53 D 4
Rio Cuarto 53 D 3
Rio de Janeiro 52 I 6
Rio de Oro 36 B 3
Rio del Rey 39 F 5
Rio Gallegos 53 C 7
Rio Grande (Argentina) 53 C 7
Rio Grande (Brazil) 53 F 3
Rio Grande do Norte 52 L 3
Rio Grande do Sul 52 G 7
Riohacha 51 B 1
Rio Itapicuru 52 I 3
Rioja, La- 53 C 2
Rioja, La-, Reg. 8 EF 2
Rio Major 9 B 4
Rio Negro Reservoir 53 E 3
Rionero, Ps. 18 E 4
Rio Pardo de Minas 52 I 5
Rio Putumayo 52 B 1
Rio Sucio 51 A 2
Rio Vaupés 49 D 3
Riozinho 52 D 3
Ripats 17 I 3
Ripiano Podolico, Mt. 1 MN 5-6
Ripoll 9 H 2
Rirca Gomba 31 G 3
Risbäck 17 F 4
Rishähr 28 M 6
Riske 16 H 4
Risör 17 C 7
Risti 17 M 7
Ristijärvi 23 G 2
Risut 38 F 4
Riva 19 C 2
Rivadavia 53 B 2
Rivas 48 C 4
Rivera 53 E 3
River Cess 39 C 4
Riversdale 41 C 5
Rivers Inlet 44 D 5
Riverston 46 E 4
Rivesaltes 11 G 5
Rivett, Mt. 57 f 3
Riviera di Levante 18 B 2-3
Riviera di Ponente 18 AB 2-3
Riyadh (Riad) 38 E 3
Rize 25 F 3
Rizzuto, Cape 18 F 5
Rjabuska 24 C 9
Rjapusovo 23 N 3-4
Rjukan 17 C 7
Roan 17 D 4
Roanne 11 G 3
Roanoke 46 M 5
Robat 38 F 1
Robert-English-Küste 57 Oo 2
Robertson 41 C 5
Robertson, Bay 57 A 2
Robertson, Island 57 n 3
Robertsport 39 B 4
Roberval 44 Q 6
Robla, La- 9 D 2
Robson, Mt. 42 GH 4
Roca, Da-, Cape 8 B 4
Roca Alijos 47 B 4
Roca Partida, Island 47 B 4
Rocas, I. 49 G 4
Rocca Eusambra, Mt. 18 D 6
Rocha 53 F 3
Rocharc, Mt. 11 E 2
Rochefort 11 E 4
Rochelle 46 L 6
Rochelle, La- 11 E 3
Roche-sur-Yon, La- 11 E 3
Rochester 46 M 4
Rockdale 55 e 10
Rockefeller, Mt. 57 Ss 2
Rockford 46 I 4
Rockhampton 55 I 4
Rock Island 46 H 4

Rock Springs 46 E 4
Rocky Mountains 42 GI 4-6
Roca, La- 9 E 4
Rocez 11 G 4
Rocnei 20 G 4
Roconit, Cape 20 D 7
Röcvig 17 E 9
Roebourne 55 B 4
Roes Welcome Sound 44 N 3
Rogacëv 23 H 8
Rogagua 52 D 4
Rogaland 17 AB 7
Rognan 17 F 3
Rogo 39 F 3
Rogue 46 B 4
Rohmoiva, Mt. 23 G 1
Roi Et 33 C 3
Roja 17 L 8
Rojas 53 D 3
Rojo, Cape 47 E 3
Rokab 37 M 6
Rokell 39 B 4
Rokiskis 17 M 9
Rokitno 20 H 2
Roldanillo 51 A 3
Rolla 46 H 5
Rolla, Island 17 G 2
Rollag 17 C 6
Rolvsöy 17 M 1
Röma (Australia) 55 H 5
Roma (Sweden) 17 H 8
Roma, Island 34 G 6
Romagna 18 CD 2
Romaine 44 S 5
Roman (Bulgaria) 21 F 6
Roman (Romania) 21 H 4
Romania 21 EH 4-5
Romanija Planina, Mt. 20 D 6
Romano, Cape 46 L 7
Romanovka 22 M 4
Romans 11 H 4
Roman Wall 3 EF 4
Romanzof, Cape 45 E 4
Rome 19 D 4
Rome 46 L 6
Romilly 11 G 2
Römö, Island 16 C 9
Romorantin 11 F 3
Rompin 33 C 6
Ron 33 D 3
Rona, North-, Island 4 D 2
Ronaldsay, North-, Island 4 E 2
Ronaldsay, South- 4 E 2
Roncador, Island 48 CD 4
Roncesvalles 8 F 2
Ronciglione 19 CD 3
Ronco 18 CD 2
Ronda 9 D 5
Rondane, Mt. 16 D 6
Ronehamn 17 H 8
Ronneby 17 F 8
Ronneim 17 F 8
Roodepoort 41 D 4
Rooi Bank 41 A 3
Roosevelt, Island 57 Tt 1
Roper 54 D 6
Roper 55 E 2
Rooi, Mt. 16 I 2
Roques, Los-, Island 51 C 1
Ror 16 C 7
Roraima, Mt. 49 D 3
Röros 17 D 5
Rorumluk, Pt. 31 E 3
Rosa, 54 L 6
Rosa, Mt. 18 AB 2
Rosario 53 D 3
Rosario de la Frontera 53 D 2
Rosario do Sul 53 F 3
Rosas 9 H 2
Roscommon 4 B 5
Roscrea 4 C 5
Rosenheim 13 DE 5
Rosetta 37 M 3
Roshage 17 C 8
Rosica 20 G 6
Rosiorii de Vede 21 G 5
Roskilde 17 E 9
Roslavl' 23 I 8
Ross (United Kingdom) 4 E 6
Ross (New Zealand) 55 g 14
Ross-Schelfeis 57 TA 2
Ross, Island. 57 a 2
Rossano 19 F 5
Rosso (USA) 42 L 6
Rost 17 D 3
Rosta 17 H 2
Rosto 16 I 2
Rostock 13 E 2
Rostov 25 E 2
Rosvinskoe 24 G 1
Roswell 46 F 6
Rota, Island 54 E 3
Rothaar-Gebirge, 12 C 3
Rothbury 4 F 4
Rothenburg 13 D 4
Roti, Island 34 F 7
Rotondo, Mt. 18 B 3
Rottweil 13 C 4
Rotterdam 15 G 3
Rotuma, Island 54 H 6
Rouen 11 F 2

Rousay, Island 4 E 2
Roussillon 11 G 5
Rov 20 HI 3
Rovaniemi 17 M-N 3
Rovereto 19 C 2
Rovigo 19 C 2
Rovigno 21 A 5
Rovno 2 N 5
Rovuma 35 G 7
Roxen 16 F 7
Roxo, Cape 39 A 3
Royal Canal 3 C 5
Royan 11 E 4
Roy Hill 55 B 4
Röykenvik 17 D 6
Rozdestvenskoe 24 C 5
Rozovka 25 D 2
Roztocze 12 L 3-4
Rtanj, Mt. 20 E 6
Rtishchevo 24 H 1
Rua'at, Er- 37 M 7
Ruaha 35 G 6
Ruapehu, Mt. 55 h 13
Rub' al-Khali, Desert (great Arabian Desert) 38 EF 3
Rubengera 40 D 3
Rubtsovsk 22 H 4
Rudbar 29 D 5
Rud-i-Mehran 38 F 2
Rud-i-Saimarreh 28 I 4
Rud-i-Sar 28 M 2
Rudki 21 F 3
Rudnicnyj 24 G 5
Rudnik, Mt. 20 E 5
Rudno 23 G 5
Rudok 31 B 4
Rufa'a 38 B 5
Ruffea 11 F 3
Rufiji 35 G 6
Rufino 53 D 3
Rufisque 37 A 7
Rügen, I. 12 EF 1
Rühimäki 17 M 6
Ruhnu, Island 16 L 8
Ruhr 12 B 3
Ruien, Mt. 20 F 6
Ruiva 16 M 4
Rujiena 17 M 8
Rumah 38 E 2
Rumaitha 28 H 5
Rumana 28 G 3
Rumbek 40 D 1
Rum Cay, Island 48 E 2
Rumija, Mt. 20 D 6
Rumoi 32 F 3
Rumuruti 40 F 2
Rundvik 17 H 5
Rungu 40 D 2
Rungue, Mt. 35 G 6
Rungwa, River 40 E 4
Ruona 17 N 4
Ruosta, Mt. 16 H 2
Ruovesi 17 M 6
Rupat, Island 34 B 4
Rupert 42 N 4
Rupert House 44 P 5
Rupper, Cape 57 S 2
Rur 14 H 3
Rururtu, Island 54 M 7
Rusan 29 F 4
Rusape 41 E 2
Rusele 17 H 4
Russia 22 CE 4
Russia, White 23 EH 8
Rustenburg 41 D 4
Rutana 40 D 3
Rutanzige, Lake 40 D 3
Rutba 28 F 4
Ruteng 34 F 6
Rutshuru 40 D 3
Ruvuvu 40 E 3
Ruwandiz 28 H 2
Ruwenzori 35 F 5
Ràza 23 L 7
Ruza 23 LM 7
Ruzomberok 21 D 3
Rwagarika 40 D 3
Rwanda 36 FG 6
Ryan 4 D 4
Ryazan' 23 N 7
Rybace 29 G 3
Rybaci Peninsula 22 C 2-3
Rybare 21 A 2
Rybinsk 23 N 5
Rybinske Res. 23 MN 5
Rybnitsa 21 I 4
Ryd 17 F 8
Ryde 55 e 10
Rygdin 16 C 6
Ryngköbing, Fj. 16 C 9
Ryonaja 22 L 2
Rypin 13 H 2
Ryû Kyû (Nansei Shoto), I. 32 BC 6-7
Rzeszow 13 I 3-4
Rzëv 23 L 6

S

Sä'adat 28 M 5
Saale 12 D 3
Saar 13 B 4

Saar, River 12 B 4
Saarbrücken 13 B 4
Saarburg 11 I 2
Saaremaa 23 D 5
Saarlouis 13 B 4
Saarijärvi 17 M 5
Saari Selkä 17 O 2
Saba 48 G 3
Sabac 21 D 5
Sabadell 9 H 3
Sabah 34 E 3
Sabaki 40 F 3
Sabalana, Island 34 E 6
Sabana, La- 53 E 2
Sabancuy 47 F 4
Sabang 34 E 4
Sabari 30 D 5
Sabatini, Monti- 18 D 3
Sabaya 52 D 5
Sab 'Biyar 28 D 4
Sabi 41 E 2-3
Sabihiyahiya 28 L 6
Sabile 17 L 8
Sabinal, 48 D 2
Sabinas 47 D 2
Sabine, River 46 G 6
Sabine, Mt. 57 a 2
Sable, Cape (Canada) 44 R 7
Sable, Cape (USA) 46 L 7
Sable, Island 44 T 7
Sablé-sur-Sarthe 11 E 3
Sabon Birni 39 F 3
Sabor 8 C 3
Sabrina, Coast 57 Dc 3
Sabugal 9 C 3
Sabya 38 D 4
Sabzawar 29 D 5
Sabzvan 29 C 4
Sacco 18 D 4
Sacedon 9 E 3
Sachigo 44 M 5
Saci 25 E 4
Sacile 19 D 1-2
Sackhere 25 G 4
Sacramento 46 B 5
Sa'da 38 D 4
Sadakhlo 25 H 5
Sa'dani 40 F 4
Sa'diya 38 C 3
Sadva 16 G 3
Sado 8 B 4
Sado, Island 32 E 4
Sadrinsk 24 N 6
Sadus 38 E 2
Safaha, Desert 28 EF 7
Safaia, es- 37 H 5
Safanya 28 L 6
Safé 37 H 7
Säffle 17 E 7
Safi 37 C 3
Safranbolu 25 B 5
Sag, Fj. 17 F 3
Saga (Indonesia) 34 H 5
Sagaing 33 B 2
Sagala 37 C 7
Sagami 27 d 13
Sagan 29 C 2
Sagana 38 C 6
Sagata 37 A 6
Sagen 17 F 6
Saggat 16 GH 3
Saghand 29 C 5
Saghez 28 I 2
Saghis 1 ST 6
Saginaw 46 L 4
Sagiz 29 B 2
Sagne 37 B 6
Sagra, La-, Mt. 8 E 5
Sagua la Grande 48 C 2
Saguenay 44 Q 6
Saguiet el Hamra 37 B 4
Sagunto 9 F 4
Sahagun 9 D 2
Sahara 35 CF 3
Saharan Atlas 35 CD 2
Saharanpur 30 C 2
Sahel 37 C 6
Sahl el-Mahra 38 F 4
Sahr-i-Yezd 29 B 5
Sahwa 38 E 4
Saïda (Algeria) 37 E 3
Saida (Libanon) 28 C 4
Saidabad 29 C 6
Saïd Bandas 40 C 1
Said Bundas 40 C 1
Saigon 33 D 4
Saih 38 E 3
Saihut 38 F 4
Saikhoa Chat 33 B 1
Sailan 38 E 4
Sailolof 34 H 5
Saim 24 O 4
Saimbeyli 28 D 1
Saindak 29 D 6
Saintes 11 E 4
Saintonge 11 E 4
Saipan, Island 54 E 3
Saipuru 52 E 5
Saiun 38 E 4
Saiyid Hasan 28 I 4
Sajama, Mt. 49 D 5
Sajo 20 E 3
Sajtanovka 24 L 3
Sajul 27 H 8
Saka (China) 31 D 5
Saka (Kenia) 40 F 3
Sakabar 39 F 3
Sakabinda 40 D 5
Sakakah 28 F 6
Sakarya 1 O 7
Sakbayème 39 G 5
Sakchu 31 N 2
Sakend, Mt. 1 R 8
Sakété 39 E 4
Sakhalin 22 P 4-5
Sakhrisjabz 29 E 4
Sakhty 25 F 2
Sakhun'ja 24 D 6
Sakishima Islands 32 B 7
Sakkijarvi 23 G 4
Sakmara 24 H 8
Sakmara, River 24 IL 8-9
Sakrivier 41 C 5
Saksaul'skij 29 D 2
Sakura 27 e 13
Sal, Island 39 a
Salaca 16 M 8
Salada, Bay 53 B 2
Salado 49 D 7
Salaga 39 D 4
Salajar, Island 34 F 6
Salak, Mt. 26 I 13
Salam, Es- 37 M 6
Salama 47 F 4
Salaman 20 I 9
Salamanca 9 D 3
Salamat, Bahr- 35 EF 4
Salangen 17 G 2
Salaverry 52 B 3
Salawati 34 H 5
Salda 24 M 5
Saldanha 41 B 5
Saldé 37 B 6
Saldus 17 L 8
Sale 55 H 7
Salé 37 C 3
Salekhard 22 F 3
Salem (India) 30 C 6
Salem (USA) 46 B 4
Salentina, Pen.- 18 FG 4
Salerno 19 E 4
Salerno, Gulf of 18 E 4
Sales 52 G 3
Salgotarjan 21 D 3
Sali 37 D 4
Salina 46 G 5
Salina, Island 18 E 5
Salina Cruz 47 E 4
Salinas (Bolivia) 52 D 5
Salinas (Ecuador) 52 A 2
Salinas, Cape de- 8 H 4
Salinas Grandes 53 CD 2-3
Salines, Les- 37 F 2
Salinopolis 52 H 2
Salins 11 H 3
Salisbury (United Kingdom) 4 F 6
Salisbury (USA) 46 M 5
Salisbury, Island 44 P 3
Salja 24 L 6
Sal'jany 25 L 6
Sallyna 30 D 3
Salmi 23 H 4
Salmon 46 C 3
Salo 17 L 6
Salò 19 C 2
Salomone,Island 54 FG 5
Salon 11 H 5
Salon, Island. 23 I 3
Salonga 40 C 3
Salor, River 8 C 4
Salou, Cape 9 G 3
Salpau Selkä, Mt. 23 EH 4
Sal-Rei 39 a
Sal'sk 25 F 2
Salso 18 E 6
Salta 53 C 1
Salte 17 FG 3
Salten, Fj. 16 F 3
Saltillo 47 D 2
Salt Lake City 46 D 4
Salt Lake, Great 46 D 4
Salto 53 E 3
Salto, El- 47 C 3
Salto, Lake 18 D 3
Salto da Divisa 52 IL 5
Salto das Sete Quedas 52 F 3
Saltoluokta 17 H 3
Salton Sea 42 H 6
Saltpond 39 D 4
Salty, Island 4 C 5
Saluen 33 B 1-3
Salum, Es- 37 L 3
Saluzzo 19 A 2
Salvador (Bahia) 52 L 4
Salvador, El- 43 LM 8
Salvora, Island 9 B 2
Salyany 29 A 4
Salzach 13 E 4-5
Salzburg 13 E 5
Salzgitter 13 CD 3
Salzwedel 13 D 2
Samaa 23 FG 4
Samaipata 52 E 5
Samalut 37 M 4
Samana, Cape 48 F 3
Samar, Island 27 Q 8
Samara 1 S 5
Samarat 55 I 2
Samarga 32 E 2
Samarinda 34 E 5
Samarkand 29 E 4
Samarra 28 G 3
Samassi 18 B 5
Samawa 28 H 5
Samba 40 D 3
Sambalpur 30 D 4
Sambas 34 C 4
Sambava 41 c 6
Sambio 41 C 2
Sambo 40 B 5
Sambor 21 F 3
Sambre 14 FG 3
Sambu 27 h 16
Samman 28 N 3
Samneua 33 C 2
Samos 20 H 9
Samoa, Island 54 I 6
Samokov 21 F 6
Samothraki 20 G 7
Samouki 24 D 5
Sampacho 53 D 3
Sampit 34 D 5
Sampit, River 34 D 5
Sampwe 40 D 4
Samsö, Island 16 D 9
Samsun 25 D 5
Samsun, Mt. 20 H 9
Samtredia 25 G 4
Samut Prakan 33 C 4
San (Cambodia) 33 D 4
San (India) 26 M 7
San (Poland) 12 L 4
San'a 38 D 4
Sana, River 20 C 5
Sanaga 35 E 5
Sanana 34 G 5
Sänandj 28 I 3
Sancti Spiritus 48 D 2
Sancursk 24 D 6
Sand 17 B 7
Sandakan 34 E 3
Sandarshahr 30 B 3
Sandata 25 F 2
Sanday, Island 3 E 2
Sanderson 46 F 6
Sandflo egg, Mt. 17 B 7
Sandhornöv 17 F 3
Sandia 52 D 4
Sandö, Island 17 a
Sandoa 40 C 4
Sandover Creek 55 F 4
Sandoway 33 A 3
Sandnes 17 A 7
Sandnesjöen 17 E 4
Sandras Dag, Mt. 20 I 9
Sandwich, Islands. 54 IL 2
Sandwich Islands, South 57 mM 4
Sandwip 27 b 11
Sandy 4 F 5
Sandy, Cape 55 I 4
Sanga 39 E 3
Sanga, River 35 E 5
Sangar 22 N 3
Sangaréa, Bay 39 B 4
Sangatanga 39 F 6
Sangau 34 D 4
Sangeang, Island 34 E 6
Sangha, River 40 B 2
Sangli 30 B 5
Sangmélima 39 G 5
Sangon 31 IL 2-3
Sangonera 8 F 5
Sangro 18 E 3
Sangue, Rio do- 52 F 4
Sanguesa 9 F 2
Sangwin 39 C 4
Sanitatas 41 A 2
Sankarani 37 C 7
Sankishia 40 D 4
San Kolonkan 37 D 7
Sankra 30 D 4
S. Adresse 11 F 2
S. Afrique 11 G 5
S. Agnese, Island 4 C 7
S. Albans 46 N 4
S. Amand-en-Puisaye 11 G 3
S. Amaro 52 L 4
S. Ambrosio, Island 50 C 6
S. Ana (Bolivia) 52 D 4
S. Ana (Brazil) 52 I 4
S. Ana (El Salvador) 47 G 5
S. Andrés (Colombia) 51 B 2
S. Andrés (Mexico) 47 E 4
S. Andrés, Island 48 C 4
S. Andrews 4 E 3
S. Andrews, Bay 46 I 7
S. Andrija 21 B 6
S. Angelo (Brazil) 52 G 7
S. Angelo (USA) 46 F 6
S. Fé (Argentina) 53 D 3
S. Fé (USA) 46 E 5
S. Antioco 18 AB 5
S. Antao 52 E 4
S. Antonio (Island Principe) 39 F 5
S. Antonio (USA) 46 G 7
S. Antonio, Cape (Argentina) 53 E 4
S. Antonio, Cape (Cuba) 48 C 2
S. Antonio. 39 a
S. Antonio Abad 9 G 4
S. Antonio de los Cobres 53 C 1
S. Antonio do Rio Madeira 52 E 3
S. Antonio Oeste 53 D 5
S. Antonio Peak, Mt. 46 C 6
S. Augustin 41 b 8
S. Barbara (USA) 46 C 6
S. Barbara (Venezuela)) 51 B 2
S. Barthélemy 48 G 3
S. Benedetto del Tronto 19 E 3
S. Benedicto, Island 47 B 4
S. Benoît 41 a
S. Bernardino 46 C 6
S. Bernard, Great 18 A 2
S. Bernard, Little 18 A 2
S. Bernardo 53 B 3
S. Blas 47 C 3
S. Blas, Cape 46 I 7
S. Blas, Pt. 48 D 5
S. Borja (Bolivia) 52 D 4
S. Borja (Brazil) 52 F 7
S. Brieuc 11 D 2
S. Brieuc, B. 11 D 2
S. Calais 11 F 3
S. Carlos (Argentina) 53 C 3
S. Carlos (Brazil) 52 H 6
S. Carlos (Philippines) 34 F 2
S. Carlos (Cojedes) 51 C 2
S. Carlos (Amazonas) 51 C 3
S. Carlos de Bariloche 53 B 5
S. Carlos de la Rapita 9 G 3
S. Catalina, Island 46 C 6
S. Catarina 52 G 7
S. Catarina, Island 52 H 7
S. Charles 46 H 5
S. Clara 48 C 2
S. Claude 11 H 3
S. Clemente, Island 46 C 6
S. Cloud 46 H 3
S. Cristobal (Argentina) 53 D 3
S. Cristobal (Venezuela) 51 B 2
S. Cristobal, Island 52 a
S. Cristobal de las Casas 47 F 4
S. Croce, Island 54 G 6
S. Cruz (Argentina) 53 C 7
S. Cruz (Bolivia) 52 E 5
S. Cruz (Brazil) 52 C 3
S. Cruz (Philippines) 34 F 2
S. Cruz (USA) 46 B 5
S. Cruz, River 46 D 6
S. Cruz, (Galapagos Islands) 49 B 4
S. Cruz (USA) 46 C 6
S. Cruz, Rio 53 BC 7
S. Cruz de la Palma 37 A 4
S. Cruz del Sur 48 D 2
S. Cruz de Mud 9 E 4
S. Cruz de Tenerife 37 A 4
S. Cruz do Sul 52 G 7
S. David's Head 4 D 6
S. Denis (France) 11 G 2
S. Denis (Réunion Islands) 41 a
S. Dié 11 12
S. Diego 46 C 6
S. Diego, Cape 53 C 7
S. Dizier 11 H 2
S. Domingo (Dominican Republic) 48 F 3
S. Domingo (Mexico) 47 B 2
S. Domingo (Spain) 9 E 2
S. Domino 18 E 3
S. Donà di Piave 19 D 2
S. Elena, Bay 41 B 5
S. Elena, Cape 48 B 4
S. Elena, Island 36 C 7
S. Elena, Pt. 52 A 2
S. Elias, Mts. 45 L 4
S. Estanislao 52 F 6
S. Étienne 11 H 4
S. Eufemia, Gulf of 18 E 5
S. Eustatius 48 G 3
S. Fé, Island 52 a
S. Felice, Island 49 B 6
S. Felipe (Campeche) 47 F 4
S. Felipe (Yucatan) 47 G 3
S. Felipe (Venezuela) 51 C 1
S. Feliu de Guixols 9 H 3
S. Felix, Island 50 B 6
S. Fernando (Chile) 53 B 3
S. Fernando (Philippines) 34 F 1
S. Fernando (Union) 34 F 1
S. Fernando (Trinidad Island) 51 D 1
S. Fernando (Spain) 9 C 5
S. Fernando de Apure 51 C 2
S. Fernando de Atabapo 51 C 3
S. Filomena 52 H 3
S. Flour 11 G 4
S. Foy-la-Grande 11 F 4
S. Francisco (Argentina) 53 D 3
S. Francisco (Brazil) 52 D 4
S. Francisco (USA) 46 B 5
S. Francisco, Island 52 H 7
S. Francisco, Pass 49 D 6
S. Francisco, Rio 52 L 3
S. Francisco do Sul 52 H 7
S. Francisco Novo 52 G 2
S. Gabriel 50 D 3
S. Gallen 13 C 5
S. Gaudens 11 F 5
S. George (Australia) 55 H 5
S. George (USA) 46 D 5
S. Georges (Canada) 44 Q 6
S. Georges (France Guayana) 51 F 3
S. Georges (Grenada Island) 51 D 1
S. George's Channel 3 D 5-6
S. Germain-en-Laye 11 G 2
S. Gildas, Pass de- 10 D 3
S. Gilles 11 H 5
S. Gilles-sur-Vie 11 E 3
S. Gheorghe (Romania) 21 I 5
S. Giovanni in Fiore 19 F 5
S. Girons 11 F 5
S. Gotardo 52 H 5
S. Gotthard 18 B 1
S. Groix, Island 48 G 3
S. Helena Bay 41 B 5
S. Ignacio 52 E 5
S. Inés, Island 53 B 7
S. Isabel (Brazil., Mato Gr.) 52 F 4
S. Isabella, Island 54 F 5
S. Ives 4 D 6
S. James G. 44 C 5
S. Javier 53 D 3
S. Jean 51 F 2
S. Jean-du-Gard 11 G 4
S. Jeronimo 52 G 6
S. Joao 9 C 3
S. Joao, Island 52 I 2
S. Joao da Barra 52 I 6
S. Joâo del Rei 52 I 6
S. Joao do Araguaia 52 H 3
S. Joao do Piaui 52 I 3
S. Joao Pinheiro 52 H 5
S. Joaquim 52 D 1
S. Joaquin 46 B 5
S. John 44 R 6
S. John's 44 U 6
S. Jorge-G. of 53 C 6
S. Jorge, Island 37 a
S. José (Bolivia) 52 E 5
S. José (Costa Rica) 48 C 5
S. José (Philippines) 34 F 1
S. José (Guatemala) 43 L 8
S. José (USA) 46 B 5
S. José, Island 47 B 2-3
S. José de Acume 51 B 3
S. José de Buenavista 34 F 2
S. José del Cabo 47 C 3
S. José del Guaviare 51 B 3
S. José do Rio Prêto 52 H 6
S. Joseph 46 H 5
S. Juan (Argentina) 53 C 3
S. Juan (Peru) 52 C 4
S. Juan (Puerto Rico) 48 F 3
S. Juan (Venezuela) 51 C 1
S. Juan. Cape 53 D 7
S. Juan, River 46 DE 5
S. Juan, Rio 48 C 4
S. Juan Bautista 52 F 7
S. Juan de Guadalupe 47 D 3
S. Juan del Norte 48 C 4
S. Juan del Sur 48 B 4
S. Julian 53 C 6
S. Just, Sierra de- 9 F 3
S. Justo 53 D 3
S. Kitts 48 G 3
S. Laurence 55 H 4
S. Laurent de la Salanque 11 G 5
S. Lawrence, G. of 42 O 5
S. Lawrence I. 45 D 4
S. Lawrence, River 42 N 5
S. Lazaro, Cape 47 B 3
S. Leopoldo 52 G 7
S. Lô 11 E 2
S. Lorenzo, Cerro de- 8 E 2
S. Lorenzo, Cape (Ecuador) 52 A 2
S. Lorenzo de la Parrilla 9 E 4
S. Louis (Senegal) 37 A 6
S. Louis (USA) 46 H 5
S. Lourenço 52 F 5
S. Lourenço do Sul 53 F 3
S. Lucia. Bay 34 E 4
S. Lucia, Cape 41 E 4
S. Lucia Island 50 D 2
S. Lucrecia 47 E 4
S. Luis 53 C 3
S. Luis (Maranhao) 52 I 2
S. Luis Obispo 46 B 5
S. Luis Potosi 47 D 3
S. Luziania 52 H 5
S. Malo 11 D 2
S. Malo, Gulf of 10 DE 2
S. Manuel 52 F 3
S. Manza, Gulf of 18 B 4
S. Marc 48 E 3
S. Marcelino 51 C 3
S. Marcos 52 I 2
S. Marcos, Island 47 B 2
S. Margarita, Island 47 B 3
S. Maria (Bolivia) 52 E 5
S. Maria (Brazil) 52 G 7
S. Maria (Peru) 52 C 2
S. Maria Cape of (Portugal) 9 C 5
S. Maria, Island (Azores) 37 a
S. Maria, (Galapagos) 52 a
S. Marie 41 c 7
S. Marie, Cape 52 B 4
S. Maria di Leuca, Cape 18 FG 5
S. Maries, Gulf of 11 H 5
S. Marino 19 CD 3
S. Marta 51 B 1
S. Marta, Cape (Angola) 41 A 1
S. Marta, Cape (Brazil) 52 H 7
S. Martin (Argentina) 53 D 1
S. Martin (Colombia) 51 B 3
S. Martin Lake 53 B 6
S. Martinho 52 F 3
S. Martin, Island 48 G 3
S. Martin's, Island 4 C 7
S. Mary's (Neuw South Wales) 55 d 10
S. Marys (Tasmania) 55 b 9
S. Mary's, Island 4 C 7
S. Mateo 9 G 3
S. Mateus (Espirito Santo) 52 L 5
S. Matias, G. of 53 D 5
S. Matthew Island 45 D 4
S.Mathieu, P.te de- 10 C 2
S. Matthew Island 54 E 5
S. Matthews Island 33 B 5
S. Matveevka 24 G 7
S. Maur 19 A 1
S. Méen 11 D 2
S. Michael 45 F 4
S. Midt, Mt. 16 B 7
S. Miguel 47 G 5
S. Miguel, Island (Azores) 37 a
S. Miguel, Island (USA) 46 B 6
S. Miguel, Rio 52 E 5
S. Miguel de Huachi 52 D 5
S. Miguel de Teguise 37 B 4
S. Miguelito 48 C 4
S. Moritz 19 BC 1
S. Nazaire 11 D 3
S. Nicolas (Argentina) 53 D 3
S. Nicolas, Island 46 C 6
S. Nicolau 39 a
S. Niklaas 15 G 3
S. Onofre 51 A 2
S. Pablo 34 F 2
S. Paplo, Pt. 47 B 2
S. Paulo 52 H 6
S. Paolo, Island 49 H 3
S. Paolo, State 52 GH 6
S, Paul (Réunion-Island) 41 a
S. Paul (USA) 46 H 3
S. Paul, River 39 B 4
S. Paulo de Olivença 52 D 2
S. Pedro (Argentina) 53 F 2
S. Pedro (Beni) 52 E 4
S. Pedro (Potosi) 52 D 5
S. Pedro (Ivory Coast) 39 C 5
S. Pedro (Mexico) 46 F 7
S. Pedro (Paraguay) 52 F 6
S. Pedro, Sierra de- 8 C 4
S. Pedro do Sul 9 B 3
S. Petersburg 46 L 7
S. Pierre (Canada) 44 T 6
S. Pierre (Réunion) 41 a
S. Pietro 18 AB 5
S. Pietro, Island 18 AB 5
S. Pis'mjanka 24 G 7
S. Pölten 13 F 4
S. Quentin 11 G 2
S. Quintin 47 A 1
S. Quintin, B. 46 C 6
S. Rafael 53 C 3
S. Rafael, Boca- 47 E 2
S. Rafhaël 11 I 5
S. Remo 19 AB 3
S. Rita 47 G 4
S. Romao 52 H 5
S. Roque, Cape 52 L 3
S. Rosa (La Pampa) 53 D 4
S. Rosa (Rio Negro) 53 C 4-5
S. Rosa (Colombia) 51 A 2
S. Rosa (Honduras) 47 G 5
S. Rosa, Bay 51 G 3
S. Rosa, Island 46 B 6
S. Salvador 47 G 5
S. Salvador, Island 52 a
S. Salvador (Watling) 48 E 2
S. Sebastiao, Island 52 H 6
S. Sever 11 E 6
S. Severo 19 E 4
S. Simao 52 H 6
S. Sylvina 53 D 2
S. Telmo, Pt. 47 D 4
S. Teotonio 9 B 5
S. Teresa 51 C 1
S. Thomas 44 O 7
S. Tigre 51 F 3
S. Tomas 52 C 4

S. Tomé (Argentina) 53 E 2
S. Tomé 39 F 5
S. Tomé, Cape 52 I 6
S. Tomé, Island 39 F 5
S. Tomé and Principe 39 F 5
S. Thomas Island 48 F 3
S. Tropez 11 I 5
S. Truiden 15 G 3
S. Valentin 53 B 6
S. Valery-en-Caux 11 F 2
S. Vallier 11 H 4
S. Vicente (Madera) 37 A 3
S. Vincent (El Salvador) 47 G 5
S. Vicente de Canete 52 B 4
S. Vincent Gulf 54 D 8
S. Vincent, Cape 55 F 7
S. Vicente, Gulf 8 B 5
S. Vincenzo, (Cape Verde) 39 a
S. Vincent Island 48 G 4
S. Vito 18 D 5
S. Vito al Tagliamento 19 D 2
S. Vitoria do Palmar 53 F 3
S. Vittoria, Mt. 19 B 5
S. Wendel 13 B 4
S. Yrieix 11 F 4
Sankuru 35 F 6
Sanlucar de Barrameda 9 C 5
Sanlucar la Mayor 9 C 5
Sanok 19 L 4
Sansanding 37 C 7
Sansanne 39 E 3
Santai 31 H 4
Santana 52 G 5
Santander (Columbia) 51 A 3
Santander (Spain) 9 E 2
Santany 9 H 4
Santarém (Brazil) 52 G 2
Santarêm (Portugal) 9 B 4
Santhià 19 B 2
Santiago (Brazil) 52 G 7
Santiago (Chile) 53 B 3
Santiago (Dominican Republic) 48 E 3
Santiago (Spain) 9 B 2
Santiago, Island 39 a
Santiago de Cuba 48 D 3
Santiago del Estero 53 D 2
Santipur 30 E 4
Santona 9 E 2
Santorin 20 G 9
Santos 52 H 6
San tsao, Island 27 f 15
Sanyati 41 D 2
Sanza Pombo 40 B 4
Saône 10 H 3
Saparua, Island 34 G 5
Saphane, Mt. 20 I 8
Sapkina 24 GH 1
Saposoa 52 B 3
Sapporo 32 F 3
Sapri 19 E 4
Sapudi, Island 26 m 13
Sapudi, Strait 26 m 13
Saqa, River 35 E 5
Särab 28 I 1
Sarafinian 39 B 4
Sarajevo 21 D 6
Saraktas 24 I 9
Saranda 21 D 8
Saranga 24 D 6
Saranpaul' 24 M 2
Saransk 2 R 5
Sarapul 24 G 6
Sarat 25 I 6
Saratok 34 D 4
Saratov 2 R 5
Saravane 33 D 3
Sarawak 34 D 4
Saray 25 H 6
Sardinia 3 B 4-5
Sardò 38 D 5
Saréféré 37 D 6
Sàrek, Mt. 16 G 3
Sarera Bay 34 I 5
Sari 29 B 4
Sari, Mt. 39 G 4
Sarikei 34 D 4
Sär-i-Kul 28 L 4
Sarinena 9 F 3
Sarja 24 C 5
Sarlat 11 F 4
Sarlyk 24 H 8
Sarmento 40 C 4
Sarmiento 53 C 6
Särna 17 E 6
Sârnena Gora 20 G 6
Sarno 19 E 4
Sarny 21 H 2
Saronic Gulf 20 F 9
Saros, Gulf of 20 H 7
Sarra 37 I 5
Sarralbe 11 I 2
Sarria 9 C 2
Sartene 11 a
Sarthe 10 EF 2-3
Sartynja 24 N 3
Sarur 29 C 7
Saruwaged, Mt. 26 o 14
Sarvar 21 C 4
Saryg Bulun 22 I 4
Sasaram 30 D 4
Sasare 41 E 1
Sasebo 32 C 5
Saskatchewan, State 44 HI 4-5
Saskatchewan, River 42 HI 4
Saskatoon 44 H 5
Saskylakh 22 M 2
Sassabaneh 38 D 6
Sassandra 39 C 5
Sassandra, River 39 C 4
Sassari 19 B 4
Sassnitz 13 EF 1
Sâstinska Gora 20 G 6
Satadougou 37 B 7
Satara 30 B 5
Sataraljaujhely 21 E 3
Satpura Range 26 L 7
Satui 34 E 5
Satu Mare 21 F 4
Satun 33 C 5
Sauces 52 E 5
Saude 52 I 4
Saudharkrok 17 S 12
Saudi Arabia 27 G 7
Sauer, River 14 GH 3
Saugar 30 C 4
Sauldre 10 FG 3
Saulieu 11 H 3
Saulo, Mt. 16 G 3
Sault Ste Marie 46 I 3
Saumarez Reef, Island 55 I 4
Saumlaki 34 H 6
Saumur 11 E 3
Saunders, Island 57 M 4
Saurimo 40 C 4
Sausto, Mt. 16 I 2
Sava 20 AE 4-5
Savaii, Island 54 I 6
Savalan, Mt. 1 R 8
Savalou 39 E 4
Savannah 46 L 6
Savannah, River 42 M 6
Savannakhet 33 C 3
Savanna la Mar 48 D 3
Savanne 44 M 6
Savanur 30 C 5
Sävar 17 I 4
Saveh 28 M 3
Savelli 19 F 5
Savinobor 24 I 3
Savinsk 24 D 1
Savio 18 D 2
Savona 19 B 2
Savonlinna 23 G 4
Savoye 10 I 3
Savran' 21 L 3
Savukoski 17 O 3
Sawahlunto 34 B 5
Sawai 34 G 5
Sawara 27 e 13
Sawu 34 F 7
Sawu Sea 34 F 7
Sax, Island 16 F 4
Saxby, River 55 G 3
Saxony 13 EF 3
Saxony - Anhalt 13 D 3
Saxony, Lower 13 BC 2
Say (Mali) 37 C 7
Say (Niger) 37 E 7
Sayan, Eastern 22 I 4
Sayan, Western 22 HI 4
Sayramm Nor, Island. 31 C 2
Sayn Sanda 31 I 2
Sayula 47 D 4
Sazava 20 B 3
Sba 37 E 4
Scaffel Pike, Mt. 3 E 4
Scanno 19 D 4
Scapa Flow 4 E 2
Scarborough 4 F 4
Scarcies 39 B 4
Scarpa 4 C 2
Sceikh Sa'id 38 D 5
Scel'jajur 24 G 2
Schaffhausen 13 C 5
Schärding 13 E 4
Schari 37 H 7
Schari, River 35 E 4-5
Schawabia 13 CD 4
Schelde 14 FG 3
Scheppemannsdorf 41 A 3
Schesch, Erg 35 C 3
Scheveningen 15 G 2
Schiermonnikoog, Island 15 H 2
Schio 19 C 2
Schleswig 13 C 1
Schleswig Holstein 12 C 1
Schmalkalden 13 D 3
Schneeberg 12 D 3
Schneeberg 12 F 5
Schönberg 13 D 2
Schonen 16 E 9
Schongau 13 D 5
Schongau 13 D 5
Schoff Djerid 35 D 2
Schott Welgihn 35 D 2
Schott el - Gerid 37 F 3
Schouten 34 I 5
Schreiber 44 N 6
Schroffenstein, Mt. 41 B 4
Schuckmannsburg 41 C 2
Schwabian Jura 12 CD 4
Schwandorf 13 E 4
Schwedt 13 EF 2
Schweinfurt 13 D 3
Schwerin 13 D 2
Schwyz 19 B 1
Sciacca 19 D 6
Sciattel-Arab 26 G 6-7
Scicli 19 E 6
Scilla 19 E 5
Scilly Islands 3 C 7
Scinde 41 F 2
Scingune 41 E 3
Scinko 40 C 1
Scôresby, Bay of 42 ST 2-3
Scotland 4 DE 2-4
Scott, Mt. 46 B 4
Scott Inlet 44 Q 1
Scottsbluff 46 F 4
Scranton 46 M 4
Scrivia 18 B 2
Seal 44 L 4
Seattle 46 B 3
Seba 34 F 7
Sebanga 34 B 4
Sebastian Vizcaino, Bay of 47 B 2
Sebatik 34 E 4
Sebba 39 E 3
Sebcha Azz el Matti 37 E 4
Sebcha Mekherghare 37 E 4
Sebcha Oum el-Drouss Telli 37 B 5
Sebesului, Mt. 20 F 5
Sebez 23 G 6
Sebha 37 G 4
Sebinkarahisar (Sarkî Karahisar) 25 E 5
Seblat, Mt. 34 B 5
Sebou 37 C 3
Sebuku, Island 34 E 5
Sebung, Cape 27 i 16
Secchia 18 C 2
Sechura 52 A 3
Secunderabad 30 C 5
Sedalia 46 H 5
Sedan 11 H 2
Seduva 17 L 9
Seehein 41 B 4
Sefrou 37 D 3
Segbana 39 E 3
Sege 34 H 5
Segel 34 H 5
Segorbe 9 F 4
Ségou 37 C 7
Segovia 9 D 3
Segovia, River 42 M 8
Segré 11 E 3
Segre, River 8 G 3
Seguam, Island 22 T 4
Séguéla 39 C 4
Segura 8 EF 4
Seibo 48 F 3
Seida 17 O 1
Seiland 16 L 1
Seille 10 I 2
Seille, River 10 I 2
Seine 10 FG 2
Seine, B. de la 10 E 2
Sejm 1 OP 5
Sejmcan 22 Q 3
Sejny 13 L 1
Sekadau 34 D 5
Sekaju 34 B 5
Sekenke 40 E 3
Sekirjany 21 H 3
Sekondi-Takoradi 39 D 5
Seksna 23 N 5
Selaru, Island 34 H 6
Selatan 34 B 5
Selawik 45 G 3
Selb 13 E3
Selbjörn, Fj. 17 A 7
Selböy 17 A 6
Sele 18 E 4
Selemdzha 26 QR 4
Selemiyeh 28 D 3
Selenga 31 G 1
Sélestat 11 I 2
Seletin 21 G 4
Sélibaby 37 B 6
Selima 36 F 3
Selipuk Gomba 31 C 4
Selizarovo 23 I 6
Selkirk 4 E 4
Selkirk, Mt. 42 H 4-5
Sella di Conza, Pt. 18 E 4
Sella di Spinazzola, Pt. 18 F 4
Sellye 21 C 5
Selma 46 I 6
Selon' 23 GH 6
Selota 23 O 4
Selty 24 G 6
Selukwe 41 E 2
Selvaggens, Island 37 A 3
Selvas Catingas 49 CF 4
Selwin 55 G 4
Selwyn, Mt. 54 E 7
Sem, Cape 37 I 3
Semangka, Bay 26 1 13
Semarang 34 D 6
Semau 34 F 7
Semeni 20 D 7
Semënov 24 C 6
Semenovka 23 I 8
Semeru, Mt. 34 D 6
Semiozernyj 29 D 1
Semipalatinsk 22 H 4
Semitau 34 D 4
Senftenbreg 13 E 3
Sengilej 24 E 8
Senhor do Bomfim 52 I 4
Seniavin, Cape 45 F 5
Senigallia 19 D 3
Seniku 33 B 1
Senja, Island 16 G 2
Senkaya 25 G 5
Senkevic 21 G 2
Senkursk 24 B 3
Sennar 36 G 4
Senno 23 G 7
Senozero 23 H 1
Sens 11 G 2
Sent Janz 21 B 5
Senyavin, Island 54 F 4
Seo de Urgel 9 G 2
Seonath 30 D 4
Seongjin 31 N 2
Seoni 30 C 4
Seoul 31 N 3
Sepandjang, Island 34 E 6
Sepetovka 20 H 2
Sepik 26 o 14
Sept, Island 11 D 2
Sept Iles 44 R 5
Sepulveda 9 E 3
Seputih 26 1 13
Sequillo 9 D 3
Serafimovic 25 G 1
Seraing 15 G 3
Serakhs 29 D 4
Serampore 30 E 4
Serang 34 C 6
Serangoon 27 h 16
Serbia 21 E 5-6
Serdeles 37 G 4
Serdò 38 D 5
Sereflikoçhisar 25 B 6
Seremban 33 C 6
Serena, La- 53 B 2
Serenje 40 E 5
Seret 20 G 3
Sergac 24 C 7
Sergievskij 24 G 6
Sergipe 52 L 4
Serian 34 D 4
Serifos 20 G 9
Serinam 41 b 7
Serio 18 B 2
Serir Kalansho 37 I 4
Serir Tibesti 37 H 5
Sermata, Island 34 G 6
Sernyj Zavod 22 E 5
Serouenout 37 F 5
Serov 22 F 4
Serowe 41 D 3
Serpa 9 C 5
Serpeddi 18 B 5
Serpukhov 23 M 7
Serrä (Greece) 20 F 7
Serra Acarar 51 E 3
Serra di Borborema 49 G 4
Serra da Cinta 52 H 3
Serra da Desordem 49 F 4
Serra da Ibiapaba 49 F 4
Serra da Luna 51 DE 3
Serra das Araras 52 G 5
Serra das Divisoes 49 E 5
Serra de Maracaju 49 E 5-6
Serra de Misiones 52 G 7
Serra de S. Maria 52 H 4
Serra do Apiacas 52 F 4
Serra do Araripe 52 IL 3
Serra do Caperao 49 F 5-6
Serra do Chachimbo 52 FG 3
Serra do Congoji 52 IL 4
Serra do Cordoba 49 D 7
Serra do Espinacio 49 F 5-6
Serra do Estrondo 52 H 3-4
Serra do Gurupi 52 H 2-3
Serra Dolcedorme 18 EF 4-5
Serra do Mar 49 F 6
Serra do Piaui 49 F 4-5
Serra do Rio Prêto 52 H 5
Serra do Roncador 52 G 4
Serra do Tombador 49 F 5
Serra dos Agudos 52 G 6
Serra dos Aimores 52 I 5
Serra dos Carajas 52 G 2-3
Serra dos Chavantes 52 H 4
Serra dos Dourados 52 G 6
Serra dos Gradaus 52 G 3
Serra Dourada 52 H 4
Serra Formosa 52 FG 4
Serra Geral 49 E 6
Serra Geral de Goias 49 F 5
Serra Geral Espinhacho 52 I 5
Senegambia 37 A-B6-7
Semliki 40 DE 2
Semlino 21 E 5
Semmering, Pas 12 FG 5
Semois 14 G 4
Semur 11 H 3
Sena, La- 53 C 3
Senador Pompeu 52 L 3
Senafè 38 C 5
Senaja 34 E 3
Sena Madureira 52 D 3
Senanga 41 C 2
Sendai 32 F 4
Sendlingsdrift 41 B 4
Senegal 36 B 4
Senegal, River 35 B 4
Serra Ibiapaba 52 I 2
Serra Imeri 49 D 3
Serrana, Island 48 CD 4
Serra Negra 52 H 3
Serra Pacaraima 49 D3
Serra Paranapiacaba 52 H 6
Serra Parima 49 D 3
Serra Tapirapeco 51 CD 3
Serra Tumuc Humac 49 E 3
Serrezuela 53 C 3
Serrinha 52 L 4
Sêrro 52 I 5
Sersouf 37 F 5
Sertao de Camapua 52 G 5-6
Serua, Island 34 H 6
Seruli 41 D 3
Servia 21 E 7
Sesheke 41 C 2
Sesia 18 B 2
Sesimbra 9 B4
Sestakova 22 P 3
Sestriere 18 A 2
Sestri Levante 19 B 2
Sestroretsk 23 GH 4
Sete 11 G 5
Sete Lagôas 52 I 5
Sétif 37 F 2
Setit 35 G 4
Settat 37 C 3
Sette Isole 56 a
Setubal 9 B 4
Setubal, Bay of 8 B 4
Seven Lake 25 H 5
Sevastopol 25 B3
Seven Pans 41 C 4
Sévérac-le-Château 11 G 4
Severn (Canada) 42 LM 4
Severn (United Kingdom) 3 E 5
Severnaja 22 F 3
Severnaya Zemlya 22 HI 1-2
Severnoe 22 G 4
Severoural'sk 24 M 4
Sevilla 9 D 5
Sevre 10 E 3
Sevsk 23 L 8
Sevula, Mt. 21 G 3
Sewa 39 B 4
Seward 45 I 4
Seward, Mt. 57 O 2
Seward Pen. 45 EF 3-4
Seydisfjördur 17 U 12
Seyne-sur-Mer, La- 11 H 5
Seytan 20 H 7
Seytan D., Mt. 28 A 2
Sezanne 11 G 2
Sezze 19 D 4
Sfax 37 G 3
Sgurr Mor, Mt. 4 D 3
Shaba (Katanga) 36 F 6-7
Shaba Gomba 31 D 4
Shaballe 38 D6
Shabasha 37 M 7
Shabrud 2 ST 8
Shabunda 40 D 3
Shabwa 38 E 4
Sha ching 27 f 15
Shackleton Inlet 57 tA 1
Shadwan Island 28 B 7
Shaghar 28 E 5
Shahbazpur 27 b 11
Shah Dab 29 C 5
Shahjahanpur 30 C 3
Shahjui 29 E 5
Shahran 38 D 4
Shah Reza 28 M 4
Shahr Kurd 28 M 4
Shahsavar 28 M 2
Shah Shur 28 N 3
Sha hsien 31 L 5
Shaikh Sa'ad 28 I 4
Shakar Bolagh 28 I 2
Shake-Shake 40 F 4
Shakleton, Mt. 57 MI 1
Shakol, Cape 38 C 4
Shalar 28 L 4
Shambe 40 E 1
Shammar, Jabal- 26 G 7
Shamo 31 HI 2
Shamo, Lake 38 C6
Shamva 41 E 2
Shan 31 DE 3
Shang 31 F 3
Shangani 41 D 2
Shang chiu 31 L 4
Shanghai 31 M 4
Shang hang 31 L 5
Shang hsien 31 H 4
Shang jao 31 L 5
Shang tu 31 I 2
Shangyu 31 I 5
Shan hsi 31 I 3
Shanio 26 p 17
Shankha 31 G 1
Shannon 3 BC 5
Shan Shan 31 E 2
Shantan 31 G 3
Shan tang Chiao, Cape 31 M 3
Shan tou 31 L 6
Shan tung 31 LM 3
Shanwa 40 E 3
Shao hsing 31 M 5
Shao wu 31 L 5
Shao yang 31 I 5
Shapinsay 13 E 2
Shaqa Shamiya 38 D 3
Shaqua 38 E 2
Shara (Kan su) 31 EF 2-3
Shara (Inner Mongolia) 31 LM 2
Sharafkane 28 H 1
Sharamuren 31 I 2
Sharasume (Alo tai) 31 D 1
Shardu 30 C 1
Shargat 28 G 3
Sharja 29 C6
Shark Bay 55 A 5
Sharm Munaibara 38 C 2
Shasha 41 D 3
Shashih 31 I 4
Shasta, Mt. 42 G 5
Shatojevsk 25 H 4
Sha tou chiao 27 g 15
Shatra 28 I 5
Shatt-al-Arab 1 R 9
Shavli 17 L 9
Shawan 31 D1
Shaya 31 C 2
Shayib, Mt. 35 G 3
Shazia 31 C 4
Shababit 37 M 6
Sheboygan 46 I 4
Shebshi, Mt. 39 G 4
Shechkung 31 I 6
Sheffield 4 F 5
Shegarkhung Lung 31 D 4
She hsien 31 L 5
Sheikh Musa Oenawi 40 D 1
Sheikria 37 C 4
Shek Husen 38 D 6
Shekar Dzong 31 D 5
Shelby 46 D 3
Shelenda 40 D 5
Shelikof Gulf 22 Q4
Shelikof Strait 45 H 5
Shellborough 55 B 4
Shen chüan 27 g 15
Shendi 38 B 4
Shen hsi 31 H 3-4
Shenmu 31 I 3
Shentsa 31 D 4
Shen yang 31 M 2
Sheopur 30 C 3
Shepara, Island 57 r 2
Sherbrooke 44 Q 6
Shër-Gjergj 21 E 7
Sheridan 46 E 4
Sherman 46 G 6
Sherra Gimira 38 G 6
Shetland Islands 12 F 1
Shetland Islands South 57 On 3
Sheyenne 46 G 3
Shibam 38 E 4
Shibarghan 29 E 4
Shibata 32 E4
Shib-Kuh 29 B 6
Shibushi 32 D5
Shigatse 31 D 5
Shih chia chuang 31 I 3
Shih chiao 27 f 15
Shih chien 31 H 5
Shih chuan 31 H 4
Shih lung 27 f 14
Shih ping 31 G 6
Shihr 38 E 5
Shih tao 31 M 3
Shih tzu Yang 27 f 15
Shih wei 32 A 1
Shikarpur 29 E 6
Shiki 27 d 13
Shikotan, Island 32 G 3
Shilingol 31 L 2
Shilla, Mt. 30 C 2
Shillong 30 F 3
Shimoga 30 C 6
Shimonoseki 32 D 5
Shin 3 D 2
Shinafiya 38 D 1
Shinjo 32 F 4
Shinyanga 40 E 3
Shipki, Pass 30 C 2
Shiraz 28 N 6
Shire 35 G 7
Shir Kuh, Mt. 1 S 9
Shirwa 41 F 2
Shizuoka 32 E 5
Shkodër 21 D 6
Shköder, Lake 20 D 6
Shkumbi 20 D 7
Shoa 35 G 5
Sholapur 30 C 5
Shorapur 30 C 5
Shoshone 46 D 4
Shreveport 46 H 6
Shrewsbury 4 E 5
Shuang cheng 31 N 1
Shü cheng 31 L 4
Shufu 31 F 5
Shugden Gomba 31 F 5
Shui kou 31 L 5
Shumagin Is. 45 G 6
Shumaisa 38 E 3
Shunte 27 f 15
Shuo hsien 31 I 3
Shuqra 38 E 5
Shur 29 C 5
Shurma 38 D 3
Shuruppak 28 H 5
Shush 28 L 4

Shushona 41 D 3
Shushtar 28 L 4
Shuwaq 38
Si 31 I 6
Siah Kuh. Mt. 38 F 2
Sialkot 29 F 5
Siam 26 NO 8
Siam, Gulf of 26 O 8-9
Sian 31 H 4
Siang 31 I 5
Siapa 51 C 3
Siargao, Island 34 G 3
Siaskotan, Island 22 Q 5
Siauliai 17 L 9
Siau Sangihe, Island 34 G 4
Siba 39 E 3
Sibenik 21 B 6
Siberia 27 LT 3
Siberut, Island 34 A 5
Sibi 29 E 6
Sibiti 40 A 3
Sibiu 21 G 5
Siboa 34 F 4
Sibolga 34 A 4
Sibu 34 D 4
Sibutu, Island 34 E 4
Sibuyan, Island 34 F 2
Sicie, Cape 11 H 5
Sicilian Channel 19 CD 6
Sicily 18 DE 5-6
Sidamo 38 C 6
Sideros, Cape 20 H 10
Sidhpur 30 B 4
Sidi Barrani 37 L 3
Sidi-Bel-Abbès 37 D 2
Sidi Ifni 37 B 4
Sidi Moussa, u. 37 E 4
Sidley, Mt. 57 R 2
Sidney 44 T 6
Sidor 37 H 3
Sidorovsk 22 H 3
Sidra, Gulf of 37 H 3
Siedlce 13 L 2
Sieg 12 B 3
Siegburg 13 B 3
Siegen 13 C 3
Siem Reap 33 C 4
Siena 19 C 3
Sieppijärvi 17 M 3
Sieradz 13 H 3
Sierning 7 H 2
Sierpc 13 H 2
Sierra, La- 9 E 3
Sierra Blanca, Mt. 46 E 6
Sierra Charagua, Mt. 52 E 6
Sierra Colorada 53 C 5
Sierra da Chela, Mt. 41 A 2
Sierra da Neve, Mt. 41 A 1
Sierra de Divisor 52 C 3
Sierra de la Giganta 47 B 2
Sierra de los Organos 48 C 2
Sierra de Perija 49 C 2-3
Sierra de Pira 42 M 8
Sierra Imataca 51 D 2
Sierra Leone 36 B 5
Sierra Madre 34 F 1
Sierra Madre del Sud 42 IL 8
Sierra Madre Ocidental m. 42 I 7
Sierra Madre Oriental 42 IL 7
Sierra Maestra 48 D 2
Sierra Maigualida 51 CD 2
Sierra Nevada 42 GH 6
Sierra Nevada de S. Marta, 51 B 1
Sierras de Cordoba 53 D 3
Sierra Tumucumache 51 EF 3
Sierra Upanda 35 E 7
Sif Fatima 37 F 3
Sifnos 20 G 9
Sigean 11 G 5
Sighet 21 F 4
Sighisoara 21 G 4
Sigli 34 A 3
Siglufjördur 17 S 11
Signakhy 25 H 5
Signo 21 C 6
Sigovo 23 N 4
Sigtuna 17 G 7
Sigüenza 9 E 3
Siguiri 39 C 3
Sigulda 17 M 8
Sih sien 31 I 3
Siika 16 M 4
Siikainen 17 I 6
Siikajoki 17 M 4
Siika vaara, Mt. 17 N 4
Siipyy 17 I 5
Siirt 28 F 2
Sija 24 A 3
Sikasso 37 C 7
Sikhote Alin, Mt. 26 R 5
Si kiang 26 P 7
Sikinos 20 G 9
Sikkim 30 E 3
Sikonge 40 E 4
Sikosi 41 C 2
Sikotan, Island 22 P 5
Siksjö 17 G 4
Siksjön 17 H 4
Siktjakh 22 N 2

Sil 9 C 2
Sila, La- 18 F 5
Silale 17 L 9
Silba 21 B 5
Silchar 33 A 2
Sildegap, Island 17 A 5
Sile 21 I 7
Silesia 13 FG 3
Silet 37 E 5
Silgarhi Doti 30 D 3
Silian 16 F 6
Silifke 28 B 2
Siliguri 30 E 3
Silistra 21 H 5
Silit 38 D 5
Silka 22 M 4
Silka, River 22 MN 4
Silkeb 17 C 8
Siltou 37 H 6
Silvânia 52 H 5
Silver King 41 D 1
Silverton 46 E 5
Silvretta, Mt. 13 CD 5
Sim 24 I 7
Sim, River 24 I 7
Simay 21 I 8
Simakhina 22 L 4
Simanggang 34 D 4
Simanovsk 22 N 4
Simao Dias 52 L 4
Simav 20 I 7
Simba Congo 40 C 2
Simba (Kenia) 40 F 2
Simbach 13 E 4
Simbirsk (Ulyanovsk) 24 E 7
Simbor 30 B 4
Simenga 22 L 3
Simeto 19 E 6
Simeulue, Island 34 A 4
Simferopol 25 C 3
Simla 30 C 2
Simola 23 G 4
Simpang 34 B 4
Simplon 18 AB 1
Simirishamn 17 F 9
Simusir, Island 22 Q 5
Sinabang 34 A 4
Sinadagö 38 E 6
Sinai 35 G 3
Sinai, Mt. 28 B 6
Sinaloa 47 C 2
Sinamaica 51 B 1
Sinan 28 F 2
Sinauen 37 G 3
Sincelejo 51 A 2
Sind 26 I 7
Sindangan 34 F 3
Sindangbarang 34 C 6
Sindara 40 A 3
Sinder 37 E 7
Sine 37 B 7
Sinel'nikovo 25 C 1
Sines 9 B 5
Sineviju 31 M 2
Singa 38 B 5
Singapore 33 C 6
Singapore, Strait of 33 C 6
Singaraja 34 E 6
Singen 13 C 5
Singida 40 E 3
Singitik G. 20 FG 7
Singkawang 34 C 4
Singkep, Island 34 B 5
Singkil 34 A 4
Singö 17 H 6
Singora 33 C 5
Siniatsikon, Mt. 20 E 7
Siniscola 19 B 4
Sinkat 38 C 4
Sinnamary 51 F 2
Sinni 18 F 4
Sinoe 39 C 4
Sinop 25 C 4-5
Sinskoe 22 N 3
Sintang 34 D 4
Sinut, Es- 37 L 7
Siofok 21 D 4
Sion (Peru) 52 B 3
Sion (Switzerland) 19 A 1
Sioule 10 C 3
Sioux 44 M 5
Sioux City 46 G 4
Sioux Falls 46 G 4
Siple, Mt. 57 R 2
Sipolilo 41 E 2
Sipora, Island 34 A 5
Siquijor, Island 34 F 3
Sirba 37 E 7
Sirdalen 16 B 7
Sir Darja 29 E 3
Sir-Edward-Pellew-Gruppe 55 F 3
Sire elv 17 B 7
Siresi 24 D 7
Sirhan, Wadi- 28 DE 5
Siria 21 E 4
Sirino 19 EF 4
Sirna 20 H 9
Siro 37 B 7
Sironj 30 C 4
Siros 20 G 9
Sirpur 30 C 5
Sirra, U. 38 D 3
Sirri, Island 29 B 6

Sirsa 30 C 3
Sirte 37 H 3
Sirte Desert 37 H 3-4
Sisak 21 C 5
Sisaket 33 C 3
Sisi 41 D 3
Sisophon 33 C 4
Sisteron 11 H 4
Sithonia 20 F 7
Sitia 21 G 10
Sitio Grande 52 H 4
Sitka 45 M 5
Sitkalidak 45 H 5
Sitno, Mt. 20 D 3
Sittona 38 C 5
Situbondo 34 D 6
Siua 36 F 3
Siuruan 16 MN 4
Siva 24 H 6
Sivas 25 D 6
Siverek 28 E 2
Siwa 37 L 4
Sjaelland 17 DE 9
Sjul'dzjukjar 22 M 3
Sjutkja, Mt. 20 G 7
Skaftaros, G. 17 T 13
Skaga, Fj. 16 S 12
Skagen 17 D 8
Skagens Horn 16 D 8
Skagerrak 16 BC 7-8
Skaget, Mt. 16 C 6
Skal Fjeld, Mt. 16 F 5
Skalka Randi 16 H 3
Skara 17 E 7
Skaraborg 17 EF 7
Skarstind, Mt. 17 C 5
Skebo 17 H 7
Skeena 44 D 4-5
Skegness 4 G 5
Skellefte 16 HI 4
Skellefteaa 16 I 4
Skerries 4 C 5
Skhira, Es- 37 F 3
Skiathos 20 F 8
Skibbereen 4 B 6
Skien 17 C 7
Skierniewice 13 I 3
Skikda 37 F 2
Skind, Mt. 16 M 1
Skiold 17 A 7
Skipton 4 E 5
Skiros 21 G 8
Skive 17 C 8
Skjaldbreid, Mt. 16 R 12
Skjalfanda, Fj. 17 T 12
Skjalfandafljot 16 T 12
Skjalfandi 16 T 11
Skjak 17 C 6
Skjerstad 17 F 3
Skjoldungen 44 W 2
Sklov 23 H 7
Skodje 17 B 5
Skog 17 G 6
Skogeröy, Island 17 F 2
Skopelos 20 F 8
Skopin 23 N 8
Skopje 21 E 6
Skotterud 17 E 6
Skövde 17 E 7
Skovorodino 27 Q 4
Skröven 17 I 3
Skuo 17 a
Skuodas 17 I 8
Skutskar 17 G 6
Skvira 21 I 3
Skwierzyna 13 F 2
Skye, Island 3 C 3
Slagelse Köge 17 E 9
Slak 24 H 8
Slamet, Mt. 26 I 13
Slaney 3 C 5
Slantsy 23 G 5
Slatina (Yugoslavia) 21 C 5
Slatina (Romania) 21 G 5
Slatoust 22 E 4
Slave 44 G 3
Slave Coast 39 E 4-5
Slave Lake, Great 44 FG 3
Slave Lake, Lesser 44 F 4
Sleepers, Island 44 P 4
Sleitmute 45 G 4
Slesla 21 CD 2-3
Slezovka 22 Q 3
Slidre 17 C 6
Sligo 4 B 4
Slina 23 IL 6
Sline Head 3 A 5
Sliven 21 H 6
Slivnica 21 F 6
Sljudjanka 22 L 4
Slobodskoj 24 F 5
Slobozia 21 H 5
Sloka 17 L 8
Slonim 23 E 8
Slonta 37 I 3
Slotten 17 M 1
Slowakia 20 DE 3
Slovenia 21 B 4
Slupca 13 G 2
Slupsk 13 G 1
Slutsch 20 H 2

Slutsk 23 F 8
Smara 37 B 4
Smederevo 21 E 5
Smela 25 A 1
Smethwick 4 E 5
Smidovic 32 D 2 (n.d.S. S.R.)
Smidovic (Novaja Zemlja) 22 E 2
Smiley, Cape 57 o 2
Smith Bay 45 H 2
Smith, Cape 44 P 3
Smith, Island 57 O 3
Smith, Strait 56 Q 2
Smjörfjoll, Mt. 17 U 12
Smöla, Italy 16 B 5
Smolensk 23 I 7
Smoljan 21 G 7
Smorstak, Mt. 16 B 6
Snaefell, Mt. 16 U 12
Snäfells Jökull, Mt. 16 Q 12
Snake Lake 44 H 4
Snake, Rio 42 H 5
Snasa 16 D 4
Sneek 15 G 2
Sneeu Berge, Mt. 41 C 5
Snehatta, Mt. 16 C 5
Sniardwy, L. 12 I 2
Sniezka 12 F 3
Snina 21 F 3
Sno nut, Mt. 17 B 7
Snowdon, Mt. 3 D 5
Snowy 55 H 7
Soalala 41 c 7
Soang 39 G 4
Soanlahti 23 H 3
Soata 51 B 2
Sob 20 I 3
Sobane 39 B 3
Sobat 35 G 5
Sobolevka 21 I 3
Sobral 52 I 2
Sobrarbe 9 G 3
Soche 31 D 1
Socorro (Colombia) 51 B 2
Socorro (USA) 46 E 6
Socorro, Island 47 B 4
Socotra, Island 27 H 8
Soc Trang 33 D 5
Sodankylä 17 N 3
Soddu 38 C 6
Söderhamn 17 G 6
Söderköping 17 G 7
Södermanland 17 G 7
Södertälje 17 G 7
Soekmekaar 41 D 3
Sofala 41 E 2
Sofala, Gulf 35 G 8
Sofia 21 F 6
Sofia, River 41 c 7
Sofievka 25 B 1
Sofijsk 22 O 4
Sofyskoe 22 OP 4
Sogamoso 51 B 2
Sogne 19 B 7
Sogne Fjord, Fj. 16 AB 6
Sogn og Fiordane 17 AB 6
Sogoja 23 N 5
Sogra 30 D 3
Sohag 37 M 4
Sohna 37 H 4
Soisson 11 G 2
Sojana 23 P 2
Sojmigora 23 I 3
Sokal 21 G 2
Soké (Gabon) 40 A 3
Söke (Turkey) 21 H 9
Sokode 39 E 4
Sokolka 13 L 2
Sokolow 13 L 2
Sokone 37 A 7
Sokoto 35 D 4
Sokoto, River 35 D 4
Sokusti, Mt. 16 N 2
Sola 23 M 4
Solb 37 C 4
Solberg, Fj. 17 G 2
Sole 38 C 6
Solec 13 H 2
Soledad, Island 53 E 7
Solikamsk 24 I 5
Solimoes 52 D 2
Solingen 13 B 3
Soller 9 H 4
Sollia 17 D 6
Solling, Mt. 12 C 3
Sollum 36 F 2
Solna 17 F 7
Solo 26 m 13
Solo, River 26 m 13
Sologne 10 FG 3
Solok 34 B 5
Solokiga 20 FG 2
Solor, Island 34 F 6
Solothurn 18 B 5
Solta, Island 20 C 6
Soltanabad 28 L 5
Soltanabad (Iraq) 28 L 3
Soltaniyek 28 L 2
Soltau 13 CD 2
Sol'tsy 23 H 5
Soluk Dagi, Mt. 25 C 5

Solun 31 M 1
Solund, Island 16 A 6
Sol'vycegodsk 24 D 4
Solway Firth 3 DE 4
Somalia 36 H 5
Somar 28 H 4
Sombor 21 D 5
Sombreiro 39 F 5
Sombrerete 47 D 3
Sombrero, El- 51 C 2
Somero 17 L 6
Somerset 46 L 5
Somerset Island 44 M 1
Somerset East 41 D 5
Somerset West 41 B 5
Somes 20 F 4
Somesul 20 F 4
Somino 23 L 5
Somkele 41 E 4
Somme 10 FG 1-2
Somontano 9 FG 3
Somosierra, Pass 8 E 3
Sompi 37 D 6
Sompolno 13 H 2
Somport 10 E 5
Son 30 D 3-4
Sona 48 C 5
Sonchon 31 M 3
Sonda, Island 26 OQ 10
Sonda, Sea 26 PQ 10
Sondali 23 I 3
Sönderborg 17 C 9
Söndre 17 D 6
Söndre Strömfjord, 42 PQ 3
Sondrio 19 C 1
Sonepur 30 D 4
Song Cha 33 CD 3
Song Chu 33 CD 2-3
Song Coi 33 CD 2
Songea 40 F 5
Songina 31 F 1
Songkhla 33 C 5
Song Khon 33 D 3
Songo 39 B 4
Songoya 39 B 4
Songue 40 B 5
Sonhat 30 D 4
Sonmiani 29 E 6
Sono, Rio do- 52 H 4
Sonora, West 42 H 6
Sonora, Rio 47 B 2
Sonson 51 A 2
Sonsorol, Island 34 H 3
Soekmekaar 41 D 3
Sopot 13 H 1
Sopron 13 G 5
Sorak San, Mt. 31 N 3
Soraba 48 G 5
Sorel, Island 54 E 4
Sorong 34 H 5
Sororoca 51 D 3
Sorot, 23 G 6
Soroca 52 H 6
Sorocinsk 24 G 8
Soroki 21 I 3
Sorong 34 H 5
Sorong 34 H 5
Soroti 40 E 2
Sorraia 9 B 4
Sorrento 19 E 4
Sorsav 37 F 3
Sorsele 17 G 4
Sorsogon 34 F 2
Sortavala 23 H 4
Sörröndelag 17 CD 4-5
Sörvemaa 17 L 7
Sosa, Coronel Francisco- 53 D 4
Sosna 23 MN 8
Sosnovka 23 O 1
Sosnovo 23 H 4
Sosnowiec 13 H 3
Sostanj 23 B 4
Sosva 1 U 3
Soteir 37 M 6
Sotra, Island 16 A 6
Sotteftea 17 G 5
Souanké 39 G 5
Soubakaniedougou 39 D 3
Soubré 39 C 4
Souillac 11 F 4
Soulabot 39 G 5
Soure 52 H 2
Souris 44 H 4
Sous 37 C 3
Sousa 52 L 3
Sousel 52 G 2
Sousse 37 G 2
Souterraine, La- 11 F 3
South Africa 36 F 8-9
Southampton, Island 44 NO 3

South Bend 46 I 4
South Canale 4 B 5
South Carolina 46 LM 6
South China Sea 26 OP 8-9
South Dakota 46 FG 4
Southern Cross 55 B 6
South Negril, Pt. 48 D 3
South Platte 46 F 4
Southport 55 I 5
South Shields 4 F 4
South East Cape 55 b 9
Southwest Cape 55 f 15
Southwold 4 G 5
Sövde 17 A 5
Sovet Gavan 22 P 5
Sovetsk 17 I 9
Sovetskaja 25 F 3
Sovetskaja Gavan 32 F 2
Soviet Union 22 DT 1-5
Sovietsk 23 C 7
Soyo 40 A 4
Soz 23 HI 7-8
Sozopol 21 H 6
Spa 15 G 3
Spain 9 DE 2-5
Spalding 4 F 5
Spanta, Cape 20 F 10
Sparta 21 F 9
Spartanburg 46 L 6
Spassk-Dalnij 31 O 2
Spasskoe 24 D 5
Speikkogel 12 F 5
Spencer (Nebraska) 46 G 4
Spencergolf 55 F 6
Spencer. Cape 55 F 7
Spercheios 20 F 8
Sperrin Mts. 12 C 4
Spessart 12 C 3-4
Spetsä 20 F 9
Spey 3 E 3
Speyer 13 C 4
Spezzia, Island 20 F 9
Spinazzola 18 F 4
Spitsbergen 22 AB 1-2
Spitsbergen, West 22 A 2
Split 21 C 6
Splügen 18 B 1
Spokane 46 C 3
Spokojnyj 22 N 4
Spoleto 19 D 3
Sporades 20 GH 9
Sporades, Northern 20 FG 8
Spornyj 22 Q 3
Spratli, Islands 34 D 3
Spree 13 F 3
Spremberg 13 E 3
Springbok 41 B 4
Springfield (Illinois) 46 I 5
Springfield (Mass.) 46 N 4
Springfield (Missouri) 46 H 5
Springfield (Ohio) 46 L 5
Springfontein 41 D 5
Spring Hill 46 H 6
Springs 41 D 4
Springsure 55 H 4
Spurn Head 3 G 5
Squillace, Gulf of 18 F 5
Sredec 21 H 6
Sredne Kamchatsk 22 Q 4
Sredni Rodopi, Mt. 21 G 7
Srepoh 33 D 4
Sretensk 22 M 4
Sre Umbell 33 C 4
Srikakulam 30 D 5
Srirangam 30 D 6
Srivardhan 30 B 5
Srivilluputur 30 C 7
Sschüan 31 GH 4
Ssu mao 31 G 6
Ssunan 31 H 5
Ssu ping chieh 31 M 2
Staaten, River 55 G 3
Stadhur 17 Q 13
Stadland 16 A 5
Stafafell 17 U 12
Stafford 4 E 5
Staika, Mt. 16 G 3
Stalin 21 E 7
Stalon 17 F 4
Standerton 41 D 4
Stange 17 D 6
Stanger 41 E 4
Stangvik 17 C 5
Stanovoy Ranger 22 NO 4
Stanwell Park 55 d 11
Star, Fl. 17 B 7
Staraja Russa 23 H 5-6
Stara Zagora 21 G 6
Starbuck, Island 54 M 5
Stargard 13 F 2
Staritsa 23 L 6
Starobel'sk 25 E 1
Starodub 23 I 8
Starokonstantinov 21 H 3
Start Point 3 E 6
Staszow 13 I 3
Staunton 46 M 5
Stavanger 17 A 7
Staveren 15 G 2
Steamboat Spring 46 E 4
Steenwijk 15 H 2
Steep Pass 55 A 5
Stefanie, Lake 38 C 7

Stefansson 44 HI 1
Steigen 17 F 3
Steinkier 17 D 4
Steinkopf 41 B 4
Stella 18 B 3
Stellenbosch 41 B 5
Stendal 13 D 2
Stenkjar 16 D 5
Stensele 17 G 4
Stepan' 21 H 2
Stepanakert 25 I 6
Stepanovo 25 C 2
Stepnjak 22 G 4
Sterling Greeley 46 F 4
Sterlitamak 22 E 4
Stettin (Szczecin) 13 EF 2
Stewart Island 55 f 15
Steyr 13 F 4
Steytlerville 41 C 5
Stif 37 F 2
Stilo 18 F 5
Stilo, C. 19 F 5
Stip 21 F 7
Stirling 4 D 3
Stjernöy 16 L 1
Stjörna 17 C 5
Ston, Mt. 21 D 6
Stockerau 13 G 4
Stockholm 17 H 7
Stockport 4 E 5
Stockton (United Kingdom)
  4 F 4
Stockton (USA) 46 B 5
Stogovo Planina, Mt. 20 E 7
Stojba 22 O 4
Stoke 4 E 5
Stokhod 20 G 2
Stokköy 17 C 4
Stokkseyri 17 R 13
Stökksnes 17 U 12
Stolac 21 C 6
Stolbovaja 22 Q 3
Stolbovoj, Island 22 D 2
Stolbtsy 23 F 8
Stölleberg, Mt. 17 E 6
Stolzenfels 41 B 4
Stonehaven 4 E 3
Stora Lulevatten 16 H 3
Storavan 17 H 4
Stordoy, Island 16 A 7
Stören 17 D 5
Storenup, Mt. 16 B 7
Stor Fjord,. 56 a
Storfoshei 17 F 3
Storlien 17 E 5
Stormberg 41 D 5
Storm Berge, Mt. 41 D 5
Stornoway 4 C 1
Storöya, Island 56 a
Storozevsk 24 G 4
Storozinets 21 G 3
Storren 16 E 5
Storstein 17 G 2
Storsteinnes 17 H 2
Storvätteshagna, Mt. 16 E 5
Storvigelen, Mt. 16 E 5
Stor Vindeln 16 G 4
Storvola,Mt. 16 D 5
Stour (Dorset) 3 EF 6
Stour (Suffolk) 3 G 5-6
Stralsund 13 E 1
Strangways Springs 55 F 5
Strasbourg 11 I 2
Strathy Point, 4 D 2
Straubing 13 E 4
Strazov, Mt. 20 D 3
Strelka 22 L 3
Stridenburg 41 C 4
Strömbacka 17 G 5
Stromboli 18 E 5
Strömö 17 a
Strömsbro 17 G 6
Stromstad 17 D 7
Strömsund (Jämtland)
  17 F 5
Strömsund (Västerbotten)
  17 G 4
Stronsay, Island 12 E 2
Struer 17 C 8
Strule 4 C 4
Struma 20 F 7
Strumica 21 F 7
Strumica 20 F 7
Stryj, 21 F 3
Stryj, River 20 F 3
Stryn 17 B 5
Strimon Gulf of 20 F 7
Strypa 20 G 3
Strzelecki Creek 55 G 5
Strzelno 13 G 2
Stung Treng 33 D 4
Stura 18 A 2
Sturge 57 a 3
Sturt Desert 55 G 5
Stutterheim 41 D 5
Stuttgart 13 C 4
Stuven, Island 53 A 6
Stwiga 20 H 2
Styr 20 G 2
Stria 13 F 5
Suakin 38 C 4
Suarez, Coronel- 53 D 4
Subar-kuduk 29 C 2
Subata 23 EF 6
Subic 34 F 2
Subotica 21 D 4

Sucan 22 O 5
Suceava 21 H 4
Suchan 31 O 2
Su chien 31 L 4
Su chou 31 M 4
Su chou (Chui chuan)
  31 F 3
Suck 3 B 5
Sucre 52 D 5
Sucuaro 51 C 3
Suda 23 LM 4-5
Sudan 36 FG 4
Sudbury 44 O 6
Suderö, Island 17 a
Sudetes 12 FG 3
Sue 40 D 1
Sueca 9 F 4
Suez 28 B 6
Suez Canal 28 B 5
Suez, Gulf of 28 B 6
Sufeina 38 D 3
Suffolk 3 G 5
Suglan 22 P 2
Suglut 44 P 3
Sugoj 22 Q 3
Suhl 13 D 3
Sui chiang 31 G 5
Sui chuan 31 I 5
Sui chung 31 M 2
Sui hsien 31 I 4
Sui hua 31 N 1
Suilai 31 D 2
Sui leh 31 I 3
Sui ping 31 H 4
Suippes 11 H 2
Suir 3 C 5
Sui ting 31 C 2
Sui Yüan 31 HI 2-3
Sukabumi 34 C 6
Sukamara 34 D 5
Suke 40 K 4
Sukhneh 28 E 3
Sukhona 24 BD 4-5
Sukhumi 25 F 4
Sukkertoppen 44 U 2
Sukkur 29 E 6
Sukromlja 23 L 6
Suksu 24 E 6
Suksun 24 I 6
Sula 24 F 1
Sula Islands 34 G 5
Sulaiman Range 26 IL 6-7
Sulaimaniya 28 H 3
Sulaimiya 38 E 3
Sulaiyil 38 E 3
Sulak 24 E 9
Sulawesi Island 34 EF 5
Sulb 37 M 5
Sulima 39 B 4
Sulina 21 I 5
Sulingen 13 C 2
Sulitjelma 16 G 3
Sullana 52 A 2
Sullivan, Island 33 B 4
Sulmona 19 DE 3-4
Su lo ho 31 F 3
Sultan, Es- 37 H 3
Sultanabad 38 G 2
Sultanpur 30 D 3
Sulu Archipelago 34 F 3
Sulu See 34 EF 3
Suluq 37 I 3
Sumatra, Island 26 NO 9-10
Sumba, Island 34 EF 6
Sumbawa 34 E 6
Sumbing, Mt. 26 lm 13
Sumbu, Island 22 Q 4
Sumburgh Head 3 F 2
Sumen 20 H 6
Sumgait 25 L 5
Sumikha 24 N 7
Sumpa Kangri, Mt. 31
Sumperk 13 G 4
Sumprabum 33 B 1
Sunda Islands, Greater
  26 OQ 10
Sunda Islands, Lesser
  34 EF 6
Sunda Strait 34 C 6
Sundarbans 27 a 12
Sundays River 41 CD 5
Sundbyberg 17 G 7
Sunde 17 A 7
Sunderland 4 F 4
Sund 16 E 9
Sundsjö 17 F 5
Sundsvall 17 G 5
Sung 39 D 4
Sun'ga 23 L 3
Sungaipenuk 34 B 5
Sungari 26 QR 5
Sungari, Lake 31 N 2
Sungikai 37 M 7
Sungpan 31 G 4
Sungurlu 25 C 5
Sunija, Lake 28 I 4
Sunndal 17 C 5
Sunndals 16 C 5
Suntar 22 M 3
Suntsar 29 D 6
Suola selkä, Mt. 17 MN 2
Suomen Selkä, Mt. 16 L 5
Suonenjoki 17 N 5
Supé 52 B 4
Superior 46 H 3

Superior, Lake 42 LM 5
Supiori 34 I 5
Suppé 38 C 6
Suq Ash-Shuyukh 28 I 5
Sur (Libano) 28 C 4
Sur (Oman) 27 H 7
Sura (South Arabia) 28 C 7
Sura (Soviet Union) 24 C 3
Sura, Cape 38 E 5
Surabaya 34 D 6
Surag 29 C 6
Surakarta 34 D 6
Surat 30 B 4
Suratgarh 30 B 3
Surat Thani 33 B 5
Suraz (Brjansk) 28 I 8
Suraz (Weißrußland) 23 H 7
Surgat 22 G 3
Surigao 34 G 3
Surinam 50 E 3
Surinam, Rio 51 E 3
Surovo 22 L 4
Surpresa 52 D 4
Surukh 28 L 3
Susa 19 A 2
Susanville 46 B 4
Susitna 45 H 4
Susoh 34 A 4
Susques 53 C 1
Sussex 3 FG 6
Susuman 22 P 3
Sutherland (Australia)
  55 e 11
Sutherland (South Africa)
  41 C 5
Sutley 26 L 6-7
Sutvik, Island 45 G 5
Suursaari, Island 23 F 4
Suvadiva, Island 26 L 9
Suva Planina, Mt. 20 F 6
Suvasv, Island. 23 G 3
Suvorow, Island 54 L 6
Suwaira 28 H 4
Suwalki 13 L 1
Suweon 31 N 3
Svalbard (Spitsbergen)
  22 AB 1-2
Svalbardh 17 U 11
Svannäs 17 H 3
Svanöy 17 A 6
Svärholt 16 N 1
Svärtisen, Mt. 16 F 3
Svay Rieng 33 D 4
Svealand 17 EH 7
Sveksna 17 I 9
Svencionis 23 F 7
Svendborg 17 D 9
Svenner, Island 57 F 3
Sventoji 16 M 9
Sverdlask 22 F 4
Sverdlovsk 24 M 6
Sverdrup Islands 42 IL 2
Svetlaya 32 E 2
Svetlogorsk 19 I 9
Svid 23 N 4
Svilaja, Mt. 21 C 6
Svinecea 20 EF 5
Svinö 17 4
Svinö, Island. 3 a
Svir 23 IL 4
Svistov 21 G 6
Svjatoj, Cape 1 P 2
Svobodnyj 22 N 4
Svoge 21 F 6
Svolvär, Island 17 F 2
Swabia 13 CD 4-5
Swabian Jura 12 C 4
Swainbost 4 C 2
Swain Reefs, Island 55 I 4
Swakopmund 41 A 3
Swale 4 F 4
Swan, Island 47 H 4
Swansea 4 D 6
Swaziland 36 G 8
Swebo 38 B 1
Sweden 17 DL 2-9
Swellendam 41 C 5
Swettenham 33 C 6
Swica 20 FG 3
Swidwin 13 F 2
Swindon 4 F 6
Switzerland 13 BC 5
Sycevka 23 L 7
Syderö 3 a
Sydney 55 I 6
Sydney, North- 55 e 10
Sydney, Island 54 I 5
Sydpröven 44 V 3
Syktyvkar 24 F 4
Sylakh 22 N 3
Sylhet 30 F 4
Sylt 12 C 1
Sylte, Fj. 17 P 1
Sylva 24 I 6
Synshövd, Mt. 17 C 6
Syracuse 19 E 6
Syracuse 46 M 4
Syrdarya 26 IL 5
Syria 28 DE 3-4
Syrian Desert 28 OG 3-4
Syrkum 32 F 1
Syväjärvi 17 L 2
Syzran 24 E 8
Syzran' 24 DE 8
Szczebrzeszyn 13 L 3
Szczecin (Stettin) 13 EF 2

Szczuczyn 13 L 2
Szeged 21 E 4
Szegszara 21 D 4
Székesfehérvar 21 D 4
Szengen 31 H 6
Szentes 21 E 4
Szigetvar 21 C 4
Szob 21 D 4
Szolnok 21 E 4
Szombathely 21 C 4
Szubin 13 G 2

T

Ta 28 B 2
Taal 34 F 2
Taba 28 F 7
Tabaco 34 F 2
Tabarqa 37 F 2
Tabas 29 D 5
Tabatinga 52 D 2
Tabatoult 37 E 6
Tabelbala 37 D 4
Tabelbalet 37 F 4
Tabelcosa 37 E 4
Taberg, 16 F 8
Tabila 40 B 1
Tabira 39 E 4
Tablas, Las- 48 C 5
Tablas, Island 34 F 2
Taboca 52 D 2
Taboleiro 52 F 3
Tabor 21 B 3
Tabora 40 E 3
Tabory 24 O 5
Tabou 39 C 5
Tābris 28 I 1
Tabuk 28 D 6
Tabun 37 M 6
Tabynsk 24 I 8
Tacaagle 53 E 1
Ta cheng 31 C 1
Tachikawa 27 d 13
Tacloban 34 G 2
Tacna (Colombia) 52 C 2
Tacna (Perù) 52 C 5
Tacoma 46 B 3
Tacuarembo 53 E 3
Tademaït, 35 D 3
Tadjemout 37 E 4
Tadjoura 37 G 3
Tadmor 28 E 3
Tadpatri 30 C 6
Tadzhikistan 22 FG 6
Tafalla 9 F 2
Tafilalet 37 CD 3
Tafiré Soba 39 C 4
Tafolli 37 A 6
Tafraout 37 B 4
Tagaedoufat 37 F 6
Taganai, Mt. 24 L 7
Taganrog 25 E 2
Tagant 35 B 4
Tagaung 33 B 2
Tagbilaran 34 F 3
Taghit 37 D 3
Tagil, River 24 MN 5
Tadjoura 37 G 3
Tagoujalet 37 C 5
Taguatinga 54 H 4
Taguerzimt 37 A 5
Tagus 8 ED 3-4
Ta hai, Strait 27 f 15
Ta hat, Mt. 37 F 5
Ta Heng Chin, Island 27 f 15
Tahiti, Island 54 M 6
Tahlab Rud 29 D 6
Tahoua 37 F 6
Tahsien 31 H 4
Ta Hsing an ling Shanmo,
  (Great Khingan
  Mountaing) 31 LM 1-2
Ta Hsüeh Zhan 31 G 5
Tahta 37 M 4
Tai 39 C 4
Taian 31 L 3
Taichung 31 M 6
Taif 38 D 3
Taiga 22 H 4
Tai Hu 31 M 4
Taikang 31 I 4
Taiku 31 I 3
Tailem Bend 55 F 7
Taima 28 E 7
Tai mo, Mt. 27 g 15
Tain 4 D 3
Tainan 31 M 6
Tai o 31 f 15
Taipale 23 G 3
Taipei 31 M 5
Tai ping (China) 27 f 15
Taiping (Malaysia) 33 C 6
Taira 32 F 4
Taishan 31 I 6
Taishun 31 L 5
Taitao, Pen. 53 AB 6
Taitao, Cape 53 B 6
Taitung 31 M 6
Taiwan (Taiwan) 26 Q 7
Taiyüan (Yang chu) 31 I 3
Ta'izz 38 D 5

Tajmyr (Dolgano-Nentsy)
  22 HI 2
Tajmyr, River 22 I 2
Tajset 22 I 4
Tajumulco 42 L 8
Tajuna 8 E 3
Tak 33 L 3
Takada 32 E 4
Takaka 55 g 14
Takalan 34 E 6
Takamatsu 32 D 5
Takaoka 32 E 4
Takase 38 C 5
Takaungu 40 F 3
Takaw 33 B 2
Takeo 33 C 4
Take Shima, Island 32 D 4
Takhadid 28 H 5
Takhta Bazar 22 F 6
Takingeun 34 A 4
Takla Makan, West 26 M 6
Taku 31 L 3
Takuan 31 G 5
Takuna 34 G 4
Takaimannar 30 C 7
Takakan 32 D 2
Takamone 19 C 3
Taka Mungongo 40 B 4
Takara 52 A 2
Takass 29 F 3
Talaud Islands 34 G 4
Talavera de la Reina 9 D 3
Talbert, Cape 10 D 2
Talbot, Cape 55 D 2
Talca 53 B 4
Talcahuano 53 B 4
Talcher 30 E 4
Taldy-Kurgan 22 G 5
Taleh 38 E 2
Tali (Shenhsi) 31 H 4
Tali (Yünnan) 31 G 5
Taliabu, Island 34 FG 5
Talima 51 E 3
Talitsa 24 N 6
Taliwang 34 E 6
Tal-i-Khsrovi 38 F 1
Talkheh Rud 28 HI 1-2
Tallin 23 E 5
Tallahassee 46 L 6
Talodi 37 M 7
Talorza 37 B 6
Talsi 17 L 8
Taltal 53 B 2
Taluk 34 B 5
Talung 31 G 3
Talung, River 31 G 3
Talvik 17 L 1
Talyzino 24 C 7
Tama 27 d 13
Tamada 37 E 5
Tamaïa 37 F 6
Tama'in 37 I 7
Tamale 39 D 4
Tamar 3 D 6
Tamaské 37 F 7
Tamaya 52 C 3
Tamba 39 B 3
Tambacounda 37 B 7
Tambalan 34 E 4
Tambaoura 37 B 7
Tambara 41 E 2
Tambawel 39 E 3
Tambo 55 H 5
Tambohorano 41 b 7
Tambora, Mt. 34 E 6
Tambov 2 Q 5
Tambre 8 B 2
Tambura 40 D 1
Tamdy Bulak 29 D 3
Tame 51 B 2
Tamega 8 B 3
Tamelloso 9 E 4
Tamenghest 37 F 5
Tamentit 37 D 4
Tamerna 37 F 3
Tamerza 37 F 3
Tamgak, Mt. 37 F 6
Tamgrout 37 C 3
Tamgue, Mt. 39 B 3
Tamluk 27 a 11
Tammerfors 17 L 6
Tampa 46 L 7
Tampere 17 L 6
Tampico 47 E 3
Tamrau, Mt. 26 n 14
Tamsweg 13 E 5
Tamtsak Bulak 31 L 1
Tamowe 40 C 4
Tamuk 31 F 5
Tan 31 I 4
Tana 17 O 1
Tana (Kenia) 35 GH 6
Tana (Norvegia) 16 N 1-2
Tana, Fj. 17 O 1
Tana, Lake 35 C 4
Tanabu 32 F 3
Tanaga, Island 22 T 4
Tanahbala, Island 34 A 5
Tanahdjamp, Island 34 F 6
Tanahgrogot 34 E 5

Tanahmasa, Island 34 A 5
Tanak Merah 33 C 5
Tanami 55 E 3
Tanana 45 H 3
Tanana, River 45 I 4
Tanaro 18 A 2
Tandag 34 G 3
Tandaué 41 B 2
Tandil 53 E 4
Tandinsk 22 O 3
Tandjung 34 E 5
Tandjungbalai (Karimun)
  27 h 16
Tandjungbalai (Sumatra)
  34 A 4
Tandjungpandan 34 C 5
Tandjungpinang 27 i 17
Tandjungselor 34 E 4
Tanega, Island 32 D 5
Ta-n-Elak 37 F 4
Tanezrouft 37 DE 5
Tanezrouft-n-Ahenet 37 E 5
Tang, Pass 31 E 4
Tanga 40 F 4
Tangalane, Pt. 41 F 2
Tanganyika, Lake 40 DE 3-4
Tangatau, Lake 54 O 6
Tang chia kuan 27 f 15
Tanggamus, Mt. 34 B 6
Tangier 37 C 2
Tang shan (An huei) 31 L 4
Tang shan (Ho pei) 31 L 3
Tang tou hsia 27 g 15
Tanimbar Islands 34 H 6
Tanjay 34 F 3
Tanjore 30 D 6
Tanmi, Mt. 26 N 4
Tännäs 17 E 5
Tano 39 D 4
Tanoumbella 37 F 4
Tanout 37 F 7
Tanpa 31 G 4
Tan Shui 31 M 5
Tansi 39 E 3
Tansing 30 D 3
Tanta 37 M 3
Tanzania 36 G 6
Tao 31 G 4
Taoan 31 M 1
Tao erh 31 M 1
Taofu 31 G 4
Taokhe 41 C 2
Taokou 31 I 3
Taonan 31 M 1
Taongi, Island 54 G 3
Taormina 19 E 6
Taorta 37 B 6
Taoudenni 37 D 5
Taourirt 37 E 4
Taouz 37 D 3
Tapa 17 M 7
Tapachula 47 F 5
Tapagé 52 F 2
Tapaios 52 F 2
Tapaktuan 34 A 4
Tapanahoni 51 E 3
Ta Pa Shan, Mt. 26 OP 6
Tapaua 52 D 3
Ta peng 27 g 15
Tapera 52 E 2
Ta pieh Shan, Mt. 31 L 4
Tapline 28 E 5
Tapo 39 E 3
Tapolca 21 C 4
Tapsing 31 F 4
Tapti 30 C 4
Tapu 31 L 6
Tapuru 52 E 2
Tapuruqua 52 D 2
Taquaretinga 52 L 3
Taquari, Rio 52 F 5
Tara 22 G 4
Tara, River 20 D 6
Taraba 39 G 4
Tarakan 34 E 4
Taran 22 G 2
Tarancon 9 E 3
Taransay 4 C 3
Taranto 19 F 4
Taranto, G. of 18 F 4-5
Tarapaca 52 D 5
Tara Planina, Mt. 20 D 6
Tarapoto 52 B 3
Taraqua 52 D 2
Tarasca 25 A 1
Tarapoto 52 B 3
Tarata 52 D 5
Tarauaca 52 C 3
Tarauaca, River 52 C 3
Taravo 11 a
Tarawa, Island 54 H 4
Tarbagatai (Chuguchak),
  31 CE 1
Tarbagatai, Mt. (Mongolia)
  31 FG 1
Tarbagatai, Mt.
  (Soviet Union) 22 H 5
Tarbes 17 F 3
Tarce 55 I 6
Tarcaul, Mt. 20 H 4
Tarcoola 55 E 6
Tardienta 9 F 3
Tärendo 17 L 3

Tarfaya 37 B 4
Tarf Shaqq-al'Abd 28 D 7
Targane 37 F 6
Targoviste 21 H 6
Tarhaouaout 37 F 5
Tarhuna 37 G 3
Tarifa 9 D 5
Tari Hai 31 L 2
Tarija 52 D 6
Tarim 38 E 4
Tarim 26 LM 5-6
Tarjannes 16 L 5
Tarkastad 41 D 5
Tarkwa 39 D 4
Tarlac 34 F 1
Tarma 52 B 4
Tarn 10 FG 4-5
Tärna 17 F 4
Tarna, River 20 E 4
Târnava Mare 20 G 4
Tarnava Micà 20 G 4
Tarnogrod 13 L 3
Târnovo 21 G 6
Tarnow 13 I 3
Taro 18 C 2
Taroom 55 H 5
Taroudant 37 C 3
Tarragona 9 G 3
Tarrasa 9 G 3
Tarso Tiéroko, Mt. 37 H 5
Tarsus 28 C 2
Tartagal 53 D 1
Tartary Strait 22 P 4-5
Tartu 23 F 5
Tartus 28 C 3
Tarum 26 I 13
Tarusa 23 M 7
Tarutino 21 I 4
Tarutung 34 A 4
Tarvisio 19 D 1
Tarzo Uri, Mt. 37 H 5
Tarz Ulli 37 F 4
Tasaliout 37 E 6
Tasauz 22 F 5
Taschereau 44 P 6
Tash bulaq 31 E 2
Tashigang Dzong 33 A 1
Tashigong 31 B 4
Ta shih 27 f 14
  31 LM 1-2
Tashkent 29 E 3
Tash Qurghan 31 B 3
Tasikmalaja 34 C 6
Tasinge 17 D 9
Tasköprü 25 C 5
Tasman, Sea 54 G 7-8
Tasmanien 57 b 5
Tasmansee 57 B 5
Tasr 37 G 7
Tassili d. Ajjer, Mt. 35 DE 3
Tassili Oua-n-Ahaggar
  37 EF 5-6
Tassili Ta-n-Adrar 37 E 5
Tastagol 37 M 7
Tas-Timus 22 O 2
Tata 37 C 4
Tatakoto, Island 54 O 6
Tatidno 40 B 1
Tatarsk 22 G 4
Tatnam, Cape 44 M 4
Tatra, High 20 DE 3
Tatra, Low 20 D 3
Tatrart 37 B 6
Tatta 29 E 7
Tatung 31 G 2
Tau 31 I 5
Taua 52 I 3
Tauapeçaçu 52 E 2
Taubaté 52 H 6
Tauber 12 C 4
Tauere, Island 54 N 6
Tauern, Hohe- 12 E 5
Tauern, Niedere- 12 EF 5
Taufikia 38 B 6
Taufstein, Mt. 18 C 3
Taumarunui 55 h 13
Taumaturgo 52 C 3
Taung 41 C 4
Taunggyi 33 B 2
Taunton 4 E 6
Taunus 12 C 3
Taupo 55 h 13
Ta'uq 28 H 3
Taurage 17 L 9
Tauri 55 H 1
Tauride 1 O 6
Taurus 1 OP 8
Tausa, Mt. 16 F 3
Tauysk 22 Q 5
Tavda 22 F 4
Tavda, River 22 F 3-4
Tavira 9 C 5
Tavolara 18 BC 4
Tavoliere di Puglia 18 E 4
Tavoy 33 B 4
Tavsi 28 E 2
Tavoy, Island 33 B 4
Tawaiya 38 D 4
Tawao 34 E 4
Taweche, Mt. 26 p 17
Taweisha 38 C 7
Tawil, Mt. 38 C 2
Tay, River 12 E 3
Tay, L. 3 D 3

Tay, Firth of 3 E 3
Tayabamba 52 B 3
Taygetos 20 F 9
Taymyr, Lake 22 L 2
Taymyr Peninsula 22 HM 2
Tay Ninh 33 D 4
Taytay 34 E 2
Tayü 31 I 5
Taz 22 GH 3
Taza 37 D 3
Tazenakht 37 C 3
Tazerbo 36 F 3
Tazewell 46 L 5
Tazovskoe 22 G 3
Te Anau 55 f 15
Teano 19 E 4
Teapa 47 F 4
Teba 9 D 5
Tébessa 37 F 2
Tebrau 27 h 16
Tebrau, Strait 27 h 16
Tebrau, River 27 h 16
Techa 53 B 5
Techin 31 F 5
Techir-Ghiol 21 I 5
Tecoanapa 47 E 4
Tecuci 21 H 5
Tedjedi 37 F 4
Tedzher 29 D 4
Teelin Head 3 B 4
Tees 3 F 4
Tefé 52 E 2
Tefé, Rio 52 D 2-3
Tefedest 37 F 4-5
Tegal 34 C 6
Tegama 37 F 6
Tegelträsk 17 F 5
Teguèma 37 G 6
Teharu 34 G 5
Tehciou 31 L 3
Tehko 31 F 4
Tehran 28 M 3
Tehuantepec 43 L 8
Tehuantepec, Isthmus of
  42 L 8
Tehuantepec, Gulf of
  47 EF 4-5
Teide, Pico de 37 A 4
Teifi 3 DE 5
Teixeira 52 L 3
Teja 22 I 3
Tejerhi 37 G 5
Tekapo 55 g 14
Tekir 20 H 7
Tekirdag 21 H 7
Tekna Dra 37 BC 4
Tekong, Island 27 i 16
Tekro 37 I 6
Tel 30 D 4
Tel Abyad 28 E 2
Telavi 25 H 5
Tel Aviv-Jaffa 28 C 4
Telemark 17 C 7
Telén 53 C 4
Teleno, El-, Mt. 8 C 2
Télimélé 39 B 3
Teljace 25 L 2
Tell 35 D 2
Tell Abu Dhahir 28 G 2
Tellmr 45 E 3
Telli Nor 31 D 1
Tell-Sheikh Ahmed 28 F 3
Telok Anson 33 C 6
Tel'pos-iz, Mt. 24 L 3
Telsiai 17 L 9
Telukbakau 27 i 16
Telukbetung 34 C 6
Telukdalam 34 A 4
Tema 39 D 3
Temasint 37 F 5
Témassinin 37 F 4
Temax 47 G 3
Tembellaga 37 F 6
Tembenchi 27 N 3
Tembenci 22 IL 3
Tembo-Aluma 40 B 4
Tembwe 40 D 4
Temirlik 31 E 3
Temora 55 H 6
Tempe 20 F 8
Temple 46 G 6
Temrjuk 25 D 3
Temuco 53 B 4
Tena 52 B 2
Tenasserim 33 B 4
Tenasserim, Desert 26 N 8
Tenda 18 A 2
Ten Degree Channel 33
  A 4-5
Tendelti 37 M 7
Tenedos 20 H 8
Teneghir 37 C 3
Tenekert 37 E 6
Téneraro, Island 54 O 7
Ténéré 37 FG 5-6
Tenerife 37 A 4
Teng ching 31 F 4
Teng chung 31 F 5
Teng hsien 31 L 4
Tengko 31 F 4
Tenke 40 D 5
Tenkodogo 39 E 3

Teng kou 31 H 3
Tengiz, Lake 1 V 5
Tengréla 37 C 7
Tenna 18 D 3
Tennant Creek 55 E 3
Tennessee 46 I 5
Tennessee, River 48 I 5-6
Tennio 16 O 3
Tenom 34 E 3
Tensift 37 C 3
Teofilo Otoni 52 I 5
Teofipol' 21 H 3
Tepa 34 G 6
Tepic 47 D 3
Teplik 21 I 3
Teploe 23 M 8
Ter 8 H 2
Tera 37 E 7
Tera, River 8 C 2
Teramo 19 DE 3
Terceira 37 a
Terebovlija 21 G 3
Terenga 24 E 8
Teresina 52 I 3
Terhazza 37 C 5
Terkama 37 I 7
Terkos 21 I 7
Termez 22 F 5
Termini Imerese 19 DE 5
Terminillo, Mt. 18 D 3
Termoli 19 E 3
Ternei 31 P 1
Ternej 22 O 5
Terni 19 D 3
Ternopol' 21 G 3
Terpenija Bay 33 F 2
Terpenija, Cape 32 F 2
Terra Alessandra, Island 22
  D 1
Terracina 19 D 4
Terra di Bari 18 F 4
Terra d'Otranto 18 FG 4
Terralba 19 B 5
Terrasson 11 F 4
Terril, Sierra- 8 D 5
Terschelling, Island 14 G 2
Teruel 9 F 3
Tervel 21 H 6
Tervola 17 L 3
Tesanj 21 C 5
Tesaua 37 G 4
Tesinga 26 p 17
Tes-Khem, River 31 E 1
Teslin 44 C 3
Teslin, River 44 C 3
Tessalit 37 E 5
Tessaoua 37 F 7
Tessenei 38 C 4
Tessine 18 B 2
Test 3 F 6
Tete (Mozambique) 41 E 2
Tété (Central Africa Republic)
  40 C 1
Tetela 47 E 4
Tetere 22 L 4
Teterev 20 I 2-3
Teterow 13 E 2
Tetschen 13 E 3
Tolga 37 F 3
Tol'ka 22 H 3
Teterey, 20 IL 2
Teterow 13 E 2
Tetes Pires 50 E 4
Tetjukhe 31 P 2
Tetjusi 24 E 7
Tetovo 21 E 6
Tetrino 23 N 1
Tetuan 37 C 2
Tetulia 27 b 11
Teuco 53 D 2
Teuini 52 D 3
Teulada 19 B 5
Teulada, Cape 18 B 5
Teun, Island 34 G 6
Teutoburger Wald 12 BC 2-3
Teviot 3 E 4
Tevriz 22 G 4
Texarkana 46 H 6
Texas 46 FG 6
Texel, Island 14 G 2
Tezpur 33 A 1
Thachap Gangri, Mt. 31 C 4
Thaibinh 33 D 2
Thailand 33 BC 3-5
Thakhek 33 C 3
Thal 29 F 5
Thale 13 D 3
Thames 3 FG 6
Thames 55 h 13
Thammu 26 p 17
Thangmoche 26 p 17
Thanh Hoa 33 D 3
Thar Desert 26 L 7
Thargomindah 55 G 5
Tharrawaddy 33 B 3
Thasos 20 G 7
Thaton 33 B 3
Thaungdut 33 A 2
Thayetmyo 33 B 3
Thebai 21 F 8
The Barcoo 55 F 5
The Granites 55 E 4
The Hague 15 G 2-3
Theodore 55 I 4

The Pas 44 I 5
Thermopylae 21 F 8
Theron, Mt. 57 MI 2
Thessaloniki 21 F 7
Thessaloniki, G. of 20 F 7
Thessaly 21 EF 8
Thetford 4 G 5
Thiers 11 G 4
Thies 37 A 7
Thimphu 30 E 3
Thionville 11 I 2
Thiorsa 16 S 12
Thirsk 4 F 4
Thisted 17 C 8
Thistil, Fj. 17 U 11
Thok Daurakpa 31 D 4
Thok Jalung 31 C 4
Thomson 55 G 4
Thorshavn 17 a
Thouars 11 E 3
Thowa 40 F 3
Thrace 21 GH 7
Three Kings Islands 55 g 12
Thule 42 O 2
Thule, Southern 57 M 4
Thun 19 A 1
Thunder Bay (F. William)
  44 N 6
Thuner See 18 A 1
Thuringia 13 D 3
Thuringian Forest 12 D 3
Thurles 4 C 5
Thurso 4 E 2
Thurso, River 3 E 2
Thurston Pen. 57 p 2
Thyangboche 26 p 17
Thykkvabäjklaistur 17 S 13
Tiaggelvas, Island. 16 GH 3
Tiassalé 39 D 4
Tibagi 37 G 6
Tibagi, Rio 52 G 6
Tibati 39 G 4
Tiber 18 D 3
Tiberias, Lake 1 P 9
Tibesti, Mt. 35 E 3
Tibet 26 MN 6
Tibni 28 E 3
Tiburon, Cape 48 E 3
Tiburon, Island 47 B 2
Tidaholm 17 E 7
Tidikelt 37 E 4
Tidjenaouine 37 F 5
Tidjikja 37 B 6
Tieh ling 31 M 2
Tiembougou 37 C 7
Tien Chian 31 L 4
Tien shui 31 H 4
Tien tsin 31 L 3
Tierra del Fuego 53 C 7
Tiéta 8 D 3
Tieté 52 G 6
Tiflis 37 I 3
Tigara 45 E 3
Tigil 22 Q 4
Tigre 36 G 4
Tigre, Rio 52 B 2
Tigris 1 QR 8-9
Tiguentourine 37 F 4
Tihama 38 CD 3-5
Tihert 37 E 2
Ti hua (Urumchi) 31 D 2
Titilan mäki, Mt. 23 G 3
Tikahau 54 N 6
Tikaré 39 D 3
Tikhonsk 24 D 5
Tikhoretsk 25 F 3
Tikhtozero 23 H 2
Tikhvin 23 I 5
Tikhvinya 23 IL 5
Tikrit 28 G 3
Tiksi 22 N 2
Tikuyu 40 E 4
Tilamuta 34 F 4
Tilburg 15 G 3
Tilemses 37 E 6
Tilghemt 37 E 3
Tiliciki 22 R 3
Tiligul 20 L 4
Tilimsen 37 D 3
Tillabery 37 E 7
Tillanchong, Island 33 A 5
Tilmas el-Mra 37 E 4
Tilmas Inedi 37 F 4
Tilos 20 H 9
Timani 24 FG 1-2
Timaru 55 g 14
Timbedra 37 C 6
Timbon 55 a 8
Timbuktu 37 D 6
Timghe, Mt. 37 F 6
Timimoun 37 E 4
Timis 20 F 5
Timisoara 20 E 5
Timmoudi 37 D 4
Timok 20 F 5
Timokhino 23 M 5
Timor Sea 55 D 2
Timor, Island 34 FG 6-7
Timosevskaja 25 E 3
Timpahute Range 46
  C 5
Timsiaouine 37 E 5
Tin, Ras et-, Cape 37 I 3
Tina 41 D 5
Ti-n-Daouine 37 F 6
Ti-n-Didine 37 D 5

Tindouf 37 C 4
Tinef 37 E 5
Tineo 9 C 2
Tin Fouchaye 37 F 4
Ting hsien 31 I 3
Ting hsin 31 F 2
Ting nan 31 I 6
Ting pien 31 H 3
Ting si 31 G 3
Tingri Dzong 31 D 5
Tingsryd 17 F 8
Tinguéré 39 G 4
Tinian, Island 54 E 3
Tinkisso 39 BC 3
Tinn 17 C 6
Tinombo 34 F 4
Tinos 20 G 9
Tinouradj 37 D 4
Tin Rherhoh 37 E 5
Tin Tehoun 37 D 6
Ti-n-Toumma 37 G 6
Tin Zaouaténe 37 E 5
Tipuani 52 D 5
Tiram 27 h 16
Tirana (Tiranë) 21 D 7
Tiraspol' 21 I 4
Tire 21 H 8
Tirebolu 25 E 5
Tirgoviste 21 G 5
Tirgu-Fr 21 H 4
Tirgu-Jiu 21 F 5
Tirgu-Ocna 21 H 4
Tirich Mir 29 F 4
Tiririca 52 I 4
Tiririne 37 F 5
Tiris 35 B 3
Tirljanskij 24 L 7
Tirol 13 DE 5
Tirso 18 B 4
Tiruchendur 30 C 7
Tiruchirappalli 30 D 6
Tirunelveli 30 C 7
Tiruntan 52 C 3
Tiruvannamalai 30 C 6
Tisa 20 E 4-5
Tishibobo, Pt. 40 A 3
Tishit 37 C 6
Tit 37 F 5
Titaf 37 D 4
Titai Damer 38 C 4
Titicaca, Lake 49 D 5
Titograd 21 D 6
Titov-Veles 21 E 7
Titu, Island 26 P 8
Titule 40 D 2
Tivaouane 37 A 7
Tiverton 4 E 6
Tivoli 19 D 3-4
Tizegui 37 B 6
Tizimin 47 G 3
Tizi Ouzou 37 E 2
Tiznit 37 C 4
Tjacev 21 F 3
Tjareme, Mt. 26 I 13
Tjeldöy 17 G 2
Tjidtjack, Mt. 16 G 3
Tjikuraj, Mt. 26 I 13
Tjörn, Island 16 D 8
Tjorro Fjed, Mt. 16 G 3
Tjotta 17 E 4
Tjumen 22 F 4
Tjung 22 MN 3
Tjup-kildi 24 H 7
Tljarata 25 I 4
Tlokh 25 I 4
Tméssa 37 H 4
Tni Haïa 37 D 5
Toamasina 41 C 7
Toau, Island 54 N 6
Toba, Lake 34 A 4
Tobago, Island 51 D 1
Tobermory 4 C 3
Tobi, Island 54 D 4
Toboali 34 C 5
Tobocal 52 E 2
Tobol 1 UV 4-5
Tobol, River 22 F 4
Tobolsk 22 F 4
Tobriand, Island 54 F 5
Tobruk 37 I 3
Tocantinia 52 H 3
Tocatins 52 H 2-4
Toce 18 B 1
Töckfors 17 D 7
Tocopilla 52 C 6
Tocuyo, El- 51 C 2
Tocuyo, Rio 51 C 1
Todi 19 D 3
Tödi, Mt. 12 C 5
Todjo 34 F 5
Todos os Santos, Bay de-
  52 L 4
Todos Santos (Bolivia)
  52 D 5
Todos Santos (Mexico)
  47 B 3
Tofau, Island 54 I 6
Togawa 27 e 13
Toghral Ombo 31 C 3
Togliatti 24 E 8

Togo 36 D 5
Tohen 38 F 5
Tohmajärvi 23 H 3
Tohumbiri 40 B 3
Tok 24 GH 8
Tokala 34 F 5
Tokar 38 C 4
Tokara Islands 32 C 6
Tokat 25 D 5
Tokelau, Island 54 I 5
Tokorozawa 27 d 13
Tokoto 31 I 2
Tokushima 32 D 5
Tokyo 32 E 4
Tokyo, (Bay) 27 de 13
Tola, La- 52 B 1
Tola, (River) 31 H 1
Tolbuhin 21 H 6
Toledo (Spain) 9 D 4
Toledo (USA) 46 L 4
Toledo, Montes de- 8 D 4
.Tol'ka 22 H 3
Toliary 41 b 8
Tolima, Mt. 49 C 3
Tolitoli 34 F 4
Tolmezzo 19 D 1
Tolna 21 D 4
Tolo (Kongo) 40 B 3
Tolo, Gulf of 34 F 5
Tolò, Mt. 38 C 5
Tolosa 9 E 2
Tolox, Sierra de- 8 D 5
Toluca 47 E 4
To Iun 31 L 2
Tom 26 M 4
Tomakomai 32 F 3
Tomar (Brazil) 52 E 2
Tomar (Portugal) 9 B 4
Tomari 22 P 5
Tomaszow Lubelski 13 L 3
Tomaszow Mazowiecki
  13 H-I 3
Tomativi, Mt. 54 H 6
Tombé (Mali) 37 B 7
Tombe (Sudan) 40 E 1
Tombigbee 46 I 6
Tombouctou (Timbuktu)
  37 D 6
Tomea, Island 34 F 6
Tomini, Gulf of 34 F 5
Tomma 17 E 3
Tommot 22 N 4
Tomo 51 C 2
Tomor, Mt. 20 E 7
Tompo 22 O 3
Tomsk 22 H 4
Tomskaja 24 O 5
Tomtaback 17 F 8
Tonala 47 F 4
Tonale 18 C 1
Tonantins 52 D 2
Tönder 17 C 9
Tondibi 37 D 3-4
Tone 27 e 13
Tonga, Island 54 I 6
Tongareva, Island 54 M 5
Tongobory 41 b 8
Tongoy 53 B 3
Tonj 40 D 1
Tonk 30 C 3
Tonkhil 31 E 1
Tonking 33 CD 2
Tonking, Gulf of 26 O 7-8
Tonlé Sap 33 C 4
Tonneins 11 F 4
Tonopah 46 C 5
Tönsberg 17 D 7
Tonstad 17 B 7
Tonto 47 E 4
Toowoomba 55 I 5
Top 1 O 2
Topdals 16 C 7
Topeka 46 G 5
Toplica 20 E 6
Topoj, Mt. 20 F 3
Topoli 25 M 1
Topolovgrad 21 H 6
Toqsun 31 D 2
Torat 38 C 5
Torbali 21 H 8
Torbat-i-Shaikh Jam 29 D 4
Tordesillas 9 D 3
Töre 17 L 4
Torekov 17 E 8
Torell, Land 56 a
Torgau 13 E 9
Torit 40 E 2
Tormes 8 CD 3
Torne 17 IL 3
Tornea 17 M 4
Tornea, River 16 HL 2-3
Tornio 17 M 4
Tornquist 53 D 4
Toro 9 D 3
Toroni, G. of 20 F 7
Toronto 44 P 7
Toropets 23 H 6
Tororo 40 E 2
Torpa 17 D 6
Torquay 4 E 6
Torre de Moncarvo 9 C 3
Torrelavega 9 D 2

Torren 55 F 6
Torreon 47 D 2
Tôrres 52 H 7
Tôrres Novas 9 B 4
Torres Strait 54 E 5
Torres Vedras 9 B 4
Torrevieja 9 F 4
Torrowangee 55 G 6
Torsby 17 E 6
Torsö 17 E 7
Tortona 19 B 2
Tortosa, Cape 8 G 3
Tortue, La-, Island 48 E 2
Tortuga, La-, Island 51 C 1
Torun 16 H 2
Torup 17 E 8
Tory, Island 4 B 4
Torzok 23 L 6
Tosaye 37 D 6
Toscana 19 C 2-3
Tosebai 39 C 4
Tostado 53 D 2
Tosya 25 BC 5
Totana 9 F 5
Toté 39 C 4
Toteng 41 C 3
Totes Gebirge 13 F 5
Tot'ma 24 B 5
Totskoe 24 G 8
Tottenham 55 H 6
Touat 37 DE 4
Touba 39 C 4
Toubkal, Mt. 35 C 2
Toucy 11 G 3
Toufourine 37 D 5
Tougan 39 D 3
Touggour 37 D 3
Tougué 39 B 3
Touil 37 E 2-3
Touila 37 C 4
Toul 11 H 2
Toulépleu 39 C 4
Toulon 11 H 5
Toulouse 11 F 5
Tou men 27 f 15
Toumobi 39 D 4
Toumtouma 37 I 7
Tounasine 37 D 4
Toungoo 33 B 3
Touraine 11 F 3
Tourcoing 11 G 1
Tourinam, Cape 8 B 2
Tournai 15 F 3
Tournon 11 H 4
Touros 52 L 3
Touroua 39 G 4
Tours 11 F 3
Toussidé, Mt. 37 H 5
Tovar 51 B 2
Tovik 17 G 2
Tower 46 H 3
Townsville 55 H 3
Towy 3 DE 6
Toyala 17 L 6
Toyama 32 E 4
Toyohashi 32 E 5
Töysä 17 L 5
Tozeur 37 F 3
Traby 23 E 7
Trabzon 25 E 5
Trafalgar, Cape 9 C 5
Trajanswall 20 I 5
Trakai 17 M 9
Tralee 4 B 5
Tralee Bay 4 B 5
Tranas 17 F 7
Trancoso (Brazil) 52 L 5
Trancoso (Portugal) 9 C 3
Tranemo 17 E 8
Trang 33 B 5
Trangan 34 H 6
Trani 19 F 4
Transcaspia 1 T 7
Transkaukasien 1 QR 7
Transhimalaia 26 MN 6-7
Transvaal 35 F 8
Transylvania 21 FG 4
Transylvanian Alps 20 FH 5
Trapani 19 D 5
Trashi Gompa 31 E 4
Trasimeno, Lake 18 CD 3
Tras os Montes 9 C 3
Trat 33 C 4
Traun 12 F 4
Traunsee 12 E 5
Traversay Island 57 M 4
Tra Vinh 33 D 4
Travnik 21 C 5
Trbovlje 21 B 4
Trebbia 18 B 2
Trebinje 21 D 6
Treguier 11 D 2
Trehörningsjö 17 H 5
Treinta y Tres 53 F 3
Trelleborg 17 E 9
Tremadoc Bay 12 D 5
Tremblade, La- 11 E 4
Tremiti Islands 18 E 3
Tremp 9 G 2
Trenque Lauquen 53 D 4
Trent 3 F 5
Trentino-Alto Adige 19 C 1-2
Trento 19 C 1
Trenton 46 O 4
Trepassey 44 U 6
Tréport, Le- 11 F 1
Tres Arroyos 53 D 4
Três Casas 52 E 3
Tres Cerros 53 C 6
Três Coraçoes 52 H 6
Três Irmaos, Pt. 52 L 3
Treska, River 20 E 7
Treskavica, Mt. 21 D 6
Tres Lagoas 52 G 6
Tres Marias, Islands 47 C 3
Tres Montes, Cape 53 A 6
Três Pontas, Cape das- 40 A 5
Tres Puntas, Cape 53 C 6
Tres Virgines, Las-, Mt. 47 B 2
Treviglio 19 BC 2
Treviso 19 D 2
Tricarico 19 EF 4
Tricase 19 G 5
Trichur 30 D 6
Trier 13 B 4
Trieste 19 DE 2
Triest, G. of 18 D 2
Triglav 20 AB 4
Trigno 18 E 3-4
Trigueros 9 C 5
Trillo 9 E 3
Trim 4 C 5
Trincomalee 30 D 7
Trinidad (Bolivia) 52 E 4
Trinidad (Colombia) 51 B 2
Trinidad (Cuba) 48 C 2
Trinidad (USA) 46 F 5
Trinidad, Island (Argentina) 53 D 4
Trinidade, Island 49 H 6
Trinidad and Tobago 51 D 1
Trinity 46 G 6
Trinity, Island 45 H 5
Trino 19 AB 2
Trionto, Cape 18 F 5
Tripoli (Lebanon) 28 C 3
Tripoli (Libya) 37 G 3
Tripolis (Greece) 21 F 9
Tripolitania 37 GH 3-4
Tripura 27 b 11
Tristan da Cunha, Island 36 BC 9
Triunfo 52 C 2
Trivandrum 30 C 7
Trjavna 20 G 6
Trnava 21 C 3
Trœstö 17 DE 9
Trogir 21 C 6
Troglav, Mt. 20 C 6
Trois Rivieres 44 Q 6
Troitsk 23 O 3
Troitskoe 32 E 2
Troitsk 22 F 4
Troitsko Pecorsk 22 E 3
Trojan 21 G 6
Trölla dyngja, Mt. 17 T 12
Trollhättan 17 E 7
Trollheim, Mt. 16 C 5
Trombetas, River 52 F 1-2
Tromda 31 E 5
Tromsö 17 H 2
Tronador, Mt. 53 B 5
Trondheim 17 D 5
Trondheim, Fj. 16 D 5
Tronto 19 E 3
Troodos, Mt. 1 O 9
Tropea 19 E 5
Trosa 17 G 7
Trostan, Mt. 12 C 4
Trouville 11 F 2
Trowbridge 4 E 6
Troy (Turkey) 21 H 8
Troy (USA, Alabama) 46 I 6
Troy (USA, New York) 46 N 4
Troyes 11 H 2
Trubcevsk 23 I 8
Truchas, M. 46 E 5
Trudy, River 23 M 8
Trujillo (Honduras) 47 G 4
Trujillo (Peru) 52 B 3
Trujillo (Spain) 9 D 4
Trujillo (Venezuela) 51 B 2
Truk, Island 54 F 4
Truro 44 S 6
Truyère 10 G 4
Trysil 17 E 6
Trysil, River 16 D 6
Trysil, Mt. 16 E 6
Tsagan Olom 31 F 1
Tsagan Sanji 31 E 2
Tsaidam 31 EF 3
Tsambur 26 p 17
Tsang hsien 31 L 3
Tsang men 27 F 15
Tsangpo 26 M 7
Tsang wu (Wu chow) 31 I 6
Tsaobis 41 B 3
Tsaratanana 41 c 6
Tsatsein 31 E 1
Tsau 41 C 3
Tsavo 40 F 3
Tschebon 6 I 3
Tschela 40 A 3
Tsehleh (China) 31 C 3
Tse inograd 22 G 4
Tserseg 31 E 1
Tsessebe 41 D 3
Tsetserlig 31 G 1
Tshangola 40 D 5
Tshikapa 40 C 4
Tshinsenda 40 D 5
Tshofa 40 D 4
Tshopo 40 D 2
Tshuapa 40 C 3
Tsigara 41 D 3
Tsihombe 41 c 9
Tsilma 24 EF 2
Tsimljansk Res. 25 G 1-2
Tsing hsien 31 H 5
Tsinguédi 40 A 3
Tsipikan 22 M 4
Tsiribihina 41 b 7
Tsitsihar (Lungkiang) 31 M 1
Tsivilsk 24 D 7
Tsjurupinsk 25 B 2
Tsna, River 23 IL 6
Tsodornaya 31 O 2
Tsokang 31 L 1
Tsu 32 E 5
Tsugaru Strait 32 F 3
Tsula Dzong 31 E 5
Tsumeb 41 B 2
Tsumerka, Mt. 20 E 8
Tsuni 31 H 5
Tsuruga 32 E 4
Tsuruoka 32 E 4
Tsushima 32 C 5
Tsuyama 32 D 4
Tsu yung 31 G 5-6
Tua 8 C 3
Tual, Island 34 H 6
Tuam 4 B 5
Tuamotu (Paumotu), Island 54 NO 6-7
Tuapse 25 E 3
Tuban 34 D 6
Tubarao 52 H 7
Tübingen 13 C 4
Tubuai, Island 54 MN 7
Tubuai Manu, Island 54 M 6
Tucabaca 52 F 5
Tucacas 51 C 1
Tucavaca 52 F 5
Tu chüan 31 M 1
Tucson 46 D 6
Tucuman 53 C 2
Tucupita 51 D 2
Tudela 9 F 2
Tudela de Duero 9 D 3
Tug Der 38 E 6
Tuggurt 37 F 3
Tuguegarao 34 F 1
Tugur 22 O 4
Tugurig Somon 31 G 1
Tuilianpuri 27 c 11
Tuito, El- 47 C 3
Tukaiyia 28 H 6
Tukangbesi, Island 34 F 6
Tukums 17 L 8
Tula (Mexico) 47 E 3
Tula (Soviet Union) 23 M 7
Tulan 31 F 3
Tulare 46 B 5
Tulbagh 41 B 5
Tulcan 52 B 1
Tulcea 21 I 5
Tuleh 28 L 4
Tuli 41 D 3
Tuli, River 41 D 3
Tulivara 23 H 3
Tullamore 4 C 5
Tulle 11 F 4
Tulli 38 D 6
Tulnici 21 H 5
Tuloma 1 NO 2
Tulovo 21 G 6
Tulpau 24 I 4
Tulsa 46 G 5
Tulua 51 A 3
Tulun 22 L 4
Tulungagun 34 D 6
Tulymskij Kamen, Mt. 24 L 4
Tumaco 51 A 3
Tumany 22 Q 3
Tumba 40 C 3
Tumca 23 H 1
Tumen 31 N 2
Tumkur 30 C 6
Tummo, Mt 37 G 5
Tumnin, River 32 F 1-2
Tumu 39 D 3
Tumut 55 H 7
Tumutuk 24 G 7
Tun 29 C 5
Tundubai 37 L 6
Tundza 20 H 6
Tung 31 IL 6
Tungbhadra 30 C 5
Tungan 31 O 1
Tung chiang 32 D 2
Tung hsing 31 H 6
Tung hua 31 N 2
Tung huan 31 E 2
Tungie 39 B 4
Tung jen 31 H 5
Tung kuan (Kuang tung) 27 f 14
Tung kuan (Shen hsi) 31 I 4
Tung lan 31 H 6
Tung liao 31 M 2
Tung ping 31 L 3
Tung pu 31 F 4
Tung shan 31 L 4
Tung tai 31 M 4
Tung te 31 G 4
Tung Ting Hu 31 I 5
Tunguska, Lower 22 I 3
Tunguska, Stony 22 IL 3-4
Tur hu 31 I 3
Turis 37 G 2
Turis, Gulf of 18 C 6
Turesia 36 DE 2
Turja 51 B 2
Türsk 24 E 7
Tunuyan 53 C 3
Tuo 26 p 17
Tupelo 46 I 6
Tupinambarana 52 F 2
Tuque, La- 44 Q 6
Tur 20 F 3-4
Tura (India) 30 F 3
Tura (Soviet Union) 22 L 3
Tura, River 1 UV 4
Turaba 38 D 3
Turakh 27 Q 2
Turan 26 HI 5
Turano 18 D 3
Turarà 52 C 2
Turbat 29 D 6
Turbo 51 A 2
Turchino, Pass 18 B 2
Turda 21 F 4
Tureia, Island 54 O 7
Turek 13 H 2-3
Turfan 31 D 2
Turfan Depression 26 N 5
Turgai Senke 29 CD 1
Turgais 1 UV 5-6
Turgaj 22 F 5
Turgart, Pass 26 L 5
Turgun Ula, Mt. 31 E 1
Turgutlu 21 H 8
Turia 8 F 4
Turiaçu 52 H 2
Turiaçu, Bay do- 52 H 2
Turiaçu, Rio 52 H 2
Turija 20 G 2
Turin 19 AB 2
Turinsk 24 N 5
Tur'ja 24 F 3
Turkana, Lake 40 F 2
Turkestan 22 F 5
Turkestan, East 26 LM 5-6
Turkestan, West 29 BE 3-4
Turkey 2 NQ 7-8
Turkmänchai 28 I 2
Turkmenistan 22 EF 5-6
Turks, Island 48 E 2
Turku (Finland) 17 L 6
Turku (Mongolia) 31 G 1
Turku-Pori 17 L 6
Turneffe Island 47 G 4
Turnhout 15 G 3
Turnu Magurele 21 G 6
Turr 38 D 6
Turriff 4 E 3
Turrington 46 F 4
Tursi 19 F 4
Turtkul 29 D 3
Turtola 17 M 3
Turukhansk 22 H 3
Turut 29 C 4
Tuscaloosa 46 I 6
Tuscan Archipelago 18 BC 3
Tu shan 31 H 5
Tustna 17 C 5
Tutaev 23 N 6
Tuticorin 30 C 7
Tutoia 52 I 2
Tutrakan 21 H 5
Tuttlingen 13 C 5
Tutuila, Island 54 I 6
Tutunlu 25 G 5
Tuy Hoa 33 D 4
Tuva 27 N 4
Tuxpan 47 E 3
Tuxtla Gutiérrez 47 F 4
Tuy 9 B 2
Tu yün 71 H 5
Tuz, L. 25 B 6
Tuza 24 D 6
Tuz Khurmatli 28 H 3
Tuzla 21 D 5
Tuzlu 25 B 6
Tuzly 21 L 5
Tvedestrand 17 C 7
Tveitsund 17 C 7
Tweed 3 E 4
Twin Falls 46 D 4
Tydal 17 D 5
Tyland 17 C 8
Tymfristos, Mt. 20 E 8
Tymsk 22 H 4
Tyndinskij 22 N 4
Tyrä 17 C 4
Tyree, Island 3 C 3
Tyri, Fj. 17 D 6
Tyrka 22 L 4
Tyrma 32 D 1-2
Tyrrel 55 G 7
Tyrrhenian Sea 18 BE 3-5
Tys, fj. 17 G 2
Tyui 24 I 6-7
Tzuchien 31 F 5
Tzukung (Tingyanying) 31 H 3
Tzu Kao, Mt 31 M 6
Tzu yang 31 L 3

U

Uadai 35 EF 4
Ua Huka, Island 54 O 5
Uan hsien 31 H 3
Uapu, Island 54 N 5
Uargla 37 F 3
Uarini 52 D 2
Uaso Niyro 40 FG 2
Uatuma 52 F 2
Uau 40 D 1
Uaupes, Rio 49 D 3
Uba (Brazil) 52 I 6
Uba (Nigeria) 39 G 3
Ubait 28 E 6
Ubaitaba 52 L 4
Ubaiyidh, U. al- 38 D 1
Ubal 38 D 4
Ubanghi, Mts. 35 EF 5
Ubanghi, River 35 E 5
Ubangi 40 B 2
Ubari 37 G 4
Ubeda 9 E 4
Uberaba 52 H 5
Uberlândia 52 H 5
Ubombo 41 E 4
Ubort' 21 H 2
Ubort, River 20 HI 2
Ubricehamn 17 E 8
Ubsa Nur 31 E 1
Ubundu 40 D 3
Ucayali 52 C 3
Uchab 41 B 2
Uchiza 52 B 3
Uch Turfan (Wushih) 31 B 2
Ucur 22 O 4
Uda, (Irkutsk) 22 LM 4
Uda, (Khabarovsk) 22 O 4
Udaipur 30 B 4
Uddevalla 17 D 7
Udipi 30 B 6
Ud Jaure 16 H 4
Udjunglamura 34 E 5
Udomlja 23 L 6
Udon Thani 33 C 3
Uea, Island 54 I 6
Uebi 38 D 6-7
Ueda 32 E 4
Uele 40 C 2
Uelen 22 TU 3
Ufa 22 E 4
Ufa 24 HI 6-8
Ufipa 40 E 4
Ugalla 35 G 6
Uganda 36 G 5-6
Ugashih 45 G 5
Uglegorsk 22 P 5
Uglic 23 N 6
Ugogo 40 F 4
Ugra 23 IM 7
Uhehe 40 F 4
Uige 40 B 4
Uil 22 E 5
Uil, River 1 ST 6
Uinskoe 24 I 6
Uist, North- 3 C 3
Uist, South- 3 C 3
Uitenhage 41 D 5
Uj 1 U 5
Ujiain 30 C 4
Ujiji 40 D 3
Uji Yamada 32 E 5
Ujung Pandang (Makassar) 34 E 6
Ujung Pandang, Strait of 34 E 4-5
Uka 22 R 4
Ukak 45 G 5
Ukamas 41 B
Ukamba 35 G 6
Ukhta (Karelien) 23 H 2
Ukhta (Komi) 22 E 3
Ukhtozersk 23 M 4
Ukmerge 17 M 9
Ukonongo 40 E 4
Ukraine 21 GH 2
Ulan 31 E 4
Ulan Bator 31 H 1
Ulan Chonchi 31 G 2
Ulan Goom 31 E 1
Ulan hoto 31 M 1
Ulan Khusu 31 D 1
Ulan Pass 31 D 1
Ulan Ude 22 L 4
Ulas 25 D 6
Ulbagan 1 U 5
Uldza 31 I 1
Uldza, River 31 IL 1
Uleia 40 E 4
Ulety 22 M 4
Ulgei 31 D 1
Uliassulai 31 F 1
Ulindi 40 D 3
Ulithi, Island 54 E 4
Ulla 23 G 7
Ulla, (Spain) 9 B 2
Ulla (Soviet Union) 23 G 7
Ullared 17 E 8
Ullap 4 D 3
Ulldecona 9 G 3
Ullung Do, Island 32 D 4
Ulm 13 CD 4
Ulmer, Mt. 57 P 2
Ulnes 17 C 6
Ulovo 27 T 2
Ulöy 17 I 2
Ulsan 31 N 3
Ulsberg 17 C 5
Ulster 4 BC 4
Ulster Channel 3 C 4
Ulubua 52 D 3
Ulug Muztagh, Mt. 31 D 3
Uluguru 40 F 4
Ulutau 29 E 2
Ulva 17 DE 6
Ulvöar 17 H 5
Ulyanovsk (Simbirsk) 24 E 7
Ulyungur Nor 31 D 1
Uman' 25 A 1
Umanak 44 U 1
Umanak, Fj. 44 U 1
Umbegogo 40 D 1
Umboi, Island 26 o 14
Umbria 19 D 3
Ume 16 H 4
Umea 17 I 5
Umgwasena 41 D 2
Umiat 45 H 3
Umma 28 H 5
Umm Bel 37 L 7
Umm el-Abid 37 H 4
Umm Habila 37 L 7
Umm Ishram 38 B 5
Umm Kaddada 37 M 8
Umm Keddada 37 L 7
Umm Lajj 38 C 2
Umm Qasr 28 I 6
Umm Ruwaba 37 M 7
Umm Saneita 37 L 6
Umnak, Island 22 U 4
Umtata 41 D 5
Umvuma 41 E 2
Una 52 L 5
Una, River 20 C 5
Unac 20 C 5
Unalakleet 45 F 4
Unalaska 22 U 4
Unango 40 F 5
Unari 32 F 2
Unari 17 M 3
Uncia 52 D 5
Undi 40 F 5
Undory 24 E 7
Undredal 17 B 6
Undur Khan 31 I 1
Uneca 23 I 8
Ungava Pen. 44 PQ 3
Ungava Bay 44 R 4
Unggi 31 O 2
Ungoni 40 EF 5
Uniao 52 I 2
Uniao da Vitoria 52 G 7
Unije 20 B 5
Uniket 31 L 1
Unimak 45 F 6
Unini, Rio 52 E 2
Union, La- (El Salvador) 47 G 5
Union, La- (Spain) 9 F 5
Union, La- (Venezuela) 48 F 5
Uniondale 41 C 5
United Arab Emirates 27 H 7
United States 43 HM 6
Unst, Island 3 F 1
Unstrut 12 D 3
Unyamwezi 35 G 6
Unye 25 D 5
Unza 24 BC 5
Unza, River 24 BC 5-6
Upa 23 M 8
Upanda, Mt. 40 B 5
Upemba, Lake 40 D 4
Upernavik 43 PQ 2
Upington 36 F 8
Uplands, Southern- 3 DE 4
Upolu, Island 54 I 6
Upper Palatinate 12 DE 4
Upper Seal Lake 44 Q 4
Uppland 17 G 6-7
Uppsala 17 G 7
Uqsor, El- 37 M 4
Ur 28 I 5
Uracoa 51 D 2
Uraga 27 d 13
Uraga, Strait 27 d 13
Urakawa 32 F 3
Ural 1 ST 5-6
Ural Mountains 22 EF 3-4
Ural, Middle 24 LM 4-6
Ural, South 24 IL 7-9
Ural, North 24 LO 13
Urali Selvosi, Mt. 1 TU 4-5
Uralsk 22 E 4
Urandangi 55 F 4
Urandi 52 I 4
Uranium City 43 I 4
Uraricoera 51 D 3
Ura Tyube 29 E 4
Urawa 27 d 13

Urazovo 25 E 1
Urbana, La- 51 C 2
Urbino 19 D 3
Urbion, Sierra de- 8 E 2
Urda 25 I 1
Urdzar 22 H 5
Ure 3 F 4
Urfa 28 D 2
Urga 29 C 3
Urga (Ulan Bator) 31 H 1
Urgenc 22 F 5
Uri 18 B 1
Uribia 51 B 1
Urjala 17 L 6
Urla 21 H 8
Urmia, 1 R 8
Urmia, Lake 1 R 8
Urotsk 24 H 5
Urti Vaara, Mt. 17 L 2
Uru 35 F 6
Uruapan 47 D 4
Urubamba 52 C 4
Urubicha 52 E 5
Urucara 52 F 2
Urucui 52 I 3
Urucuic 52 H 4
Uruguaiana 52 F 7
Uruguay 50 E 7
Uruguay, Rio 49 E 6-7
Urumchi (Ti hua) 31 D 2
Urungu 31 D 1
Urup, Island 22 Q 5
Uruwira 40 E 4
Urville, Cape 54 D 5
Urville, Island 55 g 14
Urziceni 21 H 5
Urzum 24 F 6
Usa 22 EF 3
Usadisce 23 I 5
Usagara 40 F 4
Usakos 41 B 3
Usakova, Island 22 G 1
Usangu 40 E 4
Ushirombo 40 E 3
Ushnuiyeh 28 H 2
Ushuaia 53 C 7
Usk 3 E 6
Usküdar 21 I 7
Usole 24 I 5
Uspenka 25 E 1
Ussel 11 G 4
Ussuri 31 O 1-2
Ussuriysk 27 R 5
Usta 24 CD 6
Ust'Aldan 22 N 3
Ust'Caun 22 S 3
Ust'Bol'seretsk 22 Q 4
Usti 13 F 3
Ustica 18 D 5
Ustica, Island 18 D 5
Ust'Ilimpeja 22 L 3
Ust'ja 24 BC 4
Ust'Judoma 22 O 4
Ustjuzna 23 M 5
Ustka 13 G 1
Ust'-Kamchatsk 22 R 4
Ust'Kamenog 22 H 4-5
Ust'-Kulom 24 G 4
Ust'-Lyza 24 I 2
Ust'Maya 22 O 3
Ust'Mil 22 O 4
Ust'Nera 22 P 3
Ust'-Padenga 24 B 4
Ust'Pit 22 I 4
Ustrem 24 O 2
Ust'Talaja 22 M 4
Ust'Tapsuj 24 M 3
Ust Tsilma 22 E 3
Ust Tungir 22 N 4
Ust'Uda 22 L 4
Ust'-Ujskoe 24 N 7
Ust-Un'ja 24 I 4
Ust-Usa 24 I 2
Ust-Vaga 24 B 3
Ust-Voja 24 I 2
Ustyurt 29 CD 4
Usumacinta 47 F 4
Usva 24 IL 5
Usvjaly 23 H 7
Utah 46 D 5
Utara 34 B 5
Utena 23 E 7
Utenhage 36 F 9
Utete 40 F 4
Utiariti 52 F 4
Utica 46 M 4
Utiel 9 F 4
Utinga 52 I 4
Utö, Island 17 H 7
Utrecht 15 G 2-3
Utrera 9 D 5
Utsjoki 17 N 2
Utsonomiya 32 E 4
Uttaradit 33 C 3
Uukuniemi 23 G 4
Uurainen 17 M 5
Uusikaupunki 17 I 6
Uusimaa 17 M 6
Uvac 20 D 6
Uvaly 24 FG 4-5
Uvea, Island 54 G 7
Uvira 40 D 3
Uyedineniye Island 22 H 2
Uyo 39 F 4
Uyuni 52 D 6
Uyuni, Salar de- 52 D 6

Uz 21 IL 2
Uzaramo 40 F 4
Uzbekistan 22 F 5-6
Uzen 1 R 5-6
Uzerche 11 F 4
Uzgorod 21 F 3
Uzigua 40 F 4
Uzok 21 F 3
Uzunköprü 21 H 7
Uzur 22 Hl 4
Uzventis 17 L 9

V

Vaal 35 F 8
Vaala 16 N 4
Vaalwater 41 D 3
Vaasa 17 I 5
Vac 21 D 4
Väddö 17 H 6
Vadso 2 N 1
Vaduz 19 B 1
Vaegi 22 S 3
Vaeröy 16 E 3
Vaga 17 C 6
Vaga, River 24 B 3-4
Vagavatn, River 16 C 6
Vagö 3 a
Vagsöy 16 A 5
Vaidava 23 F 6
Vaigac 22 EF 2-3
Vaigat 44 U 1
Vaika 40 D 3
Vailapu, Island 54 H 5
Vainode 17 I 8
Vairaalea, Island 54 N 6
Vakh 22 GH 3
Valaam, Island 23 H 4
Valadares, Governador- 52 I 5
Valcheta 53 C 5
Valdai 23 I 6
Valdaj, Mt. 23 I 5-6
Valdemarsvik 17 G 7
Valdepenas 9 E 4
Valderas 9 D 2
Valdeverdeja 9 D 4
Valdez 45 I 4
Valdés, Pen 53 D 5
Valdivia 53 B 4
Valdosta 46 L 6
Vale 46 C 4
Valenc 11 G 1
Valença (Brazil) 52 L 4
Valença (Portugal) 9 B 3
Valença do Piaui 52 I 3
Valençay 11 F 3
Valence 11 H 4
Valencia (Spain) 9 F 4
Valencia, Gulf of 8 F 4
Valencia (Venezuela) 51 C 1
Valencia, Island 4 A 6
Valencia de Alcan 9 C 4
Valencia de Don Juan 9 D 2
Valentin 31 O 2
Valentine 46 F 4
Valenza, Prov. 9 FG 3-2
Valga 23 F 6
Valjevo 21 D 6
Valka 17 N 8
Valki 25 C 1
Valladolid (Mexico) 47 G 3
Valladolid (Spain) 9 D 3
Valle, Rio del- 53 D 1
Valle d'Aosta 19 A 2
Valle de la Pascua 51 C 2
Valledupar 51 B 1
Vallenar 53 B 2
Valles 47 E 3
Valletta 19 D 7
Vallgrund, Island 16 I 5
Valls 9 G 3
Valmiera 17 M 8
Valnera, Mt. 8 E 2
Valparaiso 53 B 3
Valsey, Island 3 F 1
Valsjö 17 F 4
Valtimo 23 G 3
Valverde 37 A 4
Valverde del Camino 9 C 5
Van 2 Q 8
Van, Lake 26 G 6
Vanajan 16 M 6
Vanavara 22 L 3
Vancouver 44 E 6
Vancouver, Island 44 D 6
Vandea 10 E 3
Van Diemen Gulf 55 E 2
Vandys 23 O 4
Vänern, Lake 16 E 7
Vang 17 C 6
Vanga 40 F 3
Vangaindrano 41 c 8
Vangel 17 FG 5
Vänjaurträsk 17 H 4
Vännäs 17 H 5
Vannes 11 D 3
Vannöy, Island 16 H 1
Vansittart 44 O 2
Vanua Levu, Island 54 H 6
Vanwyksvlei 41 C 5
Vanylvs, Fj. 17 A 5

Vaqra 38 F 2
Var, Fj. 16 L 1
Vara 18 B 2
Varanasi 30 D 3
Varanger Fj 1 N 1-2
Varanger Pen. 17 O 1
Varano, L. di- 19 EF 3-4
Varazdin 21 C 4
Varberg 17 E 8
Vardar 20 F 7
Varde 17 C 9
Varde, River 16 C 9
Vardousia, Mt. 20 EF 8
Varella, Cape 26 O 8
Vares 21 D 5
Varese 21 N B 2
Varginha 52 H 6
Varkaus 23 F 3
Varmland 17 E 6-7
Varna 21 H 6
Värnamo 17 F 8
Varnavino 24 C 5
Varnja 23 F 5
Varto 25 H 3
Vartsilä 23 H 3
Varzuga, Town 23 M 1
Varzuga, River 23 M 1
Vasa 17 I 5
Vash Shahri 31 D 3
Vasht 29 D 6
Vasilevka 24 G 8
Vasil'kov 21 L 2
Vasil'sursk 24 CD 6
Vaska 24 DE 2-3
Vaski 23 N 4
Vasko 16 MN 2
Vaslui 21 H 4
Vassdals egg, Mt. 17 B 7
Vassouras 52 I 6
Västeras 17 G 7
Västerbotten 17 FH 4
Västerdal 16 EG 6
Vasternorrland 17 G 5
Västervik 17 G 8
Västmanland 17 G 6-7
Vasto 19 E 3
Vastra 17 E 7
Vastra Ed 17 G 7
Vatan 11 F 3
Vatersay, Island 4 C 3
Vatican City 19 E 4
Vaticano, Cape 19 E 5
Vatna Jökull, Mt. 17 T 12
Vatneyri 17 Q 12
Vatomandry 41 c 7
Vatra-Dornei 21 G 4
Vättern, Lake 16 F 7
Vatyna 22 S 3
Vauz 28 L 3
Vavau, Island 54 I 6
Vavitu, Island 54 N 7
Vavoz 24 F 6
Vaxholm 17 H 7
Väwjö 17 F 8
Vaxna 16 F 6
Vazgort 24 D 2-3
Vazin 23 I 4
Vechte 14 GH 2
Vedea 20 G 5-6
Veendam 15 H 2
Vega, La- 48 E 3
Vega, Island 16 D 4
Vegas, Las- (Nevada) 46 D 5
Vegas, Las- (New Mexico) 46 E 5
Vegoritis, Lake 20 EF 7
Veinticinco de Majo 53 D 4
Velcome, Pt. 56 a
Vel'e 23 G 7
Velebit 20 B 5
Velez 51 B 2
Vélez de Benaudalla 9 E 5
Vélez Malaga 9 D 5
Velfjord 17 E 4
Velika 20 H 6
Velikaj 24 E 5
Velikaja-Guba 23 L 3
Velikiye Luki 23 H 6
Velikij-Ustjug 24 D 4
Velingara 37 B 7
Velino 18 D 3
Veliz 23 H 7
Velle 17 C 9
Velletri 19 D 4
Vellur 30 C 6
Velnas, Rio das- 52 I 5
Vel'sk 24 B 4
Venado 47 D 3
Venda 41 D E 3
Vendôme 11 F 3
Vendyssel 17 C 8
Veneto 18 CD 2
Venëv 23 N 7
Venezuela 50 D 3
Venezuela, Cordillera del- 49 D 3
Venezuela, Gulf of 51 B 1
Vengsöy, Island 17 H 2
Vengurla 30 B 5
Venice 19 D 2
Venice, G. of 18 D 2
Venosta 19 C 1
Venta 16 I 8
Ventimiglia 19 AB 3

Ventoux 10 H 4
Ventspils 23 C 6
Venturi 51 C 3
Vera 9 F 5
Vera, La- 9 D 3
Veracruz 47 E 4
Veramin 28 M 3
Veravalo 30 B 4
Verbania 19 B 1-2
Verbicaro 19 E 5
Vercelli 19 AB 2
Verde, Cape 35 B 4
Verde, Rio 52 G 5
Verdina 23 I 7
Verdinho 52 G 5
Verdon 10 I 5
Verdun 11 H 2
Vereeniging 41 D 4
Vereja 23 M 7
Verescagino 22 H 3
Verga, Cape 39 B 3
Vergara 9 E 2
Verghereto, Ps. 18 D 3
Verin 9 C 3
Verkh-Kigi 24 L 7
Verkhne Imbatskoe 22 H 3
Verkhne-Ural'sk 24 L 8
Verkhnjaja Lata 25 F 4
Verkhojansk 22 O 3
Verkhoyansk Ranger 22 NO 3
Verkhopuja 23 O 4
Verkhoture 24 M 5
Verkh Palenga 24 B 2
Verkh Tojma 24 C 3
Verkola 24 C 3
Vermont 46 N 4
Verneuil 11 F 2
Vernon 46 G 6
Verona 19 C 2
Versailles 11 G 2
Vertus 11 H 2
Verviers 15 G 3
Vervins 11 G 2
Ves'egonsk 23 M 5
Veseli 21 B 3
Veselinovo 25 A 2
Vesëlye Terny 25 B 1
Veskaima 24 D 7
Vesle 10 GH 2
Vesljana 24 F 3
Vesoul 11 I 3
Vessigebro 17 E 8
Vest, Fj. 16 EF 2-3
Vest Agder 17 B 7
Vesteralen 16 F 2
Vestfold 17 M 7
Vestmannaeyjar, Island 17 R 13
Vest-Vagöy 16 E 2
Vesuvius 18 E 4
Veszprém 21 C 4
Vetka 23 H 8
Vetlanda 17 F 8
Vetljanka 25 I 2
Vetluga 24 C 6
Vetluga, Island 24 CD 5-6
Vetren 21 F 6
Vettore 18 D 3
Veurne 15 F 3
Vevey 19 A 1
Veymont, Grand-, Mt. 11 H 4
Veynes 11 H 4
Vezen, Mt. 20 G 6
Vézère, River 10 F 4
Vezirköprü 25 K 5
Viacha 52 C 4
Viadana (Congo) 40 C 2
Viadana (Italy) 19 C 2
Viana do Alentejo 9 B 4
Viana do Castelo 9 B 3
Vianna 52 I 2
Viareggio 19 BC 3
Vibo Valentia 19 F 5
Vic-en-Bigorre 11 F 5
Vicenza 19 C 2
Vich 9 H 3
Vichada 51 BC 3
Vichy 11 G 3
Vicksburg 46 H 6
Viçosa do Ceara 52 I 2
Victor Harbour 55 F 7
Victoria (Argentina) 53 D 3
Victoria (Cameroon) 39 F 5
Victoria (Chile) 53 B 4
Victoria (Guinea) 39 B 2
Victoria (Hong Kong) 31 I 6
Victoria Falls 41 D 2
Victoria, Lake 40 E 3
Victoria, Mt. 34 E 3
Victoria Nile 40 E 3
Victoria, River 55 E 3
Victoria, Great Desert 55 CD 5
Victoria, Mt. 55 H 1
Victoria, State 55 GH 7
Victoria Peak, Mt. 44 D 5
Victoria River Downs 55 E 3
Victorino 51 C 3
Viderö, Island 3 a
Vidin 21 F 5

Vidlitsa 23 I 4
Vie 11 E 3
Viedma, L. 53 D 5
Viedma 53 B 6
Vieira 9 B 4
Viella 9 G 3
Vienna 13 G 4
Vienne 11 H 4
Vienne, River 10 F 3
Vientiane 33 C 3
Vientos, Los- 53 C 1
Vierfontein 41 D 4
Vierzon-Vile 11 G 3
Vieste 19 F 4
Vigan 34 F 1
Vigan, Le- 11 G 4
Vigia 52 H 2
Vigo 9 B 4
Vigo, Ria de- 8 B 2
Vihanti 17 M 4
Vihren, Mt. 20 F 7
Vijayavada 30 D 5
Vik (Norway) 17 F 2
Vik (Sogn og Fiordane) 17 B 6
Vikna 16 D 4
Vila Armindo Monteiro 34 A 3
Vila Bittencourt 52 D 2
Vila Cabral 36 G 7
Vila das Lagens 37 a
Vila de Sena 41 E 2
Vila do Porto 37 a
Vila Fontes 41 F 2
Vila Machado 4 E 2
Vila Murtinho 52 D 4
Vilanculos 41 E 3
Vila Nova de Gaia 9 B 3
Vila Nova de Malaca 34 G 6
Vila Paiva de Andrada 41 E 2
Vila Pery 41 E 2
Vila Real 9 C 3
Vila Salazar Timor, Island 34 G 6
Vila Vasco da Gama 41 E 1
Vila Velha 9 C 4
Vilcanota, Mt. 52 C 4
Viled 24 DE 4
Vilejka 23 F 7
Vil'gort 24 I 4
Viliga 22 Q 3
Vilija 23 EF 7
Viljandi 17 M 7
Viljui 22 MN 3
Viljui, Mt. 22 M 3
Vilkelmina 17 G 4
Vilkovo 21 I 5
Villa Baleira 37 A 3
Villa Castelli 53 C 2
Villacidro 19 B 5
Villa Cisneros 37 A 5
Villach 13 E 5
Villa del Salvador 53 C 3
Villadiego 9 D 2
Villa Dolores 53 C 3
Villafranca 9 F 2
Villafranca del Bierzo 9 C 4
Villafranca de Los Barros 9 C 4
Villagarcia 9 B 2
Villaguay 53 E 3
Villa Hayes 52 F 6
Villahermosa 47 F 4
Villa Huidobro 53 D 3
Villajoyosa 9 F 4
Villalpando 9 D 3
Villa Maria 53 D 3
Villa Montes 52 E 6
Villanueva de Cordova 9 D 4
Villanueva de la Serena 9 D 4
Villanueva y Geltru 9 G 3
Villaputzu 19 BC 5
Villarcayo 9 E 2
Villareal 9 F 4
Villarrica 52 F 7
Villarrobledo 9 E 4
Villarrubia 9 E 4
Villars 11 H 3
Villa Teixeira da Silva 40 B 5
Villavicencio 51 B 3
Villaviciosa 9 D 2
Villefranche 11 H 4
Villefranche 11 F 5
Villegas, General- 53 D 3
Villena 9 F 4
Villeurbanne 11 H 4
Villingen 13 C 4
Villoresi, Canal 18 B 2
Vilnius 23 E 7
Vilos, Los- 53 B 3
Vils 12 E 4
Vilshofen 13 E 4
Vilyuisk 22 N 3
Vimmerby 17 F 8
Vina del Mar 53 B 3
Vinalapo 8 F 4
Vinaroz 9 G 3
Vincennes 46 I 5

Vincennes Bay 57 d 3
Vinchiaturo, Pass 18 E 4
Vinkovci 21 D 5
Vindava 17 I 8
Vindel 16 H 4
Vindhya Mountains 26 L 7
Vinh 33 D 3
Vinnitza 21 I 3
Vintjärn 17 G 6
Vinuesa 9 E 3
Virac 34 F 2
Viramgam 30 B 4
Viransehir 28 E 2
Vire 11 E 2
Vire, River 11 E 2
Virgen, Serra de la 9 F 3
Virgenes C. 53 C 7
Virgin Island 48 G 3
Virginia 41 D 4
Virginia, State 46 LM 5
Virovitica 21 C 5
Virserum 17 F 8
Virtaniemi 16 O 2
Virtasalmi 23 F 3
Virtus 17 L 7
Viru 52 B 3
Viryuga 24 C 2
Vis 20 BC 6
Visby 17 H 8
Visegrad 21 D 6
Visentin, Col- 18 D 1
Visera 24 IL 4
Viseu 52 H 2
Vishakhapatnam 30 D 5
Visimo-Utkinsk 24 L 6
Viskan 16 E 8
Vislanda 17 F 8
Visoko 21 D 5
Vista 17 I 4
Vista Alegre 51 C 3
Vistula 12 M 2-3
Visunsk 25 B 2
Vit 20 G 6
Vitberg, Mt. 16 I 4
Vitebsk 23 H 7
Viterbo 19 D 3
Viti, Island 54 H 6
Vitiaz, Strait 26 o 14
Vitichi 52 D 6
Vitigudino 9 C 3
Viti Levu, Island 54 H 6
Vitim 22 M 4
Vitim, River 22 M 4
Vitor 52 C 5
Vitoria (Brazil) 52 I 6
Vitoria (Spain) 9 E 2
Vitoria da Conquista 52 I 4
Vitorog, Mt. 20 C 5
Vitosa Planina, Mt. 20 F 6
Vitré 11 E 2
Vitry-le-François 11 H 2
Vitsi, Mt. 20 E 7
Vittangi 17 I 3
Vittorio Véneto 19 D 1
Vivero 9 C 2
Vivi 22 I 3
Vizas 24 I 3
Vizianagaram 30 D 5
Vizille 11 H 4
Vizinga 24 E 4
Viziru 21 H 5
Vizzini 19 E 6
Vjatka (Kirov) 24 E 5
Vjatka, River 24 EF 6
Vjatshje-Poljany 24 F 6
Vjazemskij 32 Q 3
Vjeca 20 G 7
Vjosë 20 D 7
Vladimir 23 O 6
Vladimirovka 25 B 2
Vladivostok 22 O 5
Vlasic, Mt. 20 C 5
Vlasotinci 21 F 6
Vlasov 25 G 1
Vlieland, Island 15 G 2
Vlorë 21 D 7
Vltava 12 F 4
Voc 24 CD 5
Vodla 23 M 3
Vogel Klip, Mt. 41 B 4
Vogelkop 34 H 5
Vogelsberg 12 C 3
Vohémar 41 c 6
Vohipeno 41 c 8
Voi 40 F 3
Voim Sj 16 G 4
Voiron 11 H 4
Voivod 21 D 5
Voivodina 21 DE 5
Vojnitsa 23 H 2
Voj-Voz 24 H 3
Vokhma 24 D 5
Vokhma 24 D 5
Voknavolok 23 H 2
Volcano, Island 27 S 7
Volda 17 B 5
Volga 23 IN 6
Volga Heights 24 D 8
Volgograd 25 GH 1
Volinia 20 HI 2
Volkhov 23 I 5
Volkhov, River 23 H 5
Volksrust 41 D 4
Volocaevka 32 D 2
Volocisk 21 H 3

Vologda 23 N 5
Vologda, River 23 N 5
Volognes 11 E 2
Volokanka 22 I 2
Volokolamsk 23 LM 6
Volos 21 F 8
Volos, G. of 21 F 8
Voloska, River 23 NO 4
Volovo 23 M 8
Volsini, Mts. 18 CD 3
Vol'sk 24 D 8
Volta 39 E 4
Volta, Lake 39 DE 4
Volterra 19 C 3
Volturino, Mt. 18 EF 4
Volturno 18 E 4
Vomano 19 D 3
Vondrove 41 b 8
Vonozero 23 L 4
Vopna, Fj 16 U 12
Vorkuta 22 F 3
Vormsele 17 H 4
Voronez 2 P 5
Voronez 1 PQ 5
Vorosilov 22 O 5
Vorosilovgrad 25 E 1
Vorosilovsk 25 E 1
Võru 23 F 6
Vosges 10 I 2-3
Vosilevsk 23 N 5
Voskresenskoe 24 C 6
Voss 17 B 6
Vosten 16 G 3
Vostok, Island 54 M 5
Võsu 17 M 7
Votkinsk 24 G 6
Votkinsk Res. 24 H 6
Vouga 8 B 3
Vour 37 H 5
Voves 11 F 2
Vovodo, River 40 C 1
Vöyri 17 L 5
Vozgora 24 E 2
Vozmogora 23 L 3
Voznesen'e 23 L 4
Voznesenka 29 F 1
Voznesensk 25 A 2
Voznesenskoe 32 E 1
Vraca 21 F 6
Vranica Planina, Mt. 21 C 6
Vranje 21 E 6
Vranograc 21 B 5
Vratnik, Mt. 20 H 6
Vrbas 21 D 5
Vrede 41 D 4
Vrijheid 41 E 4
Vrsac 21 E 5
Vrutky 21 D 3
Vryburg 41 C 4
Vskhody 23 L 7
Vucja, Mt. 21 C 5
Vuka 20 D 5
Vukovar 21 D 5
Vulcano 18 E 5
Vulture 18 E 4
Vunasa, Mt. 20 E 8
Vuokatti, Mt. 23 G 2
Vuokki 23 G 2
Vuokso 23 G 4
Vuolvoy 16 H 3
Vutcani 21 H 4
Vyartka 24 EG 5-7
Vyaz'ma 23 L 7
Vyborg 23 G 4
Vycegda 24 DH 3-4
Vyg 23 L 3
Vygozero 23 L 3
Vyhorlat, Mt. 20 F 3
Vym 24 F 3
Vyrts, Lake 16 M 7
Vyshka 29 B 4
Vysnij Voloсěk 23 L 6
Vysoka, Mt. 20 C 3
Vysokoe 21 F 1
Vytegra 23 M 4
Vytegra, River 23 M 4

W

Wa 39 D 3
Waal 14 G 3
Waarnambool 55 a 8
Wabash 46 I 4
Wabiskaw 44 FG 4
Waco 46 G 6
Wad Banda 37 L 7
Waddington, Mt. 44 E 5
Wadhwan 30 B 4
Wadi 30 C 5
Wadi Halfa 37 M 5
Wad Medani 38 B 5
Wad Nimr 37 M 7
Wadowice 13 H 4
Wafra 28 L 6
Wager Bay 44 M 2
Wagga Wagga 55 H 7
Wahai 34 G 5
Wahpeton 46 G 3
Wai 30 B 5
Waiau 55 g 14
Waibeem 34 H 5
Waicherie 55 G 6

Waidhofen 13 F 5
Waidhofen 13 F 4
Waigeo, Island 34 H 5
Wai Hai 27 f 15
Waikabubak 34 E 6
Waikato 55 h 13
Wainganga, River 30 CD 4-5
Waingapu 34 F 6
Wainwright 45 G 2
Wairau 55 g 14
Waitaki 55 g 14
Wajabula 34 G 4
Waih 38 C 2
Wajima 32 E 4
Wajir 40 G 2
Waka 40 C 3
Wakalipu 55 f 14
Wakayama 32 E 5
Wake, I. 54 G 3
Wake, Island 54 G 3
Wakhjir - Pass 29 F 4
Wakkanai 32 F 2
Wakre 34 H 5
Walachia 20 FH 5
Walbrzych 13 G 3
Walcheren Island 14 F 3
Walden 4 G 5
Wales 13 E 5-6
Walgreen Coast 57 Q 2
Walikale 40 D 3
Wallaroo 55 F 6
Walla Walla 46 C 3
Walsham North 4 G 5
Walsk 55 d 11
Walthamstow 4 G 6
Walvis Bay 41 A 3
Walvis Bay, City 41 AB 3
Wamba (Congo) 40 D 2
Wamba (Nigeria) 39 F 4
Wamba, River 40 B 4
Wamlana 34 G 5
Wanaaring 55 h 4
Wanaka 55 f 14
Wanapiri 34 I 5
Wan chuan (Kalgan) 31 I 2
Wandunya 55 D 5
Wang 33 B 3
Wanganui 55 h 13
Wanganui, River 55 h 13
Wangaratta 55 H 7
Wangiwangi, Island 34 F 6
Wan hsien 31 H 4
Wanie Rukula 40 D 2
Wankuai, Mt. 31 I 6
Wantgela 55 H 1
Warangal 30 C 5
Warburton 55 F 5
Wardha 30 C 4
Waren 13 E 2
Waren (New Guinea) 34 I 5
Warendorf 13 B 3
Warkopi 34 H 5
Warmbad (Namibia) 41 B 4
Warnow 12 DE 2
War Poga 34 I 5
Warrego 55 H 5
Warren 55 B 6
Warrenton 41 C 4
Warrina 55 F 5
Warsaw 13 I 2
Warta 13 F 2
Warthe 12 G 2
Waru 34 H 5
Warwick 55 I 5
Wasatch Ra. 42 H 5-6
Wash, The- 4 G 5
Washington 46 M 5
Washington, Island 54 L 4
Washington, Mt. 46 N 4
Washington, State 46 BC 3
Wasserburg 13 E 4
Wasserkuppe 12 CD 3
Watau 55 f 15
Waterberg 41 B 3
Waterberg, Mt. 41 B 3
Waterfall 55 d 11
Waterford 4 C 5
Waterloo (Belgiun) 15 G 3
Waterloo (Sierra Leone) 39 B 4
Waterloo (USA) 46 H 4
Waterpoort 41 D 3
Watertown (USA, N. York) 46 M 4
Watertown (USA, S. Dakota) 46 C 3
Waterville (Ireland) 4 A 6
Waterville (USA) 46 C 3
Watgell 55 H 6
Watling, Island 48 E 2
Watsa 40 D 2
Watsi-Kenge 40 C 3
Watson Lake 44 D 3
Watzmann, Mt. 13 E 5
Wau 40 D 1
Wau El-Kebir 37 H 4
Wausau 46 I 3
Waveney 3 G 5
Waycross 46 L 6
Wazirabad 29 E 4
Wear 3 F 4
Weda 34 G 4
Weddell Sea 57 Nm 2
Weert 15 G 3

Wegrow 13 L 2
Wei 31 IL 5
Wei chiang 31 GH 5
Weiden 13 E 4
Wei fang 31 L 3
Wei hai 31 M 3
Wei ho Town 31 N 2
Wei ho River 26 O 6
Wei hsi 31 F 5
Weilburg 13 BC 3
Wei ni 31 G 5
Weimar 13 D 3
Weiser 46 C 4
Weissenburg 13 D 4
Weissrand 41 B 3-4
Weisswasser 13 F 3
Weldon 46 M 5
Weld Springs 55 C 4
Welega 38 C 6
Welo 38 CD 5
Wellesley, Island 55 F 3
Wellington 55 h 14
Wellington, Island 53 A 6
Wells 44 E 5
Wells, Lake 55 C 5
Wells next the Sea 4 G 5
Welshpool 4 E 5
Wema 40 C 3
Wen chou 31 M 5
Wenchuan 27 P 5
Wenden 17 M 8
Wenlock 55 G 2
Wen shan 31 G 6
Wentworth 55 G 6
Weonsan 31 N 3
Wepener 41 D 4
Werra 13 C 3
Wersar 34 H 5
Wert 34 H 5
Weser 12 C 2
Wesergebirge 12 C 2
Weslurhopsholar 17 R 12
Wessel Islands 55 F 2
West Bromwich 4 F 5
Westerwald 12 BC 3
Westfries Islands 15 GH 2
West Frisian Island 14 GH 2
Westirian 34 H 5
Westkap 55 f 15
West Hartlepool 4 F 4
West Lamma Channel 27 g 15
Westleigh 41 D 4
Western Cordillera 49 C 3
Westl. Morava 20 E 6
West Nicholson 41 E 3
Weston 34 E 3
West Palm Beach 46 L 7
Westphalia 12 BC 3
Westport (Iceland) 4 B 5
Westport (New Zealan) 55 g 14
Westport (USA) 46 B 3
Westray, Island 4 E 2
Westray Firth, Strait 13 E 2
West Siberian Plain 22 F 3-4
West Virginia 46 L 5
Wetar, Island 34 G 6
Wetz 13 F 5
Wexford 4 C 5
Wey 3 F 6
Weymouth 4 E 6
Whale 44 R 4
Whanharei 55 g 13
Wharanui 55 g 14
Wharfe 3 F 5
Wharton 46 G 7
Wheeler Peak, Mt. 46 D 5
Whernside, Mt. 3 E 4
White, Bay 44 T 5
White Island 22 FG 2
Whitehaven 4 E 4
Whitehorse 44 B 3
White Mountains 20 C 3
White Nile 35 G 4
White River 44 N 6
White River (USA, S. Dakota) 46 F 4
White River (USA, Texas) 46 F 6
White Russia 23 EH 8
White Sea 23 LO 1-2
White Volta 35 C 4-5
Whitney, Mt. 42 H 6
Whittle, Cape 44 T 5-6
Whyalla 55 F 6
Wichita 46 G 5
Wichita Falls 46 G 6
Wick 4 E 2
Wickow 4 C 5
Wicklow Mts. 3 C 5
Widan 38 D 4
Widawka 12 H 3
Wied 13 C 1
Wiener Neustadt 13 G 5
Wiesbaden 13 BC 3
Wight, Island 3 F 6
Wijdel Fjord 56 a
Wilba 55 F 1
Wilcannia 55 G 6
Wildhorn, Mt. 12 B 5
Wildspitze 18 C 2
Wilhelmshaven 13 BC 2
Wilkes I and 57 Cd 2

Wilkins Coast 57 O 3-2
Wilkomir 17 M 9
Willemstad 51 C 1
Willesden 4 F 6
Willham, Mt. 55 B 6
Williamsport 46 M 4
Willis In. 55 I 3
Williston (South Africa) 41 C 5
Williston (USA) 46 F 3
Willowmore 41 C 5
Wilmington (USA, Delaware) 46 M 5
Wilmington (USA, N. Carolina) 46 M 6
Wilson, Cape 44 O 2
Wilson Mts. 46 E 5
Wilson Cape 55 b 8
Wilton 55 E 2
Wiluna 55 C 4
Wimbledon 4 F 6
Winchester 46 I 5
Windehsi 34 H 5
Windham 55 D 3
Windhoek 41 B 3
Windorah 55 G 5
Windsor (Canada) 44 O 7
Windsor (United Kingdom) 4 F 6
Windward Passage 48 E 2-3
Winfreda 53 D 4
Winisk 44 N 5
Winneba 39 D 4
Winnemucca 46 C 4
Winnipeg 44 L 6
Winnipeg, Lake 44 L 5
Winnipegosis, Lake 44 I 5
Winona 46 H 4
Winslow 46 D 5
Winston Salem 46 L 5
Winter Hoek, Gr. Mt. 41 B 5
Winterthur 13 C 5
Winton 55 G 4
Wisbech 4 G 5
Wisconsin 46 H 4
Wisconsin, State 46 HI 3-4
Wismar 13 D 2
Wissen 13 B 3
Witagron 51 E 2
Witbank 41 D 4
Witham 3 F 5
Witputs 41 B 4
Wittemberge 13 D 2
Wittenberg 13 E 3
Wittingen 13 D 2
Wittlich 13 B 2
Wittow 13 E 1
Wittstock 13 E 2
Witu 40 G 3
Witwaters Rand 41 D 4
Wkra 12 I 2
Wlcclawek 13 H 2
Woкam, Island. 34 H 6
Wo f, Island 52 a
Wo gast 13 EF 1
Wo gogrod 25 HI
Wo ho, Island 54 G 3
Wo hynia 20 HI 2-3
Wolaston, Cape 44 E 1
Wolaston, Lake 44 H 4
Wolaston Pen. 44 FG 2
Wollongong 55 d 11
Wollogorang13 55 F 3
Wolow 13 G 3
Wolseley 55 G 7
Wolsztyn 13 G 2
Wolverhampton 4 E 5
Woma 39 G 3
Wompo 31 D 4
Wonthaggi 55 b 8
Woodlans 27 h 16
Woods, Island 55 E 3
Woodward 46 G 5
Woolgar 55 G 3
Wooloomber 55 C 4
Woomera 55 F 6
Worcester (United Kingdom) 4 E 5
Worcester (South Africa) 41 B 5
Worcester (USA) 46 N 4
Workai, Island 34 H 6
Workington 4 E 4
Worms 13 BC 4
Wormsi 17 L 7
Wornitz 12 D 4
Worthing 4 F 6
Wosi 34 G 5
Wowoni, Island 34 F 5
Wrangel Island 22 ST 2
Wrath, Cape 3 D 2
Wray 46 F 5
Wreck Reef, Island 55 L 4
Wrexham 4 E 5
Wriezen 13 F 2
Wrigley Gulf 57 R 2
Wrocław 19 G 3
Wronki 13 G 2
Wrzesnia 13 G 2
Wtodawa 21 F 2
Wu, (Che chiang) 31 LM 5
Wu (Kuei Chou) 31 H 5
Wu chow (Tsang wu) 31 I 6
Wu chuan 31 H 5
Wu chung pao 31 H 3

Wuhan 31 I 4
Wu hsi 31 M 4
Wu hsing 31 M 4
Wu hsüen 31 L 5
Wu hu 31 L 4
Wui Shan, Mt. 26 P 7
Wu kang 31 I 5
Wuliaru, Island 34 H 6
Wun Rog 40 D 1
Wuonta 48 C 4
Wuppertal 13 B 3
Würmsee 12 D 4
Wurno 39 F 3
Würzburg 13 C 4
Wushih (Uch Turfan) 31 B 2
Wüstenkönig 41 B 4
Wu su 31 C 2
Wutai Shan. Mt. 26 P 6
Wuting (China, Shang tung) 31 L 3
Wu ting (China, Yünnan) 31 G 5
Wu tu 31 H 4
Wu wei 31 G 3
Wu yüan 31 H 2
Wu yun 32 C 2
Wyatong 55 H 6
Wyches, Islands 56 a
Wye 3 E 5-6
Wyoming 46 E 4
Wyvis, Ben-, Mt. 3 D 3

X

Xai Xai 41 E 4
Xangongo 41 A 2
Xanti 21 G 7
Xapuri 52 D 4
Xbonil 47 F 4
Xerias 20 F 8
Xeron, Mt. 20 F 8
Xh que Xhique 52 I 4
Xieng Khouang 33 C 3
Xirgu Rio 50 E 4

Y

Ya an 31 G 4
Yaapeel 55 G 7
Yabassi 39 F 5
Yablonovy Ranger 22 M 4
Yabrud 28 D 4
Yacuiba 52 E 6
Yacuma, Rio 52 D 4
Yagaba 39 D 3
Yaguas, Rio 52 C 2
Yague, Rio 48 E 3
Yahisuli 40 C 3
Yakamatsu 32 E 4
Yakiang 31 G 4
Yakima 46 B 3
Yakka, Mt. 40 D 1
Yako 39 D 3
Yakoma 40 C 2
Yaku, Island 26 R 6
Yakuluku 40 D 2
Yakut A.S.S.R. 22 MP 3
Yakutsk 22 N 3
Yala (Kenia) 40 E 2
Yala (Thailand) 33 C 5
Yalgoo 55 B 5
Yalta (Krasnoarmeisk) 25 C 3
Yalu (China) 31 M 1
Yalu (Corea) 31 N 2
Yalun 31 G 5
Ya lung 31 F 4
Yamagata 32 F 4
Yamaguchi 32 D 5
Yamal Peninsula 22 FG 2-3
Yambéring 39 B 3
Yambio 40 D 2
Yamethin 33 B 2
Yamma Yamma, Island 55 G 5
Yamoussoukro 39 C 4
Yamuna 27 a 11
Yanam 30 D 5
Yanayacu 52 B 2
Yanbu 78 C 3
Yanga 40 C 3
Yanga, River 39 E 3
Yang chiang 31 I 6
Yang chou 31 L 4
Yang chu (Taiwan) 31 I 3
Yangihissar 31 B 3
Yengi Shahr 31 B 3
Yangon 40 C 1
Yang tse 31 FI 4-5
Yang tze kiang River 26 NP 6-7
Yangyang (Corea) 31 N 3
Yang Yang (Senegal) 37 A 6
Yankton 46 G 4
Yankwama 40 C 2
Yannarie 55 A 4
Yanonge 40 D 2
Yao 37 H 7
Yao an 31 G 5
Yaou 39 D 4

Yaounde 39 G 5
Yap, Island 54 D 4
Yaqui, Rio 47 B 2
Yaquina 46 B 4
Yaraka 55 G 4
Yaral 26 p 17
Yarangüme 21 I 9
Yarda 37 H 6
Yari, Rio 51 B 3
Yarkand 31 B 3
Yarmouth 44 R 7
Yaroslavka 24 IL 7
Yaroslavl 23 N 6
Yary 51 F 3
Yas, Island 29 B 7
Yat 37 G 5
Yatakala 39 E 3
Yatenga 39 D 3
Yathkyed 44 L 3
Yatua, Rio 51 C 3
Yauli 52 B 4
Yauyos 52 B 4
Yavari, Rio 52 C 3
Yayero, Rio 52 C 4
Yaviza 48 D 5
Yawatanama 32 D 5
Yayladagi 28 D 3
Yazdan 29 D 5
Yazoo City 46 I 6
Ye 33 B 3
Yecla 9 F 4
Yedseram 39 G 3
Yeggueba 37 G 6
Yeh hsien 31 M 3
Yehposhow 31 L 2
Yei 40 E 2
Yei, River 40 E 1
Yeji 39 D 4
Yélimané 37 B 6
Yell, Island 3 F 1
Yellandlapad 30 D 5
Yellowknife 44 G 3
Yellowknife, River 42 I 5
Yellow River (Huang) 31 L 3
Yellow Sea 31 M 3
Yellowstone, Lake 46 D 4
Yeltes 8 C 3
Yeluca, Mt. 48 C 4
Yelwa 39 E 3
Yemelyano 23 H 3
Yemen 27 GH 8
Yen 31 HI 3
Yenang-yaung 33 A 2
Yenanma 33 A 3
Yen Bay 33 C 2
Yen cheng 31 M 4
Yen chi 31 N 2
Yendi 39 E 4
Yeni 37 E 7
Yeniseysk 27 N 4
Yenki 31 D 2
Yenta 31 G 4
Yeo, Island 55 C 5
Yeosu 31 N 4
Yeotmal 30 C 4
Yeovil 4 E 6
Yerevan 25 H 5
Yerim Bulaq 31 E 2
York (United Kingdom) 4 F 5
York (USA) 46 I 6
York, K. 55 G 2
York Pen. 55 F 6
York Factory 44 M 4
Yorkton 44 I 5
Yoro 47 G 4
Yorosso 37 D 7
Yosu 31 N 4
Youghal 4 C 6
Youkou 39 C 4
Young, Island 57 a 3
Yozgat 25 C 6
Ystad 17 E 9
Ytterolden 17 E 5
Ytterøy 17 D 5
Yuan 31 I 5
Yuan kiang 26 O 7
Yüan ling 31 I 5
Yucatan, Strait 47 GH 3
Yucatan 42 LM 8
Yü chi 31 G 6
Yü Chiang 31 H 6
Yüeh sui 31 G 5
Yüeh yang 31 I 5
Yuen long 27 g 15
Yu hsien 31 I 3
Yu hu 31 I 2
Yü huan 31 M 5
Yukon 44 BC 3
Yukon, River 45 FG 4
Yerudamiar 28 B 2
Yesil Irmak 25 CD 5
Ye-u 33 B 2
Yeu 10 D 3
Yezd 2 S 9
Yin chou Hu 27 f 15
Yinchuan 27 O 6
Yin hsien 31 I 3
Yin ko, Cape f 15
Ying kou 31 M 2
Ying te 31 I 6
Yläne 17 L 6
Yikiiminki 17 N 4
Ylitornio 17 L 3
Yllästunturi, Mt. 17 LM 3
Yo 39 G 3

Yobe 37 G 7
Yokadouma 40 B 2
Yokaichiba 27 e 13
Yoko 39 G 4
Yokohama 32 E 4
Yokoshiba 27 e 13
Yokosuka 32 E 4
Yokote 32 F 4
Yola 39 G 4
Yonago 32 D 4
Yonaguni, Island 32 B 7
Yonezawa 32 F 4
Yonne 10 G 3
Yono 27 e 13
York (Alaska) 45 E 3
Yugoslavia 21 BF 5-7
Yulghun Bulaq 31 E 2
Yu lin 31 H 3
Yuma 46 D 6
Yumba 40 B 2
Yümen 31 F 2
Yunaska, Island 22 U 4
Yungas 49 D 5
Yung jen 31 G 5
Yung ning (China,
  Kuangsi) 31 H 6
Yung ning (China, Yünnan)
  31 G 5
Yung sheng 31 G 5
Yungstown 46 L 4
Yung sui 31 H 5
Yung sun 31 H 5
Yün tsi 31 I 4
Yü hsien 31 I 4
Yün lung 31 F 5
Yünnan 31 FG 5
Yura 52 C 5
Yura 16 L 9
Yur'ev-Pol'skij 23 N 6
Yurimaguas 52 B 3
Yurkand 31 B 3
Yü shu 31 F 4
Yusun Bulak 31 F 1

Yütien (Keriya) 31 C 3
Yu wang 31 H 3
Yu yang 31 H 5
Yuzhno-Sakhalinsk 22 P 5

Z
Zaandam 15 G 2
Zab, Great 1 Q 8
Zab, Little 1 QR 8
Zabok 21 B 4
Zabol 29 D 5
Zabrze 13 H 3
Zacatecas 47 D 3
Zadar 21 B 5
Zadonsk 23 N 8
Zadavka 24 D 8
Zafra 9 C 4
Zafrana, Island 20 H 9
Zagare 17 L 8
Zagazig, Ez- 37 M 3
Zagnanado 39 E 4
Zagorsk 23 N 6
Zagreb 21 C 5
Zagros, Mt. 1 RS 8-9
Zagube 23 I 4
Zagubica 21 E 5
Zagyva 20 DE 4
Zahidan 29 D 6
Zahlen 28 C 4
Zahran 38 D 3-4
Zaidam 26 N 6
Zaidiya 38 D 4
Zainde 28 MN 4
Zainsk 24 G 7
Zaire 36 F 5-6
Zaire, River 40 AD 2-4
Zaj 24 FG 7
Zajarsk 22 L 4
Zajecar 21 F 6
Zaisan, Lake 26 M 5
Zak 41 C 5

Zakataly 25 I 5
Zakho 28 G 2
Zakinthos 21 E 9
Zala 20 C 4
Zalaegerszeg 21 C 4
Zalangoye 40 A 2
Zalau 21 F 4
Zalew Wislany 12 H 1
Zalingei 37 I 7
Zalise 22 Q 3
Zambezi 35 FG 7
Zambia 36 FG 7
Zamboanga 34 F 3
Zamora (Mexico) 47 D 4
Zamora (Spain) 9 D 3
Zamora, Rio 52 B 2
Zamosc 4 L 3
Zana 25 D 5
Zancara 8 E 4
Zanguya 31 B 3
Zänjan 28 L 2
Zanjon, Rio 53 C 3
Zanlasso 39 C 3
Zante, Island 20 E 9
Zanthus 55 C 6
Zanzibar 40 F 4
Zanzur 37 G 3
Zapala 53 C 4
Zapatoca 51 B 2
Zaporozje 25 C 2
Zara (Turkey) 25 D 6
Zaragoza 9 F 3
Zarajsk 23 N 7
Zarand 29 C 5
Zaranou 39 D 4
Zarasai 23 F 7
Zarate 53 E 3
Zaravecchia 21 B 6
Zaraza 51 C 2
Zardob 25 I 5
Zarghun, Mt. 26 I 6
Zarghun Shahr 29 E 5

Zaria 39 F 3
Zarik 29 F 2
Zarkamys 29 C 2
Zarma 22 H 5
Zaruma 52 B 2
Zarzaitine 37 F 4
Zasiversk 22 P 3
Zastron 41 D 5
Zatas 8 B 4
Zavitaja 22 N 4
Zaviyeh 25 H 6
Zavodoukovskij 22 F 4
Zawi 36 G 7
Zawira 38 D 4
Zbaszyn 13 FG 2
Zdanice 21 C 3
Zdunska Wola 13 H 3
Zealand 14 FG 3
Zealand 16 DE 9
Zeberged, Island 38 C 3
Zebid 38 D 5
Zebila 39 D 3
Zeebrugge 15 F 3
Zeehan 55 b 9
Zegamra 37 D 3
Zeguerelli 37 B 6
Zeila 38 D 5
Zeitz 13 DE 3
Zeja 22 N 4
Zeja, River 22 NO 4
Zelenga 25 L 2
Zelenvj, Island 22 P 5
Zeleznod 17 I 9
Zelijn, Mt. 20 E 6
Zella 37 H 4
Zell-am-See 13 E 5
Zelten 37 H 4
Zemen 21 F 6
Zémio 40 D 1
Zemmour 37 B 4
Zemorgo 40 D 1
Zenica 21 C 5
Zep, Mt. 20 D 5

Zeravsham 26 I 6
Zerebkova 21 I 4
Zesfontein 41 A 2
Zeta 20 D 6
Zézere 8 BC 3-4
Zhdanoy 25 D 2
Zhob 29 E 5
Ziada, Pt. 38 E 5
Zibar 28 G 2
Zidacov 21 F 3
Zidouh 37 C 3
Zielona Gora 13 F 3
Zierikzee 15 F 3
Zigansk 22 N 3
Ziguei 37 H 7
Ziguinchor 37 A 7
Zigulёvask 24 E 8
Zile 25 C 5
Zilina 21 D 3
Zima 22 L 4
Zimbabwe 41 E 3
Zimovniki 25 G 2
Zinder 37 F 7
Zipaquira 51 B 2
Zira 28 M 6
Zirgan 24 H 8
Zitomir 2 N 5
Zivarih 25 B 6
Zizdra 23 L 8
Zlatoust 24 L 7
Zlin 21 C 3
Zliten 37 G 3
Zlobin 23 H 8
Zlot 21 E 5
Zlynka 23 H 8
Znaim 13 FG 4
Zobia 40 D 2
Zolotonasa 25 AB 1
Zomba (Malawi) 41 F 2
Zomba (Moz.) 21 C 3
Zongo 40 B 2

Zonguldak 25 A 5
Zongwe 40 E 4
Zoo Baba 37 G 6
Zorn 10 I 2
Zouar 37 H 5
Zouerate 37 B 5
Zrenjanin 21 E 5
Zubaida, Pt. 38 C 2
Zubtsov 23 L 6
Zuetina, ez- 37 I 3
Zuevka 24 F 5
Zug (Western Sahara) 37 B 5
Zug (Swatzerland) 19 C 5
Zugdidi 25 F 4
Zugspitze 12 D 5
Zuila 37 H 4
Zujar 9 E 5
Zujar, River 8 D 4
Zulu 35 G 8
Zumbo 41 E 2
Zungeru 39 F 4
Zupa 21 C 5
Zupanja 21 D 5
Zupanova 22 Q 4
Zura 24 G 6
Zürich 19 B 1
Zürich Lake 18 B 1
Zuru 39 F 3
Zurumata 51 E 3
Zut, Island 21 B 6
Zuwara 37 G 3
Zverevo 25 F 1-2
Zvolen 21 D 3
Zvorn 21 D 5
Zvoz 24 B 3
Zwenigorod 23 M 7
Zwetti 13 F 4
Zwickau 13 E 3
Zwolle 15 G 2
Zypern 2 o 8-9
Zyrjanka 22 Q 3
Zyrjanovsk 22 H 5